EUROPCAR GOLF GUIDE

D.P.S.
9-11, rue Benoit-Malon,
92150 SURESNES
FRANCE - Tel. (1) 45.06.40.12
Fax. (1) 42.04.77.25

CONTENTS

Every effort has been made to ensure that the rates and general information contained in this guide are correct, however the publisher cannot accept any liability or responsability for any inaccuracies or changes that may arise.

HOW TO USE THE GUIDE

For each country the golf courses of 9 holes or more are classified in alphabetical order under the name of the nearest town or city.
For England and Scotland there is the same classification by region.
For Ireland the classification is in alphabetical order by county.

How to find your golf course :
At the beginning of each country there is a list showing the nearest city to each golf course. The golf courses of 18 holes or more have a reference indicating their location on the map of each country or region.

EXPLANATION OF THE SYMBOLS

★★★ → Great golf course.

★★ → Very good golf course.

★ → Recommended golf course.

✡ → Holiday golf course.

18 → Number of Holes.

→ Closing days for visiting golfers.

GF → Price of average greenfees :
$ moderate
$$ expensive

→ Dated on which the golf club was first opened.

→ Name(s) of the architect(s).

S → The club has a pro-shop.

→ Clubs may be hired.

→ The club has a children's playground.

→ The club has one or several tennis courts.

→ The club has a swimming pool.

R → There is a restaurant and/or bar on the golf course.

L → Length of the course with Par.
Example : 5460 P 65 = 5460 meters Par 65. 5460 y P 65 = 5460 yards Par 65.

→ The club has hosted an Open or a Championship.

→ Seaside course.

→ Mountain golf course.

H → There is a hotel on the course.

COMMENT SE SERVIR DU GUIDE

Pour chaque pays les golfs de 9 trous et plus sont répertoriés par ordre alphabétique.
Pour l'Angleterre, l'Écosse et l'Irlande il y a un même classement par région.

Pour retrouver votre golf :
En début de chaque pays, un tableau indique la ville et le golf le plus proche, ainsi qu'une référence pour les golfs de 18 trous et plus, pour la carte qui suit.

EXPLICATION DES SYMBOLES

★★★ → Excellent parcours.

★★ → Très bon parcours.

★ → Parcours recommandé.

✡ → Golf de vacances.

18 → Nombre de trous.

→ Jour de fermeture pour visiteurs.

GF → Prix du Greenfees :
$ raisonnable
$$ haut standing

→ Date de création du Golf.

→ Nom du ou des architectes du Golf.

S → Le Golf possède un Pro-Shop.

→ On peut louer des clubs.

→ Le Golf a une garderie d'enfants.

→ Le Golf possède un ou plusieurs courts de tennis.

→ Le Golf possède une piscine.

R → Le Golf possède un bar ou/et restaurant.

L → Distance du parcours ainsi que le Par. Exemple : 5460 P 65 = 5460 mètres Par 65. 5460 y P 65 = 5460 yards Par 65.

→ Le Golf a reçu un Open ou un Championnat.

→ Le Golf est en bord de mer.

→ Le Golf est en montagne.

H → Il y a un hôtel sur le golf.

COMO SERVIRSE DE LA GUÍA

Para cada país, los campos de golf de 9 hoyos o más figuran en el repertorio por orden alfabético.
Para Inglaterra y Escocia, se ha previsto una sola clasificación por región.
Para Irlanda se hace una clasificación por condado.

Para hallar su campo de golf :
Al principio de cada país se indica en un cuadro la ciudad y el campo de golf más cercano. Cada golf de 18 hoyos o más tiene su referencia para el mapa que se encuentra a continuación.

EXPLICACIÓN DE LOS SÍMBOLOS

★★★ → Recorrido excelente.

★★ → Recorrido superior.

★ → Recorrido interesante.

☼ → Ideal para vacaciones.

18 → Número de hoyos del Golf.

→ Cerrado semanalmente : o una época del año.

GF → Precio del Greenfees :
$ precios razonables
$$ precios bastante elevados

→ Fecha de creación del Golf.

→ Apellido del o de los arquitectos del Golf.

S → El Golf tiene un Pro-Shop.

→ Se alquila palos y carritos.

→ El Golf tiene una guarderia para niños.

→ El Golf tiene uno o varios campos de tenis.

→ El Golf tiene una piscina.

R → Hay un restaurante y/o bar en el Golf.

L → La longitud del campo y el Par. Ejemplo :
5460 P 65 = 5460 metros Par 65.
5460 y P 65 = 5460 yards Par 65.

→ El Golf ha recibido un Open o un Campeonato.

→ El Golf está a la orilla del mar.

→ El Golf está en la montaña.

H → Hay un hotel en el Golf.

GEBRAUCHSANLEITUNG

Für jedes Land finden Sie, alphabetisch geordnet, die Golfplätze mit 9 Löcher und mehr.
Für England und Scottland gibt es eine gleiche Klassifizierung pro Bezirk.

Um Ihr Golfplatz zu finden :
Für jedes Land gibt es ein Verzeichnis der Städte und der nächstliegenden Golfplätze. Für die Golfplätze mit 18 Löchern und mehr gibt es eine Referenz in der darauffolgenden Karte.

ZEICHENERKLÄRUNG

★★★ → Ausgezeichnet.

★★ → Sehr gut.

★ → Interessant.

☼ → Ideal für Ferien

18 → Anzahl der Löcher auf dem Golfplatz.

→ Tag der Schliessung und Saison.

GF → Greenfee Preis
$ Niedrig
$$ Teuer

→ Datum der Entstehung des Golfplatzes.

→ Name des oder der Architekten.

S → Zum Golf gehört ein Pro-Shop.

J → Schlägerverleih.

→ Der Golf hat einen Kindergarten.

→ Der Golf besitzt einen oder mehrere Tennisplätze.

→ Der Golf besitzt ein Schwimmbad.

R → Der Golf hat ein Restaurant und/oder eine Bar.

L → Distanz des Parcours sowie der Par. Beispiel : 5460 P 65 = 5460 Meter Par 65. 5460 y P 65 = 5460 Yards Par 65.

→ Auf dem Golfplatz wurde oder wird eine Offene Meisterschaft oder eine Meisterschaft ausgetragen.

→ Golfplatz am Meer.

→ Golfplatz im Gebirge.

H → Hotel auf dem Golf.

凡例

★★★ → 名門コース

★★ → 優良コース

★ → 推薦コース

✡ → レジャー・コース

18 → ホール数

→ ビジター不可日

GF → グリーン・フィー
$＝中級，$$＝高級

→ ゴルフ場開設年月日

→ コース設計者名

S → プロショップ有

→ クラブレンタル可

→ 託児所有

→ テニスコート有

→ プール施設有

R → バー・レストラン施設有

L → コース全長及びパー
例：5460P65＝5460m，パ－65
5460YP65＝5460ヤード，パ－65

→ オープン・選手権開催地

→ シーサイド・コース

→ 山岳コース

H → ゴルフ場内ホテル有

SYMBOLS

Great golf course

Very good golf course

Recommended golf course

Catering facilities on the Golf Course

Holiday golf course

Championship course

Seaside

Clubs for hire

Architect

In the mountains

Children's playground

Pro-shop

Hotel on the Golf Course

Tennis court

Closing days

Number of Holes

Swimming pool

Length and Par

$ moderate
$$ expensive
Greenfees

Date when founded

PHOTOGRAPHY CREDITS

A.F.P. : Denmark.
G.F. Allen : Wales.
Austrian Tourist Authority.
P. Bernström : Sweden.
D. Bötcher-Ramdohr : Germany.
British Tourist Authority.
L. Calas : France.
Club Méditerranée : Spain.
F.J. Daehn : Wales.
Danish Tourist Board.
P. Dazelay : England – Scottand.
G. Defaix : France
T. Declercq : Belgique – Ireland.
P. Ducrey : Switzerland.
D. Dunn : England.
P. Engler : Sweden.
Enit : Italie.
Finnish Tourist Authority.
Focus.
France Golf : France – Spain – Tunisie – Maroc.
R.W. Fream : Portugal.
J. Gapany : Greece.
Golf Contact : Germany.
Golf Gazette : Austria.
T. Grenfell : England.
C. Hansen : Denmark.
D. Harradine : Austria – France – Germany – Switzerland.
G.W. Harvey : Scotland.
Hawtree : Wales.
R. Holsson : Sweden.
K. Holthe : Norway.
Irish Tourist Board.
Israel Tourist Office.
Italian Tourist Authority.
B. Jonsson : Sweden.
H.R. Karlsson : Sweden.
T. Lönnroth : Sweden.
L. Lundberg : Sweden.
H. Meier : Switzerland.
P. Merland : Wales.
B. Middlehurst : England.
B. Morgan : Scotland – Ireland – England.
J.F. Naumann : Norway
H.W. Neale.
W. Nigel Hugues : Wales.
H. Nilson : Sweden.
Pix Photos : Wales.
Portuguese Tourist Authority.
S & G Press Agency : England.
A.F. Raymond : England.
Relais & Châteaux : Spain.
M. Rene : Denmark.
J. Ritchie : Scotland.
T. Roberts : Wales.
Rockett : England.
P. Rolin : Belgium.
C.E. Rosenberg : Sweden.
S. Schmitt : Spain.
P. Sheldon : England – Scotland.
D. Simonin : France.
Spanish Tourist Authority.
F. Stenström : Sweden.
Svensk Golf.
Swiss Tourist Office.
The Cork Examiner : Ireland.
Tissies : Switzerland.
S. Van de Kerkhove : Italy.
W. Vennemann : Germany.
Waveney Photographic : England.
Wilson Photographics : Scotland.
Brenstol Limited

Car Rental

Reservation/Information telephone number :

Country code :	Telephone number :
43	**222/5054200**

Headquarters address :

DENZEL AUTOVERMIETUNG
Linke Wienzeile 120/2, 1060 Vienna
Tel. : (43) 222/5970041
Telex : 112181
Fax : (43) 222/5971431

50 GOLF COURSES, 12 000 PLAYERS

★★★ Great golf course
★★ Very good golf course
$ 80-400 Ö. Sch.
★ Recommended golf course
☆ Holiday golf course
$ $ 400-550 Ö. Sch.

TOWN	GOLF COURSE		TEL	MAP REF.
Baden bei Wien	Schloss Ebreichsdorf		(02254) 3888	20
Badgastein	Badgastein		(06434) 2775	•
Bad Gleichenberg	Bad Gleichenberg		(03159) 3717	•
Bad Ischl	Salzkammergut	☆	(06132) 6340	17
Bad Kleinkirchheim	Bad Kleinkirchheim	☆	(04275) 594	12
Deutschlandsberg	Schloss Frauenthal		(03462) 5717	•
Donnerskirchen	Delta Donnerskirchen	☆	(02683) 8110	14
Enzesfeld	Enzesfeld	★★★	(02256) 812721	3
Fernschnitz	Amstetten-Fernschnitz		(07473) 8293	•
Frohnleiten	Murhof	★★	(03127) 2101	5
Fürstenfeld	Fürstenfeld		(03382) 8533)	21
Goldegg	Goldegg		(06415) 8585	•
Hainburg	Hainburg *(ext. to 18 holes)*		(02165) 2628	•
Haugschlag/Litschau	Waldviertel		(02865) 8441	22
Innsbrück	Innsbrück Igls	★ ☆	(05223) 8177	7
	Lans Sperberegg		(05222) 77165	•
Irdning	Schloss Pichlarn	☆	(03682) 24393	11
Kitzbühel	Kitzbühel Schloss Kaps		(05356) 3007	•
	Kitzbühel-Schwarzsee	☆	(05356) 71645	16
	Rasmushof		(05356) 5252	•
Kössen	Kaiserwinkel Kössen	☆	(05375) 2122	23
Laaben	Wienerwald		(0222) 823111	•
Lebring	Gut Murstätten		(03182) 3555	
Liezen	Weissenbach		(03612) 24774	30
Linz	Linz – St-Florian		(07223) 2873	1
Niedergrünbach	Ottenstein		(02826) 7476	24
Pertisau	Achensee		(05243) 5377	•
Pörtschach	Austria Wörthersee	☆	(04272) 83486	25
Saalfelden	Brandlhof	☆	(06582) 2176	10
Salzburg	Am Mondsee		(06232) 3835	13
	Gut Altenann		(06214) 6026	15

TOWN	GOLF COURSE	TEL	MAP REF.
Salzburg	Salzburg Klesheim	(0662) 850851	•
	Schloss Fuschl	(06229) 2390	•
Schladming	Dachstein-Tauern ✡	(03686) 2630	31
Schönborn	Schloss Schönborn	(02267) 2879	26
Seefeld	Seefeld Wildmoos ★★★	(05212) 3003	8
Semmering	Semmering	(02664) 8154	•
St. Kanzian	Klopeiner See-Turnersee ✡	(04239) 38000	32
St. Pölten	St. Pölten	(02741) 7360	27
Steinakirchen	Schloss Ernegg ✡	(07488) 214	28
Velden	Kärntner ★ ✡	(04273) 2515	6
	Velden Kostenberg ✡	(04274) 7045	18
Wels	Wels	(07243) 6038	19
	Maria Theresia	(07732) 3691	33
Wien	Colony Gutenhof	(02235) 880550	34
	Wien ★★	(0222) 2189564	2
	Wienerwald	(0222) 823111	•
	Brunn am Gebirge	(02236) 31572	29
Wiener Neustadt	Wiener Neustadt Föhrenwald	(02622) 29171	4
Zell am See	Europa Sport Region ✡	(06542) 6161	9

NEW GOLF COURSES (18 HOLES OR MORE) TO OPEN SOON

Alpen Leutasch
6105 Leutasch/Tirol
Tel. : (05214) 6207

Golfclub Laudachtal-Kirchham
4810 Gmunden

Golfclub Schönfeld
2291 Schönfeld
Tel. : (0222) 261320

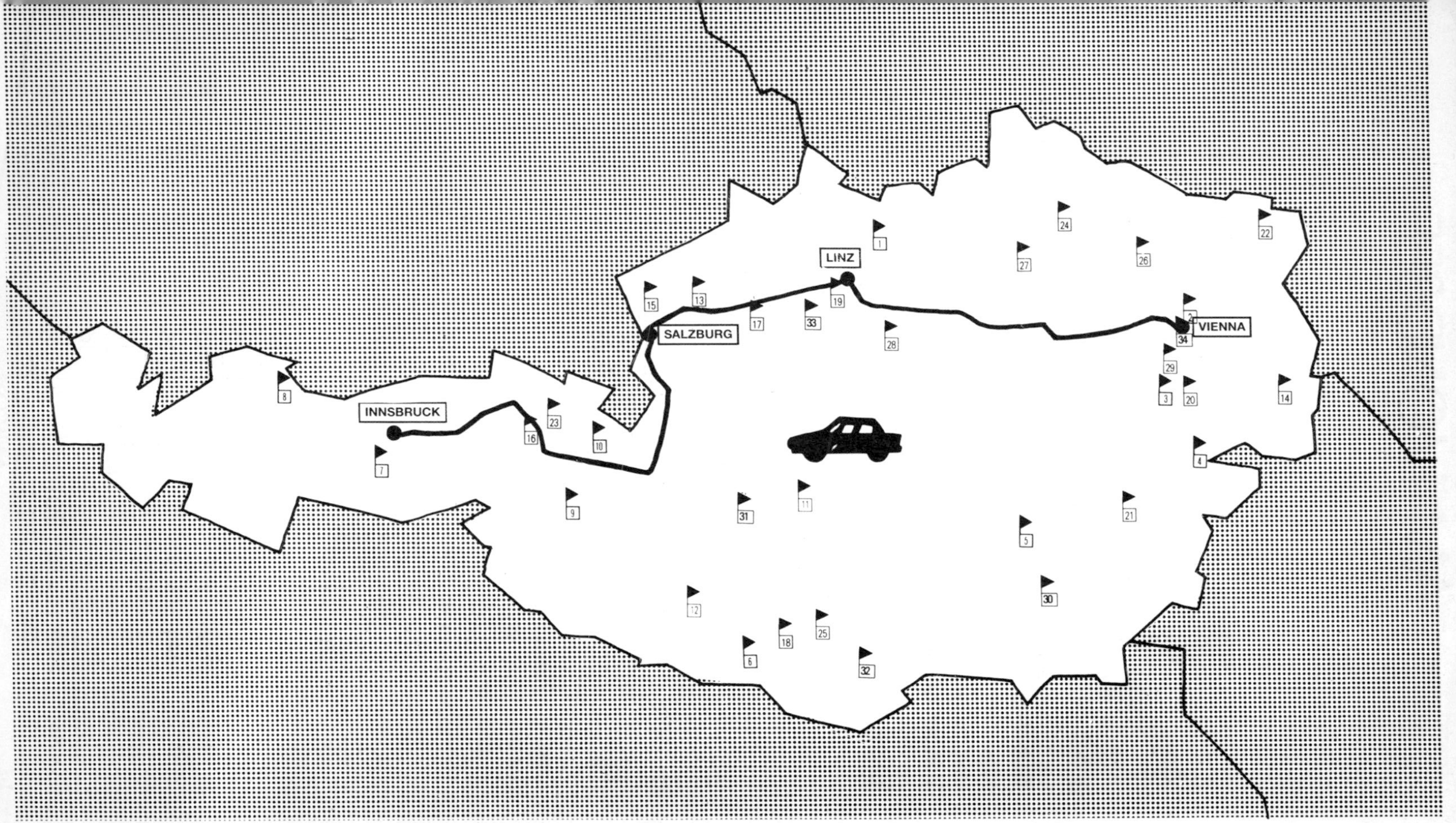

All cities represented on the map are Europcar locations.

AM MONDSEE

TEL : (06232)3835
LOCATION : 12 km E. Salzburg
ADDRESS : 5310 St-Lorenz-Drachensee
HOTEL :
Seehof-Loibichl am Mondsee
Tel : (06232)2550
Eschlböck-Plomberg am Mondsee
Tel : (06232)3572
Weisses Kreuz-Mondsee
Tel : (06232)2254
RESTAURANT : Weisses Kreuz-Mondsee
Tel : (06232)2254

Only twelve kilometres outside Salzburg, this is a fine lakeside course bordering the Mondsee lake and the scenic Drachensee lake. The gently rolling, luxuriantly wooded countryside offers magnificent scenery with the mountains in the background. The course itself is flat with several holes played over the 'Drachensee'. *SSS 72*

GF $

1988

18

Mondays

M. Lamberg

L 6197 P 72

R S

Required : Handicap Certificate
Best days : Any day

HOLE	LENGTH MEDAL-TEE	PAR	STROKE INDEX
1	342	4	
2	322	4	
3	160	3	
4	384	4	
5	415	4	
6	333	4	
7	444	5	
8	174	3	
9	512	5	
TOTAL	3086	36	TOTAL

HOLE	LENGTH MEDAL-TEE	PAR	STROKE INDEX
10	297	4	
11	564	5	
12	378	4	
13	367	4	
14	351	4	
15	193	3	
16	306	4	
17	166	3	
18	489	5	
TOTAL	3111	36	TOTAL

AUSTRIA WÖRTHERSEE

TEL : (04272)83486
LOCATION : 4 km Pörtschach/2 km Moosburg
ADDRESS : Golfstrasse 2 - 9062 Moosburg
HOTEL :
Schloss Seefels - Pörtschach
Tel : (04272)2377
Schloss Leonstein - Pörtschach
Tel : (04272)2816
Wallerwirt - Pörtschach
Tel : (04272)2316

Situated in a popular holiday area in Kärnten just 4km from the scenic Lake Wörthersee, this recently opened championship golf course will undoubtedly become one of Austria's popular golfing venues. Relatively flat, it features long holes with groups of trees separating some of the fairways. Golf arrangements have been made with most of the excellent holiday hotels in Pörtschach. *SSS 72*

GF $

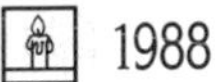

1988

18

November to April

—

L 5823 P72

S

R

Required : Handicap Certificate
Best days : Any day

HOLE	LENGTH MEDAL-TEE	PAR	STROKE INDEX
1	500	5	
2	300	4	
3	407	4	
4	137	3	
5	340	4	
6	118	3	
7	286	4	
8	322	4	
9	435	5	
TOTAL	2845	36	TOTAL

HOLE	LENGTH MEDAL-TEE	PAR	STROKE INDEX
10	143	3	
11	320	4	
12	381	4	
13	445	5	
14	370	4	
15	170	3	
16	354	4	
17	502	5	
18	293	4	
TOTAL	2978	36	TOTAL

BAD KLEINKIRCHHEIM

TEL : (04275)594
LOCATION : 36 km Villach
ADDRESS : 9546 Bad Kleinkirchheim
HOTEL :
Pulverer – Bad Kleinkirchheim
Tel : (04240)550
Das Ronacher – Bad Kleinkirchheim
Tel : (04240)282
St Oswald – Bad Kleinkirchheim
Tel : (04240)591
Trattlerhof – Bad Kleinkirchheim
Tel : (04240)8172

This is one of Austria's excellent alpine courses, designed by the Swiss based architect Donald Harradine, and ideal for holiday golf. Set amidst hills and mountains nearly 1000m above sea level, in Kärntner Oberland, the course is undulating with many holes going uphill or downhill through woods. *SSS 72*

GF $

1985

18

November to April

D. Harradine

L 6127 P 72

R S

Required : None
Best days : Any day

HOLE	LENGTH MEDAL-TEE	PAR	STROKE INDEX
1	441	5	15
2	418	4	5
3	332	4	11
4	383	4	9
5	146	3	17
6	386	4	7
7	138	3	13
8	540	5	3
9	430	4	1
TOTAL	3214	36	TOTAL

HOLE	LENGTH MEDAL-TEE	PAR	STROKE INDEX
10	299	4	10
11	123	3	12
12	472	5	4
13	382	4	14
14	509	5	2
15	387	4	8
16	350	4	18
17	124	3	16
18	267	4	6
TOTAL	2913	36	TOTAL

BRANDLHOF

TEL : (06582)2176
LOCATION : 20 km Zell am See
ADDRESS : 5760 Saalfelden
HOTEL : HR
Gut Brandlhof
Tel : (06582)2176-0
Dick – Saalfelden
Tel : (06542)2215
Gasthof Hindenburg – Saalfelden
Tel : (06542)2303

Set in natural surroundings near the Steiernen Lake amongst a pine forest in the foothills of the Austrian Alps in Salzburger Land, this is an attractive gently rolling golf course following the flow of the Saalach river. The course is ideal for holiday golf and belongs to Sporthotel Gut Brandlhof, a luxurious complex with numerous sporting facilities including a golf academy, children's playground, riding school, tennis and squash courts, bowling greens, windsurfing, indoor swimming pool, health and fitness programmes, sauna, private game and fish reserve. *SSS 72*

GF $

1983

18

November to April

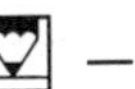 —

L 5902 P 72

Required : None
Best days : Any day

HOLE	LENGTH MEDAL-TEE	PAR	STROKE INDEX
1	295	4	15
2	358	4	7
3	435	5	17
4	180	3	3
5	312	4	11
6	192	3	9
7	330	4	5
8	142	3	13
9	526	5	1
TOTAL	2770	35	TOTAL

HOLE	LENGTH MEDAL-TEE	PAR	STROKE INDEX
10	452	5	4
11	394	4	8
12	144	3	12
13	512	5	6
14	393	4	2
15	177	3	10
16	457	5	14
17	326	4	16
18	277	4	18
TOTAL	3132	37	TOTAL

BRUNN

TEL : (02236)31572
LOCATION : 30 km Wien
ADDRESS : Rennweg 2345 - Brunn am Gebirge
HOTEL :
City Club - Wien Vösendorf
Tel : (0222)693535
Babenbergerhof - Mödling
Tel : (02236)22246-0
Jagdhof - Guntramsdorf
Tel : (02236)52225

At about 20 minutes from the center of Vienna, this golf course lies in fairly flat countryside facing the lush Wiener woods and the splendid Schloss Liechtenstein. There is an interesting pattern of holes, with old trees alternating with young plantations flanking the fairways, and several well placed tracts of water. The ultra modern clubhouse has an indoor swimming pool, a sauna, and a fitness center. *SSS 72*

GF $

1989

18

—

C. Fialik

L 5876 P 72

Required : Handicap Certificate
Best days : Weekdays

HOLE	LENGTH MEDAL-TEE	PAR	STROKE INDEX
1	407	4	4
2	359	4	10
3	150	3	18
4	408	4	2
5	314	4	16
6	493	5	6
7	152	3	14
8	451	5	12
9	371	4	8
TOTAL	3105	36	TOTAL

HOLE	LENGTH MEDAL-TEE	PAR	STROKE INDEX
10	463	5	7
11	309	4	3
12	275	4	17
13	169	3	5
14	321	4	13
15	140	3	15
16	296	4	11
17	349	4	9
18	449	5	1
TOTAL	2771	36	TOTAL

COLONY GUTENHOF

TEL : (02235)880550
LOCATION : 22 km S. Wien
ADDRESS : Gutenhof 2325-Himberg
HOTEL :
Marriott - Wien
Tel : (0222)51518
Alba - Wien
Tel : (0222)554686
Sacher - Wien
Tel : (0222)51456

At about 20 km from Vienna stands the Colony Gutenhof golf course. Its 36 holes (East and West course) wind their way through flat woodland. Most of the fairways are tree-lined with deep bunkers. Quite a number of lakes serve as obstacles and a few holes are actually played over them. *SSS 72/73*

 $$

 —

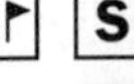 

🏠 1989

 K. Rossknecht

36

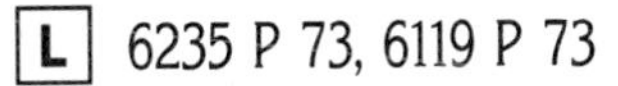 6235 P 73, 6119 P 73

Required : Handicap Certificate
Best days : Weekdays

HOLE	LENGTH MEDAL-TEE	PAR	STROKE INDEX
1	320	4	17
2	470	5	5
3	351	4	11
4	190	3	7
5	362	4	3
6	386	4	1
7	150	3	15
8	454	5	13
9	340	4	9
TOTAL	3023	36	TOTAL

HOLE	LENGTH MEDAL-TEE	PAR	STROKE INDEX
10	165	3	10
11	440	5	18
12	326	4	12
13	420	4	4
14	547	5	6
15	384	4	2
16	145	3	14
17	305	4	16
18	480	5	8
TOTAL	3212	37	TOTAL

HOLE	LENGTH MEDAL-TEE	PAR	STROKE INDEX
1	367	4	4
2	145	3	12
3	473	5	10
4	295	4	18
5	375	4	2
6	299	4	4
7	189	3	6
8	483	5	16
9	347	4	8
TOTAL	2973	36	TOTAL

HOLE	LENGTH MEDAL-TEE	PAR	STROKE INDEX
10	459	5	15
11	140	3	17
12	335	4	5
13	386	4	1
14	470	5	7
15	162	3	11
16	343	4	13
17	408	4	3
18	443	5	9
TOTAL	3146	37	TOTAL

DACHSTEIN-TAUERN

✡

TEL : (03686)2630
LOCATION : on B146 between Schladming and Haus
ADDRESS : Oberhaus 59-8967 Haus/Ennstal
HOTEL :
Alpen Schütterhof - Schladming
Tel : (03687)61205
Alte Post - Schladming
Tel : (03687)22571
Matschner - Ramsau
Tel : (03687)817210

The German golf champion Bernard Langer designed this fine natural golfing venue which rises 750 m above sea level near the famous ski resort of Schladming. The course, backed by towering snow capped mountains, is surprisingly flat with its fairways cutting through small densely covered hills. Four holes, the short 6th, the 9th, the 15th and the 18th are played over picturesque lakes. The club features a pretty chalet style clubhouse overlooking the alpine scenery. *SSS 71*

GF $$
1990
18

November to April
B. Langer
L 5393 P 71

R S

Required : Handicap Certificate
Best days : Weekdays

HOLE	LENGTH MEDAL-TEE	PAR	STROKE INDEX
1	260	4	15
2	262	4	16
3	447	5	11
4	127	3	18
5	458	5	4
6	117	3	14
7	361	4	5
8	182	3	7
9	357	4	1
TOTAL	2571	35	TOTAL

HOLE	LENGTH MEDAL-TEE	PAR	STROKE INDEX
10	369	4	2
11	128	3	17
12	458	5	9
13	312	4	12
14	344	4	3
15	157	3	6
16	460	5	10
17	156	3	13
18	438	5	8
TOTAL	2822	36	TOTAL

DELTA GOLF DONNERSKIRCHEN

TEL : (02683)8110
LOCATION : 45 km Wien/10 km Eisenstadt
ADDRESS : Golfplatz-7082 Donnerskirchen
HOTEL :
Seehotel Rust-Rust
Tel : (02685)381
Gasthof am Spitz Hölzl-Donnerskirchen
Tel : (02683)5519
RESTAURANT : Gasthof Engel - Donnerskirchen
Tel : (02683)8502

The picturesque village of Donnerskirchen is famous for its wine culture and was awarded the 'Trophy of the world's best wine' in 1976. The new golf course is set on flat countryside amidst fields and meadows not far from the 'Neusiedlersee' lake.The main difficulty of the course is presented by seven large lakes, as the majority of the holes are actually set alongside these lakes and played across them. Facilities include a driving range with a short game practice area and a very attractive clubhouse. *SSS 71.*

GF $

1990

18

Dec. to March

K. Rossknecht

L 5905 P 72

R S

Required : Handicap Certificate
Best days : Any day

HOLE	LENGTH MEDAL-TEE	PAR	STROKE INDEX
1	325	4	
2	505	5	
3	180	3	
4	360	4	
5	480	5	
6	350	4	
7	325	4	
8	400	4	
9	145	3	
TOTAL	3070	36	TOTAL

HOLE	LENGTH MEDAL-TEE	PAR	STROKE INDEX
10	495	5	
11	300	4	
12	165	3	
13	470	5	
14	135	3	
15	345	4	
16	315	4	
17	150	3	
18	460	5	
TOTAL	2835	36	TOTAL

ENZESFELD

TEL : (02256)812721
LOCATION : 15 km Baden/35 km Wien
ADDRESS : 2551 Enzesfeld
HOTEL :
Krainerhutte – Baden bei Wien
Tel : (02252)44511
Almschlössl – Baden bei Wien
Tel : (02252)48240
Grandhotel Sauerhof – Baden bei Wien
Tel : (02252)41251
RESTAURANT : Schloss Weikersdorf – Baden bei Wien
Tel : (02252)44071

The Enzesfeld course is one of Austria's most attractive and demanding golf courses, one of Europe's best. The course is set on undulating countryside near Vienna and has a varied layout. Most of its fairways are narrow and heavily wooded with deep bunkers and large greens, demanding accuracy from tee to green. Among its feature holes is the 18th with a difficult tee shot over a ravine downhill to a well-bunkered green. There is a pleasant and very comfortable clubhouse overlooking the 9th green with tennis courts and a swimming pool in the country club nearby. The Enzesfeld course has been the scene of many international tournaments. *SSS 72*

GF $$

 1970

November to April

J. Harris

L 6048 P 72

S

R

Required : Handicap Certificate
Best days : Mondays to Fridays; Weekends in July and August only

HOLE	LENGTH MEDAL-TEE	PAR	STROKE INDEX
1	322	4	6
2	104	3	18
3	428	5	16
4	461	5	2
5	331	4	10
6	198	3	14
7	397	4	4
8	357	4	3
9	178	3	15
TOTAL	2776	35	TOTAL

HOLE	LENGTH MEDAL-TEE	PAR	STROKE INDEX
10	466	5	7
11	190	3	13
12	395	4	1
13	376	4	9
14	452	5	5
15	438	5	17
16	202	3	11
17	373	4	12
18	380	4	8
TOTAL	3272	37	TOTAL

EUROPA SPORT REGION

TEL : (06542)6161
LOCATION : 4 km Zell am See/Kaprun
ADDRESS : Golfstrasse 25 – 5700 Zell am See
HOTEL :
Erlhof – Zell am See
Tel : (06542)3173
Porschehof – Zell am See
Tel : (06542)7248
Tirolerhof – Zell am See
Tel : (06542)3721

Picturesquely situated at over 750 m above sea level between the holiday resorts of Kaprun and Zell am See, overlooking the snow clad peaks of the Alps, this is a fine and flat holiday course. Laid out in the scenic Pinzgau valley, it features numerous ponds and streams serving as hazards on seven fairways, as well as three testing dogleg holes. The course is certainly an enjoyable experience for the holiday golfer. *SSS 72*

GF $

1984

27

November to April

D. Harradine

L 6218 P 72

R S

Required : Handicap Certificate 35
Best days : Any day

HOLE	LENGTH MEDAL-TEE	PAR	STROKE INDEX
1	504	5	7
2	215	3	9
3	321	4	17
4	377	4	1
5	357	5	5
6	463	4	13
7	361	3	5
8	176	3	15
9	519	4	11
TOTAL	3293	37	TOTAL

HOLE	LENGTH MEDAL-TEE	PAR	STROKE INDEX
10	399	4	4
11	295	4	12
12	364	4	6
13	167	3	14
14	303	4	16
15	173	3	18
16	318	4	10
17	387	4	2
18	519	5	8
TOTAL	2925	35	TOTAL

FURSTENFELD

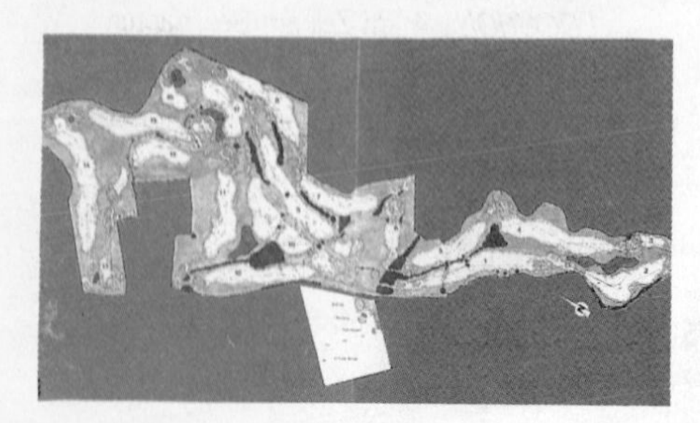

TEL : (03382)8533
LOCATION : 8 km Fürstenfeld/60 km Graz
ADDRESS : 8282 Gillersdorf 50
HOTEL :
3 Jahreszeiten - Loipersdorf
Tel : (03382)8385
Leitner - Loipersdorf
Tel : (03382)8575
RESTAURANT : Kowald - Loipersdorf
Tel : (03382)

This fairly technical course, situated near the well known thermal spa resort of Loipersdorf, blends into the lovely rolling countryside of Eastern Styria. Four rather large spreads of water demand precise shots on some of the holes. This is an ideal base for a combined thermal cure and golfing holiday. *SSS 72*

GF $

1989

18

November to March

H. Zisser/G. Hunt

L 6135 P 72

S

R

Required : Club Membership Card
Best days : Any day

HOLE	LENGTH MEDAL-TEE	PAR	STROKE INDEX
1	435	5	
2	360	4	
3	130	3	
4	390	4	
5	330	4	
6	160	3	
7	350	4	
8	340	4	
9	490	5	
TOTAL	2985	36	TOTAL

HOLE	LENGTH MEDAL-TEE	PAR	STROKE INDEX
10	415	4	
11	370	4	
12	380	4	
13	190	3	
14	470	5	
15	405	4	
16	175	3	
17	300	4	
18	445	5	
TOTAL	3150	36	TOTAL

GUT ALTENANN

TEL : (06214)6026
LOCATION : 11 km Salzburg
ADDRESS : 5302 Henndorf am Wallersee
HOTEL :
Schloss Fuschl-Salzburg Hof
Tel : (06229)22530
Caspar Moser-Henndorf am Wallersee
Tel : (06214)228
Pension Gollackner-Henndorf am Wallersee
Tel : (06214)509
RESTAURANT : Schnecken-Neumarkt am Wallersee

Scenically set in Henndorf on the popular Lake Wallersee, this will certainly become one of Europe's finest championship golf courses. It is one of Jack Nicklaus' first creations in continental Europe. The 18 holes wind through hilly countryside, typical of 'Salzkammergut', with two lakes, streams and marshes serving as hazards. The course is framed by majestic mountains and luxuriant wooded hills. A five star hotel is planned in the near future, and will be equipped with squash and tennis courts, a swimming pool, a beauty farm, a winter golf school and facilities for seminars. *SSS 72.*

GF $$ — November to March — R S
1988 — J. Nicklaus
18 — L 6180 P 72

Required : Special introduction by a member

HOLE	LENGTH MEDAL-TEE	PAR	STROKE INDEX
1	308	4	
2	456	5	
3	398	4	
4	182	3	
5	323	4	
6	403	4	
7	363	4	
8	466	5	
9	154	3	
TOTAL	3053	36	TOTAL

HOLE	LENGTH MEDAL-TEE	PAR	STROKE INDEX
10	328	4	
11	383	4	
12	165	3	
13	363	4	
14	368	4	
15	491	5	
16	170	3	
17	388	4	
18	471	5	
TOTAL	3127	36	TOTAL

GUT MURSTÄTTEN

TEL : (03182)3555
LOCATION : 25 km S. Graz
ADDRESS : Oedt 14-8403 Lebring
HOTEL :
Gollner - Lebring
Tel : (03182)2521
Stangl - Lebring
Tel : (03182)7300
Rasthaus Thaller - Lebring
Tel : (03182)2506

Laid out by the Dutch architect Dudok van Heel, this well designed course stands on flat landscape in the province of Steiermark not far from the Yougoslavian border. The centrepiece of the course consists of a large lake which influences play on at least 9 holes. Besides the championship layout, there is a public 9 hole course and a 9 hole compact course. *SSS 72*

GF $ — November to March

1989 — D. van Heel

27 — L 6103 P 72, 2964 P 36

Required : Handicap Certificate
Best days : Weekdays

HOLE	LENGTH MEDAL-TEE	PAR	STROKE INDEX	HOLE	LENGTH MEDAL-TEE	PAR	STROKE INDEX	HOLE	LENGTH MEDAL-TEE	PAR	STROKE INDEX
1	339	4	13	1	407	4	9	1	382	4	5
2	358	4	3	2	354	4	5	2	173	3	7
3	503	5	10	3	460	5	11	3	293	4	15
4	370	4	6	4	150	3	16	4	437	5	9
5	145	3	14	5	389	4	2	5	130	3	17
6	464	5	8	6	291	4	18	6	366	4	11
7	148	3	15	7	368	4	7	7	354	4	3
8	361	4	1	8	506	5	4	8	351	4	13
9	302	4	17	9	188	3	12	9	478	5	1
TOTAL	2990	36	TOTAL	TOTAL	3113	36	TOTAL	TOTAL	2964	36	TOTAL

INNSBRUCK-IGLS

TEL : (05223)8177
LOCATION : in Rinn
ADDRESS : Oberdorf 11 – 6074 Rinn
HOTEL : HP
Gästehaus Golf Rinn
Tel : (05222)83176
Geisler – Rinn
Tel : (05223)8168
Judenstein – Rinn
Tel : (05223)8168

The 18 hole course Rinn, situated 5km from Sperberegg above the city of Innsbrück, is sheltered by the Tyrolian Alps and scenically laid out amongst a pine forest. The average golfer won't find this course too much of a test. The pleasant 9 hole course is located in Sperberegg itself near the spa resort of Igls. *SSS 71*

GF $$

 1956

27

November to April

M. Hauser

L 5488 P 71, 4709 P 68

Required : Handicap Certificate
Best days : Weekdays

HOLE	LENGTH MEDAL-TEE	PAR	STROKE INDEX
1	300	4	17
2	320	4	15
3	123	3	13
4	326	4	3
5	495	5	1
6	308	4	5
7	172	3	7
8	320	4	11
9	466	5	9
TOTAL	2830	36	TOTAL

HOLE	LENGTH MEDAL-TEE	PAR	STROKE INDEX
10	109	3	14
11	383	4	4
12	321	4	12
13	392	4	2
14	202	3	6
15	118	3	18
16	451	5	8
17	246	4	16
18	436	5	10
TOTAL	2658	35	TOTAL

KAISERWINKL KÖSSEN

TEL : (05375)2122
LOCATION : 30 km Kufstein and Kitzbühel/70 km Salzburg
ADDRESS : Mühlau I - 6345 Kössen
HOTEL :
Alpina - Kössen
Tel : (05375)6453
Schick - Kössen
Tel : (05374)5331
Post - Kössen
Tel : (05375)6276

Built on a site facing snow capped mountain peaks, this lovely alpine course set amidst valleys, meadows, birch trees and pine forest has a mountain river meandering its way all through the course. There is a fine clubhouse with a very cosy and typical tyrolian restaurant (Mayer's restaurant). *SSS 71*

GF $

1988

18

November to April

D. Harradine

L 5947 P 73

R 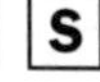

Required : Handicap Certificate
Best days : Weekdays

HOLE	LENGTH MEDAL-TEE	PAR	STROKE INDEX
1	313	4	
2	118	3	
3	455	5	
4	464	5	
5	307	4	
6	202	3	
7	307	4	
8	293	4	
9	373	4	
TOTAL	2832	36	TOTAL

HOLE	LENGTH MEDAL-TEE	PAR	STROKE INDEX
10	158	3	
11	513	5	
12	448	5	
13	492	5	
14	321	4	
15	344	4	
16	344	4	
17	323	4	
18	172	3	
TOTAL	3115	37	TOTAL

KÄRNTNER

TEL : (04273)2515
LOCATION : 8 km Velden
ADDRESS : 9082 Dellach Maria Wörth
HOTEL : HR
Lamplhof Maria Wörth
Tel : (04273)2503
Tannenhof Maria Wörth
Tel : (04274)4142
Astoria – Maria Wörth
Tel : (04273)2279
Seehaus Jamek – Pörtschach
Tel : (04272)31960

This scenic and fine championship course is a lakeside course laid out on the borders of the Wörther See near the Carinthian holiday resorts of Velden and Maria-Wörth. Many of its gently rolling fairways are tree-lined and overlook the lake. The course is ideally situated for holiday golf with two hotels in its grounds and having direct access to the Wörther See for sailing, swimming, windsurfing, etc.. (Lamplhof and Tannehof) *SSS 70*

GF $

1927

18

November to April

 —

L 5745 P 70

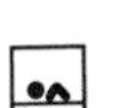 

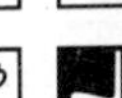

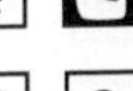 

Required : Handicap Certificate
Best days : Any day

HOLE	LENGTH MEDAL-TEE	PAR	STROKE INDEX
1	320	4	11
2	350	4	9
3	450	5	5
4	150	3	15
5	410	4	1
6	480	5	7
7	120	3	17
8	310	4	13
9	370	4	3
TOTAL	2960	36	TOTAL

HOLE	LENGTH MEDAL-TEE	PAR	STROKE INDEX
10	330	4	12
11	130	3	18
12	580	5	2
13	160	3	8
14	450	5	16
15	390	4	4
16	175	3	14
17	360	4	10
18	210	3	6
TOTAL	2785	34	TOTAL

KITZBÜHEL-SCHWARZSEE

TEL : (05356)71645
LOCATION : In Kitzbühel Reith
ADDRESS : 6370 Kitzbühel
HOTEL :
Bichlhof-Kitzbühel
Tel : (05356)4022
Rasmushof-Kitzbühel
Tel : (05356)5252
Schloss Lebernberg-Kitzbühel
Tel : (05356)4301

Located a few kilometres from the international holiday resort of Kitzbühel at over 800m above sea level, this alpine course is of championship standard. Its 18 holes wind through a scenic valley covered with firwood and broadleaf, and are surrounded by majestic snow clad mountain peaks. The first nine holes have a flat character, the second nine are hilly with the scenic mountain stream 'Reither Ache' separating them. Small lakes affect play on 8 holes. *SSS 73*

GF $$

1988

18

November to April

Hauser Golf Company

L 6320 P 72

S

R

Required : Handicap Certificate
Best days : Weekdays

HOLE	LENGTH MEDAL-TEE	PAR	STROKE INDEX
1	530	5	
2	425	4	
3	365	4	
4	285	4	
5	360	4	
6	510	5	
7	160	3	
8	400	4	
9	185	3	
TOTAL	3220	36	TOTAL

HOLE	LENGTH MEDAL-TEE	PAR	STROKE INDEX
10	315	4	
11	355	4	
12	360	4	
13	485	5	
14	150	3	
15	395	4	
16	170	3	
17	320	4	
18	550	5	
TOTAL	3100	36	TOTAL

KLOPEINER SEE - TURNERSEE

TEL : (04239)38000
LOCATION : 25 km E. Klagenfurt
ADDRESS : Grabelsdorf 94-9122 St. Kanzian
HOTEL :
Sonne - St. Kanzian
Tel : (04239)2337
Alice - St. Kanzian
Tel : (04239)2602
Amerika - St. Kanzian
Tel : (04239)2212

This sporty course is situated in south Kärnten in a fine tourist region dominated by three lakes near the resort of St.Kanzian. Sheltered by majestic mountains with the scenic Klopeiner and Turner See nearby, it spreads out over fairly flat open countryside with two tricky ponds serving as obstacles.

GF $

1989

18

October to March

D. Harradine

L 5545 P 72

R S

Required : Handicap Certificate
Best days : Any day

HOLE	LENGTH MEDAL-TEE	PAR	STROKE INDEX
1	297	4	15
2	443	5	5
3	332	4	7
4	118	3	9
5	353	4	1
6	305	4	11
7	450	5	3
8	124	3	13
9	307	4	17
TOTAL	2729	36	TOTAL

HOLE	LENGTH MEDAL-TEE	PAR	STROKE INDEX
10	309	4	18
11	426	5	6
12	149	3	8
13	347	4	2
14	301	4	16
15	129	3	12
16	366	4	4
17	318	4	14
18	471	5	10
TOTAL	2816	36	TOTAL

LINZ-ST-FLORIAN

TEL : (07223)2873
LOCATION : 8 km Linz
ADDRESS : Tillysburg 28
4490 St-Florian
HOTEL :
Lauriacum – Enns
Tel : (07223)2315
Franz Ferdinand – St Florian bei Linz
Tel : (07224)254
Grüne Traube – St Florian bei Linz
Tel : (07224)3644

Quietly situated close to the Linz/Vienna highway, exit Asten, just before the magnificent Chateau Tillysburg, this is a pleasant inland course set in the foothills of the Alps at 290m above sea level. Laid out on flat terrain one of the two water hazards on the course is a strategically placed lake between the tee and green of the short 7th hole. There is a rustic clubhouse overlooking the fairways. *SSS 72*

GF $

1960

18

November to April

D. Harradine

L 5707 P 70

R S

Required : Club Membership Card
Best days : Mondays to Fridays

HOLE	LENGTH MEDAL-TEE	PAR	STROKE INDEX
1	490	5	5
2	395	4	7
3	155	3	17
4	362	4	3
5	345	4	1
6	300	4	15
7	145	3	9
8	500	5	13
9	290	4	11
TOTAL	2982	36	TOTAL

HOLE	LENGTH MEDAL-TEE	PAR	STROKE INDEX
10	300	4	16
11	120	3	18
12	470	5	4
13	330	4	12
14	150	3	14
15	420	4	2
16	150	3	8
17	390	4	6
18	395	4	10
TOTAL	2725	34	TOTAL

MARIA THERESIA

TEL : (07732)3691
LOCATION : 35 km Wels, 65 km Linz
ADDRESS : Letten 5-4680 Haag - Geboltskirchen
HOTEL : HR
Maria Theresia
Tel : (07732)3691
Traunpark - Wels
Tel : (07242)82236
Post - Wels
Tel : (07242)5409

This new and challenging championship layout is set in charming surroundings within views of the magnificent Alps. The slightly undulating fairways linger through sweeping woodlands and numerous water hazards come into play on at least 9 holes. The 3rd hole is Austria's longest and the 7th and 14th share a unique bunkered double green.
The course is part of an exclusive leisure complex proposing 96 freehold apartments, an indoor golf school, a fitness center, a beauty farm, tennis courts, a swimming pool and its own unique thermal spring. *SSS 72*

GF $

1990

18

November to March

H. Angstl

L 6050 P 72

R S

Required : Club Membership Card
Best days : Weekdays

HOLE	LENGTH MEDAL-TEE	PAR	STROKE INDEX
1	330	4	13
2	210	3	5
3	560	5	1
4	380	4	9
5	390	4	3
6	320	4	11
7	490	5	7
8	330	4	15
9	120	3	17
TOTAL	3130	36	TOTAL

HOLE	LENGTH MEDAL-TEE	PAR	STROKE INDEX
10	460	5	12
11	300	4	18
12	350	4	2
13	340	4	10
14	470	5	6
15	160	3	14
16	320	4	16
17	210	3	4
18	310	4	8
TOTAL	2920	36	TOTAL

MURHOF

TEL : (03127)2101
LOCATION : 24 km N. Graz B 67
ADDRESS : 8130 Frohnleiten
HOTEL : HF
Golfhotel Murhof
Tel : (03127)2228
Alba Wiesler – Graz
tel : (0316)913241
Gasthaus – Frohnleiten
Tel : (03126)2443

Ideal for a golfing holiday when one is in Steiermark, the Murhof championship course is one of the leading ones in Austria hosting the 1987 European Amateur Championship. Encircled by a river, it is set in the wooded foothills of the Alps on mostly flat countryside. The course has a pleasant layout with narrow fairways and a lake on the 2nd and 3rd holes. The Golf hotel is built in a rustic style and has a typical Austrian atmosphere with facilities such as 2 tennis courts, an indoor swimming pool and a sauna. *SSS 72*

GF $$
1963
18

Mondays ; November to April
B. v. Limburger
L 6159 P 72

Required : Handicap Certificate
Best days : Weekdays

HOLE	LENGTH MEDAL-TEE	PAR	STROKE INDEX
1	342	4	15
2	205	3	11
3	412	4	3
4	132	3	17
5	400	4	5
6	406	4	1
7	446	5	7
8	330	4	13
9	480	5	9
TOTAL	3153	36	TOTAL

HOLE	LENGTH MEDAL-TEE	PAR	STROKE INDEX
10	462	5	6
11	367	4	4
12	305	4	12
13	197	3	10
14	465	5	8
15	395	4	2
16	150	3	18
17	310	4	14
18	355	4	16
TOTAL	3006	36	TOTAL

OTTENSTEIN

TEL : (02826)7476
LOCATION : 20 km Zwettl/30 km Krems
ADDRESS : 3532 Niedergrünbach I
HOTEL :
Ottenstein - Peygarten Ottenstein
Tel : (02826)251
Schweighofer - Friedersbach
Tel : (02826)293-0
RESTAURANT : Fischelmayer -
4 Niedergrünbach
Tel : (02826)280

This new championship course, situated in unspoiled landscape near Lake Ottenstein, not far from the Czechoslovakian border, will be fully operational in the middle of 1990. Its holes climb over hillsides and cross lush forests while several ponds serve as hazards.
SSS 71

GF $

1989

18

November to March

K. Preston, P. Zinterl

L 6034 P74

R S

Required : Handicap Certificate
Best days : Any day

HOLE	LENGTH MEDAL-TEE	PAR	STROKE INDEX
1	345	4	7
2	339	4	1
3	453	5	9
4	174	3	15
5	309	4	11
6	501	5	13
7	271	4	3
8	456	5	5
9	169	3	17
TOTAL	3017	37	TOTAL

HOLE	LENGTH MEDAL-TEE	PAR	STROKE INDEX
10	345	4	8
11	339	4	2
12	453	5	10
13	174	3	16
14	309	4	12
15	501	5	14
16	271	4	4
17	456	5	6
18	169	3	18
TOTAL	3017	37	TOTAL

SALZKAMMERGUT

TEL : (06132)6340
LOCATION : 6 km Bad Ischl
ADDRESS : Postfach 506 – 4820 Bad Ischl
HOTEL :
Waldhof - Fuschl am See
Tel : (06226)264
Im Weissen Rössl-St Wolfgang
Tel : (06138)23066
Margaretha am See-St Wolfgang
Tel : (06138)23790
RESTAURANT : Zauner - Bad Ischl
Tel : (06132)3722

Situated between the picturesque holiday resorts of Strobl and Bad Ischl, the landscape is typical of the 'Salzkammergut'region. It is framed by mountains and set among groves of silver birch, pines and oaks with panoramic views over valleys and meadows. Recently extended to 18 holes, it features spacious fairways and big greens following the undulations of the terrain. *SSS 71*

GF $

1933/1988

18

November to April

K. Rossknecht

L 5855 P 71

Required : Handicap Certificate
Best days : Weekdays

HOLE	LENGTH MEDAL-TEE	PAR	STROKE INDEX
1	450	5	
2	130	3	
3	460	5	
4	180	3	
5	370	4	
6	450	5	
7	357	4	
8	350	4	
9	170	3	
TOTAL	2917	36	TOTAL

HOLE	LENGTH MEDAL-TEE	PAR	STROKE INDEX
10	260	4	
11	470	5	
12	355	4	
13	153	3	
14	409	4	
15	410	4	
16	165	3	
17	386	4	
18	330	4	
TOTAL	2938	35	TOTAL

SCHLOSS EBREICHSDORF

TEL : (02254)3888
LOCATION : 35 km Wien/15 km Baden bei Wien
ADDRESS : Schlossallee 1 - Baden bei Wien 2483 Ebreichsdorf
HOTEL :
Seminar - Baden bei Wien
Tel : (02252)886620
Park - Baden bei Wien
Tel : (02252)44386
Rauch -Baden bei Wien
Tel : (02252)44561

Set on flat and easy walking ground in the mature parklands of Ebreichsdorf Castle, some of the holes work their way through forests, others run through open countryside. The greens are wide and of first quality. The spacious clubhouse, on an elevated site, commands fine views over the driving range and a part of the course. ***SSS 72***

GF $$

1988

18

November to April

K. Preston

L 6047 P 72

S

R

Required : Handicap Certificate
Best days : Mondays to Saturdays incl.

HOLE	LENGTH MEDAL-TEE	PAR	STROKE INDEX
1	341	4	11
2	460	5	13
3	390	4	1
4	297	4	15
5	190	3	7
6	472	5	9
7	139	3	17
8	362	4	5
9	359	4	3
TOTAL	3010	36	TOTAL

HOLE	LENGTH MEDAL-TEE	PAR	STROKE INDEX
10	357	4	14
11	355	4	2
12	158	3	16
13	497	5	10
14	149	3	8
15	361	4	4
16	331	4	12
17	445	5	18
18	384	4	6
TOTAL	3037	36	TOTAL

SCHLOSS ERNEGG

TEL : (07488)214
LOCATION : 100 km W. Wien A1 exit Ybbs
ADDRESS : 3261 Steinakirchen
HOTEL : HR
Schloss Ernegg
Tel : (07488)214

At 15km south of the Ybbs exit on the Vienna/Salzburg motorway, near the medieval village of Steinakirchen, this course lies amidst magnificent forests in the foothills of the Alps with views over the Danube valley. The 18 hole course, built in the shadows of the romantic 12th century castle 'Schloss Ernegg', cuts across and runs alongside the river Erlauf. Many ponds and bunkers come into play. Schloss Ernegg has been converted into a fine hotel with 20 rooms. Other facilities include an English style clubhouse, riding stables, trout fishing, deer stalking and a clay pigeon shoot. *SSS 70*

GF $$

1971/1988

27

November to May

J. Day, D. Tucker

L 5670 P 72, 4152 P 64

R S

Required : None
Best days : Weekdays

HOLE	LENGTH MEDAL-TEE	PAR	STROKE INDEX
1	421	4	5
2	269	4	12
3	475	5	3
4	231	3	15
5	398	4	11
6	156	3	17
7	307	4	9
8	384	5	1
9	314	4	10
TOTAL	2955	36	TOTAL

HOLE	LENGTH MEDAL-TEE	PAR	STROKE INDEX
10	251	4	16
11	300	4	13
12	270	4	14
13	131	3	18
14	447	4	2
15	200	3	7
16	401	5	6
17	460	5	4
18	345	4	8
TOTAL	2805	36	TOTAL

SCHLOSS PICHLARN

TEL : (03682)24393
LOCATION : 15 km Liezen
ADDRESS : 8952 Irdning/Ennstal
HOTEL : Hr
Schloss Pichlarn
Tel : (03682)22841
Falkenhof – Irdning
Tel : (03682)22412
Landhaus Pichlarn – Irdning
Tel : (03682)23004

Recently extended to 18 holes, the course is scenically situated in the Enns valley in Steiermark at 700m above sea level and is surrounded by snow capped mountain peaks. The luxury 900 year old castle hotel 'Schloss Pichlarn' is well-known for its many sport and leisure facilities including 5 tennis courts, an indoor swimming pool, gliding, hiking, summer skiing on the Dachstein glacier, a riding school, and health and fitness programmes. *SSS 72*

 $

1970

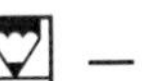

18

November to April

—

L 5906 P 72

Required : Handicap Certificate
Best days : Any day

HOLE	LENGTH MEDAL-TEE	PAR	STROKE INDEX
1	366	4	5
2	131	3	18
3	475	5	11
4	336	4	3
5	152	3	16
6	441	5	12
7	308	4	14
8	530	5	6
9	365	4	2
TOTAL	3104	37	TOTAL

HOLE	LENGTH MEDAL-TEE	PAR	STROKE INDEX
10	365	4	8
11	387	4	4
12	450	5	1
13	310	4	13
14	324	4	9
15	190	3	7
16	310	4	15
17	318	4	10
18	148	3	17
TOTAL	2802	35	TOTAL

SCHLOSS SCHÖNBORN

TEL : (02267)2879
LOCATION : 45 km N. Wien A 22/S 3 exit Obermallebarn
ADDRESS : 2013 Schönborn
HOTEL :
Bauer - Stockerau
Tel : (02266)2930
Lenaustuben - Stockerau
Tel : (02266)2812

Laid out in the grounds of the stately and historical 'Schloss Schönborn' the course with three loops of nine holes (red, green and yellow course) is set in lush parkland dotted with majestic trees and natural water expanses.

GF $$

1988

27

—

K. Rossknecht, M. Erhart

L 3082 P 36, 3146 P 37, 2913 P 36

Required : Handicap Certificate
Best days : Weekdays

HOLE	LENGTH MEDAL-TEE	PAR	STROKE INDEX	HOLE	LENGTH MEDAL-TEE	PAR	STROKE INDEX	HOLE	LENGTH MEDAL-TEE	PAR	STROKE INDEX
1	329	4	9	1	367	4	6	1	269	4	10
2	339	4	3	2	177	3	14	2	320	4	12
3	521	5	11	3	267	4	16	3	519	5	8
4	402	4	1	4	467	5	10	4	405	4	2
5	190	3	7	5	145	3	18	5	382	4	6
6	365	4	5	6	410	4	2	6	148	3	14
7	467	5	15	7	466	5	8	7	268	4	16
8	328	4	17	8	350	4	12	8	481	5	4
9	141	3	13	9	497	5	4	9	121	3	18
TOTAL	3082	36	TOTAL	TOTAL	3146	37	TOTAL	TOTAL	2913	36	TOTAL

SEEFELD-WILDMOOS

TEL : (05212)3003/2313
LOCATION : 4 km Seefeld/20 km Innsbrück
ADDRESS : 6100 Seefeld
HOTEL :
Prachenskyhof – Seefeld
Tel : (05212)2722
Klosterbräu – Seefeld
Tel : (05212)2621
Lärchenhof – Seefeld
Tel : (05212)2383
RESTAURANT : Tyrol-Seefeld
Tel : (05212)2221

Classified as one of Europe's most fascinating alpine golf courses, this undulating championship course is scenically situated on the Wildmoos plateau and surrounded by thickly wooded mountains with snow clad peaks. The course has a very varied lay-out with several well-contrived dogleg holes, 27 bunkers and two strategic lakes. Many of its fairways are lined by larch and birch trees. There are magnificent mountain views. The Tyrolian style clubhouse with its fine terrace is set near the imposing Hohe Munde mountain peak. *SSS 72*

GF $$
1968
18

October to May
D. Harradine
L 6135 P 72

S
R

Required : Handicap Certificate, Club Membership Card
Best days : Mondays to Fridays

HOLE	LENGTH MEDAL-TEE	PAR	STROKE INDEX
1	475	5	7
2	400	4	3
3	300	4	13
4	355	4	5
5	225	3	9
6	355	4	11
7	525	5	1
8	260	4	15
9	145	3	17
TOTAL	3040	36	TOTAL

HOLE	LENGTH MEDAL-TEE	PAR	STROKE INDEX
10	370	4	6
11	290	4	12
12	520	5	8
13	165	3	10
14	550	5	4
15	380	4	2
16	310	4	16
17	170	3	18
18	340	4	14
TOTAL	3095	36	TOTAL

ST. PÖLTEN

TEL : (02741)7360
LOCATION : 8 km St. Pölten/60 km Wien
ADDRESS : 3100 St. Pölten Goldegg
HOTEL :
Golfhotel – St. Pölten
Tel : (02741)7575
Elisabeth - St. Pölten
Tel : (02742)62714
Maria Graf - St. Pölten
Tel : (02742)2757

Set on both hilly and flat landscape, this promising championship course located in Nieder Osterreich offers a challenging variety of holes. The old castle 'Schloss Goldegg', with the modern clubhouse adjacent to it, dominates the course. *SSS 73*

GF $$ — November to April
1988 — Hauser Golf Company
18 — L 6055 P 73

S

R

Required : Handicap Certificate, Club Membership Card
Best days : Any day

HOLE	LENGTH MEDAL-TEE	PAR	STROKE INDEX
1	499	5	5
2	138	3	17
3	340	4	7
4	160	3	11
5	482	5	9
6	395	4	3
7	145	3	15
8	329	4	13
9	521	5	1
TOTAL	3009	36	TOTAL

HOLE	LENGTH MEDAL-TEE	PAR	STROKE INDEX
10	324	4	6
11	453	5	14
12	343	4	2
13	334	4	4
14	315	4	16
15	358	4	8
16	438	5	10
17	162	3	12
18	319	4	18
TOTAL	3046	37	TOTAL

VELDEN KOSTENBERG

TEL : (04274)7045
LOCATION : 8 km Velden/12 km Villach -
ADDRESS : 9231 Koestenberg
HOTEL :
Seehotel Europa - Velden
Tel : (04274)2770
Schloss Velden-Velden
Tel : (04274)2655
Seehotel Auenhof-Velden
Tel : (04274)111

Set at 750m above sea level near the fine holiday resort of Velden and the scenic 'Wörther See' lake, the new Velden Köstenberg golf course lies in luxuriant woodland with mature trees flanking the holes. There are panoramic views of the surrounding mountain scenery. Seven ponds and seven small streams create problems on several holes. An indoor golf academy is presently under construction.

GF $

1988

27

November to April

Rossknecht, Erhardt

L 5858 P 72

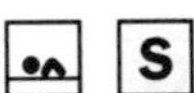

Required : Handicap Certificate
Best days : Any day

HOLE	LENGTH MEDAL-TEE	PAR	STROKE INDEX
1	462	5	14
2	281	4	18
3	164	3	10
4	377	4	12
5	525	5	4
6	333	4	16
7	315	4	2
8	152	3	8
9	380	4	6
TOTAL	2989	36	TOTAL

HOLE	LENGTH MEDAL-TEE	PAR	STROKE INDEX
10	360	4	5
11	371	4	1
12	359	4	7
13	130	3	15
14	419	5	17
15	304	4	9
16	307	4	13
17	468	5	11
18	151	3	3
TOTAL	2869	36	TOTAL

WALDVIERTEL

TEL : (02865)8441
LOCATION : NE of Gmünd, in Haugschlag
ADDRESS : 3874 Haugschlag 160
HOTEL :
Feriendorf – Königsleitn
Tel : (02865)5393

Situated close to the Czechoslovakian border, the Waldviertel course promises to be an extremely challenging one. It overlooks 70ha of unspoiled rolling countryside of woodlands and marshlands, with several natural ponds serving as hazards. A feature hole is the short 4th hole with its treacherous island green. At 5km from the club in Litschau lies Austria's first 18 hole compact course (which also belongs to the same complex). The clubhouse is equipped with childrens' playgrounds, saunas and a billiard room. *SSS 72*

GF $ — November to April

1989 — Austrogolf

18 — L 6039 P 72

Required : Handicap Certificate
Best days : Any day

HOLE	LENGTH MEDAL-TEE	PAR	STROKE INDEX
1	440	5	17
2	341	4	11
3	349	4	7
4	150	3	13
5	437	5	3
6	390	4	5
7	355	4	15
8	378	4	1
9	170	3	9
TOTAL	3010	36	TOTAL

HOLE	LENGTH MEDAL-TEE	PAR	STROKE INDEX
10	360	4	10
11	461	5	8
12	340	4	6
13	199	3	4
14	330	4	18
15	364	4	12
16	473	5	2
17	157	3	16
18	345	4	14
TOTAL	3029	36	TOTAL

WELS

TEL : (07243)6038
LOCATION : 8 km Wels
ADDRESS : Weyerbach 37 - 4512 Weisskirchen
HOTEL :
Austrotel-Wels
Tel : (07242)45361
Posthotel-Wels
Tel : (07242)45409
Stadtkrug-Wels
Tel : (07242)62941

The course, created in 1981, has been recently extended to 18 holes. Set in flat countryside in 'Oberösterreich' with some undulations, it is surrounded by woodland with trees bordering the fairways. Water affects play on several holes. *SSS 72*

GF $ — November to April — R S

1981 — Hauser Golf Company — 

18 — L 6130 P 72 — 

Required : Club Membership Card
Best days : Weekdays

HOLE	LENGTH MEDAL-TEE	PAR	STROKE INDEX
1	350	4	17
2	325	4	11
3	370	4	13
4	335	4	9
5	455	5	1
6	460	5	3
7	155	3	7
8	430	4	15
9	365	4	5
TOTAL	3245	37	TOTAL

HOLE	LENGTH MEDAL-TEE	PAR	STROKE INDEX
10	330	4	16
11	365	4	8
12	325	4	4
13	465	5	14
14	200	3	18
15	470	5	2
16	180	3	6
17	390	4	10
18	160	3	12
TOTAL	2885	35	TOTAL

WIEN

★★

TEL : (0222)2189564
LOCATION : 5 km Center Wien, near the Praterbrücke
ADDRESS : Freudenau 65 A – 1020 Wien
HOTEL :
Arenberg-Wien
Tel : (0222)525291-0
Alba Palace – Wien
Tel : (0222)58850-0
Im Palais Schwarzenberg – Wien
Tel : (0222)784515
RESTAURANT : Sacher-Wien
Tel : (0222)51456-0

Located very near to the Austrian capital, the course, which is the country's oldest, is of the parkland type with mature trees bordering the mostly flat fairways. The course is cunningly bunkered with a water hazard on the 5th fairway. Wien is of championship standard, and has hosted the Austrian Open several times. *SSS 71*

GF $$

1901

18

 —

—

L 5861 P 70

R S

Required : Handicap Certificate
Best days : Mondays and Tuesdays; Weekends by introduction only

HOLE	LENGTH MEDAL-TEE	PAR	STROKE INDEX
1	300	4	17
2	398	4	3
3	475	5	9
4	359	4	5
5	157	3	15
6	318	4	11
7	184	3	13
8	555	5	1
9	203	3	7
TOTAL	2949	35	TOTAL

HOLE	LENGTH MEDAL-TEE	PAR	STROKE INDEX
10	314	4	16
11	383	4	4
12	470	5	10
13	345	4	12
14	130	3	18
15	379	4	2
16	364	4	6
17	169	3	14
18	358	4	8
TOTAL	2912	35	TOTAL

WIENER NEUSTADT-FÖHRENWALD

TEL : (02622)29171
LOCATION : 6 km Wiener Neustadt B 54
ADDRESS : P.O. Box 105 – 2700 Wiener Neustadt
HOTEL :
Corvinus – Wiener Neustadt
Tel : (02622)24134
Zentral – Wiener Neustadt
tel : (02622)23169
RESTAURANT : Goldener Hirsch-Wiener Neustadt

A pleasant inland course with its eighteen holes running through gently undulating woodland. Several streams meander their way through the course serving as hazards on nine holes. There is a well-appointed clubhouse. *SSS 72*

GF $$ — R 

1968 M. Hauser 

18 L 5879 P 72 

Required : Handicap Certificate, Club Membership Card
Best days : Weekdays

HOLE	LENGTH MEDAL-TEE	PAR	STROKE INDEX
1	442	5	17
2	353	4	3
3	185	3	11
4	365	4	1
5	498	5	7
6	353	4	5
7	455	5	9
8	165	3	15
9	167	3	13
TOTAL	2983	36	TOTAL

HOLE	LENGTH MEDAL-TEE	PAR	STROKE INDEX
10	476	5	6
11	470	5	12
12	165	3	14
13	345	4	2
14	347	4	8
15	346	4	4
16	136	3	18
17	161	3	16
18	450	5	10
TOTAL	2896	36	TOTAL

46 GOLF COURSES, 21 000 PLAYERS

★★★ Great golf course
★★ Very good golf course
$ 250-800 B. Frs
★ Recommended golf course
✡ Holiday golf course
$ $ 800-2000 B. Frs

TOWN	GOLF COURSE		TEL	MAP REF.
Andenne	d'Andenne		(085) 843404	•
Antwerpen	Bossenstein		(03) 4856446	21
	Cleydael		(03) 8870079	18
	Rinkven		(03) 3840784	6
	Royal Antwerpen	★★★	(03) 6668456	5
	Ternesse		(03) 3530292	7
Brugge	Damme		(050) 353572	22
Bruxelles	Brabantse		(02) 7518205	30
	Kampenhout		(016) 651216	31
	Overijse		(02) 6875030	•
	Royal Anderlecht		(02) 5211687	•
	Royal Belgique	★★★	(02) 7675801	11
	Royal Waterloo	★★★	(02) 6331850	12
	Sept Fontaines		(02) 3530246	23
	Steenpoel		(02) 5696981	•
Dinant	Château Royal d'Ardenne		(082) 666228	17
Gelk	Spiegelven		(011) 359616	24
Genappe	Genappe		(067) 771571	•
Gent	Royal Latem	★	(091) 825411	4
Grez-Doiceau	Bercuit		(010) 841501	13
Hasselt	Flanders Nippon		(011) 223793	25
	Limburg		(011) 383543	8
Henri-Chapelle	Charlemagne		(015) 234961	•
	Henri-Chapelle		(087) 881991	32
Keerbergen	Keerbergen		(015) 234961	14
Kortrijk	Waregem Happy		(056) 608808	26
Knokke-Heist	Royal Zoute	★ ✡	(050) 601227	2
Leuven	Winge		(016) 634053	19
Liège	International Gomzé		(041) 609207	27
	Royal Sart Tilman		(041) 362021	15
Malmedy	Malmedy		(080) 337603	•
Melsbroek	Brabantse		(02) 7518205	

TOWN	GOLF COURSE	TEL	MAP REF.
Mol	Inter Mol	(014) 589449	•
	Kempense	(014) 816234	33
Mons	Mont Garni	(065) 622719	34
	Royal Hainaut	(065) 229474	9
Namur	Falnuée	(081) 633090	28
Nivelles	La Bruyère	(071) 877267	35
	La Tournette	(067) 219525	20
Oostende	Koninklijke Oostende ★ ✩	(059) 233283	1
Oudenaarde	Oudenaarde	(055) 315481	3
Spa	Royal Fagnes ★★	(087) 771613	16
Turnhout	Lilse	(014) 551930	•
Villers-la-Ville	Rigenee	(071) 877765	10
Wavre	Château de la Bawette	(010) 223332	29
	Louvain-la-Neuve	(010) 452801	36

NEW GOLF COURSES (18 HOLES OR MORE) TO OPEN SOON

Golf d'Hulencourt
1472 Vieux-Genappe
Tel. : (067) 780124

Golfclub Kampenhout
3090 Kampenhout
Tel. : (016) 651216

Mean
5372 Mean
Tel. : (086)323232

Rougemont
5170 Profondville
Tel. : (081) 411418

Steenhoven Country Club
2400 Postel
Tel. : (014) 377250

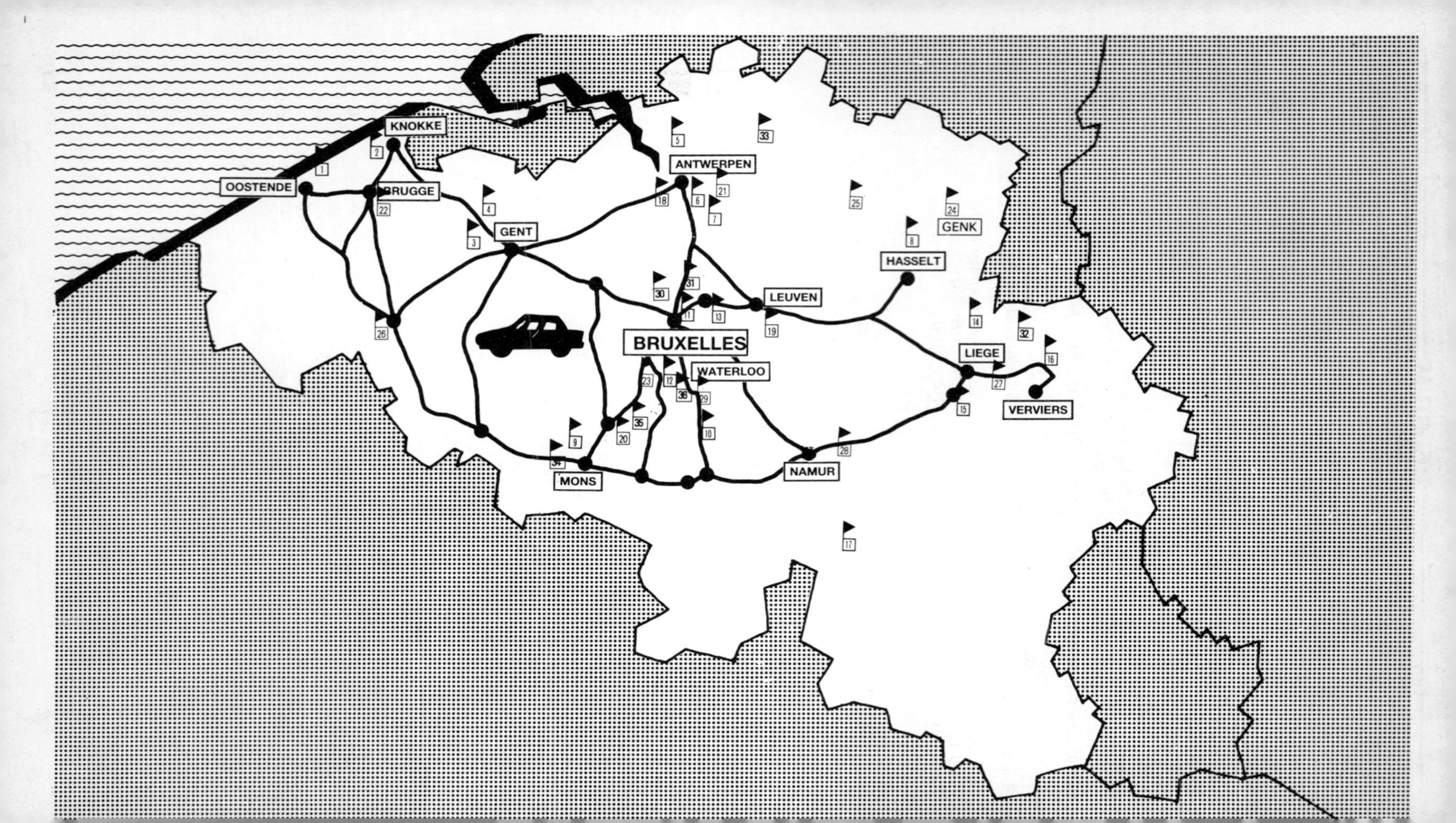

KNOKKE
OOSTENDE
BRUGGE
GENT
ANTWERPEN
BRUXELLES
LEUVEN
HASSELT
GENK
LIEGE
VERVIERS
WATERLOO
NAMUR
MONS
1
2
3
4
5
6
7
8
9
10
11
12
13
14
15
16
17
18
19
20
21
22
23
24
25
26
27
28
29
30
31
32
33
34
35
36

BERCUIT

★★

TEL : (010)841501
LOCATION : 25 km Bruxelles E 40/N24
ADDRESS : Les Gottes 3 – 5980 Grez-Doiceau
HOTEL :
Etap-Lauzelle
Tel : (010)410751
Le Domaine des Champs – Wavre
Tel : (010)227525
RESTAURANT : La Cuisine des Champs – Wavre Eik
Tel : (010)225462

A beautiful and peacefully situated inland course with age-old trees bordering the undulating fairways. The course is of championship standard and was designed by Robert Trent Jones (one of his first creations in Europe) who included several strategically placed water hazards. *SSS 72*

GF $$ — 1965 — 18

— R. Trent Jones — L 5986 P 72

S R

Required : Handicap Certificate
Best days : Weekdays

HOLE	LENGTH MEDAL-TEE	PAR	STROKE INDEX
1	327	4	9
2	467	5	11
3	361	4	7
4	438	5	15
5	132	3	17
6	358	4	5
7	378	4	1
8	200	3	13
9	531	5	3
TOTAL	3192	37	TOTAL

HOLE	LENGTH MEDAL-TEE	PAR	STROKE INDEX
10	184	3	10
11	376	4	4
12	369	4	8
13	460	5	2
14	148	3	18
15	343	4	14
16	159	3	16
17	450	5	6
18	305	4	12
TOTAL	2794	35	TOTAL

BOSSENSTEIN

TEL : (03)4856446
LOCATION : 7 km Lier/15 km Antwerpen
E 313-E 39 exit 19
ADDRESS : Moor 16 - 2520 Broechem
HOTEL :
Switel - Antwerpen
Tel : (03)2316780
Carlton - Antwerpen
Tel : (03)2311515
RESTAURANT : 't Fornuis - Antwerpen
Tel : (03)2336270

Set within the grounds of the restored 14th century fortress «Castle Bossenstein», this is a well balanced course with several expanses of water laid out on flat countryside. The clubhouse, overlooking the 1st hole, features an english style bar and an elegant restaurant. Another main activity of this new country club is its polo club with stabling facilities for 50 polo ponies. Adjoining the clubhouse is a squash court, and hotelrooms for guests are planned for 1990. *SSS 72*

GF

1988

27

Mondays

P. Rolin

L 6148 P 72, 1436 P 29

S

R

Required : Handicap Certificate
Best days : Weekdays

HOLE	LENGTH MEDAL-TEE	PAR	STROKE INDEX
1	240	4	17
2	342	4	7
3	350	4	5
4	382	4	3
5	464	5	9
6	385	4	11
7	405	4	1
8	167	3	13
9	339	4	17
TOTAL	3074	36	TOTAL

HOLE	LENGTH MEDAL-TEE	PAR	STROKE INDEX
10	337	4	10
11	289	4	18
12	424	4	2
13	349	4	8
14	489	5	4
15	337	4	14
16	174	3	12
17	365	4	16
18	365	4	6
TOTAL	3129	36	TOTAL

BRABANTSE

TEL : (02)7518205
LOCATION : 10 km NE. Bruxelles near Zaventem airport
ADDRESS : Steenwagenstraat 11-1820 Melsbroek
HOTEL :
Sheraton Airport - Zaventem
Tel : (02)7251000
Novotel - Diegem
Tel : (02)7205830
RESTAURANT : Comme chez Soi - Bruxelles
Tel : (02)5122921

Built on a typical flemish landscape, this friendly club is right by the motorway ring around Bruxelles and Zaventem airport. Though comparatively short, it features several interesting holes running through flat open terrain with trees and shrubs. The course is centered around an old attractive castle which now serves as clubhouse. *SSS 65*

GF $

1988

18

—

P. Rolin

L 4618 P 69

S

R

Required : Handicap Certificate
Best days : Any day

HOLE	LENGTH MEDAL-TEE	PAR	STROKE INDEX
1	278	4	17
2	229	4	15
3	178	3	1
4	474	5	13
5	250	4	11
6	262	4	9
7	305	4	5
8	315	4	7
9	154	3	3
TOTAL	2445	35	TOTAL

HOLE	LENGTH MEDAL-TEE	PAR	STROKE INDEX
10	459	5	16
11	324	4	8
12	199	3	2
13	130	3	12
14	271	4	10
15	220	4	14
16	84	3	6
17	242	4	18
18	274	4	4
TOTAL	2203	34	TOTAL

CHÂTEAU DE LA BAWETTE

TEL : (010)223332
LOCATION : 25 km Bruxelles E 411 exit N° 5
ADDRESS : Chaussée du Château de la Bawette 5 - 1300 Wavre
HOTEL :
Le Domaine des Champs - Wavre
Tel : (010)227525
Etap - Lauzelle
Tel : (010)410751
RESTAURANT : Le Grand Duc - Wavre
Tel : (010)227517

The Irish architect Tom McAuley designed this sporting and varied course which is set in a private estate of unspoiled landscape (95ha). The holes run through rolling parkland, cross forests and are flanked by ageld trees. Scenic lakes and ponds affect play on the second nine holes. The imposing clubhouse comprises a sauna and a fitness club. *SSS 72*

GF $

1988

27

—

T. Mc Auley, J. Capart

L 6049 P 72, 2130 P 33

S

R

Required : Handicap Certificate
Best days : Weekdays

HOLE	LENGTH MEDAL-TEE	PAR	STROKE INDEX
1	331	4	9
2	342	4	11
3	499	5	15
4	176	3	17
5	347	4	13
6	190	3	5
7	439	5	7
8	371	4	1
9	380	4	3
TOTAL	3075	36	TOTAL

HOLE	LENGTH MEDAL-TEE	PAR	STROKE INDEX
10	376	4	4
11	247	4	16
12	465	5	18
13	329	4	10
14	153	3	14
15	351	4	2
16	445	5	12
17	221	3	6
18	397	4	8
TOTAL	2984	36	TOTAL

CHÂTEAU ROYAL D'ARDENNE

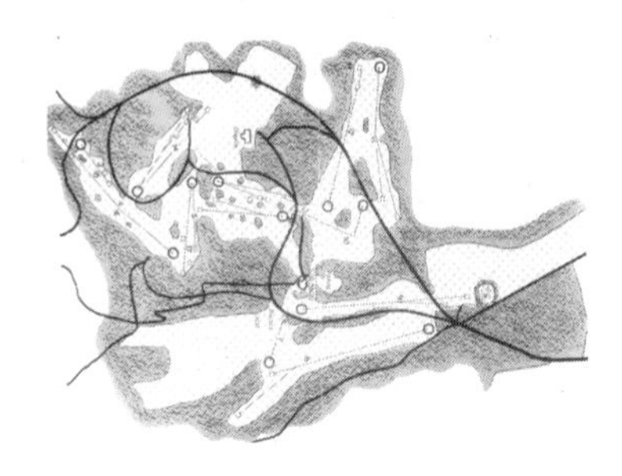

TEL : (082)666228
LOCATION : 18 km Dinant N48/N29
ADDRESS : Tour Léopold – Ardenne 6 – 5560 Houyet
HOTEL :
Marquisette – Houyet
Tel : (082)666429
Le Fenil – Celles
Tel : (082)666760
Val Joli – Celles
Tel : (082)666363
RESTAURANT : Lesse – Houyet
Tel : (082)666402

Laid out in typical Ardenne landscape, this is an attractive inland course, set on lush and well-wooded countryside. Although not of championship length, the course is a fine test for the average golfer having several picturesque holes.

GF $ — — S

1910 — 

18 L 5333 P 71 R

Required : None
Best days : Weekdays

HOLE	LENGTH MEDAL-TEE	PAR	STROKE INDEX
1	272	4	9
2	235	4	11
3	140	3	15
4	512	5	1
5	183	3	5
6	250	4	13
7	164	3	17
8	486	5	3
9	433	5	7
TOTAL	2675	36	TOTAL

HOLE	LENGTH MEDAL-TEE	PAR	STROKE INDEX
10	303	4	12
11	340	4	6
12	359	4	2
13	194	3	10
14	304	4	8
15	140	3	18
16	512	5	4
17	256	4	14
18	250	4	16
TOTAL	2658	35	TOTAL

CLEYDAEL

TEL : (03)8870079
LOCATION : 8 km S. Antwerpen to Bruxelles
ADDRESS : Château Cleydael - Cleydael-laan-36 - 2630 Aartselaar
HOTEL :
H Castle Cleydael
Tel : (03) 8870079
Kasteelhoeve Groeninghe-Aartselaar
Tel : (03)4579586
Crest-Antwerpen
Tel : (03)2372900
RESTAURANT : Lindenbos-Aartselaar
Tel : (03)8880965

The new 18 hole 'Cleydael' golf club, situated in the parish of Aartselaar near Antwerpen, is laid out in the grounds of the scenic 13th century 'Château Cleydael', a former property of Cromwell's uncle. It runs through flat and luxuriant parkland with majestic trees lining the fairways, alternating with rhododendrons and clumps of azaleas. Several lakes serve as hazards. The clubhouse is located in the outbuildings of the château, the club restaurant and golfhotel are situated in the château itself, which is surrounded by a moat, with access by help of a drawbridge. *SSS 72*

GF $ — Mondays in winter — S

1988 — P. Rolin

18 — L 6059 P 72 — R

Required : Handicap Certificate
Best days : Weekdays

HOLE	LENGTH MEDAL-TEE	PAR	STROKE INDEX
1	478	5	11
2	364	4	5
3	171	3	15
4	289	4	17
5	381	4	9
6	458	5	3
7	384	4	1
8	351	4	7
9	128	3	13
TOTAL	3004	36	TOTAL

HOLE	LENGTH MEDAL-TEE	PAR	STROKE INDEX
10	307	4	14
11	380	4	12
12	451	5	10
13	300	4	16
14	148	3	18
15	414	4	2
16	206	3	4
17	474	5	8
18	375	4	9
TOTAL	3055	36	TOTAL

DAMME

TEL : (050)353572
LOCATION : 7 km Brugge N 49 exit Damme
ADDRESS : Doornstraat 16 - 8340 Damme-Sijsele
HOTEL :
Orangerie - Brugge
Tel : (050)341649
Oud Huis Amsterdam - Brugge
Tel : (050)341810
De Gulden Kogge - Damme
Tel : (050)354217
RESTAURANT : Bruegel - Oostkerke
Tel : (050)500346

This charming golf course is just a short drive from the coast and from the magnificent ancient city of Bruges. Set on flat green pasture land amidst poplars and willows, it is encircled by bodies of water totaling 4ha. A former farmhouse has been converted into a cosy clubhouse. *SSS 72*

  $

 1988

 27

 —

 D. van Heel

 5886 P 72

Required : Handicap Certificate
Best days : Any day

HOLE	LENGTH MEDAL-TEE	PAR	STROKE INDEX
1	345	4	9
2	373	4	5
3	468	5	7
4	278	4	13
5	137	3	17
6	282	4	15
7	416	4	1
8	186	3	11
9	438	5	3
TOTAL	2923	36	TOTAL

HOLE	LENGTH MEDAL-TEE	PAR	STROKE INDEX
10	285	4	14
11	378	4	2
12	461	5	6
13	208	3	16
14	368	4	4
15	335	4	12
16	473	5	10
17	145	3	18
18	310	4	8
TOTAL	2963	36	TOTAL

FALNUÉE

TEL : (081)633090
LOCATION : 18 km NW Namur/6 km Gembloux
ADDRESS : Chaussée de Nivelles 34 - 5032 Mazy
HOTEL :
Les 3 Clés - Gembloux
Tel : (081)611617
Château de Namur - Namur
Tel : (081)222546
RESTAURANT : Prince de Liège - Gembloux
Tel : (081)611244

This attractive golf club lies at the confluence of two rivers 'l'Orneau and la Ligne' on 50ha of rolling valleys. Hillocks and forests lined by natural streams make up this natural landscape. In the center of the course stands the historical farmhouse/château de Falnuée which dates back to the 13th century and now serves as the clubhouse. *SSS 69*

GF $
1988
18

Mondays
J. Jottrand
L 5445 P 70

S

R

Required : Handicap Certificate
Best days : Weekdays

HOLE	LENGTH MEDAL-TEE	PAR	STROKE INDEX
1	140	3	9
2	356	4	5
3	490	5	3
4	169	3	13
5	347	4	17
6	321	4	1
7	182	3	7
8	500	5	11
9	127	3	15
TOTAL	2632	34	TOTAL

HOLE	LENGTH MEDAL-TEE	PAR	STROKE INDEX
10	361	4	2
11	310	4	16
12	243	4	14
13	327	4	10
14	338	4	6
15	267	4	8
16	368	4	4
17	158	3	12
18	441	5	18
TOTAL	2813	36	TOTAL

FLANDERS-NIPPON

TEL : (011)223793
LOCATION : 3 km Hasselt to Diepenbeek University
ADDRESS : Vissenbroekstraat 15 - 3500 Hasselt
HOTEL :
Scholteshof - Stevoort
Tel : (011)250202
Park - Hasselt
Tel : (011)211652
RESTAURANT : Kasteel St. Paul - Lummen
Tel : (013)521809

Situated in the province of Limburg close to the Dutch border, the golf club has been founded on the initiative of the City of Hasselt, twin city of Itami in Japan in the aim of promoting the economic and culturel relations between Flanders and Japan. It features a varied 18 hole course and a 9 hole junior course. Both are laid out on flat landscape, featuring parkland and meadowland, with groups of tall trees separating some of the fairways. The clubhouse offers a European and a Japanese cuisine. *SSS 72*

GF $

1988

27

—

P. Rolin, J. Wirtz

L 5992 P 72, 1779 P 31

S

R

Required : Handicap Certificate
Best days : Any day

HOLE	LENGTH MEDAL-TEE	PAR	STROKE INDEX
1	338	4	7
2	285	4	11
3	396	4	1
4	164	3	15
5	328	4	5
6	466	5	13
7	150	3	17
8	469	5	3
9	350	4	9
TOTAL	2946	36	TOTAL

HOLE	LENGTH MEDAL-TEE	PAR	STROKE INDEX
10	511	5	2
11	369	4	6
12	148	3	18
13	340	4	10
14	341	4	4
15	337	4	12
16	350	4	8
17	160	3	16
18	490	5	14
TOTAL	3046	36	TOTAL

HENRI-CHAPELLE

TEL : (087)881991
LOCATION : 30 km Liège, 15 km Aachen N3
ADDRESS : rue du Vivier 3-4841 Henri Chapelle
HOTEL :
Rathaus - Eupen
Tel : (087)742812
L'Amigo - Verviers
Tel : (087)316767
RESTAURANT : Le Vivier - Henri-Chapelle
Tel : (087)880412

Only 20 minutes drive from Liège not far from the German and Dutch borders, this international golf club opened for play in 1990. The 27 holes are harmoniously laid out on 70 hectares of unspoiled rolling meadowlands with old trees and ponds guarding some of the fairways. Well shaped bunkers add an extra challenge to play on this course. The clubhouse, a converted 18th century manor house, has conference facilities, a swimming pool and a health and fitness club.

GF $ — — S
1990 — D. van Heel — R
27 — L 5608 P 72, 2220 P 34

Required : Handicap Certificate
Best days : Weekdays

HOLE	LENGTH MEDAL-TEE	PAR	STROKE INDEX
1	427	5	13
2	298	4	5
3	297	4	15
4	279	4	11
5	253	4	9
6	302	4	1
7	167	3	7
8	472	5	3
9	126	3	17
TOTAL	2621	36	TOTAL

HOLE	LENGTH MEDAL-TEE	PAR	STROKE INDEX
10	331	4	8
11	192	3	18
12	293	4	14
13	437	5	2
14	183	3	16
15	484	5	4
16	338	4	10
17	394	4	6
18	335	4	12
TOTAL	2987	36	TOTAL

INTERNATIONAL GOMZE

TEL : (041)609207
LOCATION : 15 km S. Liège E 25 exit 43 to Bastogne/Spa
ADDRESS : 30, rue Gomzé - 4941 Gomzé Andoumont
HOTEL :
Dorint -Spa
Tel : (087)772581
Auberge au Vieux Hêtre - Spa
Tel : (087)647092
RESTAURANT : Le Plein Vent - Liège
Tel : (041)516336

Laid out in lush rolling countryside between the cities of Spa and Liège, this well balanced course runs through valleys, orchards and plains dotted with century old trees. It commands some nice views of the surroundings such as the tiny village of Andoumont which is situated on a hillside overlooking the course. *SSS 72*

GF $

 Mondays

 1988

P. Rolin/J. Capart

 5623 P 72

R

Required : Handicap Certificate
Best days : Any day

HOLE	LENGTH MEDAL-TEE	PAR	STROKE INDEX
1	345	4	6
2	319	4	8
3	219	4	16
4	160	3	10
5	292	4	15
6	352	4	2
7	484	5	13
8	435	5	14
9	124	3	18
TOTAL	2730	36	TOTAL

HOLE	LENGTH MEDAL-TEE	PAR	STROKE INDEX
10	350	4	4
11	147	3	17
12	500	5	5
13	367	4	1
14	347	4	3
15	282	4	9
16	168	3	7
17	301	4	11
18	436	5	12
TOTAL	2898	36	TOTAL

KAMPENHOUT

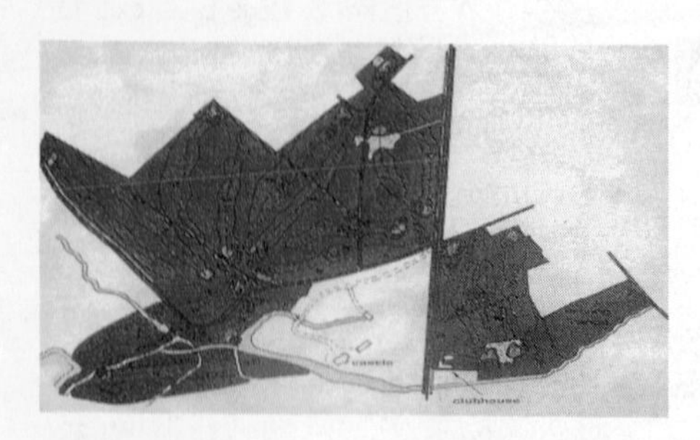

TEL : (016)651216
LOCATION : 12 km Bruxelles near Zaventem Airport
ADDRESS : Wildersedreef 56-3090 Kampenhout
HOTEL :
Holiday Inn - Diegem
Tel : (02)7205865
Novotel - Diegem
Tel : (02)7205830
RESTAURANT : Romeyer - Groenendaal
Tel : (02)6570581

Located at less than 10 minutes from the Brussel's ring road and very close to Zaventem airport, the Kampenhout course is perfectly integrated into its natural flat surroundings. Three of the holes are laid out in the lush parklands of the stately Wilder castle. Two rivers and three lakes come into play on several holes. *SSS 71*

GF $ — S

1989 R. de Vooght

18 L 5864 P 72 R

Required : Handicap Certificate
Best days : Any day

HOLE	LENGTH MEDAL-TEE	PAR	STROKE INDEX
1	331	4	5
2	329	4	11
3	124	3	17
4	286	4	13
5	326	4	3
6	454	5	7
7	378	4	1
8	327	4	15
9	346	4	9
TOTAL	2901	36	TOTAL

HOLE	LENGTH MEDAL-TEE	PAR	STROKE INDEX
10	188	3	14
11	263	4	10
12	390	4	4
13	483	5	2
14	328	4	16
15	458	5	8
16	152	3	18
17	359	4	6
18	342	4	12
TOTAL	2963	36	TOTAL

KEMPENSE

TEL : (014)816234
LOCATION : 3 km Mol, 23 km Turnhout
ADDRESS : Kiezelweg 78 2400 Mol-Rauw
HOTEL :
Molinas - Mol
Tel : (014)313764
Ritz - Balen Wezel
RESTAURANT : De Engel - Balen
Tel : (014)811906

Laid out in the Flemish province of Kempen close to the Dutch border, this course stretches out over flat countryside landscaped by trees. A strategic river and some ponds affect play on several holes. A road divides the course.

GF $

1990

18

—

—

L 5756 P 72

S

R

Required : Club Membership Card
Best days : Weekdays

HOLE	LENGTH MEDAL-TEE	PAR	STROKE INDEX
1	494	5	8
2	126	3	17
3	350	4	7
4	214	3	4
5	256	4	18
6	184	3	6
7	439	5	9
8	164	3	5
9	522	5	10
TOTAL	2749	35	TOTAL

HOLE	LENGTH MEDAL-TEE	PAR	STROKE INDEX
10	343	4	3
11	299	4	16
12	540	5	1
13	435	5	12
14	144	3	14
15	140	3	13
16	512	5	11
17	129	3	15
18	465	5	2
TOTAL	3007	37	TOTAL

KEERBERGEN

TEL : (015)234961
LOCATION : 20 km Leuven, 30 km Bruxelles
ADDRESS : Vlieghavenlaan 50 – 2850 Keerbergen
HOTEL :
Hostellerie Berkenhof – Keerbergen
Tel : (015)234803
La Royale – Leuven
Tel : (016)221252
Château de Namur – Blanden
Tel : (016)226095
RESTAURANT : The Lake – Keerbergen
Tel : (015)235069

Laid out on the edge of a lake, the course lies in the middle of a wood with numerous water hazards such as a stream crossing the 4th and 6th holes, and a pond on the 12th and 16th holes. The Hostellerie Berkenhof near the course is a Relais & Châteaux hotel with seven rooms. *SSS 69*

GF $

1969

18

—

F. Pennink

L 5530 P 70

S

R

Required : Handicap Certificate
Best days : Weekdays

HOLE	LENGTH MEDAL-TEE	PAR	STROKE INDEX
1	293	4	11
2	122	3	17
3	349	4	3
4	508	5	5
5	138	3	15
6	369	4	1
7	458	5	9
8	156	3	13
9	297	4	7
TOTAL	2690	35	TOTAL

HOLE	LENGTH MEDAL-TEE	PAR	STROKE INDEX
10	147	3	18
11	410	4	2
12	440	5	8
13	176	3	14
14	355	4	4
15	141	3	16
16	449	5	12
17	357	4	10
18	365	4	6
TOTAL	2840	35	TOTAL

KONINKLIJKE OOSTENDE

TEL : (059)233283
LOCATION : 9 km Oostende N 72
ADDRESS : Koninklijke Baan 2 – 8420 De Haan
HOTEL :
Dunes – De Haan
Tel : (059)233146
Auberge des Rois – De Haan
Tel : (059)233685
Carpe Diem – De Haan
Tel : (059)233220
RESTAURANT : Cœur Volant – De Haan
Tel : (059)233567

A pleasant links course bordering the windy North Sea and laid out near the seaside resort of Oostende. The course is short and does not present many difficulties for the average golfer. There is a fine view of the sea, and inland, from the 7th tee. *SSS 68*

GF $ — — S

1902 — —

18 L 5227 P 70 R

Required : Handicap Certificate
Best days : Weekdays

HOLE	LENGTH MEDAL-TEE	PAR	STROKE INDEX
1	245	4	11
2	440	5	7
3	290	4	5
4	125	3	15
5	442	5	3
6	382	4	1
7	128	3	17
8	320	4	9
9	132	3	13
TOTAL	2504	35	TOTAL

HOLE	LENGTH MEDAL-TEE	PAR	STROKE INDEX
10	398	4	2
11	139	3	18
12	300	4	8
13	166	3	16
14	447	5	6
15	271	4	14
16	309	4	10
17	195	3	12
18	498	5	4
TOTAL	2723	35	TOTAL

LA BRUYÈRE

TEL : (071)877267
LOCATION : 15 km Nivelles, 17 km Charleroi
ADDRESS : rue de Jumerée 1-6328 Sart-Dames-Avelines
HOTEL :
Motel Nivelles - Nivelles
Tel : (067)218721
Socatel - Charleroi
Tel : (071)319811
La Falise - Nivelles
Tel : (067)773511

This course situated between the cities of Nivelles and Charleroi, has its holes heading through former farmlands on flat open landscape. *SSS 72*

GF $

—

R S

1990

F. Theys

18

L 5937 P 71

Required : Handicap Certificate
Best days : Any day

HOLE	LENGTH MEDAL-TEE	PAR	STROKE INDEX
1	254	4	18
2	314	4	17
3	189	3	5
4	324	4	9
5	406	4	1
6	322	4	14
7	202	3	13
8	510	5	3
9	409	4	2
TOTAL	2930	35	TOTAL

HOLE	LENGTH MEDAL-TEE	PAR	STROKE INDEX
10	490	5	4
11	323	4	16
12	135	3	6
13	332	4	15
14	362	4	10
15	335	4	8
16	381	4	7
17	489	5	11
18	160	3	12
TOTAL	3007	36	TOTAL

LA TOURNETTE

TEL : (067)219525
LOCATION : 29 km Bruxelles E 19
ADDRESS : Chemin de Baudemont 2-1400 Nivelles
HOTEL :
Mortel Nivelles Sud-Nivelles
Tel : (067)218721
Le Relais du Marquis-Ittre
Tel : (067)647171
RESTAURANT : L'haubergeron-Nivelles
Tel : (067)212914

This new golf complex will without doubt become one of Belgiums most prestigious golf clubs. The first 18 hole course, fully operational in 1989, was designed by the American William Amick and will be the main championship layout. The other, planned for spring 1991, will be created by Hawtree & Son. Both are built around the clubhouse, an impressive château dating back to 1635 and several old farmhouses. They run over plains and through lush parkland alternating with woodland. The American course features spacious fairways, large bunkers, big greens, and numerous water hazards.

GF $ — Mondays — S

1989 — W. Amick — R

18 — L 6495 P 72

Required : Handicap Certificate
Best days : Any day

HOLE	LENGTH MEDAL-TEE	PAR	STROKE INDEX
1	395	4	
2	340	4	
3	230	3	
4	455	5	
5	345	4	
6	510	5	
7	190	3	
8	420	4	
9	380	4	
TOTAL	3265	36	TOTAL

HOLE	LENGTH MEDAL-TEE	PAR	STROKE INDEX
10	365	4	
11	390	4	
12	545	5	
13	185	3	
14	370	4	
15	390	4	
16	150	3	
17	460	5	
18	375	4	
TOTAL	3230	36	TOTAL

LOUVAIN-LA-NEUVE

TEL : (010)452801
LOCATION : 5 km Wavre 25 km Bruxelles E411 exit n° 7
ADDRESS : Drève de Lauzelle - 1348 Louvain-la-Neuve
HOTEL :
Château de Limelette - Louvain-la-Neuve
Tel : (010)419999
Le Domaine des Champs - Wavre
Tel : (010)227525
RESTAURANT : Cuisine des Champs - Wavre
Tel : (010)225462

A typical inland course, Louvain-la-Neuve is well wooded with lush green fairways set on flat countryside. It features a well designed pattern of holes with mature trees, strategic bunkers, rolling greens and tricky water obstacles. Facilities include a golf school and a 4 hole par 3 course.

GF $ | Tuesdays | R S
1989 | D. van Heel
18 | L 6047 P 72

Required : Handicap Certificate
Best days : Any day

HOLE	LENGTH MEDAL-TEE	PAR	STROKE INDEX
1	355	4	11
2	470	5	7
3	315	4	3
4	194	3	13
5	371	4	5
6	375	4	9
7	166	3	15
8	505	5	1
9	347	4	17
TOTAL	3098	36	TOTAL

HOLE	LENGTH MEDAL-TEE	PAR	STROKE INDEX
10	340	4	8
11	272	4	14
12	488	5	12
13	376	4	4
14	125	3	16
15	413	4	2
16	175	3	18
17	324	4	6
18	436	5	10
TOTAL	2949	36	TOTAL

MONT GARNI

TEL : (065)622719
LOCATION : near Mons, exit n° 25 of A7 to Baudour
ADDRESS : rue du Mont Garni 3-7420 Saint-Ghislain
HOTEL :
Amigo - Masnuy-St.-Jean
Tel : (065)723685
Résidence - Mons
Tel : (065)311403
RESTAURANT : Brasserie Fermez - Monz
Tel : (065)644467

Designed by the British architect Tom McAuley on 65 ha of flat parkland, this course, one of the longest in Belgium, has a varied layout featuring well designed holes. Mature trees and scenic lakes create problems on some of the fairways. The club boasts a cosy Anglo-Normand style clubhouse. *SSS 73*

GF $

1990

18

—

T. Mc Auley

L 6041 P 74

 S

Required : Handicap Certificate
Best days : Weekdays

HOLE	LENGTH MEDAL-TEE	PAR	STROKE INDEX
1	303	4	15
2	170	3	5
3	431	5	7
4	378	4	1
5	161	3	11
6	426	5	9
7	439	5	13
8	294	4	17
9	376	4	3
TOTAL	2978	37	TOTAL

HOLE	LENGTH MEDAL-TEE	PAR	STROKE INDEX
10	351	4	10
11	349	4	16
12	158	3	18
13	464	5	6
14	321	4	4
15	192	3	12
16	423	5	14
17	474	5	2
18	331	4	8
TOTAL	3063	37	TOTAL

LIMBURG

TEL : (011)383543
LOCATION : 15 km Hasselt
ADDRESS : Golfstraat 1 – 3530 Houthalen
HOTEL :
Uilenspiegel – Zwartberg Genk
Tel : (011)380157
Parkhotel – Hasselt
Tel : (011)211652
Scholteshof – Stevoort
Tel : (011)250202
RESTAURANT : Steakhouse – Houthalen-Helcherten
Tel : (011)533500

The Limburg golf course lies in Flanders. It is a typical heathland course set on sandy soil with its holes running through wooded landscape. There is only one water hazard which is the pond near the clubhouse on the opening hole. *SSS 72*

GF $

1966

18

—

—

L 5687 P 72

S

R

Required : Handicap Certificate
Best days : Mondays, Wednesdays, Fridays

HOLE	LENGTH MEDAL-TEE	PAR	STROKE INDEX
1	366	4	5
2	338	4	11
3	124	3	17
4	300	4	9
5	447	5	1
6	157	3	15
7	465	5	7
8	271	4	13
9	365	4	3
TOTAL	2833	36	TOTAL

HOLE	LENGTH MEDAL-TEE	PAR	STROKE INDEX
10	267	4	16
11	183	3	10
12	386	4	2
13	449	5	8
14	348	4	6
15	149	3	18
16	337	4	4
17	292	4	14
18	443	5	12
TOTAL	2854	36	TOTAL

OUDENAARDE

TEL : (055)315481
LOCATION : 4 km Oudenaarde N 59
ADDRESS : Kortrijkstraat 52 – 9790 Wortegem-Petegem
HOTEL :
Elnik – Oudenaarde
Tel : (055)313788
Da Vinci – Oudenaarde
Tel : (055)311305
De Ranterre – Oudenaarde
Tel : (055)318988
RESTAURANT : Hostellerie Pomme d'Or – Oudenaarde
Tel : (055)311900

A picturesque parkland course with many water hazards including the river 'Oude Schelde' meandering its way through the course. The clubhouse is in a stately château with a fine terrace in front of the first tee, overlooking the course. *SSS 71*

GF $
—
S

1976
M. Baker, H. James

18
L 5673 P 72
R

Required : Handicap Certificate
Best days : Weekdays

HOLE	LENGTH MEDAL-TEE	PAR	STROKE INDEX
1	322	4	7
2	435	5	5
3	317	4	9
4	150	3	17
5	322	4	3
6	154	3	15
7	466	5	1
8	145	3	13
9	305	4	11
TOTAL	2616	35	TOTAL

HOLE	LENGTH MEDAL-TEE	PAR	STROKE INDEX
10	365	4	6
11	455	5	4
12	122	3	18
13	302	4	14
14	445	5	12
15	380	4	2
16	172	3	16
17	368	4	8
18	448	5	10
TOTAL	3057	37	TOTAL

RIGENEE

TEL : (071)877765
LOCATION : 20 km Charleroi/Namur
ADDRESS : 10 a rue du Châtelet – 6321 Villers-la-Ville
HOTEL :
De la Falise – Baisy-Thy
Tel : (067)773511
Le Méditerranée – Charleroi
Tel : (071)317424
Socatel Diplomat – Charleroi
Tel : (071)319811
RESTAURANT : De la Collégiale – Nivelles
Tel : (067)219898

Designed in 1982 by the Belgian golf architect Paul Rolin, the course runs through flat and wooded countryside. It features four water hazards, including a strategic pond guarding the 14th hole. *SSS 72*

GF $ — Tuesdays — S

1982 — P. Rolin

18 — L 5936 P 72 — R

Required : None
Best days : Weekdays

HOLE	LENGTH MEDAL-TEE	PAR	STROKE INDEX
1	282	4	17
2	344	4	9
3	364	4	5
4	343	4	15
5	168	3	13
6	475	5	1
7	196	3	7
8	470	5	11
9	357	4	3
TOTAL	2989	36	TOTAL

HOLE	LENGTH MEDAL-TEE	PAR	STROKE INDEX
10	366	4	4
11	498	5	2
12	324	4	10
13	336	4	12
14	166	3	8
15	317	4	16
16	463	5	6
17	331	4	14
18	146	3	18
TOTAL	2947	36	TOTAL

RINKVEN INTERNATIONAL

TEL : (03)3840784
LOCATION : 17 km Antwerpen E 10
ADDRESS : Sint Jobsesteenweg 120-'s-Gravenwezel – 2232 Schilde
HOTEL :
Carlton – Antwerpen
Tel : (03)2311515
Antwerp Tower – Antwerpen
Tel : (03)2340120
De Keyser – Antwerpen
Tel : (03)2340135
RESTAURANT : Halewijn-Brasschaat
Tel : (03)6472010

Designed by the Belgian architect Paul Rolin, this is one of the country's newest golf courses laid out near Antwerpen. There are three different loops of nine holes laid out on flat wooded terrain with several small ponds serving as hazards. *SSS 72*

GF $$ — 1982 — 27

— — P. Rolin — L 2890 P 36, 2956 P 37, 2816 P 36

S — R

Required : Handicap Certificate
Best days : Weekdays

HOLE	LENGTH MEDAL-TEE	PAR	STROKE INDEX	HOLE	LENGTH MEDAL-TEE	PAR	STROKE INDEX	HOLE	LENGTH MEDAL-TEE	PAR	STROKE INDEX
1	334	4	5	1	447	5	2	1	340	4	4
2	146	3	6	2	162	3	6	2	317	4	6
3	301	4	8	3	339	4	1	3	138	3	7
4	339	4	2	4	289	4	7	4	332	4	2
5	435	5	9	5	454	5	3	5	145	3	9
6	470	5	1	6	141	3	9	6	359	4	1
7	345	4	4	7	300	4	8	7	426	5	3
8	345	4	3	8	453	5	4	8	307	4	8
9	175	3	7	9	371	4	5	9	452	5	5
TOTAL	2890	36	TOTAL	TOTAL	2956	37	TOTAL	TOTAL	2816	36	TOTAL

ROYAL ANTWERP

TEL : (03)6668456
LOCATION : 20 km Antwerpen E 3
ADDRESS : George Capiaulei – 2080 Kapellen
HOTEL :
't Ven – Kalmthout
Tel : (03)6666838
Pullman Park – Antwerpen
Tel : (03)2164800
Waldorf – Antwerpen
Tel : (03)2309950
RESTAURANT : De Graal – Kapellen
Tel : (03)6665510

This outstanding golf course is one of Europe's oldest after the Pau golf club, having been founded in 1888. Laid out on woodland by Willie Park, it was redesigned in 1920 by Tom Simpson. All the eighteen holes are well-designed and testing with fairways running through heather, shrub, pine trees and silver birch. It features many difficult dog-leg holes (9th, 10th, 14th), small greens, few bunkers and several water hazards. The 17th hole, known as the 'Bloody Bidet' is the most difficult one. *SSS 72*

GF $$
1888
27

—
T. Simpson, W. Park
L 5958 P 73, 2294 P 34

S
R

Required : Handicap Certificate
Best days : Wednesdays

HOLE	LENGTH MEDAL-TEE	PAR	STROKE INDEX
1	298	4	17
2	173	3	11
3	439	5	9
4	331	4	5
5	436	5	13
6	368	4	1
7	165	3	15
8	358	4	3
9	378	4	7
TOTAL	2946	36	TOTAL

HOLE	LENGTH MEDAL-TEE	PAR	STROKE INDEX
10	376	4	4
11	424	5	14
12	149	3	10
13	350	4	2
14	437	5	8
15	450	5	16
16	121	3	18
17	341	4	6
18	346	4	12
TOTAL	3012	37	TOTAL

ROYAL BELGIQUE

TEL : (02)7675801
LOCATION : 10 km Bruxelles N 3
ADDRESS : Château de Ravenstein – 1980 Tervuren
HOTEL :
Ramada Hotel – Bruxelles
Tel : (02)5393000
Bedford – Bruxelles
Tel : (02)5127840
Jolly Atlanta – Bruxelles
Tel : (02)2170020
RESTAURANT : Maison du Cygne – Bruxelles
Tel : (02)5118244

The Royal Belgique is Belgium's noblest golf club and one of Europe's best. Laid out in Tervuren, one of Brussel's suburbs, this is a typical inland course of the parkland type, built by royal command and laid out in the royal estate 'Ravenstein'. King Baudouin is still its honorary president. The course is long and varied with several dog-leg holes, deep bunkers and no water hazards. Among its feature holes is the testing 17th. There is an imposing and beautiful clubhouse dating back to the 17th century and now declared a national monument. *SSS 70*

GF $$

Mondays (15-10/1-05)

R S

1906

T. Simpson

27

L 5825 P 73, 1960 P 32

Required : Handicap Certificate: 24 Ladies, 20 Men
Best days : Mondays, Tuesdays, Fridays

HOLE	LENGTH MEDAL-TEE	PAR	STROKE INDEX
1	435	5	9
2	344	4	1
3	132	3	17
4	371	4	3
5	459	5	7
6	176	3	13
7	335	4	11
8	324	4	5
9	300	4	15
TOTAL	2876	36	TOTAL

HOLE	LENGTH MEDAL-TEE	PAR	STROKE INDEX
10	312	4	10
11	367	4	2
12	153	3	12
13	444	5	6
14	290	4	16
15	457	5	8
16	298	4	14
17	356	4	4
18	272	4	18
TOTAL	2949	37	TOTAL

ROYAL FAGNES

TEL : (087)771613
LOCATION : 2 km Spa N 629
ADDRESS : 4880 Spa
HOTEL :
Dorint – Balmoral
Tel : (087)772581
La Heid des Pairs – Spa
Tel : (087)877346
Le Relais Ardennois – Spa
Tel : (087)771108
RESTAURANT : Grand Maur – Spa
Tel : (087)773616

Royal Fagnes is one of Belgiums most scenic golf courses laid out on beautiful countryside near Spa. The course is of excellent quality with its fairways running through gently rolling woodland with fine overall views. *SSS 70*

GF $$ — — R S
1930 —
18 L 5671 P 72

Required : Handicap Certificate, Club Membership Card
Best days : Any day

HOLE	LENGTH MEDAL-TEE	PAR	STROKE INDEX
1	425	5	9
2	132	3	16
3	431	5	5
4	310	4	11
5	396	4	1
6	107	3	18
7	380	4	3
8	163	3	13
9	453	5	7
TOTAL	2797	36	TOTAL

HOLE	LENGTH MEDAL-TEE	PAR	STROKE INDEX
10	304	4	10
11	179	3	17
12	397	4	2
13	452	5	12
14	162	3	15
15	465	5	4
16	325	4	8
17	245	4	14
18	345	4	6
TOTAL	2874	36	TOTAL

ROYAL HAINAUT

TEL : (065)229474/229610
LOCATION : 6 km Mons N 56
ADDRESS : 7434 Erbisoeul-lez-Mons
HOTEL :
Amigo – Masnuy-Saint-Jean
Tel : (065)723685
Résidence – Mons
Tel : (065)311403
RESTAURANT : Devos – Mons
Tel : (065)351335

Royal Hainaut is a pleasant inland course laid out on wooded countryside. Most of its fairways are separated from each other by age-old trees. The course features several well-defended greens demanding accuracy. An additional 9 hole course has been opened in 1990. *SSS 72*

GF $

1934

27

Tues. (Ladies Day)

—

L 6108 P 72

R S

Required : Handicap Certificate
Best days : Weekdays

HOLE	LENGTH MEDAL-TEE	PAR	STROKE INDEX
1	452	5	7
2	346	4	11
3	388	4	1
4	189	3	15
5	361	4	5
6	176	3	17
7	493	5	13
8	363	4	9
9	381	4	3
TOTAL	3149	36	TOTAL

HOLE	LENGTH MEDAL-TEE	PAR	STROKE INDEX
10	288	4	16
11	502	5	4
12	169	3	12
13	489	5	8
14	367	4	6
15	354	4	2
16	318	4	10
17	158	3	18
18	314	4	14
TOTAL	2959	36	TOTAL

ROYAL LATEM

★

TEL : (091)825411
LOCATION : 10 km Gent exit n° 14 of N 43
ADDRESS : Latemstraat 120 – 9830 St-Martens Latem
HOTEL :
Auberge du Pêcheur – Latem
Tel : (091)823144
Flanders – Gent
Tel : (091)226065
St. Jorishof – Gent
Tel : (091)242424
RESTAURANT : De Kroon – St. Martens Latem
Tel : (091)823856

Royal Latem is one of the oldest golf clubs in Belgium, having been founded in 1909 within a private property. It is a pleasant and classical course set within woodland on sandy soil with a friendly clubhouse to welcome golfers. The club hosted the Belgian Open in 1952 and 1957. *SSS 70*

GF $

1909

18

Mondays

—

L 5767 P 72

Required : Handicap Certificate
Best days : Weekdays

HOLE	LENGTH MEDAL-TEE	PAR	STROKE INDEX
1	309	4	16
2	439	5	12
3	199	3	6
4	375	4	2
5	312	4	4
6	463	5	10
7	298	4	8
8	107	3	18
9	302	4	14
TOTAL	2804	36	TOTAL

HOLE	LENGTH MEDAL-TEE	PAR	STROKE INDEX
10	481	5	7
11	331	4	3
12	443	5	13
13	363	4	1
14	128	3	17
15	340	4	5
16	149	3	15
17	348	4	11
18	380	4	9
TOTAL	2963	36	TOTAL

ROYAL SART-TILMAN

TEL : (041)362021
LOCATION : 8 km Liège N63
ADDRESS : Route du Condroz 541 – 4200 Ougrée (Liège)
HOTEL :
Hostellerie St-Roch – Comblain-la-Tour
Tel : (041)691333
Liège Moat House – Liège
Tel : (041)426020
Ramada – Liège
Tel : (041)224910
RESTAURANT : Le Franc Canard – Boncelles
Tel : (041)367465

Royal Sart-Tilman, designed by the famous English golf architect Tom Simpson, is a not too demanding golf course. It has a pleasant layout with its eighteen holes running through wooded countryside. There are no water hazards. *SSS 69*

GF $ | Mondays | S
1939 | T. Simpson | R
18 | L 5624 P 72

Required : Handicap Certificate
Best days : Tuesdays to Fridays inc.

HOLE	LENGTH MEDAL-TEE	PAR	STROKE INDEX
1	296	4	13
2	122	3	17
3	322	4	9
4	361	4	3
5	362	4	1
6	150	3	15
7	435	5	7
8	301	4	11
9	461	5	5
TOTAL	2810	36	TOTAL

HOLE	LENGTH MEDAL-TEE	PAR	STROKE INDEX
10	158	3	12
11	361	4	4
12	365	4	2
13	143	3	16
14	447	5	10
15	340	4	6
16	443	5	8
17	128	3	18
18	429	5	14
TOTAL	2814	36	TOTAL

ROYAL WATERLOO

★★★

TEL : (02)6331850/6331597
LOCATION : 4 km Waterloo, 22 km Bruxelles
ADDRESS : Vieux Chemin de Wavre 50
– 1328 Ohain
HOTEL :
Auberge de Waterloo – Ohain
Tel : (02)3585963
Le Coté Vert – Waterloo
Tel : (02)3540860
Métropole – Bruxelles
Tel : (02)2172300
RESTAURANT : Croque en Bouche – Ohain
Tel : (02)6331368

The celebrated golfer and architect Henry Cotton used to be the club's professional in 1930/34 at the original site of the Royal Waterloo. Later Fred Hawtree designed the first of the two 18 hole courses in Ohain, the present site of the golf club, and one of Belgiums famous championship courses. Both are laid out on gently rolling parkland with some fairways running through high beech wood and others over an undulating plain. Each of the thirty-six holes has its own individual character and offers a fine challenge. The Royal Waterloo golf courses are considered among the best in Europe. *SSS 73/74*

GF $$

1923

45

—

F. Hawtree

L 5871 P 73, 5858 P 72, 4286 P 66

S

R

Required : Handicap Certificate
Best days : Weekdays

La Marache Course

HOLE	LENGTH MEDAL-TEE	PAR	STROKE INDEX
1	352	4	11
2	321	4	17
3	474	5	5
4	157	3	15
5	419	5	3
6	353	4	1
7	139	3	13
8	319	4	9
9	356	4	7
TOTAL	2890	36	TOTAL

HOLE	LENGTH MEDAL-TEE	PAR	STROKE INDEX
10	357	4	16
11	349	4	4
12	166	3	10
13	360	4	2
14	341	4	6
15	142	3	18
16	411	5	8
17	448	5	12
18	407	5	14
TOTAL	2981	37	TOTAL

Le Lion Course

HOLE	LENGTH MEDAL-TEE	PAR	STROKE INDEX
1	475	5	7
2	348	4	1
3	166	3	9
4	325	4	5
5	140	3	17
6	323	4	15
7	353	4	3
8	356	4	13
9	482	5	11
TOTAL	2968	36	TOTAL

HOLE	LENGTH MEDAL-TEE	PAR	STROKE INDEX
10	319	4	12
11	155	3	14
12	290	4	16
13	328	4	10
14	175	3	6
15	463	5	8
16	375	4	4
17	333	4	2
18	452	5	18
TOTAL	2890	36	TOTAL

ROYAL ZOUTE

TEL : (050)601617/601227
LOCATION : 2 km Knokke
ADDRESS : Caddiespad 14-8300 Knokke-Heist
HOTEL : H
Dormy House
Tel : (050)601617
Bristol – Knokke Heist
Tel : (050)511220
Chenoy Manor – Duinbergen
Tel : (050)515529
RESTAURANT : Aquilon – Knokke-Heist
Tel : (050)601274

Situated near the famous seaside resort of Knokke-Le Zoute, 1km from the sea front, there are two 18 hole courses, a short one and the main championship layout encircling the shorter one. Both courses are of the parkland type with generous open fairways. The elegant clubhouse has a Dormy House with seven rooms for visiting golfers. *SSS 72/60*

GF $$ — 1910 — 36 — L 5415 P 72, 3677 P 64

S R

Required : Handicap Certificate and Club Membership Card
Best days : Weekdays ; Saturdays in low season

HOLE	LENGTH MEDAL-TEE	PAR	STROKE INDEX
1	346	4	7
2	321	4	11
3	115	3	17
4	318	4	3
5	378	5	13
6	342	4	1
7	321	4	5
8	155	3	15
9	330	4	9
TOTAL	2626	35	TOTAL

HOLE	LENGTH MEDAL-TEE	PAR	STROKE INDEX
10	301	4	4
11	156	3	16
12	428	5	8
13	355	4	2
14	302	4	14
15	382	5	10
16	125	3	18
17	428	5	6
18	312	4	12
TOTAL	2789	37	TOTAL

SEPT FONTAINES

TEL : (02)3530246
LOCATION : 15 km Bruxelles A7/E19, exit Tubize
ADDRESS : Chaussée d'Alsemberg 1021 - 1420 Braine-l'Alleud
HOTEL :
Auberge de Waterloo - St Genesius Rode
Tel : (02)3583580
Arcade Stéphanie - Bruxelles Sud
Tel : (02)5390240
RESTAURANT : 't Hoogveld - Alsemberg
Tel : (02)3803030

This new golf complex with its 2 golf courses (Le Château and La Forêt) near Bruxelles is centered around the scenic and historical Château l'Hermite, which now serves as its clubhouse. They are combined parkland/woodland courses, laid out in 100ha of lush green rolling countryside dotted with ponds. Other sports facilities include a short 9 hole course, a heated swimming pool and several tennis courts.

GF $
1988
36

Mondays
E. Rossi
L 5461 P 72, 4500 P 66

 S

R 

Required : Handicap Certificate
Best days : Any day

HOLE	LENGTH MEDAL-TEE	PAR	STROKE INDEX
1	294	4	7
2	265	4	13
3	385	5	5
4	312	4	11
5	420	5	3
6	154	3	9
7	296	4	15
8	144	3	17
9	358	4	1
TOTAL	2628	36	TOTAL

HOLE	LENGTH MEDAL-TEE	PAR	STROKE INDEX
10	349	4	2
11	328	4	16
12	145	3	18
13	310	4	14
14	417	5	4
15	307	4	8
16	350	4	6
17	181	3	10
18	446	5	12
TOTAL	2833	36	TOTAL

SPIEGELVEN

TEL : (011)359616
LOCATION : E 313 to Hasselt exit 314 to Aachen
ADDRESS : Wiemesmeerstraat 105 - 3600 Genk
HOTEL :
Condor - Genk
Tel : (011)355828
Atlantis - Genk
Tel : (011)356551
RESTAURANT : Het Riet - Genk
Tel : (011)351207

Set in typical Limburgian landscape close to the Dutch border, its 18 holes are set on fairly open countryside encircled by woodland and parkland. Strategic water spreads affect play on several holes. There is a modern and well equipped clubhouse. *SSS 72*

GF $

1989

18

—

Golf Engineering

L 6198 P 72

S

R

Required : Handicap Certificate
Best days : Mondays, Wednesdays and Fridays

HOLE	LENGTH MEDAL-TEE	PAR	STROKE INDEX
1	298	4	15
2	333	4	11
3	135	3	17
4	335	4	9
5	361	4	3
6	511	5	5
7	388	4	1
8	172	3	13
9	459	5	7
TOTAL	2992	36	TOTAL

HOLE	LENGTH MEDAL-TEE	PAR	STROKE INDEX
10	397	4	10
11	310	4	18
12	186	3	16
13	392	4	4
14	447	5	12
15	371	4	6
16	420	4	2
17	169	3	14
18	514	5	8
TOTAL	3206	36	TOTAL

TERNESSE

TEL : (03)3530292
LOCATION : 7 km Antwerpen
ADDRESS : Uilenbaan 15 – 2220 Wommelgem
HOTEL :
Waldorf-Antwerpen
Tel : (03)2309950
Alfa Congress – Antwerpen
Tel : (03)2353000
Switel – Antwerpen
Tel : (03)2316780
RESTAURANT : Ter Vennen – Wijnegem
Tel : (03)3538140

Laid out in typical Flanders landscape, Ternesse is a flat and wooded golf course with numerous water hazards such as streams, ponds and ditches bordering or crossing fifteen of its fairways. *SSS 72*

GF $

1976

18

—

M. Baker

L 5589 P 72

S

R

Required : Handicap Certificate
Best days : Wednesdays, Thursdays

HOLE	LENGTH MEDAL-TEE	PAR	STROKE INDEX
1	299	4	10
2	119	3	18
3	463	5	6
4	170	3	16
5	430	5	14
6	336	4	2
7	301	4	4
8	169	3	12
9	434	5	8
TOTAL	2721	36	TOTAL

HOLE	LENGTH MEDAL-TEE	PAR	STROKE INDEX
10	356	4	13
11	340	4	5
12	421	5	3
13	160	3	15
14	334	4	7
15	324	4	11
16	345	4	1
17	165	3	17
18	423	5	9
TOTAL	2868	36	TOTAL

WAREGEM HAPPY

TEL : (056)608808/606388
LOCATION : 15 km Kortrijk/30 km Gent
E 3 exit N° 5
ADDRESS : Krakeelhoek 41 - 8790 Waregem
HOTEL : HR
Golfhotel
Tel : (056)609737
De Peracker - Waregem
Tel : (056)600331
Broel - Kortrijk
Tel : (056)218351
RESTAURANT : 't Oud Konijntje -Waregem
Tel : (056)601937

Located between the cities of Gent and Kortrijk, this is another fine creation of Belgiums well known golf architect Baron Rolin. It has a modern layout with the first 9 holes set on hazardous landscape, and with the others being flat. Young trees border the fairways while ponds serve as hazards on the last 9 holes. The clubhouse and golfhotel with 17 rooms overlook the 10th and 18th holes. Other facitilies include 20 tennis courts, 8 of which are indoor, 3 squash courts and a fitness room. *SSS 72*

GF $ —  

1989 — P. Rolin 

18 — L 5802 P 72

Required : Handicap Certificate
Best days : Weekdays

HOLE	LENGTH MEDAL-TEE	PAR	STROKE INDEX
1	311	4	10
2	172	3	16
3	488	5	4
4	393	4	2
5	293	4	18
6	339	4	8
7	341	4	6
8	353	4	14
9	447	5	12
TOTAL	3137	37	TOTAL

HOLE	LENGTH MEDAL-TEE	PAR	STROKE INDEX
10	512	5	9
11	175	3	13
12	249	4	17
13	388	4	1
14	384	4	15
15	350	4	3
16	176	3	11
17	358	4	7
18	309	4	15
TOTAL	2901	35	TOTAL

WINGE

TEL : (016)634053
LOCATION : 13 km Leuven N. 2, 12 km Tienen
ADDRESS : Wingerstraat 6 – 3210 Sint-Joris Winge
HOTEL :
Garden Court – Leuven
Tel : (016)290770
Nouveau Monde-Tienen
Tel : (016)814321
RESTAURANT : Sire Pynnock-Leuven
Tel : (016)202532

This new golf club, set in the grounds of a scenic 17th century castle, is named after the river which winds through a part of the course and designed by Peter Townsend, a well-known professional golfer and head pro at Portmarnock. Laid out in gently rolling countryside, the holes run through forest and fields where ponds serve as hazards. Most of the fairways are tree-lined.

GF $

1988

18

Mondays

P. Townsend

L 5924 P 72

S

R

Required : Handicap Certificate
Best days : Any day

HOLE	LENGTH MEDAL-TEE	PAR	STROKE INDEX
1	326	4	5
2	160	3	13
3	314	4	9
4	122	3	17
5	473	5	1
6	304	4	15
7	436	5	11
8	395	4	3
9	344	4	7
TOTAL	2874	36	TOTAL

HOLE	LENGTH MEDAL-TEE	PAR	STROKE INDEX
10	495	5	10
11	318	4	14
12	165	3	8
13	410	4	2
14	271	4	16
15	385	4	4
16	151	3	18
17	439	5	12
18	377	4	6
TOTAL	3011	36	TOTAL

DENMARK

Car Rental

Reservation/Information telephone number :

Country code : **45**

Telephone number : **86/132133**

Headquarters address :

INTERRENT – EUROPCAR IR OSTERGAARD BILER A/S
17, Fredensgade, 8000 Aarhus C
Tel. : (45) 86132333
Telex : 64637
Fax : (45) 86199125

60 GOLF COURSES, 36 000 PLAYERS

★★★ Great golf course
★★ Very good golf course
$ 30-120 Dkr
★ Recommended golf course
☼ Holiday golf course
$$ more than 150 Dkr

TOWN	GOLF COURSE		TEL	MAP REF.
JYLLAND				
Aalbaek	Hvide Klit	★	98489021	1
Aalborg	Aalborg	★★	98341476	2
Aarhus	Aarhus		86276322	26
Bramming	Kaj Lykke		75173911	•
Brønderslev	Brønderslev		98823281	25
Ebeltoft	Ebeltoft	☼	86342641	7
Esbjerg	Esbjerg	★	75269219	8
Fanø	Fanø Vesterhavsbad	☼	75162024	9
Fjerritslev	Han Herred		98211444	•
Grenaa	Grenaa		86309090	•
Haderslev	Haderslev		74528063	28
Hejnsvig	Gyttegard		75335649	•
Herning	Herning		97211881	•
Hjørring	Hjørring		98900399	•
Holstebro	Holstebro	★★★	97485155	4
Horsens	Horsens		75616606	29
Juelsminde	Juelsminde		75693069	•
Kolding	Kolding	★	75523793	10
Lemvig	Lemvig		97485293	•
Løgstør	Himmerland	☼	98661600	3
Nykøbing	Morsø		97722811	•
Randers	Randers		86428869	•
Ribe	Ribe		75441230	•
Silkeborg	Silkeborg	★★	86853399	6
Skive	Skive		97521075	•
Skjern	Dejbjerg		97350959	•
Thisted	Nordvestjysk		97922164	•
Tinglev	Sønderjylland		74687525	•
Toftlund	Toftlund		74834403	•
Vejle	Vejle	★	75858185	11
Viborg	Viborg		86673010	36

TOWN	GOLF COURSE		TEL	MAP REF.
SJAELLAND				
Ballerup	Skovlunde		42917628	•
Birkerod	Fureso		42817444	23
Copenhagen	Copenhagen	★★	42630483	17
	Hedeland		42136169	17
	Skovlunde		42914815	•
Eskilstrup	Storstrømmen	✡	53838080	14
Frederiksvaerk	Asserbo		42641702	•
Gilleleje	Gilleleje		49718056	32
Helsingør	Helsingør	★	49212970	21
Hillerød	Hillerød	★	42265046	22
Højby Sj.	Odsherred *(ext. to 18 h.)*		59302076	•
Holbaek	Holbaek		53430500	•
Holte	Søllerød		42801784	18
Kalundborg	Kalundborg		53510900	•
Køge	Køge		53651000	16
Kokkedal	Kokkedal		42869959	20
Korsør	Korsør	★	53571836	15
Lynge	Mølleaens		42188631	33
Naestved	Sydsjaelland		53761555	31
Roskilde	Roskilde		42370180	•
Rungsted	Rungsted	★★★	42863444	19
Sorø	Midtsjaelland		53632774	•
Vallensbaek	Vallensbaek		42621899	35
FYN				
Glamsbjerg	Vestfyns		64722124	•
Nyborg	Sct. Kunds	★★	65311212	13
Odense	Odense		65959000	12
Svendborg	Svendborg		62224077	•
BORNHOLM				
Gudhjem	Nordbornholm	★ ✡	53980619	34
Nexø	Nexø		53992404	•
Rønne	Bornholm	✡	53956854	27

cities represented on the map are Europcar locations.

AALBORG

TEL : 98341476
LOCATION : 7 km Aalborg
ADDRESS : Jaegersprisvej 35 – Restrup Enge – 9000 Aalborg
HOTEL :
Slotshotellet – Aalborg
Tel : 98101400
Phoenix – Aalborg
Tel : 98120011
Park-Aalborg
Tel : 98123133
RESTAURANT : Halling – Aalborg
Tel : 98120011

The second oldest Danish golf club founded in 1908, has its fine and gently undulating course set on open ground with small woods. Water affects play on several holes. *SSS 70*

GF $

1908

18

—

C. Cotton

L 5711 P 70

R S

Required : Handicap Certificate
Best days : Any day, weekends afer 11 h.

HOLE	LENGTH MEDAL-TEE	PAR	STROKE INDEX
1	351	4	9
2	147	3	15
3	346	4	5
4	359	4	11
5	373	4	7
6	498	5	3
7	314	4	13
8	106	3	17
9	498	5	1
TOTAL	2992	36	TOTAL

HOLE	LENGTH MEDAL-TEE	PAR	STROKE INDEX
10	380	4	4
11	333	4	14
12	163	3	10
13	372	4	2
14	341	4	8
15	158	3	18
16	347	4	12
17	149	3	16
18	476	5	6
TOTAL	2719	34	TOTAL

AARHUS

TEL : 86276322
LOCATION : 5 km S. Aarhus to Odder
ADDRESS : Ny Moesgaardvej 50-8270 Højbjerg
HOTEL :
Royal-Aarhus
Tel : 86120011
Marselis-Aarhus
Tel : 86144411
RESTAURANT : Teater Bodega-Aarhus
Tel : 86121917

Extended to 18 holes in 1986, the Moesgaard course is located in an open, slightly undulating landscape with a fine view of the sea and the nearby forest. It has a mixture of quite easy holes and extremely difficult ones, hard to reach in par. Small creeks serve as hazards on six holes. There is a modern clubhouse overlooking the 18th green. The 9 hole golf course Mollerup is situated in Risskov. *SSS 70*

GF $ | — | S
1931 | B. Huggett, Coles & Dyer
27 | L 5796 P 71, 3050 P 36 | R

Required : None
Best days : Any day

HOLE	LENGTH MEDAL-TEE	PAR	STROKE INDEX
1	350	4	9
2	486	5	3
3	115	3	17
4	406	4	1
5	290	4	11
6	450	5	5
7	290	4	15
8	450	5	7
9	162	3	13
TOTAL	2999	37	TOTAL

HOLE	LENGTH MEDAL-TEE	PAR	STROKE INDEX
10	410	4	4
11	340	4	10
12	330	4	6
13	166	3	14
14	371	4	2
15	170	3	18
16	318	4	16
17	335	4	12
18	357	4	8
TOTAL	2797	34	TOTAL

BORNHOLM

TEL : 53956854
LOCATION : 3 km Rønne to Aakirkeby
ADDRESS : Plantagevej-Robbedale – 3700 Rønne
HOTEL :
Fredensborg-Rønne
Tel : 53954444
Abildgaard-Allinge
Tel : 53980955
RESTAURANT : Gildam-Rønne
Tel : 53952656

The golf course has been extended to 18 holes. It lies in fine natural surroundings amidst gently rolling and well wooded countryside on the scenic island of Bornholm. Though rather short, there is an entertaining layout with narrow fairways running through heather within a landscape that is preserved. The Fredensborg hotel is situated 2km from the golf club. *SSS 68*

GF $

1972

18

December to March

—

L 4843 P 68

S

R

Required : None
Best days : Any day

HOLE	LENGTH MEDAL-TEE	PAR	STROKE INDEX
1	315	4	8
2	298	4	10
3	237	4	16
4	240	4	14
5	471	5	4
6	391	4	2
7	165	3	12
8	173	3	6
9	114	3	18
TOTAL	2404	34	TOTAL

HOLE	LENGTH MEDAL-TEE	PAR	STROKE INDEX
10	137	3	17
11	150	3	13
12	268	4	9
13	153	3	11
14	510	5	3
15	360	4	1
16	330	4	7
17	256	4	5
18	275	4	15
TOTAL	2439	34	TOTAL

BRØNDERSLEV

TEL : 98823281
LOCATION : 3,5 km W. Brønderslev
ADDRESS : Golfvejen 83 – 9700 Brønderslev
HOTEL :
Phonix – Brønderslev
Tel : 98820100
Tylstrup Kro – Vestbjerg
Tel : 98261401
RESTAURANT : Brunderhus – Brønderslev
Tel : 98824500

Extended to 18 holes, this is a fairly hilly and well-wooded course where ponds, ditches and lakes serve as hazards on many of the holes. It features the longest hole in Denmark which is the long 18th. *SSS 71*

GF $
1971
18

—
E. Snack
L 5710 P 70

S
R

Required : None
Best days : Any day

HOLE	LENGTH MEDAL-TEE	PAR	STROKE INDEX
1	341	4	11
2	170	3	15
3	335	4	3
4	326	4	9
5	365	4	1
6	361	4	5
7	117	3	17
8	288	4	13
9	356	4	7
TOTAL	2659	34	TOTAL

HOLE	LENGTH MEDAL-TEE	PAR	STROKE INDEX
10	452	5	8
11	327	4	12
12	160	3	16
13	360	4	2
14	142	3	18
15	366	4	6
16	352	4	10
17	329	4	14
18	563	5	4
TOTAL	3051	36	TOTAL

COPENHAGEN

TEL : 42630483
LOCATION : 15 km N. Copenhagen
ADDRESS : Dyrehaven 2 – 2800 Lyngby
HOTEL :
Eremitage – Lyngby
Tel : 42887700
Palace – Copenhagen
Tel : 42144050
Raadvad Kro – Lyngby
Tel : 42806162
RESTAURANT : Den Gule Cottage – Klampenborg
Tel : 42640691

Denmarks oldest golf course lies in the middle of the royal deer park 'Dyrehaven' in an open grassy plain. The course has a very fine turf providing pasture for about 2500 fallow and red deer. There are many age-old oak trees, sometimes creating hazards. One of the finest championship courses in Denmark, the club has hosted many national championships. An attractive feature is the "Ermitage", the Royal Hunting Castle, overlooking the course. *SSS 70*

GF $$
1898
18

Tuesdays
—
L 5696 P 71

R S

Required : None
Best days : Wednesdays, Thursdays, Fridays; Saturdays & Sundays after 12 h.

HOLE	LENGTH MEDAL-TEE	PAR	STROKE INDEX
1	170	3	9
2	281	4	17
3	335	4	5
4	450	5	11
5	380	4	3
6	413	4	1
7	327	4	13
8	154	3	15
9	350	4	7
TOTAL	2860	35	TOTAL

HOLE	LENGTH MEDAL-TEE	PAR	STROKE INDEX
10	264	4	18
11	320	4	4
12	433	5	12
13	347	4	2
14	340	4	6
15	331	4	8
16	148	3	16
17	472	5	10
18	181	3	14
TOTAL	2836	36	TOTAL

EBELTOFT

TEL : 86342641/86351432
LOCATION : 0,5 km Ebeltoft
ADDRESS : Strandgaardshøj 8 – 8400 Ebeltoft
HOTEL : HR
Hvide Hus
Tel : 86341466
Ebeltoft Strand – Ebeltoft
Tel : 86343300
Molskroen – Femmoller Strand
Tel : 86362200

Located near the sea front and the seaside resort of Ebeltoft, this golf course is ideal for holiday golf. The course with short holes lies in a hilly dune landscape with lovely views over the bay, the sea and the harbour of Ebeltoft. The Hvide Hus Hotel, a fine holiday hotel with swimming pool, is adjacent to the golf course. *SSS 67*

GF $ —  

1966 F. Dreyer 

18 L 4875 P 68

Required : None
Best days : Mondays to Saturdays inc.

HOLE	LENGTH MEDAL-TEE	PAR	STROKE INDEX
1	358	4	3
2	436	5	5
3	128	3	11
4	282	4	15
5	253	4	12
6	281	4	13
7	125	3	16
8	286	4	10
9	283	4	9
TOTAL	2432	35	TOTAL

HOLE	LENGTH MEDAL-TEE	PAR	STROKE INDEX
10	303	4	7
11	152	3	17
12	382	4	1
13	292	4	14
14	315	4	6
15	169	3	8
16	331	4	4
17	127	3	18
18	372	4	2
TOTAL	2443	33	TOTAL

ESBJERG

★

TEL : 75269219/75269272
LOCATION : 15 km N. Esbjerg
ADDRESS : Sønderhedevej-Marbaek – 6710 Esbjerg
HOTEL :
Scandic Olympic – Esbjerg
Tel : 75181188
West – Esbjerg
Tel : 75135500
RESTAURANT : Korskreven – Esbjerg
Tel : 75120059

This rather hilly championship course, designed by the famous Danish golf architect Frederic Dreyer, is laid out on varied ground with heather and coniferous woods. The course is partly surrounded by a row of inland dunes, with many of its fairways and greens cunningly bunkered. *SSS 70*

GF $ | Weekends | R S
1921 | F. Dreyer
18 | L 5728 P 71

Required : Handicap Certificate
Best days : Weekdays

HOLE	LENGTH MEDAL-TEE	PAR	STROKE INDEX
1	317	4	15
2	162	3	7
3	328	4	9
4	471	5	3
5	360	4	1
6	279	4	17
7	450	5	11
8	348	4	5
9	162	3	13
TOTAL	2877	36	TOTAL

HOLE	LENGTH MEDAL-TEE	PAR	STROKE INDEX
10	337	4	10
11	381	4	2
12	342	4	6
13	121	3	18
14	461	5	12
15	366	4	8
16	340	4	4
17	151	3	16
18	352	4	14
TOTAL	2851	35	TOTAL

FANØ VESTERHAVSBADS

TEL : 75162024
LOCATION : Island Fanø/Ferry Esbjerg
ADDRESS : Spurvevej 4 – Nordby – 6720 Fanø
HOTEL :
Sonderho Kro – Fanø
Tel : 75164009
Kongen af Danmark – Fanø
Tel : 75163333
RESTAURANT : Golf – Fanø
Tel : 75163043

Located on the tiny and scenic island of Fano, this short course is a typical links with several greens in hollows. Some of the holes are blind. Twelve kilometres from the golf course is the Sonderho Kro Hotel, a charming hotel situated in a small fishing village and member of the Relais & Châteaux chain. *SSS 65*

GF $ — November to May — 

1900 — — — 

18 — L 4642 P 66 — R

Required : None
Best days : Any day

HOLE	LENGTH MEDAL-TEE	PAR	STROKE INDEX
1	294	4	15
2	280	4	9
3	156	3	13
4	350	4	17
5	182	3	7
6	173	3	11
7	305	4	3
8	327	4	5
9	355	4	1
TOTAL	2422	33	TOTAL

HOLE	LENGTH MEDAL-TEE	PAR	STROKE INDEX
10	130	3	16
11	258	4	12
12	145	3	18
13	364	4	2
14	292	4	8
15	285	4	10
16	266	4	14
17	290	4	4
18	190	3	6
TOTAL	2220	33	TOTAL

FURESO

TEL : 42817444
LOCATION : 1 km Birkerod
ADDRESS : Hestkobvaenge 4 – 3460 Birkerod
HOTEL :
Birkerod – Birkerod
Tel : 42814430
Birkerod Kro – Birkerod
Tel : 42820018
Skovriderkroen – Charlottenlund
Tel : 31626340
RESTAURANT : Bregnerod Kro – Bregnerod
Tel : 42950057

The course, recently extended to a championship course hosting the professional Swedish Golf Tour, is dominated by numerous strategically placed water hazards as well as plantations in a gently rolling landscape with mature trees. The various shapes of the well bunkered greens make approach shots interesting and demanding. The clubhouse is a small manor house situated in a beautiful park. *SSS 71*

GF $ — S
1974 J. Sederholm
18 L 5692 P 71

Required : None
Best days : Mondays, Tuesdays, Fridays, Weekends

HOLE	LENGTH MEDAL-TEE	PAR	STROKE INDEX
1	285	4	11
2	130	3	17
3	500	5	3
4	335	4	1
5	156	3	13
6	465	5	5
7	366	4	7
8	300	4	9
9	137	3	15
TOTAL	2674	35	TOTAL

HOLE	LENGTH MEDAL-TEE	PAR	STROKE INDEX
10	485	5	8
11	460	5	4
12	144	3	18
13	330	4	14
14	345	4	10
15	399	4	2
16	300	4	16
17	200	3	12
18	355	4	6
TOTAL	3018	36	TOTAL

GILLELEJE

TEL : 49718056
LOCATION : 7 km SE Gilleleje/60 km N. Copenhagen
ADDRESS : Ferlevej 52 – 3250 Gilleleje
HOTEL :
Trouville - Holbaek
Tel : 42202200
Strand - Gilleleje
Tel : 48300512
RESTAURANT : Gilleleje Havn - Gilleleje
Tel : 48300029

The club founded in 1970 developed a new 18 hole course which opened in 1989 a few kilometres from its old 9 hole course. The new course, partly hilly and partly flat, is long and presents a variety of challenges. Some holes are laid out on open land, while others are overshadowed by trees. *SSS 72*

GF $

Mondays

S

1970/1988

J. Sederholm

27

L 6044 P 72

R

Required : Handicap Certificate
Best days : Any day

HOLE	LENGTH MEDAL-TEE	PAR	STROKE INDEX
1	478	5	9
2	188	3	17
3	291	4	15
4	313	4	7
5	319	4	3
6	345	4	13
7	201	3	5
8	404	4	1
9	451	5	11
TOTAL	2990	36	TOTAL

HOLE	LENGTH MEDAL-TEE	PAR	STROKE INDEX
10	343	4	8
11	157	3	16
12	387	4	2
13	139	3	18
14	485	5	6
15	170	3	14
16	488	5	12
17	399	4	4
18	486	5	10
TOTAL	3054	36	TOTAL

HADERSLEV

TEL : 74528063/74528301
LOCATION : 1 km NW. Haderslev
ADDRESS : Egevej 22-6100 Haderslev
HOTEL :
Norden-Haderslev
Tel : 74524030
Haderslev-Haderslev
Tel : 74526010
RESTAURANT : Spiele - Haderslev
Tel : 74522307

The golf course lies in rural surroundings in the outskirts of the town of Haderslev, bordering a river. It is set within hilly countryside where mature woodland alternate with quickset hedges. Though short, precision is essential due to the many sloping and tricky fairways, the strategic lakes and several plateau greens. It features Denmarks shortest hole : the 2nd hole. The course commands fine views over Haderslev. There is a self-service restaurant. *SSS 67*

GF $
1975
18

—
K. Bossen
L 5137 P 69

S

R

Required : None
Best days : Weekdays

HOLE	LENGTH MEDAL-TEE	PAR	STROKE INDEX
1	251	4	
2	93	3	
3	349	4	
4	166	3	
5	335	4	
6	339	4	
7	347	4	
8	451	5	
9	121	3	
TOTAL	2452	34	TOTAL

HOLE	LENGTH MEDAL-TEE	PAR	STROKE INDEX
10	467	5	
11	369	4	
12	345	4	
13	255	4	
14	125	3	
15	362	4	
16	364	4	
17	111	3	
18	287	4	
TOTAL	2685	35	TOTAL

HEDELAND

TEL : 42136169
LOCATION : 25 km Copenhagen
ADDRESS : Sterkendevej 232a-2640
Hedehusene
HOTEL :
Palace - Copenhagen
Tel : 42144050
Prindsen - Roskilde

Designed by the Swedish architect Jan Sederholm, the course lies in a recently created national park close to Copenhagen. The holes are found in a pleasant setting of rolling woodlands with lakes and ponds guarding some of the fairways. *SSS 70*

GF $

1980

18

—

J. Sederholm

L 5738 P 70

S

Required : None
Best days : Weekdays

HOLE	LENGTH MEDAL-TEE	PAR	STROKE INDEX
1	436	5	15
2	346	4	3
3	193	3	13
4	525	5	7
5	340	4	11
6	486	5	5
7	353	4	9
8	142	3	17
9	354	4	1
TOTAL	3175	37	TOTAL

HOLE	LENGTH MEDAL-TEE	PAR	STROKE INDEX
10	133	3	18
11	365	4	2
12	200	3	8
13	315	4	10
14	360	4	6
15	320	4	16
16	320	4	12
17	170	3	14
18	380	4	4
TOTAL	2563	33	TOTAL

HELSINGOR

TEL : 49212970
LOCATION : 1,5 km Helsingor
ADDRESS : Gammel Hellebaekvej – 3000 Helsingor
HOTEL :
Marienlyst – Helsingor
Tel : 49211801
Foergegaarden – Helsingor
Tel : 49213946
RESTAURANT : Tikøb Kro – Helsingor
Tel : 49248250

Designed by the Swedish golf architect Anders Amilon, the course has a varied layout set on hilly ground with several small ponds and ditches on its fairways. Many holes are bordered by beautiful majestic trees. *SSS 71*

GF $$ — — — R S

1926 — A. Amilon

18 — L 5670 P 71

Required : Handicap Certificate
Best days : Weekdays

HOLE	LENGTH MEDAL-TEE	PAR	STROKE INDEX
1	285	4	15
2	365	4	3
3	310	4	11
4	140	3	17
5	500	5	5
6	175	3	7
7	320	4	9
8	435	5	13
9	335	4	1
TOTAL	2865	36	TOTAL

HOLE	LENGTH MEDAL-TEE	PAR	STROKE INDEX
10	330	4	16
11	155	3	14
12	370	4	4
13	180	3	8
14	345	4	6
15	400	4	2
16	440	5	12
17	125	3	18
18	460	5	10
TOTAL	2805	35	TOTAL

HERNING

TEL : 97211881
LOCATION : 2 km Herning
ADDRESS : Golfvej 2 – 7400 Herning
HOTEL :
Regina – Herning
Tel : 97211500
Ostergaard – Herning
Tel : 97124555
RESTAURANT : Baghuset – Herning
Tel : 97210455

A flat course with sparse vegetation set on good turf. There is a stream meandering its way through several fairways. It features a modern clubhouse, built in the style of a cube. The fine Regina Hotel is near the golf club. *SSS 70*

GF $ — November to April — R S

1965 — 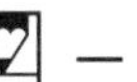 — 

18 — L 5571 P 70 — 

Required : None
Best days : Weekdays

HOLE	LENGTH MEDAL-TEE	PAR	STROKE INDEX
1	140	3	17
2	325	4	3
3	161	3	11
4	202	3	5
5	485	5	9
6	273	4	13
7	495	5	7
8	264	4	15
9	406	4	1
TOTAL	2751	35	TOTAL

HOLE	LENGTH MEDAL-TEE	PAR	STROKE INDEX
10	388	4	4
11	498	5	6
12	157	3	16
13	339	4	14
14	455	5	8
15	315	4	12
16	384	4	2
17	134	3	18
18	150	3	10
TOTAL	2820	35	TOTAL

HILLEROD

★

TEL : 42265046
LOCATION : 5 km Hillerod
ADDRESS : Nysøgardsvej-Ny Hammersholt – 3400 Hillerod
HOTEL :
Hillerod – Hillerod
Tel : 48240800
Slotskroen – Hillerod
Tel : 42260182
RESTAURANT : Slotsherrens-Kro – Hillerod
Tel : 42267516

An attractive golf course with several holes set on open ground and others laid out in woodland and meadowland. The only problem on this course is presented by the narrow fairways. There is a lake in the middle of the course. *SSS 70*

GF $$
1966
18

—
—
L 5453 P 70

Required : Handicap Certificate
Best days : Mondays, Thursdays, Fridays; Weekends after 12 h.

HOLE	LENGTH MEDAL-TEE	PAR	STROKE INDEX
1	388	4	5
2	355	4	1
3	275	4	11
4	160	3	17
5	461	5	7
6	186	3	15
7	447	5	9
8	364	4	3
9	139	3	13
TOTAL	2775	35	TOTAL

HOLE	LENGTH MEDAL-TEE	PAR	STROKE INDEX
10	371	4	8
11	380	4	2
12	347	4	6
13	143	3	14
14	280	4	12
15	327	4	4
16	245	4	18
17	131	3	16
18	454	5	10
TOTAL	2678	35	TOTAL

HIMMERLAND

TEL : 98661600
LOCATION : 14 km NW. Aars E3/35 km Hobro
ADDRESS : Centervej 1 – Gatten – 9670 Løgstør
HOTEL : HP
Himmerland
Tel : 98661600
Du Nord – Logstor
Tel : 98671711

Himmerland Golf & Country Club is an ideal holiday spot, set in the middle of West Himmerland near the small town of Gatten. It features two 18 hole golf courses (the "Old" and the "New") and a short par 3-9 hole course, both laid out on gently undulating wooded lakeland in rural surroundings where copses, brooks and ponds serve as hazards. There are 300 fully equipped chalets for rent. The resort-centre houses an indoor and outdoor swimming pool, playing fields, cycling, horse-riding paddock, windsurfing school and four tennis courts. *SSS 68*

GF $

1980/1990

36

—

J. Sederholm

L 5220 P 69, 6050 P 73

Required : Handicap Certificate
Best days : Any day

HOLE	LENGTH MEDAL-TEE	PAR	STROKE INDEX
1	350	4	
2	170	3	
3	330	4	
4	460	5	
5	370	4	
6	360	4	
7	140	3	
8	340	4	
9	450	5	
TOTAL	2970	36	TOTAL

HOLE	LENGTH MEDAL-TEE	PAR	STROKE INDEX
10	610	6	
11	360	4	
12	470	5	
13	340	4	
14	340	4	
15	150	3	
16	380	4	
17	120	3	
18	310	4	
TOTAL	3080	37	TOTAL

HOLSTEBRO

TEL : 97485155
LOCATION : 14 km W. Holstebro
ADDRESS : Brandsbjergvej 4 – Raasted – 7570 Vemb
HOTEL :
Bel Air – Holstebro
Tel : 97426666
Schaumborg – Holstebro
Tel : 97423111
RESTAURANT : Laksen – Holstebro
Tel : 97424648

One of the most beautiful courses in Denmark is the Holstebro golf course, the venue for the national and Scandinavian championships. Set in West Jutland, fourteen holes are laid out in valleys penetrating the sheltered Raasted Forest with heather and coniferous woods. The remaining four holes, each one having its own character, are in open fields. There is a modern clubhouse overlooking the 18th green. *SSS 72*

GF $ — 1970 — E. Schnack — 18 — L 6073 P 71

Required : None
Best days : Any day

HOLE	LENGTH MEDAL-TEE	PAR	STROKE INDEX
1	381	4	3
2	490	5	9
3	156	3	17
4	393	4	7
5	379	4	15
6	391	4	5
7	360	4	11
8	154	3	13
9	381	4	1
TOTAL	3085	35	TOTAL

HOLE	LENGTH MEDAL-TEE	PAR	STROKE INDEX
10	351	4	8
11	151	3	16
12	508	5	2
13	172	3	14
14	367	4	6
15	362	4	4
16	271	4	18
17	371	4	10
18	435	5	12
TOTAL	2988	36	TOTAL

HORSENS

TEL : 75616606/75615151
LOCATION : 1 km Horsens to Silkeborg
ADDRESS : Silkeborgvej 44-8700 Horsens
HOTEL :
Bygholm Park - Horsens
Tel : 75622333
Danica-Horsens
Tel : 75616022
RESTAURANT : Gastronomen - Horsens
Tel : 75618352

Designed by the Swedish architect Jan Sederhom, the 18 holes run partly through rolling and open countryside, and partly through wooded landscape. The course has been laid out with numerous lakes which encircle some of the fairways, and represent a fine challenge to players. *SSS 71*

GF $ | — | S
1985 | J. Sederholm
18 | L 6020 P 72

Required : None
Best days : Any day

HOLE	LENGTH MEDAL-TEE	PAR	STROKE INDEX
1	466	5	11
2	130	3	17
3	505	5	5
4	440	5	13
5	332	4	15
6	363	4	1
7	176	3	9
8	382	4	7
9	162	3	3
TOTAL	2956	35	TOTAL

HOLE	LENGTH MEDAL-TEE	PAR	STROKE INDEX
10	457	5	2
11	372	4	16
12	132	3	18
13	337	4	8
14	370	4	14
15	379	4	6
16	346	4	12
17	164	3	4
18	507	5	10
TOTAL	3064	36	TOTAL

HVIDE KLIT

★

TEL : 98489021
LOCATION : 2 km N. Aalbaek/24 km Frederikshavn A 10
ADDRESS : Hvideklitvej 20 – Bunken – 9982 Aalbaek
HOTEL :
Aalbaek Gl. Kro – Aalbaek
Tel : 98489022
Skagen Strand – Skagen
Tel : 98487222
RESTAURANT : Skagen Fisker – Skagen
Tel : 98443544

This fine course has a very attractive and varied layout. Slightly undulating and set within the natural landscape near the sea front, it is laid out on beautiful ground with old oak trees, conifers, bushes, junipers and heather. Due to the presence of sand dunes, parts of the course have a seaside character. There are several streams crossing the holes. *SSS 72*

GF $$ — S
1971 A. Amilon R
18 L 5875 P 72

Required : Handicap Certificate
Best days : Any day; Weekends after 12 h. only

HOLE	LENGTH MEDAL-TEE	PAR	STROKE INDEX
1	460	5	11
2	350	4	3
3	385	4	7
4	160	3	13
5	380	4	1
6	445	5	9
7	160	3	15
8	365	4	5
9	300	4	17
TOTAL	3005	36	TOTAL

HOLE	LENGTH MEDAL-TEE	PAR	STROKE INDEX
10	335	4	8
11	350	4	2
12	460	5	12
13	125	3	18
14	325	4	6
15	155	3	14
16	500	5	4
17	335	4	10
18	285	4	16
TOTAL	2870	36	TOTAL

KØGE

TEL : 53651000
LOCATION : 3 km S. Køge
ADDRESS : Golfgarden-Gammel Hastrupvej 12 – 4600 Køge
HOTEL :
Hvide Hus-Køge
Tel : 53653690
Borup Kro – Borup
Tel : 53626012
RESTAURANT : Rio Bravo – Køge
Tel : 53653820

The Koge golf course is laid out in open undulating fields and features several artificial lakes. Among its most troublesome holes are the 4th with a very difficult green (3 levels), and the 17th with a stream crossing the fairway three times. *SSS 72*

GF $

1969

18

November to April

R. Otzen

L 5924 P 72

S

R

Required : Handicap Certificate
Best days : Wednesdays, Fridays

HOLE	LENGTH MEDAL-TEE	PAR	STROKE INDEX
1	126	3	15
2	404	4	5
3	301	4	11
4	385	4	1
5	400	4	3
6	345	4	7
7	268	4	13
8	441	5	9
9	270	4	17
TOTAL	2940	36	TOTAL

HOLE	LENGTH MEDAL-TEE	PAR	STROKE INDEX
10	164	3	10
11	304	4	16
12	408	4	2
13	466	5	12
14	190	3	8
15	530	5	6
16	286	4	18
17	449	5	4
18	187	3	14
TOTAL	2984	36	TOTAL

KOKKEDAL

TEL : 42869959
LOCATION : in Horsholm, 30 km Copenhagen
ADDRESS : Kokkedal Alle 9 – 2980 Kokkedal
HOTEL :
Marina-Vedbaek
Tel : 42891711
Marienlyst – Helsingor
Tel : 42211801
RESTAURANT : Dronning Louises Kro – Niva
Tel : 42243162

Laid out in a parkland setting on undulating countryside, there is a fine overall view of the surroundings from the highest point of the course. Many of the holes are tree-lined. *SSS 72*

GF $$ — Weekends before 12h. — S

1971 — F. Pennink

18 — L 5958 P 72 — R

Required : Handicap Certificate
Best days : Weekdays

HOLE	LENGTH MEDAL-TEE	PAR	STROKE INDEX
1	333	4	5
2	359	4	7
3	133	3	11
4	452	5	9
5	371	4	1
6	461	5	13
7	370	4	3
8	253	4	17
9	138	3	15
TOTAL	2870	36	TOTAL

HOLE	LENGTH MEDAL-TEE	PAR	STROKE INDEX
10	470	5	14
11	191	3	12
12	374	4	2
13	357	4	10
14	367	4	4
15	470	5	16
16	373	4	6
17	126	3	18
18	360	4	8
TOTAL	3088	36	TOTAL

KOLDING

TEL : 75523793
LOCATION : 3 km N. Kolding
ADDRESS : Emerholtvej – 6000 Kolding
HOTEL :
Tre Roser – Kolding
Tel : 75532122
Scanticon – Kolding
Tel : 75501555
RESTAURANT : Den gyldne Hane – Kolding
Tel : 75529720

A fine golf course located on Jutland and set on undulating countryside with woods and beautiful hedgerows. Ideal for holiday golf, the Tre Roser Hotel with a swimming pool is near the course. *SSS 69*

GF $

1933

18

—

M. Steengaard

L 5376 P 69

S

R

Required : Handicap Certificate
Best days : Any day

HOLE	LENGTH MEDAL-TEE	PAR	STROKE INDEX
1	351	4	5
2	314	4	13
3	348	4	3
4	145	3	15
5	319	4	11
6	410	4	1
7	140	3	17
8	330	4	9
9	450	5	7
TOTAL	2807	35	TOTAL

HOLE	LENGTH MEDAL-TEE	PAR	STROKE INDEX
10	476	5	6
11	350	4	12
12	284	4	16
13	318	4	4
14	328	4	10
15	170	3	14
16	394	4	2
17	125	3	8
18	124	3	18
TOTAL	2569	34	TOTAL

KORSØR

TEL : 53571836
LOCATION : 1,5 km Korsør
ADDRESS : Ørnumvej 8 – 4220 Korsør
HOTEL :
Klarskovgard – Korsør
Tel : 53572322
Tommerladen – Korsør
Tel : 53570149
RESTAURANT : Lystbaadehaunens – Korsør
Tel : 53576761

A scenic lakeside course set on the hilly peninsula in Korsor Cove with lovely views over the town of Korsor. Many of the fairways are separated by fine old trees. There are numerous small lakes scattered all over, serving as hazards. *SSS 71*

GF $

1964

18

November to March

A. Amilon

L 5998 P 73

S

R

Required : None
Best days : Tuesdays, Fridays (reduced rates)

HOLE	LENGTH MEDAL-TEE	PAR	STROKE INDEX
1	297	4	13
2	349	4	7
3	141	3	17
4	339	4	11
5	446	5	9
6	302	4	4
7	502	5	1
8	147	3	15
9	326	4	5
TOTAL	2849	36	TOTAL

HOLE	LENGTH MEDAL-TEE	PAR	STROKE INDEX
10	487	5	8
11	348	4	12
12	454	5	6
13	128	3	18
14	385	4	2
15	331	4	3
16	340	4	14
17	373	4	10
18	303	4	16
TOTAL	3149	37	TOTAL

MØLLEÅEN

TEL : 42188631
LOCATION : 5 km Farum/30 km NW Copenhagen
ADDRESS : Rosenlundvej 3- Bastrup 3540 Lynge
HOTEL :
71 Nyhavn – Copenhagen
Tel : 42118585
Palace - Copenhagen
Tel : 42144050
RESTAURANT : Lynge Kro - Lynge
Tel : 42187788

Extended to 18 holes by Jan Sederholm, the course lies in nice surroundings on open ground in a gently undulating countryside close to Lake Bastrup. It features several rolling greens. There is a very pleasant clubhouse with a good restaurant. *SSS 70*

GF $

—

S

1970/1988

A. Amilon, J. Sederholm

18

L 5730 P 70

R

Required : Handicap Certificate
Best days : Mondays, Thursdays and Fridays

HOLE	LENGTH MEDAL-TEE	PAR	STROKE INDEX
1	390	4	2
2	367	4	8
3	361	4	12
4	354	4	4
5	159	3	18
6	469	5	14
7	389	4	6
8	147	3	16
9	318	4	10
TOTAL	2954	35	TOTAL

HOLE	LENGTH MEDAL-TEE	PAR	STROKE INDEX
10	480	5	1
11	161	3	9
12	314	4	17
13	364	4	7
14	143	3	13
15	316	4	11
16	497	5	3
17	143	3	15
18	358	4	5
TOTAL	2776	35	TOTAL

NORDBORNHOLM

✡

TEL : 53984200
LOCATION : 7 km Gudhjem/10 km SE Allinge
ADDRESS : Spellingevej 3 – Rø
3760 Gudhjem
HOTEL :
Friheden - Gudhjem
Tel : 53980425
Stammershalle - Gudhjem
Tel : 53984210
RESTAURANT : Rø - Rø
Tel : 53984038

This new and most promising golf course is situated on the scenic island of Bornholm adjacent to Roe airfield (light aircraft only). Nestling in rugged natural countryside, it has a unique layout with bare rocks as part of the course. The fairways run through heather and woodlands, with natural streams and lakes affecting play. *SSS 70*

GF $

1988

18

November to April

A. Amilon

L 5512 P 71

S

R

Required : None
Best days : Any day

HOLE	LENGTH MEDAL-TEE	PAR	STROKE INDEX
1	368	4	15
2	276	4	17
3	174	3	16
4	337	4	8
5	119	3	18
6	442	5	3
7	282	4	14
8	440	5	1
9	318	4	7
TOTAL	2756	36	TOTAL

HOLE	LENGTH MEDAL-TEE	PAR	STROKE INDEX
10	332	4	10
11	316	4	9
12	344	4	5
13	331	4	2
14	134	3	13
15	299	4	11
16	152	3	12
17	482	5	6
18	366	4	4
TOTAL	2756	35	TOTAL

ODENSE

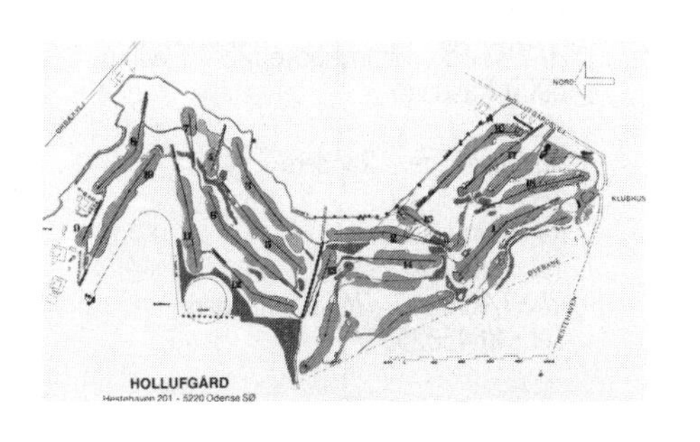

TEL : 66172134/65959000
LOCATION : 8 km Odense
ADDRESS : Hollufgaard-Hestehaven 201 – 5220 Odense Sø
HOTEL :
Grand-Odense
Tel : 66117171
H.C. Andersen – Odense
Tel : 66147800
RESTAURANT : Under Lindetraet – Odense
Tel : 66129286

Located on the island of Funen, the Odense Golf Club is a rather flat course of championship standard with a gentle fall to a boundary stream. Many of the holes are surrounded by hillocks with tightly bunkered fairways and greens. *SSS 71*

GF $ — Sundays — R S

1978 —  J. Sederholm — 

27 —  6175 P 72, 4134 P 64

Required : None
Best days : Tuesdays, Fridays

HOLE	LENGTH MEDAL-TEE	PAR	STROKE INDEX
1	450	5	13
2	367	4	3
3	476	5	7
4	154	3	15
5	416	4	1
6	495	5	9
7	171	3	11
8	364	4	5
9	146	3	17
TOTAL	3039	36	TOTAL

HOLE	LENGTH MEDAL-TEE	PAR	STROKE INDEX
10	501	5	10
11	416	4	2
12	339	4	12
13	208	3	6
14	324	4	14
15	157	3	18
16	449	5	16
17	354	4	4
18	388	4	8
TOTAL	3136	36	TOTAL

RANDERS

TEL : 86428869
LOCATION : 6 km Randers
ADDRESS : Himmelbovej 22 – Fladbro – 8900 Randers
HOTEL :
Kongens Ege – Randers
Tel : 86430300
Randers – Randers
Tel : 86423422
RESTAURANT : Mr 1 – Randers
Tel : 86430255

Recently extended to 18 holes, the course, situated close to a river, has a varied and entertaining layout. It is intersected by deep valleys, demanding a great deal of accuracy. Most of the fairways are tree-lined. *SSS 70*

GF $

1958

18

November to April

M. Cox

L 5453 P 71

S

R

Required : None
Best days : Any day

HOLE	LENGTH MEDAL-TEE	PAR	STROKE INDEX
1	228	4	12
2	154	3	2
3	315	4	8
4	265	4	18
5	255	4	4
6	506	5	14
7	398	4	16
8	309	4	16
9	175	3	10
TOTAL	2665	35	TOTAL

HOLE	LENGTH MEDAL-TEE	PAR	STROKE INDEX
10	447	5	15
11	364	4	5
12	317	4	9
13	242	4	13
14	131	3	17
15	312	4	3
16	342	4	1
17	471	5	7
18	162	3	11
TOTAL	2788	36	TOTAL

RUNGSTED

TEL : 42863444
LOCATION : 20 km N. Copenhagen
ADDRESS : Vestre Stationsvej 16 – 2960 Rungsted Kyst
HOTEL :
Marina – Vedbaek
Tel : 42891711
D'Angleterre – Copenhagen
Tel : (01)120095
Rungsted Kro – Rungsted
Tel : 42863062
RESTAURANT : Mokhen – Rungsted
Tel : 42571314

Laid out on fine woodland with a challenging and varied layout, the Rungsted golf club is one of Scandinavia's finest golf courses hosting international events. Encroached by beech woods, it is very hilly with several deep ravines. Among its feature holes is the treacherous 17th with a narrow fairway and a raised green with ravines on both sides. Many of the holes are set at the edges of old woods with leafy trees and meadowland. It has an inviting clubhouse with a terrace overlooking the 1st, 9th and 18th holes. *SSS 73*

GF $$

1937

18

—

C. Mackenzie

L 6058 P 72

Required : Handicap Certificate (24 minimum)
Best days : Any day; Weekends after 13 h. only

HOLE	LENGTH MEDAL-TEE	PAR	STROKE INDEX
1	398	4	9
2	346	4	5
3	159	3	17
4	414	4	1
5	354	4	7
6	165	3	15
7	371	4	11
8	356	4	3
9	341	4	13
TOTAL	2904	34	TOTAL

HOLE	LENGTH MEDAL-TEE	PAR	STROKE INDEX
10	370	4	6
11	452	5	2
12	296	4	16
13	312	4	14
14	327	4	8
15	111	3	18
16	479	5	4
17	363	4	12
18	444	5	10
TOTAL	3154	38	TOTAL

SCT. KNUDS

TEL : 65311212
LOCATION : 1,5 km Nyborg E 66
ADDRESS : Sliphavnsvej 16 – 5800 Nyborg
HOTEL :
Nyborg Strand – Nyborg
Tel : 65313131
Hesselet – Nyborg
Tel : 65313029
RESTAURANT : Danehofkroen – Nyborg
Tel : 65310202

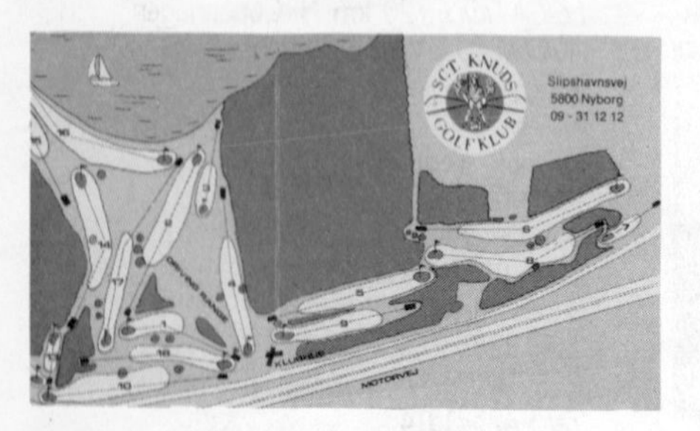

Situated on the island of Funen, east of Nyborg, this championship course of excellent quality, is set on the shores of the Store Belt (part of the Baltic Sea) on varied mostly flat ground. It is a combined parkland/woodland and seaside course with many of its fairways laid out amongst coniferous woods and the last nine holes running in every direction. The greens are undulating and fast. Ideal for holiday golf with two fine hotels 2 km away. *SSS 70*

GF $
1953
18
—
C.K. Cotton
L 5787 P 71

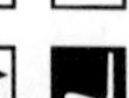

Required : Handicap Certificate
Best days : Mondays, Thursdays, Fridays

HOLE	LENGTH MEDAL-TEE	PAR	STROKE INDEX
1	305	4	17
2	383	4	3
3	196	3	7
4	317	4	13
5	360	4	1
6	143	3	15
7	457	5	9
8	387	4	5
9	293	4	11
TOTAL	2841	35	TOTAL

HOLE	LENGTH MEDAL-TEE	PAR	STROKE INDEX
10	383	4	2
11	322	4	10
12	341	4	6
13	116	3	18
14	336	4	4
15	186	3	8
16	444	5	14
17	455	5	16
18	363	4	12
TOTAL	2946	36	TOTAL

SILKEBORG

TEL : 86853399/86853399
LOCATION : 5 km Silkeborg
ADDRESS : Sensommervej 15C – Porskaer – 8600 Silkeborg
HOTEL :
Dania – Silkeborg
Tel : 86820111
Impala – Silkeborg
Tel : 86820300
RESTAURANT : Alekroen – Svejbaek
Tel : 86846033

Laid out in attractive landscape in the middle of Jutland, the Silkeborg golf club is one of Denmark's finest championship courses. Some of the fairways are laid out in an open flat and heatherclad plain, while others meander their way through more hilly wooded ground. Most of them are isolated from the rest of the course. *SSS 72*

GF $

 —

1966

F. Dreyer

18

L 5965 P 71

Required : None
Best days : Any day

HOLE	LENGTH MEDAL-TEE	PAR	STROKE INDEX
1	402	4	3
2	325	4	11
3	186	3	9
4	374	4	1
5	344	4	15
6	358	4	5
7	141	3	17
8	476	5	13
9	341	4	7
TOTAL	2947	35	TOTAL

HOLE	LENGTH MEDAL-TEE	PAR	STROKE INDEX
10	375	4	2
11	464	5	16
12	276	4	6
13	165	3	14
14	474	5	8
15	349	4	12
16	147	3	18
17	398	4	4
18	370	4	10
TOTAL	3018	36	TOTAL

SOLLEROD

TEL : 42801784
LOCATION : 19 km N. Copenhagen, 4 km Holte
ADDRESS : Øverødvej 239 – 2840 Holte
HOTEL :
Marina – Vedbaek
Tel : 42891711
Rudersdal Kro – Holte
Tel : 42424204
RESTAURANT : Sollerod Kro – Holte
Tel : 42802505

Designed by the Swedish golf architect, Anders Amilon, Sollerod is a pretty course laid out in undulating countryside with wide views of the surroundings, overlooking the Øresund sound and høse Sandbjerg. Many of the greens and fairways are cunningly bunkered. *SSS 72*

GF $$

1972

18

—

A. Amilon

L 6069 P 72

R S

Required : None
Best days : Any day

HOLE	LENGTH MEDAL-TEE	PAR	STROKE INDEX
1	442	5	13
2	355	4	7
3	395	4	1
4	146	3	17
5	276	4	15
6	171	3	11
7	419	4	3
8	493	5	5
9	324	4	9
TOTAL	3021	36	TOTAL

HOLE	LENGTH MEDAL-TEE	PAR	STROKE INDEX
10	324	4	10
11	154	3	16
12	269	4	18
13	526	5	4
14	195	3	8
15	454	5	12
16	401	4	2
17	330	4	14
18	395	4	6
TOTAL	3048	36	TOTAL

SØNDERJYLLAND

TEL : 74687525
LOCATION : 11 km SW Aabenraa
ADDRESS : Uge Hedegaard-6360 Tinglev
HOTEL :
Sonder Hostrup Kro - Sonder Hostrup
Tel : 74663446
Hvide Hus-Aabenraa
Tel : 74624700
RESTAURANT : Viking-Aabenraa
Tel : 74624335

The golf course has recenly been improved and extended to 18 holes. Located not far from the German border, it is laid out in flat landscape with several holes flanked by woodland. *SSS 70*

GF $

1970

18

—

E. Snack

L 5753 P 70

S

R

Required : None
Best days : Weekdays

HOLE	LENGTH MEDAL-TEE	PAR	STROKE INDEX
1	293	4	18
2	507	5	17
3	136	3	15
4	339	4	8
5	165	3	12
6	361	4	9
7	324	4	13
8	354	4	5
9	344	4	6
TOTAL	2803	35	TOTAL

HOLE	LENGTH MEDAL-TEE	PAR	STROKE INDEX
10	335	4	10
11	351	4	7
12	167	3	11
13	372	4	1
14	455	5	14
15	377	4	2
16	362	4	4
17	160	3	16
18	371	4	3
TOTAL	2950	35	TOTAL

STORSTROMMEN

TEL : 53838080
LOCATION : 10 km N. Nykobing
ADDRESS : Køllegaarden – Virketvej 44 – 4863 Eskilstrup
HOTEL :
Norrevang – Marielyst
Tel : 53876262
Falster – Nykobing
Tel : 53859393
RESTAURANT : Czarens Hus – Nykobing
Tel : 53852829

Located on the attractive holiday island of Falster, the Storstrommen golf club is one of Denmark's most scenic courses. It is laid out among meadows and old fields encircled by woods of pine, fir, beech and old oak trees. There is a charming Danish style clubhouse.
SSS 72

GF $

1969

18

—

A. Amilon

L 5945 P 72

R S

Required : None
Best days : Weekdays

HOLE	LENGTH MEDAL-TEE	PAR	STROKE INDEX
1	350	4	5
2	135	3	15
3	500	5	3
4	320	4	13
5	160	3	9
6	315	4	11
7	345	4	7
8	445	5	1
9	135	3	17
TOTAL	2705	35	TOTAL

HOLE	LENGTH MEDAL-TEE	PAR	STROKE INDEX
10	450	5	16
11	380	4	2
12	140	3	18
13	355	4	8
14	330	4	14
15	345	4	12
16	510	5	4
17	350	4	10
18	380	4	6
TOTAL	3240	37	TOTAL

SYDSJAELLAND

TEL : 53761553/53761503
LOCATION : 10 km S. Naestved
ADDRESS : Praestø Landevej 39 – Mogenstrup-4700 Naestved
HOTEL :
Mogenstrup Kro-Naestved
Tel : 53761130
Menstrup Kro-Menstrup
Tel : 53743003
RESTAURANT : Det Røde Pakhus-Naestved
Tel : 53729908

Set within fine natural surroundings, this is an attractive, flat inland and parkland course. It features many big and well placed bunkers, and several natural ponds serving as hazards. Restaurant facilities are available on weekends only for lunch. At 500m from the golf club is the attractive Mogenstrup Kro hotel with 45 bedrooms, sauna and solarium, and an indoor swimming pool. *SSS 70.*

GF $

1974

18

—

A. Amilon

L 5675 P 71

S

R

Required : None
Best days : Any day

HOLE	LENGTH MEDAL-TEE	PAR	STROKE INDEX
1	310	4	11
2	140	3	15
3	360	4	5
4	250	4	13
5	375	4	3
6	130	3	17
7	335	4	9
8	510	5	1
9	300	4	7
TOTAL	2710	35	TOTAL

HOLE	LENGTH MEDAL-TEE	PAR	STROKE INDEX
10	460	5	12
11	280	4	16
12	390	4	4
13	300	4	14
14	140	3	18
15	510	5	6
16	160	3	10
17	370	4	2
18	355	4	8
TOTAL	2965	36	TOTAL

VALLENSBAEK

TEL : 42621899
LOCATION : 13 km W. Copenhagen
ADDRESS : Toftevej 30-34
2625 Vallensbaek
HOTEL :
Glostrup Park - Vallensbaek
Tel : 42960038
Scandic - Vallensbaek
Tel : 31498222

Situated close to the Danish capital, this is a long and flat course with an interesting and testing layout. It has rather wide fairways and features many large tricky bunkers. A narrow stream cuts through the course. *SSS 71*

GF $

1988

18

—

F. Dreyer

L 5895 P 71

S

R

Required : Handicap Certificate
Best days : Weekdays

HOLE	LENGTH MEDAL-TEE	PAR	STROKE INDEX
1	368	4	5
2	399	4	1
3	354	4	11
4	168	3	13
5	315	4	9
6	453	5	7
7	137	3	15
8	373	4	3
9	301	4	17
TOTAL	2868	35	TOTAL

HOLE	LENGTH MEDAL-TEE	PAR	STROKE INDEX
10	488	5	6
11	389	4	2
12	312	4	14
13	202	3	8
14	361	4	4
15	366	4	12
16	157	3	16
17	290	4	18
18	462	5	10
TOTAL	3027	36	TOTAL

VEJLE

TEL : 75858185
LOCATION : 6 km Vejle
ADDRESS : Faellessletgard – Ibaekvej 46 – 7100 Vejle
HOTEL :
Munkebjerg – Vejle
Tel : 75723500
Scandic Australia – Vejle
Tel : 75824311
RESTAURANT : Huiids Vinstue – Vejle
Tel : 75832510

Located in East Jutland, in and around the beautiful and well-known Munkebjergwoods, the Vejle golf course bears all the hallmarks of the region. The course is undulating with a few holes in deep ravines. There are numerous small ponds and streams crossing or bordering the fairways. The Munkebjerg Hotel with swimming pool is nearby. *SSS 71*

GF $ — R S

1970 F. Dreyer/J. Malling

18 L 5457 P 71

Required : None
Best days : Weekdays

HOLE	LENGTH MEDAL-TEE	PAR	STROKE INDEX
1	128	3	18
2	469	5	2
3	125	3	16
4	341	4	8
5	328	4	12
6	245	4	14
7	440	5	6
8	193	3	4
9	439	5	10
TOTAL	2708	36	TOTAL

HOLE	LENGTH MEDAL-TEE	PAR	STROKE INDEX
10	145	3	11
11	304	4	17
12	374	4	3
13	278	4	13
14	200	3	9
15	456	5	7
16	361	4	1
17	332	4	5
18	299	4	15
TOTAL	2749	35	TOTAL

VIBORG

TEL : 86673010/86672660
LOCATION : 2 km E. Viborg
ADDRESS : Møllevej 26-8800 Viborg
HOTEL :
Golf - Viborg
Tel : 86610222
Missions - Viborg
Tel : 86623700

Recently moved up to 18 hole status, this friendly course runs over uneven terrain landscaped by trees. Four ponds affect play on several holes. The course has a spacious newly built clubhouse. *SSS 71*

GF $

1977/1990

18

—

J. Sederholm, F. Dreyer

L 5902 P 72

S

R

Required : None
Best days : Weekdays

HOLE	LENGTH MEDAL-TEE	PAR	STROKE INDEX
1	464	5	5
2	185	3	11
3	327	4	3
4	495	5	15
5	163	3	13
6	367	4	1
7	340	4	7
8	320	4	9
9	289	4	17
TOTAL	2950	36	TOTAL

HOLE	LENGTH MEDAL-TEE	PAR	STROKE INDEX
10	442	5	4
11	385	4	2
12	148	3	16
13	294	4	12
14	399	4	4
15	356	4	8
16	470	5	6
17	309	4	10
18	149	3	18
TOTAL	2952	36	TOTAL

FINLAND

Car Rental

Reservation/Information telephone number :

Country code :
358

Telephone number :
90/7583700

Headquarters address :

INTERRENT - EUROPCAR OY
Hitsaajankatu 7C,
P.O. Box 101,
00810 Helsinki 81
Tel. : (358) 90/7583700
Telex : 122561
Fax : (358) 90/785073

32 GOLF COURSES, 10 000 PLAYERS

★★★ Great golf course
★★ Very good golf course
$ 30-80 FM
★ Recommended golf course
☼ Holiday golf course
$$ 80-110 FM

TOWN	GOLF COURSE		TEL	MAP REF.
Åland	Aland Kastelholm		(920) 43828	•
Hamari	Virvik			•
Hameenlinna	Aulanko		(917) 74070	•
Helsinki	Espoo		(90) 811212	2
	Helsinki	★★	(90) 550235	1
	Itä-Helsingin		(90) 780122	•
	Kurk		(90) 263456	•
	Sarfvik		(90) 8012537	4
	Suur Helsinki		(90) 8558687	•
	Tuusulan		(90) 251464	•
Jyväskylä	Jyväs		(941) 244008	•
Kokkola	Kokkola		(968) 18905	•
Kotka	Kotka		(952) 14051	5
Kuopio	Tarinaharju		(971) 425299	7
Lahti	Lahti		(918) 841311	•
Lappeenranta	Viipuri		(953) 16840	•
Mikkeli	Mikkeli		(955) 19811	•
Oulu	Oulu		(981) 571192	•
Pargas	Skärgardens		(921) 740344	•
Pickala	Pickala		(90) 2966251	8
Pietarsaari	Jakobstads		(967) 30286	•
Pori	Pori		(939) 415559	•
Porvoo	Virvik		(915) 38292	•
Tampere	Tampere		(931) 613316	6
Turku	Aura	☼	(921) 589201	3
Tuusola	Krapi			•
Uotila	Rauma		(938) 230450	•
Vaasa	Vaasa		(961) 269989	•

NEW GOLF COURSES (18 HOLES OR MORE) TO OPEN SOON

Hyvinkää Golf
05830 Hyvinkää
Tel. : (914) 21501

Imatran Golf
55610 Imatra
Tel. : (954) 34954

Koski Golf
45701 Kuusankoski

Kymen Golf
48700 Kyminlinna
Tel. : (952) 14051

Master Golf
02701 Grankulla
Tel. : (90) 8537001

Neyas
01130 Sipoo
Tel. : (90) 226313

Ruukki Golf
Brödtorp
Tel. : (911) 54485

Vantaan
Kirkka
Tel. : (90) 544411

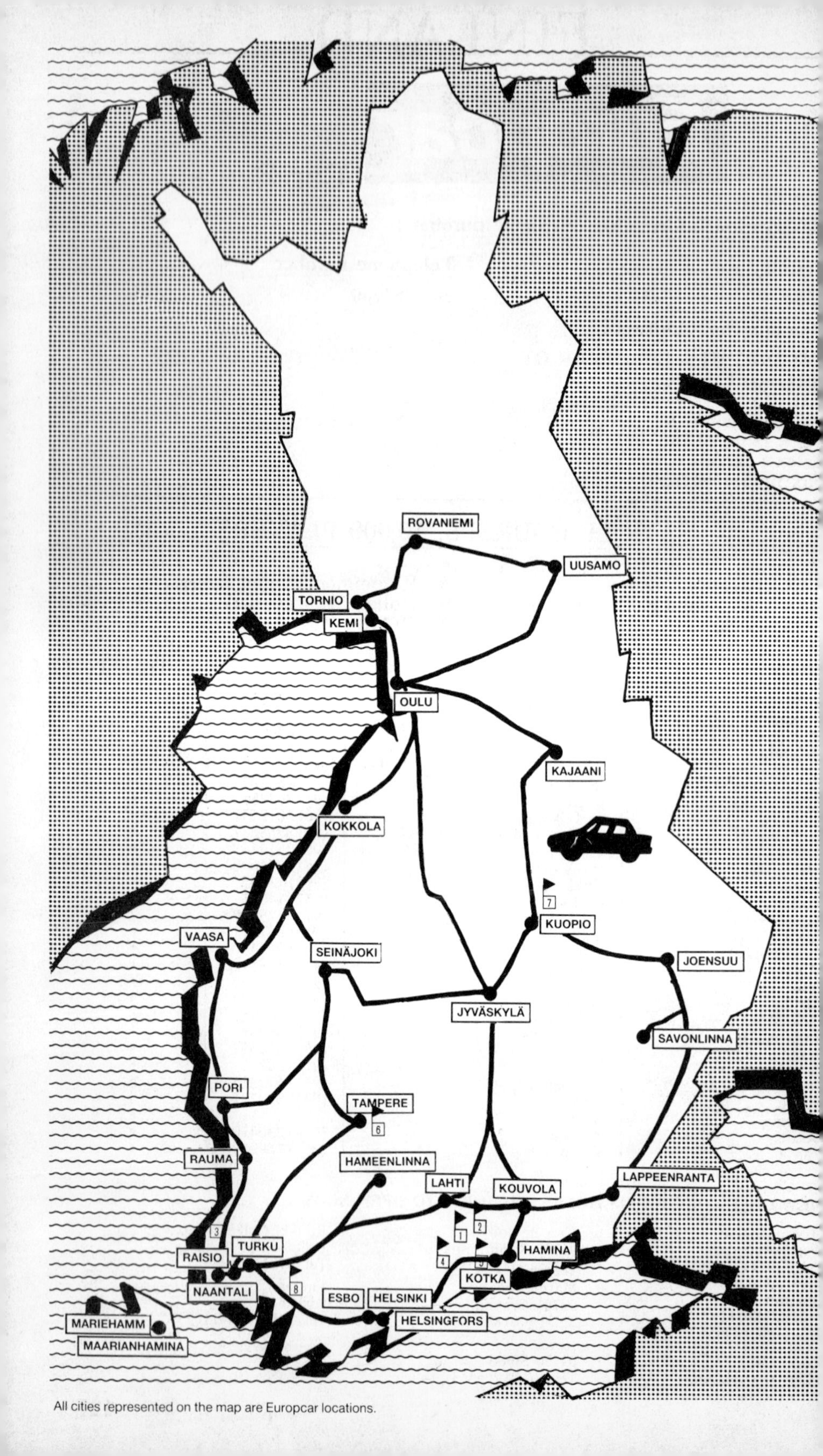

All cities represented on the map are Europcar locations.

AURA

TEL : (921)589201
LOCATION : 9 km Turku, on Ruissalo island
ADDRESS : Ruissalo 85 – 20100 Turku 10
HOTEL :
Marina Palace – Turku
Tel : (921)336300
Hamburger Börs – Turku
Tel : (921)637381
Cumulus – Turku
Tel : (921)514111

In midsummer it is possible to play golf 24 hours a day on this fine and peaceful golf course set on the island of Ruissalo on the shores of the Baltic Sea. The course is of the wooded parkland type with a large variety of mature trees bordering the fairways. Ideal for holiday golf with all kind of sport facilities available in Turku. *SSS 72*

GF $

1958

18

 November to May 15

 P. Sivula

L 5873 P 71

R

Required : None
Best days : Any day

HOLE	LENGTH MEDAL-TEE	PAR	STROKE INDEX
1	180	3	15
2	538	5	1
3	132	3	17
4	395	4	7
5	332	4	9
6	421	4	3
7	443	5	5
8	320	4	11
9	202	3	13
TOTAL	2963	35	TOTAL

HOLE	LENGTH MEDAL-TEE	PAR	STROKE INDEX
10	305	4	6
11	190	3	16
12	505	5	2
13	371	4	8
14	313	4	8
15	345	4	10
16	122	3	18
17	461	5	4
18	298	4	14
TOTAL	2910	36	TOTAL

ESPOO

TEL : (90)811212
LOCATION : 20 km NW Helsinki, 3 km S. Turku
ADDRESS : Mynttiläntie I – 02780 Espoo 78
HOTEL :
Arctia-Espoo
Tel : (90)523533
Dipoli – Espoo
Tel : (90)435811
RESTAURANT : Savoy – Helsinki
Tel : (90)176571

This is a popular and demanding course of championship standard laid out in a rolling parkland setting near the Finnish capital, with a stream presenting problems at several holes. *SSS 73*

GF $

1982

18

October to May

J. Sederholm

L 5930 P 72

S

R

Required : None
Best days : Weekdays

HOLE	LENGTH MEDAL-TEE	PAR	STROKE INDEX
1	370	4	7
2	480	5	1
3	180	3	15
4	450	5	3
5	325	4	11
6	160	3	17
7	380	4	5
8	320	4	13
9	355	4	9
TOTAL	3020	36	TOTAL

HOLE	LENGTH MEDAL-TEE	PAR	STROKE INDEX
10	150	3	16
11	490	5	2
12	130	3	18
13	355	4	8
14	310	4	14
15	435	5	4
16	330	4	10
17	380	4	6
18	330	4	12
TOTAL	2910	36	TOTAL

HELSINKI

TEL : (90)550235/557899
LOCATION : 7 km W. Helsinki
ADDRESS : Talin Kartano – 00350 Helsinki 35
HOTEL :
Academica – Helsinki
Tel : (90)440171
Savoy – Helsinki
Tel : (90)176571
RESTAURANT : Kalastajatorppa – Helsinki
Tel : (90)480100

This is the main championship course in Finland and the venue for the annual Finnish Amateur Open. It is a flat parkland course with mature trees bordering the lush fairways and a stream meandering its way through three holes. The clubhouse is a stately building with a sauna. *SSS 70*

GF $$

1935

18

October to May

—

L 5715 P 71

R S

Required : Handicap Certificate
Best days : Weekdays

HOLE	LENGTH MEDAL-TEE	PAR	STROKE INDEX
1	445	5	9
2	380	4	3
3	150	3	13
4	490	5	1
5	360	4	7
6	345	4	11
7	155	3	15
8	355	4	5
9	120	3	17
TOTAL	2800	35	TOTAL

HOLE	LENGTH MEDAL-TEE	PAR	STROKE INDEX
10	290	4	10
11	290	4	12
12	460	5	2
13	200	3	16
14	325	4	8
15	270	4	18
16	195	3	14
17	410	4	6
18	475	5	4
TOTAL	2915	36	TOTAL

KOTKA (Mussalo)

TEL : (952)604555
LOCATION : 5 km W. Kotka, on Mussalo Island
ADDRESS : 48320 Kotka
HOTEL : HR
Gasthause Santalahti
Tel : (952)604555
Seurahuone-Mussalo Island
Tel : (952)11090

Designed by the Finnish golf champion Kosti Kuronen, the Kotka golf course is located on the picturesque Mussalo island bordering the Golf of Finland. The 18 holes, encircled by water, are laid out in a typical Finnish landscape with pines and birches flanking the flat fairways. The golf club is one of the first clubs featuring 'warmed up greens'. The Santalahti hotel, 300m from the club, is part of a holiday-center which includes cottages for rent, a camping area and facilities for swimming, sailing, fishing and other sports. *SSS 72*

GF $ — November to April — R S
1989 — K. Kuronen
18 — L 5654 P 72

Required : Handicap Certificate
Best days : Weekdays

HOLE	LENGTH MEDAL-TEE	PAR	STROKE INDEX
1	303	4	13
2	465	5	1
3	176	3	15
4	282	4	7
5	435	5	3
6	313	4	11
7	147	3	17
8	350	4	9
9	370	4	5
TOTAL	2841	36	TOTAL

HOLE	LENGTH MEDAL-TEE	PAR	STROKE INDEX
10	451	5	2
11	309	4	14
12	309	4	10
13	141	3	18
14	436	5	4
15	300	4	8
16	364	4	12
17	148	3	16
18	355	4	6
TOTAL	2813	36	TOTAL

PICKALA

TEL : (90)2966251
LOCATION : 45 km W. Helsinki to Hanko
ADDRESS : Pickala Village-02580 Siuntio
HOTEL :
Savoy-Helsinki
Tel : (90)176571
Academica-Helsinki
Tel : (90)440171

The golf club is part of a large new sport complex which includes facilities for tennis, horse-riding, swimming, and sailing. The golf course is scenically set on the Baltic Sea and is laid out in flat countryside encircled by luxuriant woodland. The course, which is ideal for holiday golf, is full of creeks, with streams meandering their way through the holes. There are several well equipped chalets for rent.

GF $$

1988

27

November to May

R. Hillberg

L 2915 P 36, 2982 P 36, 2906 P 36

S

R

Required : Handicap Certificate
Best days : Weekdays before 15h. only

HOLE	LENGTH MEDAL-TEE	PAR	STROKE INDEX	HOLE	LENGTH MEDAL-TEE	PAR	STROKE INDEX	HOLE	LENGTH MEDAL-TEE	PAR	STROKE INDEX
1	297	4	6	1	441	5	2	1	355	4	5
2	332	4	3	2	393	4	4	2	106	3	9
3	149	3	9	3	152	3	9	3	473	5	2
4	513	5	1	4	306	4	7	4	334	4	6
5	372	4	4	5	381	4	3	5	347	4	3
6	461	5	2	6	157	3	8	6	161	3	8
7	162	3	8	7	329	4	5	7	478	5	1
8	336	4	5	8	466	5	1	8	323	4	4
9	293	4	7	9	357	4	6	9	329	4	7
TOTAL	2915	36	TOTAL	TOTAL	2982	36	TOTAL	TOTAL	2906	36	TOTAL

SARFVIK

TEL : (90)8012537
LOCATION : 25 km W. Helsinki
ADDRESS : PB 27-02321 Espoo
HOTEL :
Espoo-Espoo
Tel : (90)523533
Academica-Helsinki
Tel : (90)440-171

Designed by the well-known Swedish golf architect Jan Sederholm, this rather new course is laid out in open fields encircled by woodland with streams and lakes cutting the course in two.

GF $

1984

18

November to May

J. Sederholm

L 5820 P 72

S

R

Required : Handicap Certificate
Best days : Weekdays only

HOLE	LENGTH MEDAL-TEE	PAR	STROKE INDEX
1	445	5	7
2	130	3	17
3	495	5	1
4	155	3	15
5	315	4	3
6	270	4	13
7	445	5	5
8	190	3	11
9	295	4	9
TOTAL	2740	36	TOTAL

HOLE	LENGTH MEDAL-TEE	PAR	STROKE INDEX
10	485	5	4
11	140	3	18
12	485	5	2
13	170	3	16
14	375	4	6
15	330	4	14
16	385	4	8
17	335	4	12
18	375	4	4
TOTAL	3080	36	TOTAL

TAMPERE

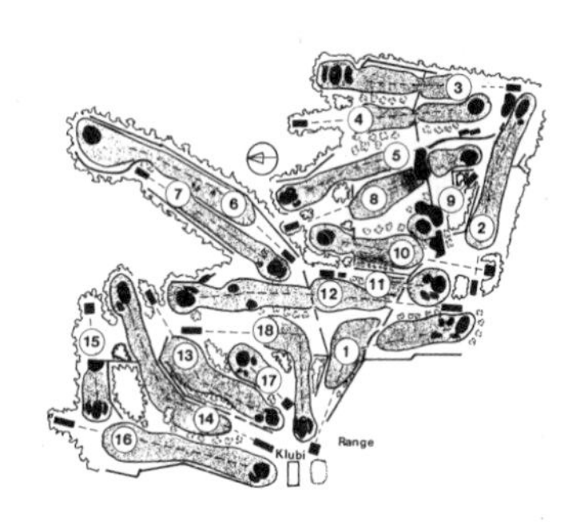

TEL : (931)613316
LOCATION : near Tampere, in Ruotula
ADDRESS : B.P. 269-33101 Tampere
HOTEL :
Rosendahl-Tampere
Tel : (931)112233
Cumulus-Tampere
Tel : (931)35500

Recently improved and extended to 18 holes, this parkland course is set on flat countryside with small rivers creating problems at several holes. *SSS 71*

GF $

1969

18

October to May

—

L 5870 P 72

S

R

Required : Handicap Certificate
Best days : Weekdays before 16h.

HOLE	LENGTH MEDAL-TEE	PAR	STROKE INDEX
1	450	5	5
2	330	4	13
3	330	4	7
4	340	4	11
5	375	4	1
6	450	5	3
7	280	4	15
8	355	4	9
9	130	3	17
TOTAL	3040	37	TOTAL

HOLE	LENGTH MEDAL-TEE	PAR	STROKE INDEX
10	310	4	12
11	190	3	16
12	510	5	2
13	325	4	10
14	450	5	4
15	155	3	14
16	390	4	6
17	160	3	18
18	340	4	8
TOTAL	2830	35	TOTAL

TARINAHARJU

TEL : (971)425299
LOCATION : 23 km Kuopio
ADDRESS : 71800 Siilinjarvi

Located in the middle of Finland, the course runs through a a varied setting with some holes bordering a lake. Several holes are laid out within a luxuriant river valley, others meander their way through pine ridge terrain. Water traps, bunkers and stands of larches serve as hazards. *SSS 72*

GF $

1987

18

—

K. Kuronen

L 5910 P 72

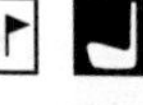

Required : Handicap Certificate
Best days : Any day

HOLE	LENGTH MEDAL-TEE	PAR	STROKE INDEX
1	340	4	9
2	155	3	17
3	370	4	7
4	445	5	3
5	160	3	15
6	310	4	14
7	350	4	10
8	545	5	1
9	140	3	18
TOTAL	2815	35	TOTAL

HOLE	LENGTH MEDAL-TEE	PAR	STROKE INDEX
10	395	4	2
11	440	5	6
12	175	3	16
13	325	4	12
14	360	4	8
15	450	5	4
16	320	4	11
17	265	4	13
18	365	4	5
TOTAL	3095	37	TOTAL

Car Rental

Reservation/Information telephone number :

Country code : 33

Telephone number : 1/30.43.82.82

Headquarters address :

EUROPCAR FRANCE
3, av. du Centre (Les Quadrants)
78881 St-Quentin-en-Yvelines – Cedex
Tel. : (33) 1/30.44.90.00
Telex : 696783
Fax : (33) 1/30.44.12.79

325 GOLF COURSES, 165 000 PLAYERS

★★★ Great golf course
★★ Very good golf course
$ 50-250 FF
★ Recommended golf course
☼ Holiday golf course
$ $ more than 350 FF

TOWN	GOLF COURSE		TEL	MAP REF.
Abbeville	Abbeville *(ext. to 18 h.)*		22.24.98.58	•
Agen	Agen		53.96.95.78	•
Aix-en-Provence	Château-L'Arc	☼	42.53.28.38	86
	Marseille-Aix		42.24.20.41	66
Aix-les-Bains	Aix-les-Bains	☼	79.61.23.35	52
Albi	Albi Lasbordes		63.54.98.07	125
	Tilbury		63.55.20.50	125
Allauch	Allauch		91.05.20.60	•
Amiens	Amiens		22.91.02.04	20
Angers	Angers		41.91.96.56	96
	Anjou		41.42.01.01	96
	Avrillé		41.69.22.50	126
Angoulème	L'Hirondelle		45.61.16.94	•
Annecy	Annecy	☼	50.60.12.89	48
Annemasse	Esery		50.36.58.70	174
Annonay	Gourdan		75.67.03.84	176
Antibes	Biot	☼	93.65.08.48	72
Arcachon	Arcachon	☼	56.83.08.51	54
	Gujan Mestras	☼	56.66.86.36	54
Arc-en-Barrois	Arc-en-Barrois		25.02.53.98	•
Arras	Arras		21.50.24.24	165
Aubusson	De la Jonchère		55.81.75.72	•
Avignon	Châteaublanc		90.33.39.08	127
	Grand Avignon		90.31.49.94	127
Baden	Baden	☼	97.57.18.96	128
Bagnoles-de-l'Orne	Andaines		33.37.81.42	•
Bar-le-Duc	Combles		29.45.16.03	•
Barneville-Carteret	La Côte des Isles		33.04.75.12	•
Bayeux	Bayeux Omaha Beach	☼	31.21.72.94	98
Beaune	Beaune		80.24.10.29	166

TOWN	GOLF COURSE		TEL	MAP REF.
Beauvais	Vivier		44.84.24.11	•
Belle-Ile-en-Mer	Belle-Ile Sauzon	☼	97.31.64.65	167
Belvès	Lolivarie		53.30.22.69	•
Benodet	Benodet-l'Odet	☼	98.57.26.16	87
Besançon	Besançon		81.55.73.54	39
Béziers	Saint-Thomas		67.98.62.01	•
Biarritz	Biarritz	☼	59.03.71.80	59
	Chiberta	★★ ☼	59.63.83.20	58
	d'Ilbarritz		59.23.74.65	•
Biscarosse	Biscarosse		56.50.92.72	•
Bitche	Bitche		87.96.00.13	100
Bonifacio *(island Corse)*	Sperone	★ ☼	95.73.13.69	182
Bordeaux	Bordeaux-Cameyrac		56.72.96.79	47
	Bordeaux-Lac		56.50.92.72	45
	Bordeaux-Pessac		56.36.24.47	129
	Bordelais		56.28.56.04	46
	Médoc	★	56.72.01.10	124
Bouc Bel Air	L'Éolienne		42.22.52.22	•
Bourg-en-Bresse	Bourg-en-Bresse		56.50.92.72	•
Bourgoin-Jallieu	Isle d'Abeau		74.43.28.84	•
Brasles	Val Secret		23.69.01.80	•
Briailles	Briailles		70.45.49.49	•
Brignoles	Barbaroux	★	94.59.07.43	97
Brive	Coiroux		55.27.25.66	81
Cabourg	Cabourg	☼	31.91.25.56	16
Calas	Cabries Calas		42.22.54.57	•
Cannes	Cannes-Mandelieu	★★ ☼	93.49.55.39	71
	Cannes-Mougins	★★ ☼	93.75.79.13	70
Cap d'Agde	Cap d'Agde	☼	67.26.34.40	130
Carnac	St-Laurent-Ploëmel	☼	97.56.85.18	29
Casteljaloux	Casteljaloux		53.93.51.60	131
Castres	Etangs de Fiac		63.70.64.70	173
Châlon-sur-Marne	La Grande Romanie		26.66.64.69	132
Chalon-sur-Saône	Chalon-sur-Saône		85.48.61.64	38
Chambon-sur-Lignon	Chambon-sur-Lignon		71.59.28.10	•
Chamonix	Chamonix	★ ☼	50.53.06.28	50
Charleville	Des Ardennes		24.35.64.65	•
Châteauroux	Val de l'Indre		54.26.59.44	184
Châtellerault	Châtelleraudais		49.86.20.21	88
	Haut-Poitou		49.62.53.62	122
Chaumont-en-Vexin	Chaumont-en-Vexin		44.49.00.81	25
	Rebetz		44.49.15.54	25
Cherbourg	Cherbourg		33.44.45.48	•
Cheverny	Cheverny		54.79.24.70	133
Cholet	Cholet		41.71.03.01	136
Clecy	Clecy-Cantelou		31.69.72.72	170
Cognac	Cognac		45.32.18.17	104
	Hautmont/Saintes		46.74.27.61	•
Compiègne	Compiègne		44.40.15.73	23
	Humières		44.42.39.51	23
Corrençon-en-Vercors	Corrençon-en-Vercors		76.95.80.42	•
Coutainville	Coutainville		33.47.03.31	•
Crécy-la-Chapelle	Montpichet		(1) 64.04.70.75	113
Deauville	Beuzeval Clair-Vallon	☼	31.91.06.97	99
	Deauville	★ ☼	31.88.20.53	17
	Saint-Gatien	☼	31.64.18.31	116
Dieppe	Dieppe	☼	35.84.25.05	8
Digne	Digne-les-Bains		92.32.38.38	171
Dijon	Bourgogne		80.35.71.10	101
Dinard	Dinard	★ ☼	99.88.32.07	14
Divonne-les-Bains	Divonne-les-Bains	★★	50.20.07.19	43
Dol-de-Bretagne	Ormes		99.48.40.27	134
Dole	Val d'Amour		84.72.24.72	•
Douai	Thumeries		20.86.58.98	•
Dunkerque	Dunkerque		28.61.07.43	172
Eauze	Guinlet		92.09.85.99	135
Epinal	Epinal		29.34.65.97	123
Etretat	Etretat	☼	35.27.04.56	9
Evian	Royal Evian	★ ☼	50.75.14.00	49
Fère-en-Tardenois	Champagne		23.71.62.08	•
Ferrières-en-Gâtinais	Domaine de Vaugouard		38.95.81.52	89
Flaine	Flaine-les-Carroz	☼	50.90.85.44	76

TOWN	GOLF COURSE		TEL	MAP REF.
Fleurance	Fleurance		62.06.26.26	•
Foix	Ariège		61.64.56.78	137
Fontenay-sur-Mer	Fontenay-en-Cotentin		33.21.44.27	•
Font-Romeu	Font-Romeu		58.30.38.09	•
Gaillon	Green Golf Gaillon		32.53.89.40	•
Gap	Gap Bayard	✡	92.50.16.83	175
Granville	Bréhal		33.51.58.88	•
	Granville	✡	33.50.23.06	15
Grenoble	Les Alberges		76.89.03.47	•
	Grenoble St-Quentin		76.93.67.28	138
	d'Uriage		76.89.03.47	•
Hardelot-Plage	Hardelot	★ ✡	21.83.73.10	3
Hossegor	Hossegor	★★★ ✡	58.43.56.99	57
	Seignosse	★ ✡	58.43.17.32	139
Houlgate	Beuzeval – Clair Vallon		31.91.06.97	99
Hyères	Valcros	✡	94.66.81.02	68
Isle Jourdan	Las Martines		62.07.27.12	•
Issoudun	Sarrays		54.49.54.49	•
Joigny	Joigny		86.73.69.87	178
La Bastide-de-Serou	L'Ariège		61.64.56.78	•
La Baule	La Baule	★ ✡	40.60.46.18	31
	La Bretèsche	★ ✡	40.88.30.03	30
Lacanau-Océan	Lacanau	✡	56.03.25.60	44
La Châtre	Les Dryades		54.30.28.00	110
La Ferté-St-Aubin	Country Club des Olleries		38.76.57.33	77
La Grande Motte	La Grande Motte	✡	67.56.05.00	108
Laguiole	Mezeyrac		65.44.41.41	•
Landerneau	Brest-Iroise	★	98.85.16.17	11
Langon	Graves et Sauternais		56.62.25.43	•
Lannemezan	Lannemezan		62.98.01.01	63
Laon	De l'Ailette		23.24.83.99	•
La Rochelle	La Prée		46.50.41.29	140
La Roche-sur-Yon	La Domangère		51.07.60.15	107
Lauzerte	Roucous Sauveterre		63.95.83.70	•
Laval	Laval		43.53.16.03	•
Le Havre	Le Havre		35.46.36.50	10
Le Mans	Le Mans		43.42.00.36	32
Le Neubourg	Champ de Bataille	★	32.35.03.72	103
Le Puy	Cros du Loup		71.09.17.77	•
Le Touquet	Le Touquet	★★★ ✡	21.05.32.62	6
Les Arcs	Arc-Chantel	✡	79.07.48.00	53
Les Rousses	Les Rousses			•
Leucate	La Pinède		68.40.70.40	•
Lille/Tourcoing	Bondues		20.23.20.62	2
	Brigode	★	20.91.17.86	5
	Flandres		20.72.20.74	•
	Le Sart	★	20.72.02.51	4
Limoges	La Porcelaine	★	55.31.10.69	109
	Limoges		55.30.21.02	41
Lons-le-Saunier	Val de Sorne			•
Lorient	Val Queven	✡	97.05.17.96	185
Loudun	Saint-Hilaire		49.98.78.06	78
Louviers	Le Vaudreuil		32.59.02.60	18
Luc-en-Diois	Pilhon		75.21.46.75	•
Luchon	Luchon		61.79.03.27	•
Lyon	Lyon	★	78.31.11.33	74
	Lyon Verger		78.02.84.20	79
	Salvagny		78.48.83.60	141
Mâcon	Château de la Salle		85.36.09.71	142
	La Commanderie		85.30.44.12	82
Marcigny	La Fredière-Céron		85.25.27.40	177
Marmande	Marmande		53.20.87.60	•
Marseille	Marseille-Aix		42.24.20.41	66
Masseube	Gascogne		62.66.03.10	•
Mazamet	La Barouge		63.61.06.72	83
Mazières-en-Gâtine	Petit Chêne		49.63.28.33	115
Megève	Mont d'Arbois	✡	50.21.29.79	51
Méribel	Méribel-les-Allues	✡	79.08.65.32	180
Mers-les-Bains	Mers-les-Bains			•
Mesnil-Saint-Laurent	Menil-St-Laurent		23.68.19.48	•
Metz	Longeville-les-Metz		87.55.26.26	•
	Metz-Cherisey		87.52.70.18	112

TOWN	GOLF COURSE		TEL	MAP REF.
Mionnay	La Dombes		78.91.84.84	•
Moissac	d'Espalais		63.29.04.56	•
Moliets	Côte d'Argent	✡	58.48.54.65	105
Montbéliard	Prunevelle	✡	81.98.11.77	40
Montbron	de la Prèze		45.23.24.74	•
Mont-de-Marsan	Mont-de-Marsan		58.75.63.05	•
Mont-Dore	Le Rigolet		73.65.00.79	•
Monte-Carlo	Monte-Carlo	★	93.41.09.11	73
Montelimar	La Valdaine		75.01.86.66	179
Montluçon	Val-de-Cher		70.06.71.15	84
Montpellier	Bombequiols		67.73.72.67	•
	Coulondres		67.84.13.75	•
	La Grande Motte	✡	67.56.05.00	108
	Massane		67.87.87.87	143
Montluçon	La Jonchère		55.62.23.05	144
Montreuil-sur-Mer	Nampont-St-Martin		22.29.92.90	7
Mooslargue	La Largue		89.25.71.11	145
Moulins	Avenelles		70.20.00.95	•
Mouriès	Servanes		90.47.59.95	146
Mulhouse	Rhin		89.26.07.86	80
Nancy	Nancy-Aingeray		83.24.53.87	27
Nans-les-Pins	Sainte-Baume	✡	94.78.60.12	119
Nantes	L'Ile d'Or		40.98.58.00	147
	Nantes		40.63.25.82	36
Nerac	Albret		53.65.53.69	148
Neuvic	Neuvic d'Ussel		55.95.98.89	•
Nevers	Nivernais		86.58.18.30	149
Nîmes	Les Hauts de Nîmes		66.23.33.33	127
	Nîmes Campagne	★★	66.70.17.37	65
Niort	Niort		49.09.01.41	•
Nogent-le-Rotrou	Perche		37.52.10.33	114
Orcines	Volcans		73.62.15.51	90
Orléans	Marcilly		38.76.11.73	111
	Sologne		38.76.57.33	120
	Val de Loire		38.59.25.15	120
Orthez	Salies-de-Béarn		59.38.37.59	•
Paimpol	Boisgelin	✡	96.22.31.24	150
Paris *(voir plus loin)*				
Pau	Pau	★	59.32.02.33	62
	Royal Artiguelouve		59.83.09.29	91
	Scottish Aubertin		59.82.70.48	151
Périgueux	La Croix de Mortemart		53.03.27.55	•
	Périgueux		53.53.02.35	•
Perpignan	St-Cyprien	✡	68.21.01.71	64
Poitiers	Haut-Poitou		49.62.53.62	122
	Poitevin		49.61.23.13	•
Pont-l'Évêque	Saint-Julien	✡	31.64.19.15	117
Pornic	Pornic		40.82.06.69	•
Poses	Léry Poses		32.59.47.42	161
Pouilly-en-Auxois	Château de Chailly		80.90.30.40	168
Quimper	Quimper		98.56.97.09	•
Reims	Champagne		23.71.62.08	24
	Reims		26.03.60.14	24
Rennes	La Freslonnière		99.60.84.09	153
	Rennes		99.64.24.18	•
Roanne	Champlong		77.69.70.60	•
Rouen	Mont-Saint-Aignan		35.76.38.65	21
	Saint-Saëns		35.34.25.24	118
Royan	Royan	✡	46.23.16.24	85
Royat	Royat Charade		73.35.73.09	•
Sables-d'Or-les-Pins	Sables-d'Or-Fréhel		96.41.42.57	•
Salbris	Salbris		54.97.21.85	•
Salies-de-Béarn	Salies-de-Béarn		59.38.37.59	•
Salon-de-Provence	Salon-de-Provence		90.53.90.90	•
Sancerre	Sancerrois		48.54.11.22	157
Sarlat	Domaine de Rochebois		53.28.18.01	•
Saumane	Saumane		90.20.20.82	•
Sauveterre	Roucous		63.95.83.70	•
Sens	Clairis		86.86.33.90	•
Septèmes-les-Vallons	Septèmes		91.96.28.59	•
Souillac	Mas del Teil		65.37.01.48	•
Strasbourg	Strasbourg		88.66.17.22	28

TOWN	GOLF COURSE		TEL	MAP REF.
Sully-sur-Loire	Sully-sur-Loire		38.36.52.08	33
St-Andre de Corcy	La Dombes		78.91.84.84	•
St-Cast	Pen Guen		96.41.91.20	•
St-Etienne	Forez		77.30.86.85	95
St-Gildas de Rhuys	Kerver	✡	97.45.30.09	154
St-Gilles Croix de Vie	Les Fontenelles		51.54.13.94	186
St-Jean-de-Luz	Chantaco	★★	59.26.14.22	61
	La Nivelle	✡	59.47.07.78	60
St-Jean-de-Monts	St-Jean-de-Monts	✡	51.58.82.73	155
St-Julien-en-Genevois	Bossey	★★	50.43.75.25	49
St-Laurent-Nouan	Les Bordes	★★	54.87.72.13	92
St-Malo	St-Malo le Tronchet	✡	99.58.96.69	93
St-Pierre d'Oléron	d'Oléron		46.47.11.59	•
St-Quay Portrieux	Ajoncs d'Or	✡	96.71.90.74	13
St-Rambert d'Albon	Albon		75.03.18.76	162
St-Raphaël	l'Esterel	✡	94.82.46.60	156
	Roquebrune	✡	94.82.92.91	156
	Valescure	✡	94.82.40.46	67
St-Saëns	St-Saëns		35.34.25.24	118
Ste-Maxime	Beauvallon		94.96.16.98	•
Tarbes	Laloubère		62.96.06.22	•
	Tumulus		62.96.14.50	183
Tende	Vievola		93.04.61.02	•
Tignes	Tignes		79.06.37.42	•
Tombebœuf	Barthe		53.88.83.31	•
Toulouse	Château de Terrides		63.95.65.20	158
	La Ramée		61.07.09.09	•
	Toulouse-Palmola	★	61.84.20.50	55
	Toulouse Seilh		61.84.20.50	159
	Vieille Toulouse		61.73.45.48	56
Tours	Ardrée		47.56.77.38	106
	Château des Sept Tours		47.24.69.75	169
	Touraine	★	47.53.20.28	37
Tregastel	St-Samson	✡	96.23.87.34	12
Troyes	La Cordelière		25.40.11.05	34
Valbonne	Val Martin		93.42.07.98	•
	Valbonne	✡	93.42.07.98	69
Valence d'Agen	Espalais		63.39.64.85	•
Valence-St-Didier	Valence-St-Didier		75.59.67.01	121
Valenciennes	Valenciennes		27.46.30.10	•
Valogne	Fontenay-sur-Mer		33.21.44.27	•
Vendôme	Bosse		54.23.02.60	•
Verneuil-sur-Avre	Bois France		32.23.50.02	•
Vichy	Vichy	✡	70.32.39.11	42
Vigneulles	Lac de Madine		29.89.56.00	•
Villars-les-Dombes	Clou		74.98.19.65	160
Villeneuve-sur-Lot	Castelnaud		53.01.74.64	94
Vittel	Vittel	★ ✡	29.08.06.38	35
Vitré	des Rochers		99.96.52.52	181
Wimereux	Wimereux		21.32.43.20	1
PARIS & SURROUNDINGS				
Bois-le-Roi	Bois-le-Roi		(1) 60.69.54.72	•
Bussy-Saint-Georges	Bussy-Saint-Georges		(1) 64.30.17.00	102
Cergy Pontoise	Ableiges		(1) 30.30.47.85	163
	Cergy Pontoise		(1) 34.21.03.48	163
	Les Templiers		44.08.73.72	75
Chantilly	Chantilly	★★★	44.57.04.43	75
	International Club du Lys	★	44.21.26.00	75
Chevry-Cossigny	La Musardière		(1) 64.25.44.39	•
Civry-la-Forêt	Vaucouleurs		(1) 34.87.62.29	75
Corbeil	St-Germain-lès-Corbeil		(1) 60.75.81.54	75
	Villeray		(1) 60.75.17.47	26
Créteil	Ormesson		(1) 45.76.20.71	75
Enghien-les-Bains	Domont-Montmorency		(1) 39 91.07.50	75
Evry	D'Etiolles		(1) 60.75.49.49	75
	Le Coudray		(1) 64.93.81.76	19
Fontainebleau	Fontainebleau	★★	(1) 64.22.22.95	75
	La Forteresse		(1) 64.31.95.10	75
	Urban Cély	✡	(1) 64.38.03.07	75

TOWN	GOLF COURSE		TEL	MAP REF.
Garches	St-Cloud	★★	(1) 47.01.01.85	75
Germigny	Lac de Germigny		40.22.04.53	•
Gif-sur-Yvette	Chevry II		(1) 60.12.40.33	•
Lésigny	Réveillon		(1) 60.02.17.33	75
Luzarches	Plessis-Bellefontaine		(1) 34.71.05.02	75
Magny-en-Vexin	Villarceaux		(1) 34.67.73.83	75
Maintenon	Château de Maintenon		37.27.18.18	75
Mantes	Guerville-Mézières		(1) 30.92.45.45	•
	Le Prieuré	★	(1) 34.76.70.12	22
	Sur Seine		(1) 30.92.45.46	•
Meaux	Meaux-Boutigny		(1) 60?25.63.98	75
	Montpichet		(1) 64.04.70.75	75
Meulan	Seraincourt		(1) 34.75.47.28	75
Montfort l'Amaury	Le Tremblay-sur-Mauldre		(1) 34.87.81.09	•
	des Yvelines	★	(1) 34.86.48.89	75
Ozoir-la-Ferrière	Ozoir-la-Ferrière		(1) 60.28.20.79	75
Plaisir	Isabella		(1) 30.54.10.62	75
Poissy	Bethemont		(1) 39.75.51.13	75
Rosny-sous-Bois	Rosny-sous-Bois		(1) 48.94.01.81	•
Saclay	St-Aubin		(1) 69.41.25.19	75
Senlis	Morfontaine	★★★	44.54.68.27	75
	Domaine de Raray		44.54.70.61	164
St-Arnoult-en-Yvelines	Rochefort	★	(1) 30.41.31.81	75
St-Germain-en-Laye	Fourqueux	★	(1) 34.51.41.47	75
	La Grenouillère		(1) 39.18.43.81	•
	St-Germain	★★	(1) 34.51.75.90	75
St-Nom-la-Bretèche	St-Nom-la-Bretèche	★★★	(1) 34.62.54.00	75
Saint-Quentin	Golf National	★★	(1) 30.43.36.00	75
Trappes	St-Quentin-en-Yvelines		(1) 30.50.86.40	75
Vaucresson	Haras Lupin		(1) 47.01.15.04	•
Versailles	La Boulie	★★	(1) 39.50.59.41	75
Villennes-sur-Seine	Villennes-sur-Seine		(1) 39.75.30.00	•

NEW GOLF COURSES (18 HOLES OR MORE) TO OPEN SOON

Château des Terrides
82100 Labourgade
Tel. : 63.95.65.20

Golf de l'Ailette
02860 Cerny
Tel. : 23.24.83.99

Golf d'Allauch
13190 Allauch
Tel. : 91.05.20.60

Golf d'Ammerschwer
68770 Ammerschwer
Tel. : 89.47.17.30

Golf d'Auriac
11330 Mouthoumet
Tel. : 68.72.57.30

Golf des Avenelles
03400 Yzeure
Tel. : 70.20.00.95

Golf de la Blanchère
84270 Vedène
Tel. : 90.31.49.94

Golf des Bois Lavau
49300 Cholet

Golf de Bombequiols
34190 Ganges
Tel. : 67.73.72.67

Golf de Bournel
25680 Rougement
Tel. : 81.86.92.15

Golf de Bresson-Jarrie
38000 Grenoble
Tel. : 76.73.65.00

Golf du Château d'Azay-le-Rideau
37190 Azay-le-Rideau

Golf de Château de Chailly
21320 Chailly-sur-Armançon
Tel. : 89.90.89.61

Golf du Château de la Perrière
49240 Avrille
Tel. : 41.69.22.50

Golf de Clairis
89150 Savigny-sur-Clairis
Tel. : 86.86.33.90

Golf de Coulondres
34980 Saint-Gely-du-Fesc
Tel. : 67.84.13.75

Golf de la Croix de Mortemar
24260 Le Bugue
Tel. : 53.03.27.55

Golf d'Embats
32000 Auch
Tel. : 62.05.20.80

Golf du Lac
65100 Lourdes
Tel. : 62.42.02.06

Golf de Marolles-en-Brie
94440 Villecresnes
Tel. : (1) 45.95.18.18

Golf du Mas del Teil
46200 Souillac
Tel. : 65.37.01.48

Golf de la Montagne Noire
81290 Labruguière
Tel. : 63.50.35.33

Golf de Montbazillac
24240 Montbazillac
Tel. : 53.58.21.21

Golf du Mont Saint-Jean
39220 Les Rousses
Tel. : 84.60.33.21

Golf de Pen-Guen
22380 Saint-Cast
Tel. : 96.41.91.20

Golf de la Picardière
18100 Vierzon
Tel. : 48.75.21.43

Golf de Pierrevent
04860 Pierrevent
Tel. : 92.72.05.69

Golf de Saintes Louis Rouyer Guillet
17100 Saintes
Tel. : 46.74.27.61

Golf du Val de Sorne
39570 Lons-le-Saunier
Tel. : 84.43.04.80

Golfclub des Avenelles
03400 Yzeure
Tel. : 70.20.00.95

Golfclub de la Vitarderie
51700 Dormans
Tel. : 26.58.25.09

Les Baux de Provence
13520 Les Baux de Provence
Tel. : 90.97.33.54

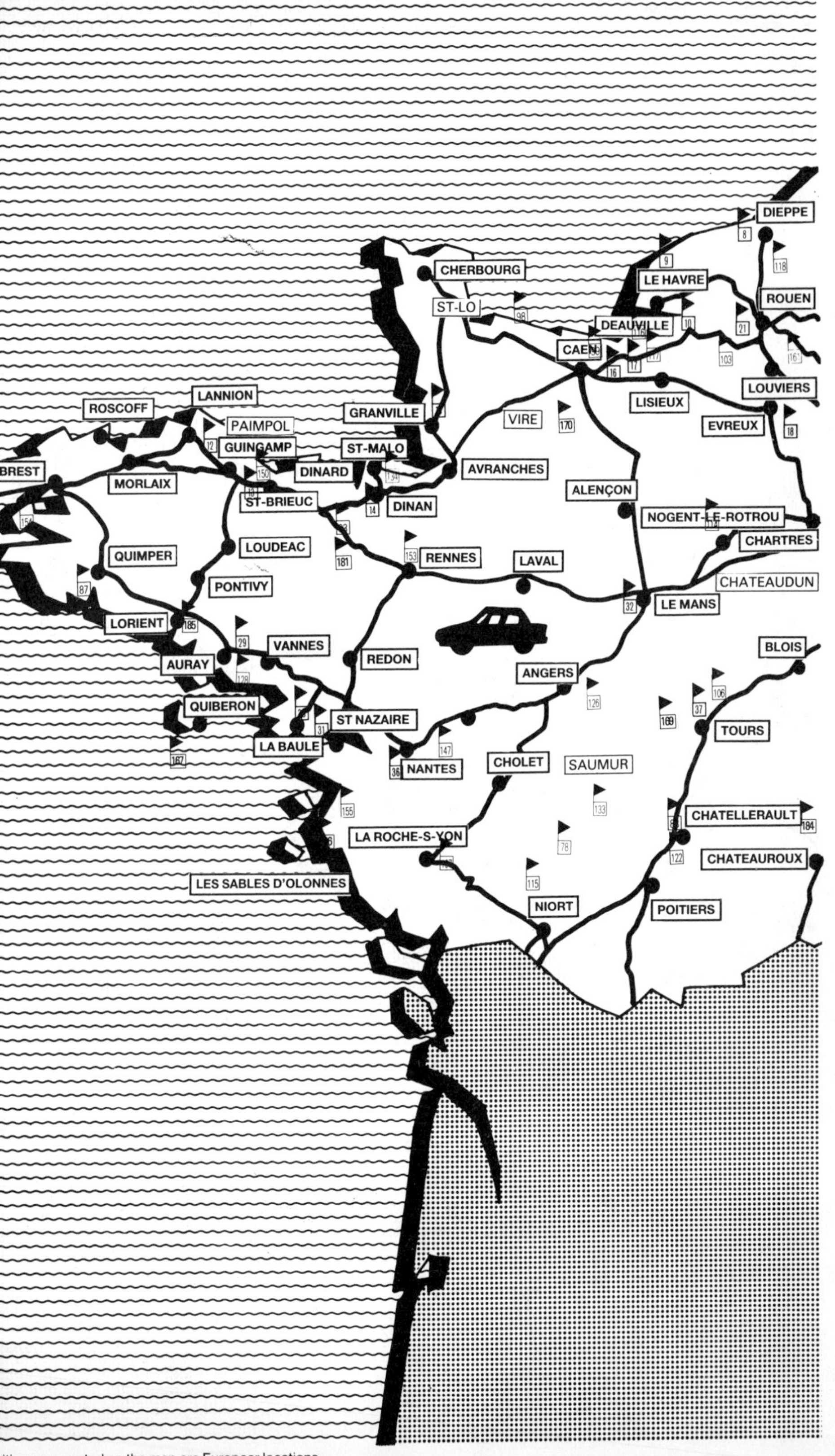

cities represented on the map are Europcar locations.

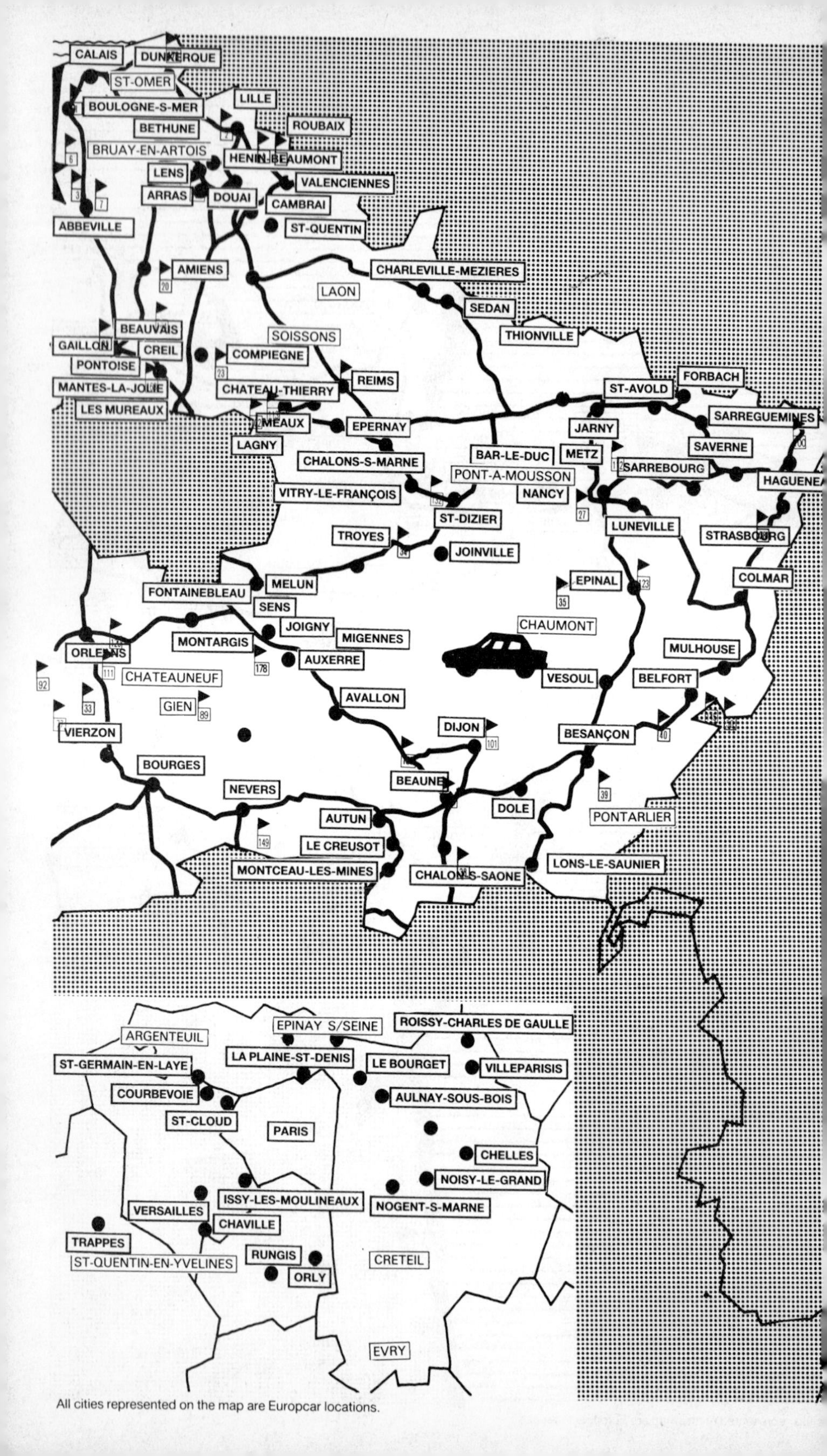

All cities represented on the map are Europcar locations.

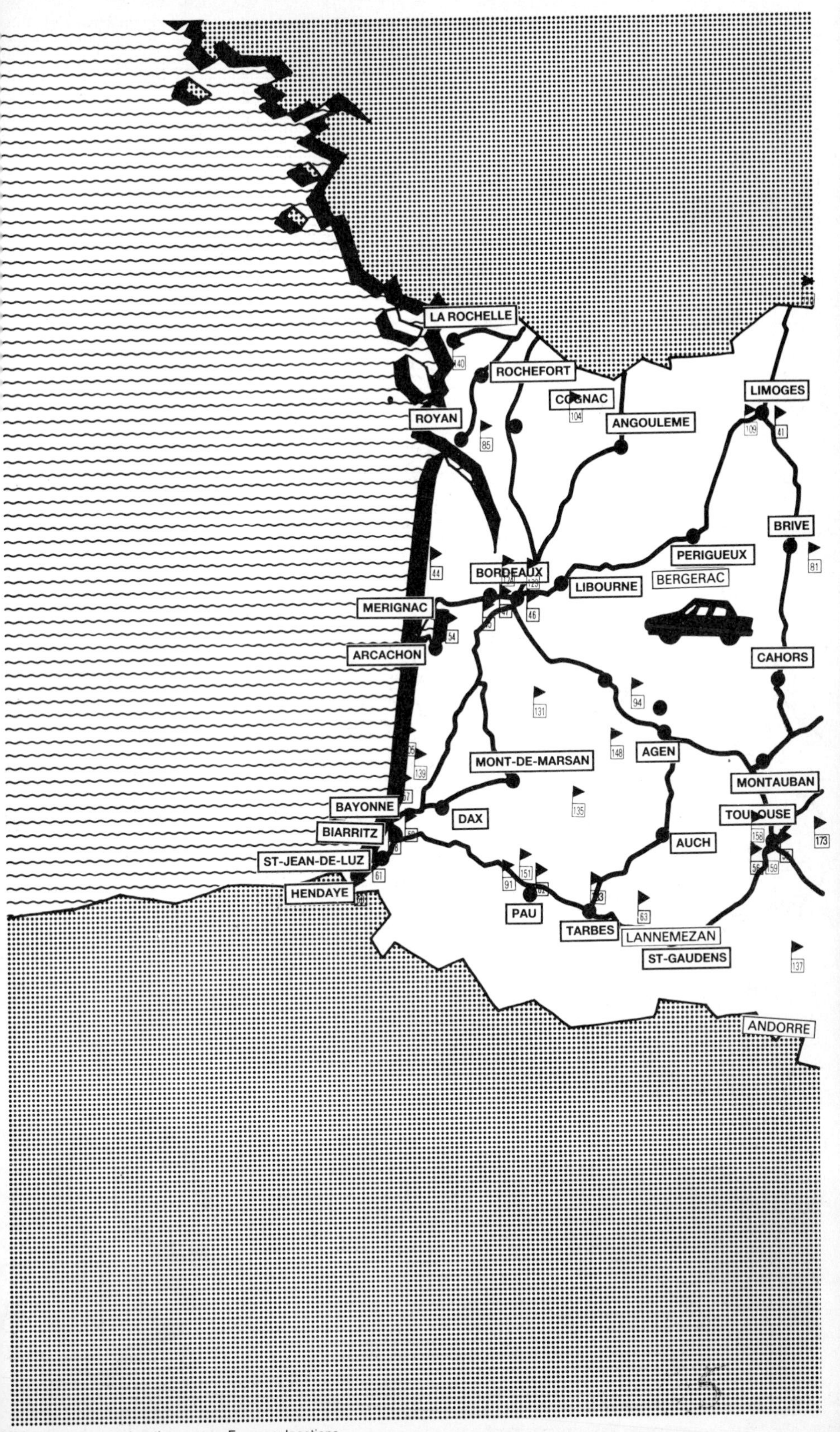

All cities represented on the map are Europcar locations.

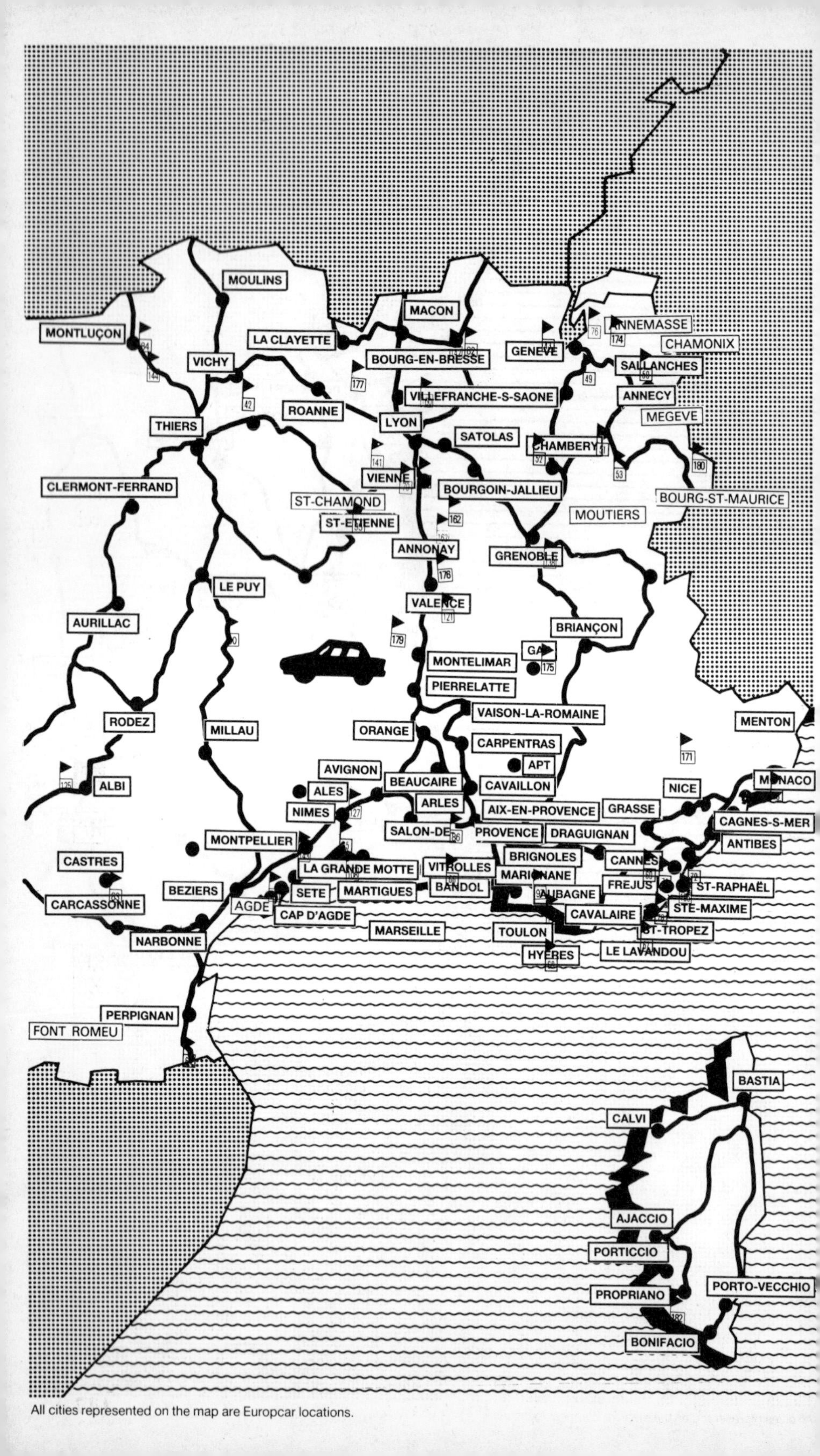

All cities represented on the map are Europcar locations.

AA-SAINT-OMER

TEL : 21385990
LOCATION : 35 km Calais A26 exit St-Omer, then 4 km on RN42
ADDRESS : Chemin des Bois Acquin - Westbecourt - 62380 Lumbres
HOTEL :
Le Bretagne - St-Omer
Tel : 21382578
Ibis - St-Omer
Tel : 21931111
Chartreuse du Val St-Esprit - Gosnay
Tel : 21628000

The Dutch architect Dudok van Heel designed this course, stretching out on gently rolling farmland in the river valley of the 'AA' in the north of France. Stately oak and beech trees border the majority of the holes and some ponds serve as obstacles.

GF $

1989

27

—

D. van Heel

L 6024 P 72, 2003 P 31

S

R

Required : Handicap Certificate
Best days : Any day

HOLE	LENGTH MEDAL-TEE	PAR	STROKE INDEX
1	340	4	
2	190	3	
3	367	4	
4	145	3	
5	281	4	
6	336	4	
7	506	5	
8	346	4	
9	453	5	
TOTAL	2964	36	TOTAL

HOLE	LENGTH MEDAL-TEE	PAR	STROKE INDEX
10	404	4	
11	458	5	
12	405	4	
13	347	4	
14	159	3	
15	445	5	
16	368	4	
17	157	3	
18	317	4	
TOTAL	3060	36	TOTAL

ABLEIGES

TEL : (1)34660605
LOCATION : 35 km Paris A15 to Mirapolis, then N14 and D28/6 km Cergy-Pontoise
ADDRESS : 95450 Ableiges
HOTEL :
Novotel - Cergy-Pontoise
Tel : (1)30303947
Ibis - Cergy-Pontoise
Tel : (1)34221144
Campanile-Pontoise *Tel :* (1)30385544
RESTAURANT : Jardin des Lavandières - Pontoise
Tel : (1)30382555

This sporting and varied course near the modern city of Cergy Pontoise spreads over 85ha of picturesque and undulating woodlands. Some of the holes are bordered by the river «La Viosne», while others run alongside pretty lakes. The club boasts a farmhouse style clubhouse. *SSS 70.*

GF $

1989

27

—

J. Garaialde, J. Pern

L 6340 P 72, 2145 P 33

R S

Required : Handicap Certificate
Best days : Weekdays Only

HOLE	LENGTH MEDAL-TEE	PAR	STROKE INDEX
1	369	4	5
2	332	4	3
3	458	5	13
4	167	3	9
5	348	4	1
6	463	5	7
7	280	4	11
8	117	3	17
9	311	4	15
TOTAL	2845	36	TOTAL

HOLE	LENGTH MEDAL-TEE	PAR	STROKE INDEX
10	435	5	14
11	383	4	8
12	144	3	16
13	345	4	6
14	258	4	18
15	431	5	10
16	298	4	2
17	147	3	12
18	348	4	4
TOTAL	2789	36	TOTAL

AIX-LES-BAINS

TEL : 79612335
LOCATION : 3 km Aix-les-Bains RN 491
ADDRESS : Avenue du Golf – 73100 Aix-les-Bains
HOTEL :
Campanile – Aix-les-Bains
Tel : 79613066
Iles Britanniques – Aix-les-Bains
Tel : 79610377
Le Manoir – Aix-les-Bains
Tel : 79614400
RESTAURANT : Chez la Mère Lille – Aix-les-Bains
Tel : 79350422

This tree-lined golf course lies a few kilometers from the spa resort of Aix-les-Bains in gently rolling and well wooded countryside. It features a stream full of trout, meandering its way through the 10th, 11th and 17th fairways. The Campanile hotel with 50 rooms is situated near the golf club. *SSS 68,6*

GF $

1936

18

Tues. in winter time

V. Bernard

L 5374 P 71

RP S

Required : Handicap Certificate
Best days : Weekdays

HOLE	LENGTH MEDAL-TEE	PAR	STROKE INDEX
1	346	4	1
2	421	5	13
3	176	3	5
4	382	4	7
5	412	5	17
6	214	3	3
7	107	3	15
8	439	5	11
9	192	3	9
TOTAL	2689	35	TOTAL

HOLE	LENGTH MEDAL-TEE	PAR	STROKE INDEX
10	135	3	6
11	275	4	12
12	93	3	18
13	302	4	10
14	301	4	14
15	497	5	8
16	460	5	16
17	330	4	2
18	292	4	4
TOTAL	2685	36	TOTAL

AIX-MARSEILLE

TEL : 42242041/42242301
LOCATION : 6 km Aix-en-Provence A 51 exit Les Milles, then RD 9 to Marignane 22 km Marseille
ADDRESS : Domaine de Riquetti – 13290 Les Milles
HOTEL :
Roy René – Aix-en-Provence
Tel : 42260301
Novotel Aix Est – Aix-en-Provence
Tel : 42274750
Pullman Le Pigeonnet – Aix-en-Provence
Tel : 42590290
RESTAURANT : Charvet – Aix-en-Provence
Tel : 42277281

A fine tree-lined course of championship length laid out on typically Mediterranean countryside, which is located between the cities of Marseille and Aix-en-Provence. *SSS 72*

GF $$ — Tuesdays — S

1935 — P. Gannon, F. Pennink — R

18 — L 6058 P 72

Required : Handicap Certificate
Best days : Mondays, Thursdays, Fridays

HOLE	LENGTH MEDAL-TEE	PAR	STROKE INDEX
1	360	4	11
2	462	5	7
3	138	3	18
4	375	4	3
5	164	3	16
6	408	4	1
7	463	5	9
8	293	4	14
9	382	4	5
TOTAL	3045	36	TOTAL

HOLE	LENGTH MEDAL-TEE	PAR	STROKE INDEX
10	328	4	13
11	388	4	2
12	376	4	6
13	444	5	10
14	177	3	17
15	340	4	8
16	168	3	15
17	351	4	4
18	448	5	12
TOTAL	3013	36	TOTAL

AJONCS D'OR

TEL : 96719074
LOCATION : 7 km St.-Quay-Portrieux
ADDRESS : Kergrain – 22410 St.-Quay-Portrieux
HOTEL :
Le Bretagne – St.-Quay-Portrieux
Tel : 96704091
Ker Moor – St.-Quay-Portrieux
Tel : 96705222
La Colombière – Etables-sur-Mer
Tel : 96706164
RESTAURANT : Le Gerbot d'Avoine – St-Quay-Portrieux
Tel : 96704116

This is a perfect holiday course located in Brittany near the seaside resorts of Binic, Etables-sur-Mer and St-Quay Portrieux. The public golf course lies on the edge of a forest on mostly flat terrain. A pond serves as a hazard on the 7th, 8th and 11th holes. *SSS 72*

GF $ — R S

1976 — G. Desheulles, J. Bourret

18 — L 6230 P 72

Required : Handicap Certificate
Best days : Any day

HOLE	LENGTH MEDAL-TEE	PAR	STROKE INDEX
1	355	4	10
2	170	3	16
3	365	4	6
4	440	5	14
5	415	4	2
6	350	4	12
7	140	3	18
8	370	4	4
9	475	5	8
TOTAL	3080	36	TOTAL

HOLE	LENGTH MEDAL-TEE	PAR	STROKE INDEX
10	375	4	5
11	390	4	1
12	215	3	9
13	445	5	13
14	340	4	11
15	145	3	17
16	400	4	3
17	340	4	15
18	500	5	7
TOTAL	3150	36	TOTAL

ALBI LASBORDES

TEL : 63549807
LOCATION : 3 km Albi
ADDRESS : Château de Lasbordes
81000 Albi
HOTEL :
St. Antoine - Albi
Tel : 63540404
St. d'Orléans - Albi
Tel : 63541656
La Réserve - Albi
Tel : 63607979
RESTAURANT : Francis Cardaillac –
Marssac-sur-Tarn
Tel : 63554190

France's most famous golfer Jean Garaialde together with Jeremy Pern, former assistant to R. Trent Jones, designed this 18 hole course, while preserving its natural setting. It is a well balanced course blending perfectly in the vallied countryside. Flanked on one side by the scenic river «Tarn», the holes stand amidst very old trees and picturesque lakes. The former Château Lasbordes has been converted into a comfortable clubhouse.

GF $ | Tuesdays | S

1989 | J. Garaialde/J. Pern | 

18 | L 6255 P 72 | 

Required : Handicap Certificate
Best days : Any day

HOLE	LENGTH MEDAL-TEE	PAR	STROKE INDEX
1	355	4	
2	320	4	
3	140	3	
4	475	5	
5	320	4	
6	395	4	
7	510	5	
8	335	4	
9	185	3	
TOTAL	3035	36	TOTAL

HOLE	LENGTH MEDAL-TEE	PAR	STROKE INDEX
10	320	4	
11	200	3	
12	415	4	
13	480	5	
14	160	3	
15	360	4	
16	495	5	
17	390	4	
18	400	4	
TOTAL	3220	36	TOTAL

ALBON

TEL : 75031876
LOCATION : 60 km S Lyon A7 exit Chanas then RN7 to Valence
ADDRESS : 26140 St-Rambert d'Albon
HOTEL :
Ibis - St-Rambert d'Albon
Tel : 75030400
Terminus - St-Vallier
Tel : 75230112

This most promising golf course lies in the Rhône Valley on beautiful sweeping woodland centered around the stately Château de Senaud. Technically excellent, the holes work their way through majestic and unspoiled countryside. They are protected by majestic trees, and bordered by rivers and lakes. *SSS 71.9*

GF $

1989

18

 Tuesdays in winter

 A. d'Ormesson

L 5925 P 72

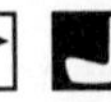 

Required : Handicap Certificate on weekends
Best days : None

HOLE	LENGTH MEDAL-TEE	PAR	STROKE INDEX
1	115	3	16
2	408	4	8
3	400	4	4
4	490	5	12
5	172	3	6
6	512	5	2
7	297	4	10
8	484	5	18
9	278	4	14
TOTAL	3156	37	TOTAL

HOLE	LENGTH MEDAL-TEE	PAR	STROKE INDEX
10	295	4	13
11	278	4	9
12	380	4	3
13	330	4	11
14	121	3	15
15	318	4	17
16	175	3	5
17	550	5	1
18	320	4	7
TOTAL	2769	35	TOTAL

ALBRET

TEL : 53655369
LOCATION : 125 km Bordeaux A62 exit Damazan Nérac, then RD 930 to Barbaste
ADDRESS : Le Pusocq - 47230 Barbaste
HOTEL :
Auberge Belle Gasconne - Poudenas Mezin
Tel : 53657158
du Château - Nérac
Tel : 53650905
d'Albret - Nérac
Tel : 53650147

Set in the rural Landes region within 50ha of fairly sweeping and sandy landscape, the course is protected on one side by a dense pinewood forest. Nearby there are facilities for archery, tennis, swimming and riding.

GF $ — Tuesdays in winter — S

1986 — J.-L. Pega

18 — L 5440 P 71 — R

Required : None
Best days : Any day

HOLE	LENGTH MEDAL-TEE	PAR	STROKE INDEX
1	315	4	7
2	328	4	2
3	185	3	6
4	299	4	11
5	363	4	12
6	110	3	10
7	453	5	16
8	253	4	18
9	498	5	4
TOTAL	2804	36	TOTAL

HOLE	LENGTH MEDAL-TEE	PAR	STROKE INDEX
10	292	4	9
11	292	4	13
12	113	3	17
13	388	4	1
14	369	4	8
15	438	5	15
16	352	4	3
17	158	3	5
18	234	4	14
TOTAL	2636	35	TOTAL

AMIENS

TEL : 22910204
LOCATION : 8 km Amiens N 29
ADDRESS : Château de Querrieu - 80115 Querrieu
HOTEL :
Novotel - Boves
Tel : 22462222
Carlton-Belfort - Amiens
Tel : 22922644
Univers - Amiens
Tel : 22915251
RESTAURANT : Chez Joséphine - Amiens
Tel : 22914738

Extended to 18 holes in 1977, the course lies on an undulating plain alongside a forest. The 10th hole commands a fine view over the city of Amiens. Most of the fairways and greens are cunningly bunkered. *SSS 71*

GF $ — Tuesdays  

1950 —  F. Pennink 

18 —  5940 P 72

Required : Handicap Certificate
Best days : Weekdays

HOLE	LENGTH MEDAL-TEE	PAR	STROKE INDEX
1	485	5	7
2	300	4	11
3	343	4	9
4	154	3	17
5	355	4	5
6	369	4	1
7	184	3	15
8	290	4	13
9	447	5	3
TOTAL	2927	36	TOTAL

HOLE	LENGTH MEDAL-TEE	PAR	STROKE INDEX
10	350	4	6
11	180	3	16
12	512	5	4
13	400	4	2
14	332	4	12
15	450	5	10
16	140	3	18
17	309	4	14
18	340	4	8
TOTAL	3013	36	TOTAL

ANGERS

TEL : 41919656/41919215
LOCATION : 8 km Angers N260
ADDRESS : Moulin de Pistrait – 49320 Saint-Jean-des-Mauvrets
HOTEL :
Anjou-Angers
Tel : 41882482
Concorde-Angers
Tel : 41873720
Le Prieuré-Gennes
Tel : 41679014
RESTAURANT : Salamandre – Angers
Tel : 41889955

Though rather short, the course is pleasant and technically interesting. It is set in a splendid natural landscape and meanders its way through luxuriant woodland, with century-old trees flanking the fairly narrow fairways. Accurate play is necessary due to the presence of numerous lakes. The charming clubhouse was once used as a mill. *SSS 69*

GF $

Tuesdays

R S

1963/1987

M. Bourret, R. Berthet

18

L 5097 P 69

Required : Handicap Certificate
Best days : Any days

HOLE	LENGTH MEDAL-TEE	PAR	STROKE INDEX
1	277	4	13
2	278	4	9
3	372	4	5
4	170	3	7
5	313	4	15
6	353	4	1
7	149	3	11
8	440	5	17
9	394	4	3
TOTAL	2746	35	TOTAL

HOLE	LENGTH MEDAL-TEE	PAR	STROKE INDEX
10	420	5	16
11	285	4	12
12	263	4	8
13	107	3	18
14	328	4	2
15	161	3	14
16	288	4	10
17	165	3	4
18	334	4	6
TOTAL	2351	34	TOTAL

ANJOU

TEL : 41420101
LOCATION : 20 km M. Angers D. 768 to Sablé
ADDRESS : Route de Cheffes – 49330 Champigné
HOTEL :
Anjou – Angers
Tel : 41882482
France – Angers
Tel : 41884942
Château des Briottières – Champigné
Tel : 41420002

Designed by the English architect Fred Hawtree, this course rolls through tranquil undulating landscape. Stately trees, new plantations and old hedgerows border the holes. Numerous ponds affect play throughout the course. The country-club with tennis courts, conference facilities and small appartments for rent will be fully operational in the summer of 1991

GF $ — Tuesdays in winter  

1990 —  F. Hawtree 

18 —  5785 P 72

Required : Handicap Certificate
Best days : Any day

HOLE	LENGTH MEDAL-TEE	PAR	STROKE INDEX
1	339	4	14
2	330	4	2
3	342	4	16
4	144	3	8
5	321	4	18
6	411	5	10
7	142	3	12
8	465	5	4
9	343	4	6
TOTAL	2837	36	TOTAL

HOLE	LENGTH MEDAL-TEE	PAR	STROKE INDEX
10	290	4	15
11	344	4	9
12	492	5	7
13	368	4	1
14	113	3	17
15	345	4	11
16	144	3	13
17	458	5	5
18	394	4	3
TOTAL	2948	36	TOTAL

ANNECY

TEL : 50601289
LOCATION : 13 km Annecy RD 909 to Talloires
ADDRESS : Echarvines – 74290 Talloires
HOTEL :
Les Dents de Lanfon – Talloires
Tel : 50601256
Abbaye – Talloires
Tel : 50607733
Hermitage et Domaine des Primevères – Talloires
Tel : 50607117
RESTAURANT : Auberge du Père Bise – Talloires
Tel : 50607201

Picturesquely situated amidst rocks (le Roc de Chère) and mountains, this well-wooded and hilly course enjoys panoramic views over the Annecy lake and the French Alps. Though short, the course is varied and rather technical with sloping fairways and small greens.

GF $

1950

18

December to March

C. Blandford

L 5016 P 69

S

R

Required : Handicap Certificate
Best days : Tuesdays, Wednesdays, Thursdays

HOLE	LENGTH MEDAL-TEE	PAR	STROKE INDEX
1	271	4	
2	157	3	
3	306	4	
4	361	4	
5	189	4	
6	111	3	
7	355	4	
8	381	4	
9	302	4	
TOTAL	2433	34	TOTAL

HOLE	LENGTH MEDAL-TEE	PAR	STROKE INDEX
10	263	4	8
11	273	4	6
12	224	3	14
13	439	5	12
14	262	4	16
15	315	4	18
16	164	3	2
17	174	3	4
18	469	5	10
TOTAL	2583	35	TOTAL

ARCACHON

TEL : 56830851
LOCATION : 3 km Arcachon, 60 km Bordeaux
ADDRESS : 35 Bd d'Arcachon – La Teste-de-Buch – 33260 La Teste
HOTEL :
Le Parc – Arcachon
Tel : 56831058
Arc – Arcachon
Tel : 56830685
Le Nautic – Arcachon
Tel : 56830148
RESTAURANT : Chez Boron – Arcachon
Tel : 56832996

Located near the popular seaside resort of Arcachon, the first nine holes are laid out in rich verdant countryside. The last nine are played on open moorland with water affecting play on several holes. The starting holes have narrow tree-lined fairways with hazardous rough demanding precision. *SSS 71, 6*

GF $$

1952

18

Tuesdays in winter

C. Blandford, P. Hirigoyen

L 5934 P 71

S

R

Required : Handicap Certificate
Best days : Weekdays

HOLE	LENGTH MEDAL-TEE	PAR	STROKE INDEX
1	360	4	11
2	219	3	5
3	535	5	1
4	372	4	3
5	147	3	17
6	311	4	13
7	504	5	5
8	386	4	4
9	439	5	15
TOTAL	3273	37	TOTAL

HOLE	LENGTH MEDAL-TEE	PAR	STROKE INDEX
10	421	4	4
11	150	3	16
12	519	5	6
13	408	4	2
14	299	4	10
15	140	3	14
16	351	4	8
17	130	3	12
18	243	4	8
TOTAL	2661	34	TOTAL

ARC-CHANTEL

TEL : 79074800
LOCATION : 12 km Bourg-St-Maurice
ADDRESS : Les Arcs 1800 – 73700 Bourg-St-Maurice
HOTEL :
Golf – Les Arcs 1800
Tel : 79072517
Les Trois Arcs – Les Arcs 1600
Tel : 79077878
RESTAURANT : Le Green – Les Arcs 1800
Tel : 79072517

This popular mountain golf course, famous as a training school, lies at 1800m above sea level amidst an impressive mountain scenery. Framed by the snow capped Alps with the majestic Mont Blanc in the background, the course is comparatively short but interesting, with several mountain streams crossing the fairways. The 2nd and 5th holes enjoy panoramic views over the 'Tarentaise' valley and the Mont Blanc. The club is not far from the Golf Hotel with a swimming pool, tennis courts, childrens' playground, health and fitness clubs. *SSS 68*

GF $

1974

18

October to June

—

L 4948 P 68

Required : Handicap Certificate
Best days : Any day

HOLE	LENGTH MEDAL-TEE	PAR	STROKE INDEX
1	280	4	13
2	122	3	9
3	360	4	1
4	413	5	7
5	331	4	5
6	155	3	15
7	170	3	3
8	275	4	11
9	177	3	17
TOTAL	2283	33	TOTAL

HOLE	LENGTH MEDAL-TEE	PAR	STROKE INDEX
10	320	4	10
11	400	4	2
12	98	3	16
13	268	4	14
14	468	5	4
15	265	4	18
16	175	3	12
17	301	4	6
18	370	4	8
TOTAL	2665	35	TOTAL

ARDREE

TEL : 47567738
LOCATION: 12 km Tours A 10, exit Tours Nord
ADDRESS : 37360 Saint-Antoine-du-Rocher
HOTEL :
Château de l'Aubrière – La Memembrole-sur-Choisille
Tel : 47515035
Jean Bardet-Tours
Tel : 47414111
Méridien-Tours
Tel : 47280080
RESTAURANT : Barrier-Tours
Tel : 47542039

The first 18 holes of this very promising 36 hole golf complex were opened in 1988. Designed by the French architect Olivier Brizon, it is set in splendid natural landscape amidst old cedars, maple-trees and copper beeches, near the famous 'Loire' châteaux. The layout is modern, featuring long and rolling fairways, well-shaped sand bunkers (85), huge greens and nine menacing water hazards. *SSS 68, 6*

GF $

1988

18

—

O. Brizon

L 5455 P 71

R S

Required : Handicap Certificate
Best days : Any day

HOLE	LENGTH MEDAL-TEE	PAR	STROKE INDEX
1	332	4	3
2	134	3	13
3	302	4	11
4	438	5	5
5	310	4	7
6	154	3	15
7	443	5	1
8	146	3	17
9	307	4	9
TOTAL	2566	35	TOTAL

HOLE	LENGTH MEDAL-TEE	PAR	STROKE INDEX
10	456	5	16
11	312	4	10
12	409	5	12
13	386	4	2
14	319	4	8
15	136	3	14
16	282	4	18
17	205	3	4
18	384	4	6
TOTAL	2889	36	TOTAL

ARIEGE

TEL : 61645678
LOCATION : 17 km Foix RD17 to Saint-Girons
ADDRESS : 09240 La Bastide de Sérou
HOTEL :
Auberge - Foix
Tel : 61655244
Pyrène - Foix
Tel : 61654866
RESTAURANT : Eychenne - St-Girons
Tel : 61662055

Blending into the lush foothills of the Pyrenees, the course overlooks splendid rugged countryside which offers a breathtaking variety of landscapes. Most of the fairways are narrow.

GF $ — 1988 — 27

— — M. Gayon — L 5954 P 71, 2947 P 36

S — R

Required : Handicap Certificate on weekends
Best days : Any day

HOLE	LENGTH MEDAL-TEE	PAR	STROKE INDEX
1	365	4	
2	325	4	
3	325	4	
4	155	3	
5	540	5	
6	131	3	
7	520	5	
8	350	4	
9	410	4	
TOTAL	3121	36	TOTAL

HOLE	LENGTH MEDAL-TEE	PAR	STROKE INDEX
10	178	3	
11	526	5	
12	135	3	
13	325	4	
14	305	4	
15	315	4	
16	468	5	
17	215	3	
18	366	4	
TOTAL	2833	35	TOTAL

ARRAS

TEL : 21502424
LOCATION : 50 km Lille A1 exit Arras, then N. 39 to St. Pol
ADDRESS : rue Briquet Taillandier - 62223 Anzin Saint-Aubin
HOTEL :
Univers - Arras
Tel : 21713401
Moderne - Arras
Tel : 21233957
RESTAURANT : La Faisanderie - Arras
Tel : 21482076

This new course is situated in the verdant valley of the river Scarpe, which meanders its way through the holes. It presents two different types of layouts : the first nine holes cut through reeds and ponds, while the last nine holes climb over a hill back to the clubhouse. It features several treacherous doglegs (4th, 6th, 13th, 15th and the difficult 18th). *SSS 69*

GF $ — S
1990 J.C. Cornillot
18 L 5455 P 72 R

Required : Handicap Certificate
Best days : Any day

HOLE	LENGTH MEDAL-TEE	PAR	STROKE INDEX
1	289	4	9
2	223	4	11
3	117	3	17
4	442	5	15
5	412	5	3
6	309	4	13
7	326	4	1
8	170	3	7
9	316	4	5
TOTAL	2604	36	TOTAL

HOLE	LENGTH MEDAL-TEE	PAR	STROKE INDEX
10	139	3	18
11	284	4	12
12	393	4	2
13	450	5	6
14	96	3	14
15	327	4	10
16	354	4	4
17	340	4	8
18	468	5	16
TOTAL	2851	36	TOTAL

AVRILLE

TEL : 41692250
LOCATION : 5 km d'Angers RN162 to Laval
ADDRESS : Château de la Perrière 49240 Avrillé
HOTEL :
Le Cavier - Avrillé
Tel : 41423045
Anjou - Angers
Tel : 41882482
Ibis - Angers
Tel : 41861515
RESTAURANT : Auberge de la Haye – Avrillé
Tel : 41693358

This very technical course set amidst a variety of deciduous trees in the Loire Valley, was designed by Robert Berthet. Its first nine holes run over vallied countryside, the second nine stretching over flat land. Water is ever present here. Six holes are affected by it and some 16 greens, some elevated, are protected by it. Sport facilities nearby : tennis and horse riding. *SSS 72*

GF $ — Tuesdays in Dec. and Jan. — S

1988 — R. Berthet

18 — L 6116 P 71 — R

Required : Handicap Certificate
Best days : Any day

HOLE	LENGTH MEDAL-TEE	PAR	STROKE INDEX
1	385	4	13
2	405	4	5
3	358	4	7
4	388	4	3
5	157	3	17
6	508	5	1
7	358	4	9
8	153	3	15
9	439	5	11
TOTAL	3151	36	TOTAL

HOLE	LENGTH MEDAL-TEE	PAR	STROKE INDEX
10	353	4	16
11	204	3	2
12	494	5	10
13	193	3	6
14	359	4	12
15	163	3	18
16	331	4	14
17	403	4	4
18	465	5	8
TOTAL	2965	35	TOTAL

BADEN

TEL : 97571896
LOCATION : 9 km Auray/Vannes on D101
ADDRESS : Kernic - 56870 Baden
HOTEL :
Les Gavrinis - Baden
Tel : 97570082
du Loch - Auray
Tel : 97564833
La Marébaudière - Vannes
Tel : 97473429

This sporting and friendly course, set in the south of Brittany, boasts three different types of landscape. Partly bordering the picturesque inlet of the Gulf of Kerdréan, or running through maritime pine forest or over hilly countryside which is typical of this Brittany region. Some of the holes are bordered by lakes. The region is famous for its sailing facilities, mild climate and good seafood. A hotel (Fairway) is planned in 1991. *SSS 72*

GF $

— RΓ S

1989

Y. Bureau

18

L 5731 P 72

Required : Handicap Certificate
Best days : Any day

HOLE	LENGTH MEDAL-TEE	PAR	STROKE INDEX
1	310	4	9
2	465	5	3
3	365	4	1
4	162	3	17
5	415	5	15
6	153	3	11
7	339	4	7
8	285	4	13
9	334	4	5
TOTAL	2828	36	TOTAL

HOLE	LENGTH MEDAL-TEE	PAR	STROKE INDEX
10	297	4	16
11	335	4	10
12	146	3	18
13	412	5	12
14	351	4	6
15	340	4	14
16	187	3	8
17	365	4	2
18	470	5	4
TOTAL	2903	36	TOTAL

BARBAROUX

TEL : 94590743
LOCATION : 50 km Toulon/Aix-en-Provence A8 exit Brignoles, then RN 7/RD 79
ADDRESS : Route de Cabasse – 83170 Brignoles
HOTEL :
Lou Paralou– Tourves
Tel : 94787039
Mas la Cascade-Brignoles
Tel : 94690149
Le Paris-Brignoles
Tel : 94690100
RESTAURANT : Grillade au Feu de Bois-Brignoles
Tel : 94697120

This superb and challenging course, set in the heart of the Var in the south of France, was the first to be designed by the famous American golf architects Pete and P.B. Dye. Along the first ten holes, set amidst hills and vineyards, there are a number of lakes as water hazards and many typical 'Dye' style bunkers. The back nine roll through lovely pine and oak forests. It features the 'Glorious 12th', a quite phenomenal hole, with a drop of 40 meters or more to the green. The clubhouse, with pool and two tennis courts, is well appointed. *SSS 72*

GF $$ — Tuesdays — S

1988 — P. & P.-B. Dye — R

18 — L 6388 P 72

Required : Handicap Certificate
Best days : Weekdays; Weekends on invitation only

HOLE	LENGTH MEDAL-TEE	PAR	STROKE INDEX
1	380	4	
2	315	4	
3	500	5	
4	410	4	
5	320	4	
6	150	3	
7	390	4	
8	550	5	
9	200	3	
TOTAL	3215	36	TOTAL

HOLE	LENGTH MEDAL-TEE	PAR	STROKE INDEX
10	385	4	
11	325	4	
12	520	5	
13	140	3	
14	520	5	
15	410	4	
16	290	4	
17	160	3	
18	423	4	
TOTAL	3173	36	TOTAL

BAYEUX OMAHA BEACH

TEL : 31217294
LOCATION : 8 km Bayeux D6
ADDRESS : La Ferme Saint-Sauveur – 14520 Port-en-Bessin
HOTEL : Hr
Altea
Tel : 31224444
Lion d'Or-Bayeux
Tel : 31920690
Novotel-Bayeux
Tel : 31921611
RESTAURANT : Relais Château d'Audrieu-Audrieu
Tel : 31802152

Set on the Normandy coast, this new and lavish golf complex is situated close to the Arromanches beaches, site of the famous landing of World War II. The course is characterised by three different types of setting. Nine 'American style' holes run along the lake on hilly countryside, another nine are laid out amidst apple groves leading to two Roman churches. The last nine run amidst dunes along the sea, overlooking the picturesque fishing village of Port-en-Bessin. It features a green built on a 'blockhaus' bordering a cliff. The modern clubhouse overlooks the fairways and the sea. The Altea Hotel with tennis courts and a swimming pool is situated on the green of the 18th hole. *SSS 72.*

GF $

1986

27

Tuesdays in winter

Y. Bureau

L 5845 P 72, 2915 P 35

R 

Required : Handicap Certificate
Best days : Any day

HOLE	LENGTH MEDAL-TEE	PAR	STROKE INDEX
1	154	3	7
2	474	5	4
3	312	4	11
4	476	5	6
5	305	4	10
6	133	3	14
7	384	4	2
8	397	4	3
9	300	4	18
TOTAL	2935	36	TOTAL

HOLE	LENGTH MEDAL-TEE	PAR	STROKE INDEX
10	496	5	12
11	133	3	17
12	304	4	9
13	278	4	16
14	498	5	5
15	403	4	11
16	371	4	8
17	156	3	13
18	271	4	15
TOTAL	2910	36	TOTAL

BEAUNE

TEL : 80241029
LOCATION : A6 exit Beaune, then D 970 to Verdun sur le Doubs and D 111
ADDRESS : Levernois – 21200 Beaune
HOTEL :
Parc – Levernois
Tel : 80222251
Poste – Beaune
Tel : 80220811
Le Cep – Beaune
Tel : 80223548
RESTAURANT : La Paix – Beaune
Tel : 80223333

At only three minutes from Beaune, the course is set in the heart of the Burgundy vineyard area on mainly flat treeless countryside. Nine menacing lakes come into play on eleven holes. *SSS 72*

GF $

1988

18

—

C. Piot

L 6112 P 72

S

R

Required : Handicap Certificate
Best days : Any day

HOLE	LENGTH MEDAL-TEE	PAR	STROKE INDEX
1	372	4	3
2	307	4	13
3	134	3	15
4	505	5	9
5	390	4	7
6	196	3	11
7	296	4	17
8	385	4	1
9	500	5	5
TOTAL	3085	36	TOTAL

HOLE	LENGTH MEDAL-TEE	PAR	STROKE INDEX
10	323	4	10
11	383	4	4
12	343	4	12
13	152	3	8
14	437	5	14
15	215	3	6
16	308	4	18
17	390	4	2
18	480	5	16
TOTAL	3031	36	TOTAL

BELLEFONTAINE

TEL : (1)34710502
LOCATION : 27 km N Paris A1 exit Le Bourget, then RN17 to Senlis exit Louvres
ADDRESS : Le Plessis-Luzarches - 95270 Bellefontaine
HOTEL :
Sofitel - Roissy Airport
Tel : (1)48622323
Ibis - Roissy Ville
Tel : (1)39880040
Holiday Inn - Roissy Ville
Tel : (1)39880022

At 15km from Roissy airport, this 27 hole course lies in hilly landscape with parts of its bordered by woodlands. It features sloping fairways with expanses of water serving as hazards. Course facilities include two tennis courts.

GF $

1988

27

—

T. Huau

L 3011 P 36, 3196 P 36, 3312 P 36

R S

Required : Handicap Certificate weekends only
Best days : Any day

HOLE	LENGTH MEDAL-TEE	PAR	STROKE INDEX	HOLE	LENGTH MEDAL-TEE	PAR	STROKE INDEX	HOLE	LENGTH MEDAL-TEE	PAR	STROKE INDEX
1	284	4	9	1	330	4	9	1	384	4	5
2	360	4	7	2	338	4	8	2	385	4	4
3	450	5	2	3	392	4	5	3	510	5	1
4	150	3	8	4	179	3	6	4	415	4	6
5	363	4	4	5	385	4	4	5	164	3	9
6	190	3	3	6	482	5	7	6	383	4	8
7	374	4	5	7	210	3	3	7	195	3	2
8	380	4	1	8	399	4	1	8	511	5	3
9	460	5	6	9	481	5	2	9	365	4	7
TOTAL	3011	36	TOTAL	TOTAL	3196	36	TOTAL	TOTAL	3312	36	TOTAL

BELLE-ILE SAUZON

TEL : 97316465 /97316551
LOCATION : on the Pointe des Poulains
ADDRESS : 56360 Belle-Ile-en-Mer
HOTEL :
Castel Clara - Port Goulphar
Tel : 97318421
Manoir de Goulphar - Port Goulphar
Tel : 97318010
Le Cardinal - Sauzon
Tel : 97316160

Standing in a glorious and unspoiled setting along the Atlantic Ocean amidst steep cliffs and deep gorges, this is a really fine holiday course on the small and beautiful island of Belle-Isle, 20 minutes by boat from Quiberon (in Brittany). Each hole has its own individual character, each offering magnificent views. None is more challenging than the 2nd which is played across the Ocean to a green set on a cliff plunging to the sea some 150 m below. Apart from the cosy clubhouse, there are several well equipped cottages for rent.

GF $ — RF S

1987 — Y. Bureau

18 — L 5291 P 71

Required : Handicap Certificate
Best days : Any day

HOLE	LENGTH MEDAL-TEE	PAR	STROKE INDEX
1	448	5	7
2	115	3	1
3	240	4	17
4	335	4	3
5	325	4	8
6	123	3	15
7	300	4	12
8	310	4	10
9	125	3	16
TOTAL	2321	34	TOTAL

HOLE	LENGTH MEDAL-TEE	PAR	STROKE INDEX
10	515	5	2
11	350	4	11
12	302	4	5
13	292	4	14
14	450	5	6
15	346	4	13
16	165	3	4
17	115	3	18
18	435	5	9
TOTAL	2970	37	TOTAL

BENODET-DE-L'ODET

TEL : 98548788
LOCATION : 4 km Benodet, 12 km Quimper
ADDRESS : Clohars-Fouesnant – 29950 Benodet
HOTEL :
Ker Moor – Benodet
Tel : 98570448
Gwel-Kaër – Benodet
Tel : 98570438
Kastel Moor – Benodet
Tel : 98570501
RESTAURANT : Ferme du Letty – Benodet
Tel : 98570127

Located in the south of Brittany between the seaside resorts of Quimper and Benodet, at 4 km from the beaches, the course is well laid out on gently rolling countryside with long and spacious tree-lined fairways, and various streams and ponds serving as hazards. Most of the greens are well defended. *SSS 73*

GF $ — S

 1987 — R. Berthet 

27 — L 5960 P 72, 1100 P27 

Required : Handicap Certificate
Best days : Any day

HOLE	LENGTH MEDAL-TEE	PAR	STROKE INDEX
1	395	4	1
2	330	4	7
3	175	3	9
4	455	5	15
5	440	5	13
6	145	3	17
7	365	4	3
8	355	4	11
9	365	4	5
TOTAL	3015	36	TOTAL

HOLE	LENGTH MEDAL-TEE	PAR	STROKE INDEX
10	435	5	18
11	475	5	10
12	180	3	12
13	280	4	14
14	330	4	2
15	360	4	14
16	360	4	6
17	165	3	16
18	360	4	8
TOTAL	2945	36	TOTAL

BESANÇON

TEL : 81557354
LOCATION : 15 km SE Besançon RN 67 to Saône
ADDRESS : La Chevillotte – 25620 Mamirolle
HOTEL :
Altea – Besançon
Tel : 81801444
Novotel – Besançon
Tel : 81501466
Mercure – Besançon
Tel : 81803311
RESTAURANT : Le Chaudanne – Besançon
Tel : 81520613

Peacefully situated amongst a pine forest, its eighteen holes wind through a well-wooded and hilly terrain. Many of the fairways, such as the 8th, 16th and 18th, are narrow, demanding accuracy from tee to green. *SSS 72*

GF $ — Tuesdays — S
1967 — M. Fenn
18 — L 6090 P 72 — R

Required : Handicap Certificate
Best days : Any day ; Sundays by arrangement

HOLE	LENGTH MEDAL-TEE	PAR	STROKE INDEX
1	264	4	13
2	359	4	15
3	333	4	5
4	213	3	7
5	320	4	17
6	156	3	9
7	386	4	3
8	364	4	1
9	460	5	11
TOTAL	2855	35	TOTAL

HOLE	LENGTH MEDAL-TEE	PAR	STROKE INDEX
10	360	4	16
11	473	5	6
12	192	3	12
13	347	4	10
14	373	4	4
15	340	4	18
16	482	5	2
17	166	3	8
18	502	5	14
TOTAL	3235	37	TOTAL

BETHEMONT

TEL : (1)39755113
LOCATION : 40 km Paris A13 exit Poissy, then to Orgeval/Chambourcy
ADDRESS : 12, rue du Parc de Béthemont 78300 Poissy
HOTEL :
Moustel - Orgeval
Tel : (1)39759760
RESTAURANT : L'Esturgeon - Poissy
Tel : (1)39650004

Lying peacefully in beautiful hilly parkland countryside not far from the French capital, the course offers a wide variety of excellent holes laid out among majestic trees and menacing lakes. Designed by the German golf champion Bernhard Langer, it features deep bunkers and fast rolling greens. The attractive 19th century clubhouse stands on a hilltop overlooking the charming surroundings. *SSS 71,7*

GF $$

Wednesdays

S

1989

B. Langer

18

L 5955 P 72

Required : Handicap Certificate
Best days : Weekdays

HOLE	LENGTH MEDAL-TEE	PAR	STROKE INDEX
1	320	4	7
2	155	3	13
3	375	4	1
4	350	4	3
5	150	3	15
6	480	5	9
7	155	3	17
8	465	5	11
9	440	5	5
TOTAL	2890	36	TOTAL

HOLE	LENGTH MEDAL-TEE	PAR	STROKE INDEX
10	340	4	14
11	510	5	8
12	325	4	6
13	160	3	12
14	490	5	16
15	365	4	2
16	375	4	10
17	155	3	18
18	345	4	4
TOTAL	3065	36	TOTAL

BEUZEVAL CLAIR-VALLON (Houlgate)

✡

TEL : 31910697
LOCATION : 15 km Deauville, 2 km Houlgate
ADDRESS : Hameau de Tolleville à Gonneville-sur-Mer – 14510 Houlgate
HOTEL :
H. 1900-Houlgate
Tel : 31910777
Centre-Houlgate
Tel : 31911815
Hostellerie Normande-Houlgate
Tel : 31912236
RESTAURANT : Auberge de la Ferme des Aulnettes-Houlgate
Tel : 31912228

Ideal for holiday golf, the Beuzeval course is set alongside the Normandy coast and offers panoramic views of the sea. The course runs partly through undulating meadowland, and partly through parkland. A scenic river meanders its way through several holes and small lakes serve as hazards. A difficulty of this course is that it is often exposed to a prevailing wind. Another nine holes are planned in the near future. Accommodation for golfers is available (apartments) at 'Les Hauts de Clair Vallon', which is situated within the grounds of the golf.

GF $

1980

18

—

P. Alis, D. Thomas

L 5439 P 73

S

R

Required : Handicap Certificate
Best days : Any day

HOLE	LENGTH MEDAL-TEE	PAR	STROKE INDEX
1	277	4	5
2	127	3	15
3	298	4	7
4	177	3	17
5	457	5	1
6	251	4	11
7	290	4	9
8	233	4	8
9	448	5	10
TOTAL	2558	36	TOTAL

HOLE	LENGTH MEDAL-TEE	PAR	STROKE INDEX
10	140	3	12
11	373	4	2
12	292	4	16
13	139	3	18
14	463	5	14
15	521	5	6
16	242	4	4
17	241	4	13
18	470	5	3
TOTAL	2881	37	TOTAL

BIARRITZ

TEL : 59037180
LOCATION : 1 km Biarritz
ADDRESS : Le Phare – Av. Edith-Cavell – 64200 Biarritz
HOTEL :
Regina et Golf – Biarritz
Tel : 59413300
Miramar – Biarritz
Tel : 59413000
Palais – Biarritz
Tel : 59240940
RESTAURANT : La Chaumière – Biarritz
Tel : 59037032

Situated in the legendary seaside resort of Biarritz on the Basque Coast, not far from the sea front, this is a pleasant but technical parkland course with its eighteen holes running through flat and lush countryside, featuring fast greens. There is an old-style clubhouse.
SSS 69

GF $$ — Tues. in low season — S

1888 — W. Dunn

18 — L 5130 P 69 — R

Required : Handicap Certificate and an introduction letter for groups
Best days : Any day

HOLE	LENGTH MEDAL-TEE	PAR	STROKE INDEX
1	445	5	17
2	164	3	5
3	428	5	9
4	347	4	3
5	141	3	7
6	310	4	13
7	336	4	11
8	192	3	1
9	279	4	15
TOTAL	2642	35	TOTAL

HOLE	LENGTH MEDAL-TEE	PAR	STROKE INDEX
10	315	4	10
11	328	4	6
12	115	3	12
13	309	4	16
14	108	3	18
15	361	4	2
16	456	5	14
17	160	3	8
18	336	4	4
TOTAL	2488	34	TOTAL

BIOT

TEL : 93650848
LOCATION : 4 km Antibes RN 7
ADDRESS : Association du golf de La Bastide-du-Roy – 06410 Biot
HOTEL :
Les Terraillers – Biot
Tel : 93650159
Hostellerie du Bois Fleuri – Biot
Tel : 93656864
Royal – Antibes
Tel : 93340309
RESTAURANT : Auberge du Jarrier – Biot
Tel : 93651168

Laid out in a valley and framed by distant mountains, the course flows over flat countryside overlooking the picturesque town of Biot. Set amidst olive trees, the course is cut in two by the scenic river 'La Brague'. Its pleasant and rustic clubhouse lies in the middle of the course. *SSS 70*

GF $

1930

18

—

M. Bardana

L 5064 P 70

S

R

Required : Handicap Certificate
Best days : Any day

HOLE	LENGTH MEDAL-TEE	PAR	STROKE INDEX
1	265	4	7
2	115	3	18
3	435	5	3
4	225	3	14
5	438	5	1
6	250	4	11
7	138	3	16
8	327	4	9
9	317	4	5
TOTAL	2510	35	TOTAL

HOLE	LENGTH MEDAL-TEE	PAR	STROKE INDEX
10	355	4	6
11	265	4	12
12	375	4	4
13	132	3	17
14	435	5	2
15	177	3	15
16	275	4	8
17	240	4	13
18	300	4	10
TOTAL	2554	35	TOTAL

BITCHE

TEL : 87961530
LOCATION : 4 km Bitche
ADDRESS : 57230 Bitche
HOTEL :
Relais des Châteaux Forts - Bitche
Tel : 87961004
Vosges du Nord-Lembach
Tel : 88944341
Alsace-Sarreguemines
Tel : 87984432
RESTAURANT : Strasbourg - Bitche
Tel : 87960044

This 27 hole public golf course is in the 'Moselle' region. It is set in the heart of a natural park (reserve for deer) in the northern Vosges mountain chain. Laid out in fine natural landscape on hilly woodland, the course has excellent views of the surroundings, including the town of Bitche. The holes are separated from each other by tall pine trees. Ideal for holiday golf with possibilities for many other sports in the region such as : fishing, archery, tennis, swimming, walking, etc. The Relais des Châteaux Forts is at 800 m from the club.

GF $

1987

27

—

P. Fromanger, M. Adam

L 5947 P 72, 2440 P 34

R S

Required : None
Best days : Any day

HOLE	LENGTH MEDAL-TEE	PAR	STROKE INDEX
1	341	4	12
2	524	5	4
3	142	3	18
4	248	4	8
5	537	5	2
6	342	4	10
7	138	3	16
8	395	4	6
9	290	4	14
TOTAL	2959	36	TOTAL

HOLE	LENGTH MEDAL-TEE	PAR	STROKE INDEX
10	288	4	15
11	551	5	1
12	311	4	11
13	492	5	7
14	189	3	13
15	321	4	3
16	360	4	9
17	359	4	5
18	115	3	17
TOTAL	2987	36	TOTAL

BOISGELIN

✡

TEL : 96223124
LOCATION : 11 km Paimpol D7
ADDRESS : Château de Coatguelen-Pléhedel - 22290 Lanvollon
HOTEL : HR
Château de Coatguelen
Tel : 96223124
Relais Brenner - Paimpol
Tel : 96201105
Marne - Paimpol
Tel : 96208216

Located in Brittany within charming and gently rolling parkland, the 18 holes are built around the scenic first class hotel 'Château de Coatguelen' (Relais & Châteaux member). The course features short holes and has a pond affecting play. The 16 bedroomed hotel has within its grounds a swimming pool, several tennis courts, a riding center and numerous forest walks.

GF $

1981

18

January to March 31

M. de Boisgelin

L 4151 P 67

S

R

Required : Handicap Certificate
Best days : Any day

HOLE	LENGTH MEDAL-TEE	PAR	STROKE INDEX
1	137	3	
2	348	4	
3	285	4	
4	325	4	
5	210	4	
6	270	4	
7	162	3	
8	140	3	
9	435	5	
TOTAL	2312	34	TOTAL

HOLE	LENGTH MEDAL-TEE	PAR	STROKE INDEX
10	200	3	
11	240	4	
12	270	4	
13	180	3	
14	240	4	
15	109	3	
16	170	4	
17	225	4	
18	205	4	
TOTAL	1839	33	TOTAL

BONDUES

TEL : 20232062
LOCATION : 7 km Tourcoing
ADDRESS : Château de la Vigne – 59910 Bondues
HOTEL :
Ibis – Tourcoing
Tel : 20248458
Fimotel – Tourcoing
Tel : 20703800
Novotel – Tourcoing
Tel : 20940770
RESTAURANT : Petit Bedon – Tourcoing
Tel : 20250051

The Bondues golf course lies in the northern part of France called 'Flandres' close to the city of Lille on flat landscape. Fred Hawtree designed the main 18 hole course with its numerous deep bunkers, which is surrounded by private houses. Robert Trent Jones designed the 9 hole course featuring six well-placed water hazards. There is a stately clubhouse, the 18th century 'Château de la Vigne'. *SSS 73*

GF $

Tuesdays

S

1967

F. Hawtree, R. Trent Jones

27

L 
2814 P 35, 3190 P 39, 3055 P 36

Required : Handicap Certificate
Best days : Weekdays

HOLE	LENGTH MEDAL-TEE	PAR	STROKE INDEX	HOLE	LENGTH MEDAL-TEE	PAR	STROKE INDEX	HOLE	LENGTH MEDAL-TEE	PAR	STROKE INDEX
1	383	4	9	10	153	3	17	1	450	5	9
2	448	5	5	11	375	4	7	2	327	4	13
3	140	3	11	12	461	5	3	3	160	3	15
4	297	4	13	13	392	4	1	4	475	5	5
5	152	3	17	14	186	3	15	5	418	4	1
6	454	5	1	15	313	4	13	6	145	3	17
7	177	3	15	16	336	4	11	7	360	4	7
8	339	4	7	17	371	4	5	8	398	4	3
9	424	4	3	18	468	5	19	9	457	5	11
TOTAL	2814	35	TOTAL	TOTAL	3055	36	TOTAL	TOTAL	3190	37	TOTAL

BORDEAUX-CAMEYRAC

TEL : 56729679
LOCATION : 18 km Bordeaux RN 89 to Beychac
ADDRESS : 33450 St-Loubes
HOTEL :
Loubat – Libourne
Tel : 56511758
Climat de France – Libourne
Tel : 57514141
Grand – Bordeaux
Tel : 56909344
RESTAURANT : Logis de la Cadène – St.-Émilion
Tel : 57247140

Bordeaux-Cameyrac winds through densely wooded and gently rolling countryside. Several deep bunkers and six stratigic water hazards serve as obstacles. It features an entertaining 11th hole with an island-green and a difficult double dog-legged 8th hole. The club is equipped with a swimming pool, 3 tennis courts and a riding school. *SSS 70*

GF $

1972

27

Mondays

J. Quenot

L 5669 P 72, 1188 P 28

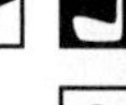

Required : Handicap Certificate
Best days : Any day

HOLE	LENGTH MEDAL-TEE	PAR	STROKE INDEX
1	445	5	18
2	309	4	8
3	340	4	6
4	147	3	14
5	312	4	16
6	138	3	10
7	472	5	12
8	462	5	4
9	351	4	2
TOTAL	2976	37	TOTAL

HOLE	LENGTH MEDAL-TEE	PAR	STROKE INDEX
10	137	3	17
11	437	5	5
12	192	3	7
13	388	4	1
14	435	5	11
15	314	4	15
16	317	4	13
17	322	4	3
18	151	3	9
TOTAL	2693	35	TOTAL

BORDEAUX-LAC

TEL : 56509272
LOCATION : 10 km Bordeaux to Blanquefort
ADDRESS : Av. de Pernon – 33300 Bordeaux
HOTEL :
Novotel – Bordeaux-Lac
Tel : 56509970
Mercure – Bordeaux-Lac
Tel : 56509030
Sofitel Aquitania – Bordeaux-Lac
Tel : 56508380
RESTAURANT : La Réserve – Pessac Alouette
Tel : 56451328

This public golf course is characterized by two different types of setting. The first nine holes run through an open area, the second nine are laid out in wooded landscape. Most of the greens are well-defended by strategic bunkers. The club boasts a modern clubhouse standing in the middle of the course. The hotels are situated around the Bordeaux lake.
SSS 72

GF $

1976

18

Tuesdays

 J. Bourret

 5874 P 72

Required : Handicap Certificate
Best days : Any day

HOLE	LENGTH MEDAL-TEE	PAR	STROKE INDEX
1	327	4	16
2	435	5	18
3	340	4	10
4	346	4	6
5	155	3	8
6	395	4	2
7	325	4	14
8	190	3	4
9	460	5	12
TOTAL	2973	36	TOTAL

HOLE	LENGTH MEDAL-TEE	PAR	STROKE INDEX
10	350	4	9
11	445	5	17
12	143	3	3
13	380	4	1
14	318	4	13
15	150	3	5
16	312	4	11
17	458	5	15
18	345	4	7
TOTAL	2901	36	TOTAL

BORDEAUX-PESSAC

TEL : 56362447
LOCATION : 4 km Bordeaux to Arcachon (exit n° 13)
ADDRESS : Rue de la Princesse
33600 Pessac
HOTEL :
Ibis - Mérignac
Tel : 56341019
La Réserve - Pessac
Tel : 56071328
Royal Brion - Pessac
Tel : 56450772

Each of the 27 holes of this golf complex has its own character. They are set amidst pine trees on rolling countryside near Bordeaux and feature sloping fairways, and greens protected by bunkers. The course is full of strategic water hazards demanding technical skill. Facilities for horse riding, tennis and trinquet (the pelotte basque) are nearby.

GF $

1988

27

Mondays in winter

O. Brizon

L 2903 P 36, 2963 P 36, 2824 P 36

Required : Handicap Certificate
Best days : Any day

HOLE	LENGTH MEDAL-TEE	PAR	STROKE INDEX	HOLE	LENGTH MEDAL-TEE	PAR	STROKE INDEX	HOLE	LENGTH MEDAL-TEE	PAR	STROKE INDEX
1	303	4	10	1	460	5	11	1	470	5	3
2	137	3	12	2	327	4	3	2	299	4	14
3	486	5	4	3	145	3	17	3	121	3	18
4	334	4	18	4	302	4	5	4	350	4	2
5	348	4	2	5	325	4	7	5	326	4	9
6	325	4	6	6	167	3	15	6	294	4	10
7	485	5	14	7	370	4	9	7	338	4	16
8	150	3	16	8	387	4	1	8	149	3	5
9	335	4	8	9	480	5	13	9	477	5	12
TOTAL	2903	36	TOTAL	TOTAL	2963	36	TOTAL	TOTAL	2824	36	TOTAL

BORDELAIS

TEL : 56285604/56281395
LOCATION : 4 km Bordeaux A 10 exit n° 7
ADDRESS : Domaine de Kater – Avenue d'Eysines – 33200 Bordeaux Cauderan
HOTEL :
Novotel – Bordeaux-Lac
Tel : 56509970
Mercure – Bordeaux-Lac
Tel : 56509030
Sofitel Aquitania – Bordeaux-Lac
Tel : 56508380
RESTAURANT : Dubern – Bordeaux
Tel : 56480344

The popular Bordelais golf course lies in the middle of a pine forest on flat terrain. It has an interesting and testing layout with several dog-leg holes, fifty-six bunkers, numerous trees, and a large lake serving as hazards. *SSS 65*

GF $

1900

18

Mondays

 —

L 4833 P 67

R S

Required : Handicap Certificate
Best days : Any day

HOLE	LENGTH MEDAL-TEE	PAR	STROKE INDEX
1	230	4	11
2	99	3	16
3	351	4	7
4	81	3	17
5	486	5	1
6	173	3	13
7	405	4	5
8	479	5	3
9	187	3	9
TOTAL	2491	34	TOTAL

HOLE	LENGTH MEDAL-TEE	PAR	STROKE INDEX
10	278	4	10
11	253	4	12
12	351	4	4
13	367	4	2
14	130	3	15
15	183	3	6
16	288	4	14
17	322	4	8
18	170	3	18
TOTAL	2342	33	TOTAL

BOSSEY

★★

TEL : 50437525
LOCATION : 6 km Genève, rte de Troinex, A 40/RN 206
ADDRESS : Château de Crevin – 74160 St Julien-en-Genevois
HOTEL :
Mercure – Gaillard
Tel : 50371927
Rey – St-Julien-en-Genevois
Tel : 50441329
RESTAURANT : Vieux-Moulins de Drize – Troinex (Suisse)
Tel : (022)422956

Designed by Robert Trent Jones Junior on hilly countryside among pine and oak trees, Bossey is situated just across the French/Swiss border near Geneva. It is scenically laid out in the foothills of the Salève mountains overlooking Lac Léman and Geneva. A technically difficult championship course with long fairways and sometimes enormous greens which are well-defended by ponds and deep bunkers. A number of fast flowing streams meander through the course. Sport facilities include several tennis and squash courts, and a swimming pool.

GF $$

1985

18

Mon.; Dec. to March

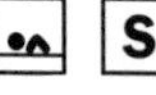

 R. Trent. Jones Jr

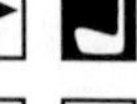

L 6022 P 71

Required : Handicap Certificate
Best days : Weekdays

HOLE	LENGTH MEDAL-TEE	PAR	STROKE INDEX
1	369	4	3
2	467	5	9
3	346	4	11
4	161	3	15
5	357	4	7
6	177	3	17
7	390	4	1
8	484	5	5
9	318	4	13
TOTAL	3069	36	TOTAL

HOLE	LENGTH MEDAL-TEE	PAR	STROKE INDEX
10	311	4	12
11	337	4	2
12	195	3	10
13	438	5	16
14	201	3	14
15	522	5	6
16	214	3	4
17	322	4	18
18	413	4	8
TOTAL	2963	35	TOTAL

BOURGOGNE

TEL : 80357110
LOCATION : 10 km N. Dijon RN 74
ADDRESS : Bois de Norges - Norges-la-Ville-21490 Ruffey-les-Echirey
HOTEL :
La Cloche-Dijon
Tel : 80301232
Altéa Château Bourgogne-Dijon
Tel : 80723113
Chapeau Rouge-Dijon
Tel : 80302810
RESTAURANT : La Chouette-Dijon
Tel : 80301810

Extended to 18 holes in 1987, the sporting Dijon golf club has two famous French members : the race-drivers Alain Prost and Jacques Lafitte. The course rolls through fine and undulating woodland and features many interesting holes. Two water traps serve as hazards on the 1st and 9th holes. The club is equipped with a pitch & putt course and six tennis courts. *SSS 72*

GF $ | — | R S
1972 | M. Fenn
18 | L 6164 P 72

Required : None
Best days : Any day

HOLE	LENGTH MEDAL-TEE	PAR	STROKE INDEX
1	412	4	4
2	160	3	17
3	510	5	15
4	420	4	1
5	370	4	8
6	358	4	10
7	368	4	5
8	190	3	13
9	479	5	9
TOTAL	3267	36	TOTAL

HOLE	LENGTH MEDAL-TEE	PAR	STROKE INDEX
10	372	4	7
11	163	3	18
12	463	5	3
13	275	4	11
14	304	4	14
15	321	4	6
16	304	4	16
17	178	3	12
18	517	5	2
TOTAL	2897	36	TOTAL

BREST-IROISE

★

TEL : 98851617
LOCATION : 3 km Landerneau on RD 770
ADDRESS : Parc des Loisirs de Lann-Rohou – 29220 Landerneau
HOTEL : HR
Club Vert
Tel : 98215221
Le Clos du Pontic – Landerneau
Tel : 98215091
Belle Aurore – Landerneau
Tel : 98216262
RESTAURANT : L'Amandier – Landerneau
Tel : 98851089

The Brest-Iroise golf course is a fine and testing course whose fairways run through windy heathland and moorland. Set on hilly and open terrain, many of its fairways are wide, with a punishing rough. Most of the greens are cunningly bunkered. Another nine hole course will be operational in 1991. The hotel Club Vert with its 48 rooms is on the course.
SSS 72

GF $

1976

27

Tuesdays

M. Fenn

L 5885 P 72

S

R

Required : Handicap Certificate
Best days : Mondays to Fridays inc.

HOLE	LENGTH MEDAL-TEE	PAR	STROKE INDEX
1	343	4	16
2	165	3	18
3	338	4	6
4	551	5	5
5	310	4	13
6	138	3	15
7	260	4	14
8	450	5	11
9	290	4	18
TOTAL	2845	36	TOTAL

HOLE	LENGTH MEDAL-TEE	PAR	STROKE INDEX
10	303	4	2
11	360	4	1
12	152	3	17
13	493	5	10
14	370	4	7
15	496	5	4
16	375	4	13
17	195	3	12
18	296	4	9
TOTAL	3040	36	TOTAL

BRIGODE

★

TEL : 20911786/20911305
LOCATION : 8 km Lille
ADDRESS : 36, Av. du Golf – 59650 Villeneuve-d'Ascq
HOTEL :
P.L.M. Grand Hôtel – Roubaix
Tel : 20701590
Flandres – Roubaix
Tel : 20723501
Grand Hotel Altea – Roubaix
Tel : 20734000
RESTAURANT : Le Caribou – Roubaix
Tel : 20708708

A pleasant inland course with spacious fairways incorporating a fine setting of trees, bunkers and lakes serving as hazards. Some of its holes run through avenues of trees, demanding accurate play. There is a mansion style clubhouse surrounded by scenic lakes. *SSS 72*

GF $

Tuesdays

1969

 M. Baker

18

 5385 P 72

Required : Handicap Certificate
Best days : Weekdays

HOLE	LENGTH MEDAL-TEE	PAR	STROKE INDEX
1	325	4	11
2	385	5	7
3	310	4	1
4	135	3	15
5	310	4	5
6	410	5	13
7	130	3	17
8	285	4	9
9	315	4	3
TOTAL	2605	36	TOTAL

HOLE	LENGTH MEDAL-TEE	PAR	STROKE INDEX
10	420	5	8
11	310	4	6
12	445	5	10
13	265	4	18
14	360	4	2
15	150	3	16
16	310	4	4
17	160	3	14
18	360	4	12
TOTAL	2780	36	TOTAL

BUSSY-SAINT-GEORGES

TEL : (1)64660000
LOCATION : 48 km Paris A 4 exit Lagny, then RD 35
ADDRESS : Promenade des Golfeurs – 77600 Bussy-Saint-Georges
HOTEL : HR
Golfhotel
Tel : (1)64301700
Grand Monarque Concorde-Melun
Tel : (1)64390440
Ibis-Melun
Tel : (1)60684245
RESTAURANT : Auberge Vaugrain-Melun
Tel : (1)64520823

The Belgian architect Paul Rolin with Jean Claude Cornillot designed this 18 hole golf course (another 9 holes are planned for 1991). It is part of a real estate development situated 48 km east of Paris near the peaceful villages of Bussy-Saint-Georges and Guermantes. Laid out in flat countryside, the golf has a modern layout featuring numerous tiered greens. Water affects play many times, especially on the three finishing holes which are surrounded by a large lake. *SSS 72.*

GF $ — Thursday mornings — R S

1987 — P. Rolin, J.-C. Cornillot — 

18 — L 5899 P 72 — 

Required : None
Best days : Any day

HOLE	LENGTH MEDAL-TEE	PAR	STROKE INDEX
1	465	5	4
2	186	3	6
3	398	4	10
4	320	4	18
5	338	4	12
6	445	5	2
7	136	3	16
8	331	4	8
9	300	4	14
TOTAL	2919	36	TOTAL

HOLE	LENGTH MEDAL-TEE	PAR	STROKE INDEX
10	384	4	11
11	170	3	13
12	318	4	15
13	495	5	9
14	337	4	7
15	295	4	17
16	339	4	1
17	182	3	5
18	460	5	3
TOTAL	2980	36	TOTAL

CABOURG

TEL : 31912556
LOCATION : 4 km Cabourg D 513
ADDRESS : Rte de Sallenelles – Le Home-sur-Mer – 14390 Cabourg
HOTEL :
Moulin du Pré – Bavant
Tel : 31788368
Le Cottage – Cabourg
Tel : 31916561
Pullmann Grand – Cabourg
Tel : 31910179
RESTAURANT : Chez Marion – Franceville Plage
Tel : 31923043

Situated near the seaside resort of Cabourg in Normandy, with several holes bordering the sea, this is an easy but rather windy golf course with a picturesque Normandy style clubhouse. A road divides the course into separate parts. *SSS 68*

GF $

 Tuesdays

1953

O. Brizon

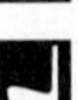

18

 5122 P 68

R

Required : None
Best days : Any day

HOLE	LENGTH MEDAL-TEE	PAR	STROKE INDEX
1	157	3	13
2	281	4	17
3	137	3	15
4	517	5	3
5	455	5	5
6	173	3	11
7	429	4	1
8	161	3	9
9	358	4	7
TOTAL	2668	34	TOTAL

HOLE	LENGTH MEDAL-TEE	PAR	STROKE INDEX
10	481	5	4
11	366	4	6
12	558	5	12
13	237	4	16
14	134	3	10
15	100	3	18
16	154	3	8
17	260	4	12
18	164	3	14
TOTAL	2454	34	TOTAL

CANNES-MANDELIEU

★★

TEL : 93495539
LOCATION : 6 km Cannes A 8/RN 7
ADDRESS : La Napoule - 06210 Mandelieu-La Napoule
HOTEL :
Saint Christophe - Miramar
Tel : 93754483
Hostellerie du Golf - Mandelieu
Tel : 93491166
La Calanque - La Napoule
Tel : 93499511
RESTAURANT : L'Oasis - La Napoule
Tel : 93499552

In a setting of scenic beauty among mimosa trees and umbrella pines, framed by mountains, this is one of the most attractive and most busy courses on the 'Côte d'Azur'. Several of the holes are laid out along the Mediterranean. It features the river Siagne which cuts the course in two. Between the 2nd and 3rd hole you have to be ferried across by a boatman. There is a rustic and well-appointed clubhouse. *SSS 71/34*

GF $$

1891

27

Tuesdays

—

L 5867 P 71, 2409 P 34

S

R

Required : Handicap Certificate plus introduction by a member
Best days : Any day

HOLE	LENGTH MEDAL-TEE	PAR	STROKE INDEX	HOLE	LENGTH MEDAL-TEE	PAR	STROKE INDEX	HOLE	LENGTH MEDAL-TEE	PAR	STROKE INDEX
1	361	4	3	10	440	5	8	1	261	4	6
2	170	3	11	11	415	4	2	2	130	3	8
3	212	3	7	12	115	3	18	3	118	3	9
4	340	4	9	13	490	5	6	4	296	4	4
5	301	4	15	14	340	4	14	5	267	4	5
6	490	5	5	15	385	4	4	6	315	4	3
7	400	4	1	16	129	3	16	7	466	5	1
8	455	5	13	17	184	3	12	8	346	4	2
9	290	4	17	18	350	4	10	9	210	3	7
TOTAL	3019	36	TOTAL	TOTAL	2848	35	TOTAL	TOTAL	2409	34	TOTAL

CANNES-MOUGINS

TEL : 93757913
LOCATION : 2 km Mougins/ 10 km Cannes RN 85
ADDRESS : 175 Route d'Antibes – 06250 Mougins
HOTEL :
Mas Candille – Mougins
Tel : 93900085
Arc – Mougins
Tel : 93757733
Manoir de l'Etang – Mougins
Tel : 93900107
RESTAURANT : Moulin de Mougins – Mougins
Tel : 93757824

One of the finest championship layouts on the Côte d'Azur with many interesting holes. It incorporates a fine setting of trees, bunkers, rivers and lakes serving as hazards. Among its feature holes are the 7th with a well-contrived dogleg, and the 17th with an elevated tee and its green defended by a small lake. The clubhouse is built in Provençal style and overlooks the 18th hole. Every year in april, the club hosts the famous 'Cannes Mougins Open' welcoming the greatest professional golfers. *SSS 72*

GF $$ — W.E. in winter time — R S

1978 — P. Allis, D. Thomas

18 — L 5641 P 72

Required : Handicap Certificate
Best days : Weekdays

HOLE	LENGTH MEDAL-TEE	PAR	STROKE INDEX
1	385	4	3
2	155	3	15
3	300	4	11
4	333	4	7
5	116	3	17
6	296	4	9
7	454	5	1
8	436	5	13
9	341	4	5
TOTAL	2816	36	TOTAL

HOLE	LENGTH MEDAL-TEE	PAR	STROKE INDEX
10	319	4	8
11	125	3	18
12	345	4	6
13	343	4	2
14	440	5	10
15	145	3	12
16	435	5	14
17	363	4	4
18	310	4	16
TOTAL	2825	36	TOTAL

CAP D'AGDE

TEL : 67265440
LOCATION : 25 km Béziers RN 112
ADDRESS : Avenue des Alizès
34300 Cap d'Agde
HOTEL :
du Golf - Cap d'Agde
Tel : 67268703
Capao - Cap d'Agde
Tel : 67269946
Pierre Barthès - Cap Agde
Tel : 67261711
RESTAURANT : La Tamarissière - La Tamarissière
Tel : 67942087

Located in the south of France in the holiday and health resort of Cap d'Agde just opposite Aqualand, this new and testing championship course promises to become one of the leading courses in France. Just 270m from the Mediterranean, it presents a challenging variety of holes with magnificent well bunkered greens some which are flanked by water, and undulating fairways bordered by olive trees and lavender. Sport facilities in Cap d'Agde include the well known Pierre Barthès tennis center and all water sports.

GF $

1989

18

—

R. Fream

L 5824 P 72

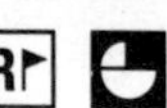

Required : None
Best days : Any day

HOLE	LENGTH MEDAL-TEE	PAR	STROKE INDEX
1	304	4	15
2	471	5	3
3	304	4	14
4	176	3	16
5	360	4	8
6	315	4	7
7	133	3	13
8	473	5	4
9	382	4	9
TOTAL	2918	36	TOTAL

HOLE	LENGTH MEDAL-TEE	PAR	STROKE INDEX
10	308	4	10
11	169	3	6
12	331	4	5
13	120	3	17
14	343	4	12
15	532	5	2
16	269	4	18
17	465	5	11
18	369	4	1
TOTAL	2906	36	TOTAL

CASTELJALOUX

TEL : 53935160
LOCATION : 75 km Bordeaux A62 to Toulouse exit Casteljaloux
ADDRESS : Route de Mont-de-Marsan 47700 Casteljaloux
HOTEL :
Château de Ruffiac - Casteljaloux
Tel : 53931863
Cordeliers - Casteljaloux
Tel : 53930219

The course displays two distinct types of landscape. The first five holes work their way through a forest of pine and oak trees while the others run to a lake. The club is part of a vast sport complex with facilities for water sports, tennis, archery and horse riding. There are fully equipped bungalows (4 persons) available adjoining the golfs' practice grounds.

GF $ — RF S

1989 M. Gayon

18 L 5484 P 72

Required : Handicap Certificate
Best days : Any day

HOLE	LENGTH MEDAL-TEE	PAR	STROKE INDEX
1	321	4	15
2	476	5	5
3	143	3	9
4	431	5	7
5	117	3	17
6	359	4	3
7	293	4	13
8	494	5	5
9	158	3	11
TOTAL	2792	36	TOTAL

HOLE	LENGTH MEDAL-TEE	PAR	STROKE INDEX
10	335	4	2
11	292	4	12
12	287	4	14
13	128	3	8
14	267	4	16
15	294	4	10
16	291	4	18
17	443	5	6
18	355	4	4
TOTAL	2692	36	TOTAL

CASTELNAUD

TEL : 53017464
LOCATION : 9 km Villeneuve-sur-Lot RN 21
ADDRESS : 47290 Castelnaud de Gratecambe
HOTEL : HR
Golf Hotel du Périgord Agenais
Tel : 53016019
Chênes – Pujols
Tel : 53490455
Les Platanes – Villeneuve-sur-Lot
Tel : 53401140

Inaugurated in 1987, the golf course lies in the heart of the Gascogne region. The course, with vast and fast greens, winds through mature trees on a lush rolling landscape. Water affects play on several holes. A feature is the charming clubhouse, converted from an old manor house dating back to the 18th century. Other facilities include a hotel with 40 bedrooms, a tennis club and a swimming pool. *SSS 73*

GF $ — 1987 — R. Berthet — 27 — L 6322 P 72, 2184 P 27 — S — R

Required : Handicap Certificate
Best days : Any day

HOLE	LENGTH MEDAL-TEE	PAR	STROKE INDEX
1	391	4	3
2	505	5	1
3	303	4	5
4	349	4	9
5	160	3	7
6	346	4	15
7	145	3	13
8	427	4	17
9	336	4	11
TOTAL	2962	35	TOTAL

HOLE	LENGTH MEDAL-TEE	PAR	STROKE INDEX
10	362	4	12
11	498	5	16
12	473	5	6
13	215	3	2
14	342	4	14
15	539	5	10
16	197	3	8
17	334	4	18
18	400	4	4
TOTAL	3360	37	TOTAL

CERGY PONTOISE

TEL : (1)34210348
LOCATION : 35 km NE Paris A15, exit n° 12
ADDRESS : 2, allée de l'Obstacle d'Eau
95000 Vaureal Cergy
HOTEL :
Novotel - Cergy
Tel : (1)30303947
Ibis - Cergy
Tel : (1)34221144
Arcade - Cergy
Tel : (1)30309393

Located near the new city of Cergy Pontoise close to Paris, this flat course features short holes with tight fairways. Several stretches of water serve as hazards. *SSS 67,5*

GF $ — Tuesdays — S
1989 — M. Gayon
18 — L 5112 P 72 — R

Required : Handicap Certificate
Best days : Any day

HOLE	LENGTH MEDAL-TEE	PAR	STROKE INDEX
1	233	4	6
2	103	3	17
3	431	5	2
4	136	3	9
5	329	4	3
6	150	3	10
7	455	5	11
8	296	4	12
9	423	5	8
TOTAL	2556	36	TOTAL

HOLE	LENGTH MEDAL-TEE	PAR	STROKE INDEX
10	233	4	6
11	103	3	17
12	431	5	2
13	136	3	9
14	329	4	3
15	150	3	10
16	455	5	11
17	296	4	12
18	423	5	8
TOTAL	2556	36	TOTAL

CHALON-SUR-SAÔNE

TEL : 85486164/85934965
LOCATION : 2 km SE Chalon-sur-Saône
ADDRESS : Zône des Sports et Loisirs de St-Nicolas – 71380 Saint-Marcel
HOTEL :
Royal – Chalon-sur-Saône
Tel : 85481586
St. Georges – Chalon-sur-Saône
Tel : 85482705
St. Regis – Chalon-sur-Saône
Tel : 85480728
RESTAURANT : Le Moulin de Martorey – Saint-Rémy
Tel : 85481298

This public golf course, situated in the 'Bourgogne', lies on the borders of the Saône river on mostly flat and open terrain admist a floral park with some 25.000 different types of roses. It is part of a sports complex with rugby and football fields. The course is cunningly bunkered. *SSS 72*

GF $

—

S

1978

M. Rio

18

L 5844 P 71

Required : Handicap Certificate
Best days : Any day

HOLE	LENGTH MEDAL-TEE	PAR	STROKE INDEX
1	267	4	17
2	162	3	15
3	336	4	11
4	362	4	9
5	175	3	13
6	387	4	3
7	410	4	1
8	500	5	7
9	367	4	5
TOTAL	2966	35	TOTAL

HOLE	LENGTH MEDAL-TEE	PAR	STROKE INDEX
10	278	4	18
11	480	5	6
12	165	3	12
13	288	4	16
14	300	4	14
15	487	5	4
16	331	4	10
17	176	3	8
18	373	4	2
TOTAL	2878	36	TOTAL

CHAMONIX

TEL : 50530628
LOCATION : 3 km Chamonix RN 506
ADDRESS : Praz de Chamonix – 74400 Chamonix Mont-Blanc
HOTEL : HR
Le Labrador
Tel : 50530625
Mont Blanc – Chamonix
Tel : 50530564
Auberge du Bois Prin – Chamonix
Tel : 50533351
RESTAURANT : Fin Godet – Chamonix
Tel : 50532004

Extended to 18 holes in 1982 by Robert Trent Jones, this is a spectacular mountain course set in a glacier valley in the foothills of the Mont Blanc and the Aiguilles Rouges with panoramic views of the surrounding snow clad mountain peaks. The course, at over 1200 m above sea level, is rather flat with most of its holes lined by tall pines. Several picturesque streams serve as hazards. There is a pretty chalet style clubhouse with an informal restaurant (La Cabane) and a recently opened three starred hotel (Le Labrador) with 31 rooms. *SSS 72*

GF $$ — October to May — R S
1982 — R. Trent Jones
18 — L 5541 P 72

Required : Handicap Certificate
Best days : Weekdays

HOLE	LENGTH MEDAL-TEE	PAR	STROKE INDEX
1	275	4	12
2	317	4	4
3	420	5	14
4	163	3	10
5	337	4	6
6	91	3	8
7	461	5	18
8	108	3	16
9	516	5	2
TOTAL	2688	36	TOTAL

HOLE	LENGTH MEDAL-TEE	PAR	STROKE INDEX
10	356	4	7
11	323	4	3
12	129	3	13
13	352	4	11
14	463	5	9
15	454	5	1
16	351	4	5
17	120	3	17
18	305	4	15
TOTAL	2853	36	TOTAL

CHAMPAGNE

TEL : 23716208
LOCATION : 26 km Reims A4 exit Dormans
ADDRESS : Villers-Agron - 02130 Fere-en-Tardenois
HOTEL :
L'Assiette Champenoise - Reims
Tel : 26041556
Boyer - Reims
Tel : 26828080
Altéa - Reims
Tel : 26885354
RESTAURANT : La Cour Souveraine - Vezilly

Situated in the heart of the famous champagne vineyards halfway between Reims and Epernay, the course is partly wooded and follows the natural undulations of the terrain. Numerous strategic water hazards serve as obstacles. *SSS 69*

GF $ — Tuesdays in winter — S

1987 — J.C. Cornillot

18 — L 5995 P 72 — R

Required : Green Card
Best days : Any day

HOLE	LENGTH MEDAL-TEE	PAR	STROKE INDEX
1	530	5	
2	320	4	
3	355	4	
4	360	4	
5	125	3	
6	430	5	
7	240	4	
8	410	4	
9	150	3	
TOTAL	2920	36	TOTAL

HOLE	LENGTH MEDAL-TEE	PAR	STROKE INDEX
10	490	5	
11	170	3	
12	290	4	
13	135	3	
14	330	4	
15	510	5	
16	420	4	
17	360	4	
18	370	4	
TOTAL	3075	36	TOTAL

CHAMP-DE-BATAILLE

★

TEL : 32350372
LOCATION : 40 km Deauville/30 km Rouen A13 exit 15
ADDRESS : 27110 Le Neubourg
HOTEL :
Auberge de l'Abbaye-Le-Bec-Hellouin
Tel : 32448602
Moulin Forêt-Bernay
Tel : 32431995
Petit Coq aux Champs-Campigny
Tel : 32410419
RESTAURANT : Auberge du Vieux Puits-Pont-Audemer
Tel : 3241018

Situated near the picturesque little Norman town of Le Neubourg, the course is built around the majestic 17th century 'Champ de Bataille' castle renowned for its classical French gardens. The course runs through beautiful rolling wooded parkland and fine pastureland with century-old trees and colourful rhododendrons lining the fairways. The clubhouse (the former stables), overlooking the French gardens, will include in the near future 22 guest rooms. *SSS 72*

GF $ | Wednesdays | S

1988 | R. Nelson, T. Huau

18 | L 5566 P 72 | R

Required : None
Best days : Any day

HOLE	LENGTH MEDAL-TEE	PAR	STROKE INDEX
1	296	4	18
2	330	4	6
3	143	3	13
4	291	4	7
5	486	5	1
6	122	3	12
7	291	4	15
8	305	4	4
9	420	5	10
TOTAL	2684	36	TOTAL

HOLE	LENGTH MEDAL-TEE	PAR	STROKE INDEX
10	371	4	9
11	448	5	11
12	305	4	14
13	309	4	17
14	368	4	3
15	442	5	8
16	135	3	2
17	342	4	16
18	162	3	5
TOTAL	2882	36	TOTAL

CHANTACO

TEL : 59261422
LOCATION : 2,5 km Saint-Jean-de-Luz RD 918
ADDRESS : Route d'Ascain – 64500 Saint-Jean-de-Luz
HOTEL : HP
de Chantaco
Tel : 59261476
Grand Hotel – Saint-Jean-de-Luz
Tel : 59261232
Plage – Saint-Jean-de-Luz
Tel : 59510344
RESTAURANT : Pablo – Saint-Jean-de-Luz
Tel : 59263781

Peacefully situated on the Basque coast near the holiday resort of Saint-Jean-de-Luz, this is an excellent course of championship standard, ideal for holiday golf. The first nine holes are thickly wooded and well-defended by bunkers. The second nine run through open and sometimes hilly parkland with picturesque water hazards. The Chantaco Golfhotel is on the course and has several tennis courts. *SSS 70*

GF $$
1928
18

Tues. in low season
H. Colt
L 5385 P 70

S

R

Required : Handicap Certificate
Best days : Any day

HOLE	LENGTH MEDAL-TEE	PAR	STROKE INDEX
1	355	4	13
2	340	4	5
3	125	3	17
4	314	4	9
5	380	4	1
6	457	5	7
7	187	3	3
8	297	4	15
9	345	4	11
TOTAL	2800	35	TOTAL

HOLE	LENGTH MEDAL-TEE	PAR	STROKE INDEX
10	125	3	18
11	289	4	6
12	127	3	14
13	475	5	2
14	316	4	10
15	445	5	4
16	312	4	16
17	172	3	8
18	324	4	12
TOTAL	2585	35	TOTAL

CHANTILLY

TEL : 44570443
LOCATION : 40 km Paris A 1 exit Survilliers, then RN 17/RN 324
ADDRESS : Vineuil-Saint-Firmin – 60500 Chantilly
HOTEL :
Château de la Tour – Gouvieux
Tel : 44570739
Campanile – Chantilly
Tel : 44573924
Hostellerie du Lys – Lys Chantilly
Tel : 44212619
RESTAURANT : Relais Condé – Chantilly
Tel : 44570575

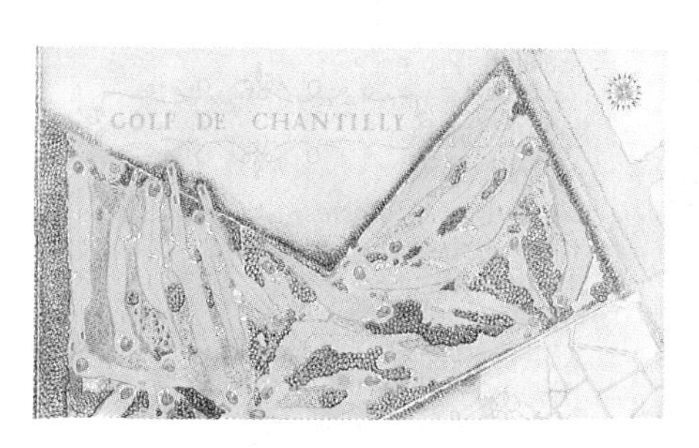

Chantilly is a noble and memorable golf course, belonging to the world's greatest. Situated near the historical town of Chantilly, famous for its horse-racing, this is a typical inland course with its long and testing holes running through beautiful and densely wooded countryside. Considered his finest achievement, master architect Tom Simpson created Chantilly in 1906, demonstrating all the hallmarks of his skill. It counts 79 bunkers, representing the greatest challenge to players. The club boasts an impressive and tastefully furnished clubhouse. *SSS 71*

GF $$ — Thursdays, Weekends

1906 — T. Simpson, M. Abercromby

27 — L 5795 P 71, 2625 P 35

Required : Handicap Certificate only for the 18 hole course
Best days : Weekdays only

HOLE	LENGTH MEDAL-TEE	PAR	STROKE INDEX	HOLE	LENGTH MEDAL-TEE	PAR	STROKE INDEX	HOLE	LENGTH MEDAL-TEE	PAR	STROKE INDEX
1	390	5	15	10	385	4	10	1	350	4	5
2	290	4	6	11	320	4	5	2	370	4	1
3	135	3	18	12	330	4	16	3	150	3	7
4	305	4	13	13	375	4	1	4	455	5	3
5	355	4	2	14	180	3	12	5	140	3	8
6	170	3	7	15	345	4	4	6	400	5	4
7	335	4	11	16	155	3	17	7	120	3	9
8	485	5	9	17	375	4	8	8	280	4	2
9	400	4	3	18	465	5	14	9	360	4	6
TOTAL	2865	36	TOTAL	TOTAL	2930	35	TOTAL	TOTAL	2625	35	TOTAL

CHATEAUBLANC

TEL : 90333908
LOCATION : 9 km S. Avignon RN7 to Salon-de-Provence
ADDRESS : Route de Châteaublanc 84310 Morières
HOTEL : HR
Le Paradou - Morières
Tél : 90882930
Europe - Avignon
Tel : 90826692
Cité des Papes - Avignon
Tel : 90862245
RESTAURANT : Hiély - Avignon
Tel : 90861707

The peacefully laid out Châteaublanc course lies on a plain in the heart of the charming Provence region. It is set amidst many trees, numerous bunkers and ponds, which serve as hazards. The three star hotel Paradou is adjacent to the club. *SSS 72*

GF $ — Tuesdays — S

1989 — T. Sprecher, G. Watine

18 — L 5945 P 72 — R

Required : None
Best days : Any day

HOLE	LENGTH MEDAL-TEE	PAR	STROKE INDEX
1	466	5	13
2	325	4	15
3	144	3	10
4	375	4	3
5	270	4	17
6	170	3	14
7	361	4	8
8	494	5	4
9	352	4	9
TOTAL	2957	36	TOTAL

HOLE	LENGTH MEDAL-TEE	PAR	STROKE INDEX
10	466	5	6
11	187	3	12
12	392	4	5
13	315	4	11
14	112	3	18
15	318	4	16
16	369	4	2
17	462	5	1
18	367	4	7
TOTAL	2988	36	TOTAL

CHATEAU DE CHAILLY

TEL : 80903040
LOCATION : 270 km Paris A6 exit Pouilly-en-Auxois, then to Saulieu
ADDRESS : Chailly-sur-Armançon – 21320 Pouilly-en-Auxois
HOTEL : HP
Château de Chailly
Tel : 80903030
Val Vert - Pouilly-en-Auxois
Tel : 80908234

The course is situated in the heart of the Burgundy region renowned for its gastronomy and wine culture. It is an attractive parkland course laid out in luxurious rolling landscape with five lakes and numerous bunkers serving as hazards. In the middle of the course stands the majestic "Château de Chailly-sur-Armançon" a mediaval 12th century fortress, classified as a National Monument which is now a luxurious hotel with 45 rooms, tennis courts and a heated swimming pool.

GF $

1990

18

—

G. Watine, T. Sprecher

L 5844 P 72

 S 

Required : None
Best days : Any day

HOLE	LENGTH MEDAL-TEE	PAR	STROKE INDEX
1	330	4	13
2	173	3	11
3	360	4	5
4	436	5	7
5	325	4	17
6	139	3	15
7	389	4	1
8	335	4	3
9	431	5	9
TOTAL	2918	36	TOTAL

HOLE	LENGTH MEDAL-TEE	PAR	STROKE INDEX
10	375	4	4
11	155	3	8
12	339	4	14
13	471	5	10
14	264	4	18
15	351	4	12
16	125	3	16
17	373	4	2
18	473	5	6
TOTAL	2926	36	TOTAL

CHÂTEAU DE CHEVERNY

TEL : 54792470
LOCATION : 15 km S. Blois
ADDRESS : La Rousselière - 41700 Cheverny
HOTEL :
France - Contres
Tel : 54795014
Les Trois Marchands - Cour Cheverny
Tel : 54799644
RESTAURANT : Botte d'Asperges - Contres
Tel : 54795049

Located in the Loire Valley,close to the famous Renaissance Château de Cheverny, the course is designed around a scenic 42 ha lake 'La Roussellière'. The holes, flanked by creeks and streams, thread their way through old wooded parkland. Another 18 hole course is planned for the near future.

GF $ — Tuesdays in winter — S

1989 — O. van der Vinckt

18 — L 5827 P 71 — R

Required : None
Best days : Any day

HOLE	LENGTH MEDAL-TEE	PAR	STROKE INDEX
1	343	4	12
2	480	5	4
3	142	3	6
4	319	4	14
5	337	4	10
6	386	4	8
7	126	3	18
8	301	4	16
9	385	4	2
TOTAL	2819	35	TOTAL

HOLE	LENGTH MEDAL-TEE	PAR	STROKE INDEX
10	345	4	1
11	360	4	5
12	188	3	9
13	368	4	11
14	294	4	17
15	449	5	15
16	345	4	7
17	184	3	13
18	475	5	3
TOTAL	3008	36	TOTAL

CHÂTEAU DE LA SALLE

TEL : 85360971
LOCATION : 4 km exit Mâcon Nord of A6 to Clessé, then RD103 and RD86
ADDRESS : 71260 La Salle
HOTEL :
Novotel - Mâcon Nord
Tel : 85360080
Mercure - St-Albain
Tel : 85331900
Bellevue - Mâcon
Tel : 85380507
RESTAURANT : Georges Blanc - Vonnas
Tel : 74500010

This course stretches over 80ha of scenic and rolling countryside in the shadow of the majestic 19th century Château de la Salle. Flanked by lush parkland, many of the holes are dotted with broom, trees and roses. There are fast greens and three lakes serve as additional hazards. The club offers a wide range of sports facilities such as a swimming pool, tennis courts and a riding center. *SSS 70, 4*

GF $ — 

1989 R. Berthet 

18 L 5895 P 71 RΓ

Required : Handicap Certificate
Best days : Any day

HOLE	LENGTH MEDAL-TEE	PAR	STROKE INDEX
1	351	4	6
2	262	4	12
3	133	3	10
4	317	4	14
5	443	5	8
6	450	5	16
7	300	4	18
8	412	4	2
9	193	3	4
TOTAL	2930	36	TOTAL

HOLE	LENGTH MEDAL-TEE	PAR	STROKE INDEX
10	396	4	1
11	348	4	9
12	145	3	13
13	334	4	11
14	317	4	17
15	199	3	3
16	390	4	5
17	370	4	7
18	466	5	15
TOTAL	2965	35	TOTAL

CHÂTEAU DE MAINTENON

TEL : (1)37271809
LOCATION : 70 km Paris N10
ADDRESS : Route de Gallardon
28130 Maintenon
HOTEL :
Château d'Esclimont - Auneau
Tel : (1)37311515
Climat - Rambouillet
Tel : (1)34856262
Le Grand Monarque - Chartres
Tel : (1)37210072
RESTAURANT : Maison des Champs - Chaises
Tel : (1)34835019

Not too distant from Paris, this golf course lies in royal historical surroundings. Facing the famous Château de Maintenon, dating back to the 12th and 18th century, and the former residence of Madame de Maintenon, the 18 holes are set within its alluring park and are divided by an aquaduct constructed by Vauban. Majestic lakes border the holes. *SSS 70,30*

GF $

1989

18

Tuesdays

M. Gayon

L 5813 P 72

R S

Required : Handicap Certificate
Best days : Weekdays only

HOLE	LENGTH MEDAL-TEE	PAR	STROKE INDEX
1	273	4	17
2	302	4	15
3	343	4	7
4	154	3	5
5	461	5	9
6	368	4	3
7	355	4	13
8	184	3	11
9	510	5	1
TOTAL	2950	36	TOTAL

HOLE	LENGTH MEDAL-TEE	PAR	STROKE INDEX
10	430	5	14
11	304	4	18
12	162	3	8
13	348	4	10
14	177	3	12
15	332	4	6
16	346	4	2
17	298	4	16
18	466	5	4
TOTAL	2863	36	TOTAL

CHÂTEAU DES ORMES

TEL : 99484027
LOCATION : 6 km Dol D795/30 km Saint-Malo N137
ADDRESS : 35120 Dol-de-Bretagne
HOTEL :
Château et Voyageurs - Combourg
Tel : 99730038
Central - Saint-Malo
Tel : 99408770
Valmarin - Saint-Malo
Tel : 99819476
RESTAURANT : Duchesse Anne - Saint-Malo
Tél : 99408533

The course extends over 100ha of lush parkland and meadows and is bordered by densely wooded forest. Most of the holes are protected by old majestic trees with picturesque ponds affecting play on many of them. The magnificent Château, dating back to the 16th century and once the residence of the bishops of Dol de Bretagne, now serves as the golfs' clubhouse. Activities within the castle's grounds include tennis courts, swimming pools and a riding school. *SSS 71,1*

GF $ — Tuesdays in winter  S

1989 — A. d'Ormesson  

18 — L 5880 P 72 — R

Required : Handicap Certificate
Best days : Any day

HOLE	LENGTH MEDAL-TEE	PAR	STROKE INDEX
1	330	4	8
2	166	3	16
3	301	4	7
4	109	3	18
5	318	4	14
6	420	4	1
7	436	5	3
8	190	3	12
9	500	5	5
TOTAL	2770	35	TOTAL

HOLE	LENGTH MEDAL-TEE	PAR	STROKE INDEX
10	290	4	10
11	380	4	2
12	490	5	4
13	192	3	11
14	340	4	15
15	328	4	9
16	500	5	6
17	150	3	17
18	440	5	13
TOTAL	3110	37	TOTAL

CHATEAU DES SEPT TOURS

TEL : 47246975
LOCATION : 27 km Tours A152 to Angers
ADDRESS :
37330 Courcelles de Touraine
HOTEL : HR
Golf Hôtel
Tel : 47246975
Jean Bardet - Tours
Tel : 47414111
RESTAURANT :
Barrier - Tours
Tel : 47542039

An attractive new course situated in the historical Loire region near the city of Tours. The 18 long holes, bordered by a wealth of trees, stand amidst dense woodlands. Six of the holes surround a magnificent 16th century Château which has been converted into a three star hotel (22 rooms) and a clubhouse. Five lakes add to the challenge of this course.

GF $ — S

1990 — O. Dongradi, D. Harradine

18 — L 6413 P 72 — RP

Required : Green Card
Best days : Any day

HOLE	LENGTH MEDAL-TEE	PAR	STROKE INDEX
1	320	4	
2	340	4	
3	190	3	
4	315	4	
5	515	5	
6	280	4	
7	370	4	
8	447	4	
9	545	5	
TOTAL	3322	37	TOTAL

HOLE	LENGTH MEDAL-TEE	PAR	STROKE INDEX
10	402	4	
11	346	4	
12	365	4	
13	180	3	
14	495	5	
15	410	4	
16	350	4	
17	155	3	
18	387	4	
TOTAL	3090	35	TOTAL

CHÂTEAU DES TERRIDES

TEL : 63956520
LOCATION : 42 km Toulouse RN113 exit Montech, then to Beaumont
ADDRESS : 82100 Labourgade
HOTEL : HR
Château des Terrides
Tel : 63956107
Sofitel - Toulouse Blagnac
Tel : 61711125
RESTAURANT : Pujol - Toulouse Blagnac
Tel : 61711358

Just 40 minutes from Toulouse, this course is situated in alluring countryside in the Garonne river valley. It has a challenging and varied layout with its 27 holes working their way through lush woodlands and scenic valleys. A number of natural lakes and streams come into play on this course. The stylish 14th century Château de Terrides has been converted into a 3 star hotel with 53 rooms, a swimming pool, archery facilities and 2 tennis courts. *SSS 71*

GF $ — 1989 — 27

— J.-P. Fourès — L 5986 P 74

S — R

Required : Handicap Certificate
Best days : Any day

HOLE	LENGTH MEDAL-TEE	PAR	STROKE INDEX
1	350	4	5
2	350	4	13
3	435	5	4
4	153	3	14
5	435	5	10
6	440	5	8
7	330	4	15
8	351	4	9
9	328	4	1
TOTAL	3172	38	TOTAL

HOLE	LENGTH MEDAL-TEE	PAR	STROKE INDEX
10	354	4	6
11	485	5	2
12	455	5	16
13	150	3	7
14	310	4	11
15	465	5	18
16	310	4	12
17	137	3	3
18	148	3	17
TOTAL	2814	36	TOTAL

CHATEAU-L'ARC

TEL : 42532838
LOCATION : 14 km Aix-en-Provence A7
ADDRESS : 13710 Fuveau
HOTEL :
Golfhotel
Tel : 42532838
Mas d'Entremont – Celony
Tel : 42234532
Pullman Le Pigonnet – Aix-en-Provence
Tel : 42590290
RESTAURANT :
Caves Henri IV – Aix-en-Provence
Tel : 42278639

Situated near the city of Aix-en-Provence, on rolling countryside facing the Sainte Victoire mountains, this is an excellent golf complex in the south of France, fully operational since 1988. It includes an 18 hole championship layout, a clubhouse with swimming pool and tennis courts, and a 4 star Golfhotel. Most of the holes are landscaped with trees. Several artificial lakes, numerous sand bunkers and large greens serve as hazards. *SSS 72*

GF $$

1986

18

—

M. Gayon

L 5973 P 72

Required : Handicap Certificate
Best days : Weekdays

HOLE	LENGTH MEDAL-TEE	PAR	STROKE INDEX
1	220	4	18
2	310	4	12
3	280	4	6
4	330	4	4
5	160	3	14
6	368	4	18
7	280	4	16
8	320	4	2
9	560	5	10
TOTAL	2828	36	TOTAL

HOLE	LENGTH MEDAL-TEE	PAR	STROKE INDEX
10	150	3	17
11	570	5	11
12	550	5	9
13	350	4	3
14	330	4	1
15	300	4	15
16	370	4	7
17	150	3	13
18	375	4	5
TOTAL	3145	36	TOTAL

CHATELLERAULT

TEL : 49862021/49861361
LOCATION : 23 km Châtellerault
ADDRESS : Parc du Connétable – 86270 La Roche-Posay
HOTEL : HR
Melusine
Tel : 49862021
Esplanade – La Roche-Posay
Tel : 49862048
Host. St. Louis – La Roche-Posay
Tel : 49862054

The Chatellerault golf course is located near the thermal spa of La Roche-Posay. Set on mostly flat terrain amidst pine trees, it features narrow fairways and a large pond in the middle of the course. There is also a short 9 hole circuit. Adjacent to the club is the thermal hotel 'Melusine' with a swimming pool and several tennis courts.

GF $

1986

18

Tues., in winter time

J. Garaialde

L 5841 P 72

 S

Required : Handicap Certificate
Best days : Any day

HOLE	LENGTH MEDAL-TEE	PAR	STROKE INDEX
1	337	4	12
2	133	3	17
3	477	5	7
4	360	4	8
5	281	4	3
6	462	5	10
7	311	4	15
8	128	3	16
9	287	4	13
TOTAL	2776	36	TOTAL

HOLE	LENGTH MEDAL-TEE	PAR	STROKE INDEX
10	417	4	1
11	490	5	4
12	366	4	9
13	172	3	14
14	360	4	6
15	244	4	18
16	178	3	11
17	378	4	5
18	460	5	2
TOTAL	3065	36	TOTAL

CHAUMONT-EN-VEXIN

TEL : 44490081
LOCATION : 6 km S. Gisors/65 km Paris A 15
ADDRESS : Château de Bertichères – 60240 Chaumont-en-Vexin
HOTEL : HR
Château de Bertichères
Tel : 44491476
Château de la Rapée – Gisors
Tel : 32551161
Moderne – Gisors
Tel : 32552351

A fine and varied inland course with six of its holes laid out on a highland plain with panoramic views of the surroundings. Most of the holes run through well-wooded terrain. There is a stream which crosses four of the fairways several times. The club is equipped with a riding school, a swimming pool, and five tennis courts. It boasts an attractive château with 17 bedrooms. *SSS 72*

GF $$

1968

18

—

D. Harradine

L 5610 P 72

S

RP 

Required : Handicap Certificate
Best days : Any day

HOLE	LENGTH MEDAL-TEE	PAR	STROKE INDEX
1	310	4	7
2	130	3	17
3	375	4	3
4	290	4	11
5	140	3	5
6	470	5	9
7	373	4	1
8	340	4	13
9	300	4	15
TOTAL	2728	35	TOTAL

HOLE	LENGTH MEDAL-TEE	PAR	STROKE INDEX
10	335	4	8
11	462	5	2
12	140	3	16
13	290	4	12
14	110	3	18
15	460	5	4
16	320	4	6
17	325	4	14
18	440	5	10
TOTAL	2882	37	TOTAL

CHIBERTA

TEL : 59638320
LOCATION : 3 km Biarritz RN 10
ADDRESS : 104, Bd des Plages – 64600 Anglet
HOTEL : HR
du Golf
Tel : 59639556
Château de Brindos – Anglet
Tel : 59231768
Eurotel – Biarritz
Tel : 59243233

Situated midway between the Basque cities of Biarritz and Bayonne, the Chiberta golf course is set within a splendid natural landscape amongst a pine forest with a lake, and several holes laid out alongside the Atlantic Ocean. There are lush green fairways and many of the greens are well-defended. The Chiberta Golf Hotel lies near the beach with a swimming pool, a riding club and various tennis courts.

 $

1927

18

Thursdays in winter

 T. Simpson

 5527 P 71

Required : Handicap Certificate
Best days : Weekdays

HOLE	LENGTH MEDAL-TEE	PAR	STROKE INDEX
1	435	5	13
2	337	4	7
3	359	4	1
4	135	3	17
5	390	5	3
6	152	3	15
7	320	4	9
8	190	3	5
9	416	5	11
TOTAL	2734	36	TOTAL

HOLE	LENGTH MEDAL-TEE	PAR	STROKE INDEX
10	145	3	18
11	362	4	4
12	455	5	12
13	286	4	14
14	164	3	10
15	396	4	2
16	348	4	8
17	281	4	16
18	356	4	6
TOTAL	2793	35	TOTAL

CHOLET

TEL : 41710501
LOCATION : 3 km Cholet to St-Léger Beaupréau
ADDRESS : Allée du Chêne Landry 49300 Cholet
HOTEL :
Poste - Cholet
Tel : 41626545
Fimotel - Cholet
Tel : 41624545
Europe - Cholet
Tel : 41620097
RESTAURANT : Le Belvédère - Cholet
Tel : 41621402

Situated in the Loire Valley, the Cholet course is partly undulating and partly wooded. Set amidst old oak trees, there is a pleasant pattern of holes featuring many water obstacles such as a large 2ha lake affecting play on 4 greens and on 3 tees. *SSS 69,6*

GF $

1989

18

—

0. Brizon

L 5605 P72

S

R

Required : Handicap Certificate
Best days : Any day

HOLE	LENGTH MEDAL-TEE	PAR	STROKE INDEX
1	357	4	14
2	160	3	16
3	402	5	11
4	368	4	1
5	100	3	18
6	506	5	5
7	357	4	9
8	149	3	3
9	370	4	7
TOTAL	2769	35	TOTAL

HOLE	LENGTH MEDAL-TEE	PAR	STROKE INDEX
10	438	5	12
11	261	4	15
12	450	5	2
13	387	4	4
14	261	4	6
15	126	3	17
16	285	4	8
17	330	4	10
18	298	4	13
TOTAL	2836	37	TOTAL

CLECY CANTELOU

TEL : 31697272
LOCATION : 34 km Caen D 565 to Flers Laval
ADDRESS : Manoir de Cantelou - 14570 Clécy
HOTEL :
Moulin du Vey - Clécy
Tel : 31697108
Galion - Flers
Tel : 33644747
RESTAURANT : Relais des Gourmets - Caen
Tel : 31860601

The course is set in 100ha of unspoiled and peaceful Normandy scenery. The holes cut alternatively through hilly woodlands and lush pasture lands and offer fine views of the surroundings. Accomodation is available in the clubs' grounds. *SSS 72*

GF $

1988

18

—

B. Baker

L 5658 P 72

S

R

Required : None
Best days : Any day

HOLE	LENGTH MEDAL-TEE	PAR	STROKE INDEX
1	309	4	3
2	330	4	9
3	436	5	5
4	127	3	15
5	290	4	13
6	165	3	7
7	390	4	1
8	302	4	11
9	475	5	17
TOTAL	2824	36	TOTAL

HOLE	LENGTH MEDAL-TEE	PAR	STROKE INDEX
10	271	4	6
11	140	3	14
12	488	5	8
13	308	4	10
14	335	4	12
15	440	5	16
16	361	4	2
17	145	3	18
18	346	4	4
TOTAL	2834	36	TOTAL

du CLOU

TEL : 74981965
LOCATION : 30 km N. Lyon RN83 to Bourg
ADDRESS : 01330 Villars-les-Dombes
HOTEL :
Le Manoir des Dombes - St-Marcel-en-Dombes
Tel : 74981965
Ribotel – Villars-les-Dombes
Tel : 74981965
RESTAURANT : Auberge des Chasseurs – Villars-les-Dombes
Tel : 74981002

This is a short but fairly technical golf course integrated into a flat landscape of forest and meadows featuring several sloping fairways. It comprises many strategic trees and expanses of water demanding accurate shots. *SSS 67*

GF $
1985
18

Tuesdays
—
L 4972 P 67

S

R

Required : Handicap Certificate on sundays only
Best days : Any day

HOLE	LENGTH MEDAL-TEE	PAR	STROKE INDEX
1	265	4	
2	159	3	
3	143	3	
4	299	4	
5	108	3	
6	507	5	
7	133	3	
8	387	4	
9	374	4	
TOTAL	2375	33	TOTAL

HOLE	LENGTH MEDAL-TEE	PAR	STROKE INDEX
10	346	4	
11	263	4	
12	140	3	
13	340	4	
14	357	4	
15	473	5	
16	195	3	
17	185	3	
18	298	4	
TOTAL	2597	34	TOTAL

COGNAC

TEL : 45321817
LOCATION : 5 km E. Cognac
ADDRESS : Saint-Brice – 16100 Cognac
HOTEL :
Le Valois-Cognac
Tel : 45827600
François Ier – Cognac
Tel : 45827600
Moderne-Cognac
Tel : 45821953
RESTAURANT : Moulin de Cierzac-Cierzac
Tel : 45830132

Laid out amidst the scenic vine-yards of the Cognac region on the borders of the river 'la Charente', this golf course offers variety. The holes run over typical rolling 'Cognac' landscape and are partly flanked by fine woodland. Among its most treacherous holes are the 12th, the 15th, the 17th and the 18th featuring a strategic pond. The clubhouse is installed in a former farmhouse. *SSS 70,2*

GF $

1986

18

Tuesdays

J. Garaialde

L 5724 P 72

R S

Required : Handicap Certificate
Best days : Any day

HOLE	LENGTH MEDAL-TEE	PAR	STROKE INDEX
1	333	4	12
2	342	4	16
3	431	5	4
4	307	4	6
5	128	3	18
6	298	4	8
7	345	4	2
8	144	3	14
9	436	5	10
TOTAL	2764	36	TOTAL

HOLE	LENGTH MEDAL-TEE	PAR	STROKE INDEX
10	324	4	5
11	346	4	1
12	472	5	11
13	318	4	13
14	345	4	9
15	159	3	7
16	449	5	15
17	404	4	3
18	143	3	17
TOTAL	2960	36	TOTAL

COIROUX

TEL : 55272566
LOCATION : between Brive and Tulle, take RN 89/RN 48
ADDRESS : Aubazine – 19190 Beynat
HOTEL :
de la Tour – Aubazine
Tel : 55257117
Château de Castel Novel – Varetz
Tel : 55850001
St Étienne – Aubazine
Tel : 55257101
RESTAURANT : La Belle Epoque – Brive
Tel : 55740875

This is an attractive well-wooded and undulating golf course set in a picturesque region. Most of the fairways are narrow and landscaped amongst pines, birches, oaks, old chestnut and beeches. Several small streams cross the scenic holes. The club has amenities such as a riding school, tennis courts, and a lake for sailing and windsurfing. The pleasant clubhouse, a former farmhouse, has 8 appartments and 7 bedrooms.

GF $
1977
18

—
H. Chesneau
L 5310 P 70

S
R

Required : None
Best days : Any day

HOLE	LENGTH MEDAL-TEE	PAR	STROKE INDEX
1	375	4	1
2	145	3	14
3	445	5	12
4	245	4	13
5	380	4	2
6	135	3	18
7	320	4	6
8	145	3	15
9	465	5	7
TOTAL	2655	35	TOTAL

HOLE	LENGTH MEDAL-TEE	PAR	STROKE INDEX
10	325	4	11
11	445	5	16
12	325	4	3
13	350	4	8
14	305	4	5
15	120	3	17
16	295	4	9
17	160	3	10
18	330	4	4
TOTAL	2655	35	TOTAL

COMPIEGNE

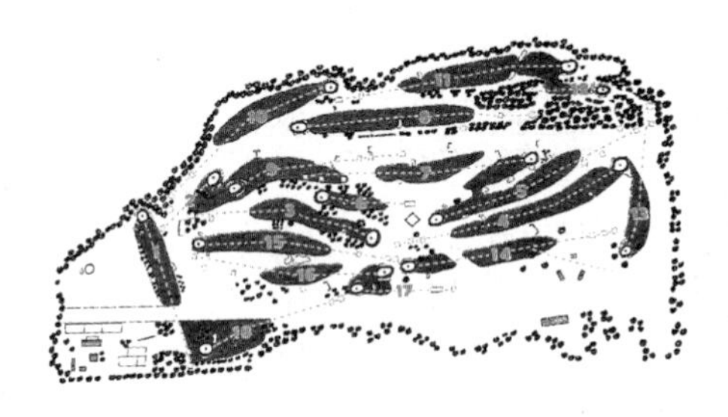

TEL : 44401573
LOCATION : exit Compiègne of A 1 then RN 31
ADDRESS : Avenue Royale – 60200 Compiègne
HOTEL :
Harlay – Compiègne
Tel : 44230150
Université – Compiègne
Tel : 44232727
Ibis – Compiègne
Tel : 44231627
RESTAURANT : Hostellerie Royal Lieu – Compiègne
Tel : 44201024

The golf club, one of the oldest in France, having been founded in 1895, lies in the middle of the horse-racing circuit of Compiegne. Laid out on flat terrain, it is flanked on one side by a dense forest. There are five tennis courts. *SSS 71*

GF $

1895

18

Thurs. and Weekends

—

L 5671 P 71

S

R

Required : Handicap Certificate
Best days : Weekdays

HOLE	LENGTH MEDAL-TEE	PAR	STROKE INDEX
1	295	4	17
2	135	3	15
3	355	4	5
4	440	5	11
5	408	4	3
6	175	3	9
7	385	4	1
8	465	5	7
9	275	4	13
TOTAL	2933	36	TOTAL

HOLE	LENGTH MEDAL-TEE	PAR	STROKE INDEX
10	370	4	4
11	438	5	8
12	135	3	12
13	284	4	16
14	382	4	2
15	367	4	6
16	350	4	14
17	164	3	10
18	248	4	18
TOTAL	2738	35	TOTAL

CÔTE D'ARGENT
(Moliets)

TEL : 58485465
LOCATION : 40 km Biarritz
ADDRESS : 40660 Moliets
HOTEL : Hr
Résidence Green Parc Océan
Tel : 58485257
Beauséjour-Hossegor
Tel : 58435107
Ermitage-Hossegor
Tel : 58435223
RESTAURANT : Les Huîtrières
du Lac-Hossegor
Tel : 58435148

The new 27 hole golf course, designed by Robert Trent Jones, is laid out in a fine, sporting holiday area (the Landes region) not far from Biarritz. The course is characterised by two different types of setting : some of the holes, set alongside the beach and the Atlantic Ocean, have a links character and run through the dunes while others are inland with tall pines bordering the fairways. Accommodation for golfers is available in the residence Green Parc Océan which is equipped with a swimming pool, eleven tennis courts and archery facilities.

GF $ — Wednesdays in winter  

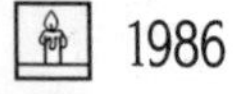 1986 —  R. Trent Jones  

 — L 5809 P 72, 1905 P 31 — R 

Required : Handicap Certificate
Best days : Weekdays

HOLE	LENGTH MEDAL-TEE	PAR	STROKE INDEX
1	333	4	11
2	385	4	1
3	498	5	9
4	340	4	13
5	450	5	5
6	179	3	7
7	382	4	3
8	140	3	17
9	330	4	15
TOTAL	3037	36	TOTAL

HOLE	LENGTH MEDAL-TEE	PAR	STROKE INDEX
10	330	4	10
11	337	4	4
12	104	3	8
13	322	4	2
14	336	4	14
15	400	5	6
16	115	3	18
17	478	5	16
18	350	4	12
TOTAL	2772	36	TOTAL

DEAUVILLE

TEL : 31882053
LOCATION : 3,5 km Deauville D 278
ADDRESS : Saint-Arnoult – 14800 Deauville
HOTEL : HR
du Golf
Tel : 31881901
Royal – Deauville
Tel : 31986633
Normandy – Deauville
Tel : 31986622
RESTAURANT : Miocque – Deauville
Tel : 31880952

The Deauville golf course lies inland from the famous seaside resort of Deauville in a undulating parkland setting, and bears the hallmarks of the region. There are three interesting loops of nine holes (one has two different 18 hole ciruits to choose from), designed by Tom Simpson and redesigned by Henry Cotton in 1965. The luxury Royal Golf Hotel with heated swimming pool lies on the course and is open to golfers from March to November. *SSS 71*

GF $$ — Tuesdays in winter

1929 — T. Simpson, H. Cotton

27 — L 2869 P 35, 3064 P 36, 3033 P 36

Required : Handicap Certificate
Best days : Weekdays

HOLE	LENGTH MEDAL-TEE	PAR	STROKE INDEX	HOLE	LENGTH MEDAL-TEE	PAR	STROKE INDEX	HOLE	LENGTH MEDAL-TEE	PAR	STROKE INDEX
1	356	4	6	1	449	5	11	1	170	3	18
2	437	5	12	2	383	4	1	2	438	5	10
3	202	3	4	3	385	4	9	3	410	4	2
4	347	4	14	4	376	4	5	4	360	4	6
5	143	3	16	5	389	4	7	5	181	3	16
6	393	4	2	6	127	3	17	6	376	4	8
7	390	4	8	7	484	5	3	7	338	4	12
8	141	3	18	8	155	3	15	8	496	5	4
9	460	5	10	9	316	4	13	9	264	4	14
TOTAL	2869	35	TOTAL	TOTAL	3064	36	TOTAL	TOTAL	3033	36	TOTAL

DIEPPE

✡

TEL : 35842505
LOCATION : 2 km Dieppe to Pourville
ADDRESS : Route de Pourville – 76200 Dieppe
HOTEL :
La Présidence – Dieppe
Tel : 35843131
Auberge Clos Normand – Martin-Église
Tel : 35827101
Univers – Dieppe
Tel : 35841255
RESTAURANT : Marmitte Dieppoise – Dieppe
Tel : 35842426

One of the oldest established clubs in France, this is a windy seaside golf course situated in Normandy with twelve holes set on flat terrain and six holes running through rolling countryside. From some of the holes (7th, 15th, 18th) there are fine views of the sea and the cliffs. The course is well-defended by some forty-eight bunkers and several ponds. *SSS 70,40*

GF $ — 1897 — 18

— W. Park — L 5763 P 70

R S

Required : Handicap Certificate
Best days : Any day

HOLE	LENGTH MEDAL-TEE	PAR	STROKE INDEX
1	369	4	10
2	108	3	18
3	350	4	4
4	326	4	8
5	425	4	16
6	362	4	6
7	186	3	14
8	360	4	12
9	445	5	2
TOTAL	2931	35	TOTAL

HOLE	LENGTH MEDAL-TEE	PAR	STROKE INDEX
10	188	3	9
11	379	4	15
12	175	3	1
13	407	4	3
14	444	5	11
15	293	4	5
16	142	3	13
17	496	5	7
18	308	4	17
TOTAL	2832	35	TOTAL

DIGNE-LES-BAINS

TEL : 92323838
LOCATION : 7 km Digne
ADDRESS : St Pierre de Gaubert - 04000 Digne
HOTEL : HF
Golf Hôtel
Tel : 92313090
L'Ermitage Napoléon - Digne
Tel : 92310109
Tonic - Digne
Tel : 92322031

Located near the thermal spa of Digne-les-Bains at 600 m above sea level, the course integrates harmoniously into a charming rolling landscape. Several sculptures, the works of local artists, sometimes serve as obstacles. The club boasts a pleasant Golfhotel with 12 rooms, tennis courts, a swimming pool and riding school. *SSS 73*

GF $

1990

18

Tuesdays in winter

 R. Berthet

L 5485 P 73

Required : Green Card
Best days : Any day

HOLE	LENGTH MEDAL-TEE	PAR	STROKE INDEX
1	360	4	8
2	235	4	17
3	455	5	3
4	445	5	9
5	120	3	15
6	280	4	14
7	240	4	13
8	125	3	7
9	140	5	16
TOTAL	2400	37	TOTAL

HOLE	LENGTH MEDAL-TEE	PAR	STROKE INDEX
10	480	5	6
11	305	4	2
12	305	4	12
13	360	4	1
14	310	4	5
15	150	3	11
16	330	4	4
17	105	3	18
18	440	5	10
TOTAL	2785	36	TOTAL

DINARD

TEL : 99883207
LOCATION : 6 km Dinard RD 786
ADDRESS : 35800 Saint-Briac-sur-Mer
HOTEL :
des Dunes – Dinard
Tel : 99461272
Émeraude Plage – Dinard
Tel : 99461579
Reine Hortense – Dinard
Tel : 99465431
RESTAURANT : Le Petit Robinson – Dinard
Tel : 99461482

A rather windy and excellent seaside course, located in Brittany, with its holes running through sand dunes, low cliffs and heather with several of them laid out alongside the beach. The course, one of the oldest in Continental Europe, is sporting and demands very accurate shots to the greens. It commands fine views of the coast and the Atlantic Ocean.
SSS 68

GF $

1883

18

—

—

L 5010 P 69

Required : Handicap Certificate
Best days : Any day

HOLE	LENGTH MEDAL-TEE	PAR	STROKE INDEX
1	365	4	9
2	408	4	1
3	309	4	13
4	420	5	7
5	271	4	15
6	312	4	3
7	107	3	17
8	323	4	5
9	145	3	11
TOTAL	2660	35	TOTAL

HOLE	LENGTH MEDAL-TEE	PAR	STROKE INDEX
10	313	4	6
11	301	4	2
12	126	3	16
13	151	3	10
14	324	4	4
15	286	4	14
16	416	5	8
17	93	3	18
18	340	4	2
TOTAL	2350	34	TOTAL

DIVONNE-LES-BAINS

TEL : 50200719
LOCATION : 20 km Genève to Divonne
RN 1/8 km Gex RD 984
ADDRESS : 01220 Divonne-Les-Bains
HOTEL : HR
du Golf/Grand Hôtel
Tel : 50200663
Château de Divonne – Divonne
Tel : 50200032
RESTAURANT : Le Champagne – Divonne
Tel : 50201313

This is one of France's great golf courses with its eighteen challenging holes winding through a beautiful rolling landscape with centuries-old trees and several picturesque and fast flowing streams serving as hazards. There is a spectacular view of Lake Geneva on one side, and of the majestic Jura mountains including the Mont Blanc, on the other. There is a stylish clubhouse. Le Grand Hôtel, a château hotel, is at 500 m from the club.
SSS 69,9

GF $$
1931
18

Weekends ; Nov. to March
M. Nakowsky
L 5607 P 72

S
R

Required : Handicap Certificate
Best days : Weekdays only

HOLE	LENGTH MEDAL-TEE	PAR	STROKE INDEX
1	140	3	15
2	265	4	11
3	355	4	3
4	360	4	1
5	170	3	9
6	431	5	13
7	435	5	17
8	450	5	5
9	325	4	7
TOTAL	2931	37	TOTAL

HOLE	LENGTH MEDAL-TEE	PAR	STROKE INDEX
10	130	3	12
11	375	4	4
12	170	3	10
13	490	5	2
14	450	5	6
15	265	4	16
16	165	3	14
17	431	5	18
18	200	3	8
TOTAL	2676	35	TOTAL

DOMAINE DE RARAY

TEL : 44547061
LOCATION : 55 km N. Paris A exit Senlis, then to Crépy-en-Valois
ADDRESS : Château de Raray - 60810 Raray
HOTEL : HR
Château de Raray
Tel : 44547061
Host. de la Porte-Bellon - Senlis
Tel : 44530305
Ibis - Senlis
Tel : 44537050

The course extends over 160ha of flat parkland and surrounds the majestic Renaissance style Château de Raray, which dates back to the 17th century. It runs through open terrain and crosses forests with old trees protecting the fairways. Accomodation is available in the château and facilities include several tennis courts. Another 18 hole course is presently under construction.

GF $

1989

27

—

I.C.V./P. Leglise

L 6155 P 72, 2925 P 35

S

R

Required : Handicap Certificate
Best days : Any day

HOLE	LENGTH MEDAL-TEE	PAR	STROKE INDEX
1	471	5	11
2	367	4	5
3	171	3	15
4	371	4	1
5	472	5	17
6	185	3	7
7	361	4	9
8	328	4	13
9	397	4	3
TOTAL	3123	36	TOTAL

HOLE	LENGTH MEDAL-TEE	PAR	STROKE INDEX
10	381	4	10
11	348	4	8
12	177	3	6
13	373	4	2
14	335	4	16
15	447	5	18
16	196	3	4
17	470	5	12
18	305	4	14
TOTAL	3032	36	TOTAL

DOMONT

TEL : (1)39910750
LOCATION : 15 km Paris A 1 exit Beauvais then RD 922
ADDRESS : Rte de Montmorency – 95330 Domont
HOTEL :
Novotel – Montsault
Tel : (1)34739305
Grand Hôtel – Enghien-les-Bains
Tel : (1)34128000
Villa Marie-Louise – Enghien-les-Bains
Tel : (1)39648221
RESTAURANT : Auberge Croix Blanche – Domont
Tel : (1)39910169

Situated 15km from Paris, Domont is an attractive well-wooded course with narrow fairways set on fairly hilly landscape. Several of the holes are laid out around a picturesque pond. There is a mansion style clubhouse with a swimming pool. *SSS 71*

GF $$ | Tuesdays
1968 | F. Hawtree
18 | L 5172 P 71

Required : Handicap Certificate, Club Membership Card.
Best days : Weekdays

HOLE	LENGTH MEDAL-TEE	PAR	STROKE INDEX
1	301	4	13
2	160	3	9
3	353	4	3
4	250	4	11
5	445	5	7
6	326	4	17
7	424	5	15
8	165	3	5
9	352	4	1
TOTAL	2776	36	TOTAL

HOLE	LENGTH MEDAL-TEE	PAR	STROKE INDEX
10	300	4	14
11	251	4	6
12	143	3	12
13	470	5	2
14	120	3	18
15	301	4	4
16	140	3	16
8	391	5	16
18	280	4	10
TOTAL	2396	35	TOTAL

DUNKERQUE

TEL : 28610743
LOCATION : 5 km SE Dunkerque D916
ADDRESS : Fort Vallières - Coudekerque Village - 59380 Bergues
HOTEL :
Altéa - Dunkerque
Tel : 28591111
Mercure - Dunkerque
Tel : 28607060
Europe - Dunkerque
Tel : 28662907

Recently extended to 18 hole status, the course lies up in the north of France close to the Belgian border on flat and rather open windy countryside not far from the sea. Some of the holes feature narrow fairways and are guarded by tricky water hazards. *SSS 71*

GF $

1986

18

Tuesdays

R. Berthet

L 5750 P 71

S

R

Required : Handicap Certificate
Best days : Any day

HOLE	LENGTH MEDAL-TEE	PAR	STROKE INDEX
1	447	5	
2	289	4	
3	175	3	
4	381	4	
5	413	4	
6	291	4	
7	490	5	
8	184	3	
9	363	4	
TOTAL	3033	36	TOTAL

HOLE	LENGTH MEDAL-TEE	PAR	STROKE INDEX
10	297	4	
11	331	4	
12	441	5	
13	389	4	
14	120	3	
15	320	4	
16	337	4	
17	201	3	
18	281	4	
TOTAL	2717	35	TOTAL

EPINAL

TEL : 29346597
LOCATION : 3 km Epinal RN 57
ADDRESS : rue du Merle-Blanc – 88001 Epinal
HOTEL : HR
Campanile
Tel : 29313838
Mercure – Epinal
Tel : 29351868
Le Colombier – Epinal
Tel : 29352005
RESTAURANT : Les Abesses – Epinal
Tel : 29825369

Extended to 18 holes in 1988, the public Epinal golf club was awarded the French 'Oscar' for their dynamism in innovating their course in the same year. The holes nestle in the foothills of the 'Vosges' mountain chain on gently rolling countryside and run through forest and marshes. Two ponds serve as water traps, and a stream runs through various holes. The Campanile hotel is adjacent to the course.

GF $

1985

18

Tues.; Nov. to March

M. Gayon

L 5242 P 72

S

RP

Required : Handicap Certificate
Best days : Any day

HOLE	LENGTH MEDAL-TEE	PAR	STROKE INDEX
1	304	4	8
2	188	3	2
3	440	5	3
4	275	4	7
5	301	4	6
6	294	4	5
7	252	4	4
8	123	3	9
9	444	5	1
TOTAL	2621	36	TOTAL

HOLE	LENGTH MEDAL-TEE	PAR	STROKE INDEX
10	304	4	8
11	188	3	2
12	440	5	3
13	275	4	7
14	301	4	6
15	294	4	5
16	252	4	4
17	123	3	9
18	444	5	1
TOTAL	2621	36	TOTAL

ÉSERY

TEL : 50365870
LOCATION : 12 km Genève to Annemasse A40, then D2 to La Roche-sur-Foron
ADDRESS : Esery - 74930 Reynier
HOTEL :
Mercure - Annemasse
Tel : 50920525
Helvetia - Annemasse
Tel : 50385980
Genève - Annemasse
Tel : 50387066

This challenging new course close to Geneva rises to 550 m above sea level and offers remarkable views of the surrounding valleys. Technically dificult, it comprises a scottish type layout featuring tight fairways set on hilly landscape. The clubhouse is a converted 14th century farmhouse. A 9 hole course will open in the summer of 1991.

GF $$ | Mondays
1990 | M. Gayon
27 | L 6350 P 72

Required : Handicap Certificate
Best days : Weekdays

HOLE	LENGTH MEDAL-TEE	PAR	STROKE INDEX
1	390	4	7
2	520	5	9
3	164	3	17
4	431	4	3
5	484	5	1
6	141	3	15
7	310	4	13
8	335	4	5
9	416	4	5
TOTAL	3191	36	TOTAL

HOLE	LENGTH MEDAL-TEE	PAR	STROKE INDEX
10	352	4	16
11	180	3	14
12	365	4	2
13	508	5	12
14	326	4	18
15	496	5	4
16	170	3	10
17	378	4	8
18	384	4	6
TOTAL	3159	36	TOTAL

ESTEREL

TEL : 94824788
LOCATION : 3 km Fréjus-St. Raphaël, exit Fréjus of A8 to Valescure/60 km Nice
ADDRESS : Avenue du Golf
83700 St-Raphaël
HOTEL : HR
Latitudes Esterel and Résidences Latitudes
Tel : 94824660

Laid out in the sparkling Côte d'Azur region just 5km from the Mediterranean sea front, this short but technically difficult course was designed by Robert Trent Jones Sr. It blends into a 100 acres of umbrella pine forest full of mimosa trees and threads its way through soft rolling landscape with Mediterranean rocks appearing regularly on the surface. Picturesque creeks flank some of the holes. The golf course is part of an international holiday complex comprising a 3 star 95 room hotel and an appartotel with 187 appartments. Facilities include 11 tennis courts, 2 swimming pools and a fitness center. *SSS 71,5*

GF $ — — RP  

1989 — R. Trent Jones 

27 — L 5921 P 71 

Required : Handicap Certificate
Best days : Any day

HOLE	LENGTH MEDAL-TEE	PAR	STROKE INDEX
1	336	4	9
2	120	3	17
3	539	5	7
4	349	4	5
5	372	4	3
6	451	5	15
7	380	4	1
8	192	3	11
9	289	4	13
TOTAL	3028	36	TOTAL

HOLE	LENGTH MEDAL-TEE	PAR	STROKE INDEX
10	369	4	6
11	507	5	12
12	139	3	16
13	318	4	10
14	305	4	14
15	125	3	18
16	391	4	2
17	382	4	4
18	357	4	8
TOTAL	2893	35	TOTAL

ETANGS DE FIAC

TEL : 63706470
LOCATION : 12 km Lavaur/27 km Castres
ADDRESS : Brazis - 81500 Lavaur
HOTEL :
Host du Château de St. Lieux - Lavaur
Tel : 63416087
Occitan - Castres
Tel : 63353420
Grand - Castres
Tel : 63590617

Wedged between rolling farmlands and bordering the river l'Agout, the course has a testing layout with lots of water covering some 7 hectares. The club became famous in France when a golfer drove his ball into one of the lakes killing instantly a large pike. A hotel with 30 rooms is scheduled to open soon. *SSS 70*

GF $ — Tuesdays — R S

1990 — F. Hawtree

18 — L 5724 P 71

Required : Handicap Certificate
Best days : Any day

HOLE	LENGTH MEDAL-TEE	PAR	STROKE INDEX
1	345	4	12
2	134	3	18
3	480	5	16
4	360	4	10
5	349	4	6
6	302	4	14
7	385	4	2
8	135	3	8
9	460	5	4
TOTAL	2950	36	TOTAL

HOLE	LENGTH MEDAL-TEE	PAR	STROKE INDEX
10	385	4	3
11	168	3	13
12	440	5	9
13	290	4	17
14	285	4	15
15	417	4	1
16	150	3	11
17	464	5	7
18	175	3	5
TOTAL	2774	35	TOTAL

ETIOLLES

TEL : (1)60754949
LOCATION : 33 km Paris A6 exit Corbeil, then Francilienne and Melun
ADDRESS : Vieux Chemin de Paris - 91450 Etiolles
HOTEL :
Novotel - Evry
Tel : (1)60778270
Campanile - Corbeil
Tel : (1)60894145
Central - Corbeil
Tel : (1)60880606

This course is laid outon the borders of the Senart Forest not far from the river Seine. The 27 holes holes, surrounded by woodlands, linger through peaceful lush landscape with 7 lakes serving as obstacles. A hotel is planned in the near future.

GF $ — 

1990 M. Gayon 

27 L 5272 P 73, 2265 P 36

Required : Handicap Certificate
Best days : Any day

HOLE	LENGTH MEDAL-TEE	PAR	STROKE INDEX	HOLE	LENGTH MEDAL-TEE	PAR	STROKE INDEX	HOLE	LENGTH MEDAL-TEE	PAR	STROKE INDEX
1	418	5	8	10	243	4	13	1	289	4	4
2	292	4	12	11	270	4	7	2	94	3	5
3	357	4	4	12	326	4	1	3	242	4	7
4	227	4	18	13	447	5	3	4	258	4	6
5	138	3	10	14	255	4	17	5	239	4	8
6	451	5	2	15	132	3	15	6	378	5	1
7	316	4	4	16	415	5	5	7	218	4	9
8	380	5	6	17	155	3	11	8	137	3	3
9	120	3	16	18	330	4	9	9	410	5	2
TOTAL	2699	37	TOTAL	TOTAL	2573	36	TOTAL	TOTAL	2265	36	TOTAL

ETRETAT

TEL : 35270489
LOCATION : In Etretat/28 km N Le Havre
ADDRESS : Route du Havre – BP 7 – 76790 Etretat
HOTEL :
Dormy House
Tel : 35270788
Falaises – Etretat
Tel : 35270277
Welcome – Etretat
Tel : 35270089
RESTAURANT : La Marine – Etretat
Tel : 35281594

This picturesque golf course is set high above the white cliffs of Etretat, commanding panoramic views of the English Channel and the surrounding countryside. It has a well designed layout with several impressive holes. Most of the fairways are exposed to the prevailing wind. The Dormy House with 50 rooms is situated 50m from the course. Presently the course is being redesigned (but open to play) and will be ready in 1992, measuring then 6 228m. *SSS 72*

GF $

1908

18

 Tuesdays

 M. Hagen

L 5842 P 72

Required : Handicap Certificate
Best days : Thursdays

HOLE	LENGTH MEDAL-TEE	PAR	STROKE INDEX
1	315	4	10
2	314	4	8
3	150	3	18
4	337	4	6
5	157	3	14
6	375	4	2
7	488	5	4
8	448	5	12
9	185	3	15
TOTAL	2769	35	TOTAL

HOLE	LENGTH MEDAL-TEE	PAR	STROKE INDEX
10	468	5	1
11	183	3	13
12	449	5	7
13	355	4	5
14	373	4	3
15	331	4	9
16	152	3	16
17	325	4	11
18	437	5	17
TOTAL	3073	37	TOTAL

EVIAN

TEL : 50751400
LOCATION : 2,5 km Evian RN 5
ADDRESS : Rive Sud du Lac de Genève – 74500 Evian
HOTEL :
Royal – Evian
Tel : 50268500
La Verniaz – Evian
Tel : 50750490
Ermitage – Evian
Tel : 50268500
RESTAURANT : Toque Royale – Evian
Tel : 50750378

Scenically situated high above Lake Geneva, this is a first class parkland course with lush fairways and greens set on relatively flat terrain. The entire course has just been redesigned by the american architect Cabell Robinson. It now offers a modern and fairly technical course enjoyable by all. The 15th counts among the most attractive of the Royal Club Evian, commanding views of the lake and the mountains. There is a pretty chalet style clubhouse. The Royal Hotel, a luxurious palace and owner of the golf club, is 1 km from the course. Hotel de la Verniaz is a former 18th century farmhouse converted into a scenic first class hotel and member of the Relais & Châteaux chain. *SSS 72*

GF $$ — December to February — S

1905/1989 — C. Robinson — 

18 — L 5651 P 72 — R

Required : None
Best days : Weekdays

HOLE	LENGTH MEDAL-TEE	PAR	STROKE INDEX
1	337	4	13
2	440	5	15
3	130	3	9
4	436	5	16
5	361	4	11
6	332	4	10
7	378	4	6
8	358	4	4
9	177	3	5
TOTAL	2949	36	TOTAL

HOLE	LENGTH MEDAL-TEE	PAR	STROKE INDEX
10	479	5	3
11	272	4	7
12	85	3	18
13	435	5	17
14	368	4	2
15	135	3	14
16	299	4	12
17	361	4	1
18	268	4	8
TOTAL	2702	36	TOTAL

FLAINE-LES-CARROZ

TEL : 50908544
LOCATION : Between Flaine and Les Carroz
ADDRESS : 74300 Flaine
HOTEL :
Les Lindars – Flaine
Tel : 50908166
Gradins Gris – Flaine
Tel : 50908110
Totem – Flaine
Tel : 50908064

One of the highest alpine courses in Europe is the Flaine-Les-Carroz golf course and playable only in summer. Laid out amidst mighty peaks between 1860m and 1920m above sea level (6th hole is the highest hole in France), the golf course runs through hilly landscape and commands fine views of the surrounding mountain scenery overlooking the Arve valley.

GF $

1985/86

18

October to June

Archigolf – R. Berthet

L 3711 P 61

Required : None
Best days : Any day

HOLE	LENGTH MEDAL-TEE	PAR	STROKE INDEX
1	205	3	
2	218	4	
3	130	3	
4	260	3	
5	210	4	
6	340	4	
7	360	4	
8	320	4	
9	146	3	
TOTAL	2189	32	TOTAL

HOLE	LENGTH MEDAL-TEE	PAR	STROKE INDEX
10	142	3	
11	99	3	
12	151	3	
13	115	3	
14	111	3	
15	114	3	
16	180	3	
17	366	4	
18	244	4	
TOTAL	1522	29	TOTAL

FONTAINEBLEAU

★★

TEL : (1)64222295
LOCATION : 1 km E. Fontainebleau RN 51
ADDRESS : Route d'Orléans – 77300 Fontainebleau
HOTEL :
Aigle Noir – Fontainebleau
Tel : (1)64223265
Legris et Parc – Fontainebleau
Tel : (1)64222424
Ibis – Fontainebleau
Tel : (1)642345225
RESTAURANT : Grand Veneur – Barbizon
Tel : (1)60664044

Located near Fontainebleau and the picturesque village of Barbizon, this is a beautiful densely wooded inland course with its narrow fairways encroached by stately pines, oaks and beeches. It features several sporting holes with small greens, demanding accuracy. There is a fine clubhouse with one tennis court. The Fontainebleau countryside is famous for rock climbing, walking and horse-riding. *SSS 72*

GF $$

Tuesdays, Weekends

1908

 T. Simpson

18

L  6012 P 72

Required : Handicap Certificate
Best days : Weekdays only

HOLE	LENGTH MEDAL-TEE	PAR	STROKE INDEX
1	307	4	11
2	166	3	17
3	480	5	7
4	378	4	3
5	327	4	9
6	396	4	1
7	168	3	15
8	505	5	5
9	296	4	13
TOTAL	3023	36	TOTAL

HOLE	LENGTH MEDAL-TEE	PAR	STROKE INDEX
10	177	3	16
11	509	5	2
12	420	5	12
13	375	4	6
14	148	3	18
15	363	4	4
16	348	4	8
17	262	4	14
18	387	4	10
TOTAL	2989	36	TOTAL

FOREZ

TEL : 77308685
LOCATION : 23 km Saint-Etienne
ADDRESS : Domaine de Presles – Craintilleux – 42210 Montrond-les-Bains
HOTEL :
Du Forez – Montrond-les-Bains
Tel : 77544228
Hostellerie La Poularde – Montrond-les-Bains
Tel : 77541006
RESTAURANT : Vieux Logis – Montrond-les-Bains
Tel : 77544271

The Golf du Forez is designed by the French architect Michel Gayon. It is located near the thermal spa of Montrond-Les-Bains on flat countryside on the Presles plateau with several ponds serving as hazards. Most of its greens are elevated and defended by bunkers.
SSS 68,3

GF $
Tuesdays
S
1986
M. Gayon
R
18
L 5313 P 70

Required : Handicap Certificate
Best days : Weekdays

HOLE	LENGTH MEDAL-TEE	PAR	STROKE INDEX
1	236	4	17
2	140	3	11
3	333	4	7
4	130	3	15
5	432	5	13
6	274	4	9
7	172	3	5
8	380	4	1
9	317	4	3
TOTAL	2414	34	TOTAL

HOLE	LENGTH MEDAL-TEE	PAR	STROKE INDEX
10	325	4	10
11	115	3	18
12	500	5	6
13	385	4	4
14	410	4	2
15	276	4	12
16	128	3	14
17	460	5	8
18	300	4	16
TOTAL	2899	36	TOTAL

FOURQUEUX

TEL : (1)34514147
LOCATION : 3 km Saint-Germain-en-Laye, 7 km Paris
ADDRESS : 36, rue de Saint-Nom – 78112 Fourqueux
HOTEL : Cazaudehore – Saint-German-en-Laye
Tel : (1) 39733660
La Forestière – St-Germain-en-Laye
Tel : (1)39733660
Pavillon Henri IV – St-Germain-en-Laye
Tel : (1)34516262
RESTAURANT : Auberge du Camélia – Bougival
Tel : (1) 39690302

The Fourqueux golf course is one of the longest courses in France, and consists of three separate loops of nine holes, designed by architects of the American P.G.A. The layout is varied and entertaining with its holes running through rather hilly and well-wooded terrain. Most of the greens are elevated and cunningly bunkered. The charming clubhouse dates back to 1635 and used to be the home of the physician of King Louis XIII. Several tennis courts are adjacent to the club. *SSS 73*

GF $$ — Tuesdays  S

1963 — US. PGA — R 

27 — L 3120 P 37, 2890 P 36, 2740 P 37

Required : Handicap Certificate
Best days : Mondays and Wednesdays

HOLE	LENGTH MEDAL-TEE	PAR	STROKE INDEX	HOLE	LENGTH MEDAL-TEE	PAR	STROKE INDEX	HOLE	LENGTH MEDAL-TEE	PAR	STROKE INDEX
1	350	4	4	1	300	4	9	1	415	5	2
2	310	4	2	2	435	5	3	2	95	3	9
3	265	4	9	3	285	4	7	3	270	4	4
4	300	4	7	4	385	4	1	4	175	3	6
5	495	5	5	5	300	4	6	5	395	5	3
6	385	4	1	6	180	3	4	6	255	4	7
7	420	4	3	7	450	5	2	7	510	5	1
8	445	5	6	8	390	4	8	8	140	3	8
9	150	3	8	9	165	3	5	9	485	5	5
TOTAL	3120	37	TOTAL	TOTAL	2890	36	TOTAL	TOTAL	2740	37	TOTAL

GAP-BAYARD

TEL : 92501683
LOCATION : on RN85
ADDRESS : Centre d'Oxygénation - 05000 Gap
HOTEL :
La Ferme Blanche - Gap
Tel : 92510341
La Grille - Gap
Tel : 92538484
Le Clos - Gap
Tel : 92513704
RESTAURANT : La Roseraie - Gap
Tel : 92514308

Nestling in the green foothills of the Alps at 750 m above sea level, the course is harmoniously integrated into the peaceful rolling landscape. Most of the holes are bordered by mature pines. Small mountain streams and lakes serve as obstacles. *SSS 69.9*

GF $

1989

18

Nov. 11 to May 15

H. Lambert

L 5638 P 72

R S

Required : None
Best days : Any day

HOLE	LENGTH MEDAL-TEE	PAR	STROKE INDEX
1	312	4	13
2	448	5	1
3	177	3	6
4	264	4	14
5	300	4	12
6	362	4	4
7	318	4	9
8	502	5	10
9	215	3	7
TOTAL	2898	36	TOTAL

HOLE	LENGTH MEDAL-TEE	PAR	STROKE INDEX
10	216	4	8
11	511	5	2
12	278	4	16
13	126	3	18
14	340	4	5
15	355	4	3
16	423	5	17
17	173	3	15
18	318	4	11
TOTAL	2740	36	TOTAL

GOURDAN

TEL : 75670384
LOCATION : exit Chanas of A7, then RN82 to Annonay
ADDRESS : Domaine de Gourdan - Saint-Clair - 07100 Annonay
HOTEL : HT
Golfhotel
Tel : 75670384
Midi - Annonay
Tel : 75332377

Quietly laid out in the rural Ardèche region within the grounds of a château, this varied course is fairly wooded. Stately trees border the fairways and lakes come into play on several holes. It boasts a comfortable hotel with 30 rooms and a swimming pool.

GF $

1988

18

—

T. Sprecher

L 5512 P 71

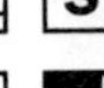
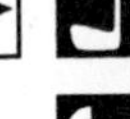

Required : None
Best days : Any day

HOLE	LENGTH MEDAL-TEE	PAR	STROKE INDEX
1	320	4	15
2	290	4	11
3	165	3	3
4	405	4	1
5	280	4	13
6	306	4	17
7	359	4	9
8	145	3	5
9	470	5	7
TOTAL	2740	35	TOTAL

HOLE	LENGTH MEDAL-TEE	PAR	STROKE INDEX
10	114	3	14
11	420	5	12
12	333	4	10
13	420	5	6
14	312	4	16
15	270	4	18
16	398	4	2
17	141	3	18
18	364	4	4
TOTAL	2772	36	TOTAL

GRAND AVIGNON

TEL : 90314994
LOCATION : 12 km Avignon A7 exit Avignon Nord
ADDRESS : Les Chênes Verts - 84270 Vedène
HOTEL :
La Mirande - Avignon
Tel : 90859393
L'Europe - Avignon
Tel : 90826692
Cité des Papes - Avignon
Tel : 90862245
RESTAURANT : Hiely - Avignon
Tel : 90861707

The Grand Avignon course opened for play in june 1990. It comprises 18 fairly technical holes set within a smart parkland setting landscaped by parasol pines, poplars, old oaks, plane and olive trees. Strategic bunkers and five vast lakes demand precision play. The greens with an average size of 600 m² are of excellent quality. Facilities include a 9 hole par 3 course and a cosy restaurant on the lakeshore.

GF $
1989
18

—
E. Vialatel
L 5648 P 71

S
R

Required : Handicap Certificate
Best days : Any day

HOLE	LENGTH MEDAL-TEE	PAR	STROKE INDEX
1	450	5	2
2	140	3	16
3	325	4	18
4	375	4	6
5	360	4	12
6	250	4	14
7	170	3	10
8	450	5	4
9	380	4	8
TOTAL	2900	36	TOTAL

HOLE	LENGTH MEDAL-TEE	PAR	STROKE INDEX
10	455	5	5
11	300	4	11
12	305	4	7
13	127	3	15
14	290	4	17
15	340	4	13
16	199	3	3
17	382	4	1
18	350	4	9
TOTAL	2748	35	TOTAL

GRANVILLE

TEL : 33502306
LOCATION : 5,5 km Granville D 971
ADDRESS : Breville – 50290 Brehal
HOTEL :
Les Bains – Granville
Tel : 33501731
Auberge des Quatre Routes – Bréville-sur-Mer
Tel : 33502010
La Mougins des Moulins à Vent – Bréville-sur-Mer
Tel : 33502241
RESTAURANT : Normandy Chaumière – Granville
Tel : 33500171

Laid out on the sand dunes in Normandy close to the Channel, the course has a links character and features numerous bunkers scattered all over. Many of the fairways are exposed to the prevailing wind. Nearby the club: tennis, riding, sailing and other water sports. *SSS 72*

GF $

1912

27

Tuesdays

H. Colt, J. Alison

L 5854 P 72, 2323 P 33

 S

Required : Handicap Certificate
Best days : Weekdays

HOLE	LENGTH MEDAL-TEE	PAR	STROKE INDEX
1	443	5	11
2	161	3	7
3	306	4	13
4	376	4	5
5	364	4	1
6	164	3	18
7	465	5	9
8	455	5	3
9	140	3	16
TOTAL	2874	36	TOTAL

HOLE	LENGTH MEDAL-TEE	PAR	STROKE INDEX
10	159	3	12
11	443	5	14
12	212	3	8
13	325	4	10
14	502	5	6
15	387	4	2
16	276	4	15
17	364	4	4
18	312	4	17
TOTAL	2980	36	TOTAL

GRENOBLE SAINT-QUENTIN

TEL : 76936728
LOCATION : 15 km Grenoble A48 exit Voreppe then RN532
ADDRESS : 38210 Saint-Quentin-sur-Isère
HOTEL :
Novotel - Voreppe
Tel : 76508144
Castel Anne - Voiron
Tel : 76058600
Abelia - Voiron
Tel : 76659000

Built on a site facing the Alps in the heart of the Isère Valley, its 18 holes are harmoniously integrated into the untouched landscape which borders the course. Quite hilly and well wooded with poplars, oaks and walnuts, some of the holes are dotted with picturesque lakes. A three star hotel is due to open in june 1991. *SSS*

GF $

—

R S

1987

J. Garaialde, J. Pern

18

L 5852 P 73

Required : None
Best days : Any day

HOLE	LENGTH MEDAL-TEE	PAR	STROKE INDEX
1	350	4	15
2	380	4	3
3	459	5	9
4	380	4	1
5	485	5	11
6	347	4	5
7	147	3	13
8	291	4	17
9	359	4	7
TOTAL	3198	37	TOTAL

HOLE	LENGTH MEDAL-TEE	PAR	STROKE INDEX
10	141	3	14
11	445	5	10
12	135	3	12
13	317	4	6
14	132	3	2
15	263	4	18
16	458	5	4
17	311	4	16
18	452	5	8
TOTAL	2654	36	TOTAL

GUINLET

TEL : 62098599
LOCATION : 5 km NE Eauze ; exit no 6 from A62, then RD931 to Eauze
ADDRESS : 32800 Eauze
HOTEL : HR
Auberge de Guinlet
Tel : 62098084
La Bonne Auberge - Manciet
Tel : 62085004
Moulin du Comte - Manciet
Tel : 62090672

Situated in the Gascogne region, the course winds its way through rolling and sometimes fairly wooded landscape and features several water obstacles. The Auberge de Guinlet with seven bedrooms and two tennis courts is adjoining the course.

GF $

1989

18

—

M. Thevenin

L 5311 P 71

R S

Required : None
Best days : Any day

HOLE	LENGTH MEDAL-TEE	PAR	STROKE INDEX
1	145	3	9
2	258	4	5
3	157	3	1
4	522	5	11
5	147	3	2
6	465	5	3
7	323	4	12
8	438	5	7
9	146	3	4
TOTAL	2601	35	TOTAL

HOLE	LENGTH MEDAL-TEE	PAR	STROKE INDEX
10	308	4	17
11	316	4	10
12	115	3	14
13	378	4	8
14	461	5	13
15	268	4	16
16	257	4	15
17	262	4	18
18	345	4	6
TOTAL	2710	36	TOTAL

GUJAN - MESTRAS

TEL : 56668636
LOCATION : 48 km Bordeaux to Arcachon, 12 km Arcachon D650
ADDRESS : Route de Sanguinet - 33470 Gujan-Mestras
HOTEL :
La Guérinière - Gujan-Mestras
Tel : 56660878
Arc - Arcachon
Tel : 56830685
Les Vagues - Arcachon
Tel : 56830375

This is a most enjoyable holiday golf course in the Landes region situated in the middle of a a pine forest near the seaside resort of Arcachon. Picturesque natural lakes guard the greens of the 5th, 9th, 11th and 18th holes. A very comfortable clubhouse with its terrace leading down to the lakeshore serves as the 19th hole. A hotel is planned in the near future. *SSS 68,5*

GF $

1990

27

—

A. Prat

L 5610 P 72, 2660 P 35

S

R

Required : Handicap Certificate
Best days : Any day

HOLE	LENGTH MEDAL-TEE	PAR	STROKE INDEX
1	435	5	17
2	350	4	7
3	110	3	13
4	270	4	15
5	350	4	1
6	160	3	9
7	435	5	11
8	330	4	5
9	330	4	3
TOTAL	2770	36	TOTAL

HOLE	LENGTH MEDAL-TEE	PAR	STROKE INDEX
10	425	5	18
11	125	3	10
12	365	4	12
13	320	4	14
14	470	5	4
15	150	3	16
16	340	4	6
17	340	4	8
18	305	4	2
TOTAL	2840	36	TOTAL

HARDELOT

TEL : 21837310
LOCATION : 1 km Hardelot-Plage
ADDRESS : Av. du Golf – 62152 Neufchâtel-Hardelot
HOTEL :
Le Regina – Hardelot
Tel : 21838188
Château de Montreuil – Montreuil
Tel : 21815304
Écusson – Hardelot
Tel : 21837152
RESTAURANT : Ecusson – Hardelot
Tel : 21837152

The golf course lies on the northern coast of France, 1km inland from the seaside resort of Hardelot. It is set within beautiful natural landscape among majestic trees. A typical parkland course of excellent quality with fine holes, all cunningly bunkered, narrow fairways, and well-defended greens. *SSS 72*

GF $

1931

 T. Simpson

18

 5870 P 72

Required : Introduction letter
Best days : Any day

HOLE	LENGTH MEDAL-TEE	PAR	STROKE INDEX
1	475	5	11
2	454	5	9
3	345	4	7
4	360	4	1
5	127	3	15
6	460	5	3
7	117	3	17
8	315	4	13
9	355	4	5
TOTAL	3008	37	TOTAL

HOLE	LENGTH MEDAL-TEE	PAR	STROKE INDEX
10	485	5	8
11	265	4	10
12	160	3	16
13	500	5	2
14	138	3	18
15	330	4	6
16	385	4	4
17	175	3	12
18	425	4	14
TOTAL	2862	35	TOTAL

HAUT-POITOU

TEL : 49625362
LOCATION : 20 km N. Poitiers, 15 km S. Châtellerault RN 10
ADDRESS : Parc de Loisirs de Saint-Cyr-86130 Jaunay-Clan
HOTEL :
Grand Hôtel-Châtellerault
Tel : 49213011
Croissant-Châtellerault
Tel : 49210177
Relais de Poitiers-Chasseneuil-du-Poitou
Tel : 49529041
RESTAURANT : Domaine de Périgny-Périgny
Tel : 49518043

Designed by the British architect Harold Bill Baker, this is a fine, public golf course located within a vast leisure park in the Poitou-Charentes region. Laid out on the shores of a lake, it is flanked on one side by the river 'Le Clain'. Several menacing streams meander their way through the holes. A part of the course is bordered by woodland. Sports facilities include sailing, archery, windsurfing, fishing and several tennis courts.

GF $

1987

27

Tuesdays

H. Baker

L 6195 P 73, 1800 P 31

Required : Handicap Certificate
Best days : Any day

HOLE	LENGTH MEDAL-TEE	PAR	STROKE INDEX
1	345	4	11
2	468	5	7
3	338	4	13
4	153	3	17
5	462	5	5
6	404	4	1
7	151	3	15
8	448	5	3
9	384	4	9
TOTAL	3153	37	TOTAL

HOLE	LENGTH MEDAL-TEE	PAR	STROKE INDEX
10	334	4	14
11	149	3	18
12	397	4	8
13	351	4	10
14	494	5	4
15	345	4	12
16	475	5	2
17	129	3	16
18	368	4	6
TOTAL	3042	36	TOTAL

HOSSEGOR

TEL : 58435699
LOCATION : 25 km Bayonne RN 10/A 63
ADDRESS : Avenue du Golf – 40150 Hossegor
HOTEL : HR
du Golf
Tel : 58435059
Beauséjour – Hossegor
Tel : 58435107
Ermitage – Hossegor
Tel : 58435222
Du Palais – Hossegor
Tel : 59240940

Located in a region called 'Les Landes', 2km from the Basque coast, this is one of the most attractive championship golf courses in France, laid out in an extensive and superb forest of pine trees. Relatively flat, no hole looks alike. There are numerous well-contrived dogleg holes, around 60 well-placed bunkers and a picturesque stream serving as a hazard on the 3rd hole. The pleasant clubhouse is built in Basque style. *SSS 71*

GF $$
1927
18

Tuesdays in winter
J. Morrison
L 5671 P 71

RP S

Required : Handicap Certificate
Best days : Any day

HOLE	LENGTH MEDAL-TEE	PAR	STROKE INDEX
1	409	5	11
2	141	3	17
3	321	4	9
4	465	5	13
5	177	3	5
6	398	4	1
7	366	4	7
8	145	3	15
9	365	4	3
TOTAL	2789	35	TOTAL

HOLE	LENGTH MEDAL-TEE	PAR	STROKE INDEX
10	371	4	2
11	355	4	12
12	409	5	10
13	349	4	6
14	119	3	18
15	430	5	8
16	366	4	4
17	166	3	16
18	317	4	14
TOTAL	2882	36	TOTAL

HUMIÈRES

TEL : 44423951
LOCATION : 85 km Paris exit n° 11/5 km Compiègne
ADDRESS : Place du Château - 60113 Monchy Humières
HOTEL : HR
Golf Hotel
Tel : 44423951
Host. Royal Lieu - Compiègne
Tel : 44201024
Université - Compiègne
Tel : 44232727
RESTAURANT : Auberge du Pont-Rethondes
Tel : 44856024

Founded and run by a Japanese woman Masako Ohya, the course lies just 45 minutes north of Paris. Standing in a tranquil setting of lush undulating woodlands and former marshlands, water hazards are omnipresent throughout this very long course.
The charming 17th century château has been converted into a hotel with 12 rooms, conference facitilies, a fine restaurant and 2 tennis courts. A riding club is nearby.

GF $

1990

18

—

J.C. Cornillot

L 6297 P 73

RP S

Required : None
Best days : Any day

HOLE	LENGTH MEDAL-TEE	PAR	STROKE INDEX
1	370	4	
2	182	3	
3	381	4	
4	455	5	
5	141	3	
6	344	4	
7	432	5	
8	392	4	
9	305	4	
TOTAL	3002	36	TOTAL

HOLE	LENGTH MEDAL-TEE	PAR	STROKE INDEX
10	467	5	
11	140	3	
12	439	5	
13	495	5	
14	195	3	
15	411	4	
16	400	4	
17	390	4	
18	358	4	
TOTAL	3295	37	TOTAL

ILE D'OR

TEL : 40985800
LOCATION : 15 km Nantes RN23 to Mauves
ADDRESS : Le Cellier - 44850 Ligné
HOTEL :
Novotel - Nantes Carquefou
Tel : 40526464
Altéa - Nantes Carquefou
Tel : 40302924
La Châtaigneraie - Suce-sur-Erdre
Tel : 40779095
RESTAURANT : Margotte - Nantes
Tel : 40732740

This charming golf course, set on an island in the Loire river, is laid out in alluring landscape. It affords panoramic views of the Loire and two scenic castles : the Château de Clermont and the Château de La Varenne. Some of the holes such as the spectacular 11th, the 12th, and the 4th are flanked by the river, serving sometimes as a hazard. The club boasts a picturesque old farmhouse as its clubhouse.

GF $ — Tuesdays — S

1989 — M. Gayon

27 — L 6292 P 72, 1217 P 27 — R

Required : None
Best days : Any day

HOLE	LENGTH MEDAL-TEE	PAR	STROKE INDEX
1	487	5	
2	180	3	
3	387	4	
4	315	4	
5	309	4	
6	402	4	
7	159	3	
8	563	5	
9	275	4	
TOTAL	3077	36	TOTAL

HOLE	LENGTH MEDAL-TEE	PAR	STROKE INDEX
10	476	5	
11	409	4	
12	156	3	
13	378	4	
14	363	4	
15	330	4	
16	417	4	
17	196	3	
18	490	5	
TOTAL	3215	36	TOTAL

INTERNATIONAL CLUB DU LYS

★

TEL : 44212600
LOCATION : 4 km Chantilly RN 16/35 km Paris
ADDRESS : Rond Point du Grand Cerf – Le Lys Chantilly – 60260 Lamorlaye
HOTEL :
Château de Montvillargene – Lamorlaye
Tel : 44215100
Campanile – Chantilly
Tel : 44573924
Host. du Lys – Lys Chantilly
Tel : 44212619
RESTAURANT : Relais Condé – Chantilly
Tel : 44570575

Two sporting golf courses (Chênes and Bouleaux) laid out on beautiful well-wooded countryside, set on the edge of the forest of Chantilly. Both courses follow the gentle undulations of the terrain. There is a varied and entertaining layout with many long holes bordered by mature oak and beech trees. Some 80 well-designed and steep bunkers serve as hazards on the narrow fairways and greens. The country club is equipped with many sports facilities such as a riding school, tennis courts, a large lake for water sports, children's playground plus a nursery, and various hockey and football fields. *SSS 71/66*

GF $$

1929

36

Tuesdays, Weekends

T. Simpson, R. Berthet

L 5214 P 71, 4798 P 66

S R

Required : Handicap Certificate
Best days : Weekdays only

HOLE	LENGTH MEDAL-TEE	PAR	STROKE INDEX
1	380	5	9
2	339	4	3
3	147	3	17
4	320	4	5
5	314	4	11
6	134	3	13
7	320	4	7
8	350	4	1
9	221	4	15
TOTAL	2525	35	TOTAL

HOLE	LENGTH MEDAL-TEE	PAR	STROKE INDEX
10	300	4	10
11	180	3	6
12	286	4	16
13	155	3	18
14	330	4	2
15	398	5	12
16	280	4	8
17	345	4	4
18	415	5	14
TOTAL	2689	36	TOTAL

ISABELLA

TEL : (1)30541062
LOCATION : 3 km E. Pontchartrin/39 km Paris A13 exit Bois d'Arcy, then D134/RN12
ADDRESS : Sainte-Appoline - 70370 Plaisir
HOTEL :
Auberge de la Dauberie - Mousseaux
Tel : (1)34878057
Le Verbois - Neauphle-le-Château
Tel : (1)34891178
RESTAURANT : L'Aubergade - Pontchartrin
Tel : (1)34890263

Recently extended to 18 holes by the Belgian architect Paul Rolin, this is a rather tight course running through flat wooded countryside with several holes played over water.

GF $ — Tuesdays — R

1969/1990 — P. Rolin

18 — L 5629 P 71

Required : Handicap Certificate
Best days : Weekdays only

HOLE	LENGTH MEDAL-TEE	PAR	STROKE INDEX
1	473	5	7
2	364	4	1
3	341	4	9
4	477	5	5
5	133	3	13
6	281	4	17
7	294	4	11
8	144	3	15
9	359	4	3
TOTAL	2866	36	TOTAL

HOLE	LENGTH MEDAL-TEE	PAR	STROKE INDEX
10	491	5	6
11	125	3	12
12	313	4	10
13	275	4	14
14	419	4	2
15	127	3	18
16	272	4	16
17	401	4	4
18	340	4	8
TOTAL	2763	35	TOTAL

JOIGNY

TEL : 86736987
LOCATION : 146 km Paris A6 exit Joigny, then D89/D955
ADDRESS : Le Château du Roncenay - 89110 Chassy
HOTEL :
La Côte St.-Jacques - Joigny
Tel : 86620970
Modern Hôtel - Joigny
Tel : 86621628

The course extends over 100 ha of vallied wooded landscape. It features tight fairways flanked by old trees and five picturesque lakes affect play on several holes. Both hotels, "La Côte St. Jacques" and "Modern Hotel" are renowned for their excellent cuisine. *SSS 72*

GF $

1990

19

Tuesdays

J. Garaialde, J. Pern

L 6140 P 72

S

R

Required : Handicap Certificate
Best days : Weekdays

HOLE	LENGTH MEDAL-TEE	PAR	STROKE INDEX
1	330	4	
2	370	4	
3	130	3	
4	330	4	
5	370	4	
6	460	5	
7	180	3	
8	340	4	
9	500	5	
TOTAL	3010	36	TOTAL

HOLE	LENGTH MEDAL-TEE	PAR	STROKE INDEX
10	520	5	
11	210	3	
12	400	4	
13	320	4	
14	160	3	
15	480	5	
16	340	4	
17	320	4	
18	380	4	
TOTAL	3130	36	TOTAL

KERVER

✡

TEL : 97453009
LOCATION : 30 km Vannes RD780 to Rhuys peninsula/3 km Arzon
ADDRESS : Ferme de Kerver
56730 St-Gildas-de-Rhuys
HOTEL :
Port du Crouesty - Port du Crouesty
Tel : 97538161
Aquarium - Vannes
Tel : 97404452
Manche Océan - Vannes
Tel : 97472646

This seaside course is located in south Brittany on the Rhuys peninsula. It spreads over rugged dune landscape alongside the ocean and in the middle is a large lake which is a nature reserve for birds. Nearby is the holiday village of Arzon with its sporting sailing harbour Port du Crouesty. Both are a part of a real estate project. *SSS 72*

GF $ — —
1989 — 0. Brizon
18 — L 5826 P 72

S

Required : None
Best days : Any day

HOLE	LENGTH MEDAL-TEE	PAR	STROKE INDEX
1	448	5	
2	160	3	
3	351	4	
4	160	3	
5	430	5	
6	354	4	
7	350	4	
8	178	3	
9	400	4	
TOTAL	2831	35	TOTAL

HOLE	LENGTH MEDAL-TEE	PAR	STROKE INDEX
10	454	5	
11	170	3	
12	432	5	
13	345	4	
14	150	3	
15	252	4	
16	361	4	
17	382	4	
18	449	5	
TOTAL	2995	37	TOTAL

LA BAROUGE

TEL : 63610672
LOCATION : 2 km N. Mazamet
ADDRESS : Pont de l'Arn – 81660 Mazamet
HOTEL : Château de Montlédier – Mazamet
Tel : 63612054
La Métairie Neuve – Bout-du-Pont-de-l'Arn
Tel : 63612331
H. Jourdan – Mazamet
Tel : 63615693
RESTAURANT : Le Grand Balcon – Mazamet
Tel : 63610115

The golf course lies in a former private property on gently rolling parkland with strategic trees in the tickly wooded foothills of the 'Montagne Noire' mountain chain in the Midi Pyrénées region. Several streams meander their way through the holes.

GF $

—

S

1956

M. Mackenzie Ross

R

18

L 5427 P 70

Required : Handicap Certificate
Best days : Any day

HOLE	LENGTH MEDAL-TEE	PAR	STROKE INDEX
1	354	4	5
2	288	4	13
3	156	3	11
4	376	4	2
5	267	4	18
6	133	3	15
7	450	5	9
8	188	3	4
9	347	4	7
TOTAL	2564	34	TOTAL

HOLE	LENGTH MEDAL-TEE	PAR	STROKE INDEX
10	170	3	14
11	505	5	3
12	268	4	16
13	275	4	17
14	174	3	10
15	393	4	1
16	318	4	12
17	310	4	8
18	450	5	6
TOTAL	2863	36	TOTAL

LA BAULE

TEL : 40604618
LOCATION : 5 km La Baule
ADDRESS : Domaine de St-Denac – St-André-des-Eaux – 44600 St-Nazaire
HOTEL :
Castel Marie Louise – La Baule
Tel : 40602060
Hermitage – La Baule
Tel : 40603700
Royal – La Baule
Tel : 40603306
RESTAURANT : L'Espadon – La Baule
Tel : 40600563

Located near the popular seaside resort of La Baule, the course is laid out in fine lush landscape with numerous water hazards such as a large and picturesque lake in the middle of the course. It has a testing and interesting layout with the last 9 holes set around the lake, going up and down. The club is equipped with a swimming pool and several tennis courts. The Castel Marie Louise Hotel is an elegant country house hotel not far from the club. *SSS 72*

GF $$
1976
18

Tues. in winter time
D. Thomas, P. Alliss
L 6157 P 72

R S

Required : Handicap Certificate
Best days : Weekdays

HOLE	LENGTH MEDAL-TEE	PAR	STROKE INDEX
1	344	4	11
2	485	5	7
3	353	4	5
4	167	3	15
5	324	4	13
6	457	5	1
7	374	4	9
8	161	3	17
9	406	4	3
TOTAL	3071	36	TOTAL

HOLE	LENGTH MEDAL-TEE	PAR	STROKE INDEX
10	146	3	18
11	441	5	4
12	379	4	10
13	474	5	2
14	386	4	8
15	342	4	6
16	353	4	12
17	162	3	16
18	403	4	14
TOTAL	3086	36	TOTAL

LA BOULIE – R.C.F.

TEL : (1)39505941
LOCATION : 2 km Versailles RN 186
ADDRESS : « La Boulie » – 78000 Versailles
HOTEL :
Trianon Palace – Versailles
TEL : (1)39503412
Holiday Inn – Vélizy
Tel : (1)39469698
Le Versailles – Versailles
Tel : (1)39506465
RESTAURANT : Trois Marches – Versailles
Tel : (1)39501321

The two championship golf courses of La Boulie belong to the exclusive sports club 'Racing Club de France'. Both are laid out in densely wooded parkland with majestic and century-old trees bordering the fairways. The 'Vallée Course' (main championship course) is set on hilly countryside, the 'Fôret Course, runs through lush woodland. Each course has around fifty bunkers and various strategic water hazards. La Boulie has hosted many important international tournaments. There is an imposing and stylish clubhouse with several tennis courts. *SSS 71/72*

GF $$

1952

45

Tuesdays

—

L 5963 P 71, 6277 P 72, 1148 P 27

S

R

Required : Handicap Certificate
Best days : Weekdays by invitation only

Vallée Course

HOLE	LENGTH MEDAL-TEE	PAR	STROKE INDEX
1	369	4	5
2	402	4	1
3	153	3	15
4	478	5	13
5	430	4	3
6	311	4	7
7	165	3	17
8	463	5	9
9	285	4	11
TOTAL	3056	36	TOTAL

HOLE	LENGTH MEDAL-TEE	PAR	STROKE INDEX
10	194	3	10
11	464	5	14
12	305	4	16
13	160	3	6
14	373	4	4
15	173	3	8
16	390	4	2
17	439	5	18
18	409	4	12
TOTAL	2907	35	TOTAL

Forêt Course

HOLE	LENGTH MEDAL-TEE	PAR	STROKE INDEX
1	373	4	10
2	127	3	18
3	451	5	11
4	431	4	1
5	436	5	13
6	344	4	8
7	415	4	3
8	351	4	6
9	172	3	15
TOTAL	3100	36	TOTAL

HOLE	LENGTH MEDAL-TEE	PAR	STROKE INDEX
10	548	5	2
11	170	3	12
12	391	4	4
13	153	3	17
14	482	5	7
15	395	4	9
16	379	4	5
17	318	4	16
18	341	4	14
TOTAL	3177	36	TOTAL

LA BRETESCHE

TEL : 40883003
LOCATION : 35 km La Baule, in Pontchâteau RN 165/RD 2
ADDRESS : Domaine de la Bretesche – 44700 Missillac
HOTEL : H
La Bretesche
Tel : 40883005

Picturesquely laid out in beautiful verdant countryside in Brittany, La Bretesche is one of France's most attractive golf courses, with a scenic 14th century Château and a large lake. The holes, featuring narrow fairways, are separated from each other by stately trees. The clubhouse is modern with a heated swimming pool and various tennis courts. The refined Golf Hotel, a former farmhouse, is adjacent to the golf course. *SSS 72*

GF $$ — —
1966 — M. Baker
18 — L 5785 P 72

Required : None
Best days : Mondays, Tuesdays, Wednesdays

HOLE	LENGTH MEDAL-TEE	PAR	STROKE INDEX
1	330	4	11
2	355	4	5
3	150	3	17
4	435	5	3
5	330	4	15
6	185	3	9
7	345	4	13
8	360	4	1
9	340	4	7
TOTAL	2830	35	TOTAL

HOLE	LENGTH MEDAL-TEE	PAR	STROKE INDEX
10	450	5	4
11	315	4	16
12	155	3	12
13	450	5	8
14	145	3	14
15	390	4	2
16	360	4	10
17	440	5	6
18	250	4	18
TOTAL	2955	37	TOTAL

LA CHAPELLE

TEL : (1)64047075
LOCATION : 29 km Meaux, 60 km Paris
A 4, exit Crécy
ADDRESS : Ferme de Montpichet – 77580
Crécy-La-Chapelle
HOTEL : Place – Coulommiers
Tel : (1)64038400
La Catounière – Sancy-les-Meaux
Tel : (1)60257174
Le Cheval Blanc – Vareddes
Tel : (1)64331803
RESTAURANT : Auberge du Moulin –
Crécy-la-Chapelle
Tel : (1)64369989

At 60km east of Paris, the golf course is laid out on mostly undulating countryside amidst young trees. It is the first French golf course to be conceived by computer, under the direction of two French golfers. The layout is modern and quite remarkable. It has several ponds serving as hazards. There is a well-appointed clubhouse, formerly a farmhouse, which dominates the course. *SSS 72*

GF $

Tuesdays

R S

 1987

O. d'Ormesson, A. Godillot

18

L 5902 P 72

Required : Handicap Certificate
Best days : Any day

HOLE	LENGTH MEDAL-TEE	PAR	STROKE INDEX
1	373	4	1
2	164	3	15
3	505	5	11
4	352	4	3
5	386	4	5
6	455	5	17
7	358	4	7
8	168	3	13
9	289	4	9
TOTAL	3050	36	TOTAL

HOLE	LENGTH MEDAL-TEE	PAR	STROKE INDEX
10	298	4	12
11	140	3	18
12	477	5	10
13	311	4	6
14	490	5	2
15	331	4	8
16	154	3	16
17	507	5	4
18	144	3	14
TOTAL	2852	36	TOTAL

LACANAU-L'ARDILOUSE

TEL : 56032560
LOCATION : 45 km Bordeaux, 3 km Lacanau-Océan
ADDRESS : 33680 Lacanau-Océan
HOTEL : HR
Les Hameaux du Golf
Tel : 56032315
Étoile d'Argent – Lacanau-Océan
Tel : 56032107
RESTAURANT : L'Oyat – Lacanau-Océan
Tel : 56031111

Set within a splendid well-wooded dune landscape, the Lacanau golf course is ideally situated for holiday golf. Only 3km from the seaside resort of Lacanau-Ocean on the Atlantic, it incorporates a fine setting of pine trees and ponds, serving as hazards. Amenities include a modern clubhouse, various bungalows and a hotel with 50 bedrooms. Nearby a tennis and squash center, a riding school, plus a windsurf and waterski center. *SSS 72*

GF $$ — — 

1980 — J. Harris — RP 

18 — L 5512 P 72 — 

Required : Handicap Certificate
Best days : Any day

HOLE	LENGTH MEDAL-TEE	PAR	STROKE INDEX
1	328	4	2
2	145	3	8
3	332	4	5
4	305	4	10
5	255	4	16
6	328	4	7
7	185	3	3
8	325	4	6
9	426	5	13
TOTAL	2629	35	TOTAL

HOLE	LENGTH MEDAL-TEE	PAR	STROKE INDEX
10	369	4	1
11	170	3	9
12	310	4	4
13	401	5	14
14	332	4	11
15	163	3	15
16	280	4	12
17	423	5	17
18	435	5	18
TOTAL	2883	37	TOTAL

LA COMMANDERIE

TEL : 85304412/85304024
LOCATION : 5 km Mâcon RN 79
ADDRESS : L'Aumusse-Crottet
01290 Pont-de-Veyle
HOTEL :
Novotel – Mâcon
Tel : 85360080
Georges Blanc – Vonnas
Tel : 74500010
La Huchette – sur route de Bourg-en-Bresse
Tel : 85310355
RESTAURANT : Georges Blanc – Vonnas
Tel : 74500010

This is a rather short but testing golf course laid out on attractive rolling countryside with trees and bunkers scattered all over. There are some strategically placed water hazards, creating problems on several holes. *SSS 69.*

GF $
1964
18
Thursdays
M. Preneuf
L 5561 P 70
S
R

Required : Handicap Certificate
Best days : Any day

HOLE	LENGTH MEDAL-TEE	PAR	STROKE INDEX
1	350	4	4
2	266	4	18
3	347	4	6
4	129	3	16
5	540	5	2
6	186	3	8
7	325	4	10
8	134	3	14
9	302	4	12
TOTAL	2579	34	TOTAL

HOLE	LENGTH MEDAL-TEE	PAR	STROKE INDEX
10	333	4	13
11	350	4	5
12	475	5	9
13	460	5	3
14	144	3	15
15	402	4	1
16	370	4	7
17	283	4	17
18	165	3	11
TOTAL	2982	36	TOTAL

LA CORDELIÈRE

TEL : 25401105
LOCATION : 30 km SE Troyes RN 71/D 444 to Chaource, then D 443 to Bar s/Seine
ADDRESS : Château de la Cordelière – 10210 Chaource
HOTEL : HR
Château de la Cordelière
Tel : 25401105
Campanile – Buchères
Tel : 25496767
Grand Hôtel – Troyes
Tel : 25799090

An attractive and technical inland course set on gently rolling woodland in the Champagne-Ardenne region. The fairways are very narrow and tree-lined. Streams and ponds serve as water traps. It features an impressive Château, dating back to the Renaissance, now operating as a stylish hotel. *SSS 72*

GF $ — Tuesdays; Nov. 15 to May 15 

1958 — J. Hirigoyen — R

18 — L 6033 P 72 — S

Required : Handicap Certificate
Best days : Weekdays

HOLE	LENGTH MEDAL-TEE	PAR	STROKE INDEX
1	401	4	6
2	275	4	16
3	402	4	4
4	460	5	10
5	177	3	14
6	400	4	2
7	318	4	12
8	133	3	18
9	463	5	8
TOTAL	3029	36	TOTAL

HOLE	LENGTH MEDAL-TEE	PAR	STROKE INDEX
10	490	5	7
11	161	3	17
12	482	5	1
13	477	5	5
14	188	3	11
15	190	3	13
16	382	4	3
17	186	3	15
18	448	5	9
TOTAL	3004	36	TOTAL

LA DOMANGERE (La Roche-sur-Yon)

TEL : 51076015
LOCATION : 7 km La Roche-sur-Yon, on route de Luçon through RD 746/RD 85
ADDRESS : Route de Nesmy – 85310 Nesmy
HOTEL : HP
Hôtel du Golf
Tel : 51076015
Ibis – La Roche-sur-Yon
Tel : 51362600
Logis de la Couperie – La Roche-sur-Yon
Tel : 51372119

At only 30 km from the popular Atlantic coast, the La Domangere golf course is set in a beautiful undulating park landscape bordering in parts the river 'L'Yon'. Several holes (the 7th is among the longest in France) are played over twelve scenic lakes. An attractive feature is the 18th century, renovated clubhouse and a charming 3 star hotel with 19 rooms with nearby a riding school and tennis courts.

GF $
1988
27

—
M. Gayon
L 6613 P 72, 1500 P 30

Required : None
Best days : Any day

HOLE	LENGTH MEDAL-TEE	PAR	STROKE INDEX
1	188	3	13
2	384	4	5
3	136	3	17
4	532	5	7
5	418	4	3
6	342	4	15
7	616	5	1
8	318	4	11
9	398	4	9
TOTAL	3332	36	TOTAL

HOLE	LENGTH MEDAL-TEE	PAR	STROKE INDEX
10	473	5	14
11	431	4	6
12	341	4	10
13	177	3	8
14	408	4	1
15	483	5	16
16	421	4	2
17	171	3	18
18	376	4	12
TOTAL	3281	36	TOTAL

LA FORTERESSE

TEL : (1)60969510
LOCATION : 27 km Fontainebleau N 6/ D 219
ADDRESS : Domaine de La Forteresse – 77156 Thoury-Ferrottes
HOTEL :
Au Moulin – Flagy
Tel : (1)60966789
L'Aigle Noir – Fontainebleau
Tel : (1)64223265
Napoleon – Fontainebleau
Tel : (1)64222039

The course is laid out admist fields in the Orvanne valley on rolling and sometimes wooded countryside near Fontainebleau. It includes several well-placed lakes and ponds serving as hazards. The cozy clubhouse is built in a former farmhouse.

GF ·$

1988

18

—

P. Fromager, M. Adam

L 5662 P 72

S

R

Required : Handicap Certificate
Best days : Any day

HOLE	LENGTH MEDAL-TEE	PAR	STROKE INDEX
1	287	4	14
2	445	5	6
3	130	3	16
4	456	5	4
5	161	3	12
6	294	4	10
7	310	4	8
8	364	4	2
9	235	4	18
TOTAL	2682	36	TOTAL

HOLE	LENGTH MEDAL-TEE	PAR	STROKE INDEX
10	542	5	1
11	373	4	3
12	416	5	5
13	300	4	17
14	188	3	9
15	295	4	15
16	151	3	13
17	337	4	11
18	378	4	7
TOTAL	2980	36	TOTAL

LA FRÉDIÈRE

TEL : 85252740
LOCATION : 30 km Roanne to Marcigny, then La Palisse/Chambilly
ADDRESS : Ceron - 71110 Marcigny
HOTEL : HR
La Frédière
Tel : 85251967
Le Charollais - Paray-le-Monial
Tel : 85810335

Situated in south Burgundy on the boundary of three departments : the Sâone, the Loire and the Allier, the holes roll through verdant and gently rolling tree-lined countryside. The course is enhanced by a scenic river and many stretches of water. Part of the course is the historical Château de la Frédière which can accomodate 12 persons. *SSS 69,23*

GF $ — Wednesdays — R S

1989 — G. Charmat, P. Garon — 

18 — L 5605 P 72

Required : Handicap Certificate
Best days : Any day

HOLE	LENGTH MEDAL-TEE	PAR	STROKE INDEX
1	297	4	
2	158	3	
3	573	5	
4	190	3	
5	324	4	
6	326	4	
7	480	5	
8	271	4	
9	323	4	
TOTAL	2942	36	TOTAL

HOLE	LENGTH MEDAL-TEE	PAR	STROKE INDEX
10	536	5	
11	107	3	
12	297	4	
13	245	4	
14	109	3	
15	476	5	
16	342	4	
17	293	4	
18	258	4	
TOTAL	2663	36	TOTAL

LA GRANDE MOTTE

TEL : 67560500
LOCATION : 15 km Montpellier
ADDRESS : 34280 La Grande-Motte
HOTEL : HR
Golfhotel
Tel : 67297200
Altea-La Grande Motte
Tel : 67569081
Mediterranée-La Grande-Motte
Tel : 67565338

Created by master architect Robert Trent Jones, the 'La Grande Motte' golf course is without doubt a sporting venue. It is located at the foot of the 'Pyramids' of the popular seaside resort 'la Grande Motte' bordering the Mediterranean. There are two 18 hole golf courses : the main championship layout 'les Flamands Roses' and the shorter 'Goélands' course. Both bear all the hallmarks of Trent Jones as they are full of large and sometimes innocent looking 'Florida' style lakes. Other difficulties are the fast rolling greens together with a large number of awkward bunkers. The complex includes a short 6 hole course and an already reputable golf school. Other facilities include the comfortable clubhouse and a new 2 star golf hotel.

GF $

—

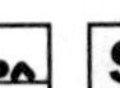 

1987

R. Trent Jones

42

L 6123 P 72, 3500 P 58

Required : Handicap Certificate
Best days : Any day

HOLE	LENGTH MEDAL-TEE	PAR	STROKE INDEX
1	370	4	11
2	365	4	15
3	462	5	3
4	328	4	7
5	125	3	13
6	427	4	5
7	507	5	1
8	160	3	17
9	385	4	9
TOTAL	3129	36	TOTAL

HOLE	LENGTH MEDAL-TEE	PAR	STROKE INDEX
10	455	5	10
11	378	4	2
12	304	4	4
13	166	3	18
14	364	4	8
15	379	4	16
16	128	3	14
17	456	5	6
18	364	4	12
TOTAL	2994	36	TOTAL

LA GRANDE ROMANIE

TEL : 26666469
LOCATION : 9 km Châlon-sur-Marne
N3/RD394 to Reims
ADDRESS : 51460 Courtisols
HOTEL :
Aux Armes de Champagne - L'Epine
Tel : 26669679
Angleterre - Châlon-sur-Marne
Tel : 26682151
Ibis - Châlon-sur-Marne
Tel : 26651665

This is a pleasant and varied course with a classical Scottish style layout. Set amidst trees on flat terrain, its 18 greens and fairways are defended by some 110 strategically placed bunkers. An old inn has been converted into a cosy clubhouse.

GF $ — Thursdays — S
1989 — A. Fribout
18 — L 5754 P 72 — R

Required : None
Best days : Any day

HOLE	LENGTH MEDAL-TEE	PAR	STROKE INDEX
1	346	4	5
2	350	4	11
3	427	5	3
4	130	3	18
5	452	5	2
6	325	4	13
7	293	4	15
8	320	4	10
9	160	3	8
TOTAL	2803	36	TOTAL

HOLE	LENGTH MEDAL-TEE	PAR	STROKE INDEX
10	330	4	12
11	314	4	9
12	312	4	7
13	180	3	17
14	350	4	4
15	470	5	14
16	363	4	6
17	165	3	16
18	467	5	1
TOTAL	2951	36	TOTAL

LA JONCHERE

TEL : 55622305
LOCATION : 30 km Montluçon, then D 990 RN145 to Gouzon/330 km Paris A71 exit Montluçon
ADDRESS : Montgrenier - 23230 Gouzon
HOTEL :
France - Aubusson
Tel : 55661022
Univers - Montluçon
Tel : 70053347
Host. du Château St-Jean - Montluçon
Tel : 70050465
RESTAURANT : Grenier à Sel
Tél : 70055379

This rather technical course extends over 68ha of alluring and unspoiled landscape. Its 18 holes climb over gentle hills, through open countryside and cross forestlands. The 5th, the difficult 6th and the short 7th holes are played over a lake. Facilities within the clubs' grounds include a riding school and several private cottages to rent which overlook the course. Nearby are several tennis courts. *SSS 69,5*

GF $ — Tuesdays in winter — R S
1988 — J.-L. Pega
18 — L 5541 P 72

Required : Handicap Certificate
Best days : Any day

HOLE	LENGTH MEDAL-TEE	PAR	STROKE INDEX
1	350	4	11
2	255	4	18
3	312	4	16
4	421	5	4
5	142	3	9
6	327	4	1
7	111	3	15
8	345	4	7
9	484	5	3
TOTAL	2747	36	TOTAL

HOLE	LENGTH MEDAL-TEE	PAR	STROKE INDEX
10	324	4	6
11	268	4	14
12	154	3	12
13	458	5	5
14	353	4	10
15	266	4	17
16	445	5	8
17	206	3	2
18	324	4	13
TOTAL	2794	36	TOTAL

LA LARGUE

TEL : 89257111
LOCATION : 30 km Basel/35 km Mulhouse A35
ADDRESS : Chemin du Largweg
68580 Mooslargue
HOTEL :
Altéa - Mulhouse
Tel : 89460123
Bourse - Mulhouse
Tel : 89561844
RESTAURANT : Auberge de la Tonnelle - Mulhouse
Tel : 89542577

This new and very attractive championship course, between Basel and Mulhouse, is prepared to play an important role on the international golf scene. Laid out in enchanting landscape amidst a variety of old trees and flowers, it features challenging water holes and demanding forest holes and has over 100 bunkers to protect its future reputation. It boasts a pleasant chalet style clubhouse with Alsatian cuisine. Another 18 holes and a hotel are scheduled. *SSS 72*

GF $$
1989
18

—
J. Garaialde/J. Pern
L 5706 P 72

Required : Handicap Certificate
Best days : Any day

HOLE	LENGTH MEDAL-TEE	PAR	STROKE INDEX
1	320	4	10
2	308	4	7
3	331	4	15
4	501	5	5
5	328	4	17
6	398	4	3
7	480	5	1
8	156	3	11
9	323	4	4
TOTAL	3145	37	TOTAL

HOLE	LENGTH MEDAL-TEE	PAR	STROKE INDEX
10	171	3	6
11	272	4	8
12	336	4	13
13	158	3	12
14	434	5	9
15	307	4	16
16	321	4	14
17	132	3	18
18	430	5	2
TOTAL	2561	35	TOTAL

LA NIVELLE

TEL : 59470778
LOCATION : 1 km Saint-Jean-de-Luz
ADDRESS : Place William-Sharp – Ciboure – 64500 Saint-Jean-de-Luz
HOTEL :
Château de Brindos – Saint-Jean-de-Luz
Tel : 59231768
La Fayette – Saint-Jean-de-Luz
Tel : 59261774
Les Goëlands – Saint-Jean-de-Luz
Tel : 59261005
RESTAURANT : Ostatua – Saint-Jean-de-Luz
Tel : 59264722

Backed by the Pyrenees with fine views over the Basque seaside resort of Saint-Jean-de-Luz, the golf course is laid out in rich verdant countryside. It is hilly with numerous dogleg holes and two water hazards. There is a stately Basque style clubhouse with one tennis court. *SSS 68*

GF $$

1907

18

Thurs. in low season

 M. Taylor

 5254 P 70

R 

Required : Handicap Certificate, Introduction letter
Best days : Any day

HOLE	LENGTH MEDAL-TEE	PAR	STROKE INDEX
1	384	5	11
2	165	3	7
3	299	4	15
4	448	5	1
5	157	3	15
6	370	4	3
7	283	4	9
8	430	5	17
9	139	3	13
TOTAL	2675	36	TOTAL

HOLE	LENGTH MEDAL-TEE	PAR	STROKE INDEX
10	337	4	6
11	329	4	16
12	308	4	10
13	332	4	12
14	356	4	2
15	160	3	8
16	235	4	18
17	202	3	4
18	320	4	14
TOTAL	2579	34	TOTAL

LANNEMEZAN

TEL : 62980101
LOCATION: 4 km Lannemezan RN 117/RD 929
ADDRESS : La Demi Lune – 65300 Lannemezan
HOTEL :
Pyrénées – Lannemezan
Tel : 62980153
Laca – Capvern-les-Bains
Tel : 62390206
Paris – Capvern-les-Bains
Tel : 62390390
RESTAURANT : Du Pont d'Espagne – Lannemezan
Tel : 62980152

Scenically situated in the foothills of the Pyrenees, providing panoramic views over the surroundings, the Lannemezan golf course lies amidst numerous pine trees on flat terrain. It borders on one side the Gimone channel. Several holes are testing due to tight fairways and several 'out of bounds'. *SSS 68,4*

GF $

1962

18

Tuesdays

 P. Hirigoyen

 5416 P 70

Required : Handicap Certificate
Best days : Any day

HOLE	LENGTH MEDAL-TEE	PAR	STROKE INDEX
1	438	5	7
2	385	4	1
3	152	3	13
4	361	4	3
5	313	4	9
6	138	3	17
7	435	5	11
8	296	4	15
9	435	5	5
TOTAL	2953	37	TOTAL

HOLE	LENGTH MEDAL-TEE	PAR	STROKE INDEX
10	129	3	14
11	128	3	16
12	297	4	12
13	374	4	4
14	134	3	18
15	375	4	16
16	374	4	2
17	311	4	10
18	341	4	8
TOTAL	2463	33	TOTAL

LA PORCELAINE

★

TEL : 55311069
LOCATION : 10 km Limoges RD 941
ADDRESS : Célicroux – 87350 Panazol
HOTEL :
Royal Limousin – Limoges
Tel : 55346530
Caravelle – Limoges
Tel : 55777529
Richelieu – Limoges
Tel : 55342282
RESTAURANT : La Chapelle Saint-Martin - Saint-Martin-du-Fault
Tel : 55758017

Located near the city of Limoges, famous for its china industry, after which the golf course is named. It has a technically interesting layout with a wide variety of holes, set on lovely rolling landscape, many of which overlook the 'Vienne' valley. Nine ponds serve as water traps. *SSS 72*

GF $ | Tuesdays | S
1988 | J. Garaialde | 
18 | L 5620 P 72 | R

Required : Handicap Certificate
Best days : Any day

HOLE	LENGTH MEDAL-TEE	PAR	STROKE INDEX
1	473	5	10
2	336	4	4
3	346	4	2
4	493	5	9
5	162	3	6
6	277	4	18
7	136	3	17
8	431	5	5
9	275	4	4
TOTAL	2929	37	TOTAL

HOLE	LENGTH MEDAL-TEE	PAR	STROKE INDEX
10	408	4	1
11	279	4	13
12	150	3	14
13	440	5	7
14	270	4	16
15	176	3	3
16	343	4	12
17	159	3	8
18	466	5	15
TOTAL	2691	35	TOTAL

LA PREE

TEL : 46012442
LOCATION : 8 km N. La Rochelle D164 to Nieul, then to Marsilly
ADDRESS : La Richardière - 17137 Marsilly
HOTEL :
Le Rochelois - La Rochelle
Tel : 46433434
Les Brises - La Rochelle
Tel : 46438937
Yachtman - La Rochelle
Tel : 46412068
RESTAURANT : Richard Coutanceau - La Rochelle
Tel : 46414819

This Scottish style links is set alongside the Atlantic Ocean, close to La Rochelle, famous for its yachting port. It has a technical and varied layout, featuring three tricky double doglegs, treacherous sand traps, tight roughs bordering the holes as well as several strategic canals and lakes. An additional hazard is the constant blowing and changing wind. The clubhouse, built high up, overlooks the coast line and the sea.

GF $

1989

18

—

O. Brizon

L 5781 P 72

R S

Required : None
Best days : Any day

HOLE	LENGTH MEDAL-TEE	PAR	STROKE INDEX
1	350	4	9
2	483	5	1
3	165	3	13
4	316	4	11
5	152	3	15
6	402	4	7
7	333	4	3
8	396	4	5
9	423	5	17
TOTAL	3020	36	TOTAL

HOLE	LENGTH MEDAL-TEE	PAR	STROKE INDEX
10	515	5	4
11	145	3	16
12	315	4	8
13	370	4	2
14	115	3	18
15	423	5	6
16	270	4	12
17	293	4	10
18	315	4	14
TOTAL	2761	36	TOTAL

LA VALDAINE

TEL : 75018666
LOCATION : 4 km Montélimar
ADDRESS : Château du Monard - 26540 Montboucher-sur-Jabron
HOTEL :
Château du Perchoir - Malataverne
Tel : 75019336
Domaine du Colombier - Malataverne
Tel : 75516586
Parc Chabeau - Montélimar
Tel : 75016566

This fine course blends harmoniously into the peaceful natural landscape. A number of holes are laid out among gently rolling valleys while others cut through large wooded areas. The course is part of a real estate project which includes a splendid clubhouse, a converted 15th century chateau. *SSS 71*

GF $

1990

18

—

T. Mc Auley

L 5341 P 71

R S

Required : Handicap Certificate
Best days : Any day

HOLE	LENGTH MEDAL-TEE	PAR	STROKE INDEX
1	437	5	13
2	281	4	15
3	146	3	6
4	457	5	7
5	243	4	18
6	154	3	5
7	280	4	16
8	184	3	10
9	330	4	14
TOTAL	2512	35	TOTAL

HOLE	LENGTH MEDAL-TEE	PAR	STROKE INDEX
10	291	4	11
11	436	5	8
12	119	3	17
13	471	5	19
14	175	3	3
15	390	4	2
16	155	3	4
17	440	5	12
18	352	4	1
TOTAL	2829	36	TOTAL

LE COUDRAY

TEL : (1)64938176
LOCATION : 37 km Paris A6 exit Corbeil Sud then RN 7
ADDRESS : 91830 Le Coudray-Montceaux
HOTEL :
Mercure – Le Coudray Montceaux
Tel : (1)64990000
Campanile – Corbeil
Tel : (1)60894145
Central – Corbeil
Tel : (1)60880606
RESTAURANT : Auberge Vaugrain – Melun
Tel : (1)64520823

The golf course lies on the left border of the river Seine, following the gentle undulations of the terrain. Many holes are tree-lined and command fine views over the valley. There is a modern clubhouse equipped with two tennis courts. *SSS 70*

GF $$

1957

27

Tuesdays

C.K. Cotton

L 5384 P 70, 1500 P 30

S

R

Required : Handicap Certificate
Best days : Thursdays

HOLE	LENGTH MEDAL-TEE	PAR	STROKE INDEX
1	343	4	7
2	330	4	5
3	133	3	9
4	455	5	13
5	382	4	3
6	147	3	11
7	290	4	17
8	296	4	15
9	485	5	1
TOTAL	2861	36	TOTAL

HOLE	LENGTH MEDAL-TEE	PAR	STROKE INDEX
10	163	3	12
11	280	4	18
12	295	4	16
13	465	5	14
14	160	3	6
15	300	4	8
16	370	4	2
17	160	3	10
18	330	4	4
TOTAL	2523	34	TOTAL

LE GOLF NATIONAL

TEL : (1)30433600
LOCATION : exit St. Quentin of A12, then A86 to Guyancourt
ADDRESS : 2, avenue du Golf - 78280 Guyancourt
HOTEL : HR
Novotel - St. Quentin-en-Yvelines
Tel : (1)30576565
Mercure - Parly II
Tel : (1)39551141
Trianon Palace - Versailles
Tel : (1)39503412

Inspired by the "Tournaments Players Club" of the USA, the French Golf Federation created the "Golf National" a golfing complex of 45 holes which extends over 140 hectares. The first 18 holes, the fascinating "Albatros" course inaugurated in October 1990, combines the pure Scottish links and the American style course. Hillocks, numerous strategically sited bunkers and vast stretches of water make this course a true test for established golfers. The Albatros course will become the permanent venue of the French Open and other international tournaments. The less testing "Aigle" course will open for play in July 91 and the 9 hole "Oiselet" course is planned for March 91. The Novotel hotel with 132 rooms is nearby. *SSS 73,4*

GF $ — S

1990 H. Chesneau, B. von Hagge 

18 L 6155 P 72

Required : Handicap Certificate
Best days : Any day

HOLE	LENGTH MEDAL-TEE	PAR	STROKE INDEX
1	350	4	8
2	170	3	16
3	460	5	12
4	385	4	4
5	350	4	6
6	330	4	14
7	390	4	2
8	180	3	18
9	495	5	10
TOTAL	3110	36	TOTAL

HOLE	LENGTH MEDAL-TEE	PAR	STROKE INDEX
10	325	4	5
11	150	3	15
12	380	4	9
13	360	4	7
14	460	5	11
15	365	4	3
16	150	3	17
17	415	4	1
18	440	5	13
TOTAL	3045	36	TOTAL

LE HAVRE

TEL : 35463650
LOCATION : 6 km Le Havre to Etretat
ADDRESS : Hameau St-Sulpice – 76930 Octeville-sur-Mer
HOTEL :
Bordeaux – Le Havre
Tel : 35226944
Le Marly – Le Havre
Tel : 35417248
Mercure – Le Havre
Tel : 35212345
RESTAURANT : Monaco – Le Havre
Tel : 35422101

Located in Normandy, the course is laid out on flat countryside. It features narrow fairways, several dog-leg holes, many well-bunkered greens, and 'out of bounds' on fourteen holes. There is an attractive local style clubhouse. *SSS 70*

GF $

1932

18

Tuesdays

—

L 5830 P 72

R S

Required : Handicap Certificate
Best days : Mondays, Thursdays, Fridays

HOLE	LENGTH MEDAL-TEE	PAR	STROKE INDEX
1	455	5	13
2	370	4	3
3	365	4	7
4	160	3	5
5	360	4	9
6	390	4	1
7	450	5	17
8	135	3	11
9	445	5	15
TOTAL	3130	37	TOTAL

HOLE	LENGTH MEDAL-TEE	PAR	STROKE INDEX
10	340	4	12
11	350	4	4
12	300	4	14
13	260	4	16
14	160	3	10
15	340	4	6
16	375	4	2
17	260	4	18
18	315	4	8
TOTAL	2700	35	TOTAL

LE MANS

TEL : 43420036
LOCATION : 12 km S. Le Mans RN 158
ADDRESS : Route de Tours – 72230 Mulsanne
HOTEL :
Novotel – Le Mans
Tel : 43852680
Concorde – Le Mans
Tel : 43241230
Novotel – Le Mans
Tel : 43852680
RESTAURANT : La Grillade – Le Mans
Tel : 43242187

The golf course lies on the famous racing circuit of Le Mans. Its fairways are narrow and flanked by strategically placed trees and heather, demanding great accuracy from tee to green. *SSS 71*

GF $
1964
18
—
A. Pennink
L 5821 P 71
S
R

Required : Handicap Certificate
Best days : Any day

HOLE	LENGTH MEDAL-TEE	PAR	STROKE INDEX
1	299	4	16
2	362	4	4
3	378	4	3
4	131	3	18
5	436	5	7
6	409	4	1
7	173	3	10
8	330	4	13
9	319	4	11
TOTAL	2837	35	TOTAL

HOLE	LENGTH MEDAL-TEE	PAR	STROKE INDEX
10	448	5	9
11	350	4	6
12	333	4	8
13	153	3	17
14	500	5	5
15	373	4	2
16	184	3	12
17	295	4	14
18	348	4	15
TOTAL	2984	36	TOTAL

LE PRIEURÉ

★

TEL : (1)34767012
LOCATION : 10 km Meulan/Mantes, 40 km Paris
ADDRESS : Sailly – 78440 Gargenville
HOTEL :
Les Glycines – Mantes
Tel : (1)34770413
Grande Pinte – Meulan
Tel : (1)34741510
Mercure – Meulan
Tel : (1)34746363
RESTAURANT : Auberge de Senneville – Mantes
Tel : (1)34766302

Two pleasant golf courses very popular with Parisian golfers. Laid out on relatively flat countryside, most of the holes are long and well-designed with strategically placed bunkers. Many of the fairways are flanked by copse. A feature of La Prieuré is the clubhouse, an ancient priory dating back to the 12th century. The club has numerous sports facilities such as tennis courts and a swimming pool. *SSS 72*

GF $$

1965

36

Tues. in winter

F. Hawtree

L 6216 P 72, 6317 P 72

R S

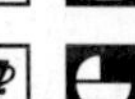

Required : Handicap Certificate
Best days : Weekdays; Weekends by arrangement

Est

HOLE	LENGTH MEDAL-TEE	PAR	STROKE INDEX
1	320	4	16
2	368	4	2
3	193	3	12
4	444	5	10
5	357	4	6
6	198	3	18
7	321	4	14
8	395	4	8
9	360	4	4
TOTAL	2956	35	TOTAL

HOLE	LENGTH MEDAL-TEE	PAR	STROKE INDEX
10	522	5	1
11	365	4	11
12	206	3	9
13	503	5	5
14	300	4	15
15	332	4	3
16	352	4	13
17	528	5	7
18	152	3	17
TOTAL	3260	37	TOTAL

Ouest

HOLE	LENGTH MEDAL-TEE	PAR	STROKE INDEX
1	175	3	17
2	403	4	3
3	381	4	11
4	391	4	5
5	495	5	1
6	215	3	9
7	393	4	7
8	489	5	13
9	191	3	15
TOTAL	3133	35	TOTAL

HOLE	LENGTH MEDAL-TEE	PAR	STROKE INDEX
10	463	5	8
11	163	3	16
12	354	4	2
13	173	3	18
14	292	4	14
15	461	5	10
16	410	4	4
17	401	5	6
18	467	5	12
TOTAL	3184	37	TOTAL

LERY POSES

TEL : 32594742
LOCATION : 25 km S. Rouen A13 exit Louviers
ADDRESS : Base de Loisirs - 27740 Poses
HOTEL :
Altéa - Louviers
Tel : 32400176
Les Saisons - Vironvay
Tel : 32400256
RESTAURANT : Host. St-Pierre - St-Pierre-du-Vauvray
Tel : 32599329

This is one of the four public golf courses located in Normandy. Laid out on the shores of a 270ha lake, it runs through rolling countryside with a pond affecting play on four holes (4,5,2,8). Another 9 holes is planned to open mid 1990. Sporting facilities include sailing, windsurfing, and swimming.

GF $
1988
18

—
H.-J. Baker
L 5934 P 72

S
RP

Required : Handicap Certificate
Best days : Any day

HOLE	LENGTH MEDAL-TEE	PAR	STROKE INDEX
1	407	5	
2	355	4	
3	137	3	
4	392	4	
5	333	4	
6	320	4	
7	144	3	
8	385	4	
9	456	5	
TOTAL	2929	36	TOTAL

HOLE	LENGTH MEDAL-TEE	PAR	STROKE INDEX
10	364	4	
11	365	4	
12	286	4	
13	159	3	
14	471	5	
15	165	3	
16	365	4	
17	484	5	
18	346	4	
TOTAL	3005	36	TOTAL

LE SART

★

TEL : 20720251
LOCATION : 7 km Lille A 10 exit Le Sart
ADDRESS : 5, rue Jean-Jaurès – 59650 Villeneuve-d'Ascq
HOTEL :
Campanile – Villeneuve-d'Ascq
Tel : 20918310
Bellevue – Lille
Tel : 20574564
Holiday Inn – Marcq-en-Barœul
Tel : 20721730
RESTAURANT : Le Flambard – Lille
Tel : 20510006

The course is divided in two by a road. Ten holes are built around the clubhouse amongst majestic and old trees. The others are laid out on gently rolling terrain. The course is short but technically difficult as most of the fairways are well wooded and narrow with well defended greens. The clubhouse (very British) is a stately 17th century château equipped with several tennis courts. *SSS 69*

GF $

1910

18

Mondays

A. Mc Beth, P. Boomer

L 5301 P 71

R S

Required : Handicap Certificate
Best days : Weekdays

HOLE	LENGTH MEDAL-TEE	PAR	STROKE INDEX
1	305	4	7
2	162	3	15
3	390	5	3
4	355	4	11
5	361	4	1
6	306	4	9
7	134	3	17
8	255	4	13
9	435	5	5
TOTAL	2703	36	TOTAL

HOLE	LENGTH MEDAL-TEE	PAR	STROKE INDEX
10	303	4	8
11	303	4	4
12	130	3	16
13	300	4	14
14	345	4	2
15	128	3	18
16	287	4	10
17	367	4	6
18	435	5	2
TOTAL	2598	35	TOTAL

LE TOUQUET

TEL : 21053262
LOCATION : 2 km Le Touquet
ADDRESS : Av. du Golf – 62520 Le Touquet Paris Plage
HOTEL : HR
Le Manoir
Tel : 21052022
Côte d'Opale – Le Touquet
Tel : 21050811
Novotel Thalamer – Le Touquet
Tel : 21052400
RESTAURANT : Flavio Club de la Fôret – Le Touquet
Tel : 21051022

Le Touquet features two championship golf courses:the 'Forest Course' and the 'Sea Course'. The Forest Course, the older one, lies inland within a lush undulating parkland landscape. The Sea Course, inaugurated in 1958, is considered one of Europe's best golf courses. It is a spectacular and testing links course, bordering the Channel, with its holes running through sandy dunes and hillocks. The course has a unique design with deep bunkers and fast greens. The French Open and other major tournaments have been played here regurarly. The charming Manoir Hotel with forty-five bedrooms, stands in the middle of the Forest Course and has facilities such as tennis courts and a swimming pool. *SSS 71/72*

GF $$
1930
45

—
W. Fernie, J. Taylor
L 6140 P72, 5910 P 71, 1350 P 28

 S

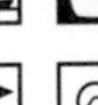

Required : Handicap Certificate
Best days : Weekdays

Sea Course

HOLE	LENGTH MEDAL-TEE	PAR	STROKE INDEX
1	470	5	5
2	299	4	13
3	464	5	1
4	459	5	7
5	323	4	11
6	151	3	15
7	348	4	9
8	410	4	3
9	120	3	18
TOTAL	3044	37	TOTAL

HOLE	LENGTH MEDAL-TEE	PAR	STROKE INDEX
10	415	4	2
11	384	4	10
12	327	4	14
13	410	4	6
14	457	5	4
15	208	3	16
16	360	4	12
17	172	3	17
18	363	4	8
TOTAL	3096	35	TOTAL

Forest Course

HOLE	LENGTH MEDAL-TEE	PAR	STROKE INDEX
1	434	5	
2	314	4	
3	175	3	
4	313	4	
5	405	4	
6	443	5	
7	366	4	
8	161	3	
9	385	4	
TOTAL	2996	36	TOTAL

HOLE	LENGTH MEDAL-TEE	PAR	STROKE INDEX
10	343	4	
11	372	4	
12	312	4	
13	170	3	
14	317	4	
15	155	3	
16	470	5	
17	388	4	
18	387	4	
TOTAL	2914	35	TOTAL

LE VAUDREUIL

TEL : 32590260
LOCATION : 6 km Louviers A 13, 25 km Rouen
ADDRESS : Le Vaudreuil – 27100 Le Vaudreuil
HOTEL : HR
du Golf
Tel : 32590294
Host. St-Pierre – St-Pierre-du-Vauvray
Tel : 32599329
Les Saisons – Vironvay
Tel : 32400256

A fine sporting golf course located in Normandy featuring various long dog-leg holes, a picturesque pond on the 10th hole and a stream behind the green of the 16th hole. The attractive Golf Hotel, a restored mansion dating back to the 18th century, has 23 bedrooms. *SSS 73*

GF $

1963

18

Tuesdays

F. Hawtree

L 5923 P 73

S

R

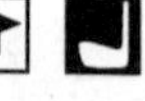

Required : Handicap Certificate
Best days : Weekdays

HOLE	LENGTH MEDAL-TEE	PAR	STROKE INDEX
1	383	4	2
2	403	4	6
3	125	3	14
4	366	4	10
5	120	3	18
6	342	4	8
7	321	4	16
8	456	5	4
9	337	4	12
TOTAL	2853	35	TOTAL

HOLE	LENGTH MEDAL-TEE	PAR	STROKE INDEX
10	147	3	17
11	330	4	7
12	483	5	1
13	358	4	3
14	321	4	11
15	438	5	9
16	150	3	15
17	412	5	13
18	431	5	5
TOTAL	3070	38	TOTAL

LES BORDES

TEL : 54877213
LOCATION : 150 km Paris, 25 km Orléans
RD 925
ADDRESS : 41220 Saint-Laurent Nouan
HOTEL : HP
Dormy House
Tel : 54877213
L'Abbaye – Beaugency
Tel : 38446735
La Tonnellerie – Tavers
Tel : 38446815
RESTAURANT : L'Ecu de Bretagne – Beaugency
Tel : 38446760

Inaugurated in 1987, 'Les Bordes' has already been acknowledged as an outstanding and very challenging golf course. Conceived by a well-known french industrialist, Baron Bich, and a Japanese industrialist, Mr. Yoshiaki Gakuraï, together with the American architect Robert Von Hagge, the course is situated south of the river Loire. It is built on a hunting property along the borders of the Sologne river on flat countryside. Robert Von Hagge designed numerous large bunkers and water hazards on twelve holes. The tastefully decorated clubhouse on the 18th hole, has five bungalows with 4 bedrooms each.

GF $$ — S

1987 R. Von Hagge 

18 L 5977 P 72 RP

Required : None
Best days : Any day

HOLE	LENGTH MEDAL-TEE	PAR	STROKE INDEX
1	341	4	8
2	453	5	4
3	326	4	10
4	140	3	18
5	377	4	6
6	332	4	14
7	454	5	2
8	124	3	16
9	339	4	12
TOTAL	2886	36	TOTAL

HOLE	LENGTH MEDAL-TEE	PAR	STROKE INDEX
10	455	5	3
11	346	4	7
12	351	4	13
13	151	3	17
14	490	5	1
15	376	4	9
16	182	3	15
17	367	4	11
18	373	4	5
TOTAL	3091	36	TOTAL

LES DRYADES

TEL : 54302800
LOCATION : 120 km Paris A 10, 40 km Châteauroux RD 943/D 940
ADDRESS : 36160 Pouligny-Notre-Dame
HOTEL : HR
Résidence du Golf
Tel : 54302800
Château Vallée Bleue-St-Chartier
Tel : 54310191
Les Tanneries-La Châtre
Tel : 54482100

The 'Dryades' golf course is part of a new and lavish sports, health and fitness complex which includes a first-class hotel (with 85 rooms), poney clubs, tennis courts, and swimming pools. Situated in the centre of France (close to Nohant, home of the famous french novelist George Sand) at 120km from Paris, not far from the 'Loire Châteaux' and the 'Bas-Berry Châteaux', this fine course lies on flat, mostly open countryside featuring old trees, many sand bunkers (51), huge greens (average size 500m) and sixteen large 'Florida-style' lakes dominating the holes.

GF $

1988

18

—

M. Gayon

L 5804 P 72

S

R

Required : Handicap Certificate
Best days : Any day

HOLE	LENGTH MEDAL-TEE	PAR	STROKE INDEX
1	280	4	17
2	385	4	5
3	455	5	1
4	150	3	13
5	303	4	15
6	441	5	7
7	334	4	11
8	180	3	3
9	307	4	9
TOTAL	2835	36	TOTAL

HOLE	LENGTH MEDAL-TEE	PAR	STROKE INDEX
10	366	4	6
11	496	5	4
12	145	3	16
13	350	4	12
14	380	4	2
15	286	4	18
16	162	3	14
17	322	4	10
18	462	5	8
TOTAL	2969	36	TOTAL

LES FONTENELLES

TEL : 51541394
LOCATION : 6 km St. Gilles-Croix-de-Vie D.6 to Coex
ADDRESS : L'Aiguillon-sur-Vie - 85220 Coex
HOTEL :
Embruns - St. Gilles-Croix-de-Vie
Tel : 51551140
Marina - St. Gilles-Croix-de-Vie
Tel : 51553097

This course is situated only a few minutes from St. Gilles Croix-de-Vie, a popular port reputed for its shellfish, and near the Atlantic Ocean. Winding through typical Vendée Country of hillocks, small woods of oak and maritime pine and overlooking stretches of water, this attractive course offers an individual setting for each of the holes. The large greens are all cunningly bunkered.

GF $ — — S

1990 — Y. Bureau

18 — L 5824 P 72 — R

Required : Handicap Certificate
Best days : Any day

HOLE	LENGTH MEDAL-TEE	PAR	STROKE INDEX
1	350	4	
2	263	4	
3	357	4	
4	443	5	
5	145	3	
6	403	4	
7	336	4	
8	476	5	
9	155	3	
TOTAL	2928	36	TOTAL

HOLE	LENGTH MEDAL-TEE	PAR	STROKE INDEX
10	327	4	
11	120	3	
12	370	4	
13	520	5	
14	347	4	
15	128	3	
16	328	4	
17	326	4	
18	430	5	
TOTAL	2896	36	TOTAL

LES HAUTS-DE-NIMES

TEL : 66233333
LOCATION : 10 km W. Nîmes D999 to Sauve
ADDRESS : Route de Sauve - Vacquerolles 30900 Nîmes
HOTEL :
Cheval Blanc - Nîmes
Tel : 66672003
Louvre - Nîmes
Tel : 66672275
Imperator - Nîmes
Tel : 66219030

Standing amidst typical "garrigue" landscape close to the Roman city of Nîmes famous for its arenas, the course offers a fine test of golf. Undulating and lushly wooded in parts, it incorporates a number of strategic bunkers demanding accuracy. There is a welcoming clubhouse with an attractive terrace overlooking parts of the course. *SSS 72*

GF $

1990

18

—

B. Baker

L 5942 P 72

S

R

Required : Handicap Certificate
Best days : Any day

HOLE	LENGTH MEDAL-TEE	PAR	STROKE INDEX
1	372	4	6
2	447	5	2
3	302	4	13
4	153	3	10
5	357	4	8
6	176	3	4
7	339	4	17
8	460	5	7
9	353	4	12
TOTAL	2959	36	TOTAL

HOLE	LENGTH MEDAL-TEE	PAR	STROKE INDEX
10	508	5	1
11	327	4	16
12	315	4	14
13	164	3	9
14	463	5	11
15	323	4	15
16	152	3	18
17	358	4	3
18	373	4	5
TOTAL	2983	36	TOTAL

LES ROCHERS

TEL : 99965252
LOCATION : 35 km Rennes
ADDRESS : Château des Rochers - route d'Argentré-du-Plessis - 35500 Vitré
HOTEL :
Pen'Roc - St. Didier
Tel : 99003302
Chêne Vert - Vitré
Tel : 99750058

Close to the medieval city of Vitré in Brittany, the golf des Rochers is built around an impressive château, once the residence of the 17th century writer Madame de Sévigné. It is laid out in tranquil and spacious parklands alongside a river where majestic chestnuts and centennial beeches line the holes. *SSS 72*

GF $ — — S
1990 — J.C. Varro
18 — L 5986 P 71 — R

Required : Club Membership Card
Best days : Any day

HOLE	LENGTH MEDAL-TEE	PAR	STROKE INDEX
1	270	4	
2	367	4	
3	395	4	
4	310	4	
5	463	5	
6	350	4	
7	420	4	
8	470	5	
9	150	3	
TOTAL	3195	37	TOTAL

HOLE	LENGTH MEDAL-TEE	PAR	STROKE INDEX
10	390	4	
11	360	4	
12	180	3	
13	330	4	
14	130	3	
15	400	4	
16	430	5	
17	330	4	
18	170	3	
TOTAL	2720	34	TOTAL

LES TEMPLIERS

TEL : 44087372
LOCATION : 60 km Paris A 15, exit Cergy-Pontoise
ADDRESS : 60173 Ivry-le-Temple
HOTEL :
Novotel – Cergy
Tel : (1)30303947
Campanile – Pontoise
Tel : (1)30385544
Ibis – Cergy
Tel : (1)34221144
RESTAURANT : Moulin de la Renardière-Osny
Tel : (1)30302113

Designed by a French and a Canadian golf architect, Patrick Fromanger and Mark Adam, this new golf course, with a modern layout, is situated near the French capital on flat countryside. It is long, with its fairways and greens defended by strategic bunkers. A lake affects play on five holes : the 9th, 11th, 17th and 18th holes are to be played over it, and the 10th has an island green. A modern, comfortable clubhouse, overlooking the course includes a club junior for children from 3 to 12 years, two tennis courts and a swimming pool. *SSS 69,3*

GF $

1988

27

Tuesdays

P. Fromanger, M. Adam

L 5628 P 71, 2400 P 34

R S

Required : None
Best days : Any day

HOLE	LENGTH MEDAL-TEE	PAR	STROKE INDEX
1	377	4	3
2	385	4	1
3	176	3	7
4	357	4	11
5	442	5	15
6	378	4	5
7	169	3	9
8	429	5	17
9	287	4	13
TOTAL	3000	36	TOTAL

HOLE	LENGTH MEDAL-TEE	PAR	STROKE INDEX
10	131	3	10
11	336	4	4
12	358	4	6
13	178	3	8
14	293	4	18
15	490	5	2
16	271	4	14
17	263	4	16
18	308	4	12
TOTAL	2628	35	TOTAL

LIMOGES

TEL : 55302102/55302801
LOCATION : 3 km S. Limoges RN 20 to Toulouse
ADDRESS : Av. du Golf – 87000 Limoges
HOTEL : HF
Albatros
Tel : 55060000
Frantel – Limoges
Tel : 55346530
Royal Limousin – Limoges
Tel : 55346530
RESTAURANT : Deux Atres – Limoges
Tel : 55796454

This public golf course lies on a flat plain overlooking the city of Limoges. Most of the fairways are tight and lined with around 3000 young and fast growing trees. Many of the holes are well-defended by bunkers, demanding accurate play. Hotel Albatros is on the course and the Frantel hotel is nearby. Sporting facilities include several tennis courts, a swimming pool, archery and a fitness center. *SSS 72*

GF $
1976
18
—
J. Bourret, H. Chesneau
L 5889 P 72
S

Required : None
Best days : Any day

HOLE	LENGTH MEDAL-TEE	PAR	STROKE INDEX
1	355	4	11
2	360	4	9
3	350	4	5
4	137	3	16
5	360	4	12
6	441	5	4
7	142	3	17
8	472	5	7
9	380	4	2
TOTAL	2997	36	TOTAL

HOLE	LENGTH MEDAL-TEE	PAR	STROKE INDEX
10	310	4	13
11	475	5	3
12	110	3	18
13	365	4	8
14	375	4	1
15	445	5	14
16	350	4	6
17	142	3	10
18	320	4	15
TOTAL	2892	36	TOTAL

LOUDUN-SAINT HILAIRE

TEL : 49987806
LOCATION : A 10 from Paris exit Maure, then RD 581
ADDRESS : Centre de Loisirs Loudun-Roiffé – 86120 Les Trois-Moutiers
HOTEL :
Mercure – Loudun
Tel : 49981922
Roue d'Or – Loudun
Tel : 49980123
Château de Marcay – Loudun
Tel : 47930347
RESTAURANT : La Reine Blanche – Loudun
Tel : 49985142

This testing golf course, belonging to a vast sports complex (tennis archery), lies in the Loire Valley at the intersection of the Anjou, Tourraine and Poitou regions on flat countryside. Its main difficulties consist of 7 doglegs, 34 well-placed bunkers and 4 ponds. In 1986 the club received an 'oscar' for their dynamism in innovating their course. The clubhouse, a former reformatory, dates back to the 19th century. *SSS 73,6*

GF $

1985

18

Tuesdays

H. Chesneau

L 6097 P 72

S

Required : Handicap Certificate
Best days : Any day

HOLE	LENGTH MEDAL-TEE	PAR	STROKE INDEX
1	382	4	4
2	377	4	1
3	483	5	6
4	357	4	9
5	310	4	18
6	156	3	16
7	480	5	12
8	330	4	7
9	152	3	15
TOTAL	3027	36	TOTAL

HOLE	LENGTH MEDAL-TEE	PAR	STROKE INDEX
10	331	4	10
11	404	4	5
12	454	5	13
13	162	3	8
14	381	4	3
15	338	4	11
16	445	5	14
17	164	3	17
18	391	4	2
TOTAL	3070	36	TOTAL

LYON

★

TEL : 78311133
LOCATION : 35 km Lyon A 42 exit 6 at Dagneux
ADDRESS : 38230 Villette-d'Anthon
HOTEL :
Sofitel – Lyon Satolas
Tel : 72227161
Climat – Lyon Satolas
Tel : 78409644
Auberge de Jons – Pont de Jons
Tel : 78312985
RESTAURANT : Mère Brazier – Lyon
Tel : 78281549

Set on the borders of the Rhône on fairly flat wooded landscape, this is a fine and sporting championship course with long tree-lined holes, around 120 bunkers and several well contrived doglegs. There are three loops of nine holes (green, blue, red), so that one has three different 18 hole circuits to choose from.

GF $
1968
27

Tuesdays
M. Fenn, F. Hawtree
L 5725 P 72, 5996 P 72, 6115 P 72

Required : Handicap Certificate
Best days : Weekdays

HOLE	LENGTH MEDAL-TEE	PAR	STROKE INDEX	HOLE	LENGTH MEDAL-TEE	PAR	STROKE INDEX	HOLE	LENGTH MEDAL-TEE	PAR	STROKE INDEX
1	457	5	15	1	357	4	16	1	390	4	7
2	333	4	12	2	325	4	10	2	383	4	9
3	337	4	6	3	454	5	2	3	487	5	14
4	265	4	18	4	292	4	17	4	211	3	5
5	154	3	9	5	172	3	5	5	349	4	17
6	470	5	1	6	450	5	13	6	409	4	3
7	134	3	7	7	357	4	4	7	147	3	16
8	355	4	3	8	370	4	8	8	538	5	2
9	320	4	14	9	180	3	11	9	371	4	12
TOTAL	2825	36	TOTAL	TOTAL	2937	36	TOTAL	TOTAL	3285	36	TOTAL

LYON-VERGER

TEL : 78028420
LOCATION : 14 km S. Lyon A 7 exit Solaize, then RN 7
ADDRESS : 69360 Saint-Symphorien-d'Ozon
HOTEL :
La Bourbonnaise – Sérezin du Rhône
Tel : 78028058
Louvre – St-Symphorien-d'Ozon
Tel : 78027005
RESTAURANT : Chez René – Saint-Romain-en-Gal
Tel : 74531972

Close to Lyon, the golf course was founded in 1977 and extended to 18 holes in 1986. It is laid out in attractive gently rolling countryside with several of the holes winding through fruit groves. Hotel du Louvre is near the golf club. *SSS 70*

GF $

1977

18

Fridays

M. de Preneuf

L 5577 P 70

R

Required : Handicap Certificate
Best days : Weekdays

HOLE	LENGTH MEDAL-TEE	PAR	STROKE INDEX
1	399	4	1
2	229	4	16
3	495	5	5
4	155	3	11
5	377	4	3
6	505	5	7
7	178	3	13
8	332	4	9
9	122	3	17
TOTAL	2792	35	TOTAL

HOLE	LENGTH MEDAL-TEE	PAR	STROKE INDEX
10	253	4	18
11	298	4	15
12	507	5	2
13	179	3	14
14	337	4	4
15	199	3	10
16	180	3	8
17	342	4	6
18	490	5	12
TOTAL	2785	35	TOTAL

MARCILLY

TEL : 38761173
LOCATION : 15 km S. Orléans RD 108
ADDRESS : Domaine de la Plaine - 45240 Marcilly-en-Villette
HOTEL :
Novotel - Orléans
Tel : 38630428
Orléans - Orléans
Tel : 38533534
Rivage - Olivet
Tel : 38660293
RESTAURANT : La Poutrière - Orléans
Tel : 38660230

Marcilly is a young and friendly golf club laid out on a former hunting estate. It runs through flat 'Sologne' landscape and some of the holes are flanked by woodland. It features several strategically placed lakes. The club also has a short 9 hole course. The picturesque clubhouse is a renovated farmhouse. *SSS72*

GF $

1987

27

Tuesdays

O. Brizon

L 5433 P 36

R S

Required : Handicap Certificate during weekends
Best days : Any day

HOLE	LENGTH MEDAL-TEE	PAR	STROKE INDEX
1	410	5	8
2	110	3	18
3	286	4	6
4	295	4	4
5	142	3	14
6	250	4	12
7	300	4	10
8	287	4	2
9	385	5	16
TOTAL	2465	36	TOTAL

HOLE	LENGTH MEDAL-TEE	PAR	STROKE INDEX
10	260	4	17
11	307	4	5
12	384	5	11
13	300	4	1
14	124	3	15
15	301	4	3
16	290	4	17
17	140	3	9
18	394	5	13
TOTAL	2500	36	TOTAL

MASSANE

TEL : 67878787
LOCATION : 10 km Montpellier A9 exit Vendargues, then RN 113
ADDRESS : Domaine de Massane 34670 Baillargues
HOTEL : HR
de Massane
Tel : 67878787
Ibis - Montpellier
Tel : 67588230
Altéa - Montpellier
Tel : 67646566
RESTAURANT : Chandelier - Montpellier
Tel : 67926162

This new and exciting golf course, with each hole offering its own challenge, is sculptered out of a former vineyard in the Languedoc-Roussillon region. Ronald Fream designed this varied championship layout incorporating undulating fairways, seven strategic ponds, three river crossings, twelve thricky doglegs and many deep sandy bunkers guarding the greens. Apart from this fine course, there is a famous golf school, a short 9 hole course, a three star hotel with a swimming pool and several tennis courts. *SSS 72, 2*

GF $

1989

18

—

R. Fream

L 5979 P 72

S

R

Required : Handicap Certificate
Best days : Any day

HOLE	LENGTH MEDAL-TEE	PAR	STROKE INDEX
1	334	4	15
2	145	3	7
3	354	4	3
4	384	4	9
5	514	5	1
6	189	3	11
7	356	4	5
8	285	4	13
9	475	5	16
TOTAL	3036	36	TOTAL

HOLE	LENGTH MEDAL-TEE	PAR	STROKE INDEX
10	361	4	18
11	481	5	12
12	111	3	17
13	301	4	4
14	493	5	6
15	285	4	10
16	360	4	14
17	170	3	8
18	381	4	2
TOTAL	2943	36	TOTAL

MEAUX-BOUTIGNY

TEL : (1) 60256398
LOCATION : 54 km E. Paris A4, 7 km S. Meaux
ADDRESS : Le Bordet – Rue de Barrois – 77100 Boutigny
HOTEL :
La Catounière – Sancy-les-Meaux
Tel : (1)60257174
Climat de France – Meaux
Tel : (1)64331547
RESTAURANT :
Auberge du Cheval Blanc – Varreddes
Tel : (1)64331803

Designed in 1986 by the French golf architect Michel Gayon, the Meaux-Boutigny golf course is laid out in a parkland setting on rolling landscape with ponds serving as hazards.

GF $

1986

27

Tuesdays

M. Gayon

L 4045 P 71, 1640 P 36

S

R

Required : Handicap Certificate
Best days : Mondays, Thursdays

HOLE	LENGTH MEDAL-TEE	PAR	STROKE INDEX
1	362	4	18
2	181	3	12
3	358	4	3
4	368	4	10
5	493	5	7
6	354	4	14
7	455	5	5
8	111	3	16
9	408	4	1
TOTAL	3090	36	TOTAL

HOLE	LENGTH MEDAL-TEE	PAR	STROKE INDEX
10	188	3	8
11	311	4	17
12	419	4	2
13	365	4	9
14	170	3	11
15	315	4	15
16	434	5	4
17	177	3	13
18	512	5	6
TOTAL	2891	35	TOTAL

MÉRIBEL

TEL : 79003267
LOCATION : 44 km Albertville, 18 km Moutiers
ADDRESS :
73550 Méribel
HOTEL :
Altiport
Tel : 79005232
Le Châlet - Méribel
Tel : 79005571
L'Orée du Bois - Méribel
Tel : 79005030

At 1850 m above sea level, the course is just 4 km above the picturesque ski resort of Méribel and is wedged between the towering snow clad peaks of the Alps.
Extended to 18 holes, the course features spacious fairways running through sweeping green valleys which are landscaped by pine woods. Within the vicinity of the excellent Altiport Hotel there is a wide choice of appartment accomodation. *SSS 68*

GF $
1990
18
Oct. 15 to June 15
T. Sprecher
L 5154 P 72

Required : Handicap Certificate
Best days : Any day

HOLE	LENGTH MEDAL-TEE	PAR	STROKE INDEX
1	258	4	
2	310	3	
3	204	5	
4	251	4	
5	170	4	
6	381	4	
7	129	3	
8	398	5	
9	278	4	
TOTAL	2379	36	TOTAL

HOLE	LENGTH MEDAL-TEE	PAR	STROKE INDEX
10	304	4	
11	150	5	
12	556	4	
13	324	3	
14	252	4	
15	327	4	
16	137	4	
17	489	3	
18	407	5	
TOTAL	2946	36	TOTAL

METZ CHERISEY

TEL : 87527018
LOCATION : 3 km Verny, 15 km Metz
RD 913
ADDRESS : Château de Cherisey – 57420
Verny
HOTEL :
Novotel – Metz
Tel : 87373839
Altéa St-Thibault – Metz
Tel : 87361769
Ibis – Metz
Tel : 87310173
RESTAURANT : Belle Vue – Borny
Tel : 87371027

Founded in 1965, the course was extended to 18 holes in 1988. Laid out around the clubhouse, a stately château, the course rolls over hilly and fairly wooded parkland. The fairways and greens are well-bunkered. The club is equipped with a tennis court. *SSS 72*

GF $

1965

18

—

D. Harradine

L 5700 P 72

R S

Required : None
Best days : Any day

HOLE	LENGTH MEDAL-TEE	PAR	STROKE INDEX
1	355	4	7
2	140	3	17
3	330	4	13
4	290	4	11
5	465	5	15
6	350	4	1
7	435	5	9
8	170	3	3
9	335	4	5
TOTAL	2870	36	TOTAL

HOLE	LENGTH MEDAL-TEE	PAR	STROKE INDEX
10	330	4	4
11	430	5	18
12	345	4	14
13	140	3	8
14	335	4	6
15	320	4	10
16	155	3	12
17	430	5	16
18	345	4	2
TOTAL	2830	36	TOTAL

MONT-D'ARBOIS

TEL : 50212979/50213151
LOCATION : 2 km Megève
ADDRESS : Mont-d'Arbois – 74120 Megève
HOTEL : HR
Chalet du Mont-d'Arbois
Tel : 50212503
Coin du Feu – Mégève
Tel : 50210494
Mont Blanc – Mégève
Tel : 50212002
RESTAURANT : Le Mont-Joly – Mégève
Tel : 50212614

Situated 2km above the town of Mégève at 1300m above sea level, surrounded by the snow-capped mountain peaks of the 'Aiguilles Croches', this is a scenic alpine course with panoramic views. Its 18 holes wind through an attractive valley with mountain streams crossing several fairways. Ideal for holiday golf with the charming Mont d'Arbois Hotel 200m from the course, with facilities such as tennis courts, a riding school and a swimming pool. *SSS 72*

GF $$
1968
18

November to May
H. Cotton
L 5855 P 72

S
R

Required : Handicap Certificate
Best days : Any day

HOLE	LENGTH MEDAL-TEE	PAR	STROKE INDEX
1	260	4	18
2	180	3	11
3	285	4	17
4	440	5	15
5	180	3	9
6	365	4	2
7	355	4	4
8	470	5	13
9	175	3	6
TOTAL	2710	35	TOTAL

HOLE	LENGTH MEDAL-TEE	PAR	STROKE INDEX
10	350	4	14
11	330	4	7
12	370	4	3
13	400	5	12
14	145	3	16
15	380	4	1
16	340	4	5
17	480	5	10
18	350	4	8
TOTAL	3145	37	TOTAL

MONTE-CARLO

TEL : 93410911
LOCATION : 11 km Monte-Carlo RD 22/ RD 53
ADDRESS : La Turbie – 06320 Cap-d'Ail
HOTEL :
de Paris – Monte Carlo
Tel : 93508080
Beach – Monte Carlo
Tel : 93782140
Napoléon – La Turbie
Tel : 93410954
RESTAURANT : Bec Rouge – Monte-Carlo
Tel : 93307491

The golf course is scenically situated on the 'Mont Agel', perching 810m above the city of Monte Carlo. Although not of championship length, the course is an interesting test featuring narrow and hilly fairways. From all part of the course it commands spectacular views of the Mediterranean, the Principality of Monaco, the Côte d'Azur, the Alps, Italy and, if the weather permits, to the coastline of Corsica. *SSS 70*

GF $$ — 1910 — 18

— W. Park — L 5667 P 71

RP S

Required : Handicap Certificate
Best days : Weekdays ; Weekends by arrangement

HOLE	LENGTH MEDAL-TEE	PAR	STROKE INDEX
1	513	5	3
2	142	3	15
3	363	4	17
4	197	3	5
5	308	4	9
6	379	5	13
7	310	4	11
8	199	3	1
9	352	4	7
TOTAL	2763	35	TOTAL

HOLE	LENGTH MEDAL-TEE	PAR	STROKE INDEX
10	422	4	4
11	409	5	12
12	151	3	14
13	366	4	8
14	154	3	10
15	267	4	16
16	400	4	2
17	450	5	6
18	285	4	18
TOTAL	2904	36	TOTAL

MORFONTAINE

TEL : 44546827
LOCATION : 10 km Senlis
ADDRESS : Mortefontaine – 60520 La Chapelle-en-Serval
HOTEL :
Croix-d'Or – Ermenonville
Tel : 44540004
Ibis – Senlis
Tel : 44537050
Host. de la Porte Bellon – Senlis
Tel : 44530305
RESTAURANT : Rabelais – Ver-sur-Launette
Tel : 44540170

A real masterpiece designed by the English architect Tom Simpson and considered one of the greatest golf courses in Europe. Laid out on fairly undulating and densely wooded heathland, the golf has many outstanding holes, each one having its own distinctive character. One of the most renowned clubs in France, one can only play here when introduced by a member. *SSS 72*

GF $$

1928

27

Tuesdays

T. Simpson

L 6063 P 70, 2585 P 35

R S

Required : Special introduction by a member
Best days : —

HOLE	LENGTH MEDAL-TEE	PAR	STROKE INDEX	HOLE	LENGTH MEDAL-TEE	PAR	STROKE INDEX	HOLE	LENGTH MEDAL-TEE	PAR	STROKE INDEX
1	434	4	7	10	342	4	8	1	290	4	4
2	201	3	15	11	153	3	18	2	120	3	9
3	437	5	1	12	477	5	2	3	285	4	2
4	178	3	13	13	148	3	16	4	150	3	7
5	330	4	17	14	350	4	4	5	440	5	1
6	370	4	11	15	420	4	10	6	420	4	5
7	402	4	3	16	434	4	6	7	310	4	6
8	400	4	5	17	168	3	14	8	435	5	3
9	356	4	9	18	463	5	12	9	135	3	8
TOTAL	3108	35	TOTAL	TOTAL	2955	35	TOTAL	TOTAL	2585	35	TOTAL

NAMPONT SAINT-MARTIN

TEL : 22299290
LOCATION : 12 km Montreuil s/Mer RN 1
ADDRESS : Château de Nampont Saint-Martin – 80120 Nampont St-Martin
HOTEL :
La Peupleraie – Nampont
Tel : 22299811
L'Auberge du Grand Tilleul – Argoulle
Tel : 22299100
Le Lion d'Or – Rue
Tel : 22257418
RESTAURANT : Auberge La Grenouillère – Montreuil
Tel : 21060722

The golf course, cut in two different parts, is 10km from the sea, and laid out around a 14th century château on fertile and sometimes hilly landscape amongst a great variety of trees. It features several island greens and some strategic lakes. The two star hotel 'La Peupleraie' is at 1km from the course. *SSS 71*

GF $

1979

18

—

T. Chatterton, R. Berthet

L 5345 P 69

R S

Required : None
Best days : Any day

HOLE	LENGTH MEDAL-TEE	PAR	STROKE INDEX
1	150	3	18
2	208	3	12
3	237	4	10
4	125	3	16
5	436	5	2
6	286	4	14
7	270	4	4
8	218	4	6
9	168	3	8
TOTAL	2098	33	TOTAL

HOLE	LENGTH MEDAL-TEE	PAR	STROKE INDEX
10	189	3	17
11	395	5	9
12	406	4	11
13	348	4	5
14	147	3	15
15	426	4	1
16	415	4	13
17	396	4	7
18	525	5	3
TOTAL	3247	36	TOTAL

NANCY-AINGERAY

TEL : 83245387
LOCATION : 10 km Nancy A 31 exit Frouard, then RD 90
ADDRESS : Aingeray – 54460 Liverdun
HOTEL :
Des Vannes – Liverdun
Tel : 83244601
Grand Hôtel de la Reine – Nancy
Tel : 83350301
Novotel – Nancy Ouest
Tel : 83966746
RESTAURANT : Le Capucin Gourmand – Nancy
Tel : 83352698

The golf course is laid out on an undulating plain in the 'La Haye' forest, not far from the Moselle river. Most of the rather short holes have tight fairways and small well-defended greens, demanding great precision. There is a well-appointed and newly built clubhouse. *SSS 69*

GF $

1964

18

Mondays

M. Fenn

L 5330 P 69

R S

Required : Handicap Certificate
Best days : Weekdays

HOLE	LENGTH MEDAL-TEE	PAR	STROKE INDEX
1	326	4	13
2	145	3	11
3	355	4	5
4	444	5	7
5	360	4	1
6	314	4	9
7	127	3	17
8	335	4	15
9	348	4	3
TOTAL	2754	35	TOTAL

HOLE	LENGTH MEDAL-TEE	PAR	STROKE INDEX
10	261	4	18
11	357	4	8
12	143	3	12
13	317	4	16
14	332	4	4
15	190	3	6
16	394	4	2
17	417	5	14
18	157	3	10
TOTAL	2548	34	TOTAL

NANTES

TEL : 40632582
LOCATION : 15 km Nantes RN 166/RD 81
ADDRESS : Rte Départ. 81 – 44360 Vigneux-de-Bretagne
HOTEL :
Domaine de la Berthelotière – Orvault
Tel : 40768402
Mercure – St-Étienne-de-Mont-Luc
Tel : 40571080
Mercure – Sautron
Tel : 40571080
RESTAURANT : La Cigale – Nantes
Tel : 40893484

The river 'Cens' divides the course into two separate parts, and serves as a hazard on seven holes. The course is of the wooded parkland type set on hilly terrain and features numerous testing dogleg holes. There is a modern clubhouse. *SSS 71,1*

GF $ — Tues. from Nov. to April 

1969 — F. Pennink

18 — L 5850 P 72

Required : None
Best days : Weekdays and Weekends in July and August

HOLE	LENGTH MEDAL-TEE	PAR	STROKE INDEX
1	303	4	12
2	364	4	4
3	259	4	18
4	127	3	16
5	354	4	8
6	411	4	2
7	161	3	14
8	362	4	10
9	439	5	6
TOTAL	2780	35	TOTAL

HOLE	LENGTH MEDAL-TEE	PAR	STROKE INDEX
10	288	3	11
11	504	4	1
12	141	4	17
13	415	5	3
14	291	4	15
15	462	5	7
16	174	3	9
17	359	4	5
18	436	5	13
TOTAL	3070	37	TOTAL

NÎMES CAMPAGNE

TEL : 66701737
LOCATION : 11 km Nîmes RD 42
ADDRESS : Route de Saint-Gilles – 30000 Nîmes
HOTEL :
Les Aubruns – Garons
Tel : 66701044
Cheval Blanc – Nîmes
Tel : 66672003
des Tuileries – Nîmes
Tel : 66213115
RESTAURANT : Alexandre – Garons
Tel : 66700899

Nîmes-Campagne is one of France's leading golf courses. It is a testing and splendid championship golf course surrounded by old cypress trees, with a varied layout set on undulating countryside. It includes seven well-contrived doglegs, and has water courses on six holes. It is especially difficult to play when the 'Mistral' dominates the course. There is a superb Georgian style clubhouse with four tennis courts, a riding school and a swimming pool. Hotel 'Les Aubruns' is at 2km from the club. *SSS 72*

GF $ — Tuesdays — R S

1968 — M. Morandi, D. Harradine — 

18 — L 5616 P 72 — 

Required : Handicap Certificate
Best days : Any day

HOLE	LENGTH MEDAL-TEE	PAR	STROKE INDEX
1	331	4	6
2	142	3	17
3	427	5	14
4	347	4	4
5	370	4	2
6	315	4	10
7	154	3	12
8	447	5	8
9	304	4	16
TOTAL	2837	36	TOTAL

HOLE	LENGTH MEDAL-TEE	PAR	STROKE INDEX
10	292	4	13
11	265	4	15
12	342	4	11
13	437	5	1
14	122	3	18
15	359	4	3
16	195	3	5
17	433	5	7
18	334	4	9
TOTAL	2779	36	TOTAL

NIVERNAIS

TEL : 86581830
LOCATION : 12 km Nevers N7 to Moulins
ADDRESS : Le Bardonnay
58470 Magny-Cours
HOTEL :
Diane - Nevers
Tel : 86572810
Loire - Nevers
Tel : 86615092
RESTAURANT : La Renaissance - Magny-Cours
Tel : 86581040

This public golf course close to the racing circuit of Magny-Cours, is situated in the Burgundy region on open and undulating landscape. It is characterized by numerous out of bounds, few trees and slow greens.

GF $

—

S

1969

Y. Bourret/M. Koening

18

L 5665 P 70

R

Required : Handicap Certificate
Best days : Any day

HOLE	LENGTH MEDAL-TEE	PAR	STROKE INDEX
1	350	4	3
2	145	3	15
3	275	4	13
4	170	3	9
5	180	3	5
6	490	5	7
7	505	5	11
8	265	4	17
9	470	5	2
TOTAL	2850	36	TOTAL

HOLE	LENGTH MEDAL-TEE	PAR	STROKE INDEX
10	300	4	14
11	275	4	18
12	355	4	16
13	375	4	4
14	415	4	1
15	165	3	10
16	280	4	8
17	170	3	6
18	480	5	12
TOTAL	2815	35	TOTAL

ORMESSON

TEL : (1)45762071
LOCATION : 8 km Créteil A4/N 4, 22 km Paris
ADDRESS : Belvedère du Parc – 94490 Ormesson-sur-Marne
HOTEL :
Novotel – Créteil
Tel : (1)42079102
Climat de France – La Queue-en-Brie
Tel : (1)45946161
Nogentel – Nogent-sur-Marne
Tel : (1)48727000
RESTAURANT : Ecu de France – Ormesson
Tel : (1)45760003

Situated close to Paris, the golf course is set on hilly terrain and landscaped with mature trees such as willows, beeches, pines and poplars. It features the river 'Morbras' meandering its way through four holes. The club boasts an elegant clubhouse. *SSS 72*

GF $

1969

18

Tuesdays

J. Harris, M. Baker

L 6180 P 72

R S

Required : Handicap Certificate 28
Best days : Weekdays

HOLE	LENGTH MEDAL-TEE	PAR	STROKE INDEX
1	425	5	9
2	405	4	3
3	330	4	13
4	410	4	1
5	155	3	15
6	360	4	7
7	325	4	17
8	490	5	5
9	190	3	11
TOTAL	3090	36	TOTAL

HOLE	LENGTH MEDAL-TEE	PAR	STROKE INDEX
10	405	4	2
11	195	3	12
12	440	5	10
13	395	4	6
14	170	3	16
15	390	4	4
16	460	5	8
17	250	4	18
18	385	4	14
TOTAL	3090	36	TOTAL

OZOIR-LA-FERRIERE

TEL : (1)60282079
LOCATION : 29 km Paris A4 exit Val Maubué then RD 51/RN 4, 2 km Ozoir-la-Ferrière
ADDRESS : Château-des-Agneaux – 77330 Ozoir-la-Ferrière
HOTEL :
Château de la Grande Romaine – Lésigny
Tel : (1)60022124
Le Manoir – Mauperthuis
Tel : (1)64092117
RESTAURANT : Relais d'Ozoir – Ozoir-la-Ferrière – Mauperthuis
Tel : (1)60282033

Laid out in luxuriant flat woodland, the picturesque holes are not very long, featuring several tight fairways, well-bunkered greens and a pond in front of the 16th green. Most of the fairways are separated from each other by avenues of tall trees. There is a stately mansion style clubhouse. *SSS 72*

GF $$ — Tuesdays  

1926 —  — 

27 — L 5235 P 72, 2235 P 33

Required : Handicap Certificate
Best days : Weekdays

HOLE	LENGTH MEDAL-TEE	PAR	STROKE INDEX	HOLE	LENGTH MEDAL-TEE	PAR	STROKE INDEX	HOLE	LENGTH MEDAL-TEE	PAR	STROKE INDEX
1	420	5	7	10	140	3	10	1	337	4	9
2	125	3	15	11	405	5	4	2	300	4	3
3	295	4	11	12	280	4	14	3	157	3	13
4	315	4	9	13	300	4	16	4	298	4	11
5	145	3	5	14	255	4	18	5	292	4	5
6	300	4	13	15	170	3	8	6	110	3	17
7	315	4	3	16	325	4	2	7	269	4	7
8	405	5	17	17	275	4	12	8	310	4	1
9	355	4	1	18	410	5	6	9	162	3	15
TOTAL	2675	36	TOTAL	TOTAL	2560	36	TOTAL	TOTAL	2235	33	TOTAL

PAU

★

TEL : 59320233
LOCATION : 2 km Pau N 117
ADDRESS : Chemin du Golf – 64140 Billère
HOTEL :
Roncevaux – Pau
Tel : 59270844
Continental – Pau
Tel : 59276931
Le Bilaa – Pau
Tel : 59810300
RESTAURANT : Chez Pierre – Pau
Tel : 59277686

One of the oldest clubs in Europe (the oldest in Continental Europe), having been founded in 1856, this is a first class golf course which recently has been transformed. The course, backed by the Pyrenees mountain chain, is laid out on flat countryside with narrow fairways having trees and strategically placed bunkers serving as hazards. The golf course borders the picturesque river 'Gave' which crosses several holes.

GF $
1856
18

—
B. Ducwing
L 5389 P 69

R S

Required : Handicap Certificate
Best days : Any day

HOLE	LENGTH MEDAL-TEE	PAR	STROKE INDEX
1	265	4	17
2	145	3	9
3	365	4	5
4	293	4	13
5	372	4	3
6	113	3	15
7	475	5	7
8	325	4	11
9	415	4	1
TOTAL	2768	35	TOTAL

HOLE	LENGTH MEDAL-TEE	PAR	STROKE INDEX
10	470	5	8
11	160	3	14
12	357	4	2
13	185	3	6
14	472	5	18
15	175	4	8
16	345	4	4
17	335	4	12
18	122	3	16
TOTAL	2621	34	TOTAL

PERCHE

TEL : 37291733
LOCATION : 130 km Paris A 11 exit Luigny, then RD 955
ADDRESS : Souancé-au-Perche – 28400 Nogent-le-Rotrou
HOTEL :
Climat – La Ferté-Bernard
Tel : 43938470
Lion d'Or – Nogent-le-Rotrou
Tel : 37520160
RESTAURANT : Moulin de Villeray – Nogent-le-Rotrou
Tel : 33733022

Situated between Paris and Le Mans, in pleasant countryside typical of the 'Eure et Loir' region, the golf course runs over plains and valleys, and is surrounded by groves of oaks and apple-trees. Four lakes serve as hazards. There is a fine clubhouse overlooking the course. It is named after the Count du Perche, the Lords of this region during the Renaissance.

GF $ — Tuesdays — R S
1988 — B. Giraud, L. Heckly
18 — L 6065 P 72

Required : Handicap Certificate
Best days : Any day

HOLE	LENGTH MEDAL-TEE	PAR	STROKE INDEX
1	500	5	
2	335	4	
3	305	4	
4	345	4	
5	200	3	
6	400	4	
7	475	5	
8	330	4	
9	140	3	
TOTAL	3030	36	TOTAL

HOLE	LENGTH MEDAL-TEE	PAR	STROKE INDEX
10	375	4	
11	510	5	
12	475	5	
13	170	3	
14	360	4	
15	310	4	
16	330	4	
17	185	3	
18	320	4	
TOTAL	3035	36	TOTAL

PETIT CHENE

TEL : 49632833
LOCATION : 18 km Parthenay RD 743 to Niort, 1 km Mazières (exit 21 from A 10)
ADDRESS : 79310 Mazières-en-Gâtine
HOTEL :
Le Logis Saint-Martin – Saint-Maixent l'Ecole
Tel : 49055868
Lika – St-Maixent l'Ecole
Tel : 49056364
St-Jacques – Parthenay
Tel : 49643333
RESTAURANT : Relais St-Antoine – Niort
Tel : 49240276

This public golf course is laid out in lush and undulating parkland in the grounds of the majestic 19th century castle du Petit Chêne which serves as the clubhouse. The holes run up and downhill with a number of strategically situated lakes and stands of hawthorn trees serving as hazards.

GF $

1987

18

Tuesdays

R. Berthet

L 5899 P 72

S

R

Required : Handicap Certificate
Best days : Any day

HOLE	LENGTH MEDAL-TEE	PAR	STROKE INDEX
1	330	4	14
2	307	4	18
3	370	4	8
4	180	3	4
5	375	4	6
6	450	5	10
7	140	3	12
8	430	5	16
9	390	4	2
TOTAL	2972	36	TOTAL

HOLE	LENGTH MEDAL-TEE	PAR	STROKE INDEX
10	365	4	1
11	355	4	7
12	385	4	3
13	162	3	5
14	460	5	9
15	350	4	13
16	150	3	15
17	270	4	17
18	430	5	11
TOTAL	2927	36	TOTAL

PIAN-MEDOC

★

TEL : 56720110
LOCATION : 20 km Bordeaux D 1
ADDRESS : Chemin de Courmateau-Louens
33290 Le Pian-Médoc
HOTEL :
Sofitel Aquitania – Bordeaux Le Lac
Tel : 56508380
Novotel – Bordeaux Le Lac
Tel : 56509970
RESTAURANT : Le Chapon Fin – Bordeaux
Tel : 56791010

Located near Bordeaux, in the Médoc vineyard area, both courses (with each hole named after one of the famous châteaux in the Médoc), designed by the American and Canadian architects Bill Coore and Rod Withman, are among the most original new French golf courses. They feature a testing and varied layout with fast undulating greens and well placed bunkers summarizing almost every challenge in the game of golf. Water hazards are omnipresent with streams meandering their way through the holes and two well placed lakes. As for the 37th hole, just walk out and visit some of the famous Bordeaux Châteaux.

GF $

Mondays

R S

1988

B. Coore, R. Withman

36

L 5745 P 71, 6291 P 70

Required : Handicap Certificate
Best days : Any day

HOLE	LENGTH MEDAL-TEE	PAR	STROKE INDEX
1	335	4	13
2	470	5	15
3	320	4	17
4	395	4	3
5	138	3	4
6	347	4	8
7	285	4	18
8	105	3	9
9	390	4	1
TOTAL	2785	35	TOTAL

HOLE	LENGTH MEDAL-TEE	PAR	STROKE INDEX
10	455	5	12
11	323	4	7
12	142	3	10
13	346	4	14
14	452	5	11
15	300	4	16
16	394	4	5
17	168	3	6
18	380	4	2
TOTAL	2960	36	TOTAL

PRUNEVELLE

★

TEL : 81981177
LOCATION : 7 km Montbéliard D 496
ADDRESS : Ferme des Petits Bans – Dampierre-sur-le-Doubs – 25420 Voujeaucourt
HOTEL :
Ibis – Montbéliard
Tel : 81902158
Bristol – Montbéliard
Tel : 81944317
Grand Hôtel du Lion – Belfort
Tel : 84211700
RESTAURANT : Tour Henriette – Montbéliard
Tel : 81910324

Set on hilly and sandy countryside, the golf course is located in a fine setting of trees serving as hazards. Most of the lush fairways are bordered by age-old trees.

GF $ — December to April — S

1930 — — —

18 — L 5446 P 72 — R

Required : Handicap Certificate
Best days : Weekdays

HOLE	LENGTH MEDAL-TEE	PAR	STROKE INDEX
1	310	4	7
2	180	3	11
3	324	4	3
4	430	5	9
5	282	4	13
6	400	5	5
7	285	4	15
8	116	3	17
9	330	4	1
TOTAL	2657	36	TOTAL

HOLE	LENGTH MEDAL-TEE	PAR	STROKE INDEX
10	327	4	10
11	420	5	4
12	144	3	16
13	270	4	18
14	318	4	6
15	185	3	12
16	333	4	2
17	450	5	8
18	342	4	14
TOTAL	2789	36	TOTAL

REBETZ

TEL : 44491554
LOCATION : 65 km Paris A 15/RN 14 to Magny-en-Vexin, then RD 43
ADDRESS : Route de Noailles – 60240 Chaumont-en-Vexin
HOTEL :
Chenal – Beauvais
Tel : 44450355
Mercure – Beauvais
Tel : 44020336
RESTAURANT : Le Grand Cerf – Chaumont
Tel : 44490057

The Rebetz golf club is part of new country club which will include in the near future 45 holes, a first-class hotel, a swimming pool and tennis courts. The first 18 holes were inaugurated in 1988. They are laid out in rolling and well-wooded countryside dominating the 'Vexin' plains. There is an interesting and technical layout featuring long holes with large greens (700m²) with 8 of them guarded by lakes. An attractive feature is the tastefully furnished clubhouse, an ancient manor house. *SSS 71*

GF $$ — R S

1988 J.-P. Foures 

27 L 6434 P 73, 3065 P 36

Required : Handicap Certificate
Best days : Any day

HOLE	LENGTH MEDAL-TEE	PAR	STROKE INDEX	HOLE	LENGTH MEDAL-TEE	PAR	STROKE INDEX	HOLE	LENGTH MEDAL-TEE	PAR	STROKE INDEX
1	460	5	7	10	345	4	2	19	335	4	
2	318	4	13	11	442	5	8	20	475	5	
3	379	4	1	12	430	5	18	21	160	3	
4	145	3	17	13	171	3	10	22	345	4	
5	355	4	3	14	322	4	12	23	485	5	
6	449	5	15	15	339	4	6	24	385	4	
7	321	4	5	16	150	3	16	25	310	4	
8	335	4	11	17	309	4	14	26	175	3	
9	134	3	9	18	481	5	4	27	395	4	
TOTAL	2896	36	TOTAL	TOTAL	2989	37	TOTAL	TOTAL	3065	36	TOTAL

REIMS

TEL : 26036014
LOCATION : 5 km Reims RN 31 to Soissons
ADDRESS : Château des Dames-de-France – 51390 Gueux
HOTEL :
Novotel – Tinqueux
Tel : 26081161
L'Assiette Champenoise – Tinqueux
Tel : 26041556
Ibis – Tinqueux
Tel : 26046070
RESTAURANT : Boyer – Reims
Tel : 26060860

This pleasant course is laid out partly on flat and lush landscape with several holes running through undulating terrain. Most of the them are tree-lined with rising greens. It features a testing 16th hole with a dogleg, a pond and a green which is well-defended by bunkers. The clubhouse, the historical 'Château des Dames' used to be the Ladies' residence of the French court when the King came to Reims to be coronated. *SSS 72*

GF $ | — | S
1928 | M. Fenn
18 | L 5097 P 72 | R

Required : Handicap Certificate
Best days : Any day; Weekends by arrangement

HOLE	LENGTH MEDAL-TEE	PAR	STROKE INDEX
1	332	4	3
2	122	3	13
3	366	5	17
4	228	4	9
5	130	3	5
6	448	5	15
7	322	4	1
8	289	4	7
9	251	4	11
TOTAL	2488	36	TOTAL

HOLE	LENGTH MEDAL-TEE	PAR	STROKE INDEX
10	287	4	10
11	301	4	2
12	133	3	12
13	288	4	16
14	410	5	14
15	309	4	4
16	395	5	18
17	150	3	16
18	336	4	18
TOTAL	2609	36	TOTAL

REVEILLON

TEL : (1)60021733
LOCATION : 30 km E. Paris A4 exit Pontault-Combault, then Lésigny
ADDRESS : Ferme des Hyverneaux
77150 Lésigny
HOTEL : HR
Le Réveillon
Tel : (1)60021733

About 25 minutes of Paris, this recent public golf course with 27 holes is set in open countryside featuring several sloping fairways. It is dotted with trees and a river meanders through several of the holes. An old farm building has been converted into the clubhouse. A hotel is scheduled to open soon. *SSS 70,0*

GF $ — S

1989 — M. Gayon

27 — L 5706 P 72, 2646 P 35 — R

Required : Handicap Certificate
Best days : Any day

HOLE	LENGTH MEDAL-TEE	PAR	STROKE INDEX
1	320	4	11
2	480	5	5
3	188	3	9
4	334	4	7
5	489	5	3
6	164	3	15
7	371	4	1
8	302	4	13
9	266	4	17
TOTAL	2914	36	TOTAL

HOLE	LENGTH MEDAL-TEE	PAR	STROKE INDEX
10	121	3	18
11	295	4	14
12	311	4	12
13	489	5	4
14	435	5	8
15	358	4	2
16	335	4	6
17	191	3	10
18	257	4	16
TOTAL	2792	36	TOTAL

RHIN

TEL : 89260786
LOCATION : 19 km E. Mulhouse RD 39
ADDRESS : Ile du Rhin – Chalampé – 68490 Ottmarsheim
HOTEL :
Château d'Isenbourg – Rouffach
Tel : 89496353
Altea – Mulhouse
Tel : 89460123
Mercure – Sausheim
Tel : 89618787
RESTAURANT : Park's – Mulhouse
Tel : 89661222

Situated near the French/German border in the Alsace, the golf course was extended to 18 holes in 1985. It lies on an island in the river Rhine on gently rolling wooded terrain with narrow fairways and strategic trees. The greens, defended by strategically placed bunkers, constitute the main difficulty. *SSS 71,3*

GF $

1972

18

Weekends

D. Harradine

L 5991 P 71

S

R

Required : None
Best days : Mondays and Tuesdays

HOLE	LENGTH MEDAL-TEE	PAR	STROKE INDEX
1	344	4	11
2	361	3	9
3	468	5	7
4	378	4	3
5	324	4	13
6	125	3	17
7	382	4	11
8	461	5	5
9	160	3	15
TOTAL	3003	35	TOTAL

HOLE	LENGTH MEDAL-TEE	PAR	STROKE INDEX
10	330	4	10
11	148	3	16
12	466	5	4
13	313	4	14
14	323	4	12
15	480	5	16
16	159	3	18
17	393	4	2
18	376	4	18
TOTAL	2988	36	TOTAL

ROCHEFORT

★

TEL : (1)30413181
LOCATION : 5 km Saint-Arnoult ; from Paris A 10 to Chartres exit Dourdan to Limours
ADDRESS : Rochefort-en-Yvelines – 78730 Saint-Arnoult-en-Yvelines
HOTEL :
Hostellerie Blanche de Castille – Dourdan
Tel : (1)64596892
L'Europe – Étampes
Tel : (1)64940296
RESTAURANT : La Remarde – Saint-Arnoult-en-Yvelines
Tel : (1)30412009

The golf club has been under Japanese management for several years. Its eighteen holes wind through a splendid forest of centuries-old tall beeches and pine trees on fairly hilly landscape. The clubhouse is situated in an impressive and historic castle, which dominates the course. *SSS 72*

GF $$

1966

18

Thursdays

F. Hawtree

L 5735 P 71

S

R

Required : Handicap Certificate
Best days : Weekdays

HOLE	LENGTH MEDAL-TEE	PAR	STROKE INDEX
1	360	4	9
2	485	5	11
3	130	3	17
4	340	4	3
5	460	5	15
6	320	4	13
7	330	4	5
8	195	3	7
9	380	4	1
TOTAL	3000	36	TOTAL

HOLE	LENGTH MEDAL-TEE	PAR	STROKE INDEX
10	165	3	8
11	455	5	18
12	150	3	14
13	365	4	2
14	440	5	10
15	305	4	16
16	365	4	16
17	150	3	12
18	340	4	6
TOTAL	2735	35	TOTAL

ROQUEBRUNE

TEL : 94829291
LOCATION : 25 min. Cannes A 8 exit Pugut-sur-Argens, then CD 7
ADDRESS : CD 7 - 83520 Roquebrune-sur-Argens
HOTEL :
Beau Séjour - St-Raphaël
Tel : 94950375
Catalogne - St-Aygulf
Tel : 94810444
Palmiers - Fréjus
Tel : 94511872

In the heart of the Côte d'Azur, between Cannes and Saintropez, perching high on the rock bearing the same name, this new course extends over wild and beautiful Mediterranean landscape. The holes are set amidst oleander, mimosa, and cork trees and various other sub tropical specimens. Each point of the course offers unique views of the Bay of Fréjus, l'Estérel and the Côte's hinterland. The course is full of natural hazards such as sloping holes, and tricky lakes. A hotel is planned in 1991. *SSS 72*

GF $

1989

18

—

U. Barth

L 5850 P 71

R S

Required : Handicap Certificate
Best days : Any day

HOLE	LENGTH MEDAL-TEE	PAR	STROKE INDEX
1	152	3	5
2	325	4	14
3	356	4	10
4	357	4	12
5	207	3	4
6	441	5	8
7	334	4	16
8	415	4	2
9	128	3	18
TOTAL	2715	34	TOTAL

HOLE	LENGTH MEDAL-TEE	PAR	STROKE INDEX
10	458	5	6
11	363	4	11
12	501	5	1
13	178	3	13
14	341	4	7
15	352	4	3
16	155	3	17
17	469	5	9
18	318	4	15
TOTAL	3135	37	TOTAL

ROUEN-
MONT-SAINT-AIGNAN

TEL : 35763865
LOCATION : 4 km N. Rouen
ADDRESS : rue Francis-Poulenc – 76130 Mont-Saint-Aignan
HOTEL :
Climat – Boisguillaume
Tel : 35616110
Dieppe – Rouen
Tel : 35719600
Ibis – Rouen
Tel : 35704818
RESTAURANT : Beffroy – Rouen
Tel : 35715527

Situated in Normandy, the golf course winds through verdant countryside with its holes following the gentle undulations of the terrain. Five of them are particularly demanding : the 8th hole having an elevated tee, and the 9th, 10th, 11th, 12th holes having narrow fairways and difficult rough. *SSS 70*

GF $

1911

18

Tuesdays

—

L 5547 P 70

R S

Required : Handicap Certificate
Best days : Weekdays

HOLE	LENGTH MEDAL-TEE	PAR	STROKE INDEX
1	339	4	8
2	253	4	16
3	385	4	2
4	101	3	18
5	257	4	14
6	309	4	10
7	161	3	12
8	380	4	6
9	327	4	4
TOTAL	2512	34	TOTAL

HOLE	LENGTH MEDAL-TEE	PAR	STROKE INDEX
10	153	3	11
11	450	5	9
12	311	4	5
13	415	4	1
14	491	5	15
15	179	3	13
16	513	5	3
17	175	3	17
18	348	4	7
TOTAL	3035	36	TOTAL

ROYAL ARTIGUELOUVE

TEL : 59830929
LOCATION : 8 km Pau RN 117 to Bayonne
ADDRESS : Domaine Saint-Michel – Artiguelouve – 64230 Lescar Cedex 02
HOTEL :
Novotel – Agora – Pau
Tel : 59842970
Bilaa – Lescar
Tel : 59810300
Le Beau Manoir – Jurançon
Tel : 59061730
RESTAURANT : Mariette – Artiguelouve
Tel : 59324508

Designed by France's most famous professional golfer, Jean Garaïalde, the Royal Artiguelouve golf course lies near the city of Pau and is backed by the Pyrenees. It belongs to a large real estate and leisure complex including a hotel, appartments for rental (2 room appartments and studios), tennis and squash courts, and a swimming pool. The american style golf course is set on flat woodland and includes three large lakes serving as hazards on eight holes.

GF $

1986

18

—

J. Garaïalde

L 5733 P 71

S

R

Required : Handicap Certificate
Best days : Any day

HOLE	LENGTH MEDAL-TEE	PAR	STROKE INDEX
1	354	4	6
2	297	4	8
3	168	3	14
4	362	4	2
5	376	4	4
6	342	4	12
7	283	4	16
8	130	3	18
9	450	5	10
TOTAL	2762	35	TOTAL

HOLE	LENGTH MEDAL-TEE	PAR	STROKE INDEX
10	393	4	1
11	155	3	11
12	438	5	13
13	328	4	7
14	302	4	17
15	330	4	9
16	162	3	15
17	377	4	3
18	486	5	5
TOTAL	2971	36	TOTAL

ROYAN

TEL : 46231624
LOCATION : 7 km Royan on ring road
ADDRESS : Maine Gaudin – La Palud – 17420 Saint-Palais
HOTEL :
Miramar – Royan
Tel : 46380364
Plage – St-Palais
Tel : 46231032
Villa Nausicaa – St-Palais
Tel : 46231478
RESTAURANT : La Grange au Grallet – Royan
Tel : 46050490

Founded in 1977, the golf course was extended to 18 holes in 1984 and bears the hallmarks of the region. It is laid out in fine natural pine forest on sloping landscape near the Atlantic seaside resorts of Royan and Saint-Palais, just 2km from the sea front.

GF $

1977

18

Tues. in low season

R. Berthet

L 6013 P 71

S

R

Required : Handicap Certificate
Best days : Any day esp. Fridays

HOLE	LENGTH MEDAL-TEE	PAR	STROKE INDEX
1	394	4	2
2	318	4	4
3	437	5	16
4	200	3	15
5	388	4	1
6	437	4	6
7	366	4	11
8	165	3	17
9	372	4	18
TOTAL	2977	35	TOTAL

HOLE	LENGTH MEDAL-TEE	PAR	STROKE INDEX
10	481	5	3
11	295	4	14
12	411	4	5
13	467	5	7
14	165	3	18
15	396	4	10
16	337	4	9
17	214	3	13
18	290	4	12
TOTAL	3036	36	TOTAL

SAINT-AUBIN

TEL : (1)69412519
LOCATION : 30 km Paris A 10 exit Saclay, then RN 306 to Gif-sur-Yvette
ADDRESS : 91190 Saint-Aubin
HOTEL :
Novotel – Saclay
Tel : (1)69418140
RESTAURANT : La Belle Epoque – Châteaufort
Tel : (1)39562166

Saint-Aubin is one of the popular public golf courses located around Paris. It is laid out on flat and windy terrain, and has a sparse vegetation. Ditches and ponds serve as hazards on half of the greens. A riding club is nearby. *SSS 70,3*

GF $

1974

27

—

M. Rio/R. Berthet

L 5817 P 71

S

R

Required : Handicap Certificate
Best days : Weekdays

HOLE	LENGTH MEDAL-TEE	PAR	STROKE INDEX
1	485	5	
2	270	4	
3	430	4	
4	366	4	
5	160	3	
6	290	4	
7	321	4	
8	378	4	
9	317	4	
TOTAL	3017	36	TOTAL

HOLE	LENGTH MEDAL-TEE	PAR	STROKE INDEX
10	158	3	
11	328	4	
12	344	4	
13	296	4	
14	450	5	
15	293	4	
16	159	3	
17	427	4	
18	345	4	
TOTAL	2800	35	TOTAL

SAINT-CLOUD

TEL : (1)47010185
LOCATION : 9 km Paris via Pont Suresnes
ADDRESS : 60, rue 19-Janvier – Parc de Buzenval – 92380 Garches
HOTEL :
Villa Henri IV – Saint-Cloud
Tel : (1)46025930
Cardinal – Rueil-Malmaison
Tel : (1)47082020
Quorum – St-Cloud
Tel : (1)47712233
RESTAURANT : El Chiquito – Rueil-Malmaison
Tel : (1)47510053

This is the golf course closest to Paris and therefore one of France's most prestigious golf clubs. The course lies in the 'Parc de Buzenval' amidst an abundance of age-old trees on undulating parkland. The Green Course is the main championship layout. Many of the fairways are tight such as the 1st, 2nd, 7th, 12th and 18th, demanding a great deal of accuracy. The 8th and 13th holes are heavily bunkered. The club, with a stylish clubhouse, was regularly used for the French Open. *SSS 71,7/66,2*

 $$

1911

36

Mondays

H. Colt, M. Serond, M. Boomer

L 5980 P 71, 5857 P 67

S

Required : Handicap Certificate plus introduction by a member
Best days : Fridays

Green Course

HOLE	LENGTH MEDAL-TEE	PAR	STROKE INDEX
1	408	4	3
2	414	4	1
3	474	5	11
4	357	4	15
5	342	4	13
6	140	3	17
7	356	4	7
8	157	3	9
9	385	4	5
TOTAL	3013	35	TOTAL

HOLE	LENGTH MEDAL-TEE	PAR	STROKE INDEX
10	423	4	4
11	148	3	16
12	395	4	2
13	167	3	8
14	283	4	12
15	435	5	18
16	278	4	14
17	453	5	10
18	385	4	6
TOTAL	2967	36	TOTAL

Yellow Course

HOLE	LENGTH MEDAL-TEE	PAR	STROKE INDEX
1	342	4	7
2	140	3	15
3	439	5	9
4	156	3	13
5	337	4	3
6	116	3	17
7	341	4	5
8	301	4	11
9	419	4	1
TOTAL	2591	34	TOTAL

HOLE	LENGTH MEDAL-TEE	PAR	STROKE INDEX
10	144	3	14
11	475	5	8
12	374	4	2
13	152	3	12
14	123	3	18
15	340	4	4
16	131	3	16
17	285	4	6
18	242	4	10
TOTAL	2266	33	TOTAL

SAINT-CYPRIEN

TEL : 68210171
LOCATION : 15 km Perpignan
ADDRESS : Mas d'Huston – 66750 St-Cyprien Plage
HOTEL :
Le Mas d'Huston and La Résidence du Golf
Tel : 68210171
La Lagune – St-Cyprien Sud
Tel : 68212424
Mar i Sol – St-Cyprien
Tel : 68210017

This fine and sporting holiday golf course lies near the Mediterranean seafront on relatively open terrain, and is backed by low wooded hills. It borders a vast lake which is a nature reserve and resting place for thousands of flamingos staying here twice a year. There are numerous tricky water holes. Facilites include two fine hotels, two swimming pools, an excellent golf school, various tennis courts and a riding school. *SSS 73*

GF $

1980

27

—

B. Wright, B. Tomlinson

L 6480 P 73, 2724 P 35

Required : Handicap Certificate
Best days : Any day

HOLE	LENGTH MEDAL-TEE	PAR	STROKE INDEX	HOLE	LENGTH MEDAL-TEE	PAR	STROKE INDEX	HOLE	LENGTH MEDAL-TEE	PAR	STROKE INDEX
1	410	4		10	380	4		1	353	4	
2	475	5		11	138	3		2	334	4	
3	182	3		12	395	4		3	135	3	
4	420	4		13	497	5		4	395	4	
5	435	5		14	377	4		5	470	5	
6	175	3		15	186	3		6	288	4	
7	460	5		16	282	4		7	274	4	
8	348	4		17	560	5		8	150	3	
9	430	4		18	330	4		9	325	4	
TOTAL	3335	37	TOTAL	TOTAL	3145	36	TOTAL	TOTAL	2724	35	TOTAL

SAINT-GATIEN

TEL : 31651999
LOCATION : 8 km Deauville
ADDRESS : 14130 Saint-Gatien-des-Bois
HOTEL :
Hélios – Deauville
Tel : 31882826
Le Clos – St-Gatien
Tel : 31651608
St-James – Trouville
Tel : 31880523
RESTAURANT : Miocque – Deauville
Tel : 31880952

Located between the famous seaside resort of Deauville and the charming harbour town of Honfleur, the golf course is set inland not far from the sea front in a typical unspoilt Normandy landscape.The first nine holes run through a sweeping and well-wooded valley, the second nine are laid out on a plateau with creeks serving as water hazards. An attractive feature is the clubhouse which is a renovated cider mill, dating back to the 18th century.

GF $

1987

27

—

O. Brizon

L 2970 P 36, 3035 P 36, 3120 P 36

R S

Required : None
Best days : Any day

HOLE	LENGTH MEDAL-TEE	PAR	STROKE INDEX	HOLE	LENGTH MEDAL-TEE	PAR	STROKE INDEX	HOLE	LENGTH MEDAL-TEE	PAR	STROKE INDEX
1	470	5	12	1	490	5	10	1	450	5	11
2	140	3	18	2	370	4	8	2	380	4	3
3	340	4	4	3	220	3	2	3	400	4	1
4	140	3	8	4	335	4	14	4	150	3	17
5	370	4	2	5	130	3	18	5	340	4	7
6	170	3	14	6	450	5	16	6	360	4	5
7	510	5	6	7	180	3	12	7	180	3	9
8	460	5	16	8	370	4	4	8	330	4	13
9	370	4	10	9	490	5	6	9	530	5	15
TOTAL	2970	36	TOTAL	TOTAL	3035	36	TOTAL	TOTAL	3120	36	TOTAL

SAINT-GERMAIN

★★

TEL : (1)34517590
LOCATION : 3 km Saint-Germain A 13
ADDRESS : Route de Poissy – 78100 Saint-Germain-en-Laye
HOTEL :
Cazaudehore – St-Germain
Tel : (1)34519380
La Forestière – St-Germain
Tel : (1)39733660
Pavillon Henri IV – St-Germain
Tel : (1)34516262
RESTAURANT : Le Coq Hardi – Bougival
Tel : (1)39690143

The course is of championship standard and lies in an attractive forest on flat terrain near the town of Saint-Germain, a picturesque suburb of Paris. Most of the holes are landscaped among a great variety of mature trees. Many of the greens are large and defended by strategic bunkers. *SSS 72*

GF $$ — Mondays
1922 — H. Colt
27 — L 6024 P 72, 2030 P 33

Required : Handicap Certificate
Best days : Weekdays; Weekends by invitation

HOLE	LENGTH MEDAL-TEE	PAR	STROKE INDEX
1	389	4	3
2	435	5	17
3	333	4	11
4	417	4	1
5	173	3	7
6	524	5	5
7	149	3	15
8	325	4	13
9	444	5	9
TOTAL	3189	37	TOTAL

HOLE	LENGTH MEDAL-TEE	PAR	STROKE INDEX
10	316	4	10
11	137	3	14
12	375	4	4
13	309	4	16
14	400	4	2
15	475	5	8
16	295	4	18
17	142	3	12
18	386	4	6
TOTAL	2835	35	TOTAL

SAINT-GERMAIN-LES-CORBEIL

TEL : (1)60758154
LOCATION : 30km Paris A6 exit Melun Sénart then D402 (La Francilienne) to St-Germain-les-Corbeil
ADDRESS : 6, avenue du Golf - 91250 Saint-Germain-les-Corbeil
HOTEL :
Central - Corbeil
Tel : (1)60880606
Campanile - Corbeil
Tel : (1)60894145

This technically difficult course, set on the edge of the Sénart forest, features nine treacherous water obstacles (4,5,6,7,8,12,13,14,15). Amongs its most testing holes is the long 13th having two greens one of them being an island green.The club boasts a welcoming Virginian style clubhouse with an excellent restaurant. *SSS 71*

GF $
—
R S
1990
P. Drancourt
18
L 5328 P 70

Required : Handicap Certificate
Best days : Any day

HOLE	LENGTH MEDAL-TEE	PAR	STROKE INDEX
1	126	3	15
2	437	5	11
3	270	4	17
4	158	3	7
5	308	4	9
6	402	4	1
7	185	3	5
8	350	4	3
9	292	4	13
TOTAL	2528	34	TOTAL

HOLE	LENGTH MEDAL-TEE	PAR	STROKE INDEX
10	265	4	12
11	352	4	16
12	450	5	10
13	440	5	4
14	140	3	18
15	527	5	2
16	158	3	8
17	156	3	14
18	312	4	6
TOTAL	2800	36	TOTAL

SAINT-JEAN-DE-MONTS

✡

TEL : 51588273
LOCATION : 76 km Nantes
RD937/RD753. From St-Jean-de-Monts take RD38 to Noirmoutiers
ADDRESS : Avenue des Pays de Monts
85160 St-Jean-de-Monts
HOTEL :
Altéa - St-Jean-de-Monts
Tel : 51591515
de la Plage - Notre-Dame-de-Monts
Tel : 51588309
L'Espadon - St-Jean-de-Monts
Tel : 51580318

This fairly technical golf course is a pleasant addition to the existing courses in the Vendee region. Set in rugged dune landscape, the holes stretch out parallel to untouched beaches along the Atlantic Ocean and are bordered on the other side by an attractive pine forest. A lake affects play on the 1st and 2nd holes. Located near the popular holiday resort of St Jean de Monts, there exists a wide choice of sporting facilities such as tennis, horse riding, swimming, sailing and health clubs. *SSS 70*

GF $

1989

18

—

Y. Bureau

L 5620 P 72

R S

Required : None
Best days : Any day

HOLE	LENGTH MEDAL-TEE	PAR	STROKE INDEX
1	303	4	9
2	414	5	7
3	157	3	13
4	331	4	5
5	365	4	3
6	132	3	17
7	312	4	11
8	486	5	1
9	252	4	15
TOTAL	2752	36	TOTAL

HOLE	LENGTH MEDAL-TEE	PAR	STROKE INDEX
10	169	3	16
11	464	5	4
12	303	4	12
13	277	4	10
14	371	4	2
15	436	5	6
16	277	4	18
17	171	3	14
18	400	4	8
TOTAL	2868	36	TOTAL

SAINT-JULIEN PONT-L'EVÊQUE

✡

TEL : 31643030
LOCATION : 15 km Deauville
ADDRESS : Saint-Julien-sur-Calonne – 14130 Pont-l'Evêque
HOTEL :
Lion d'Or – Pont-l'Evêque
Tel : 31650155
Marie-Anne – Deauville
Tel : 31883532
Vivier – Livarot
Tel : 31635029
RESTAURANT : Auberge de la Truite – Pont-l'Evêque
Tel : 31652164

The golf course lies in the heart of Normandy, only 15 km inland from the holiday resorts of Cabourg, Honfleur and Deauville. Set in fine and gently rolling landscape, the 18 holes of this recently finished course offer excellent views of the surroundings with its valleys, hills, and villages. The course has an interesting and a technically difficult layout featuring large fairways and combining obstacles such as seven strategic water traps (ponds with waterfalls) and 90 bunkers. A hotel is planned for the near future. *SSS 72*

GF $$

1988

27

Tues; Weekends in Summer

R S

A. Prat

L 5966 P 72, 2062 P 33

Required : None
Best days : Weekdays

HOLE	LENGTH MEDAL-TEE	PAR	STROKE INDEX
1	370	4	3
2	298	4	15
3	378	5	13
4	180	3	9
5	350	4	11
6	125	3	17
7	383	4	7
8	525	5	1
9	391	4	5
TOTAL	3000	36	TOTAL

HOLE	LENGTH MEDAL-TEE	PAR	STROKE INDEX
10	410	4	2
11	346	4	12
12	323	4	18
13	145	3	14
14	467	5	6
15	173	3	10
16	307	4	16
17	347	4	4
18	448	5	8
TOTAL	2966	36	TOTAL

SAINT-LAURENT-PLOËMEL

TEL : 97568518
LOCATION : 10 km Carnac RD 119 to Ploëmel
ADDRESS : 56400 Auray
HOTEL : HR
Fairway
Tel : 97568888
Diana – Carnac
Tel : 97520538
Novotel Tal Ar Mor – Carnac
Tel : 97521666
RESTAURANT : La Closerie de Kerdrain – Auray
Tel : 97566127

Located in south Brittany 5 km from the Atlantic Ocean near several well-known seaside resorts such as Quiberon and Carnac, this well bunkered golf course is peacefully situated in a forest of pine and oak trees on undulating countryside. A river meanders its way through six holes. Facilities include four tennis courts, a swimming pool and a fitness club. The elegant Fairway hotel with 42 rooms was opened in 1988. *SSS 72*

GF $

1975

27

—

M. Fenn

L 6112 P 72, 2705 P 35

R S

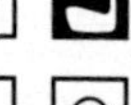

Required : Handicap Certificate
Best days : Any day

HOLE	LENGTH MEDAL-TEE	PAR	STROKE INDEX
1	266	4	15
2	326	4	17
3	430	4	1
4	176	3	13
5	400	4	3
6	412	4	5
7	190	3	11
8	460	5	9
9	243	4	17
TOTAL	2903	35	TOTAL

HOLE	LENGTH MEDAL-TEE	PAR	STROKE INDEX
10	375	4	4
11	160	3	18
12	495	5	2
13	335	4	16
14	210	3	14
15	345	4	8
16	472	5	12
17	354	4	6
18	463	5	10
TOTAL	3209	37	TOTAL

SAINT-MALO-LE TRONCHET

TEL : 99589669
LOCATION : 25 km Saint-Malo RD 73
ADDRESS : 35540 Le Tronchet Miniac Morvan
HOTEL : HR
L'Abbatiale
Tel : 99589321
La Korrigane – St-Malo
Tel : 99816585
Valmarin – St-Malo Sud
Tel : 99819476
RESTAURANT : Robert Abraham – St-Malo
Tel : 99405093

Picturesquely laid out on the banks of the Mirloup lake alongside a pine forest, this is a fine sporting golf course in Brittany. Inaugurated in 1986, the course was designed by the French golf architect Hubert Chesneau with many holes to be played over water. The clubhouse is in a former 17th century priory. The Abbatiale hotel, with 83 rooms, is adjacent to the golf course. *SSS 72*

GF $ — —  

1986 — H. Chesneau — 

27 — L 5620 P 72, 2684 P 36 — R

Required : Handicap Certificate
Best days : Weekdays, especially Tuesdays

HOLE	LENGTH MEDAL-TEE	PAR	STROKE INDEX
1	418	5	9
2	306	4	5
3	283	4	15
4	155	3	13
5	396	4	1
6	135	3	11
7	407	5	7
8	265	4	17
9	377	4	3
TOTAL	2742	36	TOTAL

HOLE	LENGTH MEDAL-TEE	PAR	STROKE INDEX
10	360	4	4
11	129	3	18
12	385	5	14
13	342	4	16
14	153	3	10
15	396	4	6
16	390	4	2
17	311	4	12
18	412	5	8
TOTAL	2878	36	TOTAL

SAINT-NOM-LA-BRETECHE

★★★

TEL : (1)34625400
LOCATION : 8 km Versailles, 25 km Paris
A 13 exit 2, then RN 186 and RN 307
ADDRESS : La Tuilerie – 78860 Saint-Nom-la-Bretèche
HOTEL :
Trianon Palace – Versailles
Tel : (1)39503412
Mercure – Le Chesnay
Tel : (1)39551141
RESTAURANT : Auberge du Vieux Logis – Saint-Nom-la-Bretèche
Tel : (1)34608143

One of the most exclusive golf clubs close to Paris is Saint-Nom-La-Breteche, ranking amongst the world's leading golf courses. There are two excellent and well-designed courses, set on rolling and fairly wooded countryside. The championship layout combines holes from both courses. Water hazards include a picturesque horseshoe lake, separating the 9th and the 18th green. It has hosted the World Cup and the French Open many times. The prestigious Trophee Lancôme returns every year in autumn, welcoming the world's greatest champions. In the grounds surrounding the course are various exclusive private villas. The club boasts a magnificent clubhouse, a 18th century farmhouse, once the property of King Louis IV. *SSS 72*

GF $$

1959

Tuesdays

F. Hawtree

L 6138 P 72, 6095 P 72

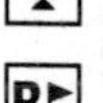 

Required : Handicap Certificate, Introduction letter
Best days : Weekdays only with advance booking

Red Course

HOLE	LENGTH MEDAL-TEE	PAR	STROKE INDEX
1	334	4	15
2	360	4	7
3	164	3	17
4	360	4	3
5	435	5	13
6	400	4	1
7	461	5	11
8	384	4	5
9	187	3	9
TOTAL	3085	36	TOTAL

HOLE	LENGTH MEDAL-TEE	PAR	STROKE INDEX
10	374	4	2
11	339	4	18
12	497	5	6
13	194	3	12
14	328	4	10
15	355	4	4
16	155	3	16
17	475	5	8
18	336	4	14
TOTAL	3053	36	TOTAL

Blue Course

HOLE	LENGTH MEDAL-TEE	PAR	STROKE INDEX
1	412	4	5
2	336	4	7
3	187	3	11
4	392	4	3
5	340	4	13
6	453	5	9
7	140	3	17
8	390	4	1
9	309	4	15
TOTAL	2966	35	TOTAL

HOLE	LENGTH MEDAL-TEE	PAR	STROKE INDEX
10	440	5	10
11	158	3	18
12	376	4	4
13	456	5	12
14	295	4	14
15	386	4	2
16	508	5	8
17	148	3	16
18	362	4	6
TOTAL	3129	37	TOTAL

SAINT-PIERRE DU PERRAY (Villeray)

TEL : (1)60751747
LOCATION : 5 km Corbeil, 30 km Paris
A 6/RD 947
ADDRESS : 91100 Saint-Pierre-du-Perray
HOTEL :
Novotel – Evry
Tel : (1)60778270
Campanile – Corbeil
Tel : (1)60894145
Central – Corbeil
Tel : (1)60880606
RESTAURANT : Aux Armes de France – Corbeil
Tel : (1)64962404

This public golf course with an excellent training center and a golf school, is laid out on flat and open terrain on the edge of a forest some thirty kilometres from the capital. It has a testing layout featuring several long and sporting dogleg holes with difficult greens.
SSS 72,2

 $  —  

 1975  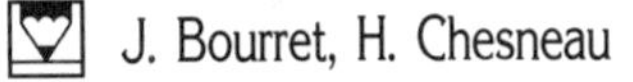 J. Bourret, H. Chesneau

  6169 P 72

Required : Handicap Certificate
Best days : Any day

HOLE	LENGTH MEDAL-TEE	PAR	STROKE INDEX
1	355	4	14
2	382	4	16
3	373	4	4
4	356	4	6
5	165	3	12
6	434	5	10
7	186	3	8
8	365	4	2
9	458	5	18
TOTAL	3074	36	TOTAL

HOLE	LENGTH MEDAL-TEE	PAR	STROKE INDEX
10	142	3	13
11	338	4	15
12	332	4	17
13	509	5	7
14	405	4	1
15	361	4	11
16	172	3	5
17	360	4	3
18	476	5	9
TOTAL	3095	36	TOTAL

SAINT-QUENTIN-EN-YVELINES

TEL : (1)30508640
LOCATION : 30 km Paris A 13 exit Trappes then RD 912
ADDRESS : 78190 Trappes
HOTEL :
Novotel - St-Quentin-en-Yvelines
Tel : (1)30576565
Mercure – Le Chesnay
Tel : (1)39551141
Urbis – Le Chesnay
Tel : (1)39633793
RESTAURANT : Trois Marches – Versailles
Tel : (1)39501321

This is a public golf course (with a training school) of excellent quality belonging to a vast sports complex. Set on varied but mostly flat landscape, both courses (Le Petit Etang and Pissaloup) border a large lake and are characterized by long and technical holes. Other facilities include a swimming pool (with waves), tennis courts, sailing and windsurfing on the lake. *SSS 71*

GF $

1982

36

January 1st

H. Chesneau

L 6033 P 71, 5768 P 70

R S

Required : Handicap certificate
Best days : Weekdays

HOLE	LENGTH MEDAL-TEE	PAR	STROKE INDEX
1	393	4	
2	178	3	
3	377	4	
4	414	4	
5	315	4	
6	425	4	
7	523	5	
8	367	4	
9	173	5	
TOTAL	3165	35	TOTAL

HOLE	LENGTH MEDAL-TEE	PAR	STROKE INDEX
10	284	4	
11	457	5	
12	472	5	
13	145	3	
14	368	4	
15	289	4	
16	185	3	
17	307	4	
18	361	4	
TOTAL	2868	36	TOTAL

SAINT-SAËNS

TEL : 35342524
LOCATION : 2 km Saint-Saëns; 30 km N. Rouen to Dieppe RN 28/RD 154
ADDRESS : B. P. 20 – 76680 Saint-Saëns
HOTEL :
Grand Cerf – Neufchatel-en-Bray
Tel : 35930002
Frantel – Rouen
Tel : 35980698
Terrasse – Varengeville-sur-Mer
Tel : 35851254
RESTAURANT : La Bucherie – Offranville
Tel : 35848310

Located in Normandy, the golf course is set in fine natural landscape bordering the 'Varenne' river. The course offers variety. The first five holes wind through the 'Varenne' valley, the 6th to the 18th run through a forest, then uphill in order to reach home. The clubhouse, an impressive 'château' set on a plain, overlooks the valley and the 'Eawy' forests. Nine more holes and several tennis courts will open shortly.

GF $

Tuesdays

1987

 D. Robinson

18

 6004 P 71

Required : Handicap Certificate
Best days : Any day

HOLE	LENGTH MEDAL-TEE	PAR	STROKE INDEX
1	318	4	
2	369	4	
3	440	5	
4	210	3	
5	348	4	
6	182	3	
7	490	5	
8	350	4	
9	200	3	
TOTAL	2907	35	TOTAL

HOLE	LENGTH MEDAL-TEE	PAR	STROKE INDEX
10	328	4	
11	163	3	
12	513	5	
13	485	5	
14	357	4	
15	373	4	
16	355	4	
17	141	3	
18	382	4	
TOTAL	3097	36	TOTAL

SAINT-SAMSON

✡

TEL : 96238734
LOCATION : 3 km S. Trégastel, 7 km Perros-Guirec
ADDRESS : Route de Kerenoc – Pleumeur-Bodou – 22560 Trebeurden
HOTEL : HR
Golfhotel
Tel : 96238734
Belle Vue – Tregastel-Plage
Tel : 96238818
Manoir de Lan-Kerellec – Trébeurden
Tel : 96235009
RESTAURANT : Corniche – Trégastel
Tel : 96238815

A pleasant and scenic golf course located in Brittany near the well-known seaside resort of Perros-Guirrec and set on rather windy tree-lined countryside bearing the characteristics of the region. Ideal for holiday golf, there is a hotel (34 rooms) on the course with various tennis courts and a swimming pool. Nearby there are facilities for riding, windsurfing and sailing.

GF $

1964

18

Tuesdays

F. Hawtree

L 5655 P 72

S

R

Required : Handicap Certificate
Best days : Any day by prior arrangement

HOLE	LENGTH MEDAL-TEE	PAR	STROKE INDEX
1	255	4	18
2	460	5	4
3	150	3	16
4	320	4	13
5	310	4	8
6	280	4	17
7	155	3	15
8	315	4	9
9	380	4	1
TOTAL	2625	35	TOTAL

HOLE	LENGTH MEDAL-TEE	PAR	STROKE INDEX
10	475	5	5
11	490	5	2
12	160	3	12
13	315	4	7
14	345	4	6
15	455	5	3
16	180	3	11
17	320	4	10
18	290	4	14
TOTAL	3030	37	TOTAL

SAINTE-BAUME

TEL : 94786012
LOCATION : 40 km E. Marseille A 50/52, 10 km Saint-Maximin RN 560
ADDRESS : 83860 Nans-les-Pins
HOTEL : HR
Domaine de Châteauneuf
Tel : 94789006
Relais de la Magdeleine – Gemenos
Tel : 94822005
Hotel Plaisance – St-Maximin
Tel : 94781674

Set inland from the Mediterranean coast between Nice and Marseille, the Sainte Baume golf course is a welcome addition to the already existing golf courses of the Côte d'Azur region. Backed by the 'Sainte-Baume' hills, the course winds through typical 'Provence' landscape. Cedars and umbrella pines, set amidst rosemary, thyme, and lavender, border the fairways. The greens are of excellent quality : rolling with numerous differences in level. A stream and four lakes serve as water traps. Situated on the course is the scenic Relais & Châteaux hotel 'Domaine de Châteauneuf', a former 17th century manor house, with a swimming pool, horse-riding and three tennis courts in its grounds.

GF $

1988

18

Tues. in winter ; February

R. Berthet

L 5878 P 72

 S

Required : Handicap Certificate
Best days : Any day

HOLE	LENGTH MEDAL-TEE	PAR	STROKE INDEX
1	423	5	
2	357	4	
3	341	4	
4	177	3	
5	384	4	
6	333	4	
7	443	5	
8	166	3	
9	369	4	
TOTAL	2993	36	TOTAL

HOLE	LENGTH MEDAL-TEE	PAR	STROKE INDEX
10	321	4	
11	181	3	
12	438	5	
13	284	4	
14	362	4	
15	423	5	
16	185	3	
17	368	4	
18	323	4	
TOTAL	2885	36	TOTAL

SALVAGNY

TEL : 78488360
LOCATION : 15 km Lyon N7 to Roanne
ADDRESS : 100 rue des Granges
69890 La Tour-de-Salvagny
HOTEL :
Cour des Loges - Lyon
Tel : 78427575
Lyon Métropole - Lyon
Tel : 78292020
RESTAURANT : Léon de Lyon - Lyon
Tel : 78281133

Just 15 minutes from Lyon, this golf course, designed by the French architect Pierre Drancourt, spreads over enchanting and fairly undulating landscape. Partly wooded, it comprises several tracts of water serving as obstacles.

GF $

1988

18

—

P. Drancourt

L 5791 P 72

S

R

Required : Handicap Certificate
Best days : Any day

HOLE	LENGTH MEDAL-TEE	PAR	STROKE INDEX
1	304	4	
2	298	4	
3	477	5	
4	361	4	
5	136	3	
6	498	5	
7	136	3	
8	393	4	
9	307	4	
TOTAL	2910	36	TOTAL

HOLE	LENGTH MEDAL-TEE	PAR	STROKE INDEX
10	429	5	
11	387	4	
12	365	4	
13	355	4	
14	161	3	
15	448	5	
16	309	4	
17	150	3	
18	277	4	
TOTAL	2881	36	TOTAL

SANCERROIS

TEL : 48541122
LOCATION : 6 km Sancerre RN7,
6 km Cosne-sur-Loire
ADDRESS : Saint-Thibault - 18300 Sancerre
HOTEL :
du Laurier - Saint-Satur
Tel : 48541720
Panoramic - Sancerre
Tel : 48542240
Le Vieux Relais - Sancerre
Tel : 86282021

This excellent course, set on the borders of the Loire with the Sancerre hill in the background, lies in the heart of the Sancerre vineyards. Its features include beautiful aged trees bordering the fairways, many elevated greens, and creeks and small streams serving as obstacles. There is a clubhouse with two fine restaurants. Another nine holes and a three star 40 room hotel are scheduled to open soon. Facilities such as 9 tennis courts (2 indoor), a swimming pool and a miniature golf are just 300m from the club. *SSS 69,5*

GF $

—

 S

1989

D. Fruchet

18

L 5523 P 71

Required : Handicap Certificate
Best days : Any day

HOLE	LENGTH MEDAL-TEE	PAR	STROKE INDEX
1	316	4	8
2	288	4	16
3	133	3	12
4	441	5	6
5	353	4	2
6	262	4	14
7	440	5	10
8	124	3	18
9	359	4	4
TOTAL	2702	36	TOTAL

HOLE	LENGTH MEDAL-TEE	PAR	STROKE INDEX
10	325	4	11
11	292	4	17
12	198	3	5
13	393	4	3
14	139	3	15
15	449	5	7
16	302	4	13
17	361	4	1
18	348	4	9
TOTAL	2821	35	TOTAL

SCOTTISH AUBERTIN

TEL : 59827373
LOCATION : 17 km Pau to Aubertin
ADDRESS : 64290 Aubertin
HOTEL :
Paris - Pau
Tel : 59273439
Continental - Pau
Tel : 59276931
Bilaa - Lescar
Tel : 59810300

Located close to Pau, the course has been designed by the Scotsman, James Fraser. It extends over lush rolling landscape overlooking partly wooded valleys and vineyards. There is a lake flanking the 14th and 15th holes, and numerous streams meander their way through the holes. The club boasts a picturesque and relaxing clubhouse.

GF $
—
S

1987
J. Fraser

18
L 4483 P 66
R

Required : None
Best days : Any day

HOLE	LENGTH MEDAL-TEE	PAR	STROKE INDEX
1	310	4	
2	120	3	
3	178	3	
4	370	4	
5	532	5	
6	145	3	
7	162	3	
8	192	3	
9	307	4	
TOTAL	2316	32	TOTAL

HOLE	LENGTH MEDAL-TEE	PAR	STROKE INDEX
10	347	4	
11	170	3	
12	245	4	
13	157	3	
14	231	4	
15	246	4	
16	240	4	
17	295	4	
18	236	4	
TOTAL	2167	34	TOTAL

SEIGNOSSE

TEL : 58431732
LOCATION : 25 km Bayonne A63 exit Hossegor, then RD 652 /1 km N. Hossegor
ADDRESS : Carrefour Boucau
40510 Seignosse
HOTEL :
Ermitage - Hossegor
Tel : 58435222
Lacotel - Hossegor
Tel : 58439350
Beauséjour - Hossegor
Tel : 58435107

Harmoniously and peacefully blending into the typical Landes countryside very close to the Atlantic coast line, this championship course winds through lush and fairly hazardous pine forest. It features picturesque water hazards and several spectacular double and triple greens. Sporting activities such as tennis, riding, surfing and other water sports are nearby. *SSS 70*

GF $

—

1988

18

R. von Hagge

L 5757 P 72

Required : Handicap Certificate
Best days : Any day

HOLE	LENGTH MEDAL-TEE	PAR	STROKE INDEX
1	377	4	10
2	279	4	8
3	350	4	6
4	411	5	14
5	127	3	17
6	335	4	4
7	465	5	12
8	108	3	16
9	314	4	2
TOTAL	2766	36	TOTAL

HOLE	LENGTH MEDAL-TEE	PAR	STROKE INDEX
10	290	4	11
11	502	5	3
12	105	3	18
13	417	4	1
14	311	4	9
15	308	4	15
16	170	3	13
17	355	4	5
18	533	5	7
TOTAL	2991	36	TOTAL

SERAINCOURT

TEL : (1)34754728
LOCATION : 5 km Meulan
ADDRESS : 95450 Gaillonnet Vigny
HOTEL :
Les Glycines – Mantes
Tel : (1)34770413
Mercure – Meulan
Tel : (1)34746363
Novotel – Cergy Pontoise
Tel : (1)30303947
RESTAURANT : La Grande Pinte – Meulan
Tel : (1)34741510

Seraincourt is a pleasant golf course, having wide and generous fairways laid out on pleasant wooded countryside not far from Paris. Very popular with golfers, the club is equipped with four tennis courts, a swimming pool and a pony club. The picturesque farmhouse style clubhouse completes the scene. *SSS 69,9*

GF $$

1982

18

—

F. Hawtree

L 5811 P 70

S

Required : Handicap Certificate
Best days : Weekdays

HOLE	LENGTH MEDAL-TEE	PAR	STROKE INDEX
1	305	4	10
2	130	3	16
3	345	4	14
4	156	3	8
5	388	4	4
6	465	5	18
7	376	4	12
8	188	3	12
9	363	4	6
TOTAL	2716	34	TOTAL

HOLE	LENGTH MEDAL-TEE	PAR	STROKE INDEX
10	356	4	5
11	392	4	1
12	113	3	17
13	357	4	7
14	361	4	3
15	328	4	13
16	469	5	9
17	140	3	11
18	467	5	15
TOTAL	2983	36	TOTAL

SERVANES

TEL : 90475995
LOCATION : 35 km Avignon A7 exit Nord Cavaillon, then N7 to Salon-de-Provence
ADDRESS : Domaine de Servanes
13890 Mouries
HOTEL : HР
Hostellerie de Servanes
Tel : 90475003
Le Pré des Baux - Maussane
Tel : 90544040
Le Valbaussenc - Maussane
Tel : 90543890

This course was designed by golf architect Thierry Sprecher and the French golf champion Gery Watine. It lies in a lush rolling valley in the heart of La Provence region and is wedged between the rocks of the Alpilles, 15km from the colourful village of Les Baux de Provence. The holes cross vineyards, run through olive groves, are sheltered by majestic rows of cypress trees, and are sometimes flanked by descending lakes. Three tricky island greens demand precise shots. The vast clubhouse is a converted 18th century building, a former oil crusher and a sheephold. L'Hostellerie de Servanes, an ancient Provençal country mansion, has 22 bedrooms and a fine swimming pool. *SSS 72*

GF $$ — Tuesdays in winter — R S

1989 — T. Sprecher, G. Watine

18 — L 5591 P 72

Required : Handicap Certificate
Best days : Any day

HOLE	LENGTH MEDAL-TEE	PAR	STROKE INDEX
1	260	4	17
2	345	4	11
3	146	3	13
4	440	5	9
5	390	4	1
6	90	3	18
7	394	4	3
8	355	4	7
9	458	5	5
TOTAL	2878	36	TOTAL

HOLE	LENGTH MEDAL-TEE	PAR	STROKE INDEX
10	297	4	14
11	310	4	16
12	173	3	2
13	475	5	6
14	309	4	15
15	109	3	10
16	330	4	8
17	232	4	12
18	478	5	4
TOTAL	2713	36	TOTAL

SOLOGNE
(Country-Club des Olleries)

TEL : 38765733
LOCATION : 25 km S. Orléans RN 20/RD 18
ADDRESS : Route de Jouy-le-Potier – 45240 Ardon
HOTEL :
Novotel – Orléans
Tel : 38630428
Auberge de la Montespan – St-Jean-de-la-Ruelle
Tel : 38881207
Perron – La Ferté-Saint-Aubin
Tel : 38915336
RESTAURANT : La Crémaillère – Orléans
Tel : 38534917

Located in Sologne, a region famous for its hunting grounds, this attractive course has a challenging layout with an abundance of fine heathered fairways running through splendid woods of pine trees, silver birch, magnificent oaks and many other varieties. Three lakes serve as hazards. Accomodation is available in the clubhouse or in several converted farmhouses. *SSS72*

GF $

1955

27

—

J. Bourret

L 6304 P 72

S

Required : None
Best days : Any day

HOLE	LENGTH MEDAL-TEE	PAR	STROKE INDEX
1	369	4	15
2	135	3	18
3	378	4	6
4	451	5	11
5	361	4	9
6	220	3	8
7	377	4	7
8	488	5	4
9	432	4	3
TOTAL	3211	36	TOTAL

HOLE	LENGTH MEDAL-TEE	PAR	STROKE INDEX
10	425	4	2
11	340	4	17
12	434	4	1
13	142	3	16
14	373	4	14
15	356	4	10
16	453	5	12
17	175	3	13
18	491	5	5
TOTAL	3189	36	TOTAL

SPERONE

TEL : 95731369
LOCATION : on the island of Corsica near Bonifacio
ADDRESS : Domaine de Sperone - 20169 Bonifacio
HOTEL :
Solemare - Bonifacio
Tel : 95730106
Etrangers - Bonifacio
Tel : 95730109
Cala Rossa - Porto Vecchio
Tel : 95716151

The first course to be opened on the beautiful island of Corsica, the "l'Ile de Beauté". Located in the southern part of the island close to the scenic town of Bonifacio, this is a truly exceptional course designed by master architect Robert Trent Jones. Set on rugged landscape bordering the Mediterranean, "Trent Jones" design is obvious in every hole. Nine links type holes are set alongside the sea offering splendid views while others head inland. Beware of several treacherous Trent Jones style water traps and bunkers. Among its feature holes : the 10th with a drive over the sea, the 15th with its green set on a cliff, and the fascinating 16th played over the sea to a high cliff. A superb clubhouse is due to open in the summer of 1991.

GF $ — Thursdays — S

1990 — R. Trent Jones 

18 — L 5464 P 72 

Required : Handicap Certificate
Best days : Any day

HOLE	LENGTH MEDAL-TEE	PAR	STROKE INDEX
1	322	4	13
2	110	3	15
3	466	5	7
4	315	4	9
5	277	4	5
6	339	4	3
7	101	3	17
8	370	4	1
9	431	5	11
TOTAL	2731	36	TOTAL

HOLE	LENGTH MEDAL-TEE	PAR	STROKE INDEX
10	299	4	16
11	309	4	4
12	133	3	10
13	263	4	12
14	356	4	8
15	304	4	18
16	430	5	2
17	145	3	14
18	494	5	6
TOTAL	2733	36	TOTAL

STRASBOURG

TEL : 88661722
LOCATION : 12 km Strasbourg A 35/ RN 83/RD 468
ADDRESS : Route du Rhin – 67400 Illkirch Graffenstaden
HOTEL :
Novotel – Illkirch Graffenstaden
Tel : 88662156
Alsace – Illkirch Graffenstaden
Tel : 88664160
Mercure – Illkirch Graffenstaden
Tel : 88660300
RESTAURANT : Maison des Tanneurs – Strasbourg
Tel : 88327970

The course is laid out in the Alsace region in an attractive parkland setting, and has a scenic layout with lots of variety. There are eleven holes running through flat countryside having spacious fairways. The others such as the 5th, 6th, 7th and 13th are more testing with narrow fairways. The course, which will be extended to 27 holes in 1991, is cunningly bunkered and has two water hazards. *SSS 70*

GF $

1934

18

—

D. Harradine

L 5675 P 72

S

Required : Handicap Certificate
Best days : Weekdays only

HOLE	LENGTH MEDAL-TEE	PAR	STROKE INDEX
1	366	4	7
2	340	4	15
3	335	4	11
4	437	5	13
5	255	4	3
6	158	3	9
7	448	5	5
8	160	3	17
9	374	4	1
TOTAL	2873	36	TOTAL

HOLE	LENGTH MEDAL-TEE	PAR	STROKE INDEX
10	323	4	10
11	154	3	6
12	284	4	8
13	452	5	4
14	338	4	2
15	290	4	12
16	144	3	18
17	453	5	14
18	323	4	16
TOTAL	2761	36	TOTAL

SULLY-SUR-LOIRE

TEL : 38365208
LOCATION : 4 km Sully-sur-Loire RD 120 to Viglain
ADDRESS : Domaine de L'Ousseau – Viglain – 45600 Sully-sur-Loire
HOTEL :
L'Auberge de Combreux – Combreux
Tel : 38594763
Poste – Sully-sur-Loire
Tel : 38352622
La Rochette – Sully-sur-Loire
Tel : 38365208
RESTAURANT : Esplanade – Sully-sur-Loire
Tel : 38362083

This pretty course, laid out in the Loire valley, is picturesquely set in varied countryside, characteristic of the 'Sologne' region (famous hunting area), only 4 km from the scenic 'Loire Château de Sully'. It incorporates a fine setting of trees and a pond, both serving as obstacles. The clubhouse is a converted Sologne style farmhouse. *SSS 72*

GF $

1963

27

Tuesdays

J. Bourret

L 3152 P 36, 3002 P 36, 3155 P 36

R S

Required : Handicap Certificate
Best days : Any day

HOLE	LENGTH MEDAL-TEE	PAR	STROKE INDEX	HOLE	LENGTH MEDAL-TEE	PAR	STROKE INDEX	HOLE	LENGTH MEDAL-TEE	PAR	STROKE INDEX
1	365	4		1	304	4		1	320	4	
2	385	4		2	474	5		2	360	4	
3	340	4		3	475	5		3	380	4	
4	475	5		4	257	4		4	200	3	
5	145	3		5	360	4		5	490	5	
6	410	4		6	156	3		6	425	4	
7	210	3		7	390	4		7	125	3	
8	450	5		8	176	3		8	475	5	
9	372	4		9	410	4		9	380	4	
TOTAL	3152	36	TOTAL	TOTAL	3002	36	TOTAL	TOTAL	3155	36	TOTAL

TILBURY

TEL : 63552050
LOCATION : 11 km Albi/Gaillac RN 88
ADDRESS : Al Bosc - 81150 Florentin
HOTEL :
La Réserve - Albi
Tel : 63607979
Host. St. Antoine - Albi
Tel : 63540404
RESTAURANT : Francis Cardaillac - Marssac
Tel : 63554190

Situated in the Tarn region in the heart of the Midi Pyrenées, the course runs through plains and valleys with treacherous water traps affecting play from the 10th to the 15th hole. A feature is the Moroccan style clubhouse with its swimming pool and terrace. A hotel with 25 rooms is planned to open in the summer of 1991. *SSS 73*

GF $

1990

18

—

R. Berthet

L 5680 P 71

S

R

Required : Handicap Certificate
Best days : Any day

HOLE	LENGTH MEDAL-TEE	PAR	STROKE INDEX
1	445	5	14
2	280	4	17
3	345	4	8
4	175	3	9
5	360	4	12
6	440	5	15
7	170	3	3
8	490	5	4
9	370	4	10
TOTAL	3075	37	TOTAL

HOLE	LENGTH MEDAL-TEE	PAR	STROKE INDEX
10	335	4	2
11	310	4	16
12	480	5	7
13	145	3	18
14	300	4	13
15	160	3	1
16	360	4	5
17	180	3	6
18	335	4	11
TOTAL	2605	34	TOTAL

TOULOUSE-PALMOLA

★

TEL : 61842050
LOCATION : 20 km Toulouse RN 88 to Albi
ADDRESS : Route d'Albi – 31380 Buzet-sur-Tarn
HOTEL :
Horizon 88 – Montastruc
Tel : 61743415
La Conseillère – Montastruc
Tel : 61842123
Mercure – Toulouse
Tel : 61231177
RESTAURANT : Darroze – Toulouse
Tel : 61623470

Toulouse-Palmola is a fine and difficult inland course with tree-lined and lush fairways and well-defended greens all set on hilly contryside. Various lakes serve as hazards. There is a spacious clubhouse with three tennis courts and a swimming pool. *SSS 72*

GF $

1974

18

Tuesdays

 M. Fenn

L 5897 P 72

Required : Handicap Certificate
Best days : Any day

HOLE	LENGTH MEDAL-TEE	PAR	STROKE INDEX
1	277	4	17
2	393	4	1
3	142	3	11
4	483	5	13
5	339	4	5
6	470	5	15
7	172	3	3
8	376	4	9
9	332	4	7
TOTAL	2984	36	TOTAL

HOLE	LENGTH MEDAL-TEE	PAR	STROKE INDEX
10	304	4	16
11	329	4	12
12	296	4	18
13	490	5	4
14	324	4	10
15	473	5	8
16	124	3	14
17	412	4	2
18	161	3	6
TOTAL	2913	36	TOTAL

TOULOUSE SEILH

TEL : 61425930
LOCATION : 12 km Toulouse to Blangnac then to Grenade
ADDRESS : Route de Grenade
31840 Aussone
HOTEL :
Novotel - Toulouse
Tel : 61493410
Hermès - Toulouse
Tel : 61476047
de l'Opéra - Toulouse
Tel : 61218266
RESTAURANT : Pujol - Blagnac
Tel : 61711358

Located near the aeronautical city of Toulouse, this golf complex with two courses is spread over 146ha of land. The main American style course (the red one) is long and rather technical. It runs partly over a plain and partly through forests and has several large water hazards affecting play. The complex comprises a golf school, a health and fitness center, plus a modern and fully equipped clubhouse. A four star hotel is scheduled soon. *SSS 69,5*

GF $

1988

36

—

J. Garaialde

L 5752 P 72, 3920 P 64

S

R

Required : Handicap Certificate
Best days : Any day

HOLE	LENGTH MEDAL-TEE	PAR	STROKE INDEX
1	309	4	15
2	305	4	9
3	157	3	13
4	399	4	1
5	455	5	14
6	173	3	5
7	318	4	11
8	437	5	7
9	313	4	3
TOTAL	2866	36	TOTAL

HOLE	LENGTH MEDAL-TEE	PAR	STROKE INDEX
10	129	3	10
11	476	5	6
12	335	4	16
13	356	4	2
14	487	5	14
15	124	3	18
16	321	4	4
17	490	5	12
18	168	3	8
TOTAL	2886	36	TOTAL

TOURAINE

TEL : 47532028
LOCATION : 11 km Tours
ADDRESS : Château de la Touche – 37510 Ballan Miré
HOTEL :
Château d'Artigny – Montbazon
Tel : 47262424
Château de Beaulieu – Joué-lès-Tours
Tel : 47532026
Domaine de la Tortinière – Montbazon
Tel : 47260019
RESTAURANT : Château de Beaulieu – Joué-lès-Tours
Tel : 47285219

This attractive golf course lies in the middle of the Loire province featuring the famous Loire Châteaux. This is one of France's most picturesque courses set in lush and undulating countryside, landscaped by trees. It features many blind holes with well-defended greens and numerous water hazards including a scenic lake guarding several of them. Its charming clubhouse, a former château, completes the scene. *SSS 71*

GF $ — 1972 — M. Fenn — 18 — L 5729 P 71

S — R

Required : Handicap Certificate during weekends only
Best days : Any day

HOLE	LENGTH MEDAL-TEE	PAR	STROKE INDEX
1	460	5	3
2	345	4	7
3	157	3	13
4	322	4	11
5	454	5	1
6	144	3	17
7	365	4	5
8	346	4	9
9	285	4	15
TOTAL	2878	36	TOTAL

HOLE	LENGTH MEDAL-TEE	PAR	STROKE INDEX
10	153	3	14
11	467	5	4
12	427	4	2
13	310	4	12
14	290	4	16
15	263	4	18
16	176	3	10
17	380	4	8
18	385	4	6
TOTAL	2851	35	TOTAL

TUMULUS

TEL : 62961450
LOCATION : 3 km Tarbes D935 to Bagnères
ADDRESS : 1, rue du Bois - 65310 Laboubère
HOTEL :
Tilleuls - Laboubère
Tel : 62931966
Président - Tarbes
Tel : 62939840
Foch - Tarbes
Tel : 62937158
RESTAURANT : Amphitryon - Tarbes
Tel : 62340899

The course lies in the foothills of the Pyrenees close to the pilgrimage town of Lourdes. Six holes cross forests dotted with natural lakes and a river, the others run through flat open landscape. The Hotel des Tilleuls is within walking distance of the course. *SSS 67*

GF $

1987

18

—

SA Lalague

L 5030 P 70

Required : None
Best days : Any day

HOLE	LENGTH MEDAL-TEE	PAR	STROKE INDEX
1	435	5	2
2	315	4	8
3	230	4	18
4	325	4	6
5	290	4	14
6	150	3	16
7	345	4	4
8	235	4	10
9	265	4	12
TOTAL	2590	36	TOTAL

HOLE	LENGTH MEDAL-TEE	PAR	STROKE INDEX
10	490	5	3
11	285	4	11
12	325	4	13
13	145	3	17
14	110	3	15
15	350	4	1
16	170	3	9
17	280	4	7
18	285	4	5
TOTAL	2440	34	TOTAL

URBAN CÉLY

TEL : (1)64380307
LOCATION : 30 km Paris A6 exit Milly-la-Forêt then to Cély
ADDRESS : Le Château - Route de St.-Germain – 77930 Cély-en-Bière
HOTEL :
Bas-Bréau - Barbizon
Tel : (1)60664005
Host. Clé d'Or - Barbizon
Tel : (1)60664096
Aigle Noir - Fontainebleau
Tel : (1) 64223265

Standing in a glorious woodland setting of majestic oak trees at 15 km from Fontainebleau and 7 km from the lovely village of Barbizon, this technically difficult championship layout will undoubtedly become one of the leading french courses. The craftily bunkered fairways and greens are surrounded by colourful flower beds, pine trees and strategic water hazards. There is a comfortable clubhouse with excellent facilities.

GF $$ — Wednesdays — S 

1990 — P. Fromager, M. Adam — 

18 — L 5739 P 72 — R

Required : Handicap Certificate
Best days : Weekdays

HOLE	LENGTH MEDAL-TEE	PAR	STROKE INDEX
1	435	5	5
2	320	4	15
3	164	3	14
4	307	4	12
5	327	4	11
6	571	5	2
7	334	4	13
8	140	3	17
9	366	4	10
TOTAL	2964	36	TOTAL

HOLE	LENGTH MEDAL-TEE	PAR	STROKE INDEX
10	408	5	6
11	306	4	16
12	331	4	8
13	308	4	9
14	184	3	3
15	505	5	1
16	132	3	18
17	310	4	7
18	291	4	4
TOTAL	2775	36	TOTAL

VALBONNE

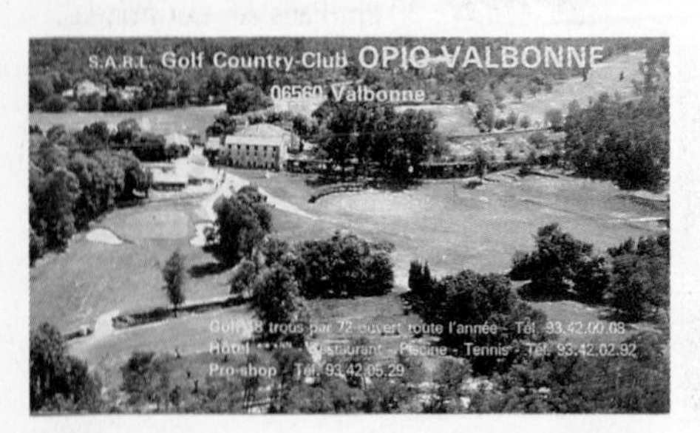

✡

TEL : 93420008
LOCATION : 12 km Cannes A 8 to Grasse exit 2, then RN 2085/RD 204
ADDRESS : Château de la Begude – 06560 Valbonne
HOTEL : HR
du Golf
Tel : 93420292
La Mourrachonne – Mouans Sartoux
Tel : 93756988
Mas Candille – Mougins
Tel : 93900085

Located 12 km from Cannes beneath the foothills of the Alps some 250 m above sea level, the golf course is built on luxuriant wooded hills and surrounded by age-old forest. It has a varied layout incorporating numerous bunkers and ponds serving as hazards. Adjoining the course is the fine clubhouse, converted from an old farmhouse, and the Golf Hotel with 20 bedrooms, tennis courts and a swimming pool.

GF $$ — S
1966 D. Harradine
18 L 5740 P 72

Required : Handicap Certificate
Best days : Fridays

HOLE	LENGTH MEDAL-TEE	PAR	STROKE INDEX
1	290	4	5
2	120	3	17
3	360	4	3
4	435	5	13
5	135	3	7
6	330	4	9
7	400	4	1
8	300	4	11
9	250	4	15
TOTAL	2620	35	TOTAL

HOLE	LENGTH MEDAL-TEE	PAR	STROKE INDEX
10	335	4	10
11	165	3	8
12	430	5	16
13	370	4	4
14	390	4	2
15	360	4	14
16	160	3	6
17	460	5	12
18	450	5	18
TOTAL	3120	37	TOTAL

VALCROS

TEL : 94668102
LOCATION : 16 km Hyères to La Londe on N 98
ADDRESS : 83250 La Londe-les-Maures
HOTEL : HR
des Cèdres
Tel : 94668073
Du Portalet – Hyères
Tel : 94653940
83 Hôtel – Le Lavandou
Tel : 94712015

Scenically and peacefully set between the Mediterranean villages of Hyères and Lavandou, its eighteen holes wind through lush valleys dotted with trees, alongside a river and small streams. The course commands excellent views of the surrounding (Porguerolles, Hyères, Port Cros). The picturesque golf hotel 'des Cedres' is on the course and has a fine swimming pool. *SSS 69*

GF $$ — Tues. in low season — R S
1965 — F. Hawtree
18 — L 4936 P 70

Required : Handicap Certificate
Best days : Any day

HOLE	LENGTH MEDAL-TEE	PAR	STROKE INDEX
1	421	5	11
2	138	3	15
3	330	4	5
4	112	3	17
5	275	4	13
6	398	4	1
7	158	3	9
8	290	4	7
9	450	5	3
TOTAL	2572	35	TOTAL

HOLE	LENGTH MEDAL-TEE	PAR	STROKE INDEX
10	138	3	10
11	240	4	14
12	421	5	4
13	482	5	2
14	117	3	16
15	334	4	6
16	260	4	8
17	110	3	18
18	262	4	12
TOTAL	2364	35	TOTAL

VAL DE CHER

TEL : 70067115
LOCATION : 17 km N. Montluçon RN 144/ RD 541
ADDRESS : 03190 Nassigny
HOTEL :
Hostellerie du Château Saint-Jean – Montluçon
Tel : 70050465
Bomotel – Montluçon
Tel : 70057622
Lion d'Or – Montluçon
Tel : 70050062
RESTAURANT : Duc de Bourbon – Montluçon
Tel : 70052279

There are nine holes laid out on flat countryside alongside the river 'Cher', featuring the 10th and the 11th holes lying on an island in the middle of the river. Five other holes are built around a scenic château on open parkland landscaped with majestic trees. *SSS 68*

GF $

1986

18

Tuesdays

G. Vigand

L 4770 P 70

S

R

Required : Handicap Certificate
Best days : Any day

HOLE	LENGTH MEDAL-TEE	PAR	STROKE INDEX
1	410	5	9
2	330	4	11
3	320	4	4
4	300	4	1
5	310	4	8
6	330	4	6
7	140	3	13
8	110	3	17
9	410	5	3
TOTAL	2660	36	TOTAL

HOLE	LENGTH MEDAL-TEE	PAR	STROKE INDEX
10	230	4	10
11	120	3	14
12	250	4	15
13	365	4	5
14	320	4	2
15	120	3	16
16	290	4	7
17	250	4	18
18	260	4	12
TOTAL	2110	34	TOTAL

VAL DE L'INDRE

TEL : 54265944
LOCATION : 12 km Châteauroux RN143 to Tours
ADDRESS : Trégonce - 36320 Villedieu-sur-Indre
HOTEL :
Elysée - Châteauroux
Tel : 54223366
Boischaut - Châteauroux
Tel : 54222234
Christina - Châteauroux
Tel : 54340177

This is a lush gentle rolling woodland course in an impressive setting of majestic cedars and centennial oaks with the picturesque river "Tregonce" meandering through three holes. It has many interesting holes particularly its challenging par 5s demanding accurate play. The course lies in the very heart of the Loire region with its 600 historical châteaux. *SSS 72*

GF $

1990

18

Tuesdays in winter

Y. Bureau

L 5716 P 72

S

R

Required : Handicap Certificate
Best days : Any day

HOLE	LENGTH MEDAL-TEE	PAR	STROKE INDEX
1	342	4	9
2	270	4	13
3	422	5	7
4	158	3	5
5	327	4	11
6	367	4	17
7	166	3	15
8	359	4	3
9	486	5	1
TOTAL	2897	36	TOTAL

HOLE	LENGTH MEDAL-TEE	PAR	STROKE INDEX
10	126	3	8
11	251	4	16
12	453	5	10
13	323	4	6
14	321	4	12
15	360	4	2
16	507	5	4
17	156	3	18
18	322	4	14
TOTAL	2819	36	TOTAL

VAL DE LOIRE

TEL : 38592515
LOCATION : 10 km E. Orléans to St.-Jean-de-Braye
ADDRESS : Château de la Touche - 45450 Donnery
HOTEL :
Novotel - St.-Jean-de-Braye
Tel : 38846565
Sofitel - Orléans
Tel : 38621739
La Capitainerie - Châteauneuf-sur-Loire
Tel : 38584216
RESTAURANT : La Crémaillère - Orléans
Tel : 38524917

The course lies in the middle of the Loire region near the city of Orléans. Originally designed by Trent Jones, the club was extended to 18 holes in 1987. It is a fairly wooded parkland course laid out on flat landscape with water coming into play on three holes. *SSS 69.7*

GF $

1953/87

18

Tuesdays in winter

R. Trent Jones, O. van der Vynckt

L 5587 P 71

S

R

Required : Handicap Certificate
Best days : Any day

HOLE	LENGTH MEDAL-TEE	PAR	STROKE INDEX
1	326	4	2
2	499	5	5
3	345	4	4
4	337	4	10
5	130	3	16
6	435	5	15
7	331	4	12
8	161	3	13
9	328	4	8
TOTAL	2892	36	TOTAL

HOLE	LENGTH MEDAL-TEE	PAR	STROKE INDEX
10	358	4	3
11	268	4	18
12	129	3	17
13	322	4	11
14	457	5	6
15	258	4	14
16	185	3	7
17	305	4	9
18	413	4	1
TOTAL	2695	35	TOTAL

VALENCE-SAINT-DIDIER

TEL : 75596701
LOCATION : 10 km Valence D 119/D 538
ADDRESS : St-Didier de Charpey-26300 Bourg-de-Péage
HOTEL :
Roch-Chabeuil
Tel : 75590023
Relais du Soleil-Chabeuil
Tel : 75590181
Hôtel 2000-Valence
Tel : 75437301
RESTAURANT : Pic-Valence
Tel : 75441532

This inland course lies in the Rhône Valley on flat countryside with three holes (3rd, 5th and 6th) running through forest. It features long and narrow fairways demanding accurate play. The golf course is often exposed to prevailing winds. There are facilities for tennis, swimming and riding nearby. *SSS 71*

GF $ — Tuesdays — S

1984 — T. Sprecher — 

18 — L 5511 P 71 — R

Required : None
Best days : Any day

HOLE	LENGTH MEDAL-TEE	PAR	STROKE INDEX
1	464	5	7
2	138	3	13
3	96	3	9
4	499	5	3
5	269	4	15
6	278	4	11
7	486	5	5
8	385	4	1
9	108	3	18
TOTAL	2723	36	TOTAL

HOLE	LENGTH MEDAL-TEE	PAR	STROKE INDEX
10	337	4	16
11	132	3	14
12	343	4	8
13	347	4	6
14	147	3	12
15	304	4	10
16	413	5	17
17	385	4	4
18	380	4	2
TOTAL	2788	35	TOTAL

VALESCURE

TEL : 94824046
LOCATION : 4 km Saint-Raphaël RN 7 to Valescure
ADDRESS : Hôtel du Golf – Valescure – 83700 Saint-Raphaël
HOTEL : HR
Mapotel Best Western
Tel : 94824031
La Cheneraie – St-Raphaël
Tel : 94836503
San Pedro – St-Raphaël
Tel : 94836569

One of the oldest clubs in France, having been founded in 1896. The short 18 hole course winds through an undulating and typically Mediterranean landscape where mature umbrella pines alternate with picturesque streams. There is a charming Provençal-style clubhouse with a fine terrace. The Golf Hotel with 40 bedrooms, is equipped with tennis courts and a swimming pool. *SSS 70*

GF $

1896

18

Weekends

—

L 4894 P 70

S

R

Required : Handicap Certificate
Best days : Weekdays only

HOLE	LENGTH MEDAL-TEE	PAR	STROKE INDEX
1	313	4	13
2	330	4	5
3	435	5	1
4	256	4	7
5	111	3	18
6	325	4	9
7	141	3	11
8	313	4	3
9	238	4	15
TOTAL	2462	35	TOTAL

HOLE	LENGTH MEDAL-TEE	PAR	STROKE INDEX
10	401	5	12
11	225	4	14
12	312	4	2
13	278	4	17
14	155	3	16
15	316	4	6
16	141	3	8
17	344	4	4
18	260	4	10
TOTAL	2432	35	TOTAL

VAL QUEVEN

TEL : 97051796
LOCATION : 5 km Lorient airport to Queven and Pont Scorf
ADDRESS : Kerrousseau - 56530 Queven
HOTEL :
Mercur - Lorient
Tel : 97213573
Lépol - Lorient
Tel : 97212316
Château de Locguénolé - Hennebont
Tel : 97762904

Set inland in southern Brittany close to several popular seaside resorts, the course skirts woods, crosses valleys, runs alongside stretches of water and even borders a tumulus. Leafy and coniferous trees line the fairways. *SSS 70*

GF $

1990

18

—

Y. Bureau

L 5752 P 72

S

R

Required : Handicap Certificate
Best days : Any day

HOLE	LENGTH MEDAL-TEE	PAR	STROKE INDEX
1	310	4	9
2	380	4	5
3	135	3	15
4	489	5	3
5	140	3	17
6	484	5	1
7	304	4	13
8	300	4	11
9	362	4	7
TOTAL	2904	36	TOTAL

HOLE	LENGTH MEDAL-TEE	PAR	STROKE INDEX
10	294	4	6
11	303	4	10
12	183	3	12
13	337	4	14
14	480	5	4
15	272	4	18
16	468	5	2
17	160	3	16
18	351	4	8
TOTAL	2848	36	TOTAL

VAUCOULEURS

TEL : (1)34876229
LOCATION : 17 km Mantes-la-Jolie to Houdan, RN 12 and RN 183
ADDRESS : 78910 Civry-la-Forêt
HOTEL :
Ibis – Mantes
Tel : (1)30596028
Plat d'Étain – Houdan
Tel : (1)30596028
Château de Berchère – Houdan
Tel : (1)37820721
RESTAURANT : La Poularde – Houdan
Tel : (1)30596050

These two recent 18 hole golf courses (the main course « La Rivière » and the shorter « Les Vallons ») are peacefully laid out on pleasant countryside amidst small and picturesque villages near Paris. Both courses feature a varied layout with its holes running along a wooded valley and incorporating an abundance of strategic lakes, large sandy bunkers and fast greens of excellent quality. The clubhouse has been converted from an old farmhouse. *SSS 74*

GF $ — Wed. in winter time — R S

1987 — M. Gayon

36 — L 6298 P 73, 5638 P 70

Required : Handicap Certificate
Best days : Weekdays

HOLE	LENGTH MEDAL-TEE	PAR	STROKE INDEX
1	326	4	17
2	507	5	7
3	198	3	11
4	300	4	13
5	495	5	5
6	403	4	1
7	154	3	15
8	461	5	9
9	385	4	3
TOTAL	3229	37	TOTAL

HOLE	LENGTH MEDAL-TEE	PAR	STROKE INDEX
10	494	5	6
11	135	3	14
12	340	4	8
13	172	3	12
14	196	3	18
15	376	4	2
16	512	5	4
17	473	5	10
18	371	4	16
TOTAL	3069	36	TOTAL

HOLE	LENGTH MEDAL-TEE	PAR	STROKE INDEX
1	290	4	17
2	177	3	7
3	477	5	5
4	170	3	9
5	434	4	1
6	291	4	11
7	130	3	13
8	286	4	15
9	516	5	3
TOTAL	2771	35	TOTAL

HOLE	LENGTH MEDAL-TEE	PAR	STROKE INDEX
10	461	5	8
11	327	4	16
12	167	3	10
13	305	4	14
14	359	4	12
15	151	3	18
16	503	5	2
17	393	4	6
18	201	3	4
TOTAL	2867	35	TOTAL

VAUGOUARD

TEL : 38958152
LOCATION : 100 km S. Paris A 6 exit Dordives/12 km Montargis
ADDRESS : Chemin des Bois – Fontenay-sur-Loing – 45210 Ferrières-en-Gâtinais
HOTEL : HR
Golf Hotel
Tel : 38957185
Climat de France – Montargis
Tel : 38982021
Gloire – Montargis
Tel : 38850469

Inaugurated in 1987 and designed by a French and a Canadian architect, its 18 holes run through wooded parkland and follow the gentle undulations of the terrain. Lakes and streams affect play on five holes. The greens are extremely large and defended by a total of 88 strategic bunkers. The golf course is the centrepiece of a large sports and leisure complex with a tennis club, a riding school, a fitness center and a hotel with 32 bedrooms.

GF $$

1987

18

—

P. Fromanger, M. Adam

L 6000 P 72

RP

Required : Handicap Certificate
Best days : Any day

HOLE	LENGTH MEDAL-TEE	PAR	STROKE INDEX
1	331	4	13
2	116	3	17
3	325	4	3
4	296	4	11
5	517	5	1
6	340	4	9
7	541	5	7
8	375	4	5
9	343	4	15
TOTAL	3184	37	TOTAL

HOLE	LENGTH MEDAL-TEE	PAR	STROKE INDEX
10	212	3	4
11	396	4	6
12	488	5	12
13	284	4	16
14	120	3	18
15	465	4	51
16	261	4	14
17	178	3	10
18	412	4	2
TOTAL	2816	35	TOTAL

VICHY

✡

TEL : 70323911
LOCATION : 2 km Vichy RN 9
ADDRESS : Allée Bougnies – 03700 Bellerive-sur-Allier
HOTEL :
Marcotel – Bellerive-sur-Allier
Tel : 70323400
Pavillon Sévigné – Vichy
Tel : 70321622
Thermalia Novotel – Vichy
Tel : 70310439
RESTAURANT : La Rhumerie – Vichy
Tel : 70315634

Located near the renowned thermal spa of Vichy, the golf course flows over gently rolling land which is densely wooded. It is varied and entertaining with several demanding holes featuring narrow fairways and well defended greens. Ponds and many strategic trees, scattered all over the course, demand accurate play. Vichy is ideal for spending a holiday as it is equipped with many sports facilities ranging from numerous tennis courts to aquatic sports on the river "l'Allier". *SSS 70*

GF $$ — Tuesdays in winter — S

1904 — P. Bourret — R

18 — L 5427 P 70

Required : Handicap Certificate
Best days : Weekdays

HOLE	LENGTH MEDAL-TEE	PAR	STROKE INDEX
1	346	4	7
2	296	4	9
3	162	3	13
4	372	4	5
5	159	3	15
6	400	4	1
7	101	3	17
8	260	4	11
9	440	5	3
TOTAL	2536	34	TOTAL

HOLE	LENGTH MEDAL-TEE	PAR	STROKE INDEX
10	297	4	16
11	407	4	2
12	130	3	18
13	459	5	4
14	298	4	12
15	295	4	14
16	359	4	6
17	181	3	10
18	465	5	8
TOTAL	2891	36	TOTAL

VIEILLE TOULOUSE

TEL : 61734548
LOCATION : 8 km N. Toulouse to Lacroix Falgarde
ADDRESS : 31230 Vieille Toulouse
HOTEL :
La Flânerie – Vieille Toulouse
Tel : 61733912
Frantel Wilson – Toulouse
Tel : 61212175
Diane – Le Mirail
Tel : 61075952
RESTAURANT : Vanel – Toulouse
Tel : 61215182

This hilly course winds through an undulating landscape, laid out above the town of Toulouse and overlooking the Garonne Valley. It is scattered with strategic trees, and features treacherous doglegs. Among its most testing holes is the 14th having a difficult green, defended by two strategic bunkers and a pond. *SSS 71*

GF $

1951

18

Tuesdays

F. Hawtree

L 5602 P 71

Required : Handicap Certificate
Best days : Weekdays

HOLE	LENGTH MEDAL-TEE	PAR	STROKE INDEX
1	480	5	6
2	246	4	4
3	134	3	16
4	359	4	10
5	178	3	8
6	287	4	18
7	462	5	9
8	130	3	17
9	475	5	11
TOTAL	2751	36	TOTAL

HOLE	LENGTH MEDAL-TEE	PAR	STROKE INDEX
10	278	4	7
11	402	4	1
12	397	4	3
13	275	4	15
14	188	3	13
15	346	4	5
16	348	4	12
17	462	5	2
18	155	3	14
TOTAL	2851	35	TOTAL

VILLARCEAUX

TEL : (1)34677383
LOCATION : 55 km Paris A 13 exit Mantes then RD 183, RD 142 and RD 86
ADDRESS : 95710 Chaussy – Bray Lu
HOTEL :
Cheval Blanc – Magny-en-Vexin
Tel : (1)34670037
Château de la Rapée – Gisors
Tel : 32551161
Moulin de Fourges – Fourges
Tel : (1)32521212
RESTAURANT : Auberge Saint-Christophe – Vétheuil
Tel : (1)34781150

This picturesque course runs over undulating open parkland featuring numerous bunkers and rolling greens with the green of the short 9th hole defended by ponds on both sides. It features an attractive clubhouse, which is a scenic château and 4 tennis courts. *SSS 72*

GF $

1970

18

Thursdays in winter

M. Becker

L 5930 P 72

Required : Handicap Certificate
Best days : Weekdays ; Weekends by arrangement

HOLE	LENGTH MEDAL-TEE	PAR	STROKE INDEX
1	352	4	13
2	390	4	3
3	201	3	9
4	437	5	11
5	339	4	7
6	437	5	17
7	371	4	5
8	401	4	1
9	166	3	15
TOTAL	3094	36	TOTAL

HOLE	LENGTH MEDAL-TEE	PAR	STROKE INDEX
10	475	5	2
11	152	3	12
12	440	5	10
13	365	4	4
14	328	4	8
15	304	4	6
16	319	4	4
17	129	3	18
18	324	4	4
TOTAL	2836	36	TOTAL

VITTEL

✡★

TEL : 29080638/29081880
LOCATION : 1 km Vittel
ADDRESS : 11, Chemin d'Enfrier – 88800 Vittel
HOTEL : HR
Ermitage
Tel : 29081880
Angleterre – Vittel
Tel : 29080842
Bellevue – Vittel
Tel : 29080798
RESTAURANT : L'Aubergade-Vittel
Tel : 29080439

Both golf courses (Mont Saint-Jean and Peulin), situated in the dynamic health resort of Vittel in the Vosges region, are administered by the 'Club Mediterranée', and laid out in beautiful and densely wooded landscape on rather hilly terrain. An abundance of strategically placed trees demand precision. The excellent Ermitage Hotel dominates the Mont Saint-Jean course. Other facilities include a short 9 hole course, numerous tennis courts, riding school, and swimming pools. There is an excellent golf school with intensive training sessions available. *SSS 72/72*

GF $

1905/1989

36

October to May

J. Morrison, T. Allison, W. Martin

L 6271 P 72, 6100 P 72

S 

RP

Required : Handicap Certificate
Best days : Any day by arrangement

HOLE	LENGTH MEDAL-TEE	PAR	STROKE INDEX
1	266	4	15
2	373	4	1
3	426	4	3
4	165	3	9
5	550	5	13
6	397	4	5
7	334	4	17
8	496	5	11
9	200	3	7
TOTAL	3207	36	TOTAL

HOLE	LENGTH MEDAL-TEE	PAR	STROKE INDEX
10	484	5	6
11	327	4	18
12	331	4	6
13	481	5	10
14	168	3	16
15	312	4	14
16	404	4	2
17	176	3	4
18	381	4	12
TOTAL	3064	36	TOTAL

VOLCANS

TEL : 73621551
LOCATION : 12 km Clermont-Ferrand RN 141
ADDRESS : La Bruyère des Moines – 63870 Orcines
HOTEL :
Pullman Splendid – Châtelguyon
Tel : 73860480
Chez Pichon – Orcines
Tel : 73621005
Relais des Puys – La Baraque
Tel : 73621051
RESTAURANT :
Auberge des Touristes – Durtol
Tel : 73378464

This 18 hole golf course is set beneath the foothills of the Puy de Dôme, an extinct volcano, in the middle of a beech and pine forest at 900m above sea level. Most of the long holes have narrow fairways, flanked by heather, and large greens, many of them having different levels. There is a short 9 hole golf course.

GF $

 —

 S

1986

L. Roux

27

L 6242 P 72

Required : Handicap Certificate
Best days : Any day

HOLE	LENGTH MEDAL-TEE	PAR	STROKE INDEX
1	357	4	11
2	484	5	13
3	350	4	6
4	350	4	8
5	169	3	10
6	463	5	15
7	429	4	1
8	197	3	16
9	389	4	3
TOTAL	3188	36	TOTAL

HOLE	LENGTH MEDAL-TEE	PAR	STROKE INDEX
10	345	4	4
11	340	4	9
12	390	4	2
13	190	3	14
14	445	5	17
15	335	4	12
16	517	5	7
17	139	3	18
18	353	4	5
TOTAL	3054	36	TOTAL

WIMEREUX

TEL : 21324320
LOCATION : 2 km N. Wimereux RD 940, 25 km Calais
ADDRESS : Route d'Ambleteuse – 62930 Wimereux
HOTEL :
Aramis – Wimereux
Tel : 21324015
Centre – Wimereux
Tel : 21324108
Paul & Virginie – Wimereux
Tel : 21324212
RESTAURANT : La Matelote – Boulogne-sur-Mer
Tel : 21301797

Set beside the sea, this is a long and popular seaside course of links character running over the dunes which are landscaped by pines. The 2nd and 12th holes commend fine views of the rugged countryside and the coast. Another 9 hole course is planned for the near future. *SSS 72*

GF $ | — | R S
1907 | T. Simpson
18 | L 5887 P 72

Required : Handicap Certificate
Best days : Weekdays

HOLE	LENGTH MEDAL-TEE	PAR	STROKE INDEX
1	514	5	7
2	202	3	9
3	295	4	13
4	342	4	3
5	349	4	5
6	164	3	17
7	471	5	1
8	301	4	15
9	339	4	1
TOTAL	2977	36	TOTAL

HOLE	LENGTH MEDAL-TEE	PAR	STROKE INDEX
10	181	3	10
11	296	4	14
12	150	3	18
13	337	4	2
14	374	4	4
15	360	4	6
16	296	4	8
17	448	5	16
18	468	5	12
TOTAL	2910	36	TOTAL

des YVELINES

★

TEL : (1)34864889
LOCATION : 45 km Paris A13 exit Bois d'Arcy, then N12 to La Queue-lez-Yvelines
ADDRESS : Château de la Couharde - 78940 La Queue-lez-Yvelines
HOTEL :
Le Verbois - Neauphile-le-Château
Tel : (1)34891178
Trianon Palace - Versailles
Tel : (1)39503412

At only 45 km from Paris near the charming village of Montfort-l'Amaury, this attractive and heavily wooded course is built around the historical Château de la Couharde which now serves as clubhouse. It stretches out over beautiful rolling parklands with centennial trees such as cedars, pines and oaks bordering the fairways. The club will certainly become one of the popular golfing venues of the french capital.

GF $$ | Tuesdays | S
1990 | B. Baker |
27 | L 6344 P 72 | R

Required : Handicap Certificate
Best days : Weekdays

HOLE	LENGTH MEDAL-TEE	PAR	STROKE INDEX
1			
2			
3			
4			
5			
6			
7			
8			
9			
TOTAL			TOTAL

HOLE	LENGTH MEDAL-TEE	PAR	STROKE INDEX
10			
11			
12			
13			
14			
15			
16			
17			
18			
TOTAL			TOTAL

GERMANY

Car Rental

Reservation/Information telephone number :

Country code : 49

Telephone number : 40/52018211

Headquarters address :

INTERRENT - EUROPCAR GmbH
Tangstedter Landstrasse 81, 2000 Hamburg 62
Tel. : (49) 40/520180
Telex : 2174308
Fax : (49) 40/52018452

300 GOLF COURSES, 130 000 PLAYERS

★★★ Great golf course
★★ Very good golf course
$ 20-50 DM
★ Recommended golf course
✡ Holiday golf course
$ $ more than 60 DM

TOWN	GOLF COURSE		TEL	MAP REF.
Aachen	Aachen		(0241) 12501	31
	Offentliche Aachen		(0241) 82300	•
Ahaus	Ahaus		(02561) 1068	•
Alfdorf	Haghof		(07182) 3040	•
Ansbach	Ansbach		(09803) 262	•
Aschaffenburg	Aschaffenburg		(06024) 7222	•
Augsburg	Augsburg		(08234) 5621	63
	Leitershofen		(0821) 434919	•
Aukrug	Mittelholsteinischer Aukrug		(04873) 595	76
Bad Bramstedt	Bad Bramstedt		(04192) 3444	•
Bad Driburg	Bad Driburg		(05253) 842349	•
Bad Ems	Mittelrheinischer	★★	(02603) 6541	34
Bad Griesbach	Rottaler		(08561) 2861	112
	Sagmühle	★ ✡	(08532) 2038	105
	Steigenberger Country Club		(08532) 7418	•
Bad Harzburg	Bad Harzburg		(05322) 1096	•
Bad Herrenalb	Herrenalb-Bernbach		(07083) 8898	•
Bad Kissingen	Bad Kissingen	✡	(0971) 3608	39
Bad König	Odenwald		(06151) 592521	•
Bad Liebenszell	Bad Liebenszell		(07052) 4353	•
Bad Mergentheim	Bad Mergentheim		(07931) 7579	•
Bad Münster	Nahetal		(06708) 2145	77
Bad Nauheim	Bad Nauheim		(06032) 2153	•
Bad Neuenahr	Bad Neuenahr-Ahrweiler	★	(02641) 6693	32
Bad Orb	Spessart		(06056) 3594	108
Bad Pyrmont	Pyrmonter		(05281) 8196	•
	Schlosshotel Schwöbber	★	(05154) 2004	88
Bad Salzdetfurth	Hildesheim		(05063) 1516	•
Bad Salzuflen	Bad Salzuflen		(05222) 10773	•
Bad Tölz	Bad Tölz		(0804) 9994	•
Bad Waldsee	Bad Waldsee	✡	(07524) 5900	51

TOWN	GOLF COURSE		TEL	MAP REF.
Bad Wiessee	Tegernseer	★ ✡	(08022) 8769	57
Bad Wildungen	Bad Wildungen		(05621) 3767	•
Bad Wörishofen	Bad Wörishofen	✡	(08346) 777	53
Baden Baden	Baden Baden	✡	(07221) 23579	46
Badenweiler	Badenweiler Rhein		(07632) 5031	78
Bamberg	Bamberg		(09547) 1524	100
Bayreuth	Oberfranken Bayreuth	★	(09228) 319	79
Bensheim	Bensheim		(06251) 67732	•
Berchtesgaden	Berchtesgaden		(08652) 2100	•
Berlin	Berlin-Wannsee		(030) 8055075	•
Beuerberg	Beuerberg		(08179) 617	64
Bielefeld	Bielefelder		(0521) 105103	•
Blieskastel	Saar-Pfalz		(06834) 8797	•
Blomberg-Cappel	Lippischer		(05236) 459	61
Bochum	Bochumer		(0234) 799832	•
Bonn	Bonn-Godesberg		(0228) 344003	58
Bottrop-Kirchhellen	Schwarze Heide		(02045) 82488	•
Braunfels	Schloss Braunfels	★★	(06442) 4530	33
Braunschweig	Braunschweig		(0531) 691369	15
Bremen	Bremen zur Vahr	★★★	(0421) 230041	11
	Oberneuland		(0421) 259321	•
Buchholz	Buchholz		(04181) 36200	89
Burg	Fehmarn		(04371) 5900	•
Burghausen	Schloss Piesing		(08679) 7001	113
Büsum	Ditmarschen		(04834) 6300	•
Celle	Herzogstadt Celle		(05086) 395	102
Chieming	Im Chiemgau	✡	(08669) 7557	65
Coburg	Schloss Tambach		(09567) 1212	•
Cuxhaven	Küsten Hohe Klint	✡	(04723) 2737	1
Darmstadt	Darmstadt Traisa		(06151) 146543	•
	Odenwald		(06151) 592521	•
Deggendorf	Rusel		(09920) 911	•
Donaueschingen	Öschberghof	★	(0771) 84525	50
Dortmund	Castrop-Rauxel		(02305) 62027	114
	Dortmunder		(0231) 774133	20
Düren	Düren		(02421) 67278	•
Düsseldorf	Auf der Lausward		(0211) 3965598	•
	Düsseldorf Kosaido		(02104) 77060	25
	Düsseldorfer	★★	(02102) 81092	24
	Hösel		(02102) 68629	91
	Hubbelrath	★★★	(02104) 72178	25
	Niederrheinischer		(0203) 721469	•
	Schloss Myllendonck		(02161) 641049	23
Ebermannstadt	Fränkische Schweiz		(09194) 9228	133
Eckernförde	Altenhof		(04351) 41227	80
Eggenfelden	Rottaler		(08561) 2861	•
Elze	Rheden		(05182) 2680	•
Ennigerloh	Schloss Vornholz		(2587) 464	•
Erding	Erding-Grünbach		(08122) 6465	132
Erfweiler	Saar Pfalz		(06843) 8797	•
Erlangen	Erlangen		(09126) 5040	•
Essen	Essen-Heidhausen		(0201) 404111	21
	Essen-Kettwig		(02054) 83911	21
	Etuf		(0201) 441426	•
Fallingbostel	Tietlingen		(05162) 3889	•
Feldkirchen	Mangfalltall		(08063) 6300	•
Föhr	Föhr		(04681) 3277	•
Frankfurt	Frankfurter	★★	(069) 666231-7	37
	Hanau	★	(06181) 82071	38
	Homburg		(06172) 38808	•
	Kronberg	★	(06173) 1426	35
	Taunus Weilrod	★	(06083) 1883	87
Freiburg	Freiburger		(07661) 5569	101
Freudenstadt	Freudenstadt		(07441) 3060	•
Fulda	Rhön-Fulda		(06657) 1334	81
Furth im Wald	Furth im Wald		(09973) 1240	•
Garmisch-Partenkirchen	Garmisch-Partenkirchen		(08824) 8344	•
	Werdenfels		(08821) 2473	•
Geiselwind	Geiselwind	★	(09556) 800	122
Geldern	Issum-Niederrhein		(02835) 3626	17
Gem	Worpswede		(04763) 7313	•
Gessertshausen	Stauden am Weiherhof		(08238) 3727	•

TOWN	GOLF COURSE	TEL	MAP REF.
Gifhorn	Gifhorn	(05371) 16737	•
Glücksburg	Förde Glücksburg	(04631) 2547	•
Gmund	Margarethenhof am Tegernsee ★ ☼	(08022) 7366	66
Göppingen	Hohenstaufen	(07162) 27171	•
Grafing	Grafing-Oberelkofen	(08092) 7494	•
Grambek	Gut Grambek	(04542) 4627	82
Grössensee	Grössensee	(04154) 6261	•
Gutach	Gütermann-Gutach	(07681) 21243	•
Gütersloh	Westfälischer Gütersloh	(05244) 2340	16
Hachenburg	Westerwald	(02666) 8220	•
Hagen	Markischer Club Hagen	(02334) 51778	•
Hamburg	Am Sachsenwald	(04104) 6120	115
	Auf der Pinnau	(04106) 81800	69
	Auf der Wendlohe ★★	(040) 5505014/5	85
	Buxtehüde	(04161) 81333	90
	Grössensee	(04154) 6261	•
	Gut Immenbeck	(04161) 87699	•
	Gut Kaden	(04193) 1420	96
	Gut Waldhof	(04194) 383	•
	Hamburg Ahrensburg ★★	(04102) 51309	3
	Hamburg Falkenstein ★★★	(040) 812177	8
	Hamburg Walddörfer ★★	(040) 6051337	7
	Hamburger Land ★	(04105) 2331	9
	Hoisdorf	(04107) 7831	5
	Jersbek	(04532) 23555	116
	Wentdorf Reinbeker	(040) 7202610	•
Hamm	Stahlberg Lippetal	(02527) 8191	•
Hannover	Burgdorf ★	(05085) 7628	14
	Hannover	(05137) 73068	13
	Herzogstadt Celle	(05086) 395	•
	Isernhagen a/Gut Lohne	(05139) 2998	103
Hechingen	Hechingen-Hohenzollern	(07471) 2600	•
Heidelberg	Heidelberg Lobenfeld ★	(06226) 40490	42
Heilbronn	Heilbronn Hohenlohe	(07941) 62801	123
Heiligenhafen	Heiligenhafen	(04362) 5505	•
Herford	Heerhof	(05228) 7453	•
	Herford	(05228) 7434	•
	Internationaler Exter	(05228) 7453	•
Herzogenaurach	Herzogenaurach	(09132) 83628	•
Hillesheim	Eifel Hillesheim	(06593) 1241	•
Hof	Hof	(09281) 437849	•
Höslwang	In Chiemgau	(08075) 714	•
Husum	Husumer Bucht	(04841) 72238	•
Hünxe	Dinslaken	(02858) 6480	•
Idstein	Idstein-Wörsdorf	(06126) 8866	129
Ingolstadt	Ingolstadt	(0841) 85778	•
	Wittelsbacher	(08431) 44118	131
Isselburg	Wasserburg-Anholt	(02874) 3444	111
Jettingen	Schloss Klingenberg-Günzburg ★	(08225) 30320	62
Kaltenkirchen	Gut Waldhof	(04194) 383	4
Kandern	Markgräflerland	(07626) 8690	•
Kassel	Kassel-Wilhelmshöhe	(0561) 33509	29
Kemnath bei Fuhrn	Oberpfälzer Wald *(15 holes)*	(09439) 466	•
Kiel	Kitzeberg	(0431) 23404	•
Kierspe	Varmert	(02269) 7299	•
Kitzingen	Schloss Maisondheim	(09324) 4656	•
Kleve	Schloss Moyland	(02824) 4947	•
Köln	Burg Overbach	(02245) 5550	92
	Köln Marienburg	(0221) 384054	•
	Köln Refrath ★★	(02204) 63114	30
	Rhein Sieg	(02242) 6501	104
	Schloss Georghausen ★	(02207) 4938	28
	Waldbrunnen	(02645) 15621	•
Königsbrunn	Auf dem Lechfeld	(08231) 32637	•
	Königsbrunn	(08231) 31153	•
Königsfeld	Königsfeld	(07725) 2477	130
Konradsheim	Burg Konradsheim	(02235) 76094	•
Konstanz	Konstanz	(07533) 5124	83
Krefeld	Krefelder ★★	(02151) 570071	22
	Stadtwald	(02151) 590243	•

TOWN	GOLF COURSE	TEL	MAP REF.
Lage	Gut Ottenhausen	(05232) 66829	•
Lahr	Ortenau	(07821) 77227	•
Lichtenau	Lichtenau	(09827) 6907	•
Lindau	Bodensee (see Switzerland) ☼	(08389) 89190	73
	Lindau Bad Schachen ★ ☼	(08382) 78090	73
Lingen	Emstal	(0591) 63837	•
Löhne	Widukindlage	(05731) 52073	•
Lüdenscheid	Gelstern	(02351) 152426	•
Lüneburg	Schloss Lüdersburg	(04153) 6715	106
	St Dionys ★	(04133) 6277	10
Mannheim	Mannheim-Viernheim	(06204) 71307	•
	Rheintal (U.S. Army)	(0621) 101055	41
Marburg	Oberhessischer	(06427) 8558	•
Marktl	Falkenhof Burghausen	(08678) 207	•
Marienfeld	Marienfeld	(05247) 8880	•
Mönchengladbach	Schloss Myllendonk	(02161) 641049	23
München	Dachau	(08131) 10879	•
	Eberle Grünwald	(089) 6414262	•
	Erding Grünbach	(08122) 6465	•
	Eschenried	(08131) 3238	•
	Feldafing ★★★ ☼	(08157) 7005/06	55
	Hohenpähl	(08808) 1330	117
	Isarwinkel	(08041) 3210	•
	München Dachau	(08131) 10879	•
	München Nord Eichenried	(08123) 1004	118
	Münchner ★	(08170) 450	54
	Münchner Thalkirchen	(089) 7231304	•
	Olching ★	(08142) 3240	60
	Schloss Reichertshausen	(08441) 7004	•
	Starnberg	(08151) 21977	109
	St Eurach ★ ☼	(08801) 1332	56
	Thalkirchen	(089) 7231304	•
	Tutzing ★★	(08158) 3600	71
	Wörthsee ★ ☼	(08153) 2425	75
Münster	Brückhausen Everswinkel	(02582) 227	•
	Münster Wilkinghage	(0251) 211201	84
	Münsterland Burgsteinfurt	(02551) 5178	•
Neheim-Hüsten	Sauerland	(02932) 31546	•
Neresheim	Hochstadt	(07326) 7979	•
Neunburg	Oberpfälzer Wald	(09439) 466	•
Neustadt	Pfalz	(06327) 2973	40
Norderney	Norderney	(04932) 680	•
Nordkirchen	Nordkirchen	(02596) 3005	•
Northeim	Göttingen	(05551) 61915	85
Nürnberg	Franken Abenberg	(09178) 5541	124
	Nürnberg ★★	(0911) 305730	45
Oberaula	Kurhessischer Oberaula	(06628) 1573	119
Oberstaufen	Oberstaufen Steibis	(08386) 8529	•
Obernkirchen	Schaumburg	(05724) 4670	•
Oberstdorf	Oberstdorf	(08322) 2895	•
Oldenburg	Oldenburg	(04402) 7240	93
Osnabrück	Dütetal	(05404) 5296	•
	Osnabrücker	(05402) 636	86
	Velper	(05456) 419	•
Ottobeuren	Allgäuer ★	(08332) 1310	94
Paderborn	Paderborner Land	(05258) 6498	•
Papenburg	Gutshof Papenburg	(04961) 74811	•
Passau	Donau Rassbach	(08501) 1313	125
Pforzheim	Karlhäuser Hof	(07237) 1284	120
Polle Holzminden	Weserbergland	(05535) 270	•
Prien	Prien Chiemsee	(08051) 62215	•
Puschendorf	Puschendorf	(09101) 7552	•
Ratingen	Düsseldorf-Hösel	(02102) 68629	•
Recklinghausen	Vestischer Recklinghausen	(02361) 26520	18
Regensburg	Regensburg	(09403) 505	49
Reichertshausen	Schloss Reichertshausen	(08441) 7004	•
Reisbach	Schlossberg	(08734) 356	97
Reit im Winkl	Reit im Winkl	(08640) 8216	•
Rendsburg	Lohersand	(04336) 3333	•
Reutlingen	Reutlingen-Sonnenbühl	(07128) 3532	126
Rickenbach	Rickenbach	(07765) 888300	•
Rotenburg	Wümme	(04263) 3352	•

TOWN	GOLF COURSE		TEL	MAP REF.
Rudelzhausen	Holledau		(08756) 1700	127
Saarbrücken	Saarbrücken	★	(06837) 841/401	44
Salzgitter	Salzgitter Liebenburg		(05341) 37376	•
Schmallenberg	Schmallenberg		(02972) 5034	•
Schmidmühlen	Schmidmühlen		(09474) 701	•
Schotten	Schotten		(06044) 1375	•
Soltau	Soltau		(05191) 14077	70
Sonthofen	Sonnenalp	★★ ✡	(08321) 7276	52
St-Peter-Ording	Nordsee		(04863) 1545	•
Starnberg	Leutstetten		(08151) 8811	128
Stromberg	Stromberg-Schindeldorf		(06724) 5204	110
Stuttgart	Golfoase Pfullinger Hof		(07138) 67442	•
	Haghof Alfdorf		(07182) 3040	•
	Neckartal Stuttgart		(07141) 871319	47
	Schloss Liebenstein	★	(07133) 16019	68
	Schloss Weitenburg	★	(07472) 8061	98
	Stuttgarter Solitude	★★	(07044) 6909	48
Sylt Island	Marine Westerland		(04651) 7037	•
	Morsum		(04654) 387	•
	St-Peter-Ording		(04863) 3545	•
	Sylt Kampen	✡	(04651) 45311	121
Tecklenburg	Tecklenburger land		(05455) 1035	•
Thyrnau bei Passau	Donau Rassbach		(08501) 1313	•
Timmendorferstrand	Timmendorferstrand	✡	(04503) 5152	2
Travemünde	Lübeck Travemünder		(04502) 74018	•
Trier	Trier-Mosel		(06507) 4374	•
Ulm	Neu-Ulm (14 holes)		(07306) 2102	•
Versmold Schulten	Hof Peckloh		(05423) 7052	•
Waldkirchen	Bayerwald		(08581) 1040	•
Waldsassen	Stiftland		(09638) 1271	•
Warendorf	Warendorfer		(02586) 1792	•
Wenden	Siegen Olpe		(02762) 7589	•
Wegberg	Schmitzhof Wegberg		(02436) 479	107
Werl	Werl		(02922) 2522	•
Wiesbaden	Main Taunus		(06122) 52208	99
	Rhein-Main		(06121) 373014	36
	Wiesbadener		(06121) 460238	•
Wiesloch	Wiesloch Hohenhardter Hof		(06222) 72081	72
Wiesmoor	Ostfriesland		(04944) 3040	59
Wiggensbach	Oberallgäu	✡	(08370) 733	74
Wildeshausen	Wildeshausen		(04431) 1232	•
Wilhelmshaven	Wilhelmshaven		(04425) 1721	•
Windhagen	Waldbrunnen		(02645) 15621	•
Winterberg	Winterberg		(02981) 1770	•
Worpswede	Worpswede		(04763) 7313	•
Wuppertal	Bergisch Land		(02053) 7177	26
	Juliana Wuppertal	★	(0202) 6475753	27
Würzburg	Würzburg Kitzingen		(09321) 4956	43
Zernien	Braasche		(05863) 556	•

NEW GOLF COURSES (18 HOLES OR MORE) TO OPEN SOON

Golf Club 'Buchenhof' Hetzbach
6124 Beerfelden im Odenwald
Tel. : (06068) 3908

Golf Club Grömitz
2433 Grömitz
Tel. : (04562) 3990

Golf Club Pfaffing
8098 Pfaffing
Tel. : (08076) 1718

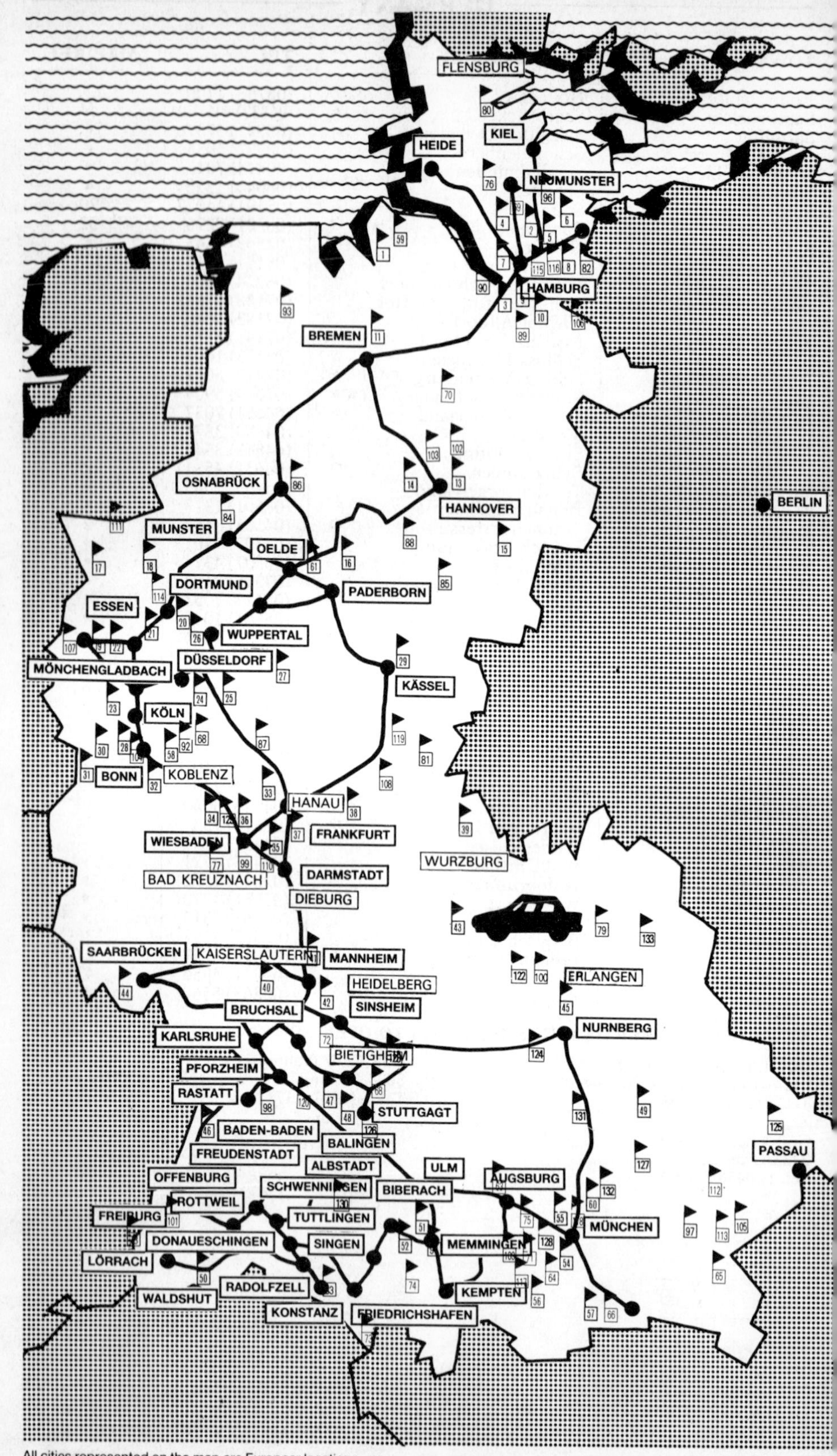

All cities represented on the map are Europcar locations.

AACHENER

TEL : (0241)12501
LOCATION : 5 km Aachen
ADDRESS : Schurzelter Strasse 300 – 5100 Aachen-Seffent
HOTEL :
Quellenhof – Aachen
Tel : (0241)152081
Aquis Grana – Aachen
Tel : (0241)4430
Novotel – Aachen
Tel : (0241)164091
RESTAURANT : La Becasse – Aachen
Tel : (0241)74444

The golf course is located close to the Dutch border on rolling parkland. Many of the fairways are flanked by stately trees. The only problem on this course is the numerous smallish greens, demanding great accuracy. The first-class Quellenhof Hotel is 3 km from the course. *SSS 71*

GF $

1927

18

November to March

H. Colt, M. Alison, J. Morrison

L 5903 P 71

S

R

Required : Handicap Certificate
Best days : Any day

HOLE	LENGTH MEDAL-TEE	PAR	STROKE INDEX
1	305	4	11
2	160	3	15
3	290	4	17
4	325	4	9
5	350	4	7
6	543	5	1
7	205	3	5
8	340	4	13
9	388	4	3
TOTAL	2906	35	TOTAL

HOLE	LENGTH MEDAL-TEE	PAR	STROKE INDEX
10	337	4	8
11	354	4	2
12	442	5	14
13	189	3	6
14	330	4	16
15	145	3	18
16	388	4	4
17	436	5	12
18	376	4	10
TOTAL	2997	36	TOTAL

ALLGAUER

★

TEL : (08332)1310
LOCATION : 15 km Memmingen to Eldern
ADDRESS : Hofgut Boschach - 8942 Ottobeuren
HOTEL :
Hirsch – Ottobeuren
Tel : (08332)799-0
Renate – Ottobeuren
Tel : (08334)1012
Algäuer Tor - Grönenbach
Tel : (08334) 6080
RESTAURANT : Landhaus Haase – Probstried
Tel : (08374)8010

Laid out in the undulating foothills of the Alps near the spa resort of Ottobeuren, this is a one of Germany's sporting championship layouts. Its main characteristics are broad fairways, various water hazards and large well-defended greens set within a sparse vegetation. Another six holes have been opened recently. There is a fine view of the basilica of Ottobeuren. *SSS 72*

GF $

1984

18

November to March

—

L 6215 P 72

R S

Required : Handicap Certificate
Best days : Any day

HOLE	LENGTH MEDAL-TEE	PAR	STROKE INDEX
1	508	5	7
2	355	4	9
3	176	3	13
4	530	5	1
5	375	4	11
6	328	4	17
7	174	3	5
8	325	4	15
9	405	4	3
TOTAL	3176	36	TOTAL

HOLE	LENGTH MEDAL-TEE	PAR	STROKE INDEX
10	350	4	8
11	345	4	10
12	480	5	4
13	164	3	16
14	405	4	2
15	460	5	12
16	310	4	14
17	140	3	18
18	385	4	6
TOTAL	3039	36	TOTAL

ALTENHOF

TEL : (04351)41227
LOCATION : 5 km S. Eckernförde
ADDRESS : 2330 Altenhof
HOTEL :
Herrenhaus – Eckernförde
Tel : (04351)41428
Seelust – Eckernförde
Tel : (04351)5075
RESTAURANT : Sandkrug – Eckernförde
Tel : (04351)41493

Located in Schleswig – Holstein about 100m from the imposing castle 'Schloss Altenhof', this is a typical parkland course built on undulating land overlooking low hills and valleys. Many of the holes are long and are lined by stately ancient trees. *SSS 72*

GF $

1971

18

November to March

—

L 6071 P 72

R S

Required : Handicap Certificate
Best days : Weekdays only

HOLE	LENGTH MEDAL-TEE	PAR	STROKE INDEX
1	462	5	
2	398	4	
3	112	3	
4	374	4	
5	423	4	
6	376	4	
7	371	4	
8	171	3	
9	475	5	
TOTAL	3162	36	TOTAL

HOLE	LENGTH MEDAL-TEE	PAR	STROKE INDEX
10	169	3	
11	480	5	
12	478	5	
13	352	4	
14	300	4	
15	140	3	
16	329	4	
17	472	5	
18	189	3	
TOTAL	2909	36	TOTAL

AM REICHSWALD-NÜRNBERG

★★

TEL : (0911)305730/50
LOCATION : 10 km Nürnberg
ADDRESS : 8500 Nürnberg-Kraftshof
HOTEL :
Schindlerhof – Nürnberg-Boxdorf
Tel : (0911)302077
Atrium – Nürnberg
Tel : (0911)47480
Maritim – Nürnberg
Tel : (0911)23630
RESTAURANT : Schwarzer Adler – Nürnberg-Kraftshof
Tel : (0911)392121

The Nürnberg golf course is of championship standard and is laid out in a setting of scenic beauty amidst centuries old trees alternating with picturesque streams and ponds. All the fairways are separated from each other by large pine trees. The clubhouse is cosy and welcoming. *SSS 72*

GF $

1960

18

December to March

—

L 6193 P 72

Required : Handicap Certificate
Best days : Weekdays

HOLE	LENGTH MEDAL-TEE	PAR	STROKE INDEX
1	350	4	11
2	175	3	15
3	455	5	7
4	385	4	3
5	155	3	17
6	300	4	13
7	500	5	5
8	410	4	1
9	355	4	9
TOTAL	3085	36	TOTAL

HOLE	LENGTH MEDAL-TEE	PAR	STROKE INDEX
10	382	4	2
11	190	3	14
12	490	5	10
13	370	4	6
14	125	3	18
15	394	4	4
16	350	4	12
17	437	5	16
18	370	4	8
TOTAL	3108	36	TOTAL

AM SACHSENWALD

TEL : (04104)6120
LOCATION : 15 km E. Hamburg
B 207/B 404
ADDRESS : Am Riesenbett
2055 Dassendorf
HOTEL :
Sachsenwald Congress - Reinbeck
Tel : (040)727610
Fährhaus Ziehl - Geesthacht
Tel : (04152)3041
RESTAURANT : Jagdhaus am Riesenbett
Dassendorf
Tel : (04104)2174

Situated on level ground and flanked by the Sachsenwald forest, the course has a varied layout. It features several long holes, strategic trees scattered all over, a stream crossing a green and some small creeks serving as hazards. *SSS 72*

GF $

1985

18

—

—

L 6118 P 72

S

R

Required : Handicap Certificate
Best days : Any day

HOLE	LENGTH MEDAL-TEE	PAR	STROKE INDEX
1	448	5	15
2	384	4	7
3	179	3	3
4	381	4	9
5	473	5	5
6	329	4	13
7	329	4	11
8	370	4	1
9	123	3	17
TOTAL	3016	36	TOTAL

HOLE	LENGTH MEDAL-TEE	PAR	STROKE INDEX
10	425	4	2
11	340	4	14
12	533	5	6
13	322	4	18
14	346	4	8
15	178	3	4
16	353	4	12
17	154	3	16
18	451	5	10
TOTAL	3102	36	TOTAL

AN DER PINNAU

TEL : (04106)81800
LOCATION : In Quickborn-Renzel/20 km Hamburg BAB to Flensburg
ADDRESS : Pinneberger Strasse 81 a – 2085 Quickborn-Renzel
HOTEL :
Sporthotel – Quickborn
Tel : (04106)4091
Quickborn – Quickborn
Tel : (04106)4091
RESTAURANT : Jagdhaus Waldfrieden – Quickborn
Tel : (04106)3771

Located on the outskirts of the city of Hamburg, the course is set in natural surroundings amongst young and old trees. The various well-placed water hazards present constant difficulties. The course is partly flanked by the river 'Pinnau'. *SSS 72*

GF $

1983

18

—

—

L 6115 P 72

R S

Required : Handicap Certificate
Best days : Weekdays

HOLE	LENGTH MEDAL-TEE	PAR	STROKE INDEX
1	340	4	5
2	325	4	9
3	490	5	1
4	167	3	15
5	315	4	7
6	343	4	11
7	405	4	17
8	181	3	13
9	355	4	3
TOTAL	2921	35	TOTAL

HOLE	LENGTH MEDAL-TEE	PAR	STROKE INDEX
10	509	5	4
11	345	4	6
12	252	4	14
13	495	5	2
14	401	4	18
15	313	4	8
16	360	4	10
17	153	3	16
18	366	4	12
TOTAL	3194	37	TOTAL

AUF DER WENDLOHE

★★

TEL : (040)5505014/5
LOCATION : 10 km Hamburg BAB to Kiel exit Hamburg Schnelsen Nord
ADDRESS : Oldesloerstrasse 251 – 2000 Hamburg 61 – Schnelsen
HOTEL :
Novotel Nord – Hamburg
Tel : (040)5502073
Alsterkrug – Hamburg
Tel : (040)513030
RESTAURANT : Zum Wattkorn – Hamburg
Tel : (040)5203797

Set in a typical 'Schleswig-Holstein' landscape near the city of Hamburg, the course is flat and surrounded by open fields and meadowland. There are water hazards on the fairways of the 2nd and 16th holes. Many of the greens are well-bunkered. *SSS 72*

GF $

1964

27

—

—

L 6070 P 72

S

R

Required : Handicap Certificate
Best days : Weekdays only

HOLE	LENGTH MEDAL-TEE	PAR	STROKE INDEX
1	360	4	3
2	340	4	13
3	540	5	1
4	165	3	15
5	320	4	17
6	450	5	9
7	200	3	7
8	370	4	5
9	335	4	11
TOTAL	3080	36	TOTAL

HOLE	LENGTH MEDAL-TEE	PAR	STROKE INDEX
10	370	4	4
11	160	3	10
12	465	5	12
13	340	4	8
14	145	3	18
15	520	5	2
16	320	4	16
17	360	4	6
18	310	4	14
TOTAL	2990	36	TOTAL

AUGSBURG

TEL : (08234)5621
LOCATION : from Augsburg B 17 to Bobingen/Strassberg
ADDRESS : Engelshofer Strasse 2 – 8903 Burgwalden/Bobingen
HOTEL :
Drei Mohren – Augsburg
Tel : (0821)510031
Zeller – Königsbrunn
Tel : (08231)4024
RESTAURANT : Die Ecke – Augsburg
Tel : (0821)510600

This sporting course is picturesquely set in Bavaria. Its 18 holes wind through rolling forest and hills, and has on one side several large lakes. A problem is presented by the continuous ups and downs of the terrain. The club boasts a cosy and a comfortable clubhouse. *SSS 71*

GF $

1959

18

November to March

—

L 5833 P 71

R S

Required : Handicap Certificate
Best days : Any day

HOLE	LENGTH MEDAL-TEE	PAR	STROKE INDEX
1	320	4	13
2	363	4	3
3	300	4	9
4	170	3	9
5	360	4	5
6	145	3	17
7	440	5	15
8	345	4	7
9	520	5	1
TOTAL	2963	36	TOTAL

HOLE	LENGTH MEDAL-TEE	PAR	STROKE INDEX
10	370	4	12
11	205	3	4
12	345	4	8
13	310	4	16
14	345	4	10
15	160	3	18
16	490	5	6
17	170	3	14
18	475	5	2
TOTAL	2870	35	TOTAL

BADEN-BADEN

TEL : (07221)23579
LOCATION : 2 km Baden-Baden
ADDRESS : Fremersberg Strasse 127 – 7570 Baden-Baden
HOTEL : HR
Fairway am Selighof
Tel : (07221)2171
Golf – Baden-Baden
Tel : (07221)23579
Kleine Prinz – Baden-Baden
Tel : (07221)3464
RESTAURANT : Zum Gott – Baden-Baden
Tel : (07223)5513

This short and fairly testing course is situated near the famous spa resort of Baden-Baden on very hilly terrain. It lies in the middle of a forest with the fairways framed by old and stately trees. A part of the course looks out over Baden-Baden. The scenic and first class Selighof Hotel stands between the 8th and 9th hole. *SSS 65*

GF $$
1901
18
November to March
—
L 4575 P 64
S
R

Required : Handicap Certificate, Club Membership Card
Best days : Any day

HOLE	LENGTH MEDAL-TEE	PAR	STROKE INDEX
1	240	4	9
2	505	5	7
3	145	3	11
4	310	4	5
5	525	5	1
6	200	3	17
7	155	3	13
8	335	4	3
9	155	3	15
TOTAL	2570	34	TOTAL

HOLE	LENGTH MEDAL-TEE	PAR	STROKE INDEX
10	100	3	16
11	240	4	14
12	95	3	18
13	425	4	2
14	325	4	4
15	230	3	8
16	210	3	6
17	175	3	12
18	205	3	10
TOTAL	2005	30	TOTAL

BAD KISSINGEN

TEL : (0971)3608
LOCATION : 2 km Bad Kissingen
ADDRESS : Euerdorfer Strasse – 8730 Bad Kissingen
HOTEL :
Steigenberger Kurhaus – Bad Kissingen
Tel : (0971)8041-0
Bristol – Bad Kissingen
Tel : (0971)824-0
Sonnenhügel – Bad Kissingen
Tel : (0971)831
RESTAURANT : Zollergarten – Bad Kissingen
Tel : (0971)65030

This well-wooded course is located near the spa resort of Bad Kissingen on a fine natural landscape. It is the river 'Fränkische Saale' that creates problems on many of the holes as it meanders its way through the course. The first class Steigenberger Kurhaus Hotel is situated 3km from the course. *SSS 69*

GF $

1911

18

November to April

 —

L 5680 P 70

S

R

Required : Handicap Certificate
Best days : Weekdays

HOLE	LENGTH MEDAL-TEE	PAR	STROKE INDEX
1	467	5	
2	219	3	
3	309	4	
4	173	3	
5	401	4	
6	354	4	
7	540	5	
8	169	3	
9	300	4	
TOTAL	2932	35	TOTAL

HOLE	LENGTH MEDAL-TEE	PAR	STROKE INDEX
10	290	4	
11	370	4	
12	350	4	
13	142	3	
14	264	4	
15	400	4	
16	154	3	
17	447	5	
18	331	4	
TOTAL	2748	35	TOTAL

BAD NEUENAHR-AHRWEILER

★

TEL : (02641)6693/2325
LOCATION : 10 km Bad Neuenahr/47 km Köln
ADDRESS : Remagener Weg – 5483 Bad Neuenahr-Ahrweiler
HOTEL :
Dorint – Bad Neuenahr
Tel : (02641)8950
Seta – Bad Neuenahr
Tel : (02641)8030
Steigenberger – Bad Neuenahr
Tel : (02641)2291
RESTAURANT : Zum Stern – Ahrweiler
Tel : (02641)34738

This attractive and sporting course lies on hilly countryside with panoramic views of the surroundings. The holes follow the undulations of the hills through meadows and woodlands. Numerous scenic ponds and streams serve as hazards. There is a short 9 hole par 3 course. A riding school is nearby. *SSS 72*

GF $

1979

18

—

—

L 6060 P 72

R S

Required : Handicap Certificate
Best days : Any day

HOLE	LENGTH MEDAL-TEE	PAR	STROKE INDEX
1	271	4	15
2	385	4	3
3	451	5	7
4	294	4	11
5	180	3	13
6	469	5	9
7	151	3	17
8	418	4	1
9	422	4	5
TOTAL	3041	36	TOTAL

HOLE	LENGTH MEDAL-TEE	PAR	STROKE INDEX
10	131	3	14
11	466	5	18
12	331	4	8
13	356	4	16
14	169	3	4
15	324	4	12
16	388	4	2
17	543	5	6
18	311	4	10
TOTAL	3019	36	TOTAL

BAD WÖRISHOFEN

TEL : (08346)777
LOCATION : 10 km Bad Wörishofen
ADDRESS : Schlingener Strasse 27 – 8951 Rieden
HOTEL :
Allgäuer Hof – Bad Wörishofen
Tel : (08247)1081
Kreuzer – Bad Wörishofen
Tel : (08247)3530
Landhaus Tanneck – Bad Wörishofen
Tel : (08247)3070
RESTAURANT : Jagdhof Schlingen – Bad Wörishofen
Tel : (08247)4879

This parkland course lies not far from the famous Bavarian spa resort of Bad Wörishofen in the foothills of the Allgäuer Alps. Set among age-old trees with two holes bordering the scenic 'Staussee' lake, the course has fine panoramic views over the mountains. *SSS 73*

GF $

1977

18

November to March

D. Harradine

L 6348 P 73

Required : Handicap Certificate
Best days : Weekdays

HOLE	LENGTH MEDAL-TEE	PAR	STROKE INDEX
1	319	4	17
2	176	3	7
3	328	4	16
4	458	5	3
5	475	5	15
6	395	4	5
7	367	4	12
8	150	3	18
9	440	5	1
TOTAL	3108	37	TOTAL

HOLE	LENGTH MEDAL-TEE	PAR	STROKE INDEX
10	330	4	13
11	175	3	8
12	353	4	12
13	502	5	6
14	357	4	11
15	526	5	2
16	422	4	4
17	190	3	10
18	385	4	9
TOTAL	3240	36	TOTAL

BAMBERG AUF GUT LEIMERSHOF

TEL : (09547)1524
LOCATION : from Bamberg B173 to Breitengüssbach
ADDRESS : 8613 Breitengüssbach
HOTEL :
Göller-Hirschaid
Tel : (09543)9138
Böttingerhaus Steinmühle-Bamberg
Tel : (0951)54074
RESTAURANT : Böttingerhaus-Bamberg
Tel : (0951)54074

The 18 holes are laid out among gently rolling hills and are partly framed by woodland. It is a technically interesting course with fairways going uphill or downhill to rolling greens with 8 strategically placed ponds serving as hazards. From several holes there are fine views over a castle (Schloss Banz) and the village of Altenhof. *SSS 72*

GF $ — Mon.; Dec. to March — S
1973 — — —
18 — L 6175 P 72 — R

Required : Handicap Certificate
Best days : Weekdays only

HOLE	LENGTH MEDAL-TEE	PAR	STROKE INDEX
1	295	4	
2	519	5	
3	149	3	
4	377	4	
5	392	4	
6	376	4	
7	161	3	
8	303	4	
9	508	5	
TOTAL	3080	36	TOTAL

HOLE	LENGTH MEDAL-TEE	PAR	STROKE INDEX
10	494	5	
11	327	4	
12	183	3	
13	362	4	
14	372	4	
15	454	5	
16	397	4	
17	317	4	
18	189	3	
TOTAL	3095	36	TOTAL

BERGISCH LAND

TEL : (02053)7177
LOCATION : 8 km Wuppertal/37 km Düsseldorf
ADDRESS : Siebeneickerstrasse 386 – 5600 Wuppertal 1
HOTEL :
Solingen – Solingen
Tel : (0212)76041
Juliana – Mollenkotten
Tel : (0202)64750
RESTAURANT : Jagdhaus Mollenkotten – Wuppertal
Tel : (0202)522643

The course is laid out in Nordrhein-Westfalen amongst stately trees on hilly countryside giving excellent views of the surroundings. Cunningly bunkered, it has generous fairways with several streams cutting them in two. *SSS 71*

GF $

1928

18

—

—

L 5920 P 71

S

R

Required : Handicap Certificate
Best days : Weekdays

HOLE	LENGTH MEDAL-TEE	PAR	STROKE INDEX
1	445	5	9
2	175	3	15
3	410	4	1
4	335	4	5
5	335	4	7
6	180	3	13
7	370	4	3
8	470	5	17
9	150	3	11
TOTAL	2870	35	TOTAL

HOLE	LENGTH MEDAL-TEE	PAR	STROKE INDEX
10	365	4	4
11	145	3	18
12	315	4	10
13	515	5	16
14	370	4	2
15	325	4	8
16	470	5	14
17	190	3	12
18	355	4	6
TOTAL	3050	36	TOTAL

BEUERBERG

TEL : (08179)617/728
LOCATION : Autobahn Garmisch exit Seeshaupt-Beuerberg
ADDRESS : Gut Sterz 1 – 8196 Beuerberg
HOTEL :
Zur Post – Königsdorf
Tel : (08179)711
Gut Faistenberg – Faistenberg
Tel : (08179)1200
RESTAURANT : Gasthof Friedenseiche – Benediktbeuern
Tel : (08857)279

Set within fine undulating forest land in the foothills of the Bavarian Alps, this attractive course is cunningly bunkered. Most of the holes have strategically placed water hazards requiring accurate play. There is a fine Bavarian-style clubhouse. *SSS 71*

GF $$
1983
18

December to April
—
L 6036 P 74

R S

Required : Handicap Certificate
Best days : Weekdays

HOLE	LENGTH MEDAL-TEE	PAR	STROKE INDEX
1	488	5	5
2	320	4	15
3	327	4	13
4	514	5	1
5	240	4	9
6	382	4	3
7	312	4	11
8	150	3	17
9	350	4	7
TOTAL	3083	37	TOTAL

HOLE	LENGTH MEDAL-TEE	PAR	STROKE INDEX
10	324	4	16
11	173	3	12
12	440	5	2
13	296	4	18
14	145	3	10
15	464	5	4
16	312	4	14
17	435	5	6
18	364	4	8
TOTAL	2953	37	TOTAL

BONN-GODESBERG

TEL : (0228)344003
LOCATION : 25 km Bonn, in Niederbachem
ADDRESS : 5307 Wachtberg-Niederbachem – Landgrabenweg
HOTEL :
Dahl – Wachtberg
Tel : (0228)341071
Dreesen – Bonn 2
Tel : (0228)82020
Parkhotel – Bonn 2
Tel : (0228)363081
RESTAURANT : St. Michael – Bonn 2
Tel : (0228)364765

Founded in 1960, the course situated in Nordrhein-Westfalen lies on an undulating plain and is entirely surrounded by dense woodland. Many of the fairways are narrow and tree-lined with water coming into play on some of the holes. *SSS 71*

GF $
1960
18
Mondays
—
L 5857 P 71
S
R

Required : Handicap Certificate, Club Membership Card
Best days : Thursdays and Fridays ; Weekends by introduction

HOLE	LENGTH MEDAL-TEE	PAR	STROKE INDEX
1	352	4	3
2	348	4	1
3	146	3	17
4	470	5	13
5	435	5	15
6	155	3	11
7	366	4	5
8	360	4	7
9	385	4	9
TOTAL	3017	36	TOTAL

HOLE	LENGTH MEDAL-TEE	PAR	STROKE INDEX
10	340	4	6
11	310	4	14
12	495	5	2
13	160	3	16
14	300	4	18
15	190	3	10
16	390	4	4
17	180	3	8
18	475	5	12
TOTAL	2840	35	TOTAL

BRAUNSCHWEIG

TEL : (0531)691369
LOCATION : 5 km Braunschweig via Salzdahlumerstrasse
ADDRESS : Schwartzkopffstr. 10 – 3300 Braunschweig
HOTEL :
Elch – Braunschweig
Tel : (0531)73079
Deutsches Haus – Braunschweig
Tel : (0531)44422
RESTAURANT : Atrium – Braunschweig
Tel : (0531)73001

An attractive course laid out on rolling countryside with its holes landscaped among majestic trees. Many of the fairways are cunningly bunkered. Precision is essential due to the presence of various well-placed ponds. *SSS 71*

GF $

1926

18

—

—

L 5893 P 71

S

R

Required : Handicap Certificate
Best days : Any day

HOLE	LENGTH MEDAL-TEE	PAR	STROKE INDEX
1	473	5	
2	307	4	
3	390	4	
4	132	3	
5	520	5	
6	182	3	
7	355	4	
8	155	3	
9	507	5	
TOTAL	3021	36	TOTAL

HOLE	LENGTH MEDAL-TEE	PAR	STROKE INDEX
10	326	4	
11	365	4	
12	516	5	
13	191	3	
14	176	3	
15	286	4	
16	372	4	
17	438	5	
18	202	3	
TOTAL	2872	36	TOTAL

BREMEN ZUR VAHR

TEL : (0421)230041/
(04795)417
LOCATION : 8 km Bremen
ADDRESS : Am Golfplatz 10 – 2861 Garlstedt – Secretary : Bürg Spitta – Allee 34 – 2800 Bremen
HOTEL :
Weisses Haus – Heilshorn
Tel : (04795)333
Strandlust – Bremen
Tel : (0421)667073
RESTAURANT : Bremen Ratskeller – Bremen
Tel : (0421)320936

One of the oldest and most prestigious sports clubs in Germany with its golf course considered as one of the world's best, often compared with Augusta (in Georgia, U.S.A., venue of the annual Masters) in layout. A technically difficult course set in the Garstedter Heath amidst thick undulating forest land. Its long and outstanding holes are dominated by tall pine trees, and count only 24 bunkers and numerous punishing dog-legs. The club is equipped with sports facilities such as tennis courts, hockey fields, and a shooting stand. *SSS 75*

GF $

1905

27

Tues., Wed., WEE.

B.v. Limburger, A. Weyhausen

L 6340 P 74, 2985 P 36

R S

Required : Handicap Certificate
Best days : Mondays, Thursdays, Fridays

HOLE	LENGTH MEDAL-TEE	PAR	STROKE INDEX	HOLE	LENGTH MEDAL-TEE	PAR	STROKE INDEX	HOLE	LENGTH MEDAL-TEE	PAR	STROKE INDEX
1	326	4	15	10	497	5	8	1	297	4	9
2	475	5	3	11	159	3	12	2	354	4	15
3	177	3	11	12	455	5	14	3	158	3	3
4	491	5	7	13	357	4	4	4	466	5	13
5	284	4	17	14	309	4	18	5	424	4	7
6	498	5	1	15	488	5	6	6	158	3	17
7	366	4	5	16	397	4	2	7	437	5	5
8	147	3	13	17	189	3	16	8	327	4	11
9	366	4	9	18	159	4	10	9	364	4	1
TOTAL	3130	37	TOTAL	TOTAL	3210	37	TOTAL	TOTAL	2985	36	TOTAL

BUCHHOLZ-NORDHEIDE

TEL : (04181)36200
LOCATION : 7 km Buchholz
ADDRESS : An der Rehm –2110 Buchholz
HOTEL :
Zur Eiche – Buchholz
Tel : (04181)8068
Frommann – Buchholz
Tel : (04181)7800
Niedersachsen – Jesteburg
Tel : (04138)2044
RESTAURANT : Landhaus Jesteburg – Jesteburg
Tel : (04183)2051

Inaugurated in 1987, this is a fine flat heathland course set among groves of ancient oak and silver birch. It presents a number of obstacles such as an attractive pond and many well-defended greens. *SSS 71*

GF $

1987

18

—

—

L 6130 P 72

S

R

Required : Handicap Certificate
Best days : Any day

HOLE	LENGTH MEDAL-TEE	PAR	STROKE INDEX
1	307	4	
2	164	3	
3	402	4	
4	368	4	
5	530	5	
6	324	4	
7	173	3	
8	312	4	
9	408	4	
TOTAL	2988	35	TOTAL

HOLE	LENGTH MEDAL-TEE	PAR	STROKE INDEX
10	344	4	
11	360	4	
12	372	4	
13	222	3	
14	472	5	
15	301	4	
16	383	4	
17	193	3	
18	495	5	
TOTAL	3142	36	TOTAL

BURGDORF

★

TEL : (05085)7628/7144
LOCATION : 13 km Hannover B 3, in Burgdorf Ehlershausen
ADDRESS : Waldstrasse 27 – 3167 Burgdorf-Ehlershausen
HOTEL :
Fürstenhof Celle – Burgdorf
Tel : (05141)2010
Bähre – Burgdorf
Tel : (05085)6006
RESTAURANT : Moormühle – Burgdorf
Tel : (05136)85008

A typical heathland course set on flat sandy soil in the province of Niedersachsen, incorporating several well-placed bunkers, tall pine trees and a small pond serving as hazards. *SSS 74*

GF $

1970

18

—

—

L 6426 P 74

S

R

Required : Handicap Certificate
Best days : Weekdays

HOLE	LENGTH MEDAL-TEE	PAR	STROKE INDEX
1	495	5	6
2	382	4	2
3	191	3	11
4	347	4	10
5	388	4	4
6	435	5	16
7	350	4	8
8	132	3	18
9	462	5	13
TOTAL	3182	37	TOTAL

HOLE	LENGTH MEDAL-TEE	PAR	STROKE INDEX
10	357	4	9
11	394	4	1
12	162	3	12
13	511	5	5
14	311	4	15
15	149	3	14
16	439	5	17
17	381	4	7
18	540	5	3
TOTAL	3244	37	TOTAL

BURG OVERBACH

TEL : (02245)5550/5519
LOCATION : 35 km Köln A4 exit Osberghausen, then B56
ADDRESS : Burg Overbach – 5203 Much
HOTEL :
Zur Schweiz – Much
Tel : (02245)4141
Parkhotel – Nümbrecht
Tel : (02293)3030
Zur Eiche – Overath
Tel : (02207)7580
RESTAURANT : Landhaus Salzmann – Much
Tel : (02245)1426

A testing inland course set in rolling countryside with fine views of the surroundings. It has a varied layout including some hundred strategic bunkers, several streams and ponds. Sports facilities include an indoor and outdoor swimming pool as well as several indoor and outdoor tennis courts. *SSS 72*

GF $

1984

18

December to March

—

L 6056 P 72

S

R

Required : Handicap Certificate
Best days : Tuesdays, Fridays

HOLE	LENGTH MEDAL-TEE	PAR	STROKE INDEX
1	343	4	9
2	165	3	13
3	351	4	1
4	350	4	11
5	445	5	7
6	135	3	15
7	350	4	3
8	322	4	17
9	505	5	5
TOTAL	2966	36	TOTAL

HOLE	LENGTH MEDAL-TEE	PAR	STROKE INDEX
10	369	4	8
11	188	3	12
12	353	4	14
13	386	4	2
14	122	3	16
15	324	4	6
16	455	5	18
17	351	4	4
18	542	5	10
TOTAL	3090	36	TOTAL

BUXTEHUDE

TEL : (04161)81333
LOCATION : 38 km Hamburg BAB 1, near Buxtehude in Daensen
ADDRESS : Zum Lehmfeld 1 – 2150 Buxtehude
HOTEL :
Zur Mühle – Buxtehude
Tel : (04161)3003
Seeburg – Buxtehude
Tel : (04161)82071
Zur Mühle – Buxtehude
Tel : (04161)3003
RESTAURANT : Seeburg – Buxtehude
Tel : (04161)82071

This well-wooded and fairly testing golf course is peacefully set on hilly countryside in the province of Niedersachsen. Most of the fairways, landscaped amongst mature trees, are wide and generous. Several water hazards affect play. *SSS 74*

GF $

1982

18

January

W. Siegmann

L 6505 P 73

R S

Required : Handicap Certificate
Best days : Weekdays

HOLE	LENGTH MEDAL-TEE	PAR	STROKE INDEX
1	505	5	13
2	155	3	5
3	355	4	17
4	360	4	11
5	385	4	7
6	515	5	1
7	335	4	15
8	180	3	9
9	535	5	3
TOTAL	3325	37	TOTAL

HOLE	LENGTH MEDAL-TEE	PAR	STROKE INDEX
10	370	4	6
11	185	3	14
12	460	5	8
13	315	4	2
14	500	5	10
15	185	3	18
16	375	4	4
17	310	3	16
18	480	5	12
TOTAL	3180	36	TOTAL

CASTROP-RAUXEL

TEL : (02305)62027
LOCATION : 5 km Castrop-Rauxel A 42 exit Dortmund-Bodelschwingh
ADDRESS : Dortmunder Strasse 383
4620 Castrop-Rauxel
HOTEL :
Wittekindshof - Dortmund
Tel : (0231)596081
Westfalenhalle - Dortmund
Tel : (0231)1204245
RESTAURANT : Haus Goldschmieding – Castrop Rauxel
Tel : (02305)32931

This testing and sporting course, in the province of Nordrhein-Westfalen, extends over 84ha of parkland flanked by forest. It is characterized by large rolling fairways, many strategic bunkers, some creeks and 2 vast water hazards which affect play on the 9th and the 18th holes. *SSS 72*

GF $
1987
18
—
—
L 6146 P 72
S

Required : Handicap Certificate
Best days : Any day

HOLE	LENGTH MEDAL-TEE	PAR	STROKE INDEX
1	343	4	
2	130	3	
3	466	5	
4	175	3	
5	385	4	
6	426	4	
7	363	4	
8	518	5	
9	308	4	
TOTAL	3114	36	TOTAL

HOLE	LENGTH MEDAL-TEE	PAR	STROKE INDEX
10	353	4	
11	321	4	
12	317	4	
13	514	5	
14	321	4	
15	450	5	
16	178	3	
17	407	4	
18	171	3	
TOTAL	3032	36	TOTAL

DONAU RASSBACH

TEL : (08501)1313
LOCATION : 10 km Passau
ADDRESS : Rassbach 8 - 8391 Thyrnau
Passau
HOTEL :
Anetseder - Thyrnau
Tel : (08501)1313
Holiday Inn - Passau
Tel : (0851)59000
Wilder Mann - Passau
Tel : (0851)35071
RESTAURANT : Kaiserin Sissi - Passau
Tel : (0851)35075

The course is set in southern Bavaria amidst sweeping valleys and lush green woodlands. The first nine holes run up and downhill through vallied landscape, the last nine wind their way through beautiful old parkland. It features large rolling greens, all craftily bunkered, and a stream which creates an omnipresent hazard on several holes. *SSS 72*

GF $

1986

18

November to March

M. von Mecklenburg

L 6097 P 72

Required : Handicap Certificate
Best days : Weekdays

HOLE	LENGTH MEDAL-TEE	PAR	STROKE INDEX
1	365	4	13
2	186	3	11
3	473	5	7
4	343	4	9
5	480	5	1
6	382	4	3
7	142	3	17
8	324	4	15
9	356	4	5
TOTAL	3051	36	TOTAL

HOLE	LENGTH MEDAL-TEE	PAR	STROKE INDEX
10	334	4	10
11	166	3	12
12	591	5	4
13	424	4	2
14	129	3	6
15	315	4	18
16	308	4	8
17	450	5	16
18	329	4	14
TOTAL	3046	36	TOTAL

DORTMUND

TEL : (0231)774133
LOCATION : 10 km Dortmund
ADDRESS : Reichsmarkstrasse 12 – 4600 Dortmund Reichsmark
HOTEL :
Lennhof – Dortmund
Tel : (0231)75726
Romberg Park – Dortmund 50
Tel : (0231)714073
Waldhotel Hülsenhain – Dortmund 50
Tel : (0231)731767
RESTAURANT : Zum Treppchen – Dortmund
Tel : (0231)431442

Laid out in the province of Nordrhein-Westfalen, Dortmund is an undulating parkland course with several long and testing holes. There are various ponds and ditches serving as hazards. *SSS 72*

GF $

Mondays

RF S

1956

—

18

L 6074 P 72

Required : Handicap Certificate
Best days : Weekdays only; Weekends with members

HOLE	LENGTH MEDAL-TEE	PAR	STROKE INDEX
1	484	5	11
2	385	4	3
3	116	3	17
4	382	4	1
5	319	4	13
6	332	4	7
7	410	4	5
8	147	3	15
9	479	5	9
TOTAL	3054	37	TOTAL

HOLE	LENGTH MEDAL-TEE	PAR	STROKE INDEX
10	181	3	10
11	371	4	6
12	437	5	14
13	335	4	12
14	346	4	4
15	276	4	16
16	397	4	2
17	158	3	18
18	459	5	8
TOTAL	3020	36	TOTAL

DÜSSELDORFER

★★

TEL : (02102)81092/83620
LOCATION : 11 km Düsseldorf BAB 3
ADDRESS : Rittergut Rommeljans – 4030 Ratingen 1
HOTEL :
Altenkamp – Ratingen
Tel : (02102)27044
Breidenbacher Hof – Düsseldorf
Tel : (0211)13030
Gut Höhne – Düsseldorf Mettmann
Tel : (02104)75006
RESTAURANT : Suitbertus Stusen – Ratingen
Tel : (02102)28967

A pleasant and busy inland course with fine views over the city of Düsseldorf, this is one of the leading golf courses in Germany. The championship course is characterized by narrow tree-lined fairways and large greens. Several of the finishing holes are crossed by meandering streams. *SSS 71*

GF $$ — January — R S
1904 — — 
18 — L 5905 P 71

Required : Handicap Certificate, Club Membership Card.
Best days : Weekdays only

HOLE	LENGTH MEDAL-TEE	PAR	STROKE INDEX
1	352	4	11
2	375	4	1
3	455	5	15
4	365	4	7
5	305	4	13
6	125	3	17
7	318	4	9
8	200	3	5
9	371	4	3
TOTAL	2866	35	TOTAL

HOLE	LENGTH MEDAL-TEE	PAR	STROKE INDEX
10	495	5	16
11	455	5	8
12	195	3	12
13	350	4	6
14	380	4	2
15	148	3	18
16	463	5	14
17	168	3	10
18	385	4	4
TOTAL	3039	36	TOTAL

DÜSSELDORF-HÖSEL

TEL : (02102)68629/69925
LOCATION : 13 km Düsseldorf BAB 3, in Ratingen
ADDRESS : In den Höfen 32 – 4030 Ratingen 6 (Hösel)
HOTEL :
Astoria – Ratingen
Tel : (02102)14005
Altenkamp – Ratingen
Tel : (02102)27044
Gut Höhna – Ratingen
Tel : (02104)75006
RESTAURANT : Haus Stemberg-Velbert
Tel : (02053)5649

Situated on the outskirts of Düsseldorf in Hösel, this fairly difficult course has a parkland character and is set on undulating terrain. The fairways are cunningly bunkered and landscaped among young trees with water affecting play on several holes. *SSS 72*

GF $

1979

18

Mondays, Weekends

—

L 6169 P 72

S

R

Required : Handicap Certificate
Best days : Weekdays only

HOLE	LENGTH MEDAL-TEE	PAR	STROKE INDEX
1	394	4	5
2	401	4	3
3	148	3	13
4	529	5	1
5	285	4	17
6	357	4	11
7	477	5	15
8	183	3	9
9	361	4	7
TOTAL	3135	36	TOTAL

HOLE	LENGTH MEDAL-TEE	PAR	STROKE INDEX
10	135	3	14
11	394	4	2
12	355	4	6
13	185	3	4
14	315	4	10
15	490	5	16
16	300	4	18
17	341	4	12
18	519	5	8
TOTAL	3034	36	TOTAL

DÜSSELDORF KOSAIDO

TEL : (02104)77060
LOCATION : 11 km Düsseldorf B7
ADDRESS : Am Schmidtberg 11 - 4000 Düsseldorf 12
HOTEL :
Gut Höhne - Düsseldorf Mettmann
Tel : (02104)75006
Steigenberger Park - Düsseldorf
Tel : (0211)8651
RESTAURANT : Im Schiffchen - Düsseldorf
Tel : (0211)401050

This course is part of the Japanese Kosaido group, which manages eleven other golf clubs around the world. It extends over hilly and luxuriant wooded parkland close to Düsseldorf-Hubbelrath and water affects play on some of the holes. The club boasts an international and a Japanses restaurant (Teppan), conference facilities, a sauna and a Japanese whirlpool. *SSS 71*

GF $$ — Tuesdays — S
1990 — — —
18 — L 5795 P 71 — R

Required : Handicap Certificate
Best days : Weekdays with booking in advance

HOLE	LENGTH MEDAL-TEE	PAR	STROKE INDEX
1	389	4	8
2	165	3	12
3	448	5	2
4	364	4	14
5	332	4	10
6	320	4	18
7	149	3	16
8	360	4	6
9	478	5	4
TOTAL	3005	36	TOTAL

HOLE	LENGTH MEDAL-TEE	PAR	STROKE INDEX
10	441	5	9
11	168	3	7
12	385	4	1
13	380	4	11
14	298	4	15
15	176	3	13
16	445	5	5
17	131	3	17
18	366	4	3
TOTAL	2790	35	TOTAL

ERDING-GRÜNBACH

TEL : (08122)6465
LOCATION : 8 km E. Erding B388
ADDRESS : Am Kellerberg - 8058
Grünbach/Erding
HOTEL :
Mayr-Wirt - Erding
Tel : (08122)7094
Isar - Freising
Tel : (08161)81004
Olymp - Eching
Tel : (089)3195073

Set in Bavaria, the holes are laid out amidst woods and fields and follow the natural undulations of the landscape. A sporty and difficult course, its features include treacherous water hazards, multi-leveled fairways and greens demanding accurate play from tee to green. *SSS 72*

GF $
1973
18

November to March
—
L 6158 P 72

S

R

Required : Handicap Certificate
Best days : Any day

HOLE	LENGTH MEDAL-TEE	PAR	STROKE INDEX
1	400	4	4
2	378	4	9
3	309	4	15
4	485	5	2
5	188	3	5
6	340	4	13
7	472	5	7
8	305	4	3
9	160	3	3
TOTAL	3037	36	TOTAL

HOLE	LENGTH MEDAL-TEE	PAR	STROKE INDEX
10	359	4	8
11	140	3	18
12	321	4	10
13	411	4	1
14	320	4	14
15	531	5	3
16	503	5	6
17	180	3	12
18	316	4	16
TOTAL	3081	36	TOTAL

ESSEN-HEIDHAUSEN

TEL : (0201)404111
LOCATION : 10 km Essen B 224
ADDRESS : Preutenborbeckstrasse 36 – 4300 Essen 16
HOTEL :
Arosa – Essen
Tel : (0201)72280
Bredeney – Essen
Tel : (0201)714081
Velbert – Essen
Tel : (02051)4920
RESTAURANT : La Buvette – Essen Werden
Tel : (0201)408048

Located in Velbert, a suburb of Essen, the course lies in a regional park. The holes are not long, but precision is essential due to the presence of several out of bounds. The second nine holes are flanked by age-old trees with a stream, the 'Rosenbach' meandering its way through many of them. There is a fine clubhouse overlooking the course. *SSS 71*

GF $

1970

18

Mon. ; Dec. to Feb.

—

L 5937 P 70

S

R

Required : Handicap Certificate
Best days : Weekdays only

HOLE	LENGTH MEDAL-TEE	PAR	STROKE INDEX
1	406	4	9
2	437	5	3
3	428	4	1
4	163	3	15
5	361	4	5
6	350	4	17
7	283	4	11
8	184	3	13
9	561	5	7
TOTAL	3173	36	TOTAL

HOLE	LENGTH MEDAL-TEE	PAR	STROKE INDEX
10	174	3	16
11	494	5	2
12	132	3	18
13	372	4	4
14	305	4	8
15	326	4	14
16	355	4	6
17	458	5	12
18	148	3	10
TOTAL	2764	35	TOTAL

ESSEN-KETTWIG HAUS OEFTE

TEL : (02054)83911
LOCATION : 10 km Essen, in Essen-Kettwig
ADDRESS :
Laupendahler Landstrasse – 4300 Essen 18
HOTEL :
Schloss Hugenpoet – Essen-Kettwig
Tel : (02054)6054
Parkhaus Hügel – Essen
Tel : (0201)471091
Burg Mintrop – Essen
Tel : (0201)57641
RESTAURANT : Seeblick – Essen-Kettwig
Tel : (02054)4556

A pleasant course laid out in the Ruhr-Valley. The 18 holes run partly through undulating countryside with mature trees, and partly through open fields. There is a stream crossing various fairways. The clubhouse is set within a castle dating back many centuries. *SSS 72*

GF $$

1959

18

December to February

—

L 6137 P 72

S

R

Required : Handicap Certificate
Best days : Any day

HOLE	LENGTH MEDAL-TEE	PAR	STROKE INDEX
1	331	4	9
2	346	4	13
3	208	3	5
4	445	5	15
5	382	4	3
6	390	4	1
7	155	3	7
8	324	4	11
9	436	5	17
TOTAL	3017	36	TOTAL

HOLE	LENGTH MEDAL-TEE	PAR	STROKE INDEX
10	312	4	16
11	510	5	8
12	326	4	14
13	360	4	10
14	169	3	12
15	426	4	2
16	524	5	4
17	138	3	18
18	355	4	6
TOTAL	3120	36	TOTAL

FELDAFING

TEL : (08157)7005/06
LOCATION : 32 km München BAB to Starnberg, in Feldafing/Obb
ADDRESS : Tutzinger Strasse 15 – 8133 Feldafing/Obb
HOTEL : HF
Golfhotel Kaiserin Elisabeth
Tel : (08157)1013
Marina – Bernried
Tel : (08158)6046

Set within splendid natural countryside in the foothills of the Bavarian Alps, this is one of the most beautiful courses in Germany. Scenically laid out on the former estate of Emperor Maximilian II with the royal castle on the 11th hole, it borders the Starnberg Lake. It is a typical inland course with majestic centuries-old trees flanking the fairways, and including around thirty bunkers and two water hazards. *SSS 70*

GF $$

1926

18

November to March

B. v. Limburger

L 5708 P 71

S

R

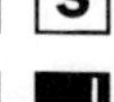

Required : Handicap Certificate
Best days : Weekdays

HOLE	LENGTH MEDAL-TEE	PAR	STROKE INDEX
1	340	4	5
2	158	3	13
3	459	5	9
4	368	4	3
5	362	4	1
6	458	5	11
7	304	4	15
8	129	3	17
9	461	5	7
TOTAL	3039	37	TOTAL

HOLE	LENGTH MEDAL-TEE	PAR	STROKE INDEX
10	290	4	16
11	112	3	18
12	352	4	8
13	382	4	2
14	196	3	10
15	380	4	6
16	161	3	14
17	340	4	4
18	456	5	12
TOTAL	2669	34	TOTAL

FRANKEN ABENBERG

TEL : (09178)5541
LOCATION : 25 km Nürnberg
ADDRESS : Am Golfplatz 19 - 8549 Abenberg
HOTEL :
Zum Heidenberg - Büchenbach Kühedorf
Tel : (09171)3040
Carlton - Nürnberg
Tel : (0911)20030
Atrium - Nürnberg
Tel : (911)47480
RESTAURANT : Schwarzer Adler - Nürnberg
Tel : (0911)392121

This mainly flat course spreads over attractive partly wooded landscape and features generous tree-lined fairways and well bunkered greens. Strategic trees and ponds demand precision in play. There is a very cosy clubhouse and a hotel is scheduled soon. *SSS 72*

GF $$

1988

18

Mon. ; Nov. to March

 Deutsche Golf Consult

 L 6127 P 72

Required : Handicap Certificate
Best days : Any day

HOLE	LENGTH MEDAL-TEE	PAR	STROKE INDEX
1	367	4	9
2	498	5	7
3	395	4	1
4	151	3	17
5	346	4	13
6	336	4	11
7	162	3	15
8	513	5	5
9	387	4	3
TOTAL	3155	36	TOTAL

HOLE	LENGTH MEDAL-TEE	PAR	STROKE INDEX
10	412	4	2
11	351	4	10
12	196	3	4
13	301	4	16
14	461	5	6
15	130	3	18
16	346	4	12
17	306	4	14
18	469	5	8
TOTAL	2972	36	TOTAL

FRANKFURTER

★★

TEL : (069)6662317/18
LOCATION : 4 km Frankfurt in Niederrad
ADDRESS : Golfstrasse 41 – 6000 Frankfurt
HOTEL :
Arabella – Niederrad
Tel : (069)66330
Gravenbuch – Frankfurt
Tel : (06102)5050
Ramada – Frankfurt
Tel : (069)39050
RESTAURANT : Bistro 77 – Niederrad
Tel : (069)614040

A demanding and rather short championship course, which constitutes a real test for players of all classes. The holes are laid out in dense flat forest and landscaped among mature trees. Most of the greens are large and well-bunkered, requiring accuracy. It has hosted the German Open many times since 1938. *SSS 71*

GF $$
1913
18

Mondays
H. Colt, J. Morrison
L 5869 P 71

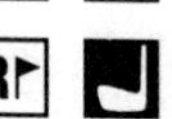

Required : Handicap Certificate
Best days : Weekdays

HOLE	LENGTH MEDAL-TEE	PAR	STROKE INDEX
1	375	4	7
2	365	4	3
3	400	4	1
4	155	3	15
5	455	5	13
6	300	4	17
7	185	3	9
8	345	4	11
9	375	4	5
TOTAL	2955	35	TOTAL

HOLE	LENGTH MEDAL-TEE	PAR	STROKE INDEX
10	325	4	16
11	150	3	8
12	355	4	10
13	365	4	2
14	304	4	14
15	435	5	12
16	150	3	18
17	435	5	6
18	395	4	4
TOTAL	2914	36	TOTAL

FRANKISCHE SCHWEIZ

TEL : (09194)9228
LOCATION : 30 km Bamberg
ADDRESS : Kanndorf 8 - 8553 Ebermannstadt
HOTEL :
Resengörg - Ebermannstadt
Tel : (09194)8174
Feiler - Wiesenthal
Tel : (09196)322
Häfner - Egloffstein
Tel : (09197)230

Recently moved up to 18-hole status, the course offers a varied layout. Some of the holes feature narrow tree-lined fairways, while others have spacious fairways winding through farmland and mature woodlands. *SSS 72*

GF $

1974

18

November to April

—

L 6040 P 72

S

R

Required : Club Membership Card
Best days : Any day

HOLE	LENGTH MEDAL-TEE	PAR	STROKE INDEX
1	340	4	9
2	140	3	16
3	376	4	2
4	502	5	4
5	195	3	5
6	339	4	14
7	430	4	7
8	342	4	11
9	451	5	13
TOTAL	3115	36	TOTAL

HOLE	LENGTH MEDAL-TEE	PAR	STROKE INDEX
10	399	4	3
11	297	4	17
12	556	5	1
13	437	5	10
14	161	3	8
15	345	4	6
16	274	4	15
17	102	3	18
18	354	4	12
TOTAL	2925	36	TOTAL

FREIBURGER

TEL : (07661)5569
LOCATION : near Freiburg, in Kirchzarten
ADDRESS : Krüttweg I-7815 Kirchzarten
HOTEL :
Schwär's Löwen-Freiburg im Breisgau
Tel : (0761)63041
Parkhotel Adler-Hinterzarten
Tel : (07652)711
Rheingold-Freiburg im Breisgau
Tel : (0761)36066
RESTAURANT : Schlossberg Dattle-Freiburg im Breisgau
Tel : (0761)31729

The Freiburger golf course is located within the water resource preserve of the city of Freiburg in a typical Black Forest landscape. The mostly flat course features long holes, many of them bordered by majestic trees which are centuries old. The main obstacles are presented by a large number of streams crossing the fairways. *SSS 72*

GF $ — Mon.; Jan. and Feb. — S

1970 — —

18 — L 6068 P 72 — R

Required : Handicap Certificate
Best days : Mondays, Fridays

HOLE	LENGTH MEDAL-TEE	PAR	STROKE INDEX
1	510	5	3
2	135	3	15
3	491	5	7
4	300	4	17
5	362	4	5
6	446	5	11
7	191	3	9
8	354	4	13
9	407	4	1
TOTAL	3196	37	TOTAL

HOLE	LENGTH MEDAL-TEE	PAR	STROKE INDEX
10	312	4	16
11	167	3	14
12	416	4	2
13	340	4	8
14	169	3	10
15	507	5	4
16	141	3	18
17	356	4	6
18	464	5	12
TOTAL	2872	35	TOTAL

GEISELWIND

★

TEL : (09556)17-0/1777
LOCATION : 45 km Nürnberg A3
ADDRESS : Friedrichstrasse 10 - 8614 Geiselwind
HOTEL : HF
Franken
Tel : (09556)17-0
Gasthaus Stern - Geiselwind
Tel : (09556)217
Gasthaus Lamm - Geiselwind
Tel : (09556)247

This pleasant and sporty championship course stands in an attractive sweeping landscape flanked by forests commanding fine views of the surroundings. Donald Harradine conceived an interesting pattern of holes running along hills featuring spacious greens (700 m2) of excellent quality.The recently opened Franken golfhotel with its 20 rooms is adjacent to the course. *SSS 72*

GF $

1990

18

November to March

 D. Harradine

 6214 P 72/73

Required : Handicap Certificate
Best days : Any day

HOLE	LENGTH MEDAL-TEE	PAR	STROKE INDEX
1	475	5	5
2	336	4	17
3	186	3	9
4	463	5	13
5	325	4	11
6	382	4	1
7	185	3	3
8	375	4	7
9	374	4	15
TOTAL	3101	36	TOTAL

HOLE	LENGTH MEDAL-TEE	PAR	STROKE INDEX
10	532	5	6
11	387	4	4
12	339	4	16
13	380	4	10
14	369	4	2
15	177	3	12
16	460	5	8
17	158	3	14
18	311	4	18
TOTAL	3113	36	TOTAL

GÖTTINGEN

TEL : (05551)61915
LOCATION : 7 km Northeim
ADDRESS : Schloss Levershausen – 3410 Northeim
HOTEL :
Waldhotel – Hartheim
Tel : (05551)2033
Burghotel Hardenberg – Nörten Hardenberg
Tel : (05503)1047
Sonne – Northeim
Tel : (05551)4071
RESTAURANT : Schwarzer Bar – Göttingen
Tel : (0551)58284

This fairly testing golf course is laid out in an attractive and undulating parkland landscape in Niedersachsen. It commands fine views of the Harz mountain chain and has several strategically placed water hazards. There is an indoor and an outdoor swimming pool. *SSS 72*

GF $

1969

18

—

—

L 6050 P 72

R S

Required : Handicap Certificate
Best days : Any day

HOLE	LENGTH MEDAL-TEE	PAR	STROKE INDEX
1	525	5	
2	355	4	
3	290	4	
4	140	3	
5	505	5	
6	330	5	
7	330	4	
8	145	3	
9	325	4	
TOTAL	2940	36	TOTAL

HOLE	LENGTH MEDAL-TEE	PAR	STROKE INDEX
10	445	5	
11	350	4	
12	145	3	
13	430	4	
14	360	4	
15	365	4	
16	335	4	
17	175	3	
18	505	5	
TOTAL	3110	36	TOTAL

GUT GRAMBEK

TEL : (04542)4627
LOCATION : 30 km Hamburg/25 km Lübeck, B 207 to Mölln
ADDRESS : Schlossstrasse 21 – 2411 Grambek bei Mölln
HOTEL :
Schwanenhof – Mölln am Schulsee
Tel : (04542)5015
Haus Hubertus – Mölln
Tel : (04542)3593
Parkhotel – Mölln
Tel : (04542)3930
RESTAURANT : Seehof – Ratzeburg
Tel : (04541)4161

Set in peaceful natural surroundings inside a vast regional park, the 'Lauenburger Seen' in Schleswig-Holstein. It is well laid out with wide and spacious fairways cutting through pine woods. The quietely situated Schwanenhof hotel is 6 km from the course and borders the "Schulsee" lake. *SSS 71*

GF $ | December to March | S

1985 | — |

18 | L 6129 P 71 | R

Required : Handicap Certificate
Best days : Weekdays

HOLE	LENGTH MEDAL-TEE	PAR	STROKE INDEX
1	317	4	13
2	475	5	5
3	172	3	9
4	309	4	17
5	343	4	7
6	380	4	1
7	149	3	15
8	364	4	11
9	389	4	3
TOTAL	2898	35	TOTAL

HOLE	LENGTH MEDAL-TEE	PAR	STROKE INDEX
10	379	4	12
11	187	3	8
12	379	4	6
13	464	5	10
14	395	4	2
15	481	5	4
16	312	4	16
17	165	3	18
18	369	4	14
TOTAL	3131	36	TOTAL

GUT KADEN

★

TEL : (04193)92021
LOCATION : 7 km Quickborn, 34 km Hamburg A 7
ADDRESS : Kadener Strasse – 2081 Alveslohe
HOTEL :
Waldfrieden – Quickborn
Tel : (04106)3771
Norderstedter Hof – Norderstedt
Tel : (040)5240046
Sporthotel Quickborn – Quickborn
Tel : (04551)8040
RESTAURANT : Scheelke – Henstedt
Tel : (04193)2207

Inaugurated in 1985, this is a sporting golf course of championship standard with long holes and large well-defended greens. Set on gently rolling terrain, the course is crossed by the scenic river, the 'Pinnau'. *SSS 72*

GF $ — Mondays  S

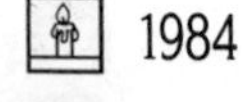 1984 — 

18 — L 6180 P 72 — R

Required : Handicap Certificate
Best days : Any day

HOLE	LENGTH MEDAL-TEE	PAR	STROKE INDEX
1	315	4	
2	170	3	
3	495	5	
4	425	4	
5	345	4	
6	135	3	
7	290	4	
8	230	4	
9	445	5	
TOTAL	2850	36	TOTAL

HOLE	LENGTH MEDAL-TEE	PAR	STROKE INDEX
10	395	4	
11	380	4	
12	405	4	
13	330	4	
14	215	3	
15	525	5	
16	155	3	
17	515	5	
18	410	4	
TOTAL	3330	36	TOTAL

GUT WALDHOF

TEL : (04194)383
LOCATION : 11 km Kaltenkirchen, 46 km Hamburg to Kiel
ADDRESS : Gut Waldhof – 2359 Kisdorferwohld
HOTEL :
Kleiner Markt – Kaltenkirchen
Tel : (04191)2105
Wiking – Henstedt-Ulzburg
Tel : (04193)5081
Zur Glashütte – Hamburg Nord
Tel : (040)5240828
RESTAURANT : Kaltenkirchner Hof – Kaltenkirchen
Tel : (04191)7861

Located near the city of Hamburg, the Gut Waldhof golf course is laid out on fairly flat open landscape, partly encircled by woodland. Most of the greens are well-bunkered demanding a great deal of accuracy. There is a friendly looking clubhouse. *SSS 72*

GF $

1969

18

 Weekends

—

L 6073 P 72

S

R

Required : Handicap Certificate
Best days : Mondays, Tuesdays, Thursdays, Fridays

HOLE	LENGTH MEDAL-TEE	PAR	STROKE INDEX
1	330	4	9
2	315	4	17
3	120	3	15
4	332	4	1
5	505	5	5
6	360	4	7
7	355	4	3
8	289	4	11
9	314	4	13
TOTAL	2920	36	TOTAL

HOLE	LENGTH MEDAL-TEE	PAR	STROKE INDEX
10	395	4	10
11	160	3	14
12	401	4	2
13	246	4	18
14	522	5	4
15	158	3	12
16	503	5	16
17	385	4	6
18	383	4	8
TOTAL	3153	36	TOTAL

HAMBURG-AHRENSBURG

★★

TEL : (04102)51309
LOCATION : 25 km Hamburg BAB to Lübeck
ADDRESS : Am Haidschlag 45 – 2070 Ahrensburg
HOTEL :
Ahrensburg – Ahrensburg
Tel : (04102)51321
Hamburg Plaza – Hamburg
Tel : (040)35020
Papendoor – Bargteheide
Tel : (04532)7041
RESTAURANT : Goldener Kegel – Ahrensburg
Tel : (04102)51031

Designed by Bernard von Limburger in 1964, the American golf architect Robert Trent Jones made alterations in 1977. Set on the borders of the Bredenbeker Lake within a typical Schleswig-Holstein landscape, the course is of championship standard. A tiny peninsula serves as an island green for the 11th hole, and as a tee-off for the 12th hole. *SSS 70*

GF $

—

1964/1977

B.v. Limburger, R. Trent Jones

18

L 5719 P 70

S

R

Required : Handicap Certificate
Best days : Weekdays only

HOLE	LENGTH MEDAL-TEE	PAR	STROKE INDEX
1	464	5	15
2	369	4	7
3	211	3	3
4	347	4	11
5	370	4	1
6	151	3	9
7	452	5	17
8	301	4	5
9	329	4	13
TOTAL	2994	36	TOTAL

HOLE	LENGTH MEDAL-TEE	PAR	STROKE INDEX
10	368	4	4
11	128	3	18
12	318	4	2
13	159	3	6
14	327	4	8
15	170	3	10
16	491	5	12
17	379	4	6
18	385	4	14
TOTAL	2725	34	TOTAL

HAMBURGER FALKENSTEIN

TEL : (040)812177
LOCATION : 10 km Hamburg BAB 7, in Blankenese
ADDRESS : In dep Bargen 59 – 2000 Hamburg 55
HOTEL :
Am Baurs Park – Blankenese
Tel : (040)860907
Seeburg – Buxtehude
Tel : (04161)82071
Zur Linde – Seevetal
Tel : (04105)2372
RESTAURANT : Süllberg – Blankenese
Tel : (040)861686

One of Germany's finest championship courses is the Hamburger Golf Club, laid out on gently undulating heathland. Its fairways, landscaped by silver birch and pines, meander through woodland and heather. The course is technically testing with several spectacular dog-leg holes and sand traps. The club has staged numerous important tournaments such as the German Open in 1965 and 1981, the European Mens Championship in 1969 and the European Junior Championship in 1986. *SSS 71*

GF $

Weekends

1906

C. Alison, J. Morrison, B.v. Limburger

18

L 5925 P 71

Required : Handicap Certificate
Best days : Weekdays in the morning

HOLE	LENGTH MEDAL-TEE	PAR	STROKE INDEX
1	301	4	15
2	510	5	9
3	196	3	5
4	436	5	11
5	371	4	7
6	383	4	1
7	327	4	13
8	166	3	17
9	388	4	3
TOTAL	3078	36	TOTAL

HOLE	LENGTH MEDAL-TEE	PAR	STROKE INDEX
10	170	3	16
11	403	4	2
12	376	4	6
13	321	4	10
14	322	4	4
15	148	3	18
16	314	4	14
17	439	5	12
18	354	4	8
TOTAL	2847	35	TOTAL

HAMBURGER LAND IN DER LÜNEBURGER HEIDE

★

TEL : (04105)2331
LOCATION : 22 km Hamburg – BAB to Bremen
ADDRESS : Am Golfplatz 24 – 2105 Seevetal
HOTEL :
Krohwinkel – Seevetal Hittfeld
Tel : (04105)2409
Meyer's – Seevetal
Tel : (04105)51561
Zur Linde – Seevetal
Tel : (04105)2372
RESTAURANT : Block House – Hamburg
Tel : (040)772437

Quietly situated, this is a good golf course with several excellent holes. Most of the fairways are narrow and landscaped among mature trees, demanding precision from tee to green. The club has a fine heated outdoor swimming pool and two tennis courts. *SSS 70*

GF $

1957

18

—

J. Morrison, H. Colt

L 5735 P 70

R S

Required : Handicap Certificate
Best days : Any day; Weekends by arrangement

HOLE	LENGTH MEDAL-TEE	PAR	STROKE INDEX
1	311	4	115
2	318	4	9
3	175	3	11
4	346	4	5
5	415	4	1
6	467	5	7
7	174	3	17
8	364	4	3
9	351	4	3
TOTAL	2921	35	TOTAL

HOLE	LENGTH MEDAL-TEE	PAR	STROKE INDEX
10	140	3	18
11	387	4	4
12	357	4	2
13	152	3	16
14	454	5	14
15	442	5	10
16	152	3	12
17	388	4	8
18	342	4	6
TOTAL	2814	35	TOTAL

HAMBURG-WALDDÖRFER

★★

TEL : (040)6051337
LOCATION : 25 km Hamburg BAB to Lübeck, in Ammersbek
ADDRESS : Schevenbarg – 2075 Ammersbek
HOTEL :
Goldener Kegel – Ahrensburg
Tel : (04102)51031
Atlantic – Hamburg 2000
Tel : (040)248001
Prem – Hamburg 2000
Tel : (040)245454
RESTAURANT : Lindenkrug – Hamburg
Tel : (040)6048005

The city of Hamburg boasts many first class golf courses including the fine Hamburg-Walddorfer championship golf course. Scenically set on the borders of the Bredenbeker lake and incorporating a fine setting of beautiful trees, numbering around 20 specimens such as oaks, chestnuts, pines, birch and lime-trees. Every hole is named after the tree, which is gestured on that fairway. The club boasts an attractive and stylish clubhouse with an indoor pool. The Walddorfer golf club has several times hosted the German National Championships. *SSS 73*

GF $ — Weekends —  S

1960 — B.v. Limburger — 

27 — L 6154 P 73 — R 

Required : Handicap Certificate
Best days : Tuesdays and Fridays ; Mondays by arrangement

HOLE	LENGTH MEDAL-TEE	PAR	STROKE INDEX
1	360	4	7
2	440	5	11
3	165	3	3
4	360	4	13
5	306	4	9
6	444	5	17
7	436	5	5
8	132	3	15
9	525	5	1
TOTAL	3168	38	TOTAL

HOLE	LENGTH MEDAL-TEE	PAR	STROKE INDEX
10	153	3	16
11	396	4	2
12	174	3	14
13	375	4	8
14	446	5	18
15	367	4	12
16	192	3	4
17	489	5	10
18	394	4	6
TOTAL	2986	35	TOTAL

HANAU

★

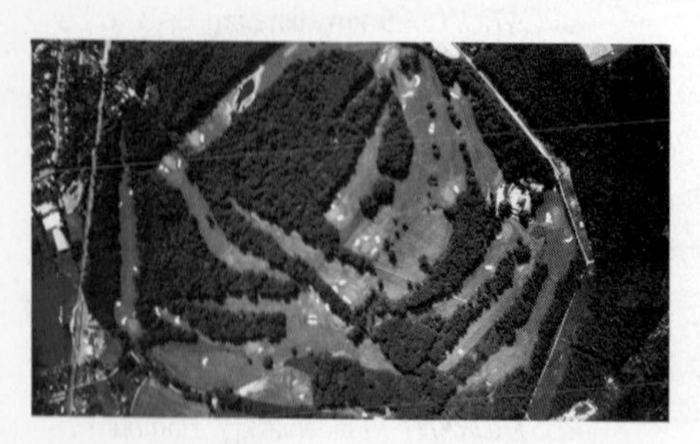

TEL : (06181)82071
LOCATION : 6 km Hanau/23 km Frankfurt
ADDRESS : Hanau am Main – Wilhelmsbader Allee 32 – 6450 Hanau-Wilhelmsbad
HOTEL : HR
Golfhotel
Tel : (06181)83219
Birkenhof – Hanau
Tel : (06181)6462
Brüder Grimm – Hanau
Tel : (06181)3060
RESTAURANT : Bei Jean Zipf – Hanau
Tel : (06181)15997

Located in Hessen, the course lies on flat countryside near the Baroque style Castle of Wilhelmsbad. It is lined by centuries-old stately trees and has water hazards on more than four holes. The course features one of the longest holes in Germany, the 7th (567m par 5). The course is of championship standard and hosted the German National Open in 87, 88 and 1989. The Golf Hotel is on the course. *SSS 73*

GF $

1959

18

Mondays

—

L 6227 P 73

Required : Handicap Certificate and Club Membership Card
Best days : Weekdays

HOLE	LENGTH MEDAL-TEE	PAR	STROKE INDEX
1	268	4	17
2	322	4	15
3	167	3	11
4	440	5	13
5	328	4	9
6	189	3	5
7	567	5	1
8	358	4	7
9	375	4	3
TOTAL	3014	36	TOTAL

HOLE	LENGTH MEDAL-TEE	PAR	STROKE INDEX
10	335	4	18
11	386	4	4
12	180	3	8
13	380	4	6
14	465	5	14
15	454	5	16
16	391	4	2
17	140	3	12
18	482	5	10
TOTAL	3213	37	TOTAL

HANNOVER

TEL : (05137)73068
LOCATION : 16 km W. Hannover E 8
ADDRESS : Am blauen See – 3008 Garbsen
HOTEL :
Garbsener Schweiz – Garbsen
Tel : (05137)75033
Landhaus Köhne – Garbsen
Tel : (05131)6011
Wildhage – Garbsen
Tel : (05137)75033
RESTAURANT : Witten's Hop – Hannover
Tel : (0511)14911

The course is cut in two by the motorway Köln/Hannover with seven holes separated from the others. Set on gently rolling parkland, the fairways are surrounded by fine old birch woods. The 11th hole lies along the scenic lake 'Blauer See'. *SSS 71*

GF $
1923
18

Weekends
B.v. Limburger
L 5900 P 71

R S

Required : Handicap Certificate
Best days : Thursdays

HOLE	LENGTH MEDAL-TEE	PAR	STROKE INDEX
1	395	4	7
2	165	3	15
3	500	5	1
4	360	4	9
5	320	4	13
6	475	5	11
7	380	4	3
8	180	3	17
9	400	4	5
TOTAL	3130	36	TOTAL

HOLE	LENGTH MEDAL-TEE	PAR	STROKE INDEX
10	300	4	16
11	455	5	10
12	345	4	2
13	200	3	8
14	460	5	6
15	140	3	18
16	345	4	4
17	360	4	14
18	165	3	12
TOTAL	2770	35	TOTAL

HEIDELBERG-LOBENFELD

★

TEL : (06226)40490/41615
LOCATION : 20 km Heidelberg
ADDRESS : Biddersbacher Hof – 6921 Lobenfeld
HOTEL :
Europaischer Hof – Heidelberg
Tel : (06221)27101
Mondial – Wiesloch
Tel : (06222)8016
Zum Ritter – Neckargemünd b. Heidelberg
Tel : (06223)7035
RESTAURANT : Zur Herrenmühle – Heidelberg
Tel : (06221)12909

The club lies in Baden-Würtemberg about 20 km from the university town of Heidelberg. Laid out on rolling countryside of the Odenwald, the course, encircled by woods and meadowland, is crossed by a little creek and a small lake. It features an attractive clubhouse built high up, overlooking the scenery. *SSS 73*

GF $

1968

18

Mon. ; Nov. to March

—

L 6215 P 72

S

R

Required : Handicap Certificate
Best days : Tuesdays and Fridays

HOLE	LENGTH MEDAL-TEE	PAR	STROKE INDEX
1	360	4	5
2	130	3	17
3	355	4	9
4	500	5	1
5	160	3	11
6	465	5	15
7	175	3	13
8	525	5	7
9	405	4	3
TOTAL	3075	36	TOTAL

HOLE	LENGTH MEDAL-TEE	PAR	STROKE INDEX
10	485	5	14
11	310	4	18
12	185	3	12
13	570	5	6
14	410	4	2
15	365	4	4
16	185	3	8
17	475	5	16
18	155	3	10
TOTAL	3140	36	TOTAL

HEILBRONN - HOHENLOHE

TEL : (07941)62801
LOCATION : exit Öhringer of BAD Heilbronn - Nürnberg, then to Sindringen
ADDRESS : Am Golfplatz - 7111 Friedrichsruhe - Öhringen
HOTEL :
Wald & Schloss - Friedrichsruhe
Tel : (07941)60870
Insel - Heilbronn
Tel : (07131)6300
Götz - Heilbronn
Tel : (07131)1550

Neigbouring Schloss Friedrichsruhe, a first class castle hotel, this course was extended to 18 holes in 1990. It is a friendly parkland course with beautiful centennial trees bordering the fairways. It features several tricky doglegs with narrow fairways and strategically placed water hazards. *SSS 71*

GF $ — November to April — S

1964 — —

18 — L 6116 P 72 — R

Required : Handicap Certificate
Best days : Any day

HOLE	LENGTH MEDAL-TEE	PAR	STROKE INDEX
1	512	5	
2	389	4	
3	358	4	
4	187	3	
5	365	4	
6	460	5	
7	170	3	
8	310	4	
9	485	5	
TOTAL	3236	37	TOTAL

HOLE	LENGTH MEDAL-TEE	PAR	STROKE INDEX
10	476	5	
11	393	4	
12	160	3	
13	362	4	
14	296	4	
15	371	4	
16	371	4	
17	342	4	
18	109	3	
TOTAL	2880	35	TOTAL

HERZOGSTADT CELLE

TEL : (05086)395
LOCATION : 7 km Celle B 191, in Garssen
52 km Hannover
ADDRESS : Beukenbusch 1 – 3100 Celle-Garssen
HOTEL :
Celler Tor-Celle
Tel : (05141)51011
Fürstenhof-Celle
Tel : (05141)2010
Zur Post-Fassberg
Tel : (05053)1077
RESTAURANT : Historischer Ratskeller-Celle
Tel : (05141)29099

Situated in Niedersachsen, this is a challenging golf course presenting a number of obstacles such as changes in level, bushes and strategic water. Old trees, some dating back 300 years, surround the fairways. The modern clubhouse enjoys fine views over the landscape.
SSS 70

GF $ | — | S
1985 | W. Siegmann |
18 | L 5934 P 72 | R

Required : Club Membership Card
Best days : Mondays and Fridays

HOLE	LENGTH MEDAL-TEE	PAR	STROKE INDEX
1	346	4	3
2	387	4	7
3	309	4	15
4	440	5	1
5	330	4	11
6	161	3	17
7	283	4	5
8	275	4	13
9	334	4	9
TOTAL	2865	36	TOTAL

HOLE	LENGTH MEDAL-TEE	PAR	STROKE INDEX
10	169	3	18
11	479	5	10
12	395	4	2
13	302	4	8
14	351	4	12
15	310	4	6
16	373	4	14
17	186	3	16
18	504	5	4
TOTAL	3069	36	TOTAL

HOHENPÄHL

TEL : (08808)1330
LOCATION : 43 km S. München BAB 2 to Starnberg-Weilheim
ADDRESS : Gut Hochschloss - 8121 Pähl
HOTEL :
Hirschberg Alm - Pähl
Tel : (08808)616
Vollmann - Weilheim
Tel : (0881)4255
Schloss Berg - Berg
Tel : (08151)50101
RESTAURANT : Hirschberg Alm - Pähl
Tel : (08808) 616

This is a natural scenic and quietly located course situated in the heart of Bavaria and offering breathtaking views of the Alps from many holes. Set amidst very old and beautiful trees, it is hilly with technically testing fairways. There are some lakes serving as hazards.
SSS 71

GF $$

1989

18

November to March 15

K. Rossknecht

L 6057 P 71

S

R

Required : Handicap Certificate
Best days : Weekdays

HOLE	LENGTH MEDAL-TEE	PAR	STROKE INDEX
1	332	4	7
2	339	4	11
3	390	4	5
4	332	4	9
5	192	3	17
6	451	5	13
7	166	3	15
8	386	4	1
9	516	5	3
TOTAL	3104	36	TOTAL

HOLE	LENGTH MEDAL-TEE	PAR	STROKE INDEX
10	488	5	4
11	323	4	12
12	349	4	10
13	397	4	2
14	338	4	8
15	146	3	16
16	348	4	14
17	172	3	18
18	392	4	6
TOTAL	2953	35	TOTAL

HOISDORF

TEL : (04107)7831/9179
LOCATION : 27 km Hamburg A 1
ADDRESS : Hof Bornbek-Hoisdorf – 2073 Lütjensee
HOTEL :
Forsthaus Seebergen – Lütjensee
Tel : (04154)7182
Fischerklause – Lütjensee
Tel : (04154)7165
RESTAURANT : Stadtkrug – Ahrensburg
Tel : (04102)57215

A technically difficult golf course laid out on former farmland. Quite hilly with continuous ups and downs in the terrain, the course has a varied layout featuring several contrived dog-leg holes and treacherous out of bounds. *SSS 71*

GF $

1977

18

Mondays

H. Peters

L 6010 P 71

R S

Required : Handicap Certificate
Best days : Weekdays only

HOLE	LENGTH MEDAL-TEE	PAR	STROKE INDEX
1	340	4	9
2	320	4	13
3	360	4	15
4	205	3	5
5	355	4	3
6	470	5	7
7	170	3	17
8	520	5	1
9	180	3	11
TOTAL	2920	35	TOTAL

HOLE	LENGTH MEDAL-TEE	PAR	STROKE INDEX
10	480	5	14
11	380	4	4
12	305	4	16
13	190	3	8
14	490	5	6
15	510	5	2
16	155	3	18
17	375	4	10
18	205	3	12
TOTAL	3090	36	TOTAL

HOLLEDAU

TEL : (08756)1700/1713
LOCATION : exit Pfaffenhofen of BAB 9/ 75 km München
ADDRESS : Weihern 3 - 8301 Rudelzhausen
HOTEL :
Post - Mainburg
Tel : (08751)1517
Isar - Freising
Tel : (08161)81004

Holledau is a new championship layout set in Bavaria just 75 km from München. Laid out in charming and slightly rolling woodland, the holes are landscaped by old and newly planted trees and feature a good pattern of well bunkered greens. There is also a 9 hole par 3 course. *SSS 72*

GF $ — Novembre to March

1986 —  —

18 — L 6085 P 72

Required : Club Membership Card
Best days : Any day

HOLE	LENGTH MEDAL-TEE	PAR	STROKE INDEX
1	410	4	1
2	455	5	5
3	300	4	13
4	405	4	3
5	155	3	17
6	445	5	7
7	321	4	11
8	160	3	15
9	440	5	19
TOTAL	3091	37	TOTAL

HOLE	LENGTH MEDAL-TEE	PAR	STROKE INDEX
10	395	4	4
11	335	4	14
12	295	4	16
13	209	3	8
14	320	4	18
15	378	4	2
16	475	5	6
17	176	3	10
18	411	4	12
TOTAL	2994	35	TOTAL

HUBBELRATH

★★★

TEL : (02104)72178/71848
LOCATION : 7 km Düsseldorf, in Hubbelrath
ADDRESS : Bergische Landstr. 700 – 4000 Düsseldorf 12
HOTEL :
Haus Bergmann – Hubbelrath
Tel : (02104)70025
Gut Höhne – Düsseldorf Mettmann
Tel : (02104)75006
Luisenhof – Düsseldorf Mettmann
Tel : (02104)53031
RESTAURANT : Rigoletto – Mettmann
Tel : (02104)22844

A few kilometres outside Düsseldorf in the heart of 'Bergisch Land' lies the exclusive Hubbelrath Golf Club with a great championship layout, designed by Germany's most famous golf architect Bernard von Limburger. Laid out on a wooded hill within fine natural countryside, the course gives panoramic views over the cities of Düsseldorf and Ratingen. Most of the fairways are tree-lined. There are various water hazards, such as a stream crossing the 12th hole, and a pond near the 18th tee. The imposing clubhouse is built high up and is equipped with an indoor swimming pool. Hubbelrath was the venue for the German Open in 1973, 1977 and 1986. *SSS 72*

GF $$

1964

36

—

B.v. Limburger

L 6042 P 72, 4325 P 66

S

R

Required : Handicap Certificate
Best days : Weekdays

Ostplatz

HOLE	LENGTH MEDAL-TEE	PAR	STROKE INDEX
1	381	4	7
2	380	4	3
3	323	4	11
4	128	3	15
5	286	4	17
6	505	5	5
7	152	3	9
8	447	5	13
9	361	4	1
TOTAL	2963	36	TOTAL

HOLE	LENGTH MEDAL-TEE	PAR	STROKE INDEX
10	337	4	16
11	185	3	14
12	440	5	18
13	345	4	4
14	202	3	10
15	366	4	2
16	362	4	12
17	500	5	6
18	342	4	8
TOTAL	3079	36	TOTAL

Westplatz

HOLE	LENGTH MEDAL-TEE	PAR	STROKE INDEX
1	315	4	14
2	95	3	12
3	305	4	4
4	140	3	8
5	260	4	16
6	265	4	18
7	275	4	10
8	255	4	2
9	125	3	6
TOTAL	2035	33	TOTAL

HOLE	LENGTH MEDAL-TEE	PAR	STROKE INDEX
10	345	4	3
11	300	4	7
12	295	4	9
13	110	3	15
14	125	3	17
15	285	4	11
16	370	4	1
17	175	3	5
18	285	4	13
TOTAL	2290	33	TOTAL

IDSTEIN-WÖRSDORF

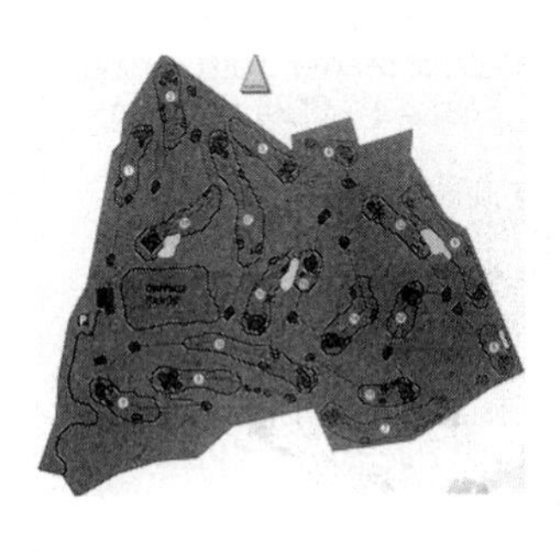

TEL : (06126)8866
LOCATION : 20 km N. Wiesbaden A66/A3
ADDRESS : Am Nassen Berg - 6270 Idstein Wörsdorf - Gut Henriettenthal
HOTEL :
Tal - Idstein
Tel : (06126)3067
Goldenes Lamm - Idstein
Tel : (06126)2080
Felsenkeller - Idstein
Tel : (06126)3351

This welcoming course merges into the soft rolling open countryside. The holes run through former farmlands and meadows landscaped by shrubs and young trees. Four water obstacles affect play. The clubhouse will be fully operational by mid 1991. *SSS 72*

GF $

1990

18

Mondays

G. Gfröhrer

L 6165 P 72

R S

Required : Handicap Certificate
Best days : Any day

HOLE	LENGTH MEDAL-TEE	PAR	STROKE INDEX
1	355	4	7
2	320	4	15
3	360	4	1
4	130	3	17
5	530	5	5
6	200	3	9
7	470	5	11
8	350	4	3
9	310	4	13
TOTAL	3025	36	TOTAL

HOLE	LENGTH MEDAL-TEE	PAR	STROKE INDEX
10	500	5	6
11	315	4	18
12	180	3	16
13	370	4	8
14	375	4	14
15	150	3	10
16	350	4	4
17	520	5	12
18	380	4	2
TOTAL	3140	36	TOTAL

IM CHIEMGAU

✡

TEL : (08669)7557
LOCATION : 10 km exit Chieming BAB München/ Salzburg, between Hart/Knesing
ADDRESS : Kötzing 1 – 8224 Chieming
HOTEL :
Gasthof Gut Ising – Ising
Tel : (08667)79-0
Malerwinkel – Seebruck Lambach
Tel : (08667)488
Wassermann – Seeon Seebruck
Tel : (08667)7155
RESTAURANT : Zum goldenen Pflug – Ising
Tel : (08667)790

This is a pleasant holiday golf course designed by the Dutch architect Dudok van Heel and located in Bavaria near the 'Chiemsee' lake. It is laid out on gently rolling terrain with wide generous fairways, many of them landscaped with tall trees. The scenic hotel "Gut Ising", set on a lake, is equipped with facilities for horse-riding, sailing, windsurfing, tennis and squash. *SSS 72*

GF $ | November to March | S
1983 | D. v. Heel |
27 | L 6070 P 72 | R

Required : Handicap Certificate
Best days : Weekdays

HOLE	LENGTH MEDAL-TEE	PAR	STROKE INDEX
1	360	4	7
2	103	3	17
3	389	4	3
4	390	4	5
5	312	4	15
6	351	4	1
7	182	3	9
8	380	4	11
9	456	5	13
TOTAL	2923	35	TOTAL

HOLE	LENGTH MEDAL-TEE	PAR	STROKE INDEX
10	317	4	12
11	168	3	14
12	453	5	8
13	385	4	4
14	205	3	2
15	485	5	6
16	347	4	10
17	343	4	16
18	444	5	18
TOTAL	3147	37	TOTAL

ISERNHAGEN AUF GUT LOHNE

TEL : (05139)2998/(0511)723030
LOCATION : 26 km Hannover B 3 to Kirchhorst
ADDRESS : Gut Lohne – 3004 Isernhagen
HOTEL :
Föhrenhof-Hannover
Tel : (0511)61721
Körner-Hannover
Tel : (0511)14666
Landhaus Ammann-Hannover
Tel : (0511)830818
RESTAURANT : Hopfenspeicher-Isernhagen
Tel : (05139)87609

The golf course is set on flat countryside typical of Niedersachsen near the city of Hannover, and is partly surrounded by woodland. Old trees, alternating with young ones, border the fairways. Several creeks run through the holes and two small lakes serve as hazards.
SSS 73

GF $ — Tuesdays — S
1984 — G. Bruns
18 — L 6379 P 73 — R

Required : Handicap Certificate
Best days : Weekdays only

HOLE	LENGTH MEDAL-TEE	PAR	STROKE INDEX
1	330	4	13
2	342	4	11
3	175	3	9
4	389	4	3
5	292	4	17
6	157	3	15
7	518	5	1
8	371	4	7
9	513	5	5
TOTAL	3087	36	TOTAL

HOLE	LENGTH MEDAL-TEE	PAR	STROKE INDEX
10	451	5	14
11	388	4	8
12	383	4	6
13	200	3	10
14	409	4	2
15	501	5	12
16	314	4	16
17	141	3	18
18	505	5	4
TOTAL	3292	37	TOTAL

ISSUM-NIEDERRHEIN

TEL : (02835)3626/1561
LOCATION : 10 km Geldern
ADDRESS : Pauenweg 68 – 4174 Issum 1
HOTEL :
Landhaus Heinen – Issum
Tel : (02835)2228
Niederrhein – Kamp Lintfort
Tel : (02842)2104
Schravelsche Heide-Kevelaer
Tel : (02832)80551
RESTAURANT : Deckers – Geldern
Tel : (02831)3626

A flat course flanked by woodland, bushes, meadowland and fruit orchards with several streams meandering their way through the holes. It is laid out in the province of Nordrhein-Westfalen. *SSS 71*

GF $

1973

18

—

—

L 5862 P 71

S

R

Required : Handicap Certificate
Best days : Mondays, Fridays

HOLE	LENGTH MEDAL-TEE	PAR	STROKE INDEX
1	440	5	
2	131	3	
3	356	4	
4	366	4	
5	331	4	
6	511	5	
7	188	3	
8	401	4	
9	388	4	
TOTAL	3112	36	TOTAL

HOLE	LENGTH MEDAL-TEE	PAR	STROKE INDEX
10	190	3	
11	287	4	
12	252	4	
13	313	4	
14	451	5	
15	416	4	
16	200	3	
17	158	3	
18	483	5	
TOTAL	2750	35	TOTAL

JERSBEK

TEL : (04532)23555
LOCATION : 3 km Bargteheide/34 km Hamburg B 434 or BAB I
ADDRESS : Oberteicher Weg 1a
2072 Gut Jersbek
HOTEL :
Forsthaus Seebergen - Frittau-Lütjensee
Tel : (04154)7182
Pirschmühle - Frittau Lütjensee
Tel : (04154)2244
RESTAURANT : Fasanenhof - Jersbek
Tel : (04532)1849

Jersbek is yet another challenging and sporting golf course in the Hamburg city area. It is set within 75ha of unspoilt and typical Holsteiner landscape. Being flat, it features many well placed lakes demanding precision play. *SSS 71*

GF $

 Mondays

1989

 M. von Schinckel

18

L 5867 P 71

Required : Handicap Certificate
Best days : Tuesdays to Fridays

HOLE	LENGTH MEDAL-TEE	PAR	STROKE INDEX
1	323	4	13
2	380	4	5
3	154	3	7
4	371	4	3
5	169	3	11
6	485	5	9
7	297	4	15
8	364	4	1
9	253	4	17
TOTAL	2796	35	TOTAL

HOLE	LENGTH MEDAL-TEE	PAR	STROKE INDEX
10	440	5	16
11	365	4	2
12	336	4	12
13	185	3	14
14	389	4	6
15	350	4	4
16	359	4	8
17	204	3	10
18	443	5	18
TOTAL	3071	36	TOTAL

JULIANA WUPPERTAL

★

TEL : (0202)647070
LOCATION : 5 km Wuppertal/38 km Düsseldorf
ADDRESS : Mollenkotten 195 – 5600 Wuppertal 2
HOTEL : HR
Juliana Golf
Tel : (0202)649630
Vesper
Tel : (0202)647070

Set on attractive hilly landscape, the course winds through woodland and meadowland. Most of the holes are tree-lined and the course commands fine views of Bergisch Land. The first class Juliana Hotel with 143 rooms, tennis courts, indoor and outdoor pools, is situated on the course near the 7th hole. Golf-Hotel Vesper is within walking distance. *SSS 71*

GF $
1978
18

Mondays
M. Peters
L 5744 P 71

S
R
◎

Required : Handicap Certificate
Best days : Weekdays

HOLE	LENGTH MEDAL-TEE	PAR	STROKE INDEX
1	347	4	7
2	393	4	1
3	215	3	9
4	302	4	13
5	449	5	3
6	287	4	17
7	172	3	11
8	464	5	5
9	105	3	15
TOTAL	2734	35	TOTAL

HOLE	LENGTH MEDAL-TEE	PAR	STROKE INDEX
10	298	4	12
11	354	4	4
12	537	5	2
13	171	3	18
14	283	4	10
15	465	5	8
16	360	4	14
17	342	4	16
18	200	3	6
TOTAL	3010	36	TOTAL

KARLHÄUSER HOF

TEL : (07237)1284/9100
LOCATION : BAB Stuttgart-Karlsruhe exit Pforzheim - Ost then B 294 to Bretten
ADDRESS : Karlhäuser Weg
7531 Ölbronn Durrn
HOTEL :
Goldene Pforte - Pforzheim
Tel : (07231)37920
Mönch's Schloss - Pforzheim
Tel : (07231)16051
RESTAURANT : Zur Linde - Mühlacker
Tel : (0721)46118

This fairly difficult course of championship standard has an attractive and modern layout. Located in the province of Baden-Würtemberg, it is a combined parkland/woodland course featuring excellent greens and many strategic water obstacles. *SSS 72*

GF $

1987

18

December to March

—

L 6050 P 72

S

R

Required : Handicap Certificate
Best days : Weekdays with booking in advance

HOLE	LENGTH MEDAL-TEE	PAR	STROKE INDEX
1	455	5	
2	328	4	
3	185	3	
4	470	5	
5	152	3	
6	363	4	
7	350	4	
8	185	3	
9	315	4	
TOTAL	2803	35	TOTAL

HOLE	LENGTH MEDAL-TEE	PAR	STROKE INDEX
10	489	5	
11	398	4	
12	139	3	
13	437	5	
14	306	4	
15	193	3	
16	489	5	
17	412	4	
18	384	4	
TOTAL	3247	37	TOTAL

KASSEL-WILHELMSHÖHE

TEL : (0561)33509
LOCATION : 15 km Kassel
ADDRESS : Am Habichtswald – 3500 Kassel
HOTEL :
Schloss – Wilhelmshöhe
Tel : (0561)30880
Kurparkhotel – Wilhelmshöhe
Tel : (0561)30972
Schweizer Hof – Wilhelmshöhe
Tel : (0561)34048
RESTAURANT : Le Français-Kassel
Tel : (0561)776649

Kassel-Wilhelmshöhe is located in the province of Hessen. Built high up, the club lies within a regional park, the 'Habichtswald' on hilly terrain with the 'Herkules', the official monument of the city of Kassel, overshadowing the holes. The course is entirely surrounded by old and stately trees with water affecting play on several holes. *SSS 70*

GF $

1958

18

November to March

—

L 5675 P 70

S

R

Required : Handicap Certificate
Best days : Weekdays only

HOLE	LENGTH MEDAL-TEE	PAR	STROKE INDEX
1	350	4	
2	145	3	
3	350	4	
4	380	4	
5	385	4	
6	460	5	
7	360	4	
8	170	3	
9	435	5	
TOTAL	3035	36	TOTAL

HOLE	LENGTH MEDAL-TEE	PAR	STROKE INDEX
10	315	4	
11	390	4	
12	130	3	
13	470	5	
14	150	3	
15	390	4	
16	335	4	
17	130	3	
18	330	4	
TOTAL	2640	34	TOTAL

KÖLN-REFRATH

TEL : (02204)63114
LOCATION : 15 km Köln, in Bergisch Gladbach
ADDRESS : Golfplatz 2 – 5060 Bergisch Gladbach
HOTEL :
Tannenhof – Bergisch Gladbach
Tel : (02202)35088
Waldhotel Mangold – Bergisch Gladbach
Tel : (02204)54011
RESTAURANT : Goethehaus – Bergisch Gladbach
Tel : (02204)54031

One of Germany's oldest and noblest clubs is the Köln-Refrath Golf und Landclub. A typical heavily wooded inland course with beautiful old trees bordering the rolling fairways. It features several well-contrived dog-leg holes with craftily bunkered greens, demanding accuracy from tee to green. The Tannenhof Hotel lies within walking distance from the course. *SSS 72*

 $$

 1906

18

Mondays (1.11/1.03)

 B. von Limburger

 6045 P 72

Required : Handicap Certificate
Best days : Weekdays only

HOLE	LENGTH MEDAL-TEE	PAR	STROKE INDEX
1	315	4	9
2	440	5	13
3	170	3	11
4	290	4	17
5	360	4	3
6	345	4	5
7	395	4	1
8	145	3	15
9	500	5	7
TOTAL	2960	36	TOTAL

HOLE	LENGTH MEDAL-TEE	PAR	STROKE INDEX
10	355	4	8
11	440	5	18
12	145	3	16
13	395	4	2
14	350	4	12
15	165	3	10
16	390	4	6
17	375	3	4
18	470	5	14
TOTAL	3085	35	TOTAL

KÖNIGSFELD

TEL : (07725)2477
LOCATION : 12 km Schramberg
ADDRESS : Angelmoos 20 - 7744
Königsfeld im Schwarzwald
HOTEL :
Schwarzwald - Königsfeld
Tel : (07725)7091
Schwarzwald Treff - Königsfeld
Tel : (07725)8080

The course lies in the middle of the Black Forest and rises 750 m above sea level. It features a challenging layout with tree-lined fairways set on lush hilly landscape surrounded by forests. *SSS 72*

GF $ — November to March — S

1990 — —

18 — L 6130 P 70

Required : Club Membership Card
Best days : Any day

HOLE	LENGTH MEDAL-TEE	PAR	STROKE INDEX
1	325	4	
2	110	3	
3	395	4	
4	350	4	
5	340	4	
6	410	4	
7	220	3	
8	360	4	
9	500	5	
TOTAL	3010	35	TOTAL

HOLE	LENGTH MEDAL-TEE	PAR	STROKE INDEX
10	420	4	
11	330	4	
12	130	3	
13	475	5	
14	425	4	
15	355	4	
16	180	3	
17	390	4	
18	415	4	
TOTAL	3120	35	TOTAL

KONSTANZ

TEL : (07533)5124
LOCATION : 15 km Konstanz, near Langenrain
ADDRESS : Hofgut Kargegg - 7753 Allensbach 3
HOTEL :
Seeblick – Konstanz
Tel : (07531)54018
Baumgartner – Konstanz
Tel : (07533)5748
Insel – Konstanz
Tel : (07531)25011
RESTAURANT : Weinstube – Konstanz
Tel : (07531)23566

The Konstanz golf course is ideal for holiday golf, peacefully laid out on rising ground above the scenic Uberlinger lake. Set on hilly terrain, the well-wooded course features several water holes and overlooks the lake. *SSS 72*

GF $$

1965

18

—

—

L 6058 P 72

S

R

Required : Handicap Certificate, Club Membership Card
Best days : Mondays to Saturdays inc.

HOLE	LENGTH MEDAL-TEE	PAR	STROKE INDEX
1	325	4	9
2	175	3	13
3	516	5	1
4	363	4	3
5	550	5	7
6	324	4	15
7	221	3	5
8	478	5	11
9	129	3	17
TOTAL	3081	36	TOTAL

HOLE	LENGTH MEDAL-TEE	PAR	STROKE INDEX
10	323	4	18
11	395	4	4
12	131	3	16
13	352	4	2
14	294	4	14
15	340	4	10
16	156	3	12
17	476	5	6
18	510	5	8
TOTAL	2997	36	TOTAL

KREFELD

★★

TEL : (02151)570071/72
LOCATION : 7 km Krefeld, 22 km Düsseldorf
ADDRESS : Eltweg 2 – 4150 Krefeld-Linn
HOTEL :
Krefelder Hof – Krefeld
Tel : (02151)584-0
Hansa – Krefeld
Tel : (02151)8290
Haus Dahmen – Krefeld
Tel : (02151)570311
RESTAURANT : Haus Dahmen – Krefeld
Tel : (02151)570311

The Krefelder is one of the best inland courses in Germany set on flat wooded landscape. Though not very long for a championship course, each hole has its own distinctive challenge. The course is cunningly bunkered and includes ten difficult dog-legs. The undulating and small greens are of excellent quality and heavily bunkered. *SSS 72*

GF $$ — Weekends — S
1930 — – — 🏆
18 — L 6060 P 72 — R

Required : Handicap Certificate
Best days : Weekdays

HOLE	LENGTH MEDAL-TEE	PAR	STROKE INDEX
1	465	5	15
2	170	3	13
3	395	4	5
4	400	4	3
5	190	3	7
6	450	5	17
7	327	4	9
8	497	4	1
9	323	4	11
TOTAL	3126	36	TOTAL

HOLE	LENGTH MEDAL-TEE	PAR	STROKE INDEX
10	170	3	14
11	445	5	6
12	335	4	4
13	137	3	18
14	400	4	2
15	465	5	12
16	166	3	10
17	444	5	16
18	372	4	8
TOTAL	2934	36	TOTAL

KRONBERG

★

TEL : (06173)1426
LOCATION : 15 km Frankfurt B 455, exit Schonberg
ADDRESS : Schloss Friedrichshof – 6242 Kronberg
HOTEL : HP
Schloss Kronberg
Tel : (06173)7011
Kronberger Hof – Kronberg
Tel : (06173)79071
Sonnenhof – Königstein
Tel : (06174)3051

An attractive parkland course with lush rolling fairways featuring a large variety of trees, including several rare specimen, lining the course. There are streams meandering their way through several holes. The magnificent Schloss Friedrichshof, adjacent to the course, used to be a royal castle, and is nowadays a luxury hotel and member of the Relais & Châteaux chain. *SSS 68*

GF $$
1954
18

Weekends
E. Kothe, B. von Limburger
L 5365 P 68

S
RP

Required : Handicap Certificate, Club Membership Card
Best days : Weekdays in the morning

HOLE	LENGTH MEDAL-TEE	PAR	STROKE INDEX
1	330	4	7
2	115	3	17
3	480	5	5
4	375	4	13
5	335	4	9
6	140	3	15
7	295	4	11
8	405	4	3
9	375	4	1
TOTAL	2850	35	TOTAL

HOLE	LENGTH MEDAL-TEE	PAR	STROKE INDEX
10	200	3	6
11	265	4	18
12	415	4	2
13	355	4	8
14	160	3	14
15	380	4	4
16	300	4	10
17	285	4	16
18	155	3	12
TOTAL	2515	33	TOTAL

KURHESSISCHER OBERAULA

TEL : (06628)1573
LOCATION : 60 km Kassel, exit Kirchheim of BAB 7 to Oberaula
ADDRESS : Am Golfplatz - 6435 Oberaula - Hausen
HOTEL :
Am Kurpark - Bad Hersfeld
Tel : (06621)1640
Zum Stern - Oberaula
Tel : (06628)8091
Motel Center - Kirchheim
Tel : (06625)108-0

A sporting and technically difficult course set on different ground levels, the holes run through hazardous and wooded landscape. It comprises deep bunkers defending greens, strategic expanses of water and many dogleg holes. Precision is a necessity while playing this new and challenging course. *SSS 72*

GF $

1987

18

November to April

Deutsche Golf Consult

L 6100 P 72

S

Required : Handicap Certificate
Best days : Any day

HOLE	LENGTH MEDAL-TEE	PAR	STROKE INDEX
1	395	4	5
2	485	5	3
3	155	3	17
4	300	4	15
5	310	4	13
6	510	5	7
7	395	4	1
8	170	3	11
9	355	4	9
TOTAL	3075	36	TOTAL

HOLE	LENGTH MEDAL-TEE	PAR	STROKE INDEX
10	445	5	10
11	185	3	16
12	325	4	12
13	150	3	18
14	410	4	2
15	365	4	4
16	290	4	14
17	445	5	8
18	410	4	6
TOTAL	3025	36	TOTAL

KÜSTEN HOHE KLINT

TEL : (04723)2737
LOCATION : 15 km Cuxhaven
ADDRESS : Rosenhof 25 – 2191 Oxstedt Cuxhaven
HOTEL :
Sternhagen – Cuxhaven
Tel : (04721)47004
Deichgraf – Cuxhaven-Döse
Tel : (04721)47091
Seepavillon Donner – Cuxhaven
Tel : (04721)38064

Situated in the province of Niedersachsen/Bremen, Küsten Hohe Klint is a wooded seaside course near the North Sea, set on sandy sub-soil. Its main obstacle is a constant prevailing sea-wind and water affecting play on several holes. *SSS 72*

GF $

1980

18

—

G. Bruns

L 6059 P 72

R S

Required : Handicap Certificate
Best days : Any day

HOLE	LENGTH MEDAL-TEE	PAR	STROKE INDEX
1	523	5	
2	167	3	
3	336	4	
4	393	4	
5	337	4	
6	469	5	
7	374	4	
8	139	3	
9	335	4	
TOTAL	3073	36	TOTAL

HOLE	LENGTH MEDAL-TEE	PAR	STROKE INDEX
10	469	5	
11	349	4	
12	138	3	
13	478	5	
14	364	4	
15	294	4	
16	328	4	
17	205	3	
18	361	4	
TOTAL	2986	36	TOTAL

LEUTSTETTEN

TEL : (08151)8811
LOCATION : 25 km München
ADDRESS : Gut Rieden - 8130 Starnberg
HOTEL :
Schloss Berg - Berg
Tel : (08151)50106
Obermühltal - Starnberg
Tel : (08151)8585
Bayerischer Hof - Starnberg
Tel : (08151)12133

Situated in the heart of Bavaria close to München, the course is found in a pleasant ascending setting and offers panoramic views of the Alps and the Starnberger lake. *SSS 72*

GF $

1989

18

November to March

—

L 5999 P 72

S

R

Required : Handicap Certificate
Best days : Mondays

HOLE	LENGTH MEDAL-TEE	PAR	STROKE INDEX
1	293	4	
2	210	3	
3	345	4	
4	317	4	
5	432	4	
6	204	3	
7	318	4	
8	289	4	
9	452	5	
TOTAL	2860	35	TOTAL

HOLE	LENGTH MEDAL-TEE	PAR	STROKE INDEX
10	312	4	
11	386	4	
12	517	5	
13	608	5	
14	251	4	
15	293	4	
16	210	3	
17	345	4	
18	317	4	
TOTAL	3239	37	TOTAL

LINDAU-BAD SCHACHEN

TEL : (08382)78090
LOCATION : In Schönbühl
ADDRESS : Schlöss Schönbühl – 8990 Lindau Bad Schachen
HOTEL :
Bad Schachen – Bad Schachen
Tel : (08382)5011
Bayerischer Hof – Lindau
Tel : (08382)5055
Reutemann – Lindau
Tel : (08382)5055
RESTAURANT : Walliser Stube – Lindau
Tel : (08382)6449

The course is picturesquely laid out around the Schönbühl Castle with magnificent views of the snow clad Alps, the island of Lindau and the Bodensee lake. It is gently rolling and features some water hazards. Ideal for holiday golf with the first class Bad Schachen hotel (with tennis courts and swimming pool) not far away. *SSS 70*

GF $ — — S
1954 — RP
18 L 5690 P 70

Required : Handicap Certificate
Best days : Any day

HOLE	LENGTH MEDAL-TEE	PAR	STROKE INDEX
1	295	4	13
2	340	4	7
3	440	5	11
4	355	4	3
5	125	3	15
6	325	4	9
7	315	4	17
8	350	4	1
9	340	4	5
TOTAL	2885	36	TOTAL

HOLE	LENGTH MEDAL-TEE	PAR	STROKE INDEX
10	370	4	6
11	165	3	16
12	310	4	18
13	470	5	10
14	310	4	12
15	155	3	14
16	375	4	4
17	425	4	2
18	225	3	8
TOTAL	2805	34	TOTAL

LIPPISCHER

TEL : (05236)459
LOCATION : In Cappel
ADDRESS : Huxollweg – 4935 Blomberg Cappel
HOTEL :
Lippischer Hof-Detmold
Tel : (05231 31041
Burghotel Blomberg – Blomberg
Tel : (05235)50010
Detmolder Hof – Detmold
Tel : (05231)28244
RESTAURANT : Deutsches Haus – Blomberg
Tel : (05235)6022

Laid out on flat open land, the course is cut in two by a row of trees which feature two majestic oaks dating back 1000 years. There are streams and three ponds serving as hazards. The average golfer won't find this course too much of a test. *SSS 72*

GF $

1983

18

—

—

L 6135 P 72

S

R

Required : Handicap Certificate
Best days : Any day

HOLE	LENGTH MEDAL-TEE	PAR	STROKE INDEX
1	455	5	11
2	350	4	17
3	315	4	13
4	510	5	5
5	140	3	15
6	410	4	1
7	195	3	9
8	395	4	3
9	360	4	7
TOTAL	3130	36	TOTAL

HOLE	LENGTH MEDAL-TEE	PAR	STROKE INDEX
10	440	5	18
11	140	3	16
12	305	4	10
13	140	3	14
14	370	4	4
15	340	4	12
16	390	4	6
17	390	4	2
18	490	5	8
TOTAL	3005	36	TOTAL

MAIN-TAUNUS

TEL : (06122)52208
LOCATION : BAB 66 to Wiesbaden exit Delkenheim
ADDRESS : Lange Seegewann 2 – 6200 Wiesbaden-Delkenheim
HOTEL :
Schwarzer Bok – Wiesbaden
Tel : (06121)3821
Nassauer Hof – Wiesbaden
Tel : (06121)1330
Penta – Wiesbaden
Tel : (06121)377041
RESTAURANT : Le Gourmet – Wiesbaden
Tel : (06121)301654

The course is set within a nature reserve for birds on flat open landscape, surrounded by fields, with young trees landscaping the holes. Ponds and ditches serve as hazards on eleven holes . *SSS 72*

GF $ | December to March | S
1980 | — |
18 | L 6044 P 72 | R

Required : Handicap Certificate
Best days : Weekdays

HOLE	LENGTH MEDAL-TEE	PAR	STROKE INDEX
1	335	4	14
2	545	5	8
3	156	3	18
4	369	4	14
5	301	4	16
6	448	5	12
7	160	3	2
8	381	4	6
9	355	4	10
TOTAL	3050	36	TOTAL

HOLE	LENGTH MEDAL-TEE	PAR	STROKE INDEX
10	326	4	7
11	289	4	17
12	359	4	15
13	342	4	3
14	508	5	11
15	170	3	9
16	346	4	5
17	193	3	1
18	461	5	13
TOTAL	2994	36	TOTAL

MARGARETHENHOF AM TEGERNSEE

✡★

TEL : (08022)74031
LOCATION : in Gmund-Marienstein
ADDRESS : Gut Steinberg – 8184 Gmund am Tegernsee
HOTEL :
Lederer am See – Bad Wiessee
Tel : (08022)8291
Terrassen Hof – Bad Wiessee
Tel : (08022)82761
Walter's Hof – Rottach Egern
Tel : (08022)2770
RESTAURANT : La Cuisine – Rottach Egern
Tel : (08022)24764

Situated in Bavaria, this is a first class championship course with several testing holes. It is laid out on gently undulating terrain and encircled by forest and mountains. The fairways are wide with many elevated greens, commanding fine views over the surroundings, including the Alps and the Tegernsee lake. *SSS 72*

GF $$

1983

18

November to April

F. Pennink

L 6010 P 72

Required : Handicap Certificate
Best days : Any day

HOLE	LENGTH MEDAL-TEE	PAR	STROKE INDEX
1	460	5	13
2	329	4	7
3	172	3	15
4	310	4	9
5	468	5	17
6	165	3	11
7	400	4	1
8	185	3	3
9	396	4	5
TOTAL	2885	35	TOTAL

HOLE	LENGTH MEDAL-TEE	PAR	STROKE INDEX
10	390	4	12
11	335	4	14
12	485	5	10
13	176	3	6
14	316	4	18
15	352	4	8
16	485	5	4
17	133	3	16
18	453	5	2
TOTAL	3125	37	TOTAL

MARITIM TIMMENDORFER STRAND

TEL : (04503)5152
LOCATION : Exit Ratekau Timmend to Putlos
ADDRESS : 2408 Timmendorfer Strand
HOTEL :
Maritim – Timmendorfer Strand
Tel : (04503)5031
Atlantis – Timmendorfer Strand
Tel : (04503)5051
Yachtclub – Timmendorfer Strand
Tel : (04503)5061
RESTAURANT : Golf – Timmendorfer Strand
Tel : (04503)4091

Designed by Bernard von Limburger, these are two fine holiday golf courses, set not far from the sea front. The main championship layout has generous fairways with well-bunkered small greens. Accuracy is essential due to a constant wind. There are many hotels by the sea, offering a wide choice of sports and leisure facilities. *SSS 72*

GF $$

— RΓ S

1973

B. v. Limburger 

36

L 6095 P 72, 3755 P 61

Required : Handicap Certificate
Best days : Weekdays

HOLE	LENGTH MEDAL-TEE	PAR	STROKE INDEX
1	345	4	11
2	510	5	1
3	155	3	17
4	320	4	15
5	355	4	9
6	200	3	5
7	355	4	3
8	465	5	13
9	345	4	7
TOTAL	3050	36	TOTAL

HOLE	LENGTH MEDAL-TEE	PAR	STROKE INDEX
10	340	4	4
11	490	5	10
12	185	3	14
13	360	4	2
14	325	4	12
15	440	5	8
16	320	4	18
17	170	3	16
18	415	4	6
TOTAL	3045	36	TOTAL

MITTELHOLSTEINISCHER AUKRUG

TEL : (04873)595
LOCATION : in Bargfeld
ADDRESS : 2356 Aukrug-Bargfeld
HOTEL : Tannhof – Neumünster
Tel : (04321)529197
Friedrichs – Neumünster
Tel : (04321)8011
Köhlerhof – Bad Bramstedt
Tel : (04192)5050
RESTAURANT : Hof Bucken – Aukrug
Tel : (04873)209

The course is set within a typical 'Holsteiner' landscape on gently rolling terrain amidst meadows and forest, with water, such as ponds and a stream, affecting play on more than six holes. Most of the fairways are narrow and flanked by trees. *SSS 72*

GF $ — October to April — S

1969 — — —

18 — L 6140 P 72 — R

Required : Handicap Certificate
Best days : Any day

HOLE	LENGTH MEDAL-TEE	PAR	STROKE INDEX
1	326	4	17
2	226	3	7
3	354	4	11
4	185	3	1
5	495	5	13
6	367	4	5
7	365	4	15
8	365	4	3
9	481	5	9
TOTAL	3164	36	TOTAL

HOLE	LENGTH MEDAL-TEE	PAR	STROKE INDEX
10	446	5	16
11	371	4	8
12	205	3	4
13	335	4	2
14	155	3	18
15	338	4	12
16	265	4	14
17	462	5	6
18	399	4	10
TOTAL	2976	36	TOTAL

MITTELRHEINISCHER

TEL : (02603)6541
LOCATION : 3 km Bad Ems/17 km Koblenz
ADDRESS : Denzerheide – 5427 Bad Ems
HOTEL :
Golf Hotel
Tel : (02603)6159
Kupferkanne – Bad Ems
Tel : (02603)14197
Parkhotel – Bad Ems
Tel : (02603)2058
RESTAURANT : Streseman – Koblenz
Tel : (0261)15464

A first class golf course picturesquely situated in the heart of 'Rheinland' on a plain some 300m above sea level. It is entirely surrounded by age-old trees and offers panoramic views over the hills of the Eifel and the Taunus. The course is of championship standard and has hosted important tournaments. *SSS 72*

 $

 —

 1930

 M. Hofmann

18

 6050 P 72

Required : Handicap Certificate
Best days : Weekdays only

HOLE	LENGTH MEDAL-TEE	PAR	STROKE INDEX
1	340	4	15
2	500	5	9
3	150	3	17
4	500	5	3
5	185	3	13
6	355	4	1
7	390	4	5
8	480	5	7
9	335	4	11
TOTAL	3235	37	TOTAL

HOLE	LENGTH MEDAL-TEE	PAR	STROKE INDEX
10	405	4	2
11	435	5	10
12	165	3	16
13	270	4	14
14	415	4	4
15	135	3	18
16	315	4	12
17	180	3	6
18	495	5	8
TOTAL	2815	35	TOTAL

MÜNCHEN NORD-EICHENRIED

TEL : (08123)1004
LOCATION : 20 km N. München B 388 to Erding
ADDRESS : Münchnerstrasse 57
8059 Eichenried
HOTEL :
Königshof - München
Tel : (089)551360
Arabella -München
Tel : (089)92321
Ferstl Braü - Eichenried
Tel : (08122)2718
RESTAURANT : Aubergine - München
Tel : (089)598171

Set in 80ha of flat and well wooded countryside near the Bavarian city of Munich, the course is flanked by forest on three sides. Its main challenge is presented by the number of water obstacles, covering more than 2ha, such as streams crossing the fairways and strategic ponds. *SSS 73*

GF $$
1988
18

November to March
—
L 6125 P 73

R S

Required : Handicap Certificate
Best days : Weekdays only

HOLE	LENGTH MEDAL-TEE	PAR	STROKE INDEX
1	386	4	7
2	188	3	5
3	374	4	1
4	314	4	9
5	290	4	17
6	432	5	15
7	392	4	3
8	174	3	11
9	481	5	13
TOTAL	3031	36	TOTAL

HOLE	LENGTH MEDAL-TEE	PAR	STROKE INDEX
10	412	4	2
11	468	5	6
12	135	3	8
13	334	4	16
14	444	5	18
15	352	4	10
16	296	4	12
17	160	3	14
18	493	5	4
TOTAL	3094	37	TOTAL

MÜNCHNER

TEL : (08170)450/7504
LOCATION : 4 km München near the zoo
ADDRESS : Tölzerstrasse – 8021 Strasslach
HOTEL :
Schloss Grünwald – Grünwald
Tel : (089)6417935
Forsthaus Wörnbrunn – Grünwald
Tel : (089)6417885
Königshof – München
Tel : (089)551360
RESTAURANT : Alpenblick – Strasslach
Tel : (08170)214

This busy championship golf course around München, is situated by the village of Strasslach in a typical Bavarian landscape. Set on rolling terrain, the course is testing, and has around 45 strategically placed bunkers and several doglegs. *SSS 72*

GF $$

1910

27

November to April

 —

L 6085 P 72, 5056 P 68

Required : Handicap Certificate, Club Membership Card
Best days : Any day

HOLE	LENGTH MEDAL-TEE	PAR	STROKE INDEX	HOLE	LENGTH MEDAL-TEE	PAR	STROKE INDEX	HOLE	LENGTH MEDAL-TEE	PAR	STROKE INDEX
1	507	5	7	1	452	5	10	1	390	4	
2	343	4	11	2	193	3	12	2	311	4	
3	163	3	15	3	338	4	16	3	302	4	
4	369	4	3	4	318	4	14	4	116	3	
5	435	5	17	5	177	3	6	5	351	4	
6	353	4	5	6	420	4	2	6	121	3	
7	137	3	13	7	380	4	4	7	327	4	
8	398	4	1	8	445	5	18	8	282	4	
9	322	4	9	9	335	4	8	9	328	4	
TOTAL	3027	36	TOTAL	TOTAL	3058	36	TOTAL	TOTAL	2528	34	TOTAL

MÜNSTER-WILKINGHEGE

TEL : (0251)211201
LOCATION : in N. Münster
ADDRESS : Steinfurter Str. 448 – 4400 Münster
HOTEL : HP
Schloss Wilkinghege – Münster
Tel : (0251)213045
Hof zur Linde – Münster
Tel : (0251)325003
Waldhotel Krautkrämer – Münster
Tel : (02501)8050

Located near the Wilkinghege castle, the course is of the parkland type, laid out on flat terrain, and has several water hazards. The stately Wilkinghege castle has been turned into a peacefully situated hotel with 38 bedrooms and tennis courts. *SSS 71*

GF $

1963

18

Weekends

W. Siegmann

L 5955 P 71

S

R

Required : Handicap Certificate
Best days : Weekdays

HOLE	LENGTH MEDAL-TEE	PAR	STROKE INDEX
1	360	4	13
2	380	4	11
3	190	3	9
4	520	5	1
5	345	4	15
6	190	3	5
7	165	3	17
8	360	4	3
9	330	4	7
TOTAL	2840	34	TOTAL

HOLE	LENGTH MEDAL-TEE	PAR	STROKE INDEX
10	460	5	14
11	375	4	2
12	445	5	6
13	335	4	16
14	345	4	8
15	205	3	12
16	460	5	4
17	130	3	18
18	360	4	10
TOTAL	3115	37	TOTAL

NAHETAL

TEL : (06708)2145/3755
LOCATION : in Bad Münster
ADDRESS : Drei Buchen Weg – 6552 Bad Münster a. St.-Ebernburg
HOTEL :
Post – Bad Münster
Tel : (06708)3026
Der Quellenhof – Bad Kreuznach
Tel : (0671)2191
Parkhotel Plehn – Bad Münster
Tel : (06708)81399
RESTAURANT : Krone – Bad Münster
Tel : (06708)2022

The Nahetal golf club lies in the province of Rheinland-Pfatz on gently rolling countryside. It is an inland course of medium difficulty with quite narrow fairways landscaped among old broadleaf trees. Water affects play on some of the holes. *SSS 72*

GF $

1971

18

—

A. Keller

L 6075 P 72

S

R

Required : Handicap Certificate
Best days : Weekdays

HOLE	LENGTH MEDAL-TEE	PAR	STROKE INDEX
1	315	4	15
2	355	4	5
3	355	4	11
4	475	5	7
5	158	3	9
6	360	4	3
7	340	4	13
8	120	3	17
9	405	4	1
TOTAL	2883	35	TOTAL

HOLE	LENGTH MEDAL-TEE	PAR	STROKE INDEX
10	445	5	18
11	167	3	10
12	335	4	14
13	395	4	4
14	200	3	2
15	480	5	16
16	380	4	8
17	445	5	6
18	345	4	12
TOTAL	3192	37	TOTAL

OBERALLGÄU ZU WIGGENSBACH

TEL : (08370)733
LOCATION : 12 km Wiggensbach
ADDRESS : Hof Waldegg – 8961 Wiggensbach/Oberallgäu
HOTEL :
Hofgut Kürnach – Wiggensbach
Tel : (08370)1211
Bürgerhaus – Wiggensbach
Tel : (08370)764
Gasthof Goldenes Kreuz – Wiggensbach
Tel : (08370)217
RESTAURANT : Goldenes Kreuz – Wiggensbach
Tel : (08370)217

The highest 18 holes in Germany with the lowest tee at 873m and the highest tee at 1004m above sea level. The short, but pleasant course is set in the foothills of the Allgäuer Alps amidst luxuriant coniferous countryside. There is a fine Bavarian-style clubhouse. *SSS 62*

GF $

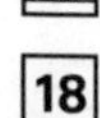 1982

18

November to April

E. Wohlfahrt-Fischberg

L 4035 P 65

 S

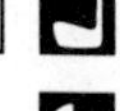

Required : Handicap Certificate
Best days : Any day

HOLE	LENGTH MEDAL-TEE	PAR	STROKE INDEX
1	170	3	5
2	335	4	1
3	240	4	15
4	235	4	13
5	85	3	17
6	255	4	9
7	135	3	7
8	235	4	11
9	190	3	3
TOTAL	1880	33	TOTAL

HOLE	LENGTH MEDAL-TEE	PAR	STROKE INDEX
10	75	3	12
11	580	5	10
12	250	4	8
13	110	3	14
14	370	4	2
15	165	3	16
16	180	3	4
17	240	4	18
18	235	4	6
TOTAL	2155	32	TOTAL

OBERFRANKEN

TEL : (09228)319/1022
LOCATION : 20 km Bayreuth
ADDRESS : Petershof - 8656 Thurnau
HOTEL :
Fränkischer Hof – Thurnau
Tel : (09228)239
Am Pollmansgarten – Thurnau
Tel : (09228)661
Königshof – Bayreuth
Tel : (0921)24094
RESTAURANT : Annecy – Bayreuth
Tel : (0921)26279

The Oberfranken golf course is an excellant inland course of championship standard, set on undulating terrain and landscaped among old trees with water coming into play on some of the holes. Several of the par 4 and 5 holes are particularly demanding. *SSS 72*

GF $

1965

18

 November to March

 B.v. Limburger, D. Harradine

L 6152 P 72

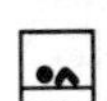

Required : Handicap Certificate
Best days : Any day

HOLE	LENGTH MEDAL-TEE	PAR	STROKE INDEX
1	334	4	13
2	360	4	5
3	546	5	3
4	109	3	17
5	390	4	1
6	369	4	9
7	332	4	15
8	503	5	7
9	147	3	11
TOTAL	3090	36	TOTAL

HOLE	LENGTH MEDAL-TEE	PAR	STROKE INDEX
10	278	4	18
11	177	3	12
12	382	4	8
13	364	4	14
14	347	4	2
15	511	5	10
16	189	3	16
17	471	5	6
18	343	4	4
TOTAL	3062	36	TOTAL

OBERSCHWABEN BAD WALDSEE

TEL : (07524)5900
LOCATION : 2 km Bad Waldsee to Eberhardzell
ADDRESS : Fürstl. Hofgut Hopfenweiler – 7967 Bad Waldsee
HOTEL :
Rössle – Bad Wurzach
Tel : (07564)2055
Kreuz – Mahenhaus
Tel : (07524)1610
Grüner Baum-Bad Waldsee
Tel : (07524)1437
RESTAURANT : Zum Ritter – Bad Waldsee
Tel : (07524)8018

Quietly set among meadowland and groves of silver birch, pines, oak and chestnut, this is a picturesque and hilly course having three ponds which serve as hazards on the 4th and 5th holes. *SSS 72*

GF $
1968
18

Mondays (1.11/1.04)
—
L 6148 P 72

S
R

Required : Handicap Certificate
Best days : Tuesdays, Fridays

HOLE	LENGTH MEDAL-TEE	PAR	STROKE INDEX
1	485	5	12
2	345	4	9
3	355	4	13
4	455	5	11
5	392	4	3
6	445	5	15
7	176	3	6
8	425	4	2
9	178	3	7
TOTAL	3256	37	TOTAL

HOLE	LENGTH MEDAL-TEE	PAR	STROKE INDEX
10	210	3	5
11	430	4	1
12	500	5	10
13	166	3	14
14	301	4	17
15	495	5	18
16	155	3	16
17	355	4	4
18	280	4	18
TOTAL	2892	35	TOTAL

OLCHING

★

TEL : (08142)3240
LOCATION : 2 km Olching/25 km München BAB to Stuttgart exit Dachau
ADDRESS : Feurstrasse 89 – 8037 Olching 2
HOTEL :
Schiller – Olching
Tel : (08142)30088
Mayer – Olching
Tel : (089)844071
Parsberg – Olching
Tel : (089)802071
RESTAURANT : Venezia – Fürstenfeldbruck
Tel : (08141)4838

A sporting championship layout set on flat terrain. The course is flanked on one side by the river 'Amper' and has five ponds which serve as hazards on more than ten holes. There is a comfortable Bavarian-style clubhouse. *SSS 72*

GF $$ — November to March — R S
1983 — — —
18 — L 6094 P 72

Required : Handicap Certificate
Best days : Any day

HOLE	LENGTH MEDAL-TEE	PAR	STROKE INDEX
1	376	4	
2	334	4	
3	154	3	
4	494	5	
5	344	4	
6	122	3	
7	492	5	
8	324	4	
9	368	4	
TOTAL	3008	36	TOTAL

HOLE	LENGTH MEDAL-TEE	PAR	STROKE INDEX
10	369	4	
11	173	3	
12	292	4	
13	408	4	
14	352	4	
15	455	5	
16	204	3	
17	483	5	
18	350	4	
TOTAL	3086	36	TOTAL

OLDENBURG

TEL : (04402)7240
LOCATION : 10 km Oldenburg
ADDRESS : Golfplatz – 2902 Rastede Wemkendorf
HOTEL :
Hof von Oldenburg – Rastede
Tel : (04402)1031
Landhaus am Schlosspark – Oldenburg
Tel : (04402)3243
Sporthotel – Oldenburg
Tel : (04402)6127
RESTAURANT : Le Journal – Oldenburg
Tel : (0441)13128

Set in the province of Niedersachsen, the course is laid out in a flat parkland setting and features several ponds, and a stream crossing two holes. Most of the fairways are landscaped with majestic trees. *SSS 72*

GF $

1964

18

November to March

—

L 6100 P 72

S

R

Required : Handicap Certificate
Best days : Weekdays

HOLE	LENGTH MEDAL-TEE	PAR	STROKE INDEX
1	350	4	7
2	188	3	15
3	336	4	13
4	388	4	1
5	140	3	17
6	353	4	9
7	325	4	3
8	490	5	5
9	485	5	11
TOTAL	3055	36	TOTAL

HOLE	LENGTH MEDAL-TEE	PAR	STROKE INDEX
10	140	3	18
11	435	5	12
12	155	3	16
13	390	4	6
14	540	5	2
15	335	4	8
16	380	4	4
17	350	4	10
18	320	4	14
TOTAL	3045	36	TOTAL

ÖSCHBERGHOF

✡

TEL : (0771)84525
LOCATION : 4 km Donaueschingen
ADDRESS : Golfplatz 1 –
7710 Donaueschingen
HOTEL : HR
Öschberghof
Tel : (0771)840
Linde – Donaueschingen
Tel : (0771)3048
Schützen – Donaueschingen
Tel : (0771)5085

Located in the province of Baden-Würtemberg, the tree-lined course is set on fairly flat terrain. Its main difficulty is a stream meandering its way through at least eight holes. Ideal for holiday golf, there is a fine hotel with a swimming pool on the course. There are open golf weeks organized in August. *SSS 74*

GF $$

1975

18

November to March

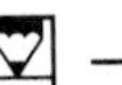 —

L 6175 P 72

RF

Required : Handicap Certificate
Best days : Mondays to Saturdays inc.

HOLE	LENGTH MEDAL-TEE	PAR	STROKE INDEX
1	430	4	3
2	340	4	11
3	175	3	9
4	505	5	5
5	390	4	1
6	360	4	7
7	140	3	15
8	445	5	13
9	305	4	17
TOTAL	3090	36	TOTAL

HOLE	LENGTH MEDAL-TEE	PAR	STROKE INDEX
10	507	5	6
11	160	3	14
12	350	4	12
13	400	4	2
14	123	3	18
15	450	5	10
16	365	4	8
17	345	4	16
18	385	4	4
TOTAL	3085	36	TOTAL

OSNABRÜCKER

TEL : (05402)636/(0541)5811
LOCATION : from Osnabrück to Lüstringen, in Jeggen bei Osnabrück
ADDRESS : Am Golfplatz 3 – 4516 Bissendorf
HOTEL :
Park – Osnabrück
Tel : (0541)46083
Hohenzollern-Osnabrück
Tel : (0541)33170
Parkhotel Burggraf – Tecklenburg
Tel : (05482)425
RESTAURANT : Chez Didier – Osnabrück
Tel : (0541)23331

Set in Niedersachsen within a nature reserve on hilly countryside, the course is framed by low wooded hills. The fairways are landscaped with old trees, and water affects play on several of them. The greens are cunningly bunkered. *SSS 71*

GF $ — Mondays — S
1955 — — —
18 — L 5881 P 71 — R

Required : Handicap Certificate
Best days : Tuesdays to Fridays

HOLE	LENGTH MEDAL-TEE	PAR	STROKE INDEX
1	382	4	5
2	154	3	17
3	329	4	7
4	436	5	11
5	194	3	13
6	324	4	15
7	453	5	3
8	171	3	9
9	487	5	1
TOTAL	2930	36	TOTAL

HOLE	LENGTH MEDAL-TEE	PAR	STROKE INDEX
10	327	4	10
11	184	3	16
12	397	4	4
13	345	4	18
14	409	4	2
15	298	4	12
16	452	5	14
17	157	3	8
18	382	4	6
TOTAL	2951	35	TOTAL

OSTFRIESLAND

TEL : (04944)2228/3040
LOCATION : 4 km Wiesmoor
ADDRESS : Fliederstrasse 1 – 2964 Wiesmoor
HOTEL : HR
Blauer Fasan
Tel : (04944)1047
Friesengeist – Wiesmoor
Tel : (04944)1044
RESTAURANT : Friedeburg – Friedeburg
Tel : (04465)367

A well-wooded inland course laid out on flat terrain with several water hazards. Its 18 holes run partly through moorland, and partly through pastureland. The golf club has organized the popular annual 'Wiesmoor-Open' since 1982. The 'Blauer Fasan', adjacent to the course, has a fine restaurant and 26 comfortable bedrooms. *SSS 73*

GF $ — January and February 

 1983 —  — 

18 — L 6256 P 73 — R

Required : Handicap Certificate
Best days : Tuesdays to Fridays inc.

HOLE	LENGTH MEDAL-TEE	PAR	STROKE INDEX
1	446	5	15
2	341	4	13
3	378	4	3
4	144	3	11
5	295	4	9
6	141	3	17
7	354	4	7
8	501	5	1
9	377	4	5
TOTAL	2977	36	TOTAL

HOLE	LENGTH MEDAL-TEE	PAR	STROKE INDEX
10	506	5	10
11	170	3	18
12	337	4	12
13	381	4	2
14	366	4	14
15	179	3	14
16	502	5	6
17	348	4	16
18	490	4	8
TOTAL	3279	37	TOTAL

PFALZ

TEL : (06327)2973
LOCATION : 11 km Neustadt B 39
ADDRESS : Geinsheim – 6730 Neustadt 22
HOTEL :
Pfalz – Hassloch
Tel : (06324)4047
Hatterer's Zum Reichsrat – Deidesheim
Tel : (06326)6011
Kurfürst – Neustadt
Tel : (06321)7441
RESTAURANT : Lang – Neustadt
Tel : (06321)32625

This wooded course lies at the edge of the 'Pfälzer' Forest in the province of Rheinland-Pfalz. Laid out on flat countryside, there is a stream crossing the course serving as a hazard on several fairways. *SSS 72*

GF $

1971

18

—

B. v. Limburger

L 6090 P 72

R S

Required : Handicap Certificate
Best days : Any day

HOLE	LENGTH MEDAL-TEE	PAR	STROKE INDEX
1	355	4	9
2	455	5	13
3	360	4	11
4	360	4	3
5	155	3	17
6	510	5	1
7	175	3	15
8	355	4	5
9	385	4	7
TOTAL	3110	36	TOTAL

HOLE	LENGTH MEDAL-TEE	PAR	STROKE INDEX
10	440	5	14
11	310	4	8
12	140	3	18
13	495	5	12
14	365	4	6
15	420	4	2
16	110	3	16
17	340	4	4
18	360	4	10
TOTAL	2980	36	TOTAL

REGENSBURG

TEL : (09403)505/1505
LOCATION : 14 km E. Regensburg, near Walhalla
ADDRESS : Jagdschloss Thiergarten – 8405 Donaustauf
HOTEL :
Tegernheimer Keller – Tegernheim
Tel : (09403)1644
Avia – Regensburg
Tel : (0941)4300
Bischofshof am Dom-Regensburg
Tel : (0941)59086
RESTAURANT : Ratskeller – Regensburg
Tel : (0941)51777

This attractive and hilly course lies within a former hunting estate featuring a scenic castle, the 'Schloss Thiergarten'. The course, located in Bavaria, is densely wooded with old conifers bordering the fairways. *SSS 72*

GF $$

1966

18

November to March

—

L 5860 P 72

S

R

Required : Handicap Certificate
Best days : Weekdays

HOLE	LENGTH MEDAL-TEE	PAR	STROKE INDEX
1	305	4	
2	500	5	
3	261	4	
4	149	3	
5	438	5	
6	397	4	
7	168	3	
8	454	5	
9	120	3	
TOTAL	2792	36	TOTAL

HOLE	LENGTH MEDAL-TEE	PAR	STROKE INDEX
10	420	4	
11	181	3	
12	437	5	
13	301	4	
14	527	5	
15	285	4	
16	390	4	
17	167	3	
18	360	4	
TOTAL	3068	36	TOTAL

REUTLINGEN - SONNENBÜHL

TEL : (07128)3532/2018
LOCATION : 20 km Reutlingen/20 km Stuttgart
ADDRESS : Im Zerg - 7419 Sonnenbühl - Undingen
HOTEL :
Hirsch - Sonnenbühl Erpfingen
Tel : (07128)2212
Fürstenhof - Reutlingen
Tel : (07121)3180
Krone - Tübingen
Tel : (07071)31036

This new championship layout comprises a sporty pattern of holes beautifully laid out along the natural lines of the land and running through 60 ha of lush meadows and woodlands. There is a welcoming clubhouse. *SSS 72*

GF $

1990

18

Mondays

—

L 6057 P 72

Required : Handicap Certificate on Weekends
Best days : Weekdays

HOLE	LENGTH MEDAL-TEE	PAR	STROKE INDEX
1	482	5	14
2	349	4	10
3	113	3	16
4	418	4	1
5	492	5	5
6	148	3	13
7	394	4	12
8	387	4	3
9	448	5	7
TOTAL	3231	37	TOTAL

HOLE	LENGTH MEDAL-TEE	PAR	STROKE INDEX
10	228	3	2
11	283	4	18
12	366	4	11
13	538	5	8
14	176	3	6
15	277	4	9
16	252	4	15
17	434	4	4
18	272	4	17
TOTAL	2826	35	TOTAL

RHEIN-SIEG

TEL : (02242)6501/1334
LOCATION : 35 km Köln BAB exit Hennef/ 7 km Hennef
ADDRESS : Haus Dürresbach-5202 Hennef
HOTEL :
Schloss Auel-Lohmar Wahlscheid
Tel : (02206)2041
Schlosshotel Wasserburg-Hennef
Tel : (02242)5024
RESTAURANT : Haus Dürresbach-Hennef
Tel : (02242)1334

Encircled by woodland and fields with the 'Siebengebirge' mountain chain in the background, the course is of medium difficulty. Mainly flat, it has spacious fairways, and large well-bunkered greens. Two picturesque lakes serve as a hazard on the 7th and the 12th holes. *SSS 72*

GF $ | Mondays | S
1971 | K. Peters
18 | L 6070 P 72 | R

Required : Club Membership Card
Best days : Tuesdays and Fridays

HOLE	LENGTH MEDAL-TEE	PAR	STROKE INDEX
1	290	4	
2	450	5	
3	185	3	
4	460	5	
5	504	5	
6	175	3	
7	386	4	
8	345	4	
9	375	4	
TOTAL	3170	37	TOTAL

HOLE	LENGTH MEDAL-TEE	PAR	STROKE INDEX
10	320	4	
11	405	4	
12	185	3	
13	305	4	
14	485	5	
15	370	4	
16	320	4	
17	155	3	
18	355	4	
TOTAL	2900	35	TOTAL

RHÖN-FULDA

TEL : (06657)1334
LOCATION : 11 km Fulda
ADDRESS : Am Golfplatz – 6417 Hofbieber
HOTEL :
Panorama – Fulda
Tel : (06657)7077
Fohlenweide – Fulda
Tel : (06657)8061
Maritim am Schlossgarten – Fulda
Tel : (0661)2820
RESTAURANT : Goldener Karpfen – Fulda
Tel : (0661)70044

The Rhön-Fulda golf club lies in the province of Hessen. Set on an undulating high plain with sparse vegetation, the course features many blind holes and commands fine views over the Rhön and the city of Fulda. *SSS 70*

GF $
1971
18
November to April
—
L 5675 P 70
R S

Required : Handicap Certificate
Best days : Weekdays

HOLE	LENGTH MEDAL-TEE	PAR	STROKE INDEX
1	287	4	
2	440	5	
3	367	4	
4	186	3	
5	191	3	
6	486	5	
7	417	4	
8	354	4	
9	180	3	
TOTAL	2908	35	TOTAL

HOLE	LENGTH MEDAL-TEE	PAR	STROKE INDEX
10	296	4	
11	373	4	
12	446	5	
13	391	4	
14	161	3	
15	313	4	
16	181	3	
17	311	4	
18	295	4	
TOTAL	2767	35	TOTAL

ROTTALER

TEL : (08561)2861
LOCATION : 10 km Bad Griesbach/6 km Eggenfelden
ADDRESS : Bergstrasse 17– 8333 Linden
HOTEL :
Bachmeier - Eggenfelden
Tel : (08721)3071
Bad Griesbach - Bad Griesbach
Tel : (08532)281
RESTAURANT : König Ludwig Stubl - Bad Griesbach
Tel : (08532)1001

Recently extended to 18 holes, this sporting course, lying in the southern part of Bavaria, winds through parkland and meadows, runs over low hills and crosses the River Rott five times. Several holes offer fine views of the surrounding villages. *SSS 72*

GF $

1972

18

November to March

—

L 6105 P 72

S

Required : Club Membership Card
Best days : Any day

HOLE	LENGTH MEDAL-TEE	PAR	STROKE INDEX
1	276	4	
2	429	4	
3	436	5	
4	324	4	
5	178	3	
6	387	4	
7	321	4	
8	205	3	
9	386	4	
TOTAL	2942	35	TOTAL

HOLE	LENGTH MEDAL-TEE	PAR	STROKE INDEX
10	317	4	
11	177	3	
12	436	5	
13	344	4	
14	520	5	
15	351	4	
16	536	5	
17	147	3	
18	335	4	
TOTAL	3163	37	TOTAL

SAARBRÜCKEN

★

TEL : (06837)841/401
LOCATION : 28 km Saarbrücken B 406.
ADDRESS : Oberlimberger Weg - 6634 Wallerfangen 7
HOTEL :
Haus Scheidberg - Wallerfangen
Tel : (06837)750
Altes Pfarrhaus Beaumarais - Saarlouis
Tel : (06831)6383
Saarhof - Völklingen
Tel : (06898)37239
RESTAURANT : Villa Fayence - Wallerfangen
Tel : (06831)62066

The Saarbrücken championship course is set on a highland plain on rolling terrain with panoramic views overlooking the Saar Valley. It incorporates a fine setting of trees, bushes and ponds, affecting play on several holes. *SSS 73*

GF $$

1961

18

January

D. Harradine

L 6231 P 72

S

R

Required : Handicap Certificate
Best days : Weekdays

HOLE	LENGTH MEDAL-TEE	PAR	STROKE INDEX
1	447	5	
2	148	3	
3	332	4	
4	326	4	
5	365	4	
6	449	5	
7	115	3	
8	384	4	
9	363	4	
TOTAL	2929	36	TOTAL

HOLE	LENGTH MEDAL-TEE	PAR	STROKE INDEX
10	180	3	
11	380	4	
12	485	5	
13	342	4	
14	146	3	
15	533	5	
16	420	4	
17	415	4	
18	401	4	
TOTAL	3302	36	TOTAL

SAGMÜHLE
Bad Griesbach

TEL : (08532)2038/36
LOCATION : 30 km Passau
ADDRESS : Schwaim 52-8394 Bad Griesbach
HOTEL :
Fürstenhof-Bad Griesbach
Tel : (08532)7051
Steigenberger – Bad Griesbach
Tel : (08532)1001
Parkhotel – Bad Griesbach
Tel : (08532)281
RESTAURANT : Schlosstaverne-Bad Füssing
Tel : (08531)2568

The pleasant Sagmühle golf course, very popular with golfers, is laid out in the scenic Rott valley, with many of its holes bordering the river Rott. The course has a varied and an entertaining layout with an arm of the Rott meandering its way through the holes. Golf facilities include one of Europe's biggest driving ranges, two 9 holes par 3 courses, a golf school and a training center. Adjacent to the golf course is the fine clubhouse and restaurant Gutshof Bad Griesbach with its terrace overlooking the river. Here, one can rent a bicycle, or a boat, or board a hot air balloon to discover the Bavarian landscape.
SSS 71

GF $

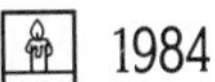

18

November to March

K. Rossknecht

L 5952 P 72

Required : Handicap Certificate
Best days : Any day

HOLE	LENGTH MEDAL-TEE	PAR	STROKE INDEX
1	352	4	15
2	360	4	13
3	465	5	11
4	154	3	7
5	300	4	5
6	464	5	9
7	345	4	1
8	292	4	3
9	126	3	17
TOTAL	2858	36	TOTAL

HOLE	LENGTH MEDAL-TEE	PAR	STROKE INDEX
10	298	4	18
11	163	3	8
12	478	5	14
13	367	4	12
14	410	4	4
15	163	3	16
16	538	5	2
17	321	4	10
18	356	4	6
TOTAL	3094	36	TOTAL

SCHLOSS BRAUNFELS

TEL : (06442)4530
LOCATION : 5 km Braunfels
ADDRESS : Homburger Hof-Golfplatz – 6333 Braunfels
HOTEL :
Schloss Braunfels – Braunfels
Tel : (06442)5051
Bürgerhof – Wetzlar
Tel : (06441)48031
Schlosshotel Weilburg – Weilburg
Tel : (06471)39096
RESTAURANT : Lika – Braunfels
Tel : (06442)5588

Situated in the province of Hessen within rolling hills, this is a championship course of excellent quality. It presents a number of natural obstacles such as trees and changes in level. There are several picturesque lakes in front of the 9th green, on the 16th hole and bordering on two sides the 18th hole. The main problem is presented by the continuous ups and downs of the terrain. The club has hosted the German Ladies Open twice. Schloss Braunfels, a castle hotel, is near the golf course. *SSS 73*

GF $$

1972

18

Weekends in the morning

B.v. Limburger

L 6288 P 73

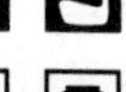

Required : Handicap Certificate
Best days : Mondays, Tuesdays, Thursdays, Fridays

HOLE	LENGTH MEDAL-TEE	PAR	STROKE INDEX
1	400	4	5
2	307	4	11
3	157	3	17
4	511	5	9
5	389	4	1
6	453	5	13
7	364	4	3
8	405	4	7
9	316	4	15
TOTAL	3302	37	TOTAL

HOLE	LENGTH MEDAL-TEE	PAR	STROKE INDEX
10	312	4	12
11	200	3	8
12	364	4	4
13	545	5	2
14	141	3	18
15	453	5	16
16	129	3	10
17	342	4	6
18	500	5	14
TOTAL	2986	36	TOTAL

SCHLOSS GEORGHAUSEN

TEL : (02207)4938
LOCATION : 30 km Köln
ADDRESS : Georghausen 8 – 5253 Lindlar-Hommerich
HOTEL : HR
Schloss Georghausen
Tel : (02207)2561
Heedt – Gummersbach
Tel : (02261)65021
Zum Holländer – Lindlar
Tel : (02266)6605

This is a very pleasant and attractive golf course with a varied but testing layout. The first nine holes meander through hilly wooded terrain, and the last nine holes are laid out on flat landscape. The scenic Schloss Hotel lies on the course and has 17 bedrooms. *SSS 72*

GF $$
1962
18
—
—
L 6045 P 72
R S

Required : Handicap Certificate
Best days : Weekdays

HOLE	LENGTH MEDAL-TEE	PAR	STROKE INDEX
1	360	4	5
2	280	4	17
3	520	5	3
4	310	4	11
5	155	3	13
6	320	4	9
7	355	4	1
8	340	4	15
9	455	5	7
TOTAL	3095	37	TOTAL

HOLE	LENGTH MEDAL-TEE	PAR	STROKE INDEX
10	185	3	12
11	450	5	14
12	315	4	18
13	320	4	16
14	195	3	6
15	400	4	2
16	190	3	10
17	525	5	8
18	370	4	4
TOTAL	2950	35	TOTAL

SCHLOSS KLINGENBURG-GÜNZBURG

★

TEL : (08225)30320
LOCATION : 24 km Ulm
ADDRESS : 8876 Jettingen-Scheppach
HOTEL :
Zettler-Günzburg
Tel : (08221)30008
Gasthof Zur Post – Leipheim
Tel : (08221)72003
Landgasthof Adler – Rammingen
Tel : (07345)7041
RESTAURANT : Adler-Jettingen
Tel : (08225)225

Designed by Donald Harradine on attractive fairly undulating landscape, this is a scenic wooded parkland course laid out among old birch, chestnut and pine trees. Numerous picturesque lakes border the holes while several streams meander their way through the fairways. *SSS 72*

GF $ — — S
1980 — D. Harradine — R
18 — L 6065 P 72 — 

Required : Handicap Certificate
Best days : Any day

HOLE	LENGTH MEDAL-TEE	PAR	STROKE INDEX
1	255	4	15
2	370	4	11
3	500	5	5
4	165	3	9
5	365	4	7
6	475	5	17
7	326	4	13
8	205	3	3
9	405	4	1
TOTAL	3066	36	TOTAL

HOLE	LENGTH MEDAL-TEE	PAR	STROKE INDEX
10	540	5	6
11	192	3	8
12	330	4	16
13	155	3	12
14	400	4	2
15	390	4	10
16	445	5	18
17	355	4	4
18	345	4	14
TOTAL	3152	36	TOTAL

SCHLOSS LIEBENSTEIN

TEL : (07133)16019
LOCATION : 53 km Stuttgart to Heilbronn
ADDRESS : 7129 Neckarwestheim
HOTEL : HR
Schloss Liebenstein
Tel : (07133)6041
Schlosshotel Mon Repos – Ludwigsburg
Tel : (07141)3020
RESTAURANT : Goldener Löwe – Marbach am Neckar
Tel : (07144)6663

Scenically set between valleys and encircled by vineyards, this is a very attractive and challenging new golf course. The smallish fairways wind through undulating woodland and a river meanders its way through the course. It features the magnificent Renaissance castle hotel 'Schloss Liebenstein'(24 bedrooms), with a scenic chapel, dating back to 1599. Both are declared National Monuments. They are built high up overlooking the scenery below. *SSS 71*

GF $$

1985

18

—

—

L 5837 P 72

S

RF

Required : Handicap Certificate
Best days : Weekdays

HOLE	LENGTH MEDAL-TEE	PAR	STROKE INDEX
1	439	5	13
2	373	4	1
3	159	3	11
4	392	4	9
5	460	5	3
6	312	4	15
7	435	5	17
8	169	3	5
9	476	5	7
TOTAL	3215	38	TOTAL

HOLE	LENGTH MEDAL-TEE	PAR	STROKE INDEX
10	130	3	10
11	170	3	14
12	320	4	4
13	379	4	2
14	436	5	6
15	152	3	16
16	332	4	12
17	310	4	18
18	393	4	8
TOTAL	2622	34	TOTAL

SCHLOSS LÜDERSBURG

TEL : (04153)6112
LOCATION : 55 km Hamburg/15 km Lüneburg
ADDRESS : 2127 Lüdersburg
HOTEL : HR
Golf-Apartments
Tel : (04153)6112
Bergström-Lüneburg
Tel : (04131)3080
Seminaris-Lüneburg
Tel : (04131)7130
RESTAURANT : Jagdschänke-Lüdersburg – Schnecke-Lüneberg
Tel : (04131)68422

Set in a typical parkland landscape, the 18 holes are laid out around the renovated stately manor house Schloss Lüdersburg which dates back to 1776. The course with its rather narrow fairways which are flanked by majestic trees, runs through flat land. There are not many bunkers, but, on the contrary, it features many water hazards including a stream which crosses the holes six times. Accomodation (golf apartments) is available for visiting golfers.

GF $

1985

18

—

W. Siegmann

L 6180 P 73

S

R

Required : Handicap Certificate
Best days : Mondays through Thursdays

HOLE	LENGTH MEDAL-TEE	PAR	STROKE INDEX
1	325	4	11
2	154	3	13
3	512	5	1
4	312	4	17
5	350	4	9
6	386	4	7
7	509	5	3
8	150	3	15
9	467	5	5
TOTAL	3165	37	TOTAL

HOLE	LENGTH MEDAL-TEE	PAR	STROKE INDEX
10	316	4	14
11	472	5	4
12	372	4	6
13	149	3	10
14	351	4	8
15	529	5	2
16	350	4	12
17	163	3	16
18	313	4	18
TOTAL	3015	36	TOTAL

SCHLOSS MYLLENDONK

TEL : (02161)641049/642152
LOCATION : 5 km Mönchengladbach, 15 km Düsseldorf
ADDRESS : Myllendonker Str 113 – 4052 Korschenbroich 1
HOTEL :
Dorint – Mönchengladbach
Tel : (02161)86060
Coenen – Mönchengladbach
Tel : (02166)10088
Parkhotel Rheydt – Möchengladbach
Tel : (02166)44011
RESTAURANT : St-Andreas – Korschenbroich
Tel : (02161)64764

The course is built around the medieval 'Castle Myllendonk', nowadays serving as the clubhouse, in a parkland setting. Laid out in flat landscape amidst age-old beautiful trees, there are numerous ditches, streams and ponds serving as hazards. *SSS 72*

  $ — —  

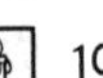  1965 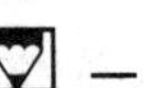 — 

18  6120 P 72 

Required : Handicap Certificate
Best days : Weekdays only

HOLE	LENGTH MEDAL-TEE	PAR	STROKE INDEX
1	527	5	5
2	165	3	9
3	434	4	1
4	494	5	10
5	302	4	13
6	375	4	7
7	400	4	3
8	303	4	15
9	137	3	17
TOTAL	3137	36	TOTAL

HOLE	LENGTH MEDAL-TEE	PAR	STROKE INDEX
10	196	3	11
11	390	4	2
12	498	5	12
13	120	3	18
14	339	4	8
15	454	5	14
16	378	4	4
17	160	3	16
18	448	5	6
TOTAL	2983	36	TOTAL

SCHLOSS PIESING

TEL : (08678)7001
LOCATION : 5 km Burghausen B 20 to Marktl
ADDRESS : Piesing 2– 8261 Haiming
HOTEL :
Burg - Burghausen
Tel : (08677)7038
Zur Post - Altötting
Tel : (08671)5040
Schlosswirtschaft - Piesing
Tel : (08678)7003
RESTAURANT : Fuchsstuben - Burghausen
Tel : (08677)62724

This new championship course will be fully operational mid 1990. It lies on three different levels amidst old trees, and surrounds the stately baroque style castle 'Schloss Piesing', which now serves as the clubhouse. The course has a well balanced layout featuring two natural lakes and seven artificial ponds as additional hazards.

GF $

1986

18

November to April

G. Mecklenburg

L 6416 P 74

R S

Required : Club Membership Card
Best days : Any day

HOLE	LENGTH MEDAL-TEE	PAR	STROKE INDEX
1	505	5	
2	334	4	
3	155	3	
4	316	4	
5	356	4	
6	181	3	
7	328	4	
8	507	5	
9	511	5	
TOTAL	3193	37	TOTAL

HOLE	LENGTH MEDAL-TEE	PAR	STROKE INDEX
10	505	5	
11	334	4	
12	155	3	
13	316	4	
14	386	4	
15	181	3	
16	328	4	
17	507	5	
18	511	5	
TOTAL	3223	37	TOTAL

SCHLOSS SCHWÖBBER

★

TEL : (05154)2004
LOCATION : 10 km Bad Pyrmont
ADDRESS : 3258 Aerzen 16
HOTEL : HR
Waldquelle-Aerzen
Tel : (05154)2277
Deutsches Haus – Starzach
Tel : (05154)1230
Landluft-Aerzen
Tel : (05154)2001
RESTAURANT : Alter Fritz – Bad Pyrmont
Tel : (05281)8669

The Schlosshotel Schwöbber golf club is a new golf course and fully operational since 1988. It includes a short 18 hole course and a 18 hole championship layout, both scenically laid out among majestic trees, shrubs and ponds. An attractive feature is the historic castle dating back to the Renaissance. Hotel Waldquelle is adjacent to the golf course. *SSS 73*

GF $$ — —

1985 — U. Barth

36 — L 6222 P 73, 2427 P 56

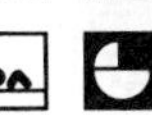

Required : Handicap Certificate
Best days : Any day

HOLE	LENGTH MEDAL-TEE	PAR	STROKE INDEX
1	359	4	5
2	102	3	17
3	523	5	3
4	308	4	15
5	177	3	11
6	446	5	9
7	336	4	7
8	372	4	1
9	462	5	13
TOTAL	3085	37	TOTAL

HOLE	LENGTH MEDAL-TEE	PAR	STROKE INDEX
10	265	4	18
11	359	4	16
12	439	5	10
13	358	4	6
14	201	3	14
15	363	4	4
16	192	3	12
17	426	4	8
18	534	5	2
TOTAL	3137	28	TOTAL

SCHLOSS WEITENBURG

★

TEL : (07472)8061
LOCATION : 50 km Stuttgart BAB 81 exit Rottenburg
ADDRESS : 7245 Starzach – Sulzau
HOTEL :
Schloss Weitenburg
Tel : (07457)8051
Würtemberger Hof – Rottenburg
Tel : (07472)6660
RESTAURANT : Waldhorn – Tübingen
Tel : (07071)61270

A new championship golf course set around the picturesque village of Sulzau in Baden-Würtemberg. Many of the holes border the winding river, the 'Neckar'. The peacefully situated Castle Weitenburg hotel with 35 bedrooms, is situated on the course and has an indoor swimming pool. *SSS 72*

GF $

 1984

27

November to April

H. Fehring

L 6069 P 72, 1068 P 27

 S

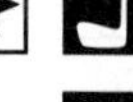

Required : Handicap Certificate
Best days : Any day

HOLE	LENGTH MEDAL-TEE	PAR	STROKE INDEX
1	436	5	6
2	332	4	2
3	105	3	18
4	308	4	12
5	170	3	8
6	435	5	16
7	160	3	14
8	562	5	4
9	201	3	10
TOTAL	2699	35	TOTAL

HOLE	LENGTH MEDAL-TEE	PAR	STROKE INDEX
10	449	5	11
11	432	4	1
12	202	3	7
13	488	5	13
14	375	4	9
15	188	3	17
16	396	4	3
17	297	4	15
18	543	5	5
TOTAL	3370	37	TOTAL

SCHLOSSBERG

TEL : (08734)356/7035
LOCATION : in Grünbach
ADDRESS : 8386 Reisbach -Grünbach
HOTEL :
Wetzel – Mühldorf am Inn
Tel : (08631)7336
Passauer Hof – Simbach am Inn
Tel : (08571)2500
Zur Post – Prienbach
Tel : (08571)2009
RESTAURANT : Seethaler – Straubing
Tel : (09421)22507

Located between the Bavarian hills, this golf course, inaugurated in 1985, is laid out in an attractive landscape among old trees and shrubs. Sometimes hilly, the course features strategically placed water hazards. *SSS 72*

GF $

1985

18

November to March

—

L 6070 P 72

Required : Handicap Certificate
Best days : Any day

HOLE	LENGTH MEDAL-TEE	PAR	STROKE INDEX
1	126	3	
2	448	5	
3	334	4	
4	352	4	
5	482	5	
6	163	3	
7	382	4	
8	420	4	
9	328	4	
TOTAL	3035	36	TOTAL

HOLE	LENGTH MEDAL-TEE	PAR	STROKE INDEX
10	165	3	
11	365	4	
12	170	3	
13	460	5	
14	385	4	
15	500	5	
16	345	4	
17	360	4	
18	285	4	
TOTAL	3035	36	TOTAL

SCHMITZHOF

TEL : (02436)479
LOCATION : 5 km Wegberg
ADDRESS : 5144 Wegberg
HOTEL :
Esser-Wegberg Kipshofen
Tel : (02161)58995
Burg Wassenberg-Wassenberg
Tel : (02432)4044
Coenen-Mönchengladbach
Tel : (02166)10088
RESTAURANT : Zur Traube-Grevenbroich
Tel : (02181)68767

Recently improved and extended to 18 holes, the Schmitzhof golf course winds through flat parkland. The holes are separated from each other by mature trees. Eight water hazards and many treacherous and strategically placed bunkers demand accurate play. *SSS 73*

GF $ | Mondays | S
1975 | D. Harradine | R
18 | L 6310 P 72

Required : Handicap Certificate
Best days : Weekdays only, esp. Tuesdays and Fridays

HOLE	LENGTH MEDAL-TEE	PAR	STROKE INDEX
1	355	4	7
2	145	3	18
3	315	4	17
4	340	4	13
5	345	4	9
6	330	4	5
7	505	5	3
8	350	4	11
9	375	4	2
TOTAL	3060	36	TOTAL

HOLE	LENGTH MEDAL-TEE	PAR	STROKE INDEX
10	530	5	4
11	155	3	15
12	420	4	1
13	355	4	6
14	330	4	16
15	340	4	14
16	225	3	12
17	370	4	8
18	525	5	10
TOTAL	3250	36	TOTAL

SOLTAU

TEL : (05191)14077
LOCATION : exit Soltau Sud BAB 7 to Tetendorf B 209
ADDRESS : Golfplatz Hof Loh – 3040 Soltau-Tetendorf
HOTEL :
Heidland – Soltau
Tel : (05191)17033
Heidehotel Anna – Soltau
Tel : (05191)15026
Landhaus Höpen – Schneverdingen
Tel : (05193)1031
RESTAURANT : Zu den Eichen – Soltau
Tel : (05191)3444

A sporting and attractive golf course, inaugurated in 1983 with a varied layout, featuring several difficult dog-legs, numerous well-placed water hazards and strategically situated trees. *SSS 73*

GF $

1983

27

—

D. Siegmann

L 6274 P 73, 2340 P 54

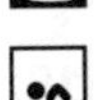

Required : None
Best days : Any day

HOLE	LENGTH MEDAL-TEE	PAR	STROKE INDEX
1	351	4	11
2	507	5	3
3	317	4	13
4	168	3	17
5	299	4	15
6	190	3	5
7	336	4	7
8	514	5	1
9	254	4	9
TOTAL	2936	36	TOTAL

HOLE	LENGTH MEDAL-TEE	PAR	STROKE INDEX
10	337	4	10
11	507	5	2
12	343	4	14
13	370	4	12
14	509	5	4
15	351	4	8
16	208	3	18
17	352	4	6
18	361	4	16
TOTAL	3338	37	TOTAL

SONNENALP

TEL : (08321)7276
LOCATION : 5 km Sonthofen
ADDRESS : 8972 Ofterschwang/Oberallgaü
HOTEL :
Sonnenalp
Tel : (08321)720/7229
Allgaüer Berghof – Sonthofen
Tel : (08321)4061
Exquisit – Oberstdorf
Tel : (08322)1034

A beautiful mountain course of championship standard, framed by the snow clad peaks of the Alps, and following the natural undulations of the valley. The course is encircled by luxuriant fir woods and features several natural lakes, serving as hazards. The fine chalet style Sonnenalp Hotel lies 500m from the course and is equipped with every imaginable sports and leisure facility ranging from gymnasium, tennis and squash courts, several swimming pools to a windsurfing school and children's playground. *SSS 72*

GF $$
1976
18

October to April
D. Harradine
L 6038 P 72

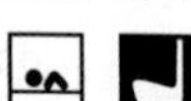
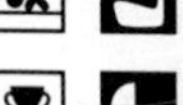

Required : Handicap Certificate
Best days : Any day

HOLE	LENGTH MEDAL-TEE	PAR	STROKE INDEX
1	358	4	2
2	253	4	18
3	151	3	16
4	475	5	12
5	192	3	10
6	354	4	6
7	167	3	14
8	557	5	4
9	190	3	8
TOTAL	2697	34	TOTAL

HOLE	LENGTH MEDAL-TEE	PAR	STROKE INDEX
10	391	4	3
11	408	4	1
12	478	5	17
13	161	3	9
14	338	4	5
15	482	5	7
16	169	3	11
17	441	5	15
18	473	5	13
TOTAL	3341	38	TOTAL

SPESSART

TEL : (06056)3594
LOCATION : 15 km Bad Orb
ADDRESS : Alsberg a.d.H.-6483 Bad Soden-Salmünster
HOTEL :
Steigenberger Kurhaus-Bad Orb
Tel : (06052)880
Madstein-Bad Orb
Tel : (06052)2028
Parkhotel Bad Orb-Bad Orb
Tel : (06052)2066
RESTAURANT : Schiesshaus-Gelnhausen
Tel : (06051)66929

Located near the spa resort of Bad Orb, the golf course is set in a rolling landscape of woods, meadows and fields. The course features rather densely wooded holes with well designed greens and several small but strategic ponds. *SSS 72*

GF $

1974

18

Mondays

E. Rowan

L 6039 P 72

S

R

Required : Handicap Certificate
Best days : Weekdays

HOLE	LENGTH MEDAL-TEE	PAR	STROKE INDEX
1	379	4	2
2	320	4	16
3	144	3	8
4	453	5	6
5	300	4	12
6	342	4	4
7	321	4	18
8	160	3	10
9	452	5	14
TOTAL	2871	36	TOTAL

HOLE	LENGTH MEDAL-TEE	PAR	STROKE INDEX
10	356	4	7
11	376	4	5
12	121	3	17
13	441	5	13
14	390	4	1
15	170	3	15
16	389	4	3
17	402	4	11
18	523	5	9
TOTAL	3168	36	TOTAL

STARNBERG

TEL : (08151)12157/21977
LOCATION : In Hadorf, 24 km München to Starnberg
ADDRESS : Tutzinger Hof-Platz 3-8130 Starnberg
HOTEL : Bayerischer Hof-Starnberg
Tel : (08151)12133
Alba Seehotel-Herrsching am Ammersee
Tel : (08152)2011
Tutzinger Hof-Starnberg
Tel : (08151)3081
RESTAURANT : Maximilian-Starnberg
Tel : (08151)6280

The new Starnberg course, situated in Bavaria, is characterized by two different types of setting. The first nine holes are set on flat landscape, the second nine run through rather hilly terrain. Precision is essential due to the presence of six strategically placed water hazards. *SSS 73*

GF $$
1986
18

Mondays
K. Rossknecht
L 6300 P 72

R S

Required : Handicap Certificate
Best days : Tuesdays and Fridays

HOLE	LENGTH MEDAL-TEE	PAR	STROKE INDEX
1	495	5	
2	420	4	
3	190	3	
4	365	4	
5	350	4	
6	315	4	
7	530	5	
8	400	4	
9	135	3	
TOTAL	3200	36	TOTAL

HOLE	LENGTH MEDAL-TEE	PAR	STROKE INDEX
10	360	4	
11	280	4	
12	520	5	
13	380	4	
14	355	4	
15	175	3	
16	370	4	
17	210	3	
18	450	5	
TOTAL	3100	36	TOTAL

ST-DIONYS

TEL : (04133)6277
LOCATION : 10 km Lüneburg B 4
ADDRESS : 2123 St-Dionys bei Lüneburg
HOTEL :
Romantik Josthof – St-Dionys
Tel : (04172)292
Heiderose – Lüneburg
Tel : (04131)44410
Seminaris – Lüneburg
Tel : (04131)713
RESTAURANT : Wellenkamp –Lüneburg
Tel : (04131)43026

St-Dionys is one of the popular golf clubs set around Hamburg. It is a sporting and flat heathland course with its 18 holes running through open fields, bushes and heather. Water affects play on several holes. *SSS 73*

GF $$

1972

18

 Mondays

—

L 6218 P 72

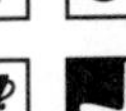

Required : Handicap Certificate
Best days : Any day

HOLE	LENGTH MEDAL-TEE	PAR	STROKE INDEX
1	360	4	5
2	343	4	7
3	355	4	3
4	525	5	1
5	150	3	13
6	355	4	9
7	340	4	17
8	189	3	11
9	475	5	15
TOTAL	3092	36	TOTAL

HOLE	LENGTH MEDAL-TEE	PAR	STROKE INDEX
10	348	4	14
11	450	5	18
12	200	3	8
13	496	5	12
14	363	4	2
15	369	4	4
16	160	3	16
17	350	4	10
18	390	4	6
TOTAL	3126	36	TOTAL

ST. EURACH

TEL : (08801)1332
LOCATION : 35 km München
ADDRESS : Eurach 8 – 8127 Iffeldorf
HOTEL :
Marina – Zernried
Tel : (08158)6046
Alpenhof Murnau-Murnau
Tel : (08841)1045
Landgasthof Osterseen-Iffeldorf
Tel : (08856)1011
RESTAURANT : Sonnenhof – Seeshaupt
Tel : (08801)760

Set in the foothills of the Bavarian Alps, St Eurach is an undulating moorland course flanked by mature trees. Among the three water obstacles, there is a ditch in front of the 1st green and a lake occupying the fairway of the 2nd hole. The club has a spacious chalet style clubhouse.

GF $$

1973

18

December to March

—

L 5888 P 71

Required : Handicap Certificate
Best days : Weekdays

HOLE	LENGTH MEDAL-TEE	PAR	STROKE INDEX
1	341	4	2
2	165	3	15
3	380	4	5
4	374	4	3
5	305	4	7
6	317	4	17
7	482	5	11
8	190	3	13
9	344	4	9
TOTAL	2898	35	TOTAL

HOLE	LENGTH MEDAL-TEE	PAR	STROKE INDEX
10	444	5	14
11	368	4	4
12	140	3	18
13	317	4	12
14	407	4	1
15	345	4	6
16	362	4	8
17	170	3	16
18	437	5	10
TOTAL	2990	36	TOTAL

STROMBERG-SCHINDELDORF

TEL : (06724)1035
LOCATION : 65 km S. Koblenz
A 61/10 km Stromberg
ADDRESS : Am Südhang 1 a-6534
Stromberg-Schindeldorf
HOTEL :
Burg-Stromberg
Tel : (06724)1026
Goldenfels-Stromberg
Tel : (06724)3605
Quellenhof-Bad Kreuznach
Tel : (0671)2191
RESTAURANT : Krone-Bad Kreuznach
Tel : (0671)2420

A new and challenging golf course situated above the old town of Stromberg at the edge of the Hunsrück mountains. It is laid out in old wooded highlands, featuring some elevated tees, and has both flat and sloping fairways. A number of small lakes serve as hazards. The course is built around a holiday park which offers a full range of facilities (squash, tennis, swimming pools, children's playgrounds, riding and nature walks) and accomodation. The clubhouse will be operational in 1990. *SSS 72*

GF $

1988

18

Mon.; Dec. to Feb.

R. Preissmann

L 6060 P 72

S

Required : Handicap Certificate
Best days : Weekdays

HOLE	LENGTH MEDAL-TEE	PAR	STROKE INDEX
1	200	4	
2	330	4	
3	500	5	
4	400	4	
5	300	4	
6	460	5	
7	190	3	
8	350	4	
9	360	4	
TOTAL	3090	36	TOTAL

HOLE	LENGTH MEDAL-TEE	PAR	STROKE INDEX
10	350	4	
11	170	3	
12	460	5	
13	360	4	
14	180	3	
15	450	5	
16	460	5	
17	170	3	
18	370	4	
TOTAL	2970	35	TOTAL

STUTTGARTER SOLITUDE

★★

TEL : (07044)6909/5852
LOCATION : 25 km Stuttgart BAB to Karlsruhe
ADDRESS : 7256 Mönsheim-Obermönsheim
HOTEL :
Eiss – Leonberg Ramtel
Tel : (07152)20041
City – Leonberg
Tel : (07152)71053
Park – Stuttgart
Tel : (0711)280161
RESTAURANT : Goldene Pforte-Pforzheim
Tel : (07231)3792

A first class well-wooded inland course of championship standard, located in Baden-Würtemberg near the city of Stuttgart. The wide and generous fairways are bordered by old stately trees. Most of the fine greens are elevated and well-defended by bunkers. The course has two artificial lakes serving as hazards. *SSS 72*

GF $$

1927

18

December to March

B. v. Limburger

L 6045 P 72

R S

Required : Handicap Certificate
Best days : Weekdays only

HOLE	LENGTH MEDAL-TEE	PAR	STROKE INDEX
1	365	4	5
2	495	5	15
3	170	3	7
4	325	4	1
5	305	4	13
6	360	4	3
7	440	5	17
8	125	3	11
9	365	4	9
TOTAL	2950	36	TOTAL

HOLE	LENGTH MEDAL-TEE	PAR	STROKE INDEX
10	190	3	6
11	370	4	2
12	320	4	12
13	350	4	10
14	475	5	16
15	170	3	14
16	320	4	18
17	405	4	4
18	495	5	18
TOTAL	3095	36	TOTAL

SYLT KAMPEN

TEL : (04651)45311
LOCATION : on island Sylt, in Wenningstedt
ADDRESS : 2283 Wenningstedt
HOTEL :
Landhaus am Meer - Wenningstedt
Tel : (04651)45100
Rungholt - Kampen
Tel : (04651)4480
Benen - Dikenhof - Keitum
Tel : (04651)31035
RESTAURANT : Gogärtchen - Kampen
Tel : (04651)41242

Donald Harradine designed this new course situated on the popular and picturesque holiday island of Sylt. The course, of the seaside type, borders the North Sea and is laid out on flat and open terrain amidst dunes, bushes, meadows and strategic water traps. Most of the greens are vast and some are protected by deep bunkers. An additional hazard is the omnipresent wind. A clubhouse is scheduled in the near future. *SSS 70.*

 GF $

— S

 1988

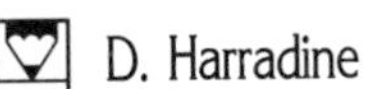 D. Harradine

 18

 5707 P 70

Required : Handicap Certificate
Best days : Weekdays

HOLE	LENGTH MEDAL-TEE	PAR	STROKE INDEX
1	370	4	11
2	462	5	5
3	315	4	13
4	146	3	15
5	371	4	3
6	345	4	9
7	355	4	7
8	155	3	17
9	397	4	1
TOTAL	2916	35	TOTAL

HOLE	LENGTH MEDAL-TEE	PAR	STROKE INDEX
10	312	4	12
11	440	5	8
12	405	4	2
13	191	3	10
14	330	4	6
15	341	4	4
16	325	4	14
17	160	3	18
18	287	4	16
TOTAL	2791	35	TOTAL

TAUNUS-WEILROD

★

TEL : (06083)1883
LOCATION: 40 km Frankfurt BAB to Kassel
ADDRESS : Merzhaüser Landstrasse – 6395 Weilrod/Altweilnau
HOTEL :
Erbismühle – Weilrod
Tel : (06083)855
Geheimrat Trapp – Bad Homburg
Tel : (06172)26047
Hardtwald – Bad Homburg
Tel : (06172)25016
RESTAURANT : Table – Bad Homburg
Tel : (06172)24425

Situated in the Valley of the Taunus, this inland course is of championship standard and presents a real test for the average golfer. Quite hilly with lots of ups and downs, most of the long holes have elevated tees and smallish fairways, demanding accurate shots. Precision is essential due to the presence of many out of bounds. *SSS 72*

GF $

1976

18

—

D. Harradine

L 6176 P 72

S

R

Required : Handicap Certificate
Best days : Any day

HOLE	LENGTH MEDAL-TEE	PAR	STROKE INDEX
1	355	4	15
2	212	3	5
3	433	4	3
4	497	5	11
5	205	3	1
6	231	4	17
7	427	4	9
8	445	5	7
9	180	3	13
TOTAL	2985	35	TOTAL

HOLE	LENGTH MEDAL-TEE	PAR	STROKE INDEX
10	300	4	16
11	496	5	4
12	172	3	14
13	425	4	2
14	469	5	12
15	314	4	10
16	324	4	8
17	301	4	18
18	390	4	6
TOTAL	3191	37	TOTAL

TEGERNSEER-BAD WIESSEE

TEL : (08022)8769
LOCATION : 1 km Bad Wiessee
ADDRESS : Robognerhof – 8182 Bad Wiessee
HOTEL :
Lederer – Bad Wiessee
Tel : (08022)8291
Marina – Bad Wiessee
Tel : (08022)81125
Sapplfeld – Bad Wiessee
Tel : (08022)82067
RESTAURANT : Freihaus Brenner – Bad Wiessee
Tel : (08022)82004

This is an idyllic Alpine lakeside course, laid out on rising parkland 800m above the Tegern See Lake and sheltered by the Bavarian Alps. The course is long and demanding with several uphill and downhill holes, 40 bunkers and a picturesque stream crossing two fairways. The green of the 10th hole lies in front of the famous St. Quinirus chapel, dating back several centuries. The course commands unforgettable panoramic views of the lake and the mountains. There is a charming Bavarian style clubhouse. *SSS 69*

GF $

1958

18

November to April

E. Durk, D. Harradine

L 5501 P 70

 S

Required : Handicap Certificate
Best days : Weekdays

HOLE	LENGTH MEDAL-TEE	PAR	STROKE INDEX
1	317	4	13
2	479	5	5
3	375	4	1
4	179	3	11
5	415	4	3
6	375	4	7
7	202	3	9
8	305	4	15
9	99	3	17
TOTAL	2746	34	TOTAL

HOLE	LENGTH MEDAL-TEE	PAR	STROKE INDEX
10	291	4	14
11	290	4	12
12	91	3	18
13	435	5	2
14	365	4	4
15	278	4	16
16	202	3	6
17	449	5	8
18	355	4	10
TOTAL	2755	36	TOTAL

TUTZING

★★

TEL : (08158)3600/1699
LOCATION : 35 km München/
10 km Starnberg to Weilheim
ADDRESS : 8132 Tutzing-Deixlfurt
HOTEL :
Seehof – Starnberg
Tel : (08151)12220
Engelhof – Tutzing
Tel : (08158)3062
Kaiserin Elisabeth – Feldafing
Tel : (08157)1013
RESTAURANT : Am See – Tutzing
Tel : (08158)490

In a setting of scenic beauty among groves of colourful trees, the course lies in the foothills of the Bavarian Alps at over 700m above sea level. The 18 holes wind through fine woodland and meadowland incorporating several picturesque streams meandering their way through the course. There is a charming chalet style clubhouse flanked by majestic trees. *SSS 73*

GF $$

1983

18

November to March

C. Kramer

L 6159 P 72

S

R

Required : Handicap Certificate, Club Membership Card
Best days : Any day

HOLE	LENGTH MEDAL-TEE	PAR	STROKE INDEX
1	404	4	3
2	466	5	9
3	390	4	13
4	360	4	5
5	161	3	17
6	371	4	11
7	362	4	7
8	138	3	15
9	565	5	1
TOTAL	3217	36	TOTAL

HOLE	LENGTH MEDAL-TEE	PAR	STROKE INDEX
10	447	5	12
11	158	3	16
12	338	4	10
13	390	4	8
14	465	5	6
15	122	3	18
16	516	5	2
17	361	4	4
18	145	3	14
TOTAL	2942	36	TOTAL

VESTISCHER RECKLINGHAUSEN

TEL : (02361)26520
LOCATION : 1 km Recklinghausen
ADDRESS : Bockholter Strasse 475 – 4350 Recklinghausen
HOTEL :
Novotel Marl – Recklinghausen
Tel : (02365)1020
Am Schlosspark – Herten
Tel : (02366)80050
Quellberg – Recklinghausen
Tel : (02361)41014
RESTAURANT : Die Engelsburg – Recklinghausen
Tel : (02361)25066

A sporting inland course featuring narrow tree-lined fairways, several dog-legs and numerous water hazards. It is laid out on flat countryside in Nordrhein-Westfalen with fairways and greens craftily bunkered. *SSS 72*

GF $ — Mondays — S
1974 — — — R
18 — L 6111 P 72

Required : Handicap Certificate
Best days : Weekdays only

HOLE	LENGTH MEDAL-TEE	PAR	STROKE INDEX
1	324	4	13
2	163	3	16
3	512	5	7
4	389	4	2
5	203	3	15
6	528	5	5
7	392	4	9
8	165	3	12
9	392	4	1
TOTAL	3068	35	TOTAL

HOLE	LENGTH MEDAL-TEE	PAR	STROKE INDEX
10	300	4	18
11	450	5	3
12	155	3	10
13	435	5	6
14	343	4	4
15	339	4	14
16	478	5	17
17	192	3	8
18	351	4	11
TOTAL	3043	37	TOTAL

WASSERBURG ANHOLT

TEL : (02874)3444
LOCATION : 4 km Anholt
ADDRESS : Am Schloss 3-4294 Isselburg Anholt
HOTEL :
Wasserburg Anholt-Isselburg
Tel : (02874)2044
Legeland-Isselburg
Tel : (02874)837
Waldhotel Tanenhäuschen-Wesel am Niederrhein
Tel : (0281)61014
RESTAURANT : Terrine-Bocholt
Tel : (02871)182767

Located near the Dutch border, the golf course is laid out in flat parkland amidst age-old trees with several water hazards affecting play. Extended to 18 holes in 1988, the average player won't find this course too testing. *SSS 72*

GF $ — November to April — S
1972 — —
18 — L 6141 P 72 — R

Required : Handicap Certificate
Best days : Any day with booking in advance

HOLE	LENGTH MEDAL-TEE	PAR	STROKE INDEX
1	358	4	15
2	540	5	5
3	386	4	3
4	400	4	1
5	490	5	11
6	325	4	13
7	119	3	17
8	378	4	9
9	161	3	7
TOTAL	3157	36	TOTAL

HOLE	LENGTH MEDAL-TEE	PAR	STROKE INDEX
10	365	4	6
11	140	3	12
12	470	5	8
13	331	4	16
14	170	3	4
15	338	4	10
16	387	4	2
17	441	5	18
18	342	4	14
TOTAL	2984	36	TOTAL

WESTFÄLISCHER GÜTERSLOH

TEL : (05244)2340
LOCATION : 6 km Gütersloh
ADDRESS : Gütersloherstrasse 127 - 4835 Rietberg 2
HOTEL :
Parkhotel - Gütersloh
Tel : (05241)850
Wiedenbrück - Rheda Wiedenbrück
Tel : (05242)7051
Stadt - Gütersloh
Tel : (05241)1711
RESTAURANT : Zur Deele und Apostel - Gütersloh
Tel : (05241)28370

A typical inland course of championship standard laid out on flat terrain amongst old beeches and oak trees. The course, with a varied layout, includes numerous ditches and lakes, and is bordered on one side by the river 'Wapel'. *SSS 72*

GF $

1969

18

—

B.v. Limburger

L 6135 P 72

Required : Handicap Certificate
Best days : Any day

HOLE	LENGTH MEDAL-TEE	PAR	STROKE INDEX
1	350	4	11
2	380	4	3
3	495	5	7
4	295	4	15
5	350	4	1
6	155	3	13
7	385	4	5
8	205	3	9
9	460	5	17
TOTAL	3075	36	TOTAL

HOLE	LENGTH MEDAL-TEE	PAR	STROKE INDEX
10	170	3	8
11	540	5	2
12	115	3	18
13	395	4	6
14	335	4	12
15	290	4	10
16	365	4	14
17	390	4	4
18	460	5	16
TOTAL	3060	36	TOTAL

WIESLOCH-HOHENHARDTER HOF

TEL : (06222)72081/74681
LOCATION : Wiesloch to Baiertal/Schatthausen
ADDRESS : Hohenhardter Hof – 6908 Wiesloch 4 – Baiertal
HOTEL :
Gänsberg-Wiesloch
Tel : (06222)4400
Mondial – Wiesloch
Tel : (06222)8016
Winzerhof – Rauenberg
Tel : (06222)62067

A very hilly course with many ups and downs and several blind holes. Trees, water courses, sand traps and several out of bounds present constant hazards. The course lies in Baden-Württemberg and is laid out around an imposing and historical manor house. *SSS 72*

GF $

1983

18

—

R. Weishaupt/D. Harradine

L 6130 P 72

S

R

Required : Handicap Certificate
Best days : Any day

HOLE	LENGTH MEDAL-TEE	PAR	STROKE INDEX
1	371	4	5
2	345	4	9
3	206	3	11
4	541	5	1
5	248	4	17
6	334	4	7
7	291	4	13
8	162	3	15
9	351	4	3
TOTAL	2849	35	TOTAL

HOLE	LENGTH MEDAL-TEE	PAR	STROKE INDEX
10	440	5	5
11	127	3	3
12	397	4	4
13	472	5	5
14	202	3	3
15	342	4	4
16	403	4	4
17	418	4	4
18	480	5	5
TOTAL	3281	37	TOTAL

WITTELSBACHER

TEL : (08431)44118/49616
LOCATION : 20 km W. Ingolstadt/84 km N. München
ADDRESS :
8858 Neubing a.d. Donau 2
HOTEL :
Ambassador - Ingolstadt
Tel : (0841)5030
Lindenhof - Neuburg
Tel : (08438)2617
Krone - Neuburg
Tel : (08438)44854

Not far from the Donau river, this is a most enjoyable scenic course featuring a sporty and challenging layout. The holes are found in an individual setting with old and majestic oak trees lining the fairways. Four water hazards such as a burn and two lakes serve as hazards. *SSS 72*

GF $

1990

18

November to March

D. van Heel

L 6065 P 72

S

R

Required : Handicap Certificate
Best days : Weekdays

HOLE	LENGTH MEDAL-TEE	PAR	STROKE INDEX
1	452	5	9
2	370	4	7
3	306	4	17
4	381	4	1
5	356	4	11
6	187	3	5
7	344	4	13
8	345	4	3
9	300	4	15
TOTAL	3041	36	TOTAL

HOLE	LENGTH MEDAL-TEE	PAR	STROKE INDEX
10	334	4	10
11	163	3	14
12	322	4	12
13	353	4	2
14	333	4	16
15	449	5	6
16	126	3	18
17	428	4	4
18	516	5	8
TOTAL	3024	36	TOTAL

WORPSWEDE

TEL : (04763)7313/
(0421)404214
LOCATION : 3 km Kuhstedt
ADDRESS : Gielermühle - 2864 Gem. Vollersode
HOTEL :
Bonner - Worpswede
Tel : (04792)2079
Deutsches Haus - Worpswede
Tel : (04792)1205
Eichenhof - Worpswede
Tel : (04792)2677
RESTAURANT : Ratsstuben - Ritterhude
Tel : (04292)9260

A typical moorland course with its 18 holes running through coniferous woodland and heather. Many of the fairways are flanked by thistles and blackberry bushes. The club is closed in November and in January due to the hunting season. *SSS 71*

GF $

 1974

18

November and January

W. v. Laguna

L 5845 P 71

Required : Handicap Certificate
Best days : Weekdays

HOLE	LENGTH MEDAL-TEE	PAR	STROKE INDEX
1	330	4	4
2	336	4	4
3	200	3	3
4	364	4	4
5	181	3	3
6	490	5	5
7	339	4	4
8	435	5	4
9	397	4	4
TOTAL	3072	36	TOTAL

HOLE	LENGTH MEDAL-TEE	PAR	STROKE INDEX
10	393	4	4
11	336	4	4
12	373	4	4
13	182	3	3
14	363	4	4
15	255	4	4
16	108	3	3
17	316	4	4
18	457	5	5
TOTAL	2773	35	TOTAL

WÖRTHSEE

TEL : (08153)2425/2699
LOCATION : 27 km München BAB to Lindau
ADDRESS : Gut Schluifeld – 8031 Wörthsee
HOTEL :
Post – Wörthsee
Tel : (08153)3619
Piushof – Herrsching
Tel : (08152)1007
Wörthsee – Steinebach
Tel : (08153)7650
RESTAURANT : Alba See – Herrsching
Tel : (08152)2011

Scenically situated near the Wörthsee lake and backed by the snow capped mountains of the Alps, the course winds through gently rolling land, lined by old oak trees and silver beeches. Most of the greens are undulating, demanding accuracy. There are four picturesque ponds serving as hazards on more than six holes. *SSS 71*

GF $$
1984
18

Mondays (1.11/1.04)
—
L 5915 P 72

R S

Required : Handicap Certificate
Best days : Weekdays only

HOLE	LENGTH MEDAL-TEE	PAR	STROKE INDEX
1	440	5	15
2	165	3	11
3	363	4	3
4	150	3	13
5	378	4	5
6	478	5	9
7	326	4	7
8	336	4	1
9	273	4	17
TOTAL	2909	36	TOTAL

HOLE	LENGTH MEDAL-TEE	PAR	STROKE INDEX
10	322	4	8
11	164	3	4
12	437	5	18
13	196	3	14
14	333	4	10
15	462	5	12
16	340	4	6
17	370	4	16
18	382	4	2
TOTAL	3006	36	TOTAL

GREECE

Car Rental

4 GOLF COURSES, 3 000 PLAYERS

★★★ Great golf course
★★ Very good golf course
$ 2000-3000 Drs
★ Recommended golf course
☼ Holiday golf course
$ $ more than 3000 Drs

TOWN	GOLF COURSE		TEL	MAP REF.
Athens	Glyfada	★★★	(01) 8931721	3
Corfu	Corfu	★ ☼	(0661) 94220	1
Porto Carras	Porto Carras	☼	(0375) 71381	2
Rhodos	Afandou	☼	(0241) 51390	4

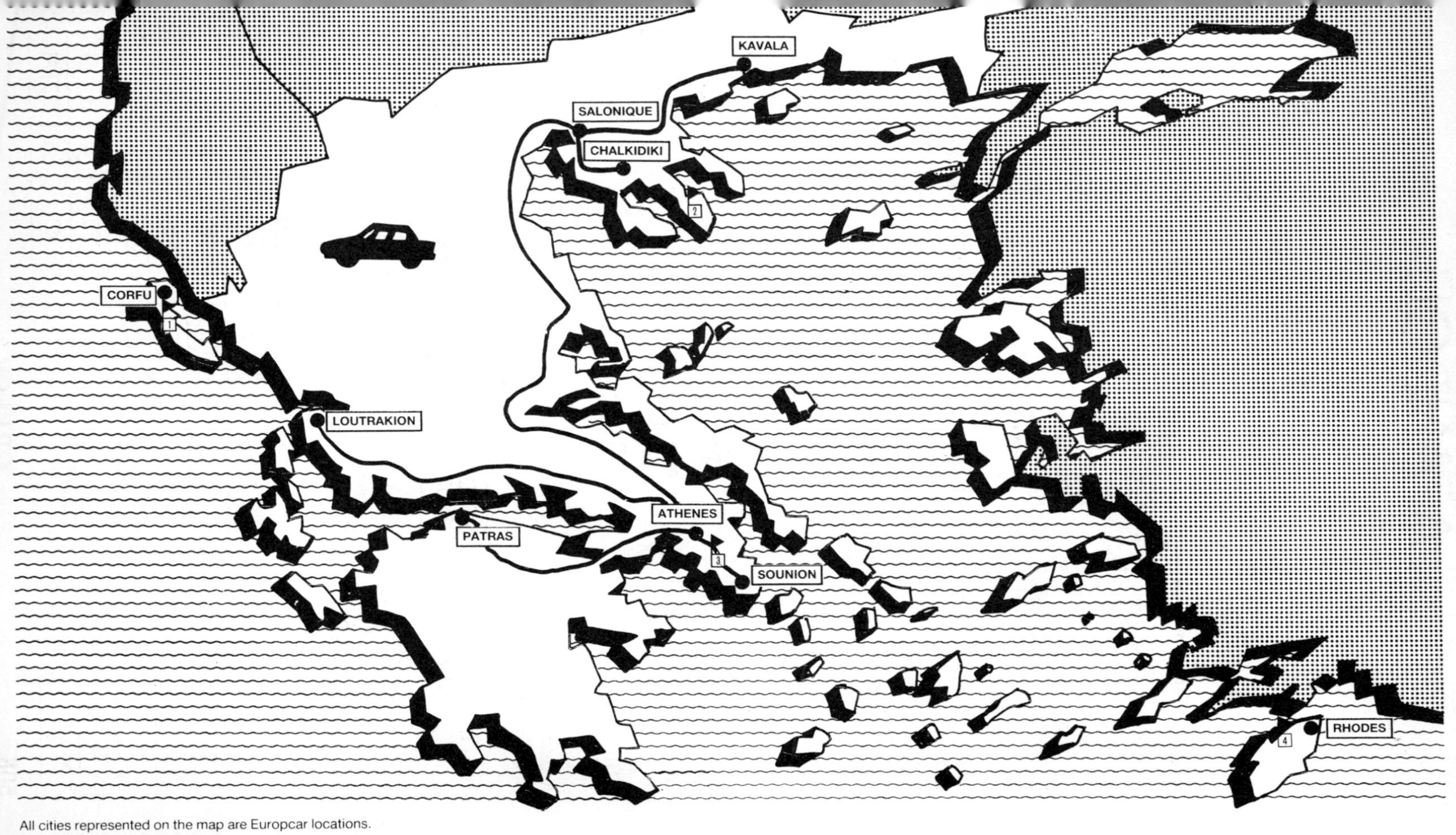

All cities represented on the map are Europcar locations.

AFANDOU

TEL : (0241)51390/51257
LOCATION : 18 km Rhodos
ADDRESS : Afandou – Rhodos
HOTEL : HF
Appolo Beach – Faliraki
Tel : (0241)85251

A fine holiday course set on the east coast of the scenic island of Rhodes. Laid out directly by the sea, which makes it the only real seaside course in Greece. The fairways are sown with bermuda grass and the greens are of excellent quality. The first nine holes are of the links type. The second nine run through an olive grove encircled by distant hills. There is a fine clubhouse set high up, with tennis courts and a swimming pool.

GF $

1973

18

—

D. Harradine

L 6090 P 72

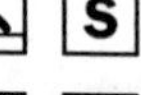
S

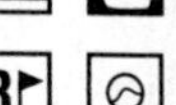

Required : Handicap Certificate
Best days : Any day

HOLE	LENGTH MEDAL-TEE	PAR	STROKE INDEX
1	380	4	
2	470	5	
3	135	3	
4	460	5	
5	320	4	
6	330	4	
7	360	4	
8	200	3	
9	395	4	
TOTAL	3050	36	TOTAL

HOLE	LENGTH MEDAL-TEE	PAR	STROKE INDEX
10	165	3	
11	320	4	
12	480	5	
13	290	4	
14	330	4	
15	510	5	
16	160	3	
17	420	4	
18	365	4	
TOTAL	3040	36	TOTAL

CORFU

TEL : (0661)94220
LOCATION : 14 km Corfu, in Ermones
ADDRESS : P.O. Box 71 – Ropa Valley – Corfu
HOTEL :
Ermones Beach – Ermones
Tel : (0661)94241

This is a superb holiday golf course set within the splendid natural landscape of the Ropa Valley. Encircled by low wooded hills, the fairways are tree-lined with cypress, and streams meander their way through several of them. There is an attractive rustic clubhouse, built from timber and local stone. The Ermones Beach Hotel is only 1km from the course, overlooking the bay.

GF $

1972

18

  —

D. Harradine

L 5807 P 72

Required : Handicap Certificate
Best days : Any day

HOLE	LENGTH MEDAL-TEE	PAR	STROKE INDEX
1	275	4	11
2	140	3	17
3	435	5	13
4	340	4	3
5	430	5	9
6	327	4	5
7	440	5	1
8	185	3	15
9	390	4	7
TOTAL	2962	37	TOTAL

HOLE	LENGTH MEDAL-TEE	PAR	STROKE INDEX
10	410	4	4
11	360	4	8
12	150	3	18
13	325	4	6
14	295	4	16
15	305	4	10
16	180	3	14
17	380	4	2
18	440	5	12
TOTAL	2845	35	TOTAL

GLYFADA

TEL : (01)8931721/8946820
LOCATION : 12 km Athens
ADDRESS : 16610 Glyfada – Athens
HOTEL :
Regina Maris – Glyfada
Tel : (01)8945050
RESTAURANT : Psaropoulos – Glyfada
Tel : (01)8945677

The Glyfada golf club is the most prestigious Greek club located near the capital. It is one of the world's best courses and has often hosted important tournaments such as the 1979 World Cup. Set in the seaside resort of Glyfada, the course itself is not situated directly by the sea. Backed by distant hills and Mount Hymettus, the course is gently undulating and has some fine views. Many of the fairways feature strategically placed umbrella pines. *SSS 70*

GF $$

1962

18

Weekends

D. Harradine, R. Trent Jones

L 5768 P 72

S

R

Required : Handicap Certificate
Best days : Weekdays

HOLE	LENGTH MEDAL-TEE	PAR	STROKE INDEX
1	337	4	9
2	317	4	13
3	429	5	5
4	339	4	11
5	134	3	15
6	375	4	3
7	480	5	7
8	161	3	17
9	368	4	1
TOTAL	2940	36	TOTAL

HOLE	LENGTH MEDAL-TEE	PAR	STROKE INDEX
10	436	5	12
11	325	4	4
12	179	3	16
13	329	4	6
14	385	4	2
15	408	5	14
16	125	3	18
17	301	4	10
18	340	4	8
TOTAL	2828	36	TOTAL

PORTO CARRAS

TEL : (0375)71381
LOCATION : 2 km Porto Carras
ADDRESS : Sithonia – Halkidiki
HOTEL : HR
Meliton Beach and Sithonia Beach – Sithonia/Village Inn
Tel : (0375)71381

Named after the Greek shipping magnate John Carras, who bought a large part of the peninsula called Sithonia and turned it into a holiday resort. The Porto Carras golf course is the newest and most promising of the Greek golf courses having been founded in 1980. Laid out between two high class hotels and the sea, and backed by wooded hills and distant mountains, the club hosted the European Boys Championship in 1986. It is part of a holiday complex with day time sports and leisure facilities including a riding school, nine tennis courts, a yachting marina, and a wide choice of water sports.

GF $

1980

18

—

G. Cornish/W. Robinson

 5601 P 72

Required : None
Best days : Any day

HOLE	LENGTH MEDAL-TEE	PAR	STROKE INDEX
1	317	4	11
2	468	5	1
3	159	3	15
4	332	4	9
5	292	4	13
6	116	3	17
7	350	4	7
8	373	4	5
9	460	5	3
TOTAL	2867	36	TOTAL

HOLE	LENGTH MEDAL-TEE	PAR	STROKE INDEX
10	309	4	12
11	290	4	14
12	318	4	10
13	320	4	8
14	372	4	2
15	140	3	16
16	418	5	4
17	125	3	18
18	442	5	6
TOTAL	2734	36	TOTAL

IRELAND

Car Rental

Reservation/Information telephone number :

Country code :	**Telephone number :**
353	**1/681777**

Headquarters address :

EUROPCAR – MURRAYS
Baggot Street Bridge, Dublin 4
Tel. : (353) 1/681777
Telex : 93784
Fax : (353) 1/602958

250 GOLF COURSES, 165 000 PLAYERS

★★★ Great golf course
★★ Very good golf course
$ 5-15 Ir. Pound
★ Recommended golf course
✡ Holiday golf course
$ $ more than 15 Ir. Pound

TOWN	GOLF COURSE		TEL	♦	MAP REF.
CO. ANTRIM					
Antrim	Massereene		(08494) 62096		4 M
Belfast	Balmoral		(0232) 381514		4 N
	Belvoir Park	★	(0232) 491693	♦	4 M
	Dunmurry		(084) 610834		4 M
	Fortwilliam		(0232) 370770		4 M
	Malone		(084) 612758	♦	4 M
	Shandon Park		(0232) 401856		4 M
	The Knock		(02318) 3251	♦	4 N
Ballycastle	Ballycastle	★★	(02657) 62536	♦	2 M
Ballymena	Ballymena		(0266) 861487	♦	3 M
Bushmills	Bushmills	•	(02657) 31317		2 L
Carrickfergus	Carrickfergus		(09603) 62203		4 N
Larne	Cairndhu	★	(0574) 83324	♦	4 N
	Larne	•	(0574) 82228		3 N
Portrush	Royal Portrush	★★★	(0265) 822311	♦	2 L
Whitehead	Whitehead		(09603) 53631		4 P
CO. ARMAGH					
Lurgan	Lurgan		(0762) 322087		5 M
Portadown	Portadown		(0762) 355356		5 M
Tandragee	Tandragee		(0762) 840727		5 M
CO. CARLOW					
Borris	Borris	•	(0503) 73143		13 L
Carlow	Carlow	★★	(0503) 31695	♦	12 L

♦ For details, see following pages.

• 9 hole golf courses.

TOWN	GOLF COURSE		TEL	◆	MAP REF.
CO. CAVAN					
Belturbet	Belturbet	•	(049) 22287		7 J
Blacklion	Blacklion	•	(072) 53024		6 H
Cavan	County Cavan		(049) 31283	◆	7 J
Kingscourt	Kingscourt	•	(042) 67160		8 L
Virginia	Virginia	•			8 K
CO. CLARE					
Ennis	Ennis		(065) 29211		12 E
	Dromoland	•	(061) 71144		3 F
Kilkee	Kilkee	•	Kilkee 48		13 D
Kilrush	Kilrush	•	Kilrush 138		13 D
Lahinch	Lahinch	★★★	(065) 81003	◆	12 D
Shannon	Shannon	★★	(061) 61020	◆	13 E
CO. CORK					
Bandon	Bandon		(023) 41111		17 F
Bantry	Bantry	•	(027) 50579		17 D
Charleville	Charleville		(063) 257		14 E
Clonakilty	Dunmore	•	(023) 33352		18 F
Cork	Douglas		(021) 291086		16 G
	Little Island (Cork)	★★★	(021) 353451	◆	16 H
	Mahon		(021) 631687		16 G
	Monkstown	★	(021) 841376	◆	17 G
	Muskerry	★	(021) 385297	◆	17 G
			(021) 385104		
Doneraile	Doneraile	•	(022) 24137		15 F
Fermoy	Fermoy		(025) 31473		15 G
Glengarriff	Glengarriff	•	(027) 63150		17 D
Kanturk	Kanturk	•	(029) 50534		15 F
Kinsale	Kinsale	•	(021) 72197		17 G
Macroom	Macroom	•	(026) 41072		16 E
Mitchelstown	Mitchelstown	•	(025) 24072		15 G
Mallow	Mallow	★	(022) 21145	◆	15 F
Skibbereen	Skibbereen	•	(028) 21227		18 D
Youghal	Youghal	★★	(024) 92787	◆	16 H
CO. DERRY					
Castlerock	Castlerock	★★	(0265) 848314	◆	2 L
Londonderry	City of Derry	★	(0504) 46369	◆	3 K
Portstewart	Portstewart	✡	(026583) 2015	◆	2 L
CO. DONEGAL					
Ballybofey/Stanorlar	Ballybofey/Stanorlar	✡	(074) 31093		4 H
Ballyliffen	Ballyliffen	★	(077) 74417	◆	1 J
Buncrana	Buncrana	•	Buncrana 1		2 J
Bundoran	Bundoran	★ ✡	(072) 41302	◆	5 G
Donegal	Donegal Town	★	(073) 34054	◆	4 H
Dunfanaghy	Dunfanaghy	✡	(074) 36335	◆	2 H
Fahan	North West		(077) 61027	◆	2 J
Greencastle	Greencastle	•	Greencastle 13		2 K
Gweedore	Gweedore	•	(075) 31140		3 G
Letterkenny	Letterkenny		(074) 21150	◆	3 J
Narin	Narin and Portnoo	★★	(075) 45107	◆	4 G
Portsalon	Portsalon	✡	(074) 59102	◆	2 J
Rathmullan	Otway	•	(074) 58319		2 J
Rosapenna	Rosapenna	★★	(074) 55301	◆	2 H
CO. DOWN					
Ardglass	Ardglass	★	(0396) 841219		6 P
Bangor	Bangor	★	(0247) 270922		4 P
	Carnalea	★	(0247) 270368	◆	4 P
	Clandeboye	★★	(0247) 271767	◆	4 P
Donaghadee	Donaghadee	✡	(0247) 883624	◆	4 P
Downpatrick	Downpatrick		(0396) 612152		5 P
Holywood	Royal Belfast	★★★	(0232) 428165	◆	4 N

◆ For details, see following pages.

• 9 hole golf course.

TOWN	GOLF COURSE		TEL	◆	MAP REF.
Newcastle	Royal County Down	★★★	(03967) 22209	◆	6 N
Newtownards	Scrabo	✡	(0247) 812355	◆	4 P
Warrenpoint	Warrenpoint		(06937) 72219		6 M
CO. DUBLIN					
Dublin & Suburbs	Balbriggan		(01) 412173	◆	9 M
	Ballinascorney	•	(01) 512515		10 N
	Beaverstown		(01) 436439	◆	10 N
	Beech Park		(01) 580522	◆	10 M
	Carrickmines	•	(01) 895676		10 N
	Castle		(01) 904207		10 N
	Clontarf		(01) 315085	◆	10 M
	Corballis		(01) 452127		9 N
	Deerpark	✡	(01) 322624	◆	10 N
	Donabate	✡	(01) 436346	◆	9 N
	Dun Laoghaire		(01) 803916	◆	10 N
	Edmondstown	✡	(01) 931082	◆	10 M
	Forest Little		(01) 401000	◆	10 M
	Foxrock	•	(01) 8893992		10 N
	Grange	★	(01) 932889	◆	10 M
	Hermitage	✡	(01) 268471	◆	10 M
	Howth	★★	(01) 323055	◆	10 N
	Killiney	•	(01) 852823		10 N
	Kilternan (Dublin Sport)		(01) 895418		11 M
	Lucan	•	(01) 280246		10 M
	Malahide	•	(01) 451428		10 N
	Milltown		(01) 977060		10 N
	Newlands		(01) 593157		10 M
	Portmarnock	★★★	(01) 323082	◆	10 N
	Rathfarnham	•	(01) 931201		10 M
	Royal Dublin	★★★	(01) 336346	◆	10 N
	Rush	•	(01) 437548		9 N
	Skerries	✡	(01) 491567	◆	9 N
	Slade Valley		(01) 582207		10 M
	St. Anne's	•	(01) 336471		10 N
	Stackstown		(01) 942338	◆	10 M
	Sutton	•	(01) 323013		10 N
	The Island	★	(01) 436104 (01) 436462	◆	10 N
	Woodbrook	★	(01) 824799	◆	11 N
CO. FERMANAGH					
Enniskillen	Enniskillen	•	(0365) 325250		5 J
CO. GALWAY					
Athenry	Athenry	•	(091) 84466		10 E
Ballinasloe	Ballinasloe		(0905) 42126	◆	10 G
Ballyconneely	Connemara	★★ ✡	(095) 23502	◆	10 B
Galway	Galway	★★	(091) 23038	◆	10 E
Gort	Gort	•	(091) 31336		11 F
Loughrea	Loughrea	•	(091) 41049		11 F
Mountbellew	Mountbellew	•	(0905) 79259		9 G
Oughterard	Oughterard		(091) 82131	◆	10 D
Portumna	Portumna	•	(0509) 41059		11 G
Tuam	Tuam		(093) 24354		9 F
CO. KERRY					
Ballybunion	Ballybunion	★★★	(068) 27146	◆	14 D
Ballyferriter	Ceann Sibeal	•	(066) 51657		13 B
Glenbeigh	Dooks	✡	(066) 68205	◆	16 C
Kenmare	Kenmare	•	(064) 41291		16 D
Killarney	Killarney	★★★	(064) 31034	◆	16 D
Parknasilla	Parknasilla	•	(064) 45122		17 C
Tralee	Tralee	★★★	(066) 36379	◆	15 C
Waterville	Waterville	★★★ ✡	(0667) 4102	◆	17 B
CO. KILDARE					
Athy	Athy	•	(0507) 31729		12 L
Curragh	Curragh		(045) 41238		11 L
Donadea	Knockanally		(045) 69322 (045) 287716	◆	10 L

TOWN	GOLF COURSE		TEL	◆	MAP REF.
Kilcock	Kilcock	•	(01) 287283		10 L
Kildare	Cill Dara		(045) 21433		11 L
Kill	Four Lakes		(045) 66003		10 L
Naas	Naas	•	(045) 97509		10 L
Sallins	Bodenstown (Old Course)		(045) 97096		10 L
	Bodenstown (New Course)		(045) 97096		10 L
CO. KILKENNY					
Callan	Callan	•	(056) 25136		13 K
Castlecomer	Castlecomer	•	(056) 41139		12 K
Kilkenny	Kilkenny		(056) 22125	◆	13 K
CO. LAOIS					
Abbeyleix	Abbeyleix	•	(0502) 31450		12 K
Mountrath	Mountrath	•	(0502) 32558		12 J
Portlaoise	The Heath		(0502) 46533	◆	1 K
Portarlington	Portarlington	•	(0502) 23115		11 K
Rathdowney	Rathdowney	•	(0505) 46170		12 J
CO. LEITRIM					
Ballinamore	Ballinamore	•	(078) 44346		7 H
Carrick-on-Shannon	Carrick-on-Shannon	•	(078) 20157		7 H
CO. LIMERICK					
Adare	Adare Manor	•	(061) 94204		13 F
Limerick	Castletroy	★	(061) 335261		13 F
	Limerick	✡	(061) 44083		13 F
Newcastle West	Newcastle West	•	(069) 62105		14 E
CO. LONGFORD					
Longford	County Longford		(043) 46310		8 H
CO. LOUTH					
Ardee	Ardee		(041) 53227		8 M
Baltray	County Louth	★★	(041) 23329	◆	8 M
Dundalk	Dundalk	★	(042) 21713		7 N
Greenore	Greenore	✡	(042) 73212		7 N
CO. MAYO					
Ballina	Ballina	•	(096) 21050		7 E
Ballinrobe	Ballinrobe	•	(092) 41448		9 E
Ballyhaunis	Ballyhaunis	•	(0907) 30014		8 F
Belmullet	Belmullet		(097) 81093		6 C
Castelbar	Castelbar		(094) 21649		8 D
Claremorris	Claremorris	•	(094) 71527		8 E
Keel	Achill	•	(098) 43202		7 C
Mulrany	Mulrany	•	(098) 36185		8 C
Swinford	Swinford	•	(094) 51378		7 E
Westport	Westport	★	(098) 25113	◆	8 D
CO. MEATH					
Kells	Headfort	★	(046) 40146	◆	8 L
Laytown/Bettystown	Laytown/Bettystown	★★	(041) 27534	◆	8 M
Navan	Royal Tara		(046) 25244		9 L
Trim	Trim	•	(046) 31463		9 L
CO. MONAGHAN					
Carrickmacross	Nuremore	•	(042) 61438		7 L
Clones	Clones	•	Scotshouse 17		6 K
Monaghan	Rossmore	•	(047) 81316		6 K
CO. OFFALY					
Birr	Birr		(0509) 20082		11 H
Edenderry	Edenderry	•	(0405) 31072		10 K
Tullamore	Tullamore		(0506) 21439		10 J
CO. ROSCOMMON					
Boyle	Boyle	•	(079) 62594		7 G
Castlerea	Castlerea	•	Castlerea 68		8 F

TOWN	GOLF COURSE		TEL	♦	MAP REF.
Roscommon	Roscommon	•	(0903) 6382		9 G
CO. SLIGO					
Ballymote	Ballymote	•	Ballymote 3460		7 G
Inniscrone	Enniscrone	★	(096) 36297	♦	6 E
Sligo	Rosses Point	★★★	(071) 77186	♦	6 G
	Strandhill		(071) 68188		6 F
CO. TIPPERARY					
Cahir	Cahir Park	•	(052) 41474		14 H
Carrick-on-Suir	Carrick-on-Suir	•	(051) 40047		14 J
Clonmel	Clonmel	★	(052) 21138	♦	14 J
Nenagh	Nenagh		(067) 31476	♦	12 G
Roscrea	Roscrea	•	(0505) 21130		12 H
Templemore	Templemore	•	(0504) 31522		12 H
Thurles	Thurles		(0504) 21983		13 H
Tipperary	Tipperary	•	(062) 51119		14 G
CO. TYRONE					
Dungannon	Dungannon		(08687) 22098		5 L
Fintona	Fintona	•	(0662) 841480		5 J
Newtownstewart	Newtownstewart		(06626) 61466	♦	4 K
Strabane	Strabane		(0504) 382271	♦	3 J
CO. WATERFORD					
Dungarvan	Dungarvan	•	(058) 41605		15 J
Lismore	Lismore	•	(058) 54026		15 H
Tramore	Tramore	★ ✡	(051) 81247		15 K
Waterford	Waterford	★	(051) 74182		15 K
CO. WESTMEATH					
Athlone	Athlone		(0902) 2073		10 H
Moate	Moate	•	(0902) 31271		10 J
Mullingar	Mullingar	★	(044) 48366		9 S
CO. WEXFORD					
Courtown	Courtown	✡	(055) 21533	♦	13 N
Enniscorthy	Enniscorthy	•	(054) 33191		14 M
New Ross	New Ross	•	(051) 21150		14 L
Rosslare	Rosslare	✡	(053) 32113	♦	15 M
Wexford	Wexford		(053) 42238	♦	14 M
CO. WICKLOW					
Arklow	Arklow	★	(0402) 32492	♦	12 N
Baltinglass	Baltinglass	•	(0508) 81350		12 L
Blainroe (Wicklow)	Blainroe	★ ✡	(0404) 68168	♦	12 N
Bray	Bray	•	(01) 862484		11 N
Delgany	Delgany	✡	(01) 874536		11 N
Greystones	Greystones	★	(01) 874136	♦	11 N
Shillelagh	Coolattin	•	(055) 29125		13 M
Wicklow	Wicklow	★	(0404) 23279		12 N
Woodbrook	Woodbrook	★	(01) 824799	♦	11 N
Woodenbridge	Woodenbridge	•	(0402) 5202		12 M

♦ For details, see following pages.

• 9 hole golf course.

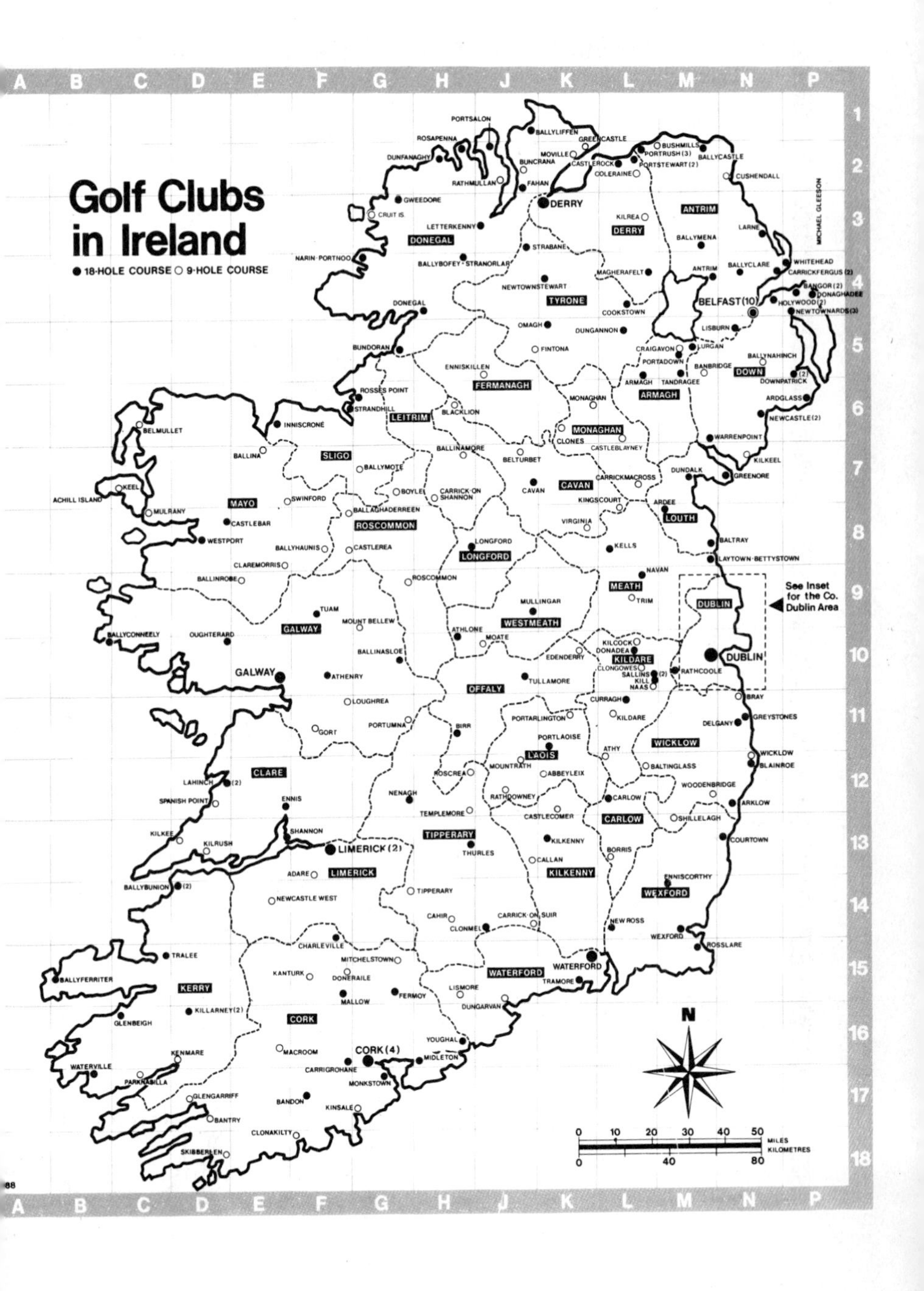

Golf Clubs in Ireland
● 18-HOLE COURSE ○ 9-HOLE COURSE
MICHAEL GLEESON
A B C D E F G H J K L M N P
1 2 3 4 5 6 7 8 9 10 11 12 13 14 15 16 17 18
DONEGAL
DERRY
ANTRIM
TYRONE
FERMANAGH
ARMAGH
DOWN
MONAGHAN
LEITRIM
SLIGO
MAYO
ROSCOMMON
CAVAN
LOUTH
LONGFORD
MEATH
WESTMEATH
DUBLIN
GALWAY
KILDARE
OFFALY
LAOIS
WICKLOW
CLARE
CARLOW
TIPPERARY
LIMERICK
KILKENNY
WEXFORD
WATERFORD
KERRY
CORK
PORTSALON
ROSAPENNA
DUNFANAGHY
BALLYLIFFEN
GREENCASTLE
MOVILLE
BUNCRANA
CASTLEROCK
BUSHMILLS
PORTRUSH (3)
PORTSTEWART (2)
BALLYCASTLE
RATHMULLAN
FAHAN
COLERAINE
CUSHENDALL
GWEEDORE
CRUIT IS.
DERRY
KILREA
LETTERKENNY
LARNE
NARIN · PORTNOO
STRABANE
BALLYMENA
BALLYBOFEY · STRANORLAR
MAGHERAFELT
ANTRIM
BALLYCLARE
WHITEHEAD
CARRICKFERGUS (2)
NEWTOWNSTEWART
BANGOR (2)
DONAGHADEE
BELFAST (10)
HOLYWOOD (2)
NEWTOWNARDS (3)
DONEGAL
COOKSTOWN
OMAGH
DUNGANNON
LISBURN
BUNDORAN
FINTONA
CRAIGAVON
LURGAN
PORTADOWN
BALLYNAHINCH
ENNISKILLEN
BANBRIDGE
ARMAGH
TANDRAGEE
DOWNPATRICK
(2)
ROSSES POINT
ARDGLASS
STRANDHILL
BLACKLION
MONAGHAN
NEWCASTLE (2)
BELMULLET
INNISCRONE
CLONES
CASTLEBLAYNEY
WARRENPOINT
BALLINA
BALLINAMORE
BELTURBET
KILKEEL
BALLYMOTE
DUNDALK
GREENORE
KEEL
BOYLE
CARRICK · ON SHANNON
CAVAN
CARRICKMACROSS
ACHILL ISLAND
SWINFORD
KINGSCOURT
ARDEE
MULRANY
BALLAGHADERREEN
CASTLEBAR
VIRGINIA
WESTPORT
LONGFORD
BALTRAY
BALLYHAUNIS
CASTLEREA
KELLS
LAYTOWN · BETTYSTOWN
CLAREMORRIS
NAVAN
BALLINROBE
ROSCOMMON
See Inset for the Co. Dublin Area
TRIM
MULLINGAR
TUAM
MOUNT BELLEW
ATHLONE
BALLYCONNEELY
OUGHTERARD
MOATE
KILCOCK
DONADEA
BALLINASLOE
EDENDERRY
DUBLIN
CLONGOWES
SALLINS
(2)
RATHCOOLE
GALWAY
KILL
NAAS
ATHENRY
TULLAMORE
CURRAGH
BRAY
LOUGHREA
KILDARE
PORTARLINGTON
GREYSTONES
PORTUMNA
BIRR
DELGANY
GORT
PORTLAOISE
ATHY
WICKLOW
MOUNTRATH
ABBEYLEIX
BLAINROE
BALTINGLASS
LAHINCH
(2)
ROSCREA
WOODENBRIDGE
NENAGH
RATHDOWNEY
CARLOW
SPANISH POINT
ENNIS
ARKLOW
TEMPLEMORE
CASTLECOMER
SHILLELAGH
KILKEE
SHANNON
KILRUSH
LIMERICK (2)
KILKENNY
COURTOWN
THURLES
CALLAN
BORRIS
ADARE
ENNISCORTHY
BALLYBUNION
(2)
TIPPERARY
NEWCASTLE WEST
CAHIR
CARRICK · ON SUIR
CLONMEL
NEW ROSS
WEXFORD
CHARLEVILLE
ROSSLARE
TRALEE
MITCHELSTOWN
KANTURK
DONERAILE
WATERFORD
TRAMORE
BALLYFERRITER
LISMORE
MALLOW
FERMOY
KILLARNEY (2)
DUNGARVAN
GLENBEIGH
YOUGHAL
KENMARE
MACROOM
CORK (4)
MIDLETON
WATERVILLE
CARRIGROHANE
PARKNASILLA
MONKSTOWN
GLENGARRIFF
BANDON
KINSALE
BANTRY
CLONAKILTY
SKIBBEREEN
N
0 10 20 30 40 50 MILES
0 40 80 KILOMETRES

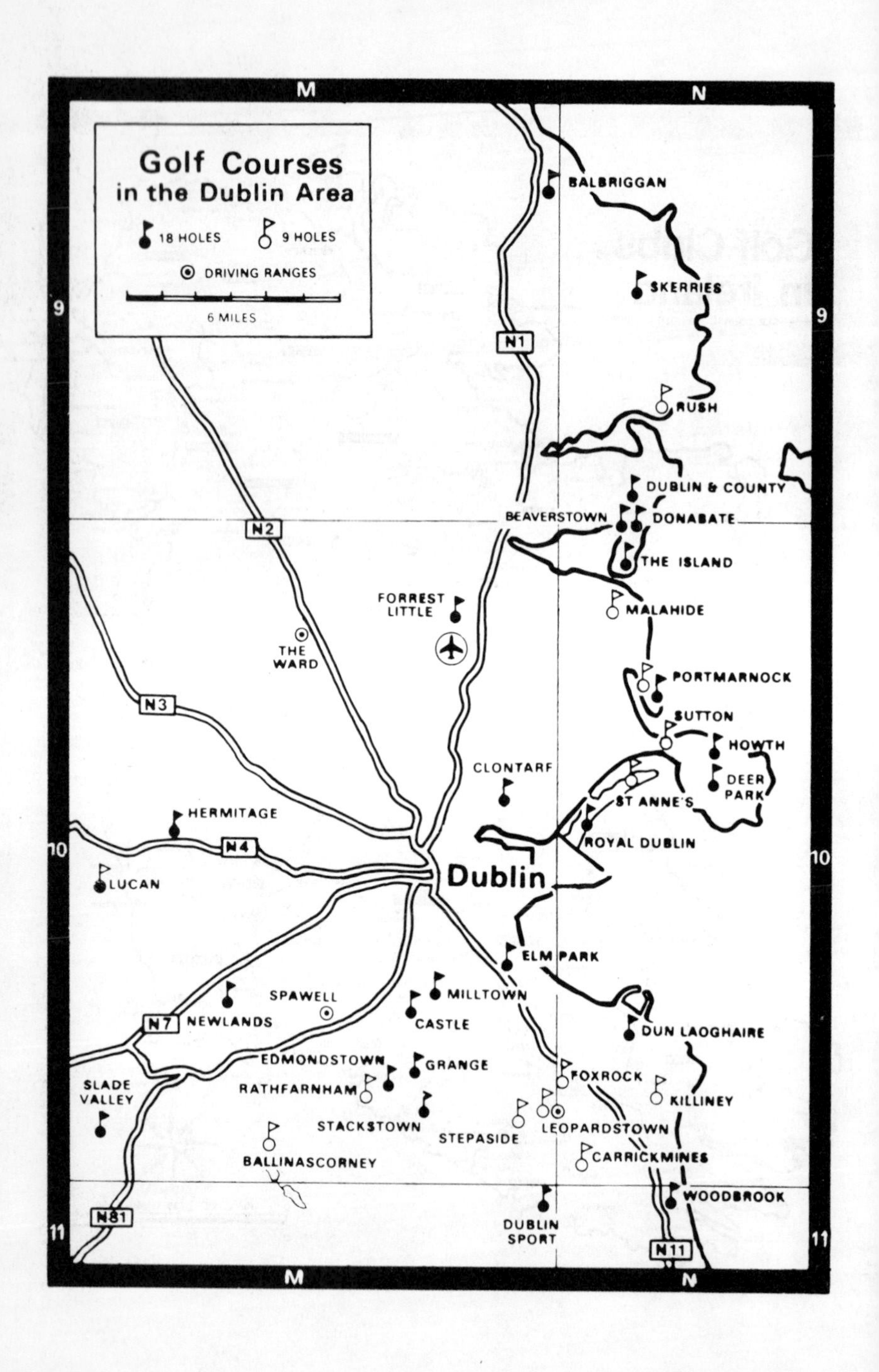
Golf Courses
in the Dublin Area
18 HOLES
9 HOLES
DRIVING RANGES
6 MILES
M
N
9
10
11
BALBRIGGAN
SKERRIES
RUSH
N1
N2
N3
N4
N7
N81
N11
DUBLIN & COUNTY
BEAVERSTOWN
DONABATE
THE ISLAND
MALAHIDE
FORREST LITTLE
THE WARD
PORTMARNOCK
SUTTON
HOWTH
DEER PARK
CLONTARF
ST ANNE'S
ROYAL DUBLIN
HERMITAGE
LUCAN
Dublin
ELM PARK
MILLTOWN
SPAWELL
NEWLANDS
CASTLE
DUN LAOGHAIRE
EDMONDSTOWN
GRANGE
FOXROCK
SLADE VALLEY
RATHFARNHAM
KILLINEY
STACKSTOWN
STEPASIDE
LEOPARDSTOWN
BALLINASCORNEY
CARRICKMINES
WOODBROOK
DUBLIN SPORT

ARDGLASS

TEL : (0396)841219
LOCATION : 8 m SE. Downpatrick
ADDRESS : Castle Place – Ardglass – County Down
HOTEL :
Portaferry Hotel – Portaferry
Tel : (02477)28231
Abbey Lodge – Downpatrick
Tel : (0396)4511
RESTAURANT : Lobsterpot – Strangford
Tel : (039686)288

Set in Northern Ireland within the Belfast area, this is a scenic seaside course laid out in lush unspoiled countryside along the Irish Sea. The short 11th hole commands excellent views of the surroundings. It features a pleasant looking mansion style clubhouse. *SSS 68*

 $

—  

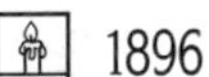 1896

— 

18

 5462 P 70 

Required : Introduction letter
Best days : Weekdays

HOLE	LENGTH MEDAL-TEE	PAR	STROKE INDEX
1	294	4	10
2	147	3	16
3	305	4	6
4	324	4	4
5	123	3	18
6	447	5	8
7	473	5	14
8	352	4	2
9	201	3	12
TOTAL	2666	35	TOTAL

HOLE	LENGTH MEDAL-TEE	PAR	STROKE INDEX
10	409	4	1
11	119	3	15
12	367	4	7
13	351	4	5
14	446	5	13
15	357	4	3
16	333	4	9
17	106	3	17
18	308	4	11
TOTAL	2796	35	TOTAL

ARKLOW

★

TEL : (0402)32401/39858
LOCATION : 1 km S. Arklow
ADDRESS : Abbeylands-Arklow – County Wicklow
HOTEL :
Arklow Bay-Arklow
Tel : (0402)32309
Tinakilly House – Rathnew
Tel : (0404)69274

A sporting and fine links featuring undulating fairways. It has been laid out with several water hazards such as streams meandering their way through the holes, and a lake guarding the 13th hole. *SSS 67*

GF $

1927

18

—

F. Hawtree, M. Taylor

L 5269 P 68

Required : Handicap Certificate
Best days : Weekdays

HOLE	LENGTH MEDAL-TEE	PAR	STROKE INDEX
1	370	4	
2	339	4	
3	153	3	
4	281	4	
5	391	4	
6	339	4	
7	113	3	
8	269	4	
9	145	3	
TOTAL	2400	33	TOTAL

HOLE	LENGTH MEDAL-TEE	PAR	STROKE INDEX
10	345	4	
11	157	3	
12	350	4	
13	175	3	
14	333	4	
15	252	4	
16	394	4	
17	402	4	
18	461	5	
TOTAL	2869	35	TOTAL

BALBRIGGAN

TEL : (01)412173
LOCATION : 0,5 km S Balbriggan off Dublin road
ADDRESS : Balbriggan – County Dublin
HOTEL :
Grand-Malahide
Tel : (01)450633
Boyne Valley - Drogheda
Tel : (041)37737

Extended to 18 holes in 1985, this gently rolling inland course is scenically situated overlooking the Cooley and Mourne mountains. There are several challenging holes, the most difficult one being the 15th, a par 4, ending in a dogleg with a water hazard in front of the green. *SSS 68*

GF $

1945

18

—

—

L 5708 P 71

R

Required : None
Best days : Weekdays except Tuesdays

HOLE	LENGTH MEDAL-TEE	PAR	STROKE INDEX
1	266	4	17
2	312	4	7
3	284	4	15
4	352	4	3
5	370	4	9
6	327	4	11
7	473	5	13
8	379	4	1
9	171	3	5
TOTAL	2934	36	TOTAL

HOLE	LENGTH MEDAL-TEE	PAR	STROKE INDEX
10	313	4	8
11	350	4	16
12	155	3	12
13	304	4	10
14	349	4	4
15	392	4	2
16	126	3	14
17	331	4	6
18	454	5	18
TOTAL	2774	35	TOTAL

BALLINASLOE

TEL : (0905)42126
LOCATION : 3 km Ballinasloe on Portumna road
ADDRESS : Rosgloss – Ballinasloe – County Galway
HOTEL :
Haydens – Ballinasloe
Tel : (0905)42347

Founded in 1911 and extended to 18 holes in 1984, this inland course has several tightly bunkered holes with water hazards. One of its most testing holes is the long par 5 fourth with a pronounced dog-leg. The course is very popular with holiday golfers. *SSS 68*

GF $

1911

18

—

—

L 6425 y P 72

R

Required : None
Best days : Any day

HOLE	LENGTH MEDAL-TEE	PAR	STROKE INDEX
1	325	4	16
2	428	4	2
3	182	3	11
4	495	5	4
5	122	3	17
6	360	4	13
7	402	4	1
8	387	4	3
9	169	3	12
TOTAL	2870	34	TOTAL

HOLE	LENGTH MEDAL-TEE	PAR	STROKE INDEX
10	362	4	6
11	177	3	15
12	166	3	8
13	366	4	7
14	344	4	10
15	273	4	18
16	388	4	5
17	188	3	14
18	488	5	9
TOTAL	2752	34	TOTAL

BALLYBUNION

TEL : (068)27146/27611
LOCATION : 1,6 km S. Ballybunion L 106
ADDRESS : Ballybunion – County Kerry
HOTEL :
Listowel Arms – Listowel
Tel : (068)21500/22524
Ambassador Golf - Ballybunion
Tel : (068)27111

The Ballybunion links rates among the best in the world. Laid out on the southern shore of the windy Shannon estuary, bordering the Atlantic and separated from the sea by huge sandhills. The Old Course was founded in 1896. The New Course was designed by the celebrated Robert Trent Jones. Both courses have spectacular holes with a unique design, each with its own distinctive character and challenge. The Old Course offers a formidable test with it long fairways and narrowly trapped greens. The New Course features three outstanding holes demanding accurate play : the 10th, 13th and 18th. *SSS 72/72*

GF $$ — — 

1896 — R. Trent Jones 

36 — L 6201 y P 71, 6116 y P 72 

Required : Handicap Certificate
Best days : Any day with booking in advance

Old Course

HOLE	LENGTH MEDAL-TEE	PAR	STROKE INDEX
1	366	4	9
2	394	4	1
3	211	3	11
4	490	5	15
5	489	5	13
6	344	4	7
7	400	4	5
8	134	3	17
9	430	4	3
TOTAL	3258	36	TOTAL

HOLE	LENGTH MEDAL-TEE	PAR	STROKE INDEX
10	336	4	10
11	400	4	2
12	179	3	16
13	480	5	8
14	125	3	18
15	207	3	4
16	482	5	14
17	368	4	12
18	366	4	6
TOTAL	2943	35	TOTAL

New Course

HOLE	LENGTH MEDAL-TEE	PAR	STROKE INDEX
1	413	4	5
2	377	4	7
3	142	3	17
4	341	4	11
5	425	4	1
6	140	3	15
7	316	4	9
8	600	5	3
9	486	5	13
TOTAL	3240	36	TOTAL

HOLE	LENGTH MEDAL-TEE	PAR	STROKE INDEX
10	317	4	12
11	133	3	18
12	251	4	14
13	370	4	4
14	351	4	10
15	476	5	2
16	133	3	16
17	476	5	8
18	369	4	6
TOTAL	2876	36	TOTAL

BALLYCASTLE

★★

TEL : (02657)62536
LOCATION : Between Portrush / Cushendall, on A 2
ADDRESS : Cushendall Rd – Ballycastle – County Antrim
HOTEL :
Bushmills Inn – Bushmills
Tel : (02657)32339
Thornlea – Cushendall
Tel : (02667)71223
RESTAURANT : Kimark – Ballycastle
Tel : (02657)63338

A fine seaside course, the first five holes being typical of an inland character with the Margy River running alongside the 1st and 2nd holes. The ruins of the former Franciscan Abbey are beside the 3rd and 4th holes. The middle part is of the 'links' type with the seashore alongside the 6th and 9th. The seven remaining holes are mountain holes with panoramic views over Rathlin Island, the Scottish coastline and the Mull of Kintyre. *SSS 69*

GF $

1891

18

—

—

L 5376 P 71

R S

Required : Handicap Certificate
Best days : Weekdays

HOLE	LENGTH MEDAL-TEE	PAR	STROKE INDEX
1	450	5	9
2	319	4	7
3	152	3	15
4	369	4	3
5	240	4	17
6	244	4	11
7	339	4	1
8	173	3	13
9	367	4	5
TOTAL	2653	35	TOTAL

HOLE	LENGTH MEDAL-TEE	PAR	STROKE INDEX
10	298	4	10
11	323	4	8
12	101	3	18
13	312	4	14
14	451	5	2
15	355	4	6
16	263	4	16
17	164	3	12
18	456	5	4
TOTAL	2723	36	TOTAL

BALLYLIFFIN

★

TEL : (077)74417/76119
LOCATION : 10 m N. Buncrana
ADDRESS : Ballyliffin – Lifford – County Donegal
HOTEL :
Strand – Ballyliffin
Tel : (077)76107

Located in County Donegal, this is a scenic links laid out alongside the Atlantic, amid sandy beaches, high sandhills and wind-sculptured sandstone. One of its feature holes is the 5th with a raised green demanding a great deal of accuracy. Golf is free to residents of the Strand Hotel. *SSS 71*

GF $

1947

18

—

E. Hackett

L 6042 P 71

R

Required : None
Best days : Weekdays

HOLE	LENGTH MEDAL-TEE	PAR	STROKE INDEX
1	371	4	
2	402	4	
3	393	4	
4	445	5	
5	176	3	
6	379	4	
7	352	4	
8	361	4	
9	100	3	
TOTAL	2979	35	TOTAL

HOLE	LENGTH MEDAL-TEE	PAR	STROKE INDEX
10	352	4	
11	374	4	
12	193	3	
13	456	5	
14	344	4	
15	366	4	
16	319	4	
17	151	3	
18	508	5	
TOTAL	3063	36	TOTAL

BALLYMENA

TEL : (0266)861487
LOCATION : 2 m Ballymena A 42
ADDRESS : Broughshane – Ballymena – County Antrim
HOTEL :
Adair Arms – Ballymena
Tel : (0266)653674
The Country House – Ballymena
Tel : (0266)891663
RESTAURANT : Leighinmohr House – Ballymena
Tel : (0266)652313

A heathland course north of Belfast with its fairways landscaped among mature trees. Most if its greens are defended by numerous sand and grass bunkers. Accuracy is essential due to the presence of several out of bounds. *SSS 67*

GF $

Saturdays

S

1903

—

R

18

L 5108 P 68

Required : None
Best days : Mondays, Thursdays, and Sundays

HOLE	LENGTH MEDAL-TEE	PAR	STROKE INDEX
1	323	4	9
2	167	3	13
3	449	5	3
4	128	3	15
5	228	4	11
6	351	4	1
7	100	3	17
8	340	4	7
9	439	5	5
TOTAL	2525	35	TOTAL

HOLE	LENGTH MEDAL-TEE	PAR	STROKE INDEX
10	172	3	18
11	404	4	2
12	375	4	6
13	268	4	12
14	197	3	16
15	357	4	4
16	192	3	14
17	323	4	8
18	295	4	10
TOTAL	2583	33	TOTAL

BEAVERSTOWN

TEL : (01)436439/436721
LOCATION : 24 km N Dublin
ADDRESS : Beaverstown – Donabate – County Dublin
HOTEL : Grand-Malahide
Tel : (01)450633
Marine – Sutton
Tel : (01)322613

One of the newest clubs in Ireland, located close to Dublin, and considered as a potentially magnificent course. It is an inland course winding through lush orchards and a wild fowl estuary having narrow fairways and fast greens. Water affects play on several holes. The Grand Hotel is situated by the sea and conveniant to Dublin airport. *SSS 72*

GF $ — Wednesdays — R

1985 — —

18 — L 5662 P 72

Required : Handicap Certificate
Best days : Mondays, Thursdays, Fridays

HOLE	LENGTH MEDAL-TEE	PAR	STROKE INDEX
1	293	4	
2	294	4	
3	161	3	
4	306	4	
5	418	4	
6	375	4	
7	125	3	
8	324	4	
9	452	5	
TOTAL	2748	35	TOTAL

HOLE	LENGTH MEDAL-TEE	PAR	STROKE INDEX
10	282	4	
11	165	3	
12	303	4	
13	308	4	
14	469	5	
15	445	5	
16	341	4	
17	132	3	
18	469	5	
TOTAL	2914	37	TOTAL

BEECH PARK

TEL : (01)580522
LOCATION : 3 km Rathcoole
ADDRESS : Johnston – Rathcoole – County Dublin
HOTEL : Baberstown Castle – Straffan – County Kildare
Tel : (01)6288157
Moygiare Manor - Maynootte
Tel : (01)6286351

Inaugurated in 1983, Beech Park is a new and sporting inland course laid out on undulating countryside with mature beech trees bordering the holes. There is a strategically placed lake crossing the 11th and 12th holes. Baberstown Castle, renowned for its cuisine and hospitality, is set in the rich pastures of Kildare, and embraces a charming blend of medieval Elizabethan and Edwardian features.

GF $

1983

18

Tuesdays, Weekends

—

L 5654 P 72

R

Required : Handicap Certificate
Best days : Mondays, Thursdays, Fridays

HOLE	LENGTH MEDAL-TEE	PAR	STROKE INDEX
1	334	4	
2	385	4	
3	382	4	
4	133	3	
5	351	4	
6	373	4	
7	513	5	
8	161	3	
9	489	5	
TOTAL	3121	36	TOTAL

HOLE	LENGTH MEDAL-TEE	PAR	STROKE INDEX
10	362	4	
11	307	4	
12	167	3	
13	515	5	
14	321	4	
15	142	3	
16	364	4	
17	479	5	
18	406	4	
TOTAL	3063	36	TOTAL

BELVOIR PARK

★

TEL : (0232)491693
LOCATION : 3 m E. Belfast
ADDRESS : Church Rd – Newtownbreda – Belfast – County Down
HOTEL :
Stormont Hotel – Belfast
Tel : (0232)658621
Wellington Park – Belfast
Tel : (0232)38111
Culloden – Belfast
Tel : (02317)5223
RESTAURANT : La Belle Epoque – Belfast
Tel : (0232)323244

Designed by Harry Colt in 1927 and set near the capital of Northern Ireland, this is a pleasant rather flat parkland course with several of its fairways bordered by mature trees. There is an attractive and well-appointed mansion style clubhouse overlooking the course.
SSS 70

GF $

1927

18

—

H. Colt

L 5738 P 70

S

RP

Required : Introduction letter
Best days : Mondays, Tuesdays and Thursdays

HOLE	LENGTH MEDAL-TEE	PAR	STROKE INDEX
1	260	4	18
2	355	4	6
3	382	4	2
4	174	3	8
5	439	5	14
6	347	4	10
7	390	4	3
8	128	3	16
9	435	5	12
TOTAL	2910	36	TOTAL

HOLE	LENGTH MEDAL-TEE	PAR	STROKE INDEX
10	425	4	5
11	156	3	15
12	395	4	1
13	338	4	9
14	153	3	13
15	435	5	11
16	175	3	7
17	388	4	4
18	363	4	17
TOTAL	2828	34	TOTAL

BLAINROE

TEL : (0404)68168
LOCATION : 4 km S. Wicklow Town
ADDRESS : Blainroe – County Wicklow
HOTEL :
Tinakilly House – Wicklow
Tel : (0404)69274
Old Rectory – Wicklow
Tel : (0404)67048
Hunters – Rathnew
Tel : (0404)40106

This pleasant seaside course has an inland character. It is bordered by the Irish Sea and rises 91 metres above sea level. There are wide and generous fairways. Among its feature holes is the 15th, which includes a strategic pond and a cunningly bunkered and elevated green. Hunters is one of Irelands oldest coaching inns set in award winning gardens. Tinakilly House and the Old Rectory pride in their antique furnishings. All three are well known for their excellent food. *SSS 72*

GF $
1978
18

—
F. Hawtree
L 6109 P 72

S
R

Required : Handicap Certificate
Best days : Weekdays

HOLE	LENGTH MEDAL-TEE	PAR	STROKE INDEX
1	330	4	15
2	394	4	2
3	384	4	5
4	480	5	13
5	445	5	9
6	332	4	3
7	338	4	11
8	193	3	7
09	335	4	14
TOTAL	3231	37	TOTAL

HOLE	LENGTH MEDAL-TEE	PAR	STROKE INDEX
10	344	4	6
11	356	4	12
12	390	4	4
13	363	4	10
14	243	4	17
15	208	3	8
16	417	4	1
17	112	3	18
18	445	5	16
TOTAL	2878	35	TOTAL

BUNDORAN

TEL : (072)41302
LOCATION : 1 m E. Bundoran
ADDRESS : Bundoran – County Donegal
HOTEL : HP
Great Northern
Tel : (072)41204
Sand House – Rossnowlagh
Tel : (072)51777

Designed in 1894 by the great golf champion Harry Vardon, this is an attractive links course laid out on undulating countryside. Some of the holes are well-bunkered and very tricky especially when the wind is blowing. An interesting and challenging links, ideal for holiday golf. The Great Northern Hotel, adjacent to the links, offers free golf to residents and special reductions for groups. *SSS 69*

GF $
1894
18

—
H. Vardon
L 5785 P 70

S
R

Required : Handicap Certificate
Best days : Weekdays

HOLE	LENGTH MEDAL-TEE	PAR	STROKE INDEX
1	327	4	14
2	459	5	11
3	117	3	18
4	331	4	6
5	197	3	12
6	366	4	2
7	325	4	8
8	356	4	4
9	356	4	10
TOTAL	2834	35	TOTAL

HOLE	LENGTH MEDAL-TEE	PAR	STROKE INDEX
10	364	4	1
11	384	4	5
12	316	4	9
13	212	3	13
14	366	4	7
15	390	4	3
16	142	3	17
17	453	5	16
18	324	4	15
TOTAL	2951	35	TOTAL

CAIRNDHU

★

TEL : (0574)83324
LOCATION : 4 m N. Larne A 2
ADDRESS : 192 Coast Rd – Ballygally – Larne – County Antrim
HOTEL :
Ballygally Castle – Ballygally
Tel : (0574)583212
Drumnagreagh – Ballygally
Tel : (0574)841651
Londonderry Arms – Carnlough
Tel : (0574)85255
RESTAURANT : Londonderry Arms – Carnlough
Tel : (0574)85255

A scenic seaside course with lots of variety, laid out on rugged terrain amid high sand dunes. The course commands fine views of the ocean and the rocky coastline. There is a pleasant white mansion style clubhouse. *SSS 69*

GF $

1928

18

Saturdays

—

L 6112 y P 70

Required : Handicap Certificate
Best days : Weekdays

HOLE	LENGTH MEDAL-TEE	PAR	STROKE INDEX
1	378	4	5
2	160	3	15
3	419	4	3
4	292	4	11
5	431	4	7
6	173	3	17
7	326	4	9
8	381	4	1
9	284	4	13
TOTAL	2844	34	TOTAL

HOLE	LENGTH MEDAL-TEE	PAR	STROKE INDEX
10	410	4	4
11	215	3	16
12	447	4	2
13	145	3	18
14	497	5	8
15	421	4	6
16	301	4	12
17	538	5	10
18	294	4	14
TOTAL	3268	36	TOTAL

CARLOW

TEL : (0503)31695
LOCATION : 3 km N. Carlow/80 km S. Dublin
ADDRESS : Deerpark - Carlow - County Carlow
HOTEL :
Seven Oaks - Carlow
Tel : (0503)31308
Royal - Carlow
Tel : (0503)31621

Designed by the celebrated golf architect Tom Simpson in the closing days of the last century, this is a very testing inland championship course. It features tree-lined fairways, a fair proportion of hills and a few strategically placed water hazards. *SSS 70*

GF $ — — S RP

1899 — T. Simpson

18 — L 5731 P 70

Required : None
Best days : Any day

HOLE	LENGTH MEDAL-TEE	PAR	STROKE INDEX
1	395	4	4
2	275	4	14
3	124	3	17
4	333	4	9
5	450	5	15
6	163	3	12
7	389	4	1
8	390	4	6
9	338	4	8
TOTAL	2857	35	TOTAL

HOLE	LENGTH MEDAL-TEE	PAR	STROKE INDEX
10	273	4	11
11	381	4	3
12	334	4	7
13	150	3	16
14	415	4	5
15	334	4	10
16	393	4	2
17	134	3	18
18	460	5	13
TOTAL	2874	35	TOTAL

CARNALEA

★

TEL : (0247)270368
LOCATION : 2 m W. Bangor
ADDRESS : Bangor – County Down
HOTEL :
Old Inn – Crawfordsburn
Tel : (0247)853255
Beresford House – Bangor
Tel : (0247)472143
Ardshane House - Hollywood
Tel : (02317)2044
Culloden – Holywood
Tel : (02317)5223
RESTAURANT : Bryansburn Inn
Tel : (0247)270173

Set in Northern Ireland on flat countryside, bordering the Belfast Lough, this is a pleasant seaside course ideal for holiday golf. It has many picturesque holes which include ten par four holes and two long par five holes. *SSS 67*

GF $

1927

18

Weekends

 J. Braid

L 5548 y P 68

 S

Required : None
Best days : Mondays, Wednesdays, Thursdays, Fridays

HOLE	LENGTH MEDAL-TEE	PAR	STROKE INDEX
1	265	4	17
2	346	4	3
3	341	4	15
4	293	4	11
5	236	3	7
6	508	5	9
7	406	4	5
8	409	4	1
9	141	3	13
TOTAL	2945	35	TOTAL

HOLE	LENGTH MEDAL-TEE	PAR	STROKE INDEX
10	223	3	2
11	157	3	14
12	328	4	12
13	176	3	18
14	276	4	16
15	182	3	8
16	491	5	10
17	336	4	6
18	434	4	4
TOTAL	2603	33	TOTAL

CASTLEROCK

TEL : (0265)848314
LOCATION : 10 km W. Coleraine A2
ADDRESS : Castlerock – County Derry
HOTEL :
Lodge Hotel – Coleraine
Tel : (0265)44848
Bohill Hotel and Country Club – Coleraine
Tel : (0265)44406
MacDuffs – Coleraine
Tel : (0265)868433
RESTAURANT : Macduff's – Coleraine
Tel : (0265868)433

A links of championship standard set in natural surroundings, bordering the Atlantic, the River Bann and a railway line. The fairways are wide and generous and most of the large greens feature strategically placed bunkers, demanding accurate play. *SSS 72*

GF $

1901

18

—

B. Sayers

L 6127 P 73

Required : Handicap Certificate
Best days : Weekdays

HOLE	LENGTH MEDAL-TEE	PAR	STROKE INDEX
1	319	4	
2	317	4	
3	471	5	
4	183	3	
5	439	5	
6	319	4	
7	373	4	
8	394	4	
9	184	3	
TOTAL	2999	36	TOTAL

HOLE	LENGTH MEDAL-TEE	PAR	STROKE INDEX
10	360	4	
11	463	5	
12	392	4	
13	344	4	
14	176	3	
15	482	5	
16	139	3	
17	447	5	
18	325	4	
TOTAL	3128	37	TOTAL

CITY OF DERRY

★

TEL : (0504)46369
LOCATION : 3 m Londonderry
ADDRESS : 47 Victoria Rd – Prehan – County Derry
HOTEL :
Glen House Hotel – Eglinton
Tel : (0504)810527
Everglades – Londonderry
Tel : (0504)46722
White Horse Inn – Londonderry
Tel : (0504)860606
RESTAURANT : Bells – Londonderry
Tel : (0504)41078

Located near the city of Londonderry, the course has a parkland character having undulating fairways. Streams serve as hazards in front of the greens of the 5th, the 6th and 7th holes. The club has hosted the British Midland Ladies Championship and the Irish Open. *SSS 71*

GF $

1912

27

—

—

L 6406 y P 71, 4280 P 66

S

R

Required : None
Best days : Any day

HOLE	LENGTH MEDAL-TEE	PAR	STROKE INDEX
1	222	3	11
2	381	4	5
3	540	5	7
4	441	4	2
5	370	4	6
6	338	4	14
7	488	5	9
8	165	3	17
9	379	4	10
TOTAL	3324	36	TOTAL

HOLE	LENGTH MEDAL-TEE	PAR	STROKE INDEX
10	362	4	15
11	507	5	8
12	175	3	13
13	412	4	4
14	435	4	1
15	142	3	18
16	299	4	16
17	401	4	3
18	349	4	12
TOTAL	3082	35	TOTAL

CLANDEBOYE

TEL : (0247)271767
LOCATION : 3 m S. Bangor
ADDRESS : Conlig – Newtownards – County Down
HOTEL :
Culloden Hotel – Bangor
Tel : (02317)5223
Royal – Bangor
Tel : (0247)471866
Old Inn – Crawfordsburn
Tel : (0247)853255
RESTAURANT : Old Inn – Crawfordsburn
Tel : (0247)853255

There are two 18 hole courses laid out on undulating parkland and heathland:the older Dufferin course of championship standard designed by William Robinson, and the Ava Course designed by Bernard von Limburger. Both are scenically situated overlooking the Irish Sea. The club was the venue for the Ladies Irish Open in 1984 and the 1987 All Ireland Cups and Shields Finals. *SSS 72/67*

 $

Saturdays

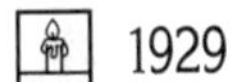 1929

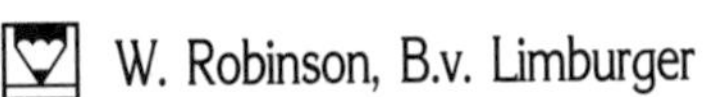 W. Robinson, B.v. Limburger

 36

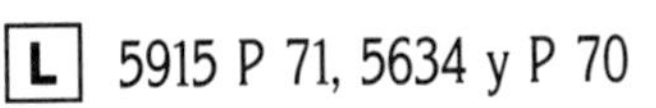 5915 P 71, 5634 y P 70

Required : Introduction letter
Best days : Weekdays

Dufferin Course

HOLE	LENGTH MEDAL-TEE	PAR	STROKE INDEX
1	346	4	9
2	163	3	17
3	376	4	7
4	347	4	3
5	168	3	13
6	463	5	15
7	327	4	11
8	405	4	1
9	363	4	5
TOTAL	2958	35	TOTAL

HOLE	LENGTH MEDAL-TEE	PAR	STROKE INDEX
10	370	4	4
11	139	3	18
12	451	5	10
13	320	4	8
14	148	3	16
15	446	5	12
16	357	4	2
17	336	4	14
18	390	4	6
TOTAL	2957	36	TOTAL

Ava Course

HOLE	LENGTH MEDAL-TEE	PAR	STROKE INDEX
1	340	4	9
2	504	5	1
3	166	3	7
4	318	4	5
5	312	4	17
6	180	3	15
7	305	4	3
8	541	5	13
9	303	4	11
TOTAL	2969	36	TOTAL

HOLE	LENGTH MEDAL-TEE	PAR	STROKE INDEX
10	156	3	12
11	426	4	2
12	171	3	10
13	476	5	14
14	346	4	4
15	127	3	18
16	313	4	6
17	319	4	16
18	331	4	8
TOTAL	2665	34	TOTAL

CLONMEL

★

TEL : (052)21138/24050
LOCATION : 3,5 km Clonmel
ADDRESS : Lyreanearla-Mountain Road-Clonmel-County Tipperary
HOTEL :
Knocklofty House
Tel : (052)38222
Clonmel Arms-Clonmel
Tel : (052)21233
Hearn's - Clonmel
Tel : (052)21611
Minella - Clonmel
Tel : (052)22388

Picturesquely and quietly set on the scenic slopes of the pine and fir covered Comeragh Mountains overlooking the famous plains of Tipperary, Clonmel is a very pleasant and hilly inland course with lots of open space. The course is of great variety and features a stream crossing three fairways. *SSS 69*

GF $ — S

1911 — E. Hackett

18 — L 5806 P 71 — R

Required : None
Best days : Weekdays

HOLE	LENGTH MEDAL-TEE	PAR	STROKE INDEX
1	343	4	8
2	368	4	4
3	135	3	18
4	455	5	12
5	341	4	10
6	344	4	6
7	309	4	16
8	361	4	2
9	172	3	14
TOTAL	2828	35	TOTAL

HOLE	LENGTH MEDAL-TEE	PAR	STROKE INDEX
10	366	4	7
11	456	5	9
12	261	4	17
13	385	4	1
14	148	3	15
15	360	4	5
16	377	4	3
17	172	3	13
18	453	5	11
TOTAL	2978	36	TOTAL

CLONTARF

TEL : (01)315085/311305
LOCATION : 4 km Dublin City Centre
ADDRESS : Malahide Road – Dublin 3 – Delete – County Dublin
HOTEL :
Marine – Sutton
Tel : (01)322613
Grey Door – Dublin
Tel : (01)763286
RESTAURANT : Patrick Guilbaud – Dublin
Tel : (01)764192

The Clontarf golfclub is the club nearest to Dublin city and therefore very popular. It is a parkland type course bordered on one side by a railway line. There are several testing and challenging holes like the 12th across a pond and a quarry. *SSS 68*

GF $$ | Weekends | S
1911 | — | 
18 | L 5459 P 69 | R

Required : None
Best days : Tuesdays to Fridays

HOLE	LENGTH MEDAL-TEE	PAR	STROKE INDEX
1	324	4	10
2	414	4	2
3	287	4	12
4	151	3	16
5	338	4	6
6	122	3	18
7	339	4	8
8	356	4	4
9	295	4	14
TOTAL	2626	34	TOTAL

HOLE	LENGTH MEDAL-TEE	PAR	STROKE INDEX
10	365	4	9
11	187	3	11
12	381	4	1
13	267	4	17
14	329	4	5
15	145	3	15
16	351	4	3
17	356	4	7
18	452	5	13
TOTAL	2833	35	TOTAL

CONNEMARA

TEL : (095)23502
LOCATION : 13 km S. Clifden
ADDRESS : Ballyconneely – Clifden – County Galway
HOTEL :
Rockclen Manor House – Clifden
Tel : (095)21035
Abbeyglen Castle – Clifden
Tel : (095)21201
RESTAURANT : Shades – Clifden
Tel : (095)21215

A scenic and testing championship links located in the famous Connemara region. The course is set in fine natural surroundings backed by the twelve Bens mountain range. There are long and well laid-out holes with numerous sandy bunkers, and raised greens. Water affects play on three holes. Holiday golf at its best. *SSS 73*

GF $$

1973

18

—

E. Hackett

L 6186 P 72

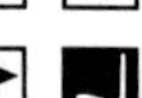

Required : Handicap Certificate
Best days : Mondays to Saturdays

HOLE	LENGTH MEDAL-TEE	PAR	STROKE INDEX
1	331	4	7
2	366	4	5
3	145	3	17
4	339	4	11
5	342	4	9
6	175	3	13
7	482	5	15
8	418	4	1
9	344	4	3
TOTAL	2942	35	TOTAL

HOLE	LENGTH MEDAL-TEE	PAR	STROKE INDEX
10	383	4	6
11	151	3	18
12	399	4	2
13	189	3	12
14	460	5	16
15	349	4	8
16	370	4	4
17	468	5	10
18	475	5	14
TOTAL	3244	37	TOTAL

CORK

TEL : (021)353451
LOCATION : 8 km E. Cork
ADDRESS : Little Island – County Cork
HOTEL :
Ashbourne House – Glounthaune
Tel : (021)353319
Rochestown Park – Cork
Tel : (021)892233
RESTAURANT : Arbutus Lodge – Cork
Tel : (021)501237

Picturesquely situated overlooking the charming Cork harbour, this is a memorable inland course of championship standard. At five holes one gets the impression of playing within a quarry due to the fact that about 100 years ago limestone was cut here where there are now fairways and greens. The club has hosted the Irish Mens' and Ladies' Championships at various times. *SSS 70*

GF $$ — Thursdays — R S
1888 — A. McKenzie
18 — L 5848 P 72

Required : Handicap Certificate
Best days : Weekdays

HOLE	LENGTH MEDAL-TEE	PAR	STROKE INDEX
1	335	4	5
2	442	5	13
3	244	4	17
4	402	4	1
5	442	5	9
6	272	4	15
7	158	3	7
8	374	4	3
9	170	3	11
TOTAL	2839	36	TOTAL

HOLE	LENGTH MEDAL-TEE	PAR	STROKE INDEX
10	358	4	2
11	450	5	14
12	286	4	12
13	149	3	18
14	380	4	8
15	366	4	4
16	315	4	16
17	335	4	10
18	370	4	6
TOTAL	3009	36	TOTAL

COUNTY CAVAN

TEL : (049)31283
LOCATION : 2 km W. Cavan to Killeshandra
ADDRESS : Arnmore House – Drumelis – Cavan – County Cavan
HOTEL :
Farnham Arms – Cavan
Tel : (049)32577
Kilmore – Cavan
Tel : (049)32288

A scenic parkland course and a very popular venue set in the undulating Drumlin Hills of Cavan with spectacular views to the mountains in the west. The course heavily planted with mature oak, beech and lime trees is a challenging test of golf in an idyllic surrounding. The clubhouse is located in the beautifully restored and extented Dower-House of the Farnham Estate of which the course once formed a part. *SSS 69*

GF $ — RP

1894 Gaffney & Cullivan 

18 L 5519 P 70

Required : None
Best days : Any day

HOLE	LENGTH MEDAL-TEE	PAR	STROKE INDEX
1	288	4	11
2	291	4	13
3	371	4	1
4	161	3	15
5	350	4	3
6	312	4	7
7	488	5	9
8	142	3	17
9	303	4	5
TOTAL	2706	35	TOTAL

HOLE	LENGTH MEDAL-TEE	PAR	STROKE INDEX
10	189	3	12
11	326	4	6
12	171	3	14
13	323	4	8
14	316	4	16
15	338	4	4
16	358	4	2
17	447	5	18
18	347	4	10
TOTAL	2813	35	TOTAL

COUNTY LOUTH (BALTRAY)

TEL : (041)22329
LOCATION : 6 km Drogheda
ADDRESS : Baltray – County Louth
HOTEL :
Conyngham Arms – Slane
Tel : (041)24155
Boyne Valley – Drogheda
Tel : (041)37737

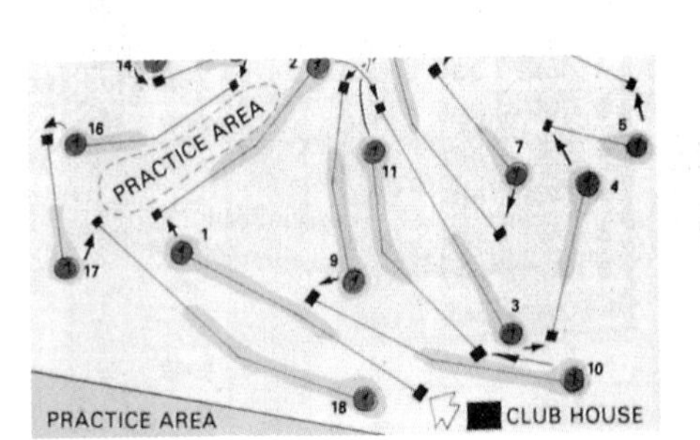

Very often named after the local village called 'Baltray', this is an excellent championship links with many interesting and testing holes. It is laid out bordering the Irish Sea with its holes running through sand dunes. Accomodation is available for eighteen golfers in the clubhouse. *SSS 72*

 $$

 1892

18

 Tuesdays

 T. Simpson

L 6693 y P 74

Required : Handicap Certificate
Best days : Weekdays except Tuesdays

HOLE	LENGTH MEDAL-TEE	PAR	STROKE INDEX
1	412	4	3
2	476	5	17
3	539	5	9
4	334	4	15
5	165	3	13
6	521	5	7
7	165	3	5
8	396	4	11
9	409	4	1
TOTAL	3417	37	TOTAL

HOLE	LENGTH MEDAL-TEE	PAR	STROKE INDEX
10	381	4	4
11	498	5	16
12	418	4	2
13	419	4	6
14	339	4	12
15	157	3	18
16	392	4	8
17	187	3	10
18	495	5	14
TOTAL	3286	36	TOTAL

COUNTY SLIGO

★★★

TEL : (071)77186/77134
LOCATION : 8 km Sligo
ADDRESS : Rosses Point – County Sligo
HOTEL :
Markree Castle – Collooney
Tel : (071)67800
Ballincar House – Rosses Point
Tel : (071)45361

One of Ireland's famous natural sandy links with scenic views of the the mountains, the Atlantic and the undulating Sligo area. Popularly know as Rosses Point, it is set high upon the cliffs with a panoramic view from the 5th tee of about 12 holes. One of the main obstacles is the constantly blowing wind. *SSS 71*

GF $$

1894

18

Tuesdays

H. Colt, J. Allison

L 6003 P 71

S

R

Required : Handicap Certificate
Best days : Weekdays except Tuesdays

HOLE	LENGTH MEDAL-TEE	PAR	STROKE INDEX
1	381	4	4
2	353	4	4
3	497	5	5
4	165	3	3
5	482	5	5
6	411	4	4
7	425	4	4
8	410	4	4
9	170	3	3
TOTAL	3294	36	TOTAL

HOLE	LENGTH MEDAL-TEE	PAR	STROKE INDEX
10	382	4	4
11	402	4	4
12	495	5	5
13	174	3	3
14	440	4	4
15	408	4	4
16	215	3	3
17	457	4	4
18	361	4	4
TOTAL	3334	35	TOTAL

COURTOWN

TEL : (055)21533
LOCATION : 6 km Gorey, 1 km N. Courtown
ADDRESS : Kiltennel – Gorey – County Wexford
HOTEL :
Marfield House – Gorey
Tel : (055)21124
Clohamon House – Bunclody
Tel : (054)77253

This inland course popular with visitors, is set near the sea and is planted with a great variety of trees and shrubs bordering the fairways. Most of the greens are well-defended with strategically placed bunkers. The four par 3s present a sporting challenge. There is a large water hazard guarding the 18th hole. *SSS 70*

GF $ — Tuesdays — S

1937 — J. Harris

18 — L 5852 y P 71 — R

Required : None
Best days : Weekdays

HOLE	LENGTH MEDAL-TEE	PAR	STROKE INDEX
1	288	4	18
2	393	4	4
3	155	3	14
4	302	4	10
5	311	4	8
6	294	4	12
7	389	4	2
8	166	3	16
9	516	5	6
TOTAL	2814	35	TOTAL

HOLE	LENGTH MEDAL-TEE	PAR	STROKE INDEX
10	439	5	17
11	389	4	1
12	512	5	11
13	347	4	9
14	183	3	7
15	352	4	5
16	294	4	13
17	370	4	3
18	152	3	15
TOTAL	3038	36	TOTAL

DEERPARK

✡★

TEL : (01)322624/323489
LOCATION : 12.8 km N. Dublin
ADDRESS : Howth – County Dublin
HOTEL : HR
The Grey Door – Dublin
Tel : (01)763286
Howth Lodge – Howth
Tel : (01)390288

Deerpark is the largest public golf complex in Ireland with an 18 hole, a 9 hole, a 12 hole plus an 18 hole pitch & putt golf course, administered by the Deerpark Hotel and very popular among overseas golfers. The courses of inland character are scenically situated overlooking Dublin Bay. *SSS 69*

GF $

1965

39

—

—

L 6078 P 72, 2838 P 35

R

Required : None
Best days : Any day

HOLE	LENGTH MEDAL-TEE	PAR	STROKE INDEX
1	382	4	5
2	197	3	9
3	306	4	11
4	335	4	15
5	375	4	3
6	509	5	1
7	153	3	17
8	312	4	7
9	453	5	14
TOTAL	3022	36	TOTAL

HOLE	LENGTH MEDAL-TEE	PAR	STROKE INDEX
10	184	3	13
11	513	5	6
12	343	4	16
13	339	4	8
14	338	4	12
15	366	4	2
16	141	3	18
17	325	4	10
18	507	5	4
TOTAL	3056	36	TOTAL

DONABATE

TEL : (01)436346/436059
LOCATION : 16 m N. Dublin
ADDRESS : Balcarrick – Donabate – County Dublin
HOTEL :
Grand-Malahide
Tel : (01)450633
Marine – Sutton
Tel : (01)322613

Donabate is a typical inland course set on mostly flat countryside not far from the Irish capital. The average golfer won't find this course too much of a test. Among its most interesting and testing holes figure the 17th and 18th. There is a modern well-equipped clubhouse. *SSS 67*

GF $ — Weekends — S
1938 — — — R
18 — L 4882 P 69

Required : Handicap Certificate
Best days : Weekdays except Wednesdays

HOLE	LENGTH MEDAL-TEE	PAR	STROKE INDEX
1	127	3	14
2	389	4	8
3	369	4	10
4	380	4	4
5	300	4	1
6	275	4	12
7	250	4	6
8	262	4	16
9	117	3	18
TOTAL	2469	34	TOTAL

HOLE	LENGTH MEDAL-TEE	PAR	STROKE INDEX
10	305	4	2
11	161	3	9
12	265	4	13
13	276	4	7
14	269	4	11
15	137	3	15
16	272	4	5
17	326	4	17
18	402	5	3
TOTAL	2413	35	TOTAL

DONAGHADEE

✡

TEL : (0247)883624
LOCATION : 6 m E. Bangor/1 m W. Donaghadee
ADDRESS : Warren Rd – Donaghadee – County Down
HOTEL :
Old Inn – Crawfordsburn
Tel : (0247)853255
Beresford House – Bangor
Tel : (0247)472143
The Sands – Bangor
Tel : (0247)473696
RESTAURANT : Redpepper – Groomsport
Tel : (0266)270097

Set in an attractive holiday area, this is a pleasant gently rolling seaside course bordering the Irish Sea with many excellent greens. The 2nd, 3rd and 12th holes feature a burn across the fairways. The clubhouse is comfortable and overlooks the course, the Copeland Islands and the Irish Sea. *SSS 71*

GF $

1894

18

Saturdays

—

L 5576 P 71

S

R

Required : None
Best days : Weekdays

HOLE	LENGTH MEDAL-TEE	PAR	STROKE INDEX
1	271	4	16
2	435	5	10
3	374	4	4
4	362	4	14
5	332	4	2
6	334	4	6
7	295	4	12
8	296	4	8
9	117	3	18
TOTAL	2816	36	TOTAL

HOLE	LENGTH MEDAL-TEE	PAR	STROKE INDEX
10	370	4	1
11	319	4	5
12	441	5	15
13	145	3	9
14	362	4	3
15	309	4	11
16	304	4	17
17	170	3	7
18	340	4	3
TOTAL	2760	35	TOTAL

DONEGAL TOWN

TEL : (073)34054
LOCATION : 11 km SW. Donegal
ADDRESS : Murvagh-Ballintra – County Donegal
HOTEL :
St. Ernan's House Hotel – near Donegal Town
Tel : (073)21065
Sand House – Rossnewlagh
Tel : (072)51777

An attractive seaside course with a varied and sporting layout. Among its feature holes is the 5th with 'islands' of fairway, and the 18th hole with a blind tee shot over a ridge. Another hazard is a pond near the tee of the 4th hole. The Ernan Park Hotel offers a homely atmosphere, good food, and is ideal for a relaxing and peaceful holiday. *SSS 72*

GF $ — RP

1962 E. Hackett

18 L 6243 P 73

Required : None
Best days : Weekdays and weekends by arrangement

HOLE	LENGTH MEDAL-TEE	PAR	STROKE INDEX
1	478	5	9
2	379	4	1
3	173	3	15
4	380	4	3
5	170	3	13
6	473	5	11
7	352	4	7
8	499	5	5
9	306	4	17
TOTAL	3210	37	TOTAL

HOLE	LENGTH MEDAL-TEE	PAR	STROKE INDEX
10	320	4	14
11	340	4	8
12	503	5	6
13	145	3	18
14	379	5	4
15	370	4	2
16	209	3	12
17	323	4	16
18	344	4	10
TOTAL	2933	36	TOTAL

DOOKS

✡ ★

TEL : (066)68205
LOCATION : 6 km Killorglin
ADDRESS : Glenbeigh – County Kerry
HOTEL :
Ard-na-Sidhe – Caragh Lake
Tel : (066)69105
Towers – Glenbeigh
Tel : (066)68212

One of the oldest Irish courses, having been founded in 1889, Dooks is a fine and testing links course set between the Kerry mountains and the sea, overlooking Dingle Bay. Many of the holes have raised greens. Ideal for holiday golf, it is also a nature reserve for the protected natterjack toad. Ard-na-Sidhe, a Victorian style mansion, is beautifully situated on the edge of Caragh Lake. Special green fees for residents on Kerry's famous golf courses.
SSS 68

GF $ — —
1889 —
18 — L 5873 y P 70

Required : Handicap Certificate
Best days : Mondays to Fridays

HOLE	LENGTH MEDAL-TEE	PAR	STROKE INDEX
1	366	4	2
2	121	3	18
3	273	4	15
4	311	4	5
5	166	3	10
6	362	4	3
7	435	5	14
8	335	4	7
9	168	3	12
TOTAL	2537	34	TOTAL

HOLE	LENGTH MEDAL-TEE	PAR	STROKE INDEX
10	330	4	1
11	476	5	8
12	325	4	6
13	133	3	17
14	341	4	11
15	187	3	4
16	315	4	13
17	283	4	16
18	456	5	9
TOTAL	2846	36	TOTAL

DOUGLAS

TEL : (021)891086/895297
LOCATION : 3 m SE. Cork
ADDRESS : Douglas – County Cork
HOTEL :
Rochestown Park Hotel – Rochestown
Tel : (021)892233
Blue Haven – Kinsale
Tel : (021)772209
RESTAURANT : Lovett's – Cork
Tel : (021)294909

A challenging inland course, varied in character, with a stream bordering the fairway of the 8th and a lateral water hazard between the 14th and 16th holes. There is a fine putting green located under palm trees. The Blue Haven Hotel, situated in the picturesque fishing port of Kinsale, is small and cosy and boasts an award winning restaurant. *SSS 69*

GF $

1909

18

—

—

L 5664 P 70

R S

Required : Handicap Certificate
Best days : Weekdays except Tuesdays

HOLE	LENGTH MEDAL-TEE	PAR	STROKE INDEX
1	243	4	18
2	341	4	6
3	409	4	2
4	140	3	16
5	393	4	4
6	346	4	8
7	170	3	10
8	443	5	14
9	297	4	12
TOTAL	2782	35	TOTAL

HOLE	LENGTH MEDAL-TEE	PAR	STROKE INDEX
10	307	4	15
11	351	4	9
12	364	4	5
13	341	4	11
14	382	4	1
15	140	3	13
16	370	4	3
17	242	4	17
18	385	4	7
TOTAL	2882	35	TOTAL

DUNDALK

★

TEL : (042)21731
LOCATION : 3 km S. Dundalk
ADDRESS : Blackrock – County Louth
HOTEL :
Ballymascanlon House
Tel : (042)71124

This scenic inland course of championship standard is set on the shores of Dundalk Bay with the famous Cooley and Mourne mountains in the background. The golf club organizes several popular open weeks at the end of May and July. *SSS 70*

GF $

 1910

18

Tuesdays and Sundays

T. Shannon

L 6067 P 72

Required : None
Best days : Weekdays except Tuesdays

HOLE	LENGTH MEDAL-TEE	PAR	STROKE INDEX
1	358	4	7
2	359	4	9
3	368	4	3
4	406	4	1
5	159	3	11
6	455	5	17
7	487	5	5
8	306	4	15
9	161	3	13
TOTAL	3059	36	TOTAL

HOLE	LENGTH MEDAL-TEE	PAR	STROKE INDEX
10	454	5	16
11	391	4	2
12	464	5	8
13	162	3	12
14	294	4	18
15	359	4	6
16	392	4	4
17	172	3	14
18	320	4	10
TOTAL	3008	36	TOTAL

DUNFANAGHY

TEL : (074)36335
LOCATION : 3 km E. Dunfanaghy
ADDRESS : Dunfanaghy - County Donegal
HOTEL :
Port-na Blagh
Tel : (074)36129
Arnold's - Dunfanaghy
Tel : (074)36208
Shandon - Dunfanaghy
Tel : (074)36137

A short seaside course with various holes laid out near the beach, set near the small town of Dunfanaghy. It is ideal for holiday golf with free golf concessions for golfers staying in most of the local hotels. The golf club organizes an open week during the first week of August. *SSS 65*

GF $ — —  

1903 — 

18 L 4977 y P 68

Required : None
Best days : Any day except Sundays

HOLE	LENGTH MEDAL-TEE	PAR	STROKE INDEX
1	303	4	13
2	143	3	14
3	351	4	1
4	336	4	4
5	304	4	10
6	316	4	8
7	210	3	7
8	277	4	11
9	120	3	18
TOTAL	2360	33	TOTAL

HOLE	LENGTH MEDAL-TEE	PAR	STROKE INDEX
10	263	4	15
11	280	4	12
12	332	4	2
13	141	3	17
14	322	4	5
15	346	4	3
16	466	5	6
17	143	3	16
18	324	4	9
TOTAL	2617	35	TOTAL

DUN LAOGHAIRE

TEL : (01)803916
LOCATION : 11 km SE. Dublin City Centre
ADDRESS : Eglinton Park – Dun Laoghaire – County Dublin
HOTEL :
Royal Marine – Dun Laoghaire
Tel : (01)801911
The Grey Door – Dublin
Tel : (01)763286
RESTAURANT : Na Mara – Dun Laoghaire
Tel : (01)806767

An inland course set on gently rolling open parkland featuring a stream in front of the green of the tricky 7th hole. The most difficult hole is the 14th with a long dogleg to the green, requiring accurate placing of the tee shot. *SSS 68*

GF $$

1909

18

Thursdays, Saturdays

—

L 5463 P 70

S

R

Required : Handicap Certificate
Best days : Mondays, Tuesdays, Wednesdays and Fridays

HOLE	LENGTH MEDAL-TEE	PAR	STROKE INDEX
1	306	4	11
2	333	4	5
3	148	3	8
4	240	4	18
5	392	4	1
6	281	4	15
7	95	3	14
8	368	4	3
9	345	4	10
TOTAL	2508	34	TOTAL

HOLE	LENGTH MEDAL-TEE	PAR	STROKE INDEX
10	183	3	9
11	344	4	6
12	438	5	17
13	148	3	7
14	371	4	2
15	343	4	12
16	336	4	4
17	313	4	13
18	479	5	16
TOTAL	2955	36	TOTAL

EDMONDSTOWN

★

TEL : (01)931082/932461
LOCATION : 11 km Dublin
ADDRESS : Rathfarnham – Dublin 16 – County Dublin
HOTEL :
Shelbourne – Dublin
Tel : (01)766471
Fitzpatricks Killiney Castle – Killiney
Tel : (01)851533
RESTAURANT : Beaufield News – Stillorgan
Tel : (01)880375

A testing inland course, set on rolling countryside, which presents a number of obstacles such as a stream meandering its way through the 4th and 6th holes, many strategic trees on the fairways and well-placed rough. *SSS 69*

GF $

1944

18

—

—

L 5663 P 70

S

R

Required : Handicap Certificate
Best days : Mondays, Thursdays, Fridays

HOLE	LENGTH MEDAL-TEE	PAR	STROKE INDEX
1	295	4	16
2	339	4	8
3	130	3	18
4	507	5	6
5	391	4	2
6	368	4	4
7	462	5	14
8	181	3	12
9	344	4	10
TOTAL	2987	36	TOTAL

HOLE	LENGTH MEDAL-TEE	PAR	STROKE INDEX
10	375	4	1
11	268	4	17
12	143	3	15
13	367	4	5
14	321	4	7
15	319	4	11
16	139	3	13
17	326	4	9
18	418	4	3
TOTAL	2676	34	TOTAL

ENNISCRONE

★

TEL : (096)36297/36335
LOCATION : 1 km W. Enniscrone
ADDRESS : Enniscrone – County Sligo
HOTEL :
Mount Falcon – Ballina
Tel : (096)21172
Downhill – Ballina
Tel : (096)21033

A fine links course, ideal for holiday golf, set on the shores of Killala Bay with scenic views of the surroundings. There are several testing dogleg holes. Most of the greens are elevated and well-bunkered. The golf club organizes a popular open week during August. The Mount Falcon Hotel, set in wooded parklands, has private salmon fishing on the River Moy. *SSS 71*

GF $

1930

18

—

E. Hackett

L 6544 P 72

Required : None
Best days : Weekdays; Weekends by arrangement

HOLE	LENGTH MEDAL-TEE	PAR	STROKE INDEX
1	551	5	7
2	530	5	11
3	395	4	1
4	524	5	9
5	170	3	17
6	356	4	13
7	367	4	5
8	170	3	15
9	345	4	3
TOTAL	3408	37	TOTAL

HOLE	LENGTH MEDAL-TEE	PAR	STROKE INDEX
10	338	4	16
11	386	4	4
12	510	5	12
13	202	3	10
14	368	4	14
15	412	4	6
16	373	4	2
17	147	3	18
18	400	4	8
TOTAL	3136	35	TOTAL

FORREST LITTLE

TEL : (01)401763/401183
LOCATION : at Airport Dublin/6 m N. Dublin City Centre
ADDRESS : Cloghran – County Dublin
HOTEL :
Dublin International – Dublin Airport
Tel : (01)379211
Westbury – Dublin
Tel : (01)6791122
RESTAURANT Le Coq Hardi – Dublin
Tel : (01)684130

Located near Dublin Airport, the course is a gently undulating parkland course with mature trees, and a total of fifty-five well-placed bunkers. There is a stream cutting the course in two while crossing at the same time six fairways. *SSS 69*

GF $ — Weekends — S

1972 — F. Hawtree

18 — L 5560 P 69 — R

Required : None
Best days : Weekdays

HOLE	LENGTH MEDAL-TEE	PAR	STROKE INDEX
1	278	4	7
2	353	4	5
3	342	4	11
4	374	4	1
5	156	3	9
6	446	5	15
7	126	3	17
8	386	4	3
9	338	4	13
TOTAL	2799	35	TOTAL

HOLE	LENGTH MEDAL-TEE	PAR	STROKE INDEX
10	334	4	12
11	143	3	8
12	309	4	4
13	335	4	16
14	170	3	10
15	432	5	18
16	332	4	6
17	304	4	14
18	402	4	2
TOTAL	2761	35	TOTAL

GALWAY

★★

TEL : (091)23038/22169
LOCATION : 3 km W. Galway
ADDRESS : Blackrock – County Galway
HOTEL :
Ardilaun House – Galway
Tel : (091)21433
Connemara Coast – Furbo
Tel : (091)92108
RESTAURANT : Paddy Burke's – Clarinbridge
Tel : (091)96226

Laid out on rugged terrain in the popular seaside resort of Salthill, the course is a fine natural links of championship standard with many testing holes, overlooking the famous Galway Bay. It runs through rugged countryside which is rarely free of wind. *SSS 70*

GF $$

1904

18

—

—

L 5828 P 70

S

Required : Handicap Certificate
Best days : Weekdays except Tuesdays

HOLE	LENGTH MEDAL-TEE	PAR	STROKE INDEX
1	347	4	5
2	361	4	7
3	338	4	11
4	154	3	17
5	396	4	1
6	380	4	3
7	463	5	13
8	317	4	15
9	184	3	9
TOTAL	2940	35	TOTAL

HOLE	LENGTH MEDAL-TEE	PAR	STROKE INDEX
10	398	4	2
11	175	3	12
12	456	5	16
13	119	3	18
14	354	4	6
15	353	4	8
16	380	4	4
17	307	4	14
18	346	4	10
TOTAL	2888	35	TOTAL

GRANGE

TEL : (01)932889
LOCATION : 10 km Dublin
ADDRESS : Rathfarnham – Dublin 16 – County Dublin
HOTEL :
Fitzpatrick's Killiney Castle – Killiney
Tel : (01)851533
Kilternan – Dublin
Tel : (01)955559/893631
RESTAURANT : The Guinea Pig-Dalkey
Tel : (01)859055

A very pleasant inland course picturesquely laid out in the foothills of the Dublin mountains. Many of the holes call for great accuracy, due to the presence of strategically placed trees. Two of the most tricky holes on this course are the 4th and 18th. *SSS 68*

GF $

1911

18

—

—

L 5517 y P 68

S

R

Required : None
Best days : Ring for suitable times

HOLE	LENGTH MEDAL-TEE	PAR	STROKE INDEX
1	203	3	7
2	122	3	17
3	389	4	1
4	383	4	5
5	306	4	13
6	170	3	15
7	388	4	3
8	193	3	9
9	319	4	11
TOTAL	2473	32	TOTAL

HOLE	LENGTH MEDAL-TEE	PAR	STROKE INDEX
10	390	4	2
11	182	3	8
12	292	4	16
13	329	4	10
14	487	5	14
15	150	3	18
16	385	4	4
17	467	5	12
18	362	4	6
TOTAL	3044	36	TOTAL

GREYSTONES

TEL : (01)874136/876624
LOCATION : 32 km S. Dublin/1 km S. Greystones
ADDRESS : Greystones – County Wicklow
HOTEL :
La Touche Hotel – Greystones
Tel : (01)874401/02
RESTAURANT : Schooners – Greystones
Tel : (01)874807

A fine inland course with a varied layout. The first nine holes are flat, the second nine run through undulating land. From the 17th and 18th tee on a clear day, one can see the Welsh Mountains and the Irish Sea. There is a welcoming old-style clubhouse built of Canadian redwood. *SSS 67*

GF $ — — S
1895 — R
18 L 5296 P 69

Required : None
Best days : Mondays and Fridays

HOLE	LENGTH MEDAL-TEE	PAR	STROKE INDEX
1	263	4	
2	446	5	
3	393	4	
4	151	3	
5	360	4	
6	315	4	
7	128	3	
8	437	5	
9	125	3	
TOTAL	2618	35	TOTAL

HOLE	LENGTH MEDAL-TEE	PAR	STROKE INDEX
10	364	4	
11	327	4	
12	177	3	
13	286	4	
14	375	4	
15	329	4	
16	202	3	
17	284	4	
18	334	4	
TOTAL	2678	34	TOTAL

HEADFORT

★

TEL : (046)40146/40857
LOCATION : 1 km Kells T 35/64 km Dublin
ADDRESS : Kells – County Meath
HOTEL :
Headford Arms – Kells
Tel : (046)40063
Park – Virginia
Tel : (049)47235

This fine inland course with well-wooded fairways, has many testing and interesting holes featuring several treacherous doglegs such as the 1st, 5th, 7th, 13th and 15th holes. The golf club has hosted the Irish Club Team Championship finals. The Park Hotel, in a idyllic setting on the shores of Lough Ramor, overlooks the local nine hole golf course. The restaurant is excellent. There are mews cottages to rent in the enclosed courtyard. *SSS 69*

GF $ — Weekends — R S

1928 — –

18 — L 5914 P 72

Required : None
Best days : Weekdays except Tuesdays

HOLE	LENGTH MEDAL-TEE	PAR	STROKE INDEX
1	438	5	13
2	173	3	15
3	356	4	4
4	446	5	9
5	394	4	1
6	381	4	3
7	436	5	18
8	144	3	14
9	318	4	7
TOTAL	3084	37	TOTAL

HOLE	LENGTH MEDAL-TEE	PAR	STROKE INDEX
10	171	3	16
11	491	5	12
12	340	4	5
13	351	4	8
14	171	3	11
15	271	4	17
16	372	4	2
17	326	4	10
18	337	4	6
TOTAL	2830	35	TOTAL

HEATH

TEL : (0502)46533
LOCATION : 5 km E. Portlaoise/100 km SW. Dublin
ADDRESS : Portlaoise – County Laoise
HOTEL :
Killeshin – Portlaoise
Tel : (0502)21663
Montague – Portlaoise
Tel : (0502)26154

The seventh oldest club in Ireland, this magnificent inland course is playable all year round and is exceptionally dry in wintertime. Set in beautiful rather flat surroundings with scenic views of the rolling hills of Laois, the course incorporates three natural lakes. Noted for its roughs of heather and gorse furze, the course is a challenge to any golfer. A fully illuminated driving range provides an excellent practice area. *SSS 69*

GF $

1899

18

—

—

L 5507 P 71

S

R

Required : None
Best days : Weekdays

HOLE	LENGTH MEDAL-TEE	PAR	STROKE INDEX
1	447	5	16
2	159	3	12
3	332	4	4
4	437	5	10
5	274	4	14
6	322	4	6
7	335	4	8
8	324	4	2
9	148	3	18
TOTAL	2778	36	TOTAL

HOLE	LENGTH MEDAL-TEE	PAR	STROKE INDEX
10	296	4	7
11	127	3	17
12	327	4	11
13	378	4	1
14	346	4	9
15	337	4	3
16	449	5	15
17	141	3	13
18	328	4	5
TOTAL	2729	35	TOTAL

HERMITAGE

★

TEL : (01)268491/264781
LOCATION : 12 km W. Dublin, 3 km Lucan
ADDRESS : Lucan - County Dublin
HOTEL :
Moyglare Manor - Maynooth
Tel : (01)286351
Finnstown Country House - Lucan
Tel : (01)280644

A very picturesque parkland course, set on undulating countryside alongside the river Liffey, with tree-lined fairways always in excellent condition. Its 10th hole is one of Ireland's most photographed holes:the tee shot starts from a high tee, and is played to the green below, which is bordered by the Liffey. Moyglare Manor is a Georgian country house with antique furnishings, set in lush parklands. *SSS 70*

GF $$ — — S

1905 — R

18 L 5561 P 71

Required : Handicap Certificate
Best days : Mondays, Thursdays and Fridays

HOLE	LENGTH MEDAL-TEE	PAR	STROKE INDEX
1	340	4	
2	295	4	
3	358	4	
4	320	4	
5	290	4	
6	125	3	
7	357	4	
8	353	4	
9	425	5	
TOTAL	2863	36	TOTAL

HOLE	LENGTH MEDAL-TEE	PAR	STROKE INDEX
10	193	3	
11	400	5	
12	450	4	
13	254	4	
14	461	5	
15	172	3	
16	294	4	
17	153	3	
18	321	4	
TOTAL	2698	35	TOTAL

HOWTH

★★

TEL : (01)323055
LOCATION : 9 m N.E. Dublin, 1 m Sutton
ADDRESS : Carrickbrack Rd – Sutton – Dublin 13 – County Dublin
HOTEL :
Howth Lodge – Howth
Tel : (01)390288
The Grey Door – Dublin
Tel : (01)763286
Marine-Sutton
Tel : (01)322613
RESTAURANT : King Sitric – Howth
Tel : (01)325235

Situated on the south side of the Hills of Howth, this undulating inland course has an interesting and testing layout and is an excellent example of golf course architecture. Its fairways run downhill, uphill and along the side of the hills, calling for great accuracy from tee to green. There is a fine clubhouse overlooking about seven golf courses in the Dublin region. *SSS 69*

GF $$ | Weekends | S
1916 | — | R
18 | L 5607 P 71

Required : None
Best days : Mondays, Tuesdays and Fridays

HOLE	LENGTH MEDAL-TEE	PAR	STROKE INDEX
1	306	4	10
2	321	4	4
3	408	4	1
4	155	3	12
5	355	4	6
6	269	4	14
7	486	5	8
8	134	3	18
9	252	4	16
TOTAL	2686	35	TOTAL

HOLE	LENGTH MEDAL-TEE	PAR	STROKE INDEX
10	309	4	5
11	314	4	3
12	463	5	15
13	397	4	2
14	326	4	7
15	137	3	17
16	296	4	9
17	349	4	11
18	330	4	13
TOTAL	2921	36	TOTAL

KILKENNY

★

TEL : (056)22125/22024
LOCATION : 2 km Kilkenny, on main Dublin Road
ADDRESS : Glendine-County Kilkenny
HOTEL :
Newpark-Kilkenny
Tel : (056)22122
Mount Juliet – Thomastown
Tel : (056)24455
RESTAURANT : Langton's – Kilkenny
Tel : (056)65133
Laken House – Kilkenny
Tel : (056)61085

An excellent inland course of the parkland type, laid out in gently undulating countryside, situated on the outskirts of the medieval city of Kilkenny. The course offers fine views of Mount Leinster and the Blackstairs mountains to the east and the fabled Slievenamon to the south. Among its feature holes are the last five finishing holes necessitating carefully placed tee-shots. *SSS70*

  $

 —

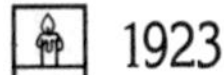 1923

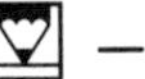 —

 5824 P 71

Required : None
Best days : Weekdays

HOLE	LENGTH MEDAL-TEE	PAR	STROKE INDEX
1	362	4	7
2	304	4	12
3	380	4	2
4	327	4	8
5	272	4	17
6	137	3	18
7	364	4	5
8	367	4	4
9	443	5	13
TOTAL	2956	36	TOTAL

HOLE	LENGTH MEDAL-TEE	PAR	STROKE INDEX
10	192	3	9
11	399	4	1
12	446	5	14
13	388	4	3
14	458	5	11
15	181	3	15
16	319	4	6
17	162	3	16
18	323	4	10
TOTAL	2868	35	TOTAL

KILLARNEY

TEL : (064)31034
LOCATION : 5 km W. Killarney
ADDRESS : Killarney – County Kerry
HOTEL :
Castlerosse – Killarney
Tel : (064)31144
Cahernane – Killarney
Tel : (064)31895
Europe – Killarney
Tel : (064)31900
RESTAURANT : Gaby's Restaurant – Killarney
Tel : (064)32519

The Killarney Golf and Fishing Club has two 18 hole courses (Killeen and Mahony's Point), both of championship standard. They count among the world's most beautiful and scenic ones, laid out in a magnificent setting amid small streams, lakes and mountains. Gently undulating, each of the 36 holes is unique, presenting different features, demanding carefully placed tee shots. Killeen Course *SSS 72*, Mahony's *SSS 72*

GF $$

1891

36

—

G. Campbell

L Killeen Course : 6389 y P 73,
Mahony's Point Course : 6152 y P 72

R S

Required : Handicap Certificate
Best days : Weekdays

HOLE	LENGTH MEDAL-TEE	PAR	STROKE INDEX
1	334	4	12
2	347	4	8
3	179	3	18
4	378	4	4
5	436	5	10
6	178	3	14
7	441	4	2
8	378	4	6
9	349	4	16
TOTAL	3020	36	TOTAL

HOLE	LENGTH MEDAL-TEE	PAR	STROKE INDEX
10	155	3	15
11	465	5	11
12	434	4	5
13	404	4	1
14	353	4	17
15	375	4	9
16	454	5	13
17	339	4	3
18	390	3	7
TOTAL	3369	37	TOTAL

KNOCKANALLY

TEL : (045)69322
LOCATION : 6 km Prosperous, 35 km Dublin
ADDRESS : Donadea - County Kildare
HOTEL :
Curryhills House - Prosperous
Tel : (045)68150
Baberstown Castle - Straffan
Tel : (01)6288157

A new golf course located in County Kildare and laid out on undulating ground. This inland course with mature trees and numerous water hazards, features a clubhouse in a tastefully modernised 120 year-old Palladian mansion with scenic views of the course. Curryhills House, a converted Georgian farmhouse, is set in beautiful natural surroundings. There is fishing and horse-riding available locally. *SSS 71*

GF $

1985

18

—

—

L 6484 y P 72

S

RP

Required : None
Best days : Any day

HOLE	LENGTH MEDAL-TEE	PAR	STROKE INDEX
1	422	4	5
2	522	5	8
3	260	4	18
4	424	4	2
5	358	4	11
6	476	5	16
7	185	3	14
8	455	4	1
9	168	3	13
TOTAL	3270	36	TOTAL

HOLE	LENGTH MEDAL-TEE	PAR	STROKE INDEX
10	392	4	4
11	142	3	10
12	364	4	6
13	401	4	7
14	364	4	12
15	163	3	17
16	393	4	3
17	476	5	15
18	519	5	9
TOTAL	3214	36	TOTAL

LAHINCH

TEL : (065)81003
LOCATION : 35 m Shannon Airport N 67, 1 m NW. Lahinch
ADDRESS : Lahinch – County Clare
HOTEL :
Aberdeen Arms – Lahinch
Tel : (065)81100
Sheedy's Spa View – Lisdoonvarna
Tel : (065)74026
RESTAURANT : Captain's Deck – Liscannor
Tel : (065)81385

The world famous championship course was laid out by Old Tom Morris in 1892 and redesigned by Alister Mac Kenzie some thirty years later. The new course, the Castle, was designed by John Harris. Both are links courses running through dunes with high sandhills overlooking the ocean and the Cliffs of Moher. The Old Course is a fine classic links with two celebrated blind holes, the 5th and the 6th. The Castle course is ideal for family golf. *SSS 70/67*

GF $$

1893

36

—

Old Tom Morris, A. McKenzie, J. Harris

L 6441 y P 72, 4888 P 67

Required : Handicap Certificate
Best days : Weekdays

HOLE	LENGTH MEDAL-TEE	PAR	STROKE INDEX
1	387	4	
2	515	5	
3	157	3	
4	424	4	
5	488	5	
6	156	3	
7	376	4	
8	341	4	
9	348	4	
TOTAL	3192	36	TOTAL

HOLE	LENGTH MEDAL-TEE	PAR	STROKE INDEX
10	453	4	
11	139	3	
12	353	4	
13	274	4	
14	486	5	
15	456	4	
16	196	3	
17	435	4	
18	520	5	
TOTAL	3312	36	TOTAL

LAYTOWN & BETTYSTOWN

TEL : (041)27534/27170
LOCATION : 1 m Laytown
ADDRESS : Laytown – County Meath
HOTEL :
Ardboyne – Navan
Tel : (046)23119
Annesbrook Country House – Duleek
Tel : (041)23293
RESTAURANT : Dunderry Lodge – Robinstown
Tel : (046)31671

A fine natural links of championship standard set beside the sea near the river Boyne. It is ideally situated for holiday golf near the fine seaside resorts of Laytown and Bettystown. Founded in 1909, many of its holes have been redesigned and lengthened.
SSS 69

GF $

1909

18

—

—

L 5482 P 70

S

Required : Handicap Certificate
Best days : Weekdays

HOLE	LENGTH MEDAL-TEE	PAR	STROKE INDEX
1	272	4	13
2	306	4	10
3	337	4	3
4	433	5	14
5	329	4	8
6	167	3	15
7	363	4	6
8	159	3	11
9	322	4	2
TOTAL	2688	35	TOTAL

HOLE	LENGTH MEDAL-TEE	PAR	STROKE INDEX
10	343	4	5
11	420	4	1
12	348	4	4
13	310	4	16
14	143	3	17
15	353	4	7
16	174	3	9
17	274	4	18
18	429	5	12
TOTAL	2794	35	TOTAL

LETTERKENNY

TEL : (074)21150
LOCATION : 2 m S. Letterkenny
ADDRESS : BarnHill – Letterkenny – County Donegal
HOTEL :
Rathmullan House – Rathmullan
Tel : (074)58188
The Manse (Bed & Breakfast) – Ramelton
Tel : (074)51047

This flat inland course is set on the shores of Lough Swilly with many testing holes. The fairways are wide and generous with short rough serving as the main obstacle. The Manse, situated in the village of Ramelton, is a charming Georgian house, (just three bedrooms), full of old world charm. *SSS 71*

GF $

—

S

1915

E. Hackett

R

18

L 6292 y P 70

Required : None
Best days : Mondays to Thursdays

HOLE	LENGTH MEDAL-TEE	PAR	STROKE INDEX
1	368	4	14
2	530	5	12
3	364	4	8
4	362	4	6
5	138	3	18
6	423	4	2
7	388	4	4
8	170	3	16
9	370	4	10
TOTAL	3113	35	TOTAL

HOLE	LENGTH MEDAL-TEE	PAR	STROKE INDEX
10	396	4	9
11	415	4	3
12	343	4	13
13	209	3	7
14	337	4	11
15	420	4	5
16	151	3	17
17	400	4	1
18	508	5	15
TOTAL	3179	35	TOTAL

LIMERICK

TEL : (061)44083/45146
LOCATION : 5 km S. Limerick
ADDRESS : Ballyclough – County Limerick
HOTEL :
Adare Manor – Adare
Tel : (061)396566
Dunraven Arms – Adare
Tel : (061)396209
RESTAURANT : Restaurant de la Fontaine – Limerick
Tel : (061)44461

A fine rolling upland course with tree-lined fairways overlooking the city of Limerick, the Shannon valley and the Clare Hills. Several holes are testing especially the par 3s. One of its most difficult ones is the 3rd hole with a ditch crossing in front of the green. The club is the third oldest in Ireland, having been founded in 1891. The Dunraven Arms Hotel, in the picturesque village of Adare, has charming bedrooms and an excellent restaurant. *SSS 71*

GF $$

1891

18

Tuesdays, Weekends

J. Braid

L 5856 y P 72

R S

Required : None
Best days : Mondays, Wednesdays and Fridays

HOLE	LENGTH MEDAL-TEE	PAR	STROKE INDEX
1	260	4	9
2	442	5	15
3	430	4	1
4	336	4	5
5	159	3	16
6	492	5	7
7	371	4	3
8	120	3	18
9	447	5	13
TOTAL	3057	37	TOTAL

HOLE	LENGTH MEDAL-TEE	PAR	STROKE INDEX
10	394	4	2
11	336	4	11
12	358	4	6
13	279	4	17
14	141	3	14
15	336	4	4
16	296	4	10
17	347	4	8
18	312	4	12
TOTAL	2799	35	TOTAL

MALLOW

TEL : (022)21145/21972
LOCATION : 2 km Mallow/34 km Cork City
ADDRESS : Ballellis-Mallow-County Cork
HOTEL :
Longueville House-Mallow
Tel : (022)47156
Blackwater Castle – Castletownroche
Tel : (022)26333
Clonmeen Lodge – Banteer
Tel : (029)56090

Extended to 18 holes by Commander J. Harris in 1960, the Mallow golf course has turned into a testing inland course of championship standard. Laid out in hilly parkland, there are fine views over the Blackwater Valley. The club is equipped with a fine clubhouse, tennis and squash courts and a sauna. The tasteful Longueville House, is a Georgian mansion set in extensive parkland. *SSS 70*

GF $

1948

18

Weekends

J. Harris

L 5687 P 72

S

R

Required : None
Best days : Weekdays except Tuesdays

HOLE	LENGTH MEDAL-TEE	PAR	STROKE INDEX
1	350	4	7
2	166	3	9
3	402	4	3
4	166	3	11
5	340	4	5
6	457	5	13
7	380	4	2
8	437	5	17
9	295	4	15
TOTAL	2993	36	TOTAL

HOLE	LENGTH MEDAL-TEE	PAR	STROKE INDEX
10	375	4	6
11	148	3	8
12	468	5	12
13	353	4	1
14	282	4	14
15	347	4	4
16	115	3	18
17	435	5	16
18	171	3	10
TOTAL	2694	35	TOTAL

MALONE

★

(FOUNDED 1895)

TEL : (084)612758
LOCATION : 6 m S. Belfast A 1
ADDRESS : 240 Upper Malone Rd – Dunmurry – Belfast – County Antrim
HOTEL :
Europa – Belfast
Tel : (0232)327000
Ash Rowan Guesthouse – Belfast
Tel : (0232)661458
Stormont – Belfast
Tel : (0232)658621
RESTAURANT : Roscoff – Belfast
Tel : (0232)331532

Malone is one of the oldest golf Clubs in Ireland. Both courses are of the parkland type, scenically laid out in an elevated position only six miles from Belfast. There is a river crossing the 18 hole layout plus a picturesque lake by the 15th and 18th holes. The imposing clubhouse is a former 17th century mansion. *SSS 71*

 $  —  

 1895  F. Hawtree

27  6395 y P 70, 2895 y P 34 

Required : None
Best days : Weekdays

HOLE	LENGTH MEDAL-TEE	PAR	STROKE INDEX
1	381	4	9
2	499	5	11
3	445	4	3
4	152	3	17
5	412	4	5
6	158	3	15
7	470	4	1
8	358	4	13
9	364	4	7
TOTAL	3239	35	TOTAL

HOLE	LENGTH MEDAL-TEE	PAR	STROKE INDEX
10	401	4	4
11	393	4	10
12	194	3	12
13	400	4	8
14	413	4	2
15	136	3	18
16	306	4	16
17	520	5	14
18	393	4	6
TOTAL	3156	35	TOTAL

MONKSTOWN

TEL : (021)841376/841225
LOCATION : 13 km S. Cork L. 66
ADDRESS : Monkstown-County Cork
HOTEL :
Fitzpatricks Silver Springs – Cork
Tel : (021)507533
Rochestown Park-Cork
Tel : (021)892233
RESTAURANT : Lovett's-Cork
Tel : (021)294909

This picturesque course is situated in the southern suburbs of Cork partly overlooking the estuary of the river Lee. It is built around the historical Monkstown castle, dating back to the 17th century, in undulating parkland landscape. The five finishing holes, including the tough 16th with the lake on its right, are especially challenging and among the best in Ireland. *SSS 68*

GF $ | Tuesdays | S
1908 | — |
18 | L 5441 P 70 | R

Required : None
Best days : Any day except Tuesdays and Thursdays

HOLE	LENGTH MEDAL-TEE	PAR	STROKE INDEX
1	172	3	10
2	330	4	6
3	480	5	16
4	230	4	18
5	291	4	4
6	160	3	12
7	270	4	14
8	344	4	2
9	334	4	8
TOTAL	2611	35	TOTAL

HOLE	LENGTH MEDAL-TEE	PAR	STROKE INDEX
10	303	4	11
11	345	4	5
12	290	4	15
13	151	3	17
14	360	4	3
15	469	5	13
16	165	3	9
17	382	4	1
18	365	4	7
TOTAL	2830	35	TOTAL

MULLINGAR

★

TEL : (044)48366/41488
LOCATION : 5 km S. Mullingar
ADDRESS : Mullingar - County Westmeath
HOTEL :
Bloomfield House - Mullingar
Tel : (044)40894
Greville Arms - Mullingar
Tel : (044)48563
RESTAURANT : Crookedwood House - Mullingar
Tel : (044)72165

An inland course of championship standard with well-wooded fairways laid out on gently rolling parkland. The short par 3s are among the most difficult holes. One of its most challenging holes is the 16th with a ditch crossing the fairway. There is a fine clubhouse overlooking the course. Mullingar is very popular with visiting groups. *SSS 70*

  $  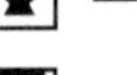 —  

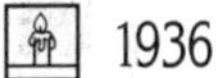 1936  J. Braid 

 L 6370 y P 72 

Required : Handicap Certificate
Best days : Weekdays except Wednesdays

HOLE	LENGTH MEDAL-TEE	PAR	STROKE INDEX
1	328	4	
2	189	3	
3	388	4	
4	495	5	
5	177	3	
6	320	4	
7	457	4	
8	338	4	
9	337	4	
TOTAL	3039	35	TOTAL

HOLE	LENGTH MEDAL-TEE	PAR	STROKE INDEX
10	444	4	
11	351	4	
12	155	3	
13	371	4	
14	478	5	
15	152	3	
16	494	5	
17	393	4	
18	493	5	
TOTAL	3331	37	TOTAL

MUSKERRY

★

TEL : (021)385297/385104
LOCATION : 11 km NW. Cork
ADDRESS : Carrigrohane – County Cork
HOTEL :
Rochestown Park – Rochestown
Tel : (021)892233
Blarney Park – Blarney
Tel : (021)385281
RESTAURANT : Lovett's – Cork
Tel : (021)294909

A typical undulating heathland course with many good testing holes. Its first five holes are mostly flat, the 6th crosses a river, the 7th to the 14th run through hilly land, and the 17th and 18th are crossed by a river. There is a panoramic view from the 11th tee overlooking the surrounding countryside, which demands accurate play. *SSS 69*

GF $ — 1897 — 18 — L 6314 y P 71 — S

Required : Handicap Certificate
Best days : Weekdays except Wednesdays and Thursdays

HOLE	LENGTH MEDAL-TEE	PAR	STROKE INDEX
1	417	4	
2	266	4	
3	387	4	
4	492	5	
5	370	4	
6	200	3	
7	479	5	
8	172	3	
9	337	4	
TOTAL	3120	36	TOTAL

HOLE	LENGTH MEDAL-TEE	PAR	STROKE INDEX
10	319	4	
11	394	4	
12	168	3	
13	408	4	
14	486	5	
15	171	3	
16	431	4	
17	427	4	
18	390	4	
TOTAL	3194	35	TOTAL

NARIN & PORTNOO

★★

TEL : (075)45107
LOCATION : 6 m N Ardara/1 m E. Narin
ADDRESS : Portnoo – County Donegal
HOTEL :
The Highland Central – Donegal Town
Tel : (073)21027
St. Ernan's House Hotel – near Donegal Town
Tel : (073)21065

This interesting seaside links on the Atlantic has a varied layout with each hole having its own characteristics. Many of the greens have protective electrified wire around them helping to keep the grazing cattle off. Some of the par 4s can be difficult to reach with two woods due to a prevailing cross wind from the sea. *SSS 68*

GF $

1930

18

—

—

L 5225 P 69

Required : Handicap Certificate
Best days : Weekdays

HOLE	LENGTH MEDAL-TEE	PAR	STROKE INDEX
1	286	4	
2	450	5	
3	143	3	
4	418	4	
5	298	4	
6	193	3	
7	294	4	
8	134	3	
9	295	4	
TOTAL	2511	34	TOTAL

HOLE	LENGTH MEDAL-TEE	PAR	STROKE INDEX
10	358	4	
11	174	3	
12	307	4	
13	170	3	
14	450	5	
15	451	5	
16	111	3	
17	372	4	
18	321	4	
TOTAL	2714	35	TOTAL

NENAGH

TEL : (067)31476/31099
LOCATION : 8 km NE. Nenagh N 7
ADDRESS : Beechwood-Nenagh – County Tipperary
HOTEL :
Gurthalougha House Terryglass – Nenagh
Tel : (067)22080

Situated in County Tipperary, this is a sporting inland course extended to 18 holes in 1972. A good all-year round course and thus very popular for off-season outings, it features five testing par 3s and a difficult 18th hole going uphill to a two-tiered green. It boasts the largest practice ground in the country and a panoramic view from the 8th tee. The small winding roads which lead to Gurthalougha House will seem endless, but the welcome and the cuisine that awaits you, will make it worthwhile. *SSS 68*

GF $

1928

18

—

E. Hackett

L 5483 P 69

R

S

Required : Handicap Certificate
Best days : Mondays to Fridays

HOLE	LENGTH MEDAL-TEE	PAR	STROKE INDEX
1	364	4	4
2	135	3	18
3	338	4	8
4	441	5	14
5	155	3	16
6	354	4	2
7	236	4	17
8	293	4	12
9	335	4	6
TOTAL	2651	35	TOTAL

HOLE	LENGTH MEDAL-TEE	PAR	STROKE INDEX
10	362	4	11
11	358	4	5
12	176	3	13
13	484	5	10
14	358	4	3
15	208	3	7
16	342	4	9
17	177	3	15
18	367	4	1
TOTAL	2832	34	TOTAL

NEWTOWNSTEWART

TEL : (06626)61466
LOCATION : 2 m Newtownstewart B84
ADDRESS : 38 Golfcourse Rd – Newtownstewart – County Tyrone
HOTEL :
Barnscourt Cottages
Tel : (06626)61013
Royal Arms – Omagh
Tel : (0662)243263
RESTAURANT : Silverbirch – Omagh
Tel : (0662)242520

A well-wooded and scenic inland course with an interesting layout set on undulating land. Its fairways run uphill and downhill through mature beech trees, tall pines and poplars. There are streams and lakes bordering various holes and serving as hazards. *SSS 69*

GF $

1915

18

—

F. Pennink

L 5468 P 70

R

Required : None
Best days : Mondays, Tuesdays and Fridays

HOLE	LENGTH MEDAL-TEE	PAR	STROKE INDEX
1	275	4	17
2	282	4	16
3	123	3	12
4	337	4	6
5	282	4	10
6	360	4	1
7	200	3	8
8	350	4	4
9	446	5	14
TOTAL	2655	35	TOTAL

HOLE	LENGTH MEDAL-TEE	PAR	STROKE INDEX
10	134	3	18
11	341	4	3
12	362	4	2
13	183	3	13
14	475	5	5
15	138	3	15
16	472	5	11
17	344	4	9
18	364	4	7
TOTAL	2813	35	TOTAL

NORTH WEST

TEL : (077)61027/61843
LOCATION : 12 m N. Derry/2 m S. Buncrana
ADDRESS : Lifford-Fahan-County Donegal
HOTEL :
White Strand-Buncrana
Tel : (077)61059
RESTAURANT : St-John's-Fahan
Tel : (077)60289

The North West links lies between the sea (the scenic Lough Swilly) and the picturesque 'Mouldy' Mountain on open and sandy terrain. The holes are very varied, with many sandy knolls and gentle undulations. *SSS69*

GF $

1891

18

—

—

L 6203 y P 69

R S

Required : None
Best days : Weekdays

HOLE	LENGTH MEDAL-TEE	PAR	STROKE INDEX
1	448	4	3
2	358	4	11
3	169	3	13
4	353	4	9
5	190	3	15
6	393	4	7
7	436	4	1
8	147	3	17
9	536	5	5
TOTAL	3030	34	TOTAL

HOLE	LENGTH MEDAL-TEE	PAR	STROKE INDEX
10	394	4	4
11	369	4	10
12	450	4	2
13	191	3	16
14	356	4	14
15	380	4	8
16	102	3	18
17	410	4	6
18	521	5	12
TOTAL	3173	35	TOTAL

OUGHTERARD

TEL : (091)82131/82381
LOCATION : 2 km Oughterard/24 km W. Galway
ADDRESS : Oughterard-County Galway
HOTEL :
Currarevagh House-Oughterard
Tel : (091)82313
Connemara Gateway-Oughterard
Tel : (091)82328
Sweeney's Oughterard House – Oughterard
Tel : (091)82207

Oughterard is a fine inland course of the parkland type, set on flat Connemara landscape. Extended to 18 holes in 1985, it is situated between Lough Corrib and the nearby mountains and is adjacent to the 14th century Aughanure castle. It features closely guarded and elevated greens demanding precision in putting. *SSS 69*

GF $ — S

1974 E. Hachett

18 L 5456 P 70 R

Required : None
Best days : Mondays to Saturdays incl.

HOLE	LENGTH MEDAL-TEE	PAR	STROKE INDEX
1	370	4	3
2	315	4	11
3	130	3	13
4	262	4	17
5	292	4	7
6	298	4	9
7	276	4	15
8	445	5	1
9	159	3	5
TOTAL	2547	35	TOTAL

HOLE	LENGTH MEDAL-TEE	PAR	STROKE INDEX
10	359	4	10
11	359	4	4
12	354	4	12
13	186	3	8
14	435	5	16
15	315	4	18
16	362	4	6
17	147	3	14
18	392	4	2
TOTAL	2909	35	TOTAL

PORTMARNOCK

TEL : (01)323082
LOCATION : 16 km N.E. Dublin
ADDRESS : Portmarnock – County Dublin
HOTEL :
Grand – Malahide
Tel : (01)450633
Marine – Sutton
Tel : (01)322613

This world famous links is situated on a peninsula, encircled by the sea on three sides, bordering Dublin Bay and the Irish Sea at the same time. The course is laid out in fine natural surroundings with its fairways running between sandhills, dunes and through marshland. It is very long with an outstanding layout, counting only three tricky short holes, and fifteen challenging long holes. The Irish Open returns here every year. *SSS 74*

GF $$

1894

27

—

G. Ross, M. Pickman

L 6489 P 72, 3286 P 36

Required : Handicap Certificate
Best days : Mondays, Tuesdays

HOLE	LENGTH MEDAL-TEE	PAR	STROKE INDEX
1	358	4	
2	344	4	
3	350	4	
4	404	4	
5	362	4	
6	545	5	
7	157	3	
8	365	4	
9	401	4	
TOTAL	3286	36	TOTAL

HOLE	LENGTH MEDAL-TEE	PAR	STROKE INDEX
10	342	4	
11	395	4	
12	138	3	
13	514	5	
14	355	4	
15	170	3	
16	472	5	
17	432	4	
18	385	4	
TOTAL	3203	36	TOTAL

PORTSALON

TEL : (074)59102
LOCATION : 32 km N. Letterkenny L 78
ADDRESS : Portsalon – County Donegal
HOTEL :
Rathmullan House – Rathmullan
Tel : (074)58188
Fort Royal – Rathmullan
Tel : (074)58100

Ideally situated for holiday golf on the scenic shores of Lough Swilly, this is a links course running through sand hills with a stream meandering its way through several fairways. Set in beautiful rolling lawns, Rathmullen House overlooks a sandy beach and Lough Swilly. There is a magnificent view from the restaurant where excellent food is served. *SSS 67*

GF $

1967

18

—

—

L 5343 P 69

R

Required : None
Best days : Weekdays

HOLE	LENGTH MEDAL-TEE	PAR	STROKE INDEX
1	358	4	2
2	169	3	10
3	326	4	16
4	301	4	8
5	183	3	12
6	320	4	6
7	446	5	18
8	169	3	14
9	306	4	4
TOTAL	2578	34	TOTAL

HOLE	LENGTH MEDAL-TEE	PAR	STROKE INDEX
10	343	4	7
11	293	4	17
12	162	3	11
13	385	4	1
14	141	3	15
15	343	4	9
16	248	4	13
17	478	5	5
18	372	4	3
TOTAL	2765	35	TOTAL

PORTSTEWART

TEL : (026583)2015
LOCATION : 4 m Coleraine A2
ADDRESS : 117 Strand Road – Portstewart – County Derry
HOTEL :
Edgewaler – Portstewart
Tel : (026583)3314
Blackheath House – Bushmills
Tel : (0265868)433
Greenhill House – Coleraine
Tel : (026585)241
RESTAURANT : McDuff's – Bushmills
Tel : (0265868)433

This seaside course, ideally situated for holiday golf, is located in the north part of Northern Ireland. It has two 18 hole layouts including the well-known Strand Course which is of championship standard. The course is bordered on one side by the river Bann. It was the venue for the 1960 Irish Open. *SSS 72*

GF $

1889

36

—

—

L 6784 y P 72, 4733 y P 64

S

R

Required : Handicap Certificate
Best days : Weekdays only, weekends by arrangement

HOLE	LENGTH MEDAL-TEE	PAR	STROKE INDEX
1	425	4	8
2	352	4	4
3	393	4	12
4	370	4	2
5	166	3	16
6	500	5	10
7	485	5	14
8	169	3	18
9	422	4	6
TOTAL	3282	36	TOTAL

HOLE	LENGTH MEDAL-TEE	PAR	STROKE INDEX
10	434	4	1
11	186	3	17
12	550	5	13
13	210	3	15
14	505	5	7
15	340	4	13
16	425	4	5
17	418	4	9
18	434	4	11
TOTAL	3502	36	TOTAL

ROSAPENNA

TEL : (074)55301
LOCATION : 2 km Downings
ADDRESS : Downings – County Donegal
HOTEL : HP
Rosapenna Golf Hotel
Tel : (074)55301

A famous championship links designed by Old Tom Morris (of St Andrews) in 1898, and redesigned by two famous golf pioneers such as James Braid and Harry Vardon. The first class Rosapenna Golf hotel, equipped with tennis courts, is adjacent to the course.
SSS 70

GF $

1898

18

—

T. Morris, J. Braid, H. Vardon

L 6254 y P 70

Required : None
Best days : Any day by arrangement

HOLE	LENGTH MEDAL-TEE	PAR	STROKE INDEX
1	281	4	11
2	428	4	5
3	446	4	1
4	386	4	9
5	255	4	15
6	167	3	17
7	367	4	13
8	485	5	7
9	185	3	13
TOTAL	3000	35	TOTAL

HOLE	LENGTH MEDAL-TEE	PAR	STROKE INDEX
10	543	5	10
11	427	4	2
12	342	4	14
13	455	4	6
14	128	3	18
15	418	4	4
16	216	3	16
17	358	4	12
18	367	4	8
TOTAL	3254	35	TOTAL

ROSSLARE

TEL : (053)32113/32370
LOCATION : 16 km Wexford/2 km N. Rosslare
ADDRESS : Rosslare - County Wexford
HOTEL :
Kelly's - Rosslare
Tel : (053)32114
Ferrycarrig - Wexford
Tel : (053)22999

Inaugurated as a 9 hole course in 1908, it was extended to 18 holes in 1926. Ideal for holiday golf, the Rosslare golf course is a testing links bordering the Irish Sea. There are undulating fairways surrounded by sand dunes. The greens are of excellent quality. Good food and wine are part of the tradition at Kelly's Hotel, where amenities for guests include tennis, squash, swimming pool, sauna, solarium and a host of activities for children.
SSS 69

GF $

1908

18

—

—

L 6495 y P 74

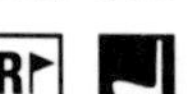

Required : Handicap Certificate
Best days : Weekdays except Tuesdays

HOLE	LENGTH MEDAL-TEE	PAR	STROKE INDEX
1	368	4	
2	170	3	
3	522	5	
4	373	4	
5	496	5	
6	310	4	
7	482	5	
8	173	3	
9	397	4	
TOTAL	3291	37	TOTAL

HOLE	LENGTH MEDAL-TEE	PAR	STROKE INDEX
10	160	3	
11	478	5	
12	476	5	
13	280	4	
14	162	3	
15	397	4	
16	362	4	
17	411	4	
18	478	5	
TOTAL	3204	37	TOTAL

ROYAL BELFAST

TEL : (0232)428165
LOCATION : 2 m E. Holywood
ADDRESS : Craigavad – Holywood – County Down
HOTEL :
Old Inn – Crawfordsbawn
Tel : (0247)853255
Culloden – Holywood
Tel : (02317)5223
RESTAURANT : Roscoff – Belfast
Tel : (0232)331532

Created in 1881, the Royal Belfast in one of Ireland's oldest and noblest clubs. It is a gently rolling parkland course set alongside the sea shore with scenic views of the coastline and the surrounding countryside. There is a spacious country house style clubhouse equipped with six tennis courts and a squash court. *SSS 70*

GF $$

1881

18

Weekends

 G. Baily

 5691 P 70

Required : Introduction letter
Best days : Weekdays only except Thursdays

HOLE	LENGTH MEDAL-TEE	PAR	STROKE INDEX
1	380	4	7
2	376	4	3
3	328	4	13
4	143	3	17
5	481	5	1
6	321	4	11
7	150	3	15
8	360	4	9
9	374	4	5
TOTAL	2913	35	TOTAL

HOLE	LENGTH MEDAL-TEE	PAR	STROKE INDEX
10	285	4	10
11	160	3	14
12	371	4	2
13	329	4	12
14	172	3	16
15	375	4	4
16	443	5	6
17	177	3	18
18	466	5	8
TOTAL	2778	35	TOTAL

ROYAL COUNTY DOWN

★★★

TEL : (03967)23314
LOCATION : 30 m Belfast A2/0,5 m E. Newcastle
ADDRESS : Newcastle - County Down
HOTEL :
Slieve Donard - Newcastle
Tel : (03967)23681
Burrendale - Newcastle
Tel : (03967)22599
Brock Cottage - Newcastle
Tel : (03967)22204
RESTAURANT : Mario's - Newcastle
Tel : (03967)23912

One of the world's greatest golf courses laid out by Old Tom Morris on the shores of Dundrum Bay with the Mountains of Mourne in the background. This magnificent undulating links has two 18 hole courses, the testing championship course and a shorter course ideal for holiday golf. The championship course has many great holes with the opening ones heading along the bay and the dunes. Among its feature holes are the tricky 7th and 14th and the long 18th. The club has welcomed all the great golf champions since its creation in 1889. *SSS 73/60*

GF $$

1889

36

Weekends

T. Morris

L 6968 y P 72, 4100 y P 65

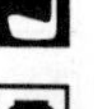

Required : Handicap Certificate and Introduction letter
Best days : Weekdays by prior arrangement

HOLE	LENGTH MEDAL-TEE	PAR	STROKE INDEX
1	506	5	
2	424	4	
3	473	4	
4	217	3	
5	440	4	
6	396	4	
7	145	3	
8	427	4	
9	486	5	
TOTAL	3514	36	TOTAL

HOLE	LENGTH MEDAL-TEE	PAR	STROKE INDEX
10	200	3	
11	440	4	
12	501	5	
13	445	4	
14	213	3	
15	445	4	
16	265	4	
17	400	4	
18	545	5	
TOTAL	3454	36	TOTAL

ROYAL DUBLIN

TEL : (01)336346
LOCATION : 6 km N. Dublin
ADDRESS : Dollymount – Dublin 3 – County Dublin
HOTEL :
Jury's – Dublin
Tel : (01)605000
Buswells – Dublin
Tel : (01)764013
RESTAURANT : Whites on the Green – Dublin
Tel : (01)751975

Another of the oldest and prestigious clubs in Ireland is the Royal Dublin, a fine and testing links course of championship standard with a challenging layout often compared with St Andrews. Set on Dublin Bay, the fairways with fine well placed bunkers are exposed to a prevailing wind. Among its many notable holes is the testing 18th: a sharply doglegged par five, with 'out of bounds' all along the right-hand side. A fine finish to a great links. The club has hosted the Irish Open several times. *SSS 71*

GF $$

1885

18

Weekends

 E. Colt

 6026 P 73

R 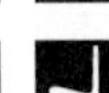

Required : Handicap Certificate
Best days : Weekdays except Wednesdays

HOLE	LENGTH MEDAL-TEE	PAR	STROKE INDEX
1	351	4	9
2	440	5	10
3	355	4	3
4	157	3	15
5	389	4	1
6	170	3	16
7	322	4	7
8	435	5	12
9	160	3	17
TOTAL	2779	35	TOTAL

HOLE	LENGTH MEDAL-TEE	PAR	STROKE INDEX
10	374	4	5
11	469	5	8
12	172	3	11
13	381	4	2
14	439	5	13
15	390	4	4
16	241	4	18
17	341	4	6
18	440	5	14
TOTAL	3247	38	TOTAL

ROYAL PORTRUSH

★★★

TEL : (0265)822311
LOCATION : 1 m E. Portrush A 110
ADDRESS : Bushmills Rd – Portrush – County Antrim
HOTEL :
Magherabuoy House – Portrush
Tel : (0265)823507
Bushmills Inn – Bushmills
Tel : (02657)32339
Bayview Hotel – Portballintrae
Tel : (0265)31453
RESTAURANT : Ramore – Portrush
Tel : (0265)823444

Another of Irelands memorable courses is set north of Belfast on the Ulster Coast near the Giant's Causeway. Undoubtedly one of the world's most famous links laid out on undulating land bordering the windy Atlantic and overlooking the distant hills of Donegal and the shores of the Hebrides islands. The most testing layout is the 'Dunluce', named after the ancestral home of the Lords of Antrim, with its narrow fairways running through high sand hills and dunes. The Valley links is less strenuous and ideal for holiday golf. The modern clubhouse lies at the 9th hole of the Dunluce course. *SSS 72/70*

GF $$
1888
36

Saturdays
H. Colt
L 6106 P 73, 6054 y P 70

Required : Introduction letter
Best days : Weekdays and Sunday afternoons by prior arrangement

Dunluce Links

HOLE	LENGTH MEDAL-TEE	PAR	STROKE INDEX
1	348	4	7
2	451	5	11
3	137	3	17
4	415	4	3
5	353	4	9
6	175	3	15
7	384	4	1
8	334	4	13
9	435	5	5
TOTAL	3032	36	TOTAL

HOLE	LENGTH MEDAL-TEE	PAR	STROKE INDEX
10	436	5	10
11	152	3	18
12	356	4	2
13	334	4	6
14	187	3	16
15	330	4	12
16	379	4	4
17	464	5	8
18	436	5	14
TOTAL	3074	37	TOTAL

Valley Links

HOLE	LENGTH MEDAL-TEE	PAR	STROKE INDEX
1	339	4	11
2	374	4	3
3	135	3	17
4	520	5	7
5	324	4	13
6	231	3	9
7	441	4	1
8	399	4	5
9	311	4	15
TOTAL	3074	35	TOTAL

HOLE	LENGTH MEDAL-TEE	PAR	STROKE INDEX
10	472	5	2
11	130	3	18
12	452	4	4
13	458	5	8
14	412	4	12
15	155	3	14
16	349	4	10
17	382	4	6
18	170	3	16
TOTAL	2980	35	TOTAL

SCRABO

TEL : (0247)812355
LOCATION : 2 m SW. Newtownards
ADDRESS : Scrabo Rd 133 – Newtownards – County Down
HOTEL :
Strangford Arms – Newtownards
Tel : (0247)814141
Beresford House – Bangor
Tel : (0247)472143
Royal – Bangor
Tel : (0247)472143
RESTAURANT : Old Schoolhouse – Conber
Tel : (0238)541182

A pleasant seaside course set on rugged open countryside on the windy shores of the Belfast Lough. Many of its interesting holes are surrounded by rocks and bounded by gorse, demanding accuracy from tee to green. *SSS 70*

GF $

1906

18

Wed., Sat.

—

L 5699 P 71

Required : None
Best days : Weekdays

HOLE	LENGTH MEDAL-TEE	PAR	STROKE INDEX
1	424	4	4
2	148	3	13
3	372	4	6
4	119	3	18
5	512	5	5
6	287	4	14
7	195	4	11
8	291	4	9
9	519	5	1
TOTAL	2867	36	TOTAL

HOLE	LENGTH MEDAL-TEE	PAR	STROKE INDEX
10	299	4	14
11	436	5	10
12	406	4	2
13	184	3	7
14	353	4	12
15	340	4	8
16	314	4	3
17	133	3	17
18	267	4	15
TOTAL	2732	35	TOTAL

SHANDON PARK

TEL : (0232)401856
LOCATION : 3 m Belfast
ADDRESS : Shandon Park 73 – Belfast – County Down
HOTEL :
Drumkeen – Belfast
Tel : (0232)491321
Stormont – Belfast
Tel : (0232)658621
Wellington Park – Belfast
Tel : (0232)381111
RESTAURANT : Rest. 44 – Belfast
Tel : (0232)244844

Located near Belfast, this is a parkland course of championship standard with a stream cutting the course in two, which meanders its way through at least nine holes. There is a comfortable and pleasant clubhouse. *SSS 70*

GF $

1926

18

—

—

L 5714 P 70

R S

Required : None
Best days : Weekdays

HOLE	LENGTH MEDAL-TEE	PAR	STROKE INDEX
1	325	4	13
2	343	4	3
3	474	5	11
4	333	4	7
5	364	4	5
6	414	4	1
7	333	4	15
8	174	3	9
9	293	4	17
TOTAL	3053	36	TOTAL

HOLE	LENGTH MEDAL-TEE	PAR	STROKE INDEX
10	118	3	18
11	479	5	8
12	317	4	10
13	155	3	16
14	363	4	4
15	152	3	12
16	386	4	2
17	367	4	6
18	324	4	14
TOTAL	2661	34	TOTAL

SHANNON

★★

TEL : (061)61020/61849
LOCATION : 22 km Limerick or Ennis
ADDRESS : Shannon Airport – County Clare
HOTEL :
Clare Inn – Shannon
Tel : (061)71161
Fitzpatricks Shannon Shamrock – Bunratty
Tel : (061)361177

The Shannon golf club lies in south-west Ireland, and is one of the best golf courses in this region. Situated near Shannon Airport, it is a typical inland course of championship standard. Laid out on mostly flat terrain, there are several tight and testing holes demanding precision, and offering a challenge for every category of golfer. *SSS 72*

GF $$ —
1966 J. Harris
18 L 6231 P 72

Required : None
Best days : All days except on special event days

HOLE	LENGTH MEDAL-TEE	PAR	STROKE INDEX
1	398	4	
2	166	3	
3	301	4	
4	476	5	
5	362	4	
6	466	5	
7	434	4	
8	152	3	
9	307	4	
TOTAL	3062	36	TOTAL

HOLE	LENGTH MEDAL-TEE	PAR	STROKE INDEX
10	199	3	
11	312	4	
12	356	4	
13	373	4	
14	352	4	
15	205	3	
16	465	5	
17	363	4	
18	464	5	
TOTAL	3089	36	TOTAL

SKERRIES

✡

TEL : (01)491567/491204
LOCATION : 29 km N Dublin/2 km S. Skerries
ADDRESS : Skerries – County Dublin
HOTEL :
Grand – Malahide
Tel : (01)450633
RESTAURANT : Red Bank – Skerries
Tel : (01)491005

This is a popular treelined parkland course at 20 km from Dublin Airport which is ideal for holiday golf. Its 18th hole is considered as one of the best finishing holes in Ireland with a semi-dogleg slightly uphill. There is an attractive clubhouse overlooking the 18th green. *SSS 70*

GF $ — Sun., Tues., Wed., Sat. — S

1906 — — — R

18 — L 5852 P 71

Required : None
Best days : Mondays, Thursdays and Fridays

HOLE	LENGTH MEDAL-TEE	PAR	STROKE INDEX
1	374	4	3
2	157	3	17
3	392	4	1
4	335	4	5
5	130	3	13
6	304	4	15
7	306	4	7
8	530	5	9
9	318	4	11
TOTAL	2846	35	TOTAL

HOLE	LENGTH MEDAL-TEE	PAR	STROKE INDEX
10	370	4	6
11	265	4	16
12	128	3	18
13	370	4	2
14	469	5	12
15	144	3	10
16	377	4	8
17	492	5	14
18	391	4	4
TOTAL	3006	36	TOTAL

STACKSTOWN

TEL : (01)942338/941993
LOCATION : 15 km S. Dublin
ADDRESS : Kellystown Road – Stackstown – Rathfarmham – Dublin 16
HOTEL :
Royal Marine – Dun Laoghaire
Tel : (01)801911
Montrose – Stillorgan
Tel : (01)693311
RESTAURANT : Beaufield Mews – Stillorgan
Tel : (01)880375

This picturesque hillside course overlooks much of Dublin City. It has a challenging layout with the first hole, a par 4, bordered by a stream to the left and an out-of-bound on the right. The uphill 16th demands a blind second shot. The main problem on this course are presented by the continuous ups and downs of the terrain. *SSS 72*

GF $ — Weekends — R

1975 — —

18 — L 5919 P 72

Required : None
Best days : Weekdays

HOLE	LENGTH MEDAL-TEE	PAR	STROKE INDEX
1	360	4	3
2	155	3	15
3	339	4	9
4	270	4	17
5	539	5	5
6	180	3	7
7	487	5	13
8	300	4	11
9	369	4	1
TOTAL	2999	36	TOTAL

HOLE	LENGTH MEDAL-TEE	PAR	STROKE INDEX
10	195	3	6
11	313	4	18
12	294	4	10
13	307	4	16
14	492	5	8
15	351	4	12
16	349	4	2
17	173	3	4
18	446	5	14
TOTAL	2920	36	TOTAL

STRABANE

TEL : (0504)382271
LOCATION : 0,5 m Strabane
ADDRESS : Ballycolman – Strabane – County Tyrone
HOTEL : HP
Fir Trees Lodge – Strabane
Tel : (0504)383003

Situated just off the main road from Strabane to Belfast, this is a welcoming inland course following the undulations of the terrain, with a fine new clubhouse and the Fir Trees Lodge Hotel adjacent to the course. *SSS 68*

GF $

1909

18

—

—

L 5332 P 69

RP

Required : None
Best days : Weekdays

HOLE	LENGTH MEDAL-TEE	PAR	STROKE INDEX
1	330	4	5
2	130	3	15
3	417	4	1
4	363	4	7
5	384	4	3
6	281	4	11
7	119	3	17
8	157	3	13
9	284	4	9
TOTAL	2465	33	TOTAL

HOLE	LENGTH MEDAL-TEE	PAR	STROKE INDEX
10	436	5	12
11	303	4	8
12	133	3	18
13	356	4	4
14	469	5	2
15	265	4	14
16	166	3	16
17	400	4	6
18	339	4	10
TOTAL	2867	36	TOTAL

THE ISLAND

TEL : (01)436205
LOCATION : 24 km Dublin
ADDRESS : Corballis – Donabate – County Dublin
HOTEL :
Grand – Malahide
Tel : (01)450633
RESTAURANT : The Old Schoolhouse – Swords
Tel : (01)402846

Set on the east coast of Ireland, this testing seaside golf course has been redesigned and promises to be one of the leading links courses in County Dublin. *SSS 72*

GF $ — 1890 — 18

— — L 6056 P 71

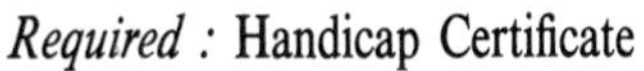

Required : Handicap Certificate
Best days : Mondays, Tuesdays and Fridays

HOLE	LENGTH MEDAL-TEE	PAR	STROKE INDEX
1	396	4	5
2	363	4	7
3	405	4	1
4	320	4	11
5	336	4	9
6	300	4	13
7	403	4	3
8	282	4	15
9	159	3	17
TOTAL	2964	35	TOTAL

HOLE	LENGTH MEDAL-TEE	PAR	STROKE INDEX
10	500	5	14
11	284	4	18
12	379	4	4
13	191	3	8
14	315	4	16
15	507	5	12
16	140	3	10
17	366	4	16
18	410	4	2
TOTAL	2964	36	TOTAL

THE KNOCK

TEL : (02318)3251
LOCATION : 5 m E. Belfast A 20
ADDRESS : Dundonald – Upper Newtownards Rd – Belfast – County Down
HOTEL :
Stormont – Belfast
Tel : (0232)658621
Drumkeen – Belfast
Tel : (0232)491321
Europa – Belfast
Tel : (0232)327000
RESTAURANT : Strand – Belfast
Tel : (0232)682266

Located in the Belfast area, this is a parkland course with very little rough but with many mature trees landscaping the holes. There are two streams criss-crossing the course. Most of the greens are craftily bunkered and of excellent quality. *SSS 71*

GF $

1895

18

Wed., Sat.

—

L 5865 P 70

S

R

Required : None
Best days : Weekdays

HOLE	LENGTH MEDAL-TEE	PAR	STROKE INDEX
1	300	4	7
2	347	4	15
3	418	4	3
4	124	3	17
5	345	4	9
6	414	4	1
7	342	4	11
8	375	4	5
9	328	4	13
TOTAL	2993	35	TOTAL

HOLE	LENGTH MEDAL-TEE	PAR	STROKE INDEX
10	437	5	8
11	381	4	4
12	134	3	18
13	345	4	10
14	409	4	2
15	386	4	6
16	169	3	16
17	247	4	14
18	364	4	12
TOTAL	2872	35	TOTAL

TRALEE

TEL : (066)36379/36355
LOCATION : 13 km Tralee on Fenit road
ADDRESS : West Barrow – Ardfert – Tralee – County Kerry
HOTEL :
The Brandon – Tralee
Tel : (066)23333
Ballygarry House – Tralee
Tel : (066)21233
RESTAURANT : Chez Jean-Marc – Tralee
Tel : (066)21377

This spectacular new links course, the first European creation of Arnold Palmer, the world famous golfer, has a magnificent layout alongside the Atlantic. Set on a scenic corner of Kerry's south-west coast, the course is expected in time to rank among the world's best. Its eighteen holes run through a lush dune landscape having gently rolling fairways and large bunkers. *SSS 71*

GF $$
1904 (new course 1984)
18

—
A. Palmer
L 5552 P 71

Required : Handicap Certificate
Best days : Weekdays ; Weekends by prior arrangement

HOLE	LENGTH MEDAL-TEE	PAR	STROKE INDEX
1	342	4	12
2	518	5	2
3	119	3	14
4	344	4	8
5	356	4	4
6	340	4	10
7	116	3	18
8	317	4	6
9	404	5	16
TOTAL	2856	36	TOTAL

HOLE	LENGTH MEDAL-TEE	PAR	STROKE INDEX
10	354	4	9
11	485	5	7
12	376	4	1
13	115	3	15
14	338	4	5
15	240	4	17
16	142	3	11
17	280	4	13
18	366	4	3
TOTAL	2696	35	TOTAL

TRAMORE

TEL : (051)86170
LOCATION : 2 km W. Tramore/13 km Waterford
ADDRESS : Newtown Hill – Tramore – County Waterford
HOTEL :
Waterford Castle – Waterford
Tel : (051)78203
Grand – Tramore
Tel : (051)81414
RESTAURANT : Candlelight Inn – Dunmore East
Tel : (051)83215

Located near the seaside resort of Tramore, this is an inland course of championship standard. There are fine holes with greens of excellent quality. Among its most testing holes are the 11th and 17th, demanding accurate tee-shots. *SSS 71*

GF $$

Weekends

1894

M. Tibbett

18

6435 y P 72

Required : Handicap Certificate
Best days : Weekdays

HOLE	LENGTH MEDAL-TEE	PAR	STROKE INDEX
1	402	4	
2	511	5	
3	176	3	
4	376	4	
5	329	4	
6	186	3	
7	405	4	
8	409	4	
9	544	5	
TOTAL	3338	36	TOTAL

HOLE	LENGTH MEDAL-TEE	PAR	STROKE INDEX
10	184	3	
11	370	4	
12	350	4	
13	364	4	
14	391	4	
15	127	3	
16	543	5	
17	300	4	
18	468	5	
TOTAL	3097	36	TOTAL

WATERVILLE

TEL : (0667)4102
LOCATION : 48 m SW. Killarney/2 m NW. Waterville
ADDRESS : Waterville – County Kerry
HOTEL : HF
Butler Arms – Waterville
Tel : (0667)4144
Great Southern – Parknasilla
Tel : (064)45122

A beautiful and great seaside course and one of the longest in Ireland. This championship links is laid out in natural surroundings in open land and huge sand dunes with water hazards, overlooking Ballinskelligs Bay and bordered on three sides by the Atlantic. A variety of tee placings gives a choice for all handicaps. The course was the venue for the 1978 World Cup Championships and in 1984 for the European Regional World Cup. Ideal for a holiday with lake Currane nearby for salmon fishing. *SSS 74*

GF $$
1880/1970
18

—
E. Hackett, J. Mulcany
L 7184 y P 72

S

Required : Handicap Certificate
Best days : Weekdays

HOLE	LENGTH MEDAL-TEE	PAR	STROKE INDEX
1	430	4	11
2	469	4	1
3	417	4	3
4	179	3	15
5	595	5	9
6	371	4	13
7	178	3	17
8	435	4	5
9	445	4	7
TOTAL	3519	35	TOTAL

HOLE	LENGTH MEDAL-TEE	PAR	STROKE INDEX
10	475	4	2
11	496	5	10
12	200	3	18
13	518	5	14
14	456	4	4
15	392	4	6
16	350	4	12
17	196	3	16
18	582	5	8
TOTAL	3665	37	TOTAL

WESTPORT

★

TEL : (098)25113
LOCATION : 3 km W. Westport
ADDRESS : Westport – County Mayo
HOTEL :
Westport – Westport
Tel : (098)25122
Newport House – Newport
Tel : (098)41222
RESTAURANT : The Asgard – Westport
Tel : (098)25319

This inland course of championship standard is one of Ireland's longest courses measured from the back tee. It is laid out on the shores of Clew Bay around the slopes of Croagh Patrick mountain. Its feature hole is the 15th with a carry from the tee across the edge of Clew Bay, with an out of bound seashore on the left, and various fairway bunkers. Newport House is a member of Relais & Châteaux. Situated in gardens and park overlooking the Newport River, it has private fishery for salmon and sea trout. *SSS 73*

GF $ — S 

1973 F. Hawtree

18 L 7012 y P 73 R

Required : Club Membership Card
Best days : Mondays to Saturdays

HOLE	LENGTH MEDAL-TEE	PAR	STROKE INDEX
1	348	4	16
2	343	4	10
3	162	3	18
4	501	5	14
5	356	4	12
6	453	4	4
7	524	5	8
8	468	4	2
9	202	3	6
TOTAL	3357	36	TOTAL

HOLE	LENGTH MEDAL-TEE	PAR	STROKE INDEX
10	579	5	11
11	433	4	1
12	220	3	7
13	455	4	3
14	189	3	9
15	580	5	5
16	363	4	15
17	316	4	17
18	520	5	13
TOTAL	3655	37	TOTAL

WEXFORD

TEL : (053)42238
LOCATION : 0,5 km Wexford on Mulgannor road
ADDRESS : Mulgannor – Wexford – Country Wexford
HOTEL :
Talbot – Wexford
Tel : (053)22566
Ferrycarrig – Wexford
Tel : (053)22999
Whites – Wexford
Tel : (053) 22311

This is a fine parkland course, situated in an area of high ground just south of the town, with extensive views of Wexford, Wexford Harbour and as far south as the Saltee Islands. The clubhouse has been recently extented to provide a new pro-shop and extra facilities for members and visitors as well as improved bar & catering facilities. *SSS 69*

GF $ — S R

1960 H. Stutt

18 L 6040 P 70

Required : None
Best days : Weekdays

HOLE	LENGTH MEDAL-TEE	PAR	STROKE INDEX
1	192	3	5
2	305	4	12
3	397	4	6
4	351	4	16
5	192	3	13
6	384	4	8
7	190	3	11
8	511	5	9
9	400	4	4
TOTAL	2922	34	TOTAL

HOLE	LENGTH MEDAL-TEE	PAR	STROKE INDEX
10	399	4	2
11	146	3	14
12	493	5	15
13	203	3	10
14	429	4	1
15	135	3	18
16	491	5	3
17	476	5	17
18	346	4	7
TOTAL	3118	36	TOTAL

WOODBROOK

★

TEL : (01)824799
LOCATION : 18 km Dublin/2 km N. Bray
ADDRESS : Bray – County Wicklow
HOTEL :
Glenview – Glen-of-the-Downs
Tel : (01)873399
RESTAURANT : Tree of Idleness – Bray
Tel : (01)863498

The Woodbrook golf club is located near the popular and picturesque seaside resort of Bray. The golf course is of the inland character with panoramic views, overlooking the Wicklow and Dublin mountains, the sea and the coast stretching from Killiney Head to Bray Head. *SSS 71*

GF $$

1921

18

Weekends

F. Hawtree

L 6034 P 72

Required : Handicap Certificate
Best days : Mondays, Thursdays and Fridays by prior arrangement

HOLE	LENGTH MEDAL-TEE	PAR	STROKE INDEX
1	458	5	12
2	177	3	6
3	344	4	8
4	362	4	4
5	460	5	16
6	315	4	10
7	402	4	2
8	335	4	14
9	130	3	18
TOTAL	2983	36	TOTAL

HOLE	LENGTH MEDAL-TEE	PAR	STROKE INDEX
10	405	4	1
11	195	3	7
12	482	5	11
13	160	3	13
14	478	5	9
15	397	4	3
16	462	5	15
17	128	3	17
18	344	4	5
TOTAL	3051	36	TOTAL

YOUGHAL

TEL : (024)92787
LOCATION : 1 km Youghal on N. 25
ADDRESS : Youghal – County Cork
HOTEL :
Devonshire Arms – Youghal
Tel : (024) 92827
Hilltop – Youghal
Tel : (024)92911
RESTAURANT : Aherne's Seafood – Youghal
Tel : (024)92424

Laid out high above the old sea port town of Youghal, overlooking Youghal Bay and the estuary of the river Blackwater, this is a fine seaside course, ideal for holiday golf, with many interesting holes featuring various strategic bunkers and trees, and tricky doglegs demanding precision from tee to green. *SSS 69*

  GF $

 —

 1898

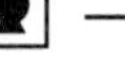  J. Harris

18

L 6223 y P 70

Required : Handicap Certificate
Best days : Weekdays except Wednesdays

HOLE	LENGTH MEDAL-TEE	PAR	STROKE INDEX
1	308	4	10
2	482	5	12
3	180	3	16
4	412	4	3
5	440	4	5
6	350	4	7
7	311	4	14
8	416	4	1
9	295	4	18
TOTAL	3194	36	TOTAL

HOLE	LENGTH MEDAL-TEE	PAR	STROKE INDEX
10	407	4	4
11	354	4	11
12	340	4	15
13	164	3	17
14	407	4	2
15	361	4	13
16	200	3	9
17	380	4	8
18	416	4	6
TOTAL	3029	34	TOTAL

Car Rental

Reservation/Information telephone number :

Country code :
39

Telephone number :
6/6888041
1678/68088 (toll-free number)

Headquarters address :

EUROPCAR ITALIA SpA
Via del Fiume Giallo, 00144 Roma Eur Torrino Sud
Tel. : (39) 6/6888029
Telex : 614202
Fax : (39) 6/5732317

101 GOLF COURSES, 32 000 PLAYERS

★★★ Great golf course
★★ Very good golf course
$ 20.000-80.000 Lire
★ Recommended golf course
☼ Holiday golf course
$ $ more than 80.000 Lire

TOWN	GOLF COURSE		TEL	MAP REF.
Abano Terme	Frassanelle		(049) 9900054	42
Alessandria	Margara		(131) 778555	14
Anzio	L'Eucalyptus		(06) 926252	43
Arenzano	Pineta		(010) 9111817	•
Asiago	Asiago		(0424) 462721	•
Aviano	Castel d'Aviano		(0434) 652302	•
Avigliana	Le Fronde		(011) 938053	13
Barlassina	Barlassina		(0362) 560621	4
Bergamo	Bergamo L'Albenza	★	(035) 640028	11
	La Rossera		(035) 838600	•
	Parco dei Colli		(035) 260444	•
Biella	Biella « Le Betulle »	★★	(015) 679151	7
Bologna	Bologna		(051) 969100	24
Brendola	Colli Berici		(0444) 601780	•
Brescia	Franciacorta		(030) 984167	38
Breuil Cervinia	Cervino		(0166) 949131	•
Carmagnola	La Margherita *(ext. 18 h.)*		(011) 9795113	•
Catanzaro	Porto d'Orra		(0961) 791045	•
Cervia	Adriatic Cervia	☼	(0544) 992786	35
Cetraro	San Michele		(0982) 91012	•
Cherasco	Le Chiocciole		(0172) 48772	•
Claviere	Claviere		(0122) 878917	•
Collecchio	La Rocca		(0521) 834037	45
Como	Carimate Parco	☼	(031) 790226	10
	La Pinetina	☼	(031) 933202	9
	Monticello	★★★	(031) 928055	6
	Villa d'Este	★★★ ☼	(031) 200200	15
Courmayeur	Courmayeur		(0165) 89103	•
Desenzano del Garda	Garda Golf	☼	(0365) 674707	39
Firenze	Firenze	★★	(055) 2301009	25
Fiuggi	Fiuggi		(0775) 55250	•
Folgaria	Trentino		(0461) 981682	•
Frassanelle	Frassanelle		(049) 9910477	50
Galzignano	Padova	☼	(049) 9130078	19
Garda	Ca'degli Ulivi		(045) 7256497	• 51
Gardone	Bogliaco		(0365) 643006	•
Garlenda	Garlenda	★ ☼	(0182) 580012	17
Gorizia	San Floriano		(0481) 884131	•

TOWN	GOLF COURSE		TEL	MAP REF.
Lanzo Intelvi	Lanzo		(031) 840169	•
Lecco	Royal Sant'Anna		(0341) 577551	•
Lerici	Marigola		(0187) 970193	•
Madonna di Campiglio	Carlo Magno		(0465) 41003	•
Menaggio	Menaggio & Cadenabbia		(0344) 32103	1
Milano	Le Rovedine		(02) 55500405	•
	Milano	★★★	(039) 303081	5
	Molinetto	★	(02) 9238500	32
	Zoate		(02) 90631861	34
Montecatini	Montecatini		(0572) 62218	41
Napoli	Napoli		(081) 8674296	•
Novara	Castelconturbia	★	(0322) 802093	33
Parma	La Rocca		(0521) 834037	•
Perugia	Perugia		(075) 795204	•
Petersberg	Petersberg		(0471) 615122	•
Piacenza	Croara		(0523) 977105	46
Ponte di Legno	Ponte di Legno		(0364) 92577	•
Poppi	Casentino		(0575) 520167	•
Premeno	Piandisole		(0323) 47100	•
Punta Ala	Punta Ala	★ ✡	(0564) 922121	26
Rapallo	Rapallo	★	(0185) 50210	18
Roma	Castelgandolfo		(06) 9313084	37
	Fioranello		(06) 608291	•
	Olgiata	★★	(06) 3789141	29
	Parco de'Medici		(06) 6553477	47
	Roma Circolo	★★★	(06) 783407	30
Rosolina	Albarella	✡	(0426) 67124	23
San Remo	San Remo	✡	(0184) 67093	16
Sestriere	Sestriere		(0122) 76276	3
Sirolo	Conero Sirolo		(071) 7360613	48
Stresa	Alpino di Stresa		(0323) 20101	•
	Iles Borromées		(0323) 30243	49
Taranto	Riva dei Tessali	✡	(099) 6439251	31
Tarquinia	Marina Velca		(0766) 812109	•
Tirrenia	Tirrenia		(050) 37518	•
Torino	I. Roveri	★★★	(011) 9235667	8
	Stupinigi		(011) 343975	•
	Torino La Mandria	★★★	(011) 9235440	12
	Vinovo		(011) 9653880	•
Trieste	Trieste		(040) 226159	•
Udine	Udine		(0432) 800418	•
Valenza	La Serra		(0131) 954778	•
Varese	Varese	★	(0332) 229302	2
Venezia	Ca Della Nave	★	(041) 5401555	36
	Lido di Venezia	★ ✡	(041) 731015	21
	Villa Condulmer	★	(041) 457062	20
Verona	Verona		(045) 510060	22
Vigevano	Santa Martretta		(0381) 76872	•
Vinovo	Vinovo		(011) 9653880	•
Vittoria Veneto	Cansiglio		(0438) 585398	•
ISOLA D'ELBA				
Portoferraio	Acquabona		(0565) 940066	•
	Hermitage		(0565) 969932	•
SARDEGNA				
Porto Cervo	Pevero	★★★ ✡	(0789) 96210	27
Pula	Is Molas	★★ ✡	(070) 9209062	28
SICILIA				
Castiglione	Il Picciole	✡	(0942) 986252	44

NEW GOLF COURSES (18 HOLES OR MORE) TO OPEN SOON

Circolo Golf Matilde di Canossa
42100 S. Bartolomeo
Tel. : (0522)955295

Eturia Golf Club
53049 Torrita di Siena
Tel. : (0577)686318

Golf Club Castello della Montecchia
35030 Selvazzano
Tel. : (049)8055550

Golf Club Le Querce
01015 Sutri
Tel. : (0761)68142

Golf Club Mettuno
00048 Mettuno
Tel. : (06)9876219

Modena
41050 Colombaro di Formigine
Tel. : (059) 553482

Picciolo Golf Club
Castiglione di Sicilia
Tel. : (0942)986252

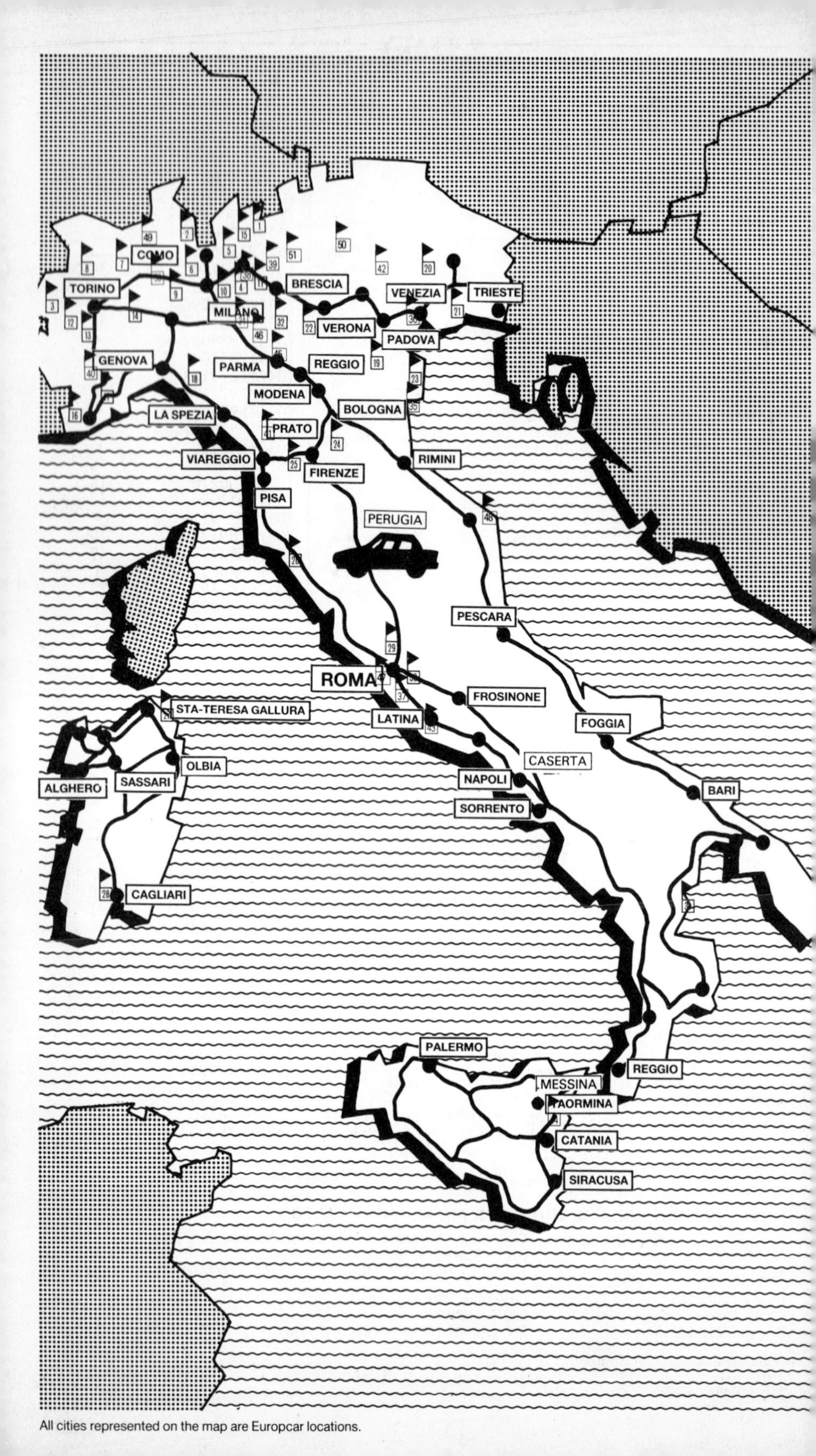

All cities represented on the map are Europcar locations.

ADRIATIC CERVIA

TEL : (0544)992786
LOCATION : 20 km Ravenna/30 km Rimini
ADDRESS : Via Jelenia Gora 2-48016 Cervia-Milano Marittima (RA)
HOTEL :
Mare e Pineta-Milano Marittima
Tel : (0544)992262
Aurelia-Milano Marittima
Tel : (0544)992082
Rouge-Milano Marittima
Tel : (0544)992201
RESTAURANT : Al Caminetto-Milano Marittima
Tel : (0544)994292

Designed by the Venetian architect Marco Croze,the course is laid out near the health and holiday resort of Cervia amidst thick maritime pinewood, sand dunes and lakes, not far from the Adriatic sea front.The club is equipped with thirteen tennis courts. *SSS 72*

GF $

1985

18

Tues.; Dec. to March

M. Croze

L 6038 P 72

R S

Required : Handicap Certificate
Best days : Any day

HOLE	LENGTH MEDAL-TEE	PAR	STROKE INDEX
1	378	4	7
2	409	4	1
3	552	5	3
4	328	4	9
5	137	3	17
6	473	5	15
7	319	4	11
8	172	3	5
9	339	4	13
TOTAL	3107	36	TOTAL

HOLE	LENGTH MEDAL-TEE	PAR	STROKE INDEX
10	320	4	18
11	286	4	14
12	351	4	4
13	506	5	8
14	202	3	6
15	468	5	12
16	360	4	2
17	157	3	10
18	281	4	16
TOTAL	2931	36	TOTAL

ALBARELLA

TEL : (0426)330124
LOCATION : 50 km Venezia
ADDRESS : 45010 Isola di Albarella-Rosolina
HOTEL : HR
Golf
Tel : (0426)330373
Alexander – Rosolina Mare
Tel : (0426)68047
Capo Nord – Isola di Albarella
Tel : (0426)330139

This is the perfect holiday course, laid out on the tiny island of Albarella situated at the mouth of the Po river. Set in fine natural surroundings amongst sand dunes, beaches and small lakes, the course has a seaside character and is of championship standard. The Golf Hotel is situated on the course with tennis courts and a swimming pool. *SSS 72*

GF $

1972

18

Tuesdays

J. Harris, M. Croze

L 6065 P 72

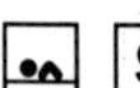 

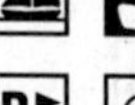 

RF

Required : Handicap Certificate
Best days : Weekdays

HOLE	LENGTH MEDAL-TEE	PAR	STROKE INDEX
1	395	4	1
2	130	3	18
3	365	4	10
4	365	4	12
5	370	4	8
6	325	4	16
7	500	5	6
8	200	3	2
9	440	5	15
TOTAL	3090	36	TOTAL

HOLE	LENGTH MEDAL-TEE	PAR	STROKE INDEX
10	350	4	5
11	330	4	17
12	440	5	13
13	315	4	11
14	200	3	4
15	490	5	9
16	185	3	3
17	345	4	7
18	320	4	14
TOTAL	2975	36	TOTAL

BARLASSINA

TEL : (0362)560621/2/3
LOCATION : 22 km Milano
ADDRESS : Via Privata Golf 42 – 20030
Lentate sul Seveso – Birago di Camnago
(Milano)
HOTEL :
Park Hotel – Figino
Tel : (031)780792
Brunelleschi – Milano
Tel : (02)312256
Manin – Milano
Tel : (02)6596511
RESTAURANT : Saviri – Milano
Tel : (02)8058343

A fine natural inland course with its wide fairways landscaped among luxuriant woodland. The course is rather testing featuring three troublesome holes: the 4th, 6th and 10th. There is an attractive mansion style clubhouse with a swimming pool, tennis courts and football field. *SSS 71*

GF $

Mondays

1955

 J. Harris

18

 6053 P 72

Required : Handicap Certificate
Best days : Tuesdays to Fridays inc.

HOLE	LENGTH MEDAL-TEE	PAR	STROKE INDEX
1	441	5	15
2	290	4	17
3	341	4	5
4	362	4	1
5	190	3	7
6	363	4	3
7	447	5	13
8	329	4	11
9	176	3	9
TOTAL	2939	36	TOTAL

HOLE	LENGTH MEDAL-TEE	PAR	STROKE INDEX
10	414	4	2
11	508	4	10
12	148	3	18
13	442	5	16
14	374	4	6
15	169	3	14
16	379	4	4
17	325	4	12
18	355	4	8
TOTAL	3114	35	TOTAL

BERGAMO L'ALBENZA

★

TEL : (035)640028
LOCATION : 13 km Bergamo
ADDRESS : Via Longoni 21 – 24030 Almenno San Bartolomeo
HOTEL :
Excelsior San Marco – Bergamo
Tel : (035)232132
Arli – Bergamo
Tel : (035)222014
Cristallo Palace – Bergamo
Tel : (035)311211
RESTAURANT : Taverna del Colleoni – Bergamo
Tel : (035)232596

Set in the thickly wooded Alpine foothills, the course was originally designed by Charles Cotton and later redesigned by John Morrison. A truly testing and very attractive inland course (three loops of nine holes: red-yellow and blue course) with its narrow fairways flanked by age-old conifers and broadleaf. Several of the holes are crossed by ditches. *SSS 71*

GF $

Mondays

R S

1960

C. Cotton, J. Morrison

27

L 3098 P 36, 3100 P 36, 2962 P 36

Required : Handicap Certificate
Best days : Weekdays

HOLE	LENGTH MEDAL-TEE	PAR	STROKE INDEX	HOLE	LENGTH MEDAL-TEE	PAR	STROKE INDEX	HOLE	LENGTH MEDAL-TEE	PAR	STROKE INDEX
1	476	5	7	10	382	4	4	1	185	3	12
2	171	3	11	11	115	3	16	2	348	4	6
3	400	4	3	12	338	4	14	3	275	4	14
4	350	4	9	13	515	5	6	4	575	5	2
5	345	4	13	14	388	4	2	5	135	3	18
6	160	3	17	15	469	5	10	6	514	5	4
7	485	5	5	16	175	3	12	7	329	4	10
8	311	4	15	17	375	4	8	8	277	4	16
9	400	4	1	18	307	4	18	9	324	4	8
TOTAL	3098	36	TOTAL	TOTAL	3100	36	TOTAL	TOTAL	2962	36	TOTAL

BIELLA « LE BETULLE »

TEL : (015)679151
LOCATION : 18 km Biella S 338
ADDRESS : 13050 Magnano – Vercelli
HOTEL :
Astoria – Biella
Tel : (015)20545
Augustus – Biella
Tel : (015)27554
Michelangelo – Biella
Tel : (015)21270
RESTAURANT : Prinz Grill – Biella
Tel : (015)30302

This is a magnificent and scenic course set in fine natural countryside backed by thickly wooded hills. The course is long and technically interesting with its undulating fairways running between majestic oak, chestnut and silver birch trees. All the holes have great character, demanding accuracy. One of the best clubs in Italy, it has hosted several major European tournaments. An attractive feature is the fine clubhouse with several bedrooms for visiting golfers. *SSS 72*

GF $ — Mon. ; Nov. to April 

1958 —  J. Morrison 

18 —  L 6045 P 73 

Required : Handicap Certificate
Best days : Weekdays

HOLE	LENGTH MEDAL-TEE	PAR	STROKE INDEX
1	354	4	5
2	170	3	17
3	359	4	11
4	356	4	7
5	174	3	15
6	344	4	1
7	462	5	9
8	351	4	3
9	446	5	13
TOTAL	3016	36	TOTAL

HOLE	LENGTH MEDAL-TEE	PAR	STROKE INDEX
10	169	3	16
11	447	5	14
12	329	4	2
13	327	4	10
14	373	4	4
15	293	4	6
16	472	5	8
17	171	3	18
18	448	5	12
TOTAL	3029	37	TOTAL

BOLOGNA

TEL : (051)969100
LOCATION : 20 km Bologna
ADDRESS : Via Sabatini 69 – 40050
Chiesa Nuova di Monte St-Pietro
HOTEL :
Della Rocca – Bazzano
Tel : (051)831217
Zolam – Bologna
Tel : (051)751101
Baglioni – Bologna
Tel : (051)225445
RESTAURANT : Al Pappagallo – Bologna
Tel : (051)232807

Set in the green and fertile plains of the Apennines, the course is pleasant with several fine holes such as the long 6th and 12th, and the testing 15th hole. There is a bungalow style clubhouse with tennis courts and a swimming pool. *SSS 72*

GF $

1959

18

Mondays

H. Cotton

L 6108 P 72

S

Required : Handicap Certificate
Best days : Weekdays

HOLE	LENGTH MEDAL-TEE	PAR	STROKE INDEX
1	343	4	
2	150	3	
3	474	5	
4	175	4	
5	405	4	
6	544	5	
7	279	4	
8	293	4	
9	261	4	
TOTAL	2924	36	TOTAL

HOLE	LENGTH MEDAL-TEE	PAR	STROKE INDEX
10	166	3	
11	465	5	
12	406	4	
13	454	5	
14	342	4	
15	375	4	
16	384	4	
17	196	3	
18	396	4	
TOTAL	3171	36	TOTAL

Ca' degli Ulivi

TEL : (045)7256497
LOCATION : 35 km Verona, near Garda
ADDRESS : Via Ghiandare 2 - 37010
Marciaga di Costermano (VR)
HOTEL :
Regina Adelaide - Garda
Tel : (045)7255013
Madrigale - Garda
Tel : (045)7256322
Beatrix - Garda
Tel : (045)7212120

Standing close to the city of Garda and the famous Garda lake, this promising new championship layout embraces the natural lines of the land and rolls through beautiful and sweeping wooded landscape dotted with scenic lakes.

GF

1988

18

Mondays

Cotton, Pennink & Partners

L 6000 P 72

 S

Required : Handicap Certificate
Best days : Weekdays

HOLE	LENGTH MEDAL-TEE	PAR	STROKE INDEX
1	290	4	
2	520	5	
3	380	4	
4	340	4	
5	320	4	
6	180	3	
7	380	4	
8	490	5	
9	340	4	
TOTAL	3240	37	TOTAL

HOLE	LENGTH MEDAL-TEE	PAR	STROKE INDEX
10	440	5	
11	320	4	
12	200	3	
13	480	5	
14	360	4	
15	140	3	
16	300	4	
17	160	3	
18	360	4	
TOTAL	2760	35	TOTAL

CA DELLA NAVE

★

TEL : (041)5401555
LOCATION : 20 km Venice
ADDRESS : Piazza della Vittoria 14-30030 Martellago (VE)
HOTEL :
Villa Conestabile-Scorzè
Tel : (041)445027
Villa Giustinian-Scorzè
Tel : (041)5700200
RESTAURANT : Auto Espresso-Scorzè
Tel : (041)939214

Arnold Palmer designed the Ca della Nave golf course which is laid out in typical Venetian countryside. The 18 holes wind through flat terrain and artificial lakes affect play on many of them. Among its feature holes is the short 14th with its fairway entirely surrounded by water. The course is located on the former estate of the ancient « Grimani Morosini » family and centered around the beautiful 16th century 'Villa' with several farm buildings dating back to the 19th century. Facilities include 4 tennis courts and 3 swimming pools. *SSS 72*

GF $$

1986

27

Tuesdays

A. Palmer

L 6373 P 72

Required : Handicap Certificate
Best days : Weekdays

HOLE	LENGTH MEDAL-TEE	PAR	STROKE INDEX
1	373	4	9
2	396	4	1
3	507	5	11
4	150	3	15
5	408	4	5
6	468	5	13
7	392	4	7
8	164	3	17
9	432	4	3
TOTAL	3290	36	TOTAL

HOLE	LENGTH MEDAL-TEE	PAR	STROKE INDEX
10	400	4	2
11	160	3	14
12	436	5	18
13	345	4	16
14	300	4	12
15	490	5	10
16	360	4	6
17	200	3	4
18	392	4	8
TOTAL	3083	36	TOTAL

CARIMATE PARCO

TEL : (031)790226/790392
LOCATION : 18 km Como S 35
ADDRESS : Via Airoldi 2 – 22060 Carimate – Como
HOTEL :
Como – Como
Tel : (031)266173
Barchetta Excelsior – Como
Tel : (031)266531
Villa Fori – Como
Tel : (031)557642
RESTAURANT : Al Torchio del Castello – Carimate
Tel : (031)791486

Not far from Lake Como, this attractive inland course has wide fairways landscaped among coniferous woods. Cunningly bunkered there is only one water hazard, a pond on the 17th hole. The modern clubhouse has three tennis courts and an attractive heart shaped swimming pool. *SSS 71*

GF $ | Mondays | S
1962 | P. Mancinelli
18 | L 5982 P 71

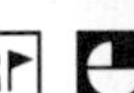

Required : Handicap Certificate
Best days : Weekdays

HOLE	LENGTH MEDAL-TEE	PAR	STROKE INDEX
1	372	4	5
2	149	3	12
3	447	5	7
4	348	4	8
5	481	5	14
6	174	3	10
7	354	4	2
8	327	4	9
9	324	4	16
TOTAL	2976	36	TOTAL

HOLE	LENGTH MEDAL-TEE	PAR	STROKE INDEX
10	354	4	4
11	529	5	6
12	361	4	7
13	349	4	13
14	377	4	3
15	170	3	18
16	372	4	1
17	169	3	11
18	325	4	15
TOTAL	3006	35	TOTAL

CASTELCONTURBIA

★

TEL : (0322)832093
LOCATION : 18 km Novara
ADDRESS : Via Suno – 28010 Agrate Conturbia
HOTEL :
La Famiglia – Novara
Tel : (0321)399316
La Rotonda – Novara
Tel : (0321)23691
Maya – Novara
Tel : (0321)452722
RESTAURANT : Giorgio – Novara
Tel : (0321)27647

Robert Trent Jones designed this promising championship layout. There are three separate loops of nine holes laid out on gently rolling parkland. The fairways are wide and generous with numerous lakes serving as hazards. A feature of the golf course is the clubhouse complex, set in the middle of the course, with gymnasium, restaurants, a Junior's Club and accomodation for golfers. Other sports facilities include two tennis courts and a large swimming pool.

GF $

1984

27

Mondays

R. Trent Jones

L 3081 P 36, 3269 P 36, 3121 P 36

Required : Handicap Certificate
Best days : Weekdays

HOLE	LENGTH MEDAL-TEE	PAR	STROKE INDEX	HOLE	LENGTH MEDAL-TEE	PAR	STROKE INDEX	HOLE	LENGTH MEDAL-TEE	PAR	STROKE INDEX
1	488	5	18	10	395	4	5	1	514	5	11/12
2	150	3	14	11	406	4	1	2	148	3	17/18
3	503	5	12	12	437	4	3	3	407	4	1/2
4	403	4	2	13	119	3	17	4	138	3	15/16
5	497	5	8	14	356	4	11	5	342	4	9/10
6	174	3	10	15	539	5	7	6	366	4	5/6
7	348	4	4	16	405	4	9	7	374	5	7/8
8	176	3	6	17	132	3	13	8	456	4	13/14
9	342	4	16	18	480	5	15	9	376	4	3/4
TOTAL	3081	36	TOTAL	TOTAL	3269	36	TOTAL	TOTAL	3121	36	TOTAL

CASTELGANDOLFO

TEL : (06)9313084
LOCATION : 25 km Roma
ADDRESS : Via di Santo Spirito 13-00040 Castelgandolfo
HOTEL :
Helio Cabala-Marino
Tel : (06)9384235
Lord Byron-Roma
Tel : (06)3609541
Parco dei Principe-Roma
Tel : (06)841071
RESTAURANT : Al Vigneto-Marino
Tel : (06)9387034

This course is located in Castelgandolfo, the Pope's summer residence and laid out in rolling lush Roman countryside amidst olive trees and maritime pinewood. It features three lakes which serve as hazards on six holes. The splendid clubhouse, a former 17th century palace, is set amidst roses, mimosa, cypress and pine trees. *SSS 71*

GF $$

1988

18

Mondays

 R. Trent Jones

 5855 P 72

Required : Handicap Certificate
Best days : Any day

HOLE	LENGTH MEDAL-TEE	PAR	STROKE INDEX
1	370	4	9
2	175	3	17
3	346	4	7
4	349	4	1
5	453	5	5
6	334	4	11
7	137	3	15
8	474	5	3
9	279	4	13
TOTAL	2917	36	TOTAL

HOLE	LENGTH MEDAL-TEE	PAR	STROKE INDEX
10	397	4	14
11	453	5	6
12	127	3	16
13	383	4	4
14	318	4	10
15	454	5	2
16	318	4	8
17	138	3	18
18	350	4	12
TOTAL	2938	36	TOTAL

CONERO SIROLO

TEL : (071)7360613
LOCATION : 20 km S. Ancona A14
ADDRESS : Via Betellico 6 - 60020 Sirolo (AN)
HOTEL :
Monteconero - Sirolo
Tel : (071)936122
Eden Gigli - Sirolo
Tel : (071)936182
Jolly - Ancona
Tel : (071)201171

About 20 km from Ancona, the course lies in the Conero National Park between Mount Colombo and the Betellico. Only two kilometers from the Adriatic Sea, it offers an interesting pattern of holes which follow the natural undulations of the open landscape. The fairways are dotted with strategic trees. A lake and a river serve as obstacles. Facilities include a short 9 hole course, tennis courts and a swimming pool.

GF $

1988

18

Mondays ; Jan.15-Feb15

M. Croze

L 6185 P 72

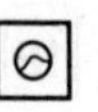

Required : Handicap Certificate
Best days : Any day

HOLE	LENGTH MEDAL-TEE	PAR	STROKE INDEX
1	480	5	
2	410	4	
3	475	5	
4	310	4	
5	150	5	
6	380	4	
7	340	4	
8	350	4	
9	200	3	
TOTAL	3095	38	TOTAL

HOLE	LENGTH MEDAL-TEE	PAR	STROKE INDEX
10	330	4	
11	410	4	
12	510	5	
13	200	3	
14	320	4	
15	490	5	
16	175	3	
17	315	4	
18	340	4	
TOTAL	3090	36	TOTAL

CROARA

TEL : (0523)977105
LOCATION : 16 km Piacenza
ADDRESS : Croara di Gazzola – 29010 Gazzola (PC)
HOTEL :
Grande Alb. Roma – Piacenza
Tel : (0523)23201
Palace - Castelsangio - Vanni
Tel : (0523)840641
Nazionale – Croara
Tel : (0532)754000
RESTAURANT : Antica Osteria del Teatro – Piacenza
Tel : (0523)23777

Recently extended to 18 holes, the course is laid out on rolling countryside in the foothills of the Apennines. It has a typical hillside character, with the river Trebbia meandering its way through the course and creating problems on more than four holes. The club features a fine clubhouse, a swimming pool, a fitness club and 5 tennis courts. *SSS 72*

GF $ — Tuesdays ; January — S

1977 — R. Buratti, M. Croze 

18 — L 6065 P 72 

Required : Club Membership Card
Best days : Mondays and Fridays

HOLE	LENGTH MEDAL-TEE	PAR	STROKE INDEX
1	409	4	2
2	372	4	12
3	335	4	16
4	315	4	4
5	195	3	8
6	460	5	14
7	145	3	18
8	351	4	10
9	502	5	6
TOTAL	3084	36	TOTAL

HOLE	LENGTH MEDAL-TEE	PAR	STROKE INDEX
10	171	3	9
11	410	4	1
12	371	4	5
13	450	5	15
14	295	4	7
15	308	4	11
16	149	3	17
17	480	5	3
18	347	4	13
TOTAL	2981	36	TOTAL

FIRENZE

TEL : (055)2301009
LOCATION : 12 km S. Firenze
ADDRESS : Strada Chiantigiana 3 – 50015 Dell'Ugolino – Grassina
HOTEL :
Villa Carlotta – Firenze
Tel : (055)220530
Croce di Malta – Firenze
Tel : (055)218351
Regency – Firenze
Tel : (055)245247
RESTAURANT : Enoteca Pinchiorri – Firenze
Tel : (055)242777

This noble hillside course follows the natural undulations of the Chianti Hills. The course is not very long but demands delicate stroke play as there are many natural hazards such as cypress, olive, pine, cork and oleander trees or changes in level of the terrain. The clubhouse has a swimming pool and various tennis courts. *SSS 70*

GF $ | Mondays
1934 | C. Blandford
18 | L 5741 P 72

Required : Handicap Certificate
Best days : Weekdays

HOLE	LENGTH MEDAL-TEE	PAR	STROKE INDEX
1	305	4	
2	258	4	
3	298	4	
4	199	3	
5	398	4	
6	472	5	
7	280	4	
8	130	3	
9	461	5	
TOTAL	2801	36	TOTAL

HOLE	LENGTH MEDAL-TEE	PAR	STROKE INDEX
10	203	3	
11	350	4	
12	148	3	
13	335	4	
14	476	5	
15	340	4	
16	325	4	
17	469	5	
18	294	4	
TOTAL	2940	36	TOTAL

FRANCIACORTA

TEL : (030)984167
LOCATION : 20 km Brescia/25 km Bergamo
ADDRESS : Loc. Castagnola-25040 Corte Franca
HOTEL :
Golfhotel Franciacorte-Paratico
Tel : (035)913333
Cristallo Palace-Bergamo
Tel : (035)311211
Vittoria-Brescia
Tel : (030)280061

Franciacorta is designed by the American Pete Dye in association with Italy's most famous architect Marco Croze. Laid out in open gently rolling countryside, it has two lakes which serve as hazards on eight holes. The course's greatest traps are the 5th and the 11th, both having island greens. There is an impressive modern clubhouse with tennis courts, a swimming pool, and a riding school. *SSS 72*

GF $

1986

27

Tuesdays

P. Dye, M. Croze

L 6065 P 72, 1150 P 27

S

R

Required : Handicap Certificate
Best days : Any day

HOLE	LENGTH MEDAL-TEE	PAR	STROKE INDEX
1	320	4	13
2	350	4	3
3	300	4	11
4	390	4	1
5	185	3	9
6	470	5	5
7	305	4	17
8	480	5	7
9	160	3	15
TOTAL	2960	36	TOTAL

HOLE	LENGTH MEDAL-TEE	PAR	STROKE INDEX
10	445	5	18
11	125	3	16
12	345	4	6
13	490	5	12
14	360	4	10
15	350	4	8
16	195	3	14
17	385	4	4
18	410	4	2
TOTAL	3105	36	TOTAL

FRASSANELLE

TEL : (049)9910477
LOCATION : 10 km Padova/20 km Vicenza
ADDRESS : 35030 Frassanelle di Rovolon (PD)
HOTEL :
Mioni Pezzato - Frassanelle
Tel : (049)668377
Bristol Biya - Frassanelle
Tel : (049)669390
La Résidence - Frassanelle

At 3 km from the thermal spa of Abano Terme near the city of Padova lies the friendly Frassanelle course designed by the Venetian architect Marco Croze. Its 18 holes are found in a pleasant and flat parkland setting with mature trees and lakes serving as hazards.

GF $ — Tuesdays — S
1988 — M. Croze
18 — L 6120 P 72 — R

Required : Handicap Certificate
Best days : Weekdays

HOLE	LENGTH MEDAL-TEE	PAR	STROKE INDEX
1			
2			
3			
4			
5			
6			
7			
8			
9			
TOTAL			TOTAL

HOLE	LENGTH MEDAL-TEE	PAR	STROKE INDEX
10			
11			
12			
13			
14			
15			
16			
17			
18			
TOTAL			TOTAL

GARDAGOLF

✡★

TEL : (0365)674707
LOCATION : 13 km Desenzano del Garda/12 km Salo
ADDRESS : Via Angelo Omodeo 2-25080 Soiano del Lago (BS)
HOTEL :
Grand-Gardone
Tel : (0365)20261
Grandhotel-Fasano
Tel : (035)21051
Villa del Sogno-Fasano
Tel : (0365)20228
RESTAURANT : Villa Fiordaliso-Gardone
Tel : (0365)20158

Set in a splendid natural landscape above Lake Garda amidst tall cypress trees, this is a promising championship course. There are magnificent views of the majestic 'Baldo' mountain chain from many of the holes. The course is varied and entertaining with scenic ponds and streams serving as hazards on seven holes. The impressive clubhouse with its spacious terrace dominates the entire course. The club is equipped with 4 tennis courts, a riding school and 3 swimming pools. *SSS 74*

GF $

1985

27

Mondays

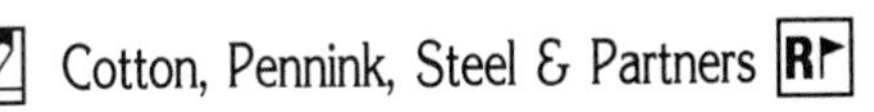

Cotton, Pennink, Steel & Partners

L 6011 P 72, 2415 P 34

S

Required : Handicap Certificate
Best days : Weekdays

HOLE	LENGTH MEDAL-TEE	PAR	STROKE INDEX
1	380	4	6
2	441	5	18
3	332	4	4
4	377	4	2
5	199	3	10
6	328	4	8
7	462	5	16
8	165	3	12
9	340	4	14
TOTAL	3024	36	TOTAL

HOLE	LENGTH MEDAL-TEE	PAR	STROKE INDEX
10	363	4	1
11	135	3	15
12	459	5	11
13	378	4	5
14	477	5	13
15	326	4	7
16	291	4	17
17	395	4	3
18	163	3	9
TOTAL	2987	36	TOTAL

GARLENDA

☆★

TEL : (0182)580012
LOCATION : 10 km Albenga / 15 km Alassio / 6 km Autostrada Dei Fiori
ADDRESS : Via del Golf 7 - 17030 Garlenda - Savona
HOTEL : HR
La Méridiana
Tel : (0182)580150
Foresteria
Tel : (0182)580013
Hermitage - Garlenda
Tel : (0182)582975

Fourteen kilometres from the Italian Riviera and the seaside resorts of Alassio and Albenga, this pleasant and peacefully situated golf course is ideal for holiday golf. Backed by luxuriant wooded hills, the flat course is cut in two by the small 'Lerrone' river. There is a cosy clubhouse with tennis courts, riding school and swimming pool. The refined Relais & Châteaux hotel 'La Meridiana' and the club's dormy house 'La Foresteria' are situated on the course. *SSS 71*

GF $

1965

18

Wednesdays (1-9/1-6)

J. Harris

L 5862 P 71

Required : Handicap Certificate
Best days : Weekdays

HOLE	LENGTH MEDAL-TEE	PAR	STROKE INDEX
1	290	4	14
2	182	3	9
3	465	5	4
4	373	4	2
5	480	5	8
6	302	4	16
7	138	3	18
8	318	4	6
9	445	5	11
TOTAL	2993	37	TOTAL

HOLE	LENGTH MEDAL-TEE	PAR	STROKE INDEX
10	278	4	17
11	382	4	5
12	388	4	1
13	185	3	12
14	438	5	10
15	146	3	15
16	387	4	3
17	349	4	7
18	316	4	13
TOTAL	2869	35	TOTAL

ILES BORROMEES

TEL : (0323)30243/29285
LOCATION : 5 km Stresa/70 km Milano
ADDRESS : Via Bono Lamberti 14 - 28049 Stresa (NO)
HOTEL :
Regina Palace - Stresa
Tel : (0323)30171
Milan Speranza - Stresa
Tel : (0323)31178
Astoria - Stresa
Tel : (0323)32566

Wedged between luxuriant hills and rising to 600 m above sea level, this course is near the historical city of Stresa and the famous "lago Maggiore" lake. Situated in a splendid natural landscape, many holes are bordered by majestic old trees and a scenic river meanders through them. *SSS 72*

GF $ — Mondays — S
1988 — M. Croze
18 — L 5910 P 72 — R

Required : Handicap Certificate
Best days : Weekdays

HOLE	LENGTH MEDAL-TEE	PAR	STROKE INDEX
1	340	4	5
2	335	4	7
3	385	4	3
4	310	4	17
5	135	3	15
6	450	5	13
7	390	4	1
8	160	3	11
9	450	5	9
TOTAL	2955	36	TOTAL

HOLE	LENGTH MEDAL-TEE	PAR	STROKE INDEX
10	340	4	5
11	335	4	7
12	385	4	3
13	310	4	17
14	135	3	15
15	450	5	13
16	390	4	1
17	160	3	11
18	450	5	9
TOTAL	2955	36	TOTAL

IL PICCIOLO

✡

TEL : (0942)986252
LOCATION : 45 km Catania/4 km Linguaglossa/25 km Taormina
ADDRESS : S.S. 120 km 200
Castiglione di Sicilia (CT)
HOTEL :
Albergo d'Orange - Francavilla
Tel : (0942)981374
San Domenico Palace - Taormina
Tel : (0942)23701
RESTAURANT : Casa degli Vlivi - Linguaglossa
Tel : (095)643593

Laid out in a unique setting of volcanic landscape not far from Mount Etna, this new and prestigious club is the only one on the scenic island of Sicily. Both hilly and flat the holes, dotted with 3 lakes, blend perfectly into the mountainous countryside and offer fine views of the surroundings. Facilities will include a hotel, tennis courts and a swimming pool.

GF $

1988

18

—

D. Steel/L. Rota Caremoli

L 4748 P 68

S

R

Required : None
Best days : Any day

HOLE	LENGTH MEDAL-TEE	PAR	STROKE INDEX
1	314	4	
2	135	3	
3	150	3	
4	272	4	
5	285	4	
6	445	5	
7	147	3	
8	145	3	
9	485	5	
TOTAL	2378	34	TOTAL

HOLE	LENGTH MEDAL-TEE	PAR	STROKE INDEX
10	312	4	
11	465	5	
12	122	3	
13	282	4	
14	165	3	
15	257	4	
16	350	4	
17	95	3	
18	322	4	
TOTAL	2370	34	TOTAL

I ROVERI

TEL : (011)9235667
LOCATION : 16 km Torino
ADDRESS : Rotta Cerbiatta 24 - 10070
Fiano - La Mandria
HOTEL :
Turin Palace - Torino
Tel : (011)515511
City - Torino
Tel : (011)540546
Jolly Ligure - Torino
Tel : (011)55641
RESTAURANT : Villa Sassi - Torino
Tel : (011)890556

Located inside La Mandria Park, a nature park for deer, pheasants, wild boar and chamois, the I Roveri golf club is one of the most exclusive clubs in Italy and one of the world's best. The course is a classical inland course set on flat terrain with numerous lakes and streams crossing the fairways. One of the longest course in Italy, most of the fairways are lined by majestic trees. The club has hosted important national and international tournaments on many occasions. *SSS 72*

GF $$ | Mon. ; Nov. to March | S

1971 | R. Trent Jones

27 | L 6218 P 72, 3107 P 36 | R

Required : Handicap Certificate
Best days : Weekdays

HOLE	LENGTH MEDAL-TEE	PAR	STROKE INDEX
1	342	4	8
2	350	4	6
3	393	4	4
4	175	3	14
5	520	5	2
6	144	3	18
7	329	4	12
8	467	5	16
9	330	4	10
TOTAL	3050	36	TOTAL

HOLE	LENGTH MEDAL-TEE	PAR	STROKE INDEX
10	351	4	5
11	500	5	11
12	160	3	9
13	354	4	13
14	381	4	3
15	184	3	17
16	364	4	7
17	410	4	1
18	464	5	15
TOTAL	3168	36	TOTAL

IS MOLAS

TEL : (070)9209062
LOCATION : 35 km Cagliari
ADDRESS : Strada Statale 195 – Santa Margherita di Pula – Sardegna
HOTEL : HR
Is Molas Golf
Tel : (070)9209907
Is Morus – Santa Margherita di Pula
Tel : (070)921171
Abamar – Pula
Tel : (070)921555
Flamingo – Pula
Tel : (070)9208361

This exciting championship course is one of Italy's finest. Situated on the south coast of Sardinia, the golf course is laid out in fine natural surroundings partly near the sea front, partly inland. There is a spectacular layout including very long holes and numerous dangerous water hazards such as a pond on the 9th and a deep ravine-style ditch on the 5th. The course follows the natural undulations of the terrain and is backed by luxuriant wooded hills. Facilities include a large clubhouse, a hotel, a swimming pool, sauna and tennis courts. The elegant Is Morus Hotel is close to the course. *SSS 72*

GF $$
1975
18

—
P. Mancinelli
L 6131 P 72

R S

Required : Handicap Certificate
Best days : Any day

HOLE	LENGTH MEDAL-TEE	PAR	STROKE INDEX
1	450	5	11
2	380	4	5
3	176	3	17
4	404	4	7
5	350	4	1
6	320	4	13
7	185	3	15
8	380	4	9
9	350	4	3
TOTAL	2995	35	TOTAL

HOLE	LENGTH MEDAL-TEE	PAR	STROKE INDEX
10	160	3	16
11	348	4	14
12	460	5	6
13	351	4	8
14	140	3	18
15	495	5	2
16	440	5	10
17	360	4	12
18	382	4	4
TOTAL	3136	37	TOTAL

LA PINETINA

TEL : (031)933202
LOCATION : 12 km Como/25 km Milano
ADDRESS : Via al Golf 4 – Appiano Gentile – Como – 22070 Carbonate
HOTEL : HR
Golf House – La Pinetina
Tel : (031)933202
Barchetta Excelsior – Como
Tel : (031)266531
Como – Como
Tel : (031)266173

Located in Brianza near Como, La Pinetina is an inland course with numerous well-wooded fairways and several water hazards. It is ideal for a relaxed golfing round, with the Golf House hotel adjacent to the course. *SSS 71*

GF $$
1971
18

Tuesdays
—
L 6002 P 71

R S

Required : Handicap Certificate
Best days : Weekdays

HOLE	LENGTH MEDAL-TEE	PAR	STROKE INDEX
1	339	4	18
2	135	3	16
3	490	5	2
4	315	4	12
5	150	3	14
6	350	4	10
7	340	4	6
8	473	5	8
9	348	4	4
TOTAL	2940	36	TOTAL

HOLE	LENGTH MEDAL-TEE	PAR	STROKE INDEX
10	375	4	9
11	329	4	11
12	205	3	7
13	385	4	1
14	400	4	5
15	157	3	15
16	375	4	3
17	331	4	17
18	505	5	13
TOTAL	3062	35	TOTAL

LA ROCCA

TEL : (0521)834037
LOCATION : 7 km Parma to Collecchio
ADDRESS : Via Campi 8 - 43038 Sala Baganza - Parma
HOTEL :
La Pineta - Collecchio
Tel : (0521)805226
Albergo Christina - Collecchio
Tel : (0521)800460
Park Toscanini - Parma
Tel : (0521)289141
RESTAURANT : Villa Maria Luigia - Collecchio
Tel : (0521)805489

Recently upgraded to 18 hole status, the course winds its way through unspoiled sweeping landscape and is sheltered by distant hills. Strategic trees and lakes serve as obstacles demanding precision in play. *SSS 71*

GF $

 Mondays ; Dec. to March

1984

M. Croze

18

L 5816 P 71

S

Required : Handicap Certificate
Best days : Any days

HOLE	LENGTH MEDAL-TEE	PAR	STROKE INDEX
1	375	4	1
2	358	4	7
3	373	4	5
4	459	5	9
5	128	3	17
6	332	4	13
7	497	5	3
8	367	4	11
9	145	3	15
TOTAL	3034	36	TOTAL

HOLE	LENGTH MEDAL-TEE	PAR	STROKE INDEX
10	376	4	6
11	294	4	16
12	460	5	8
13	310	4	10
14	357	4	2
15	155	3	12
16	383	4	4
17	142	3	18
18	305	4	14
TOTAL	2782	35	TOTAL

LE CHIOCCIOLE

TEL : (0172)48772
LOCATION : 40 km Asti, 50 km Torino; between Bra and Cherasco
ADDRESS : Località Fraschetta-12062 Cherasco (Cuneo)
HOTEL :
Elisabeth-Bra
Tel : (0172)422486
Cavalieri-Bra
Tel : (0172)413304
Savona-Alba
Tel : (0173)42381
RESTAURANT : Battaglino-Bra
Tel : (0172)412509

This course is named after the local delicacy and speciality of the region 'snails'. Recently extended to 18 holes, it is one of Italy's longest courses. It is laid out on two levels, half hilly and half flat, at the confluence of two rivers. The course is technically demanding, and features strategic water hazards and punishing out of bounds. *SSS 71*

GF $ — Tues.; Nov. to March — R S

1923/1986 — M. Croze

18 — L 5863 P 72

Required : Handicap Certificate
Best days : Weekdays

HOLE	LENGTH MEDAL-TEE	PAR	STROKE INDEX
1	341	4	11
2	295	4	8
3	426	4	1
4	120	3	17
5	445	5	9
6	330	4	13
7	161	3	12
8	398	4	3
9	520	5	7
TOTAL	3036	36	TOTAL

HOLE	LENGTH MEDAL-TEE	PAR	STROKE INDEX
10	375	4	6
11	100	3	18
12	300	4	16
13	380	4	2
14	304	4	15
15	200	3	4
16	460	5	5
17	273	4	14
18	435	5	10
TOTAL	2827	36	TOTAL

LE FRONDE

TEL : (011)938053
LOCATION : 2 km Avigliana/20 km Torino
ADDRESS : Via S. Agostino 68 – 10051 Avigliana – Torino
HOTEL :
Chalet del Lago – Avigliana
Tel : (011)938383
Hermitage – Avigliana
Tel : (011)938150
RESTAURANT : La Maiana – Avigliana
Tel : (011)938805

A pleasant hillside course set on the north slope of Mount Cuneo, it is short but technically demanding. Many of the fairways are flanked by luxuriant woodland. There are fine views from the 2nd and 4th holes over the Susa Valley, the peak of Rocciamelone and a medieval castle. *SSS 72*

GF $

Mon. ; Nov. to March

1974

J. Harris

18

L 5940 P 72

Required : Handicap Certificate
Best days : Weekdays

HOLE	LENGTH MEDAL-TEE	PAR	STROKE INDEX
1	490	5	5
2	393	4	1
3	314	4	11
4	448	5	18
5	293	4	9
6	330	4	3
7	159	3	13
8	350	4	7
9	132	3	16
TOTAL	2909	36	TOTAL

HOLE	LENGTH MEDAL-TEE	PAR	STROKE INDEX
10	309	4	10
11	478	5	14
12	364	4	6
13	166	3	17
14	337	4	4
15	480	5	12
16	203	3	8
17	361	4	2
18	333	4	15
TOTAL	3031	36	TOTAL

L'EUCALYPTUS

TEL : (06)926252
LOCATION : 20 km Roma, 10 km Anzio
On Via Nettunense SS 207/km 26.400
ADDRESS : Via Cogna 3/5 -
04011 Aprilia (LT)
HOTEL :
dei Cesari - Anzio
Tel : (06)9874751
Lido Garda - Anzio
Tel : (06)9845389
Enea - Anzio
Tel : (06)9107021

Located 20 km south west of Rome and just 10 km from the Mediterranean, this course is fairly technical. Partly hilly, the holes, some of them flanked by Eucalyptus trees and small ponds, blend perfectly into this Italian dune landscape. Facilities include a first class clubhouse with a fine swimming pool, two tennis courts and several mini appartments for rental. *SSS 72*

GF $ — Tuesdays in winter — S 

1988 — A. d'Onofrio — 

18 — L 6335 P 72 — R 

Required : None
Best days : Weekdays

HOLE	LENGTH MEDAL-TEE	PAR	STROKE INDEX
1	420	4	
2	515	5	
3	180	3	
4	400	4	
5	360	4	
6	185	3	
7	350	4	
8	480	5	
9	350	4	
TOTAL	3240	36	TOTAL

HOLE	LENGTH MEDAL-TEE	PAR	STROKE INDEX
10	390	4	
11	385	4	
12	370	4	
13	180	3	
14	440	5	
15	350	4	
16	160	3	
17	460	5	
18	360	4	
TOTAL	3095	36	TOTAL

LIDO DI VENEZIA

TEL : (041)731015/731333
LOCATION : 10 km Venezia, at west end of the Lido island
ADDRESS : Via del Forte – 30011 Alberoni-Lido di Venezia
HOTEL :
Excelsior – Lido di Venezia
Tel : (041)5260201
Des Bains – Lido di Venezia
Tel : (041)5265921
Quattro Fontane – Venezia
Tel : (041)5260227
RESTAURANT : Harry's Bar – Venezia
Tel : (041)5236797

This prestigious golf club lies on the western edge of the world famous Lido island. Encircled by water, it is built on sand dunes between the Adriatic sea and the lagoon of Venice. Apart from its unique situation, the course is demanding, with several tough holes featuring wide greens with numerous differences in level, and some water traps. Many of the fairways and greens are lined by groves of poplars, pines, ilexes and olive trees. *SSS 72*

GF $$ — Mondays

1928 — H. Cotton

18 — L 6042 P 72

Required : Handicap Certificate
Best days : Weekdays

HOLE	LENGTH MEDAL-TEE	PAR	STROKE INDEX
1	330	4	11
2	136	3	15
3	302	4	9
4	370	4	3
5	191	3	7
6	446	5	17
7	408	4	1
8	510	5	5
9	157	3	13
TOTAL	2850	35	TOTAL

HOLE	LENGTH MEDAL-TEE	PAR	STROKE INDEX
10	358	4	6
11	500	5	4
12	163	3	10
13	496	5	12
14	365	4	2
15	333	4	8
16	316	4	16
17	354	4	14
18	307	4	18
TOTAL	3192	37	TOTAL

MARGARA

TEL : (0131)778555
LOCATION : 15 km Alessandria
ADDRESS : Via Tenuta Margara 5 – 15043 Fubine
HOTEL : HR
Clubhouse
Tel : (0131)778556
Alli Due Buoi Rossi – Alessandria
Tel : (0131)445252
Lux – Alessandria
Tel : (0131)51661

Set on the borders of the provinces of Asti and Alessandris, the course is set on rolling open terrain nearing the foothills of the Monferrato hills. Many of the holes are long with wide and generous fairways landscaped among young conifers. There is a stately clubhouse with several bedrooms, two tennis courts and a big swimming pool. *SSS 71*

GF $ — Mon. ; Dec. to March 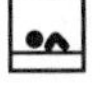 

1971 — —  

18 — L 6045 P 72 — R

Required : Handicap Certificate
Best days : Weekdays

HOLE	LENGTH MEDAL-TEE	PAR	STROKE INDEX
1	355	4	
2	359	4	
3	370	4	
4	182	3	
5	297	4	
6	324	4	
7	346	4	
8	390	4	
9	487	5	
TOTAL	3110	36	TOTAL

HOLE	LENGTH MEDAL-TEE	PAR	STROKE INDEX
10	358	4	
11	422	5	
12	156	3	
13	324	4	
14	446	5	
15	198	3	
16	329	4	
17	345	4	
18	357	4	
TOTAL	2935	36	TOTAL

MENAGGIO & CADENABBIA

TEL : (0344)32103
LOCATION : 4 km Menaggio
ADDRESS : Via Golf 12 – 22010 Grandola e Uniti – Como
HOTEL :
Albergo Bellavista – Menaggio
Tel : (0344)32136
Victoria – Menaggio
Tel : (0344)32003
Adler – Menaggio
Tel : (0344)32171
RESTAURANT : Da Paolino – Menaggio
Tel : (0344)32335

The second oldest club in Italy after Roma, the course is set within fine natural countryside on the western banks of Lake Como nearing the Swiss border. A pleasant hillside course with many uphill and downhill holes including narrow fairways. *SSS 69*

GF $$

1907

18

Tues. ; Nov. to March

J. Harris

L 5277 P 69

S

R

Required : Handicap Certificate
Best days : Weekdays

HOLE	LENGTH MEDAL-TEE	PAR	STROKE INDEX
1	390	4	7
2	167	3	11
3	162	3	15
4	265	4	17
5	474	5	13
6	376	4	9
7	176	3	5
8	330	4	3
9	380	4	1
TOTAL	2720	34	TOTAL

HOLE	LENGTH MEDAL-TEE	PAR	STROKE INDEX
10	172	3	8
11	359	4	2
12	335	4	10
13	300	4	14
14	452	5	6
15	131	3	12
16	334	4	4
17	242	4	18
18	232	4	16
TOTAL	2557	35	TOTAL

MILANO

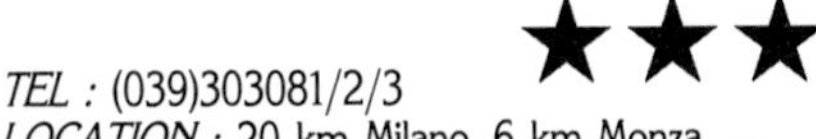

TEL : (039)303081/2/3
LOCATION : 20 km Milano, 6 km Monza
ADDRESS : 20052 Parco di Monza – Milano
HOTEL :
Hotel de la Ville – Monza
Tel : (039)382581
Della Regione – Monza
Tel : (039)387205
Leonardo da Vinci – Milano
Tel : (039)9407
RESTAURANT : Saint Georges 1er – Monza
Tel : (039)320600

Laid out within Monza Park near the race-circuit, this is a well-established inland course of great natural beauty. One of the noblest and most crowded clubs in Italy, many of the holes are laid out on flat terrain landscaped among majestic trees. There are few water hazards. Regularly used for the Italian Open and other international matches, the club boasts an impressive clubhouse with swimming pool. *SSS 73*

GF $$ — Mondays  S

1929 — C. Blandford, J. Harris — R 

27 — L 6239 P 72, 2976 P 36

Required : Handicap Certificate
Best days : Weekdays

HOLE	LENGTH MEDAL-TEE	PAR	STROKE INDEX
1	455	5	13
2	383	4	5
3	173	3	9
4	314	4	17
5	381	4	1
6	351	4	11
7	177	3	7
8	366	4	3
9	507	5	15
TOTAL	3107	36	TOTAL

HOLE	LENGTH MEDAL-TEE	PAR	STROKE INDEX
10	195	3	10
11	349	4	12
12	136	3	18
13	413	4	2
14	455	5	16
15	374	4	4
16	458	5	14
17	345	4	8
18	407	4	6
TOTAL	3132	36	TOTAL

MOLINETTO

★

TEL : (02)9238500
LOCATION : 14 km Milano S11
ADDRESS : Strada Padana Superiore 11 – 20063 Cernusco sul Naviglio (MI)
HOTEL :
Nasco – Milano
Tel : (02)2043841
Concorde – Milano
Tel : (039)2895853
Nasco – Milano
Tel : (039)202301
RESTAURANT : Lo Spiedo da Odero – Cernusco sul Naviglio
Tel : (02)9242781

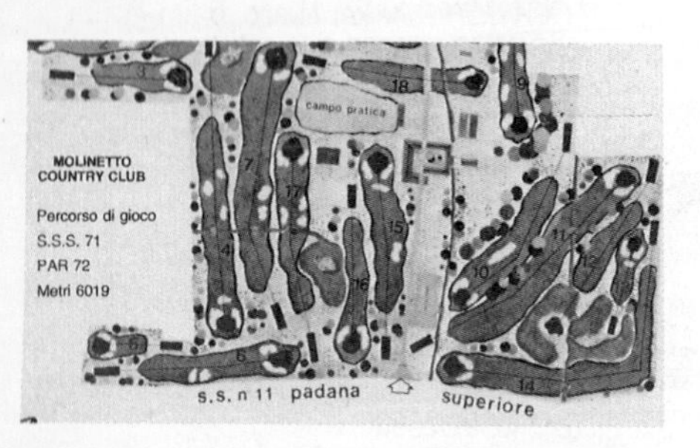

One of the finest championship courses built in 1983 and having already hosted the Italian Open, the course is testing with well-designed holes. The fairways are smallish and there are some large lakes serving as hazards. The country club includes a swimming pool and 22 tennis courts. *SSS 71*

GF $$
1983
18

Mondays
Tartaglia – Studio Polis
L 5823 P 72

Required : Handicap Certificate
Best days : Tuesdays, Thursdays, Fridays only

HOLE	LENGTH MEDAL-TEE	PAR	STROKE INDEX
1	348	4	13
2	378	4	3
3	189	3	7
4	436	5	11
5	118	3	17
6	334	4	5
7	432	5	15
8	390	4	1
9	270	4	9
TOTAL	2895	36	TOTAL

HOLE	LENGTH MEDAL-TEE	PAR	STROKE INDEX
10	329	4	14
11	440	5	16
12	311	4	8
13	173	3	10
14	473	5	6
15	291	4	18
16	205	3	4
17	340	4	12
18	366	4	2
TOTAL	2928	36	TOTAL

MONTECATINI

TEL : (0572)62218
LOCATION : 9 km Montecatini Terme
ADDRESS : Via Brogi-Loc. Pievaccia-51015 Monsummano Terme (PT)
HOTEL :
Bellavista Palace-Montecatini Terme
Tel : (0572)78122
Corallo-Montecatini Terme
Tel : (0572)78288
Croce di Malta-Montecatini Terme
Tel : (0572)75871
RESTAURANT : Gourmet-Montecatini Terme
Tel : (0572)771012

This course is set in a splendid natural landscape, typical of Toscany, near the health resort of Montecatini. Laid out on terrain which is alternatively undulating and flat, it is backed by densely wooded low lying hills. Its main features are the length and width of many of its holes and the innumerable small ponds serving as hazards. *SSS 72*

GF $ — Tuesdays — S

1985 —  M. Croze — 

18 — L 6097 P 72 — R

Required : Handicap Certificate
Best days : Weekdays

HOLE	LENGTH MEDAL-TEE	PAR	STROKE INDEX
1	365	4	17
2	290	4	13
3	400	4	11
4	490	5	1
5	305	4	3
6	155	3	15
7	375	4	7
8	495	5	9
9	150	3	5
TOTAL	3025	36	TOTAL

HOLE	LENGTH MEDAL-TEE	PAR	STROKE INDEX
10	292	4	17
11	354	4	13
12	345	4	11
13	412	4	1
14	188	3	15
15	440	5	3
16	206	3	7
17	502	5	9
18	333	4	5
TOTAL	3072	36	TOTAL

MONTICELLO

TEL : (031)928055
LOCATION : 10 km Como S 35
ADDRESS : Via Volta 4 - 22070 Cassina Rizzardi – Como
HOTEL :
Villa Flori – Como
Tel : (031)557642
Barchetta Excelsior – Como
Tel : (039)266531
Metropole Suisse – Como
Tel : (039)269444
RESTAURANT : Imbarcadero – Como
Tel : (031)277341

It is the only Italian course with 36 holes and is one of the top golf courses on the peninsula. Both courses are long and testing with an entertaining layout. Set on relatively flat open countryside, the fairways are large, tree-lined and cunningly bunkered, and include several water hazards. The clubhouse is modern, with tennis courts and a swimming pool. Founded in 1975, the club, due to its high standard, has hosted many top European tournaments and on several occasions the Italian Open. *SSS 73/72*

GF $$

1975

36

Mondays

—

L 6365 P 72, 6056 P 72

S

Required : Handicap Certificate
Best days : Weekdays

Red Course

HOLE	LENGTH MEDAL-TEE	PAR	STROKE INDEX
1	350	4	15
2	364	4	7
3	177	3	17
4	502	5	11
5	374	4	3
6	309	4	9
7	198	3	5
8	402	4	1
9	511	5	13
TOTAL	3187	36	TOTAL

HOLE	LENGTH MEDAL-TEE	PAR	STROKE INDEX
10	353	4	16
11	484	5	10
12	368	4	4
13	223	3	8
14	491	5	12
15	352	4	14
16	393	4	2
17	154	3	18
18	360	4	6
TOTAL	3178	36	TOTAL

Blue Course

HOLE	LENGTH MEDAL-TEE	PAR	STROKE INDEX
1	316	4	17
2	400	4	1
3	146	3	15
4	306	4	13
5	323	4	9
6	525	5	5
7	377	4	3
8	211	3	7
9	468	5	11
TOTAL	3072	36	TOTAL

HOLE	LENGTH MEDAL-TEE	PAR	STROKE INDEX
10	132	3	18
11	374	4	4
12	480	5	10
13	357	4	2
14	149	3	8
15	482	5	12
16	398	4	6
17	156	3	14
18	456	5	16
TOTAL	2984	36	TOTAL

OLGIATA

★★

TEL : (06)3789141
LOCATION : 19 km Roma S 2
ADDRESS : Largo dell' Olgiata 15 – 00123 Roma
HOTEL :
Lord Byron – Roma
Tel : (06)3609541
Atlante Star – Roma
Tel : (06)6564196
Forum – Roma
Tel : (06)6792446
RESTAURANT : Dal Bolognese – Roma
Tel : (06)3611426

This interesting inland course was the venue for the World Amateur Championship and is one of Italy's most respected golf clubs. Located 19km north of Rome, the course is long with undulating fairways, some of them tree-lined. Several ponds serve as hazards. There is an attractive clubhouse with a swimming pool. *SSS 72*

GF $$

1961

27

Mondays

C. Cotton

L 6185 P 72, 2968 P 34

S

R

Required : Handicap Certificate
Best days : Weekdays

HOLE	LENGTH MEDAL-TEE	PAR	STROKE INDEX
1	344	4	14
2	384	4	2
3	370	4	10
4	378	4	6
5	145	3	18
6	435	5	8
7	175	3	16
8	468	5	12
9	383	4	4
TOTAL	3082	36	TOTAL

HOLE	LENGTH MEDAL-TEE	PAR	STROKE INDEX
10	332	4	13
11	182	3	7
12	421	4	1
13	350	4	15
14	436	5	9
15	383	4	3
16	168	3	11
17	340	4	17
18	491	5	5
TOTAL	3103	36	TOTAL

PADOVA

✡

TEL : (049)9130078
LOCATION : 3 km S. Galzignano, 20 km Padova
ADDRESS : 35030 Valsanzibio di Galzignano
HOTEL :
Sporting – Galzignano
Tel : (049)525500
Green Park – Galzignano
Tel : (049)525511
Splendid – Galzignano
Tel : (049)525333
RESTAURANT : Belvedere – Galzignano
Tel : (049)528005

Ideal for holiday golf, the Padova golf club is set near the health and spa resorts of Abano and Galzignano in the Euganean hills. A pleasant and a not too difficult course, laid out on flat terrain with artificial water hazards and high trees scattered all over. The comfortable clubhouse with tennis courts and swimming pool is built high up overlooking the fairways. *SSS 72*

GF $ — Mon. ; Dec. to March
1964 — J. Harris
18 — L 6053 P 72

Required : Handicap Certificate
Best days : Weekdays only

HOLE	LENGTH MEDAL-TEE	PAR	STROKE INDEX
1	370	4	
2	382	4	
3	183	3	
4	344	4	
5	482	5	
6	340	4	
7	156	3	
8	443	5	
9	322	4	
TOTAL	3022	36	TOTAL

HOLE	LENGTH MEDAL-TEE	PAR	STROKE INDEX
10	510	5	
11	322	4	
12	164	3	
13	485	5	
14	183	3	
15	353	4	
16	456	5	
17	157	3	
18	401	4	
TOTAL	3031	36	TOTAL

PARCO DE MEDICI

TEL : (06)6553477
LOCATION : 10 km Roma to L. da Vinci airport
ADDRESS : Autostrada Roma - Fiumicino - km 45-00148 Roma
HOTEL :
Sheraton - Roma Città Giardino
Tel : (06)5453
Shangri Là - Roma Città Giardino
Tel : (06)5916441
Lord Byron - Roma Norte
Tel : (06)3609541

Just 10 minutes from the center of Rome, this golf club was developed on the former shooting grounds of Pope Leo X (15th century) within the "Raccordo Anulare" (ring road) at ten minutes from the centre of Roma. It stands on 70ha of flat typical Roman countryside with plantations of 4000 plants. Its main difficulties are a large number of well placed lakes and burns. An original feature of this course is that some of the holes are enriched by sculptures of contemporary artists. There is a first class spacious clubhouse with tennis courts and a swimming pool. A hotel is scheduled. *SSS 72*

GF $$
1989
27

Tuesdays
D. Merzacane, P. Fazio
L 5427 P 72, 2415 P 34

R S

Required : Handicap Certificate
Best days : Weekdays

HOLE	LENGTH MEDAL-TEE	PAR	STROKE INDEX
1	396	5	9
2	191	3	15
3	427	5	5
4	132	3	17
5	242	4	13
6	275	4	1
7	163	3	11
8	428	5	7
9	324	4	13
TOTAL	2578	36	TOTAL

HOLE	LENGTH MEDAL-TEE	PAR	STROKE INDEX
10	337	4	16
11	376	4	4
12	170	3	18
13	297	4	10
14	445	5	6
15	146	3	14
16	283	4	2
17	315	4	12
18	480	5	8
TOTAL	2849	36	TOTAL

PEVERO

TEL : (0789)96210/96072
LOCATION : 18,5 km Arzachena
ADDRESS : Costa Smeralda – 07020 Porto Cervo – Sardegna
HOTEL :
Cala di Volpe – Porto Cervo
Tel : (0789)96083
Pitrizza – Arzachena
Tel : (0789)92000
Romazzino – Arzachena
Tel : (0789)96020
RESTAURANT : La Fattoria – Arzachena
Tel : (0789)92214

The Pevero Golf Club is one the world's most renowned golf courses, magnificently set on the 'Costa Smeralda' of Sardinia, on a promontory separating the Bays of Pevero and Cala di Volpe. Masterminded by Robert Trent Jones(probably his finest achievement), the championship course is laid out in a beautiful landscape of rocks and cliffs overlooking the Mediterranean. A truly testing and long course numbering 90 bunkers and 6 menacing water hazards plus a sometimes prevailing wind, the 'Mistral'. One of the most scenic holes is the 15th with a lovely view over the coastline and the sea. There is an equally magnificent clubhouse with terrace and a fine swimming pool built high up, with panoramic views over the two bays and the course. *SSS 72*

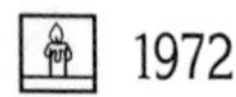

GF $$
1972
18

Tues. (1-10/1-03)
R. Trent Jones
L 5838 P 72

Required : Handicap Certificate
Best days : Any day

HOLE	LENGTH MEDAL-TEE	PAR	STROKE INDEX
1	376	4	9
2	350	4	3
3	474	5	1
4	351	4	13
5	175	3	17
6	306	4	7
7	166	3	11
8	339	4	5
9	454	5	15
TOTAL	2991	36	TOTAL

HOLE	LENGTH MEDAL-TEE	PAR	STROKE INDEX
10	169	3	18
11	484	5	4
12	351	4	8
13	354	4	6
14	170	3	16
15	436	5	2
16	262	4	12
17	132	3	14
18	489	5	10
TOTAL	2847	36	TOTAL

PUNTA ALA

TEL : (0564)922121
LOCATION : 42 km Grosseto
ADDRESS : 58040 Punta Ala
HOTEL : HR
Gallia Palace
Tel : (0564)922022
Golf Hotel – Punta Ala
Tel : (0564)9222026
Piccolo Alleluja – Punta Ala
Tel : (0564)922050

This superb golf course is ideal for holiday golf, set in the unspoiled and peaceful surroundings of Punta Ala. Its fine fairways meander their way through heathland to the Mediterranean sea. Most of them are isolated and separated by mature trees. The very attractive Gallia Palace Hotel is near the course and is a member of the Relais & Châteaux chain. *SSS 72*

GF $

1964

18

—

G. Cavalsani

L 6190 P 72

R S

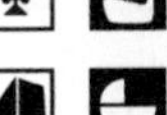

Required : Handicap Certificate
Best days : Any day

HOLE	LENGTH MEDAL-TEE	PAR	STROKE INDEX
1	310	4	17
2	160	3	15
3	350	4	9
4	470	5	7
5	390	4	3
6	170	3	13
7	500	5	5
8	393	4	1
9	357	4	11
TOTAL	3100	36	TOTAL

HOLE	LENGTH MEDAL-TEE	PAR	STROKE INDEX
10	470	5	10
11	190	3	12
12	430	4	2
13	475	5	8
14	380	4	6
15	145	3	18
16	360	4	4
17	345	4	14
18	295	4	16
TOTAL	3090	36	TOTAL

RAPALLO

★

TEL : (0185)50210/57187
LOCATION : 2 km Rapallo
ADDRESS : Via Mameli 377 – 16035
Rapallo-Genova
HOTEL :
Eurotel – Rapallo
Tel : (0185)60981
Grand Bristol – Rapallo
Tel : (0185)273313
Rosa Bianca – Rapallo
Tel : (0185)50390
RESTAURANT : Riviera – Rapallo
Tel : (0185)502481

Located near the seaside resort of Rapallo, this is a very fine course and certainly an enjoyable experience for any golfer. Though not very long, it is testing with each hole offering a challenge. There are numerous natural obstacles such as tall trees, three streams crossing the fairways and well-defined greens. The most attractive hole is the 7th with a fine view of the Monastero Valle Christi, which dates back to the 12th century. *SSS 70*

GF $

1931

18

Tuesdays

M. Maffei

L 5694 P 70

R S

Required : Handicap Certificate
Best days : Weekdays

HOLE	LENGTH MEDAL-TEE	PAR	STROKE INDEX
1	255	4	17
2	518	5	7
3	363	4	5
4	162	3	15
5	414	4	1
6	282	4	13
7	435	5	11
8	371	4	3
9	176	3	9
TOTAL	2976	36	TOTAL

HOLE	LENGTH MEDAL-TEE	PAR	STROKE INDEX
10	372	4	2
11	385	4	4
12	376	4	8
13	314	4	12
14	302	4	18
15	171	3	14
16	309	4	16
17	269	4	10
18	220	3	6
TOTAL	2718	34	TOTAL

RIVA DEI TESSALI

TEL : (099)6439251
LOCATION : 40 km Taranto SS 106
ADDRESS : 74011 Castellaneta – Taranto
HOTEL : HR
Golf Hotel
Tel : (099)6439251
Villa Giusy – Castellaneta Marina
Tel : (099)643036

A good holiday course situated near the shores of the Ionian sea. It is set within a peaceful parkland landscape, with the fairways lined by mature trees and several ponds serving as hazards. The newly built Golf Hotel with tennis courts, swimming pool and private beach, is situated on the course. *SSS 71*

GF $$

1972

18

Tues. (1-10/1-05)

M. Croze

L 5738 P 71

S

R

Required : Handicap Certificate
Best days : Weekdays

HOLE	LENGTH MEDAL-TEE	PAR	STROKE INDEX
1	320	4	11
2	164	3	17
3	507	5	3
4	361	4	7
5	312	4	13
6	346	4	9
7	195	3	5
8	379	4	1
9	305	4	15
TOTAL	2889	35	TOTAL

HOLE	LENGTH MEDAL-TEE	PAR	STROKE INDEX
10	305	4	12
11	363	4	2
12	494	5	8
13	143	3	18
14	300	4	10
15	164	3	14
16	461	5	6
17	354	4	4
18	265	4	16
TOTAL	2849	36	TOTAL

ROMA-CIRCOLO (Aquasanta)

TEL : (06)783407
LOCATION : 12 km SE. Roma near Ciampino
ADDRESS : Via dell'Acquasanta 3 – Via Appia Nuva 716/A – 00178 Roma
HOTEL :
Golf – Roma
Tel : (06)6439251
Eden – Roma
Tel : (06)4743551
Villa Giusy – Roma
Tel : (06)6433036
RESTAURANT : Campana – Roma
Tel : (06)655273

The oldest Italian golf club having been founded in 1903, this is a memorable course and one of the world's best courses. It has a unique setting in historic surroundings next to the famous Acquasanta springs, backed by a Roman aqueduct, and bordering the legendary Appian Way. Laid out in low hills, there are strategically placed pines and several meandering streams (mineral sources) on the course. The greens are generally quite small. There is a stylish clubhouse with a swimming pool overlooking the beautiful surroundings. *SSS 71*

GF $$ — Mondays — S
1903 — — — R
18 — L 5854 P 71

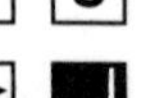

Required : Handicap Certificate
Best days : Weekdays

HOLE	LENGTH MEDAL-TEE	PAR	STROKE INDEX
1	299	4	
2	131	3	
3	318	4	
4	344	4	
5	183	3	
6	341	4	
7	497	5	
8	366	4	
9	365	4	
TOTAL	2844	35	TOTAL

HOLE	LENGTH MEDAL-TEE	PAR	STROKE INDEX
10	440	5	
11	118	3	
12	406	4	
13	347	4	
14	312	4	
15	332	4	
16	314	4	
17	375	4	
18	366	4	
TOTAL	3010	36	TOTAL

SANREMO

TEL : (0184)557093
LOCATION : 5 km N. Sanremo
ADDRESS : Via Campo Golf 43 - 18038 Sanremo degli Olivi
HOTEL :
Royal – Sanremo
Tel : (0184)79991
Miramare – Sanremo
Tel : (0184)882381
Principe Résidence – Sanremo
Tel : (0184)83565
RESTAURANT : Pesce d'Oro – Sanremo
Tel : (0184)66332

Located near the legendary seaside resort of Sanremo, the course is picturesquely set in the foothills of the mountains with panoramic views over the Mediterranean. Many of the fairways meander their way through the Val Gogna olive groves. Though short, the course demands delicate stroke play. *SSS 67*

GF $$
1932
18

Tuesdays
P. Gannon
L 5203 P 69

S
R

Required : None
Best days : Any day

HOLE	LENGTH MEDAL-TEE	PAR	STROKE INDEX
1	270	4	13
2	180	3	9
3	250	4	11
4	345	4	5
5	300	4	7
6	340	4	3
7	235	4	15
8	385	4	1
9	85	3	17
TOTAL	2390	34	TOTAL

HOLE	LENGTH MEDAL-TEE	PAR	STROKE INDEX
10	365	4	8
11	180	3	14
12	330	4	18
13	260	4	16
14	210	3	4
15	435	5	2
16	228	3	6
17	365	4	12
18	440	5	10
TOTAL	2813	35	TOTAL

SESTRIERE

TEL : (0122)76276
LOCATION : Centre Sestriere, 93 km Torino
ADDRESS : Piazza Agnelli 4 – 10058 Sestriere
HOTEL :
Grand – Sestriere
Tel : (0122)76476
Cristallo – Sestriere
Tel : (0122)77234
Miramonti – Sestriere
Tel : (0122)77048
RESTAURANT : La Balta – Sestriere
Tel : (0122)77496

This is Europe's highest course, over 2000m above sea level. Set in the Western Alps, this is a typical mountain course with sparse vegetation. There are several ponds and streams serving as hazards. *SSS 65*

GF $

1932

18

September to July

 —

L 4598 P 67

R

Required : Handicap Certificate
Best days : Any day

HOLE	LENGTH MEDAL-TEE	PAR	STROKE INDEX
1	195	3	5
2	165	3	9
3	484	5	3
4	100	3	17
5	260	4	15
6	246	4	11
7	301	4	13
8	373	4	1
9	319	4	7
TOTAL	2443	34	TOTAL

HOLE	LENGTH MEDAL-TEE	PAR	STROKE INDEX
10	269	4	6
11	159	3	12
12	260	4	10
13	126	3	18
14	292	4	2
15	137	3	14
16	282	4	16
17	480	5	4
18	150	3	8
TOTAL	2155	33	TOTAL

TORINO-LA MANDRIA

TEL : (011)9235440
LOCATION : 20 km N. Torino
ADDRESS : Via Grange 137 – 10070 Fiano Torinese – Torino
HOTEL :
Villa Sassi – Torino
Tel : (011)890556
Grand Hotel Sitea – Torino
Tel : (011)5570171
Jolly Ambasciatori – Torino
Tel : (011)5752
RESTAURANT : Al Gatto Nero – Torino
Tel : (011)590414

Located inside La Mandria Park, now a regional park, but once a former stud farm, the Torino golf club is one of Italy's prestigious clubs and one of Europe's greatest. It is laid out on slightly undulating terrain with lakes, canals and streams serving as hazards. The main course is of the classical parkland type, with wide and generous fairways, and is among centuries-old beech trees. La Mandria has hosted many international championships such as the Italian Open and the European Amateurs in 1967. *SSS 72*

GF $$

1956

36

Mon. ; Dec. to March

J. Harris

L 6217 P 72, 6208 P 72

Required : Handicap Certificate
Best days : Weekdays

HOLE	LENGTH MEDAL-TEE	PAR	STROKE INDEX
1	464	5	
2	354	4	
3	371	4	
4	332	4	
5	172	3	
6	417	4	
7	339	4	
8	140	3	
9	373	5	
TOTAL	2962	36	TOTAL

HOLE	LENGTH MEDAL-TEE	PAR	STROKE INDEX
10	387	4	
11	354	4	
12	466	5	
13	156	3	
14	308	4	
15	516	5	
16	192	3	
17	395	4	
18	381	4	
TOTAL	3155	36	TOTAL

VARESE

★

TEL : (0332)229302
LOCATION : 6 km Varese/35 km Como
ADDRESS : Via Vittorio Veneto 32 – 21020 Luvinate
HOTEL :
Palace – Varese
Tel : (0332)312600
Acquario – Varese
Tel : (0332)260550
City – Varese
Tel : (0332)281304
RESTAURANT : Lago Maggiore – Varese
Tel : (0332)231183

Scenically situated with panoramic views over five lakes (including the Varese and Lago Maggiore) and the Monte Rosa mountains, this is a typical hillside course with numerous natural hazards. The beautiful clubhouse is a former Romanesque church, dating back to the 12th century. *SSS 71*

GF $

Mondays

S

1934

C. Blandford

18

L 5942 P 72

R

Required : Handicap Certificate
Best days : Weekdays

HOLE	LENGTH MEDAL-TEE	PAR	STROKE INDEX
1	288	4	16
2	332	4	8
3	134	3	17
4	348	4	4
5	362	4	3
6	460	5	11
7	274	4	18
8	512	5	6
9	136	3	15
TOTAL	2846	36	TOTAL

HOLE	LENGTH MEDAL-TEE	PAR	STROKE INDEX
10	342	4	13
11	376	4	2
12	482	5	14
13	194	3	7
14	361	4	5
15	489	5	12
16	373	4	1
17	176	3	9
18	303	4	10
TOTAL	3096	36	TOTAL

VERONA

TEL : (045)510060
LOCATION : 10 km Verona
ADDRESS : Cà del Sale 15 – 37066 Sommacampagna – Verona
HOTEL :
Due Torri – Verona
Tel : (045)595044
Accademia – Verona
Tel : (045)596222
Grand – Verona
Tel : (045)595600
RESTAURANT : 12 Apostoli – Verona
Tel : (045)596999

This inland course has a varied layout set in rolling countryside. The first nine holes have small fairways, requiring accuracy. The last holes are longer with wider fairways. There is a fine clubhouse with various tennis courts and a swimming pool (reserved for members).
SSS 72

GF $

Tuesdays

S

1962

 J. Harris

18

L 6037 P 72

Required : Handicap Certificate
Best days : Mondays

HOLE	LENGTH MEDAL-TEE	PAR	STROKE INDEX
1	335	4	
2	128	3	
3	330	4	
4	270	4	
5	437	5	
6	503	5	
7	159	3	
8	384	4	
9	167	3	
TOTAL	2713	35	TOTAL

HOLE	LENGTH MEDAL-TEE	PAR	STROKE INDEX
10	505	5	
11	300	4	
12	380	4	
13	383	4	
14	291	4	
15	202	3	
16	351	4	
17	487	5	
18	424	4	
TOTAL	3324	37	TOTAL

VILLA CONDULMER

★

TEL : (041)457062
LOCATION : 17 km N. Venezia/13 km S. Treviso
ADDRESS : Via della Croce 3 – 31020 Zerman di Mogliano Veneto
HOTEL : HR
Villa Condulmer
Tel : (041)457100
Continental – Treviso
Tel : (0422)57216
Cà del Galletto – Treviso
Tel : (0422)23831

Situated in the Venetian Villa Condulmer parkland, this is a very attractive course. The second nine holes are more interesting than the starting holes due to various 'out-of-bounds' and well-defended greens. The hotel Villa Condulmer, an ancient Venetian Villa dating back to the 18th century, is near the clubhouse. Facilities include a swimmingpool, a riding school and several tennis courts. *SSS 71*

GF $

1961

27

Mondays

J. Harris, M. Croze

L 5955 P 71, 1670 P 29

Required : Handicap Certificate
Best days : Weekdays

HOLE	LENGTH MEDAL-TEE	PAR	STROKE INDEX
1	275	4	17
2	340	4	18
3	365	4	2
4	180	3	14
5	130	3	18
6	505	5	4
7	160	3	10
8	450	5	15
9	320	4	6
TOTAL	2725	35	TOTAL

HOLE	LENGTH MEDAL-TEE	PAR	STROKE INDEX
10	190	3	13
11	390	4	1
12	380	4	7
13	540	5	3
14	200	3	9
15	345	4	6
16	360	4	11
17	485	5	12
18	340	4	5
TOTAL	3230	36	TOTAL

VILLA D'ESTE

TEL : (031)200200
LOCATION : 7 km Como
ADDRESS : Via per Cantù 13 – 22030
Montorfano – Como
HOTEL :
Santandrea Golf – Montorfano
Tel : (031)200220
Como – Como
Tel : (031)266173
Barchetta Excelsior – Como
Tel : (031)266531
RESTAURANT : Da Pizzi – Como
Tel : (031)266100

One of Europe's noblest clubs, set on the banks of the scenic Lake Montorfano. It is a typical hillside course with numerous testing holes landscaped among majestic chestnut, pines and birch trees. One of the finest Italian courses, it was the venue for several international championships. There is a splendid clubhouse overlooking the fairways. *SSS 69*

GF $$ — Dec. to March — R S
1926 — P. Gannon
18 — L 5581 P 69

Required : Handicap Certificate
Best days : Weekdays only

HOLE	LENGTH MEDAL-TEE	PAR	STROKE INDEX
1	537	5	6
2	353	4	4
3	187	3	8
4	293	4	14
5	134	3	18
6	289	4	16
7	178	3	12
8	383	4	2
9	355	4	10
TOTAL	2709	34	TOTAL

HOLE	LENGTH MEDAL-TEE	PAR	STROKE INDEX
10	169	3	13
11	381	4	3
12	327	4	9
13	486	5	7
14	192	3	5
15	403	4	1
16	153	3	17
17	450	5	15
18	311	4	11
TOTAL	2872	35	TOTAL

ZOATE

TEL : (02)90631861/90632183
LOCATION : 17 km Milano
ADDRESS : Via Verde – 20067 Zoate di Tribiano (MI)
HOTEL :
Jolly President – Milano
Tel : (02)7746
Grand Hotel – Milano
Tel : (02)870757
Manin – Milano
Tel : (02)6596511
RESTAURANT : Savini – Milano
Tel : (02)8058343

This not too difficult course, founded in 1984, lies near Milan on the main Crema road. A popular inland course with several long holes and numerous streams and canals bordering greens and fairways. There are two clubhouses with a swimming pool. Other sports facilities include football and volleyball grounds. *SSS 72*

GF $ — Mondays — RF S 

1984 — M. Marmori 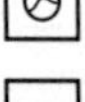

18 — L 5943 P 72 

Required : Handicap Certificate
Best days : Weekdays

HOLE	LENGTH MEDAL-TEE	PAR	STROKE INDEX
1	280	4	5
2	303	4	17
3	140	3	15
4	490	5	13
5	172	3	11
6	480	5	7
7	420	4	3
8	422	4	1
9	350	4	9
TOTAL	3057	36	TOTAL

HOLE	LENGTH MEDAL-TEE	PAR	STROKE INDEX
10	160	3	10
11	315	4	6
12	320	4	8
13	190	3	4
14	321	4	16
15	505	5	2
16	480	5	12
17	295	4	14
18	300	4	18
TOTAL	2886	36	TOTAL

Car Rental

Reservation/Information telephone number :

Country code :

352

Telephone number :

404228
487684

Headquarters address :

INTERRENT - EUROPCAR SARL
84, route de Thionville 2610 Luxembourg - Bonnevoie
Tel. : (352) 487684
Telex : 3488
Fax : (352) 40.33.44

---

2 GOLF COURSES, 5 000 PLAYERS

★★★ Great golf course
★★ Very good golf course
$ 250-650 B. Frs
★ Recommended golf course
✡ Holiday golf course
$ $ 650-1000 B. Frs

TOWN	GOLF COURSE		TEL	MAP REF.
Luxembourg	Grand Ducal de Luxembourg	★★	34090	1
	Kikuoka Country Club « Chant Val »		356135	2

GRAND DUCAL DE LUXEMBOURG

★★

TEL : 3 40 90
LOCATION : 7 km Luxembourg
ADDRESS : Senningerberg – Luxembourg
HOTEL :
Aerogolf Sheraton – Luxembourg
Tel : 3 45 71
Cravat – Luxembourg
Tel : 4 16 16
Host. Grunewald – Dommeldange
Tel : 4 37 81
Le Royal – Luxembourg
Tel : 4 16 16
RESTAURANT : St-Michel – Luxembourg
Tel : 2 32 15

The oldest 18 hole golf club in Luxembourg is the championship course 'Grand Ducal' situated 7km from the city. A very attractive course in a parkland setting with fairways separated from each other by centuries old trees. The club boasts a fine and comfortable clubhouse. *SSS 71*

GF $
1936
18
—
—
L 5765 P 71
R S

Required : Handicap Certificate 28
Best days : Weekdays

HOLE	LENGTH MEDAL-TEE	PAR	STROKE INDEX
1	342	4	9
2	464	5	7
3	293	4	17
4	183	3	11
5	399	4	1
6	422	4	3
7	181	3	13
8	280	4	15
9	354	4	5
TOTAL	2918	35	TOTAL

HOLE	LENGTH MEDAL-TEE	PAR	STROKE INDEX
10	336	4	10
11	484	5	4
12	184	3	14
13	334	4	8
14	145	3	16
15	455	5	2
16	331	4	12
17	143	3	18
18	435	5	6
TOTAL	2847	36	TOTAL

KIKUOKA « Chant Val »

TEL : 356135
LOCATION : 15 km Luxembourg E29
ADDRESS : Scheierhaff - 5412 Canach
HOTEL : HF
Kikuoka Country Club
Tel : 356135
Royal – Luxembourg
Tel : 41616
Cravat – Luxembourg
Tel : 21975

Set in the sweeping Scheierhaff valley in the heart of Europe amidst the gentle slopes and the fruitful orchards of the Moselle vineyards, the promising international championship course « Chant Val » will be among the most modern and sophisticated in Europe devised to host international tournaments. The holes, running over lush rolling countryside, are framed by small shrubs, bushes, trees and Japanese style gardens. Strategic bunkers and lakes demand precison play. Facilities include a spacious clubhouse, a five star hotel with 69 rooms (opening oct. 91), squash and tennis courts, a gymnasium and a swimming pool.

GF $$

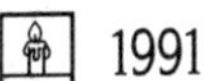
1991

18

Mondays

I. Uematsu

L 5780 P 72

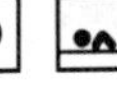

Required : Handicap Certificate, Introduction by a member
Best days : Any day

HOLE	LENGTH MEDAL-TEE	PAR	STROKE INDEX
1	350	4	
2	454	5	
3	135	3	
4	370	4	
5	350	4	
6	460	5	
7	160	3	
8	355	4	
9	337	4	
TOTAL	2971	36	TOTAL

HOLE	LENGTH MEDAL-TEE	PAR	STROKE INDEX
10	345	4	
11	129	3	
12	467	5	
13	317	4	
14	315	4	
15	336	4	
16	321	4	
17	446	5	
18	133	3	
TOTAL	2809	36	TOTAL

Car Rental

Reservation/Information telephone number :

Country code :
31

Telephone number :
20/6654141

Headquarters address :

EUROPCAR AUTOVERHUUR B.V.
Wibautstraat 224 a, 1097 DN Amsterdam
Tel. : (31) 20/5909111
Telex : 17191
Fax : (31) 20/6657016

62 GOLF COURSES, 45 000 PLAYERS

★★★ Great golf course
★★ Very good golf course
$ 20-40 Dfl.
★ Recommended golf course
✡ Holiday golf course
$ $ more than 55 Dfl.

TOWN	GOLF COURSE		TEL	MAP REF.
Alkmaar	Noordhollandse		(072) 156177	•
Almere	Almeerderhout		(03240) 21818	15
Alphen aan de Rijn	Zeegersloot		(01720) 74567	24
Amsterdam	Amsterdamse		(020)943650	•
	Olympus		(020) 799362	•
Apeldoorn	Veluwse		(05769) 275	•
Arnhem	Edese		(08308) 1985	•
	Rosendaelsche	★★	(085) 421438	8
Axel	De Woeste Kop		(01155) 4467	•
Beetsterzwaag	Lauswolt		(05126) 2594	•
Bergen op Zoom	Wouwse Plantage		(01657) 593	•
Breda	Noordbrabantse « Toxandria »	★	(01611) 1200	10
Brunssum	Brunssummerheide		(045) 270968	16
Den Bosch	De Dommel		(04105) 2316	•
Den Haag	Haagsche	★★★	(01751) 79607	5
Den Helder	Helderse		(02230) 14035	•
	Nieuwediep		(02230) 42484	•
Deventer	Sallandsche « De Hoek »		(05709) 1214	•
Doetinchem	Keppelse		(08348) 1416	•
Domburg	Domburgsche		(01188) 1573	•
Dordrecht	De Merwelanden		(078) 211221	•
Eindhoven	Best		(04998) 96696	22
	De Schoot		(04138) 73011	•
	De Tongelreep		(040) 520962	•
	Eindhovensche	★	(04902) 12713	11
	Haviksoord		(04906) 1818	•
Emmen	Drentse « Gelpenberg »		(05917) 1784	•
Enschede	Enschedese		(053) 337992	•
Gasselte	De Semslanden		(05990) 64661	•

TOWN	GOLF COURSE		TEL	MAP REF.
Groesbeek	Het Rijk van Nijmegen	★	(08891) 76644	17
Groningen	Noord-Nederlandse		(05906) 1275	12
Gulpen	Wittem		(04455) 1397	•
Haarlem	Spaarnwoude		(023) 382708	1
Hattem	Hattemse		(05206) 41909	•
Havelte	Havelte		(05214) 2200	•
Hengelo	Twentsche		(074) 912773	•
Hilversum	Hilversumsche	★★	(035) 857060	6
Leusden	De Hoge Kleij		(033) 616944	18
Maarsbergen	Anderstein		(03433) 1330	•
Nieuwegein	Nieuwegein		(03407) 2231	•
Noordwijk	Noordwijkse	★★ ☆	(02523) 73761	3
Nunspeet	Nunspeetse	★	(03412) 58034	19
Ommen	De Hooge Graven		(05291) 7503	•
Purmerend	Purmerend		(02990) 44646	23
Rilland-Bath	Reymerswael		(01135) 1265	•
Roden	Holthuizen		(05908) 15103	•
Rotterdam	Kleiburg		(01810) 14225	9
	Broekpolder		(010) 4748140	13
	Oude Maas		(01890) 16165	•
	Rotterdamse Kralingen		(010) 4527646	•
Sneek	Sint Nicolaasga		(05138) 99850	25
Utrecht	De Haar		(03407) 2860	•
	De Pan	★★	(03404) 55223	7
Venray	Geysteren		(04784) 1809	14
Voerendaal	Hoenshuis		(045) 753300	20
Wassenaar	Haagsche	★★★	(01751) 79607	5
	Rozenstein		(01751) 17846	•
Weert	Crossmoor		(04950) 18438	•
Wierden	De Koepel		(05496) 76150	•
Wijchen	De Berendonck		(08894) 20039	•
Zaandam	Zaanse		(075) 160253	•
Zandvoort	Kennemer	★★★ ☆	(02507) 12836	2
Zeewolde	Zeewolde		(03242) 2103	21

NEW GOLF COURSES (18 HOLES OR MORE) TO OPEN SOON

GC Capelle a/d Ijssel
Capelle a/d Ijssel
Tel. : 01807-16477

GC Cromstrijen
3280 Numansdorp
Tel. : 01865-1077

GC De Brugse Vaart
Brugse Vaart 10-4501 Oostburg
Tel. : 01170-3410

GC Edda Huzid
Hunnenweg 16-3781 Voorthuizen
Tel. : 03429-1661

GC Flevoland
Bosweg 1-Lelystad
Tel. : 03200-30077

GC Grevelingenhout
Oudendijk-Bruinisse
Tel. : 01113-2650

GC Veldzijde
Bovendijk 41-3648 Wilnis
Tel. : 02979-81143

Rijswijkse
Lange Kleiweg 2b-2288 Rijswijk
Tel. : 070-901826

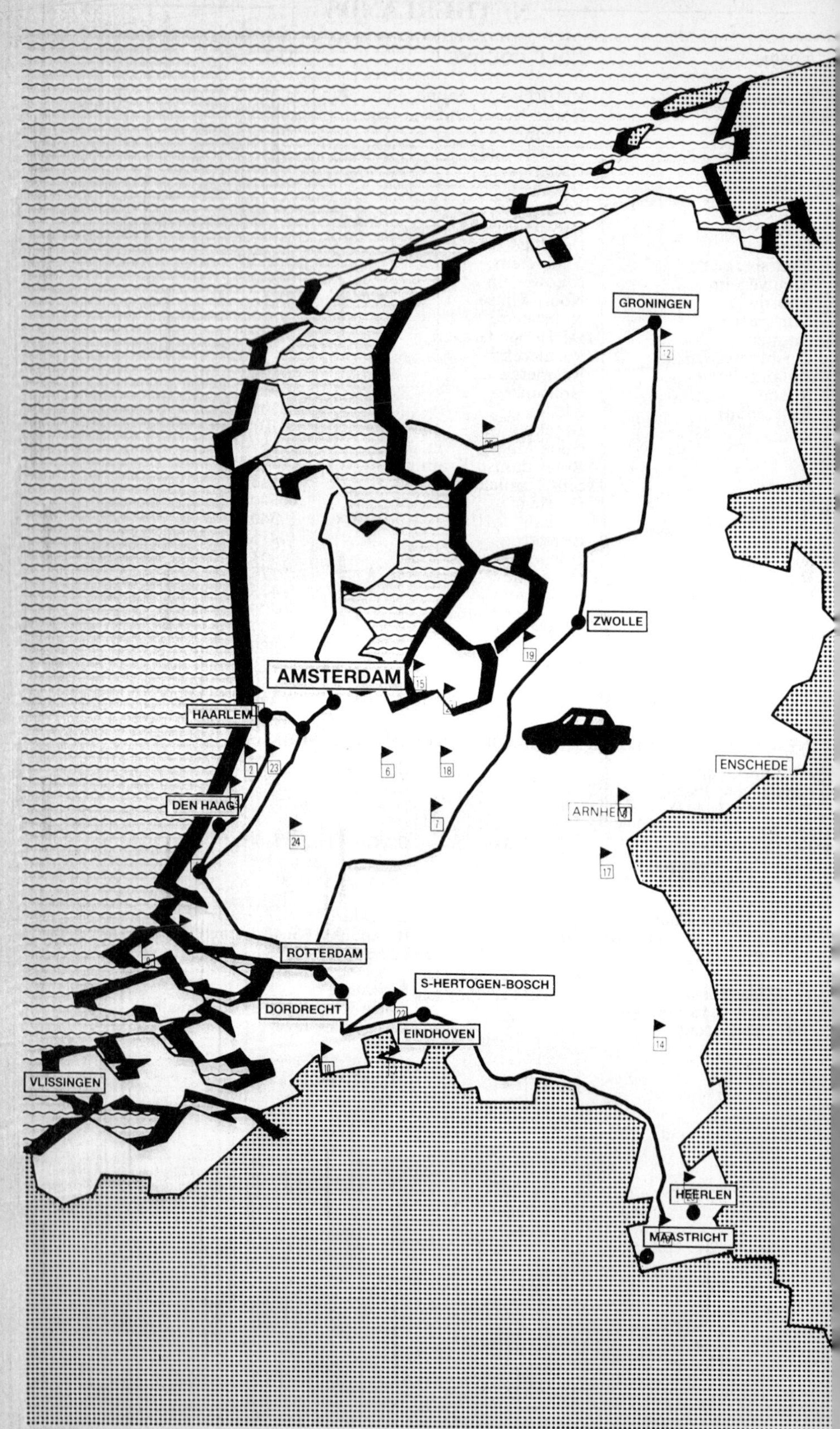

All cities represented on the map are Europcar locations.

ALMEERDERHOUT

TEL : (03240)21818/23818
LOCATION : between Huizen and Almere N. 27
ADDRESS : Watersnipwep 19-21-Almere-Flevoland
HOTEL :
Jan Tabak-Bussum
Tel : (02159)59911
Barbizon Centre-Amsterdam
Tel : (020)851351
Pulitzer-Amsterdam
Tel : (020)228333
RESTAURANT : Auberge La Provence-Laren
Tel : (02153)97874

Inaugurated in 1988, the golf course is situated not far from Amsterdam in the middle of a polder called Flevoland. The 18 holes run through flat and partly hazardous landscape of 450 acres woodland. An originality of Almeerderhout is that it is the natural habitat of a variety of birds and small animals all year round. There is a short par 3 nine hole course. *SSS 69*

GF $ | — | S
1986 | D. van Heel |
18 | L 5593 P 72 | R

Required : Handicap Certificate
Best days : Any day

HOLE	LENGTH MEDAL-TEE	PAR	STROKE INDEX
1	294	4	11
2	478	5	3
3	108	3	17
4	300	4	13
5	336	4	9
6	158	3	5
7	443	5	7
8	361	4	1
9	276	4	15
TOTAL	2754	36	TOTAL

HOLE	LENGTH MEDAL-TEE	PAR	STROKE INDEX
10	458	5	4
11	142	3	18
12	314	4	6
13	306	4	14
14	164	3	16
15	438	5	8
16	377	4	2
17	307	4	12
18	333	4	10
TOTAL	2839	36	TOTAL

BEST

TEL : (04998)96696
LOCATION : 10 km Eindhoven to Den Bosch
ADDRESS : Golflaan 1-5683 RZ Best
HOTEL :
Days Inn - Best
Tel : (04998)91650
Novotel - Eindhoven
Tel : (040)526575
RESTAURANT : Quatre Bras - Best
Tel : (04998)71450

This parkland course, designed by the former golf champion Dudok van Heel, is situated close to the city of Eindhoven in the south of Holland. The first nine holes work their way through lush woodland, the second nine are laid out on more open countryside with young plantations. Several spreads of water flank the holes. *SSS 72*

GF $$ — S
1989 D. van Heel
18 L 5935 P 72 R

Required : Club Membership Card
Best days : Any day

HOLE	LENGTH MEDAL-TEE	PAR	STROKE INDEX
1	343	4	7
2	365	4	13
3	110	3	15
4	363	4	1
5	375	4	5
6	151	3	11
7	320	4	9
8	492	5	3
9	282	4	17
TOTAL	2801	35	TOTAL

HOLE	LENGTH MEDAL-TEE	PAR	STROKE INDEX
10	473	5	4
11	339	4	16
12	198	3	6
13	435	5	12
14	396	4	2
15	480	5	10
16	314	4	8
17	152	3	18
18	347	4	14
TOTAL	3134	37	TOTAL

BROEKPOLDER

TEL : (010)4748140
LOCATION : 12 km Rotterdam
ADDRESS : Watersportweg 100 –
3138 HD Vlaardingen
HOTEL :
Delta Crest – Vlaardingen
Tel : (010)4345477
Novotel – Schiedem
Tel : (010)4713322
Rijnhotel – Rotterdam
Tel : (010)4333800
RESTAURANT : Taverne d'Ouwe Haven –
Vlaardingen
Tel : (010)4353000

This busy golf course is situated near Vlaardingen, an important harbour. It is laid out on flat countryside in a typical Dutch 'polder landscape' with ditches and reeds encircling some of the fairways. The average golfer won't find this course too much of a test.
SSS 68

GF $$ | — | R S
1981 | F. Pennink
18 | L 6048 P 72

Required : Handicap Certificate
Best days : Weekdays

HOLE	LENGTH MEDAL-TEE	PAR	STROKE INDEX
1	342	4	11
2	335	4	5
3	457	5	17
4	157	3	15
5	351	4	7
6	474	5	9
7	381	4	1
8	352	4	3
9	170	3	13
TOTAL	3019	36	TOTAL

HOLE	LENGTH MEDAL-TEE	PAR	STROKE INDEX
10	441	5	16
11	357	4	10
12	381	4	2
13	158	3	14
14	462	5	8
15	329	4	12
16	134	3	18
17	369	4	6
18	395	4	4
TOTAL	3029	36	TOTAL

BRUNSSUMERHEIDE

TEL : (045)270968/311545
LOCATION : 25 km Maastricht
ADDRESS : Rimburgerweg 50-Brunssum
HOTEL :
Zuid Limburg-Epen
Tel : (04455)1818
Derlon-Maastricht
Tel : (043)216770
Ons Krijtland-Epen
Tel : (04455)1557
RESTAURANT : Kasteel Wittem-Wittem
Tel : (04450)1208

This is a public golf course located in the southern part of Holland not far from the German border. It is laid out on rolling heathland where mature and young trees alternate. There are several lakes guarding the holes. The course, which is divided by a road, has some cycle and riding tracks crossing it. There is a short par 3-9 hole course. *SSS 69*

GF $

1985

18

—

D. van Heel

L 5457 P 71

S

RP

Required : Handicap Certificate
Best days : Any day

HOLE	LENGTH MEDAL-TEE	PAR	STROKE INDEX
1	381	4	5
2	262	4	11
3	159	3	15
4	296	4	9
5	330	4	7
6	81	3	17
7	513	5	3
8	368	4	1
9	330	4	13
TOTAL	2720	35	TOTAL

HOLE	LENGTH MEDAL-TEE	PAR	STROKE INDEX
10	314	4	4
11	336	4	12
12	274	4	10
13	486	5	2
14	107	3	16
15	294	4	8
16	180	3	14
17	305	4	18
18	441	5	6
TOTAL	2737	36	TOTAL

DE HOGE KLEIJ

TEL : (033)616944
LOCATION : 20 km Utrecht/4 km Amersfoort
ADDRESS : Appelweg 4-3832 RK Leusden
HOTEL :
Den Treek-Leusden
Tel : (033)947479
Malie-Utrecht
Tel : (030)316424
Pays Bas-Utrecht
Tel : (030)333321
RESTAURANT : Van der Wiel-Leusden
Tel : (033)947479

Located in a densely wooded part of Holland, many of the fairways of de Hoge Kleij are bounded by trees. Partly flat and partly hilly, there are some fine views over the surrounding countryside from several of the holes. Most of the greens are well-defended by bunkers. *SSS 72*

GF $$ — S

1987 — F. Pennink, D. Steel 

18 — L 6053 P 72 — R

Required : Handicap Certificate
Best days : Weekdays only, upon reservation

HOLE	LENGTH MEDAL-TEE	PAR	STROKE INDEX
1	363	4	7
2	202	3	13
3	463	5	11
4	356	4	5
5	147	3	17
6	460	5	15
7	374	4	3
8	331	4	9
9	380	4	1
TOTAL	3076	36	TOTAL

HOLE	LENGTH MEDAL-TEE	PAR	STROKE INDEX
10	361	4	4
11	320	4	12
12	473	5	6
13	388	4	2
14	173	3	16
15	301	4	14
16	439	5	8
17	168	3	18
18	354	4	10
TOTAL	2977	36	TOTAL

DE PAN

★★

TEL : (03404)55223
LOCATION : 13 km Utrecht E8/A28
ADDRESS : Amersfoortseweg 1 - 3735 LJ Bosch en Duin
HOTEL :
Oud London - Zeist
Tel : (03439)1245
Figi - Zeist
Tel : (03404)27411
Kerkebosch - Zeist
Tel : (03404)14734
RESTAURANT : Hoefslag - Bosch-en-Duin
Tel : (03404)284395

One of Holland's finest golf courses with its gently rolling fairways running through a beautiful forest. This rather short championship course is characterized by sandy hillocks projected into several of them, calling for accuracy from tee to green. The well-appointed clubhouse lies in the middle of the course. *SSS 70*

GF $$
1929
18

—
H. Colt
L 5702 P 72

Required : Membership Card and Handicap Certificate
Best days : Weekdays

HOLE	LENGTH MEDAL-TEE	PAR	STROKE INDEX
1	438	5	13
2	339	4	7
3	153	3	17
4	346	4	3
5	460	5	11
6	361	4	1
7	285	4	9
8	187	3	15
9	347	4	5
TOTAL	2916	36	TOTAL

HOLE	LENGTH MEDAL-TEE	PAR	STROKE INDEX
10	309	4	12
11	454	5	6
12	145	3	18
13	356	4	2
14	317	4	10
15	151	3	16
16	333	4	4
17	275	4	14
18	446	5	8
TOTAL	2786	36	TOTAL

EINDHOVENSCHE

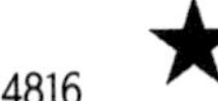

TEL : (04902)12713/14816
LOCATION : 8 km Eindhoven A2/E9
ADDRESS : Eindhovenseweg 300 – 5553 VB Valkenswaard
HOTEL :
Eindhoven Motel – Eindhoven
Tel : (040)116033
Cocagne – Eindhoven
Tel : (040)444755
Mandarin – Eindhoven
Tel : (040)125055
RESTAURANT : Heerlijkheid – Valkenswaard
Tel : (04902)15176

Set in the middle of a pine forest, this is an attractive well-wooded course of championship standard with mature trees bordering each fairway. Several of them are located around a lake. The 8th hole features a heavily bunkered green. The club hosted the European Amateur Championship in 1986. There is a sociable clubhouse overlooking the 1st, 9th, 10th and 18th holes. *SSS71*

GF $ — R S

1930 — H. Colt

18 — L 5897 P 72

Required : Handicap Certificate
Best days : Weekdays

HOLE	LENGTH MEDAL-TEE	PAR	STROKE INDEX
1	366	4	6
2	279	4	16
3	174	3	8
4	477	5	4
5	312	4	14
6	335	4	12
7	382	4	2
8	100	3	18
9	447	5	10
TOTAL	2872	36	TOTAL

HOLE	LENGTH MEDAL-TEE	PAR	STROKE INDEX
10	389	4	3
11	163	3	17
12	380	4	1
13	325	4	11
14	356	4	5
15	439	5	7
16	154	3	15
17	461	5	9
18	358	4	13
TOTAL	2872	36	TOTAL

GEYSTEREN

TEL : (04784)1809
LOCATION : 5 km Venray
ADDRESS : Het Spekt 2 – 5862 AZ Geysteren
HOTEL :
Zwaan – Venray
Tel : (04780)86969
Bovenste Molen – Venlo
Tel : (077)541045
Novotel – Venlo
Tel : (077)544141
RESTAURANT : Gasterij – Venray
Tel : (04780)84473

Founded in 1974, the golf course has recently been extended to 18 holes. It is a pretty course set in a pine and loaf forest in the south of Holland. The last five holes run through open land with a pond serving as hazard on the 14th, 15th and 18th holes. *SSS 72*

GF $

1974

18

—

—

L 6063 P 72

S

R

Required : Handicap Certificate
Best days : Weekdays only

HOLE	LENGTH MEDAL-TEE	PAR	STROKE INDEX
1	361	4	5
2	289	4	17
3	387	4	1
4	331	4	11
5	344	4	7
6	347	4	3
7	178	3	13
8	471	5	9
9	171	3	15
TOTAL	2879	35	TOTAL

HOLE	LENGTH MEDAL-TEE	PAR	STROKE INDEX
10	463	5	2
11	356	4	12
12	189	3	14
13	373	4	4
14	447	5	6
15	153	3	16
16	446	5	10
17	377	4	18
18	380	4	8
TOTAL	3184	37	TOTAL

HAAGSCHE

TEL : (01751)79607
LOCATION : 6 km Den Haag A44
ADDRESS : Groot Haesebroekseweg 22 – 2243 EC Wassenaar
HOTEL :
Duinoord – Wassenaar
Tel : (01751)19332
Wassenaar – Wassenaar
Tel : (01751)19218
Bijhorst – Wassenaar
Tel : (01751)19344
RESTAURANT : Kieviet – Wassenaar
Tel : (01751)19232

Though laid out 3km from the sea front in the middle of the Dutch dunes, the course is often compared with the British links courses in layout. Undoubtedly one of the most testing courses in Europe, it is set on undulating rugged terrain with its narrow fairways running through tricky dunes with deep hollows. Often exposed to the prevailing wind, one of its feature holes is the tough 6th. Hosting many championships, there is a handsome clubhouse and terrace with a fine view of the 18th hole. *SSS 71*

GF $$

1939

18

—

H. Colt, J. Allison, M. Morrison

L 5674 P 72

S

R

Required : Handicap Certificate
Best days : Weekdays only

HOLE	LENGTH MEDAL-TEE	PAR	STROKE INDEX
1	451	5	13
2	340	4	7
3	318	4	5
4	166	3	11
5	437	5	15
6	388	4	1
7	296	4	9
8	184	3	17
9	320	4	3
TOTAL	2900	36	TOTAL

HOLE	LENGTH MEDAL-TEE	PAR	STROKE INDEX
10	435	5	12
11	358	4	6
12	149	3	16
13	337	4	2
14	314	4	10
15	336	4	4
16	261	4	14
17	133	3	18
18	451	5	8
TOTAL	2774	36	TOTAL

HET RIJK VAN NIJMEGEN

★

TEL : (08891)76644
LOCATION : 5 km Nijmegen
ADDRESS : Postweg 17-6561 KJ Groesbeek
HOTEL :
Val Monte-Berg en Dal
Tel : (08895)41704
Sionshof-Groesbeek
Tel : (080)227727
Erica-Berg en Dal
Tel : (08895)43514
RESTAURANT : Het Golvend Land-Groesbeek
Tel : (08891)76644

Set within fine natural surroundings close to the German border, this is the largest golf complex in Holland. Apart from the 18 hole championship course, there is an interesting 9 hole course set in a hilly landscape with all blind holes and another 9 hole course ideal for beginners. The main course has a wooded layout with tree-lined fairways following the undulations of the terrain. The golf course offers beautiful panoramas along this regious hilly landscape. *SSS 72*

GF $

1988

36

—

P. Rolin

L 6048 P 72, 2412 P 34, 1924 P 33

S

R

Required : Handicap Certificate, Club Membership Card
Best days : Any day

HOLE	LENGTH MEDAL-TEE	PAR	STROKE INDEX
1	320	4	11
2	326	4	17
3	475	5	3
4	386	4	1
5	176	3	15
6	480	5	5
7	190	3	7
8	355	4	9
9	328	4	13
TOTAL	3036	36	TOTAL

HOLE	LENGTH MEDAL-TEE	PAR	STROKE INDEX
10	340	4	6
11	495	5	4
12	165	3	16
13	496	5	2
14	357	4	10
15	350	4	12
16	126	3	18
17	338	4	14
18	345	4	8
TOTAL	3012	36	TOTAL

HILVERSUMSCHE

TEL : (035)857060
LOCATION : 3 km Hilversum
ADDRESS : Soestdijkerstraatweg 172 – 1213 XJ Hilversum
HOTEL :
Jan Tabak – Bussum
Tel : (02159)59911
Hof van Holland – Hilversum
Tel : (035)857060
Lapershoek – Hilversum
Tel : (035)231341
RESTAURANT : Palace Résidence – Hilversum
Tel : (035)19994

This is an attractive heavily wooded course whose mostly flat holes run between beautiful trees and heather. Several of the fairways and greens are craftily bunkered. The clubhouse is comfortable and modern. The Hilversumsche golf club hosted the 1987 and 1988 Dutch Open. *SSS 71*

  $$

 1910

18

 —

 —

L 5861 P 72

RP 

Required : Handicap Certificate, Club Membership Card
Best days : Any day

HOLE	LENGTH MEDAL-TEE	PAR	STROKE INDEX
1	448	5	15
2	310	4	11
3	356	4	5
4	373	4	3
5	190	3	13
6	395	4	1
7	439	5	7
8	123	3	17
9	299	4	9
TOTAL	2933	36	TOTAL

HOLE	LENGTH MEDAL-TEE	PAR	STROKE INDEX
10	135	3	16
11	385	4	4
12	320	4	8
13	437	5	12
14	111	3	18
15	410	4	2
16	336	4	6
17	350	4	14
18	444	5	10
TOTAL	2928	36	TOTAL

HOENSHUIS

TEL : (045)753300
LOCATION : 17 km Maastricht
ADDRESS : Hoensweg 17-6367 GM Voerendaal
HOTEL :
Prinses Juliana-Valkenburg
Tel : (04406)12244
Grand Hotel-Heerlen
Tel : (045)713846
Erenstein-Kerkrade
Tel : (045)13333
RESTAURANT : Winselerhof-Landgraaf
Tel : (045)464343

Designed by Belgium's finest golf architect Paul Rolin, this golf course is of championship standard. Laid out in the province of Limburg near the holiday resort of Valkenburg, it is a long open course set in hilly countryside with fine views of the typical Limburgian countryside. It features several blind holes and strategic water hazards, requiring precision. The 18th hole is an interesting par 3 with a teeshot across a 150 meter expanse of water. Many a match is settled at this hole. The clubhouse is located in an old Limburgian farm dating back to the 14th century. *SSS 71*

GF $ — — S

1986 P. Rolin 

18 L 6126 P 72 R

Required : Handicap Certificate
Best days : Weekdays only

HOLE	LENGTH MEDAL-TEE	PAR	STROKE INDEX
1	375	4	11
2	343	4	7
3	346	4	3
4	335	4	9
5	154	3	17
6	474	5	13
7	371	4	1
8	141	3	15
9	506	5	5
TOTAL	3047	36	TOTAL

HOLE	LENGTH MEDAL-TEE	PAR	STROKE INDEX
10	391	4	2
11	475	5	6
12	364	4	14
13	375	4	8
14	350	4	16
15	170	3	12
16	455	5	4
17	293	4	18
18	200	3	10
TOTAL	3079	36	TOTAL

KENNEMER

TEL : (02507)12836
LOCATION : 10 km Haarlem
ADDRESS : Kennemerweg 78-80 –
2042 XT Zandvoort
HOTEL :
Queenie – Zandvoort
Tel : (02507)13599
Hoogland – Zandvoort
Tel : (02507)15541
Zuiderbad – Zandvoort
Tel : (02507)12613
RESTAURANT : Bokkedoorn – Heemstede
Tel : (023)263 600

Designed by Harry Colt, this was Holland's first seaside course. It is a fine natural and traditional links, amongst the world's best with a challenging layout. The 27 holes are (Van Hengel-A, Pennink-B, Colt-C) set amidst hilly sand dunes, some of them flanked by pine trees and exposed to the prevailing westerly wind. Among its most difficult holes are the 10th (B course) with a blind drive, and the 15th (B course) with deep impressive bunkers. Many times host to leading international tournaments, it boasts an elegant clubhouse built high up overlooking the course. *SSS 71*

GF $$

1927/1985

27

Mondays

H. Colt, F. Pennink

L A: 2951 P 36, B: 2874 P 36, C: 2864 P 36

S R

Required : Handicap Certificate
Best days : Weekdays

HOLE	LENGTH MEDAL-TEE	PAR	STROKE INDEX	HOLE	LENGTH MEDAL-TEE	PAR	STROKE INDEX	HOLE	LENGTH MEDAL-TEE	PAR	STROKE INDEX
1	368	4	9	1	392	4	7	10	314	4	12
2	479	5	3	2	133	3	17	11	404	4	4
3	134	3	17	3	478	5	3	12	467	5	8
4	316	4	13	4	291	4	13	13	296	4	14
5	348	4	13	5	297	4	5	14	339	4	2
6	325	4	1	6	435	5	11	15	139	3	16
7	475	5	11	7	317	4	3	16	435	5	6
8	158	3	15	8	150	3	15	17	140	3	18
9	348	4	5	9	381	4	9	18	330	4	10
TOTAL	2951	36	TOTAL	TOTAL	2874	36	TOTAL	TOTAL	2864	36	TOTAL

KLEIBURG

TEL : (01810)14225
LOCATION : 34 km Rotterdam
ADDRESS : Krabbeweg 9 – 3231 NB Brielle
HOTEL :
Zalm – Brielle
Tel : (01810)13388
Duinoord – Oostvoorne
Tel : (01815)2044
Wapen Van Marion – Oostvoorne
Tel : (01815)9399
RESTAURANT : Pablo – Brielle
Tel : (01810)12960

Extended to 18 holes in 1986, this public golf course lies on the edge of a canal called 'Hartelkanaal' on flat and heavy clayey terrain. Built partly on a dyke, it is landscaped with young trees, bushes and shrubs. There are two large lakes guarding several holes.

GF $

—

S

1974

F. Pennink

18

L 5534 P 70

R

Required : Handicap Certificate
Best days : Wednesdays and Fridays

HOLE	LENGTH MEDAL-TEE	PAR	STROKE INDEX
1	311	4	8
2	288	4	18
3	304	4	14
4	289	4	16
5	163	3	4
6	315	4	6
7	261	4	12
8	446	5	10
9	198	3	2
TOTAL	2575	35	TOTAL

HOLE	LENGTH MEDAL-TEE	PAR	STROKE INDEX
10	310	4	13
11	393	4	7
12	416	4	1
13	319	4	9
14	368	4	5
15	163	3	17
16	444	5	11
17	157	3	15
18	389	4	3
TOTAL	2959	35	TOTAL

NOORD NEDERLANDSE

TEL : (05906)1275/2004
LOCATION : 15 km Groningen A28/E35
ADDRESS : Pollselaan 5 –
9756 CJ Glimmen
HOTEL :
Motel Haren – Haren
Tel : (050)347041
Paterswolde – Paterswolde
Tel : (05907)5400
Motel Westerbroek – Westerbroek
Tel : (05904)2205
RESTAURANT : Auberge Le Grillon –
Glimmen
Tel : (05906)1392

Situated in the north of Holland, the course is laid out alongside a scenic river called 'Drentse A'. Its holes run partly through flat woodland and partly through pastureland, with blossoming rhododendrons colouring the fairways in spring time. *SSS 70*

GF $

—

S

1950

F. Pennink, D. Steel

R

18

L 5677 P 70

Required : Handicap Certificate
Best days : Mondays, Wednesdays, Fridays

HOLE	LENGTH MEDAL-TEE	PAR	STROKE INDEX
1	364	4	5
2	431	4	1
3	257	4	13
4	129	3	17
5	307	4	9
6	289	4	11
7	372	4	3
8	467	5	7
9	141	3	15
TOTAL	2757	35	TOTAL

HOLE	LENGTH MEDAL-TEE	PAR	STROKE INDEX
10	287	4	16
11	389	4	2
12	173	3	18
13	492	5	8
14	393	4	4
15	369	4	6
16	321	4	14
17	163	3	10
18	333	4	12
TOTAL	2920	35	TOTAL

NOORDBRABANTSE « TOXANDRIA »

★

TEL : (01611)1200
LOCATION : 8 km Breda
ADDRESS : Veenstraat 89 – 5124 NC Molenschot
HOTEL :
Mastbosch – Breda
Tel : (076)650050
Mercury – Breda
Tel : (076)220200
Novotel – Breda
Tel : (076)659220
RESTAURANT : Auberge De Arent – Breda
Tel : (076)144601

This very attractive course lies in the middle of a densely wooded part in the south of Holland. It is entirely surrounded by lush forests with majestic trees bordering most of the fairways. The fine clubhouse has panoramic views over several of the holes. *SSS 70*

GF $

— S

1929

M. Morrison

18

L 5759 P 72

R

Required : Club Membership Card
Best days : Weekdays only

HOLE	LENGTH MEDAL-TEE	PAR	STROKE INDEX
1	322	4	6
2	457	5	2
3	328	4	8
4	124	3	18
5	259	4	14
6	337	4	4
7	275	4	16
8	436	5	12
9	163	3	10
TOTAL	2701	36	TOTAL

HOLE	LENGTH MEDAL-TEE	PAR	STROKE INDEX
10	390	4	1
11	408	4	3
12	348	4	7
13	148	3	17
14	461	5	11
15	348	4	5
16	176	3	13
17	458	5	15
18	321	4	9
TOTAL	3058	36	TOTAL

NOORDWIJKSE

TEL : (02523)73761
LOCATION : 25 km Den Haag A 44
ADDRESS : Randweg 25 –
2204 AB Noordwijk
HOTEL :
Witte Raaf – Noordwijkerhout
Tel : (02523)75984
Alexander – Noordwijk
Tel : (01719)18900
Hof van Holland – Noorwijk Binnen
Tel : (01719)12255
RESTAURANT : Graaf van het Hoogeveen – Noordwijk
Tel : (01719)11308

This is a first class links course designed by Frank Pennink in 1972, and hosting the Dutch Open in 1978, 79, 85 and 1986. Set in natural surroundings amid pine forest and hilly sand dunes, there are several fine holes demanding accuracy. The modern clubhouse is built high up overlooking the North Sea and the course. *SSS 72*

GF $$

1972

18

—

F. Pennink

L 5899 P 72

S

R

Required : Handicap Certificate
Best days : Weekdays only

HOLE	LENGTH MEDAL-TEE	PAR	STROKE INDEX
1	345	4	13
2	503	5	5
3	139	3	17
4	365	4	1
5	354	4	9
6	165	3	15
7	345	4	3
8	328	4	11
9	472	5	7
TOTAL	3016	36	TOTAL

HOLE	LENGTH MEDAL-TEE	PAR	STROKE INDEX
10	356	4	2
11	442	5	14
12	140	3	18
13	333	4	6
14	439	5	10
15	344	4	8
16	333	4	4
17	161	3	12
18	335	4	16
TOTAL	2883	36	TOTAL

NUNSPEETSE

★

TEL : (03412)58034
LOCATION : 25 km Zwolle, 35 km Amersfoort A 28
ADDRESS : PlesmanLaan 30-8072 PT Nunspeet
HOTEL :
Malle Jan-Vierhouten
Tel : (05771)241
Wientjes-Zwolle
Tel : (038)254254
Postiljon Motel-Zwolle
Tel : (038)216031
RESTAURANT : Schouw-Nunspeet
Tel : (03412)52829

The Nunspeetse golf course lies within a magnificent pine forest. It provides a fine test of golf with three loops of nine (North, South and East Course) holes meandering their way through undulating sand dunes and scenic woodland. Two strategically positioned ponds create problems on several holes. Nunspeet is Holland's first golf course featuring two-level greens. It boasts an attractive and comfortable clubhouse with fine views over three holes. *SSS 72*

GF $$

1987

27

—

P. Rolin

L 2931 P 36, 2935 P 36, 2930 P 36

S

R

Required : Handicap Certificate
Best days : Any day

HOLE	LENGTH MEDAL-TEE	PAR	STROKE INDEX	HOLE	LENGTH MEDAL-TEE	PAR	STROKE INDEX	HOLE	LENGTH MEDAL-TEE	PAR	STROKE INDEX
1	331	4	3	1	326	4	6	1	477	5	6
2	141	3	17	2	435	5	10	2	262	4	18
3	466	5	7	3	139	3	18	3	136	3	16
4	309	4	15	4	362	4	4	4	477	5	2
5	336	4	11	5	383	4	2	5	296	4	12
6	367	4	1	6	309	4	14	6	359	4	4
7	173	3	5	7	326	4	12	7	187	3	14
8	469	5	13	8	174	3	16	8	345	4	8
9	339	4	9	9	481	5	8	9	391	4	10
TOTAL	2931	36	TOTAL	TOTAL	2935	36	TOTAL	TOTAL	2930	36	TOTAL

PURMEREND

TEL : (02990)44646
LOCATION : 25 km N. Amsterdam
A7/E22
ADDRESS : Westerweg 60
1445 AD Purmerend
HOTEL :
De Saense Schans - Zaandijk
Tel : (075)211911
Garden - Amsterdam
Tel : (020)642121
RESTAURANT : De Hoop op d'Swarte
Walvis - Zaandijk
Tel : (075)165629

Laid out in authentic polder landscape bordering on the «Ijsselmeer» in the north of Holland, the 27 holes run through flat parkland. The Irish architect Tom McAuley designed this challenging layout incorporating as obstacles many bunkers, canals and ponds. A first class 70 room hotel is planned to open in 1991. *SSS 72*

GF $

1990

27

—

T. Mc Auley

L 6062 P 72

S

RP

Required : Handicap Certificate
Best days : Weekdays

HOLE	LENGTH MEDAL-TEE	PAR	STROKE INDEX
1	344	4	8
2	320	4	10
3	196	3	4
4	505	5	6
5	140	3	17
6	326	4	12
7	287	4	16
8	445	5	14
9	406	4	2
TOTAL	2969	36	TOTAL

HOLE	LENGTH MEDAL-TEE	PAR	STROKE INDEX
10	372	4	13
11	343	4	15
12	189	3	3
3	253	4	11
14	452	5	9
15	147	3	18
16	404	4	7
17	418	4	1
18	515	5	5
TOTAL	3093	36	TOTAL

ROSENDAELSCHE

★★

TEL : (085)421438
LOCATION : 5 km Arnhem N 50
ADDRESS : Apeldoornseweg 450 – 6816 SN Arnhem
HOTEL :
Groot Warnsborn – Arnhem
Tel : (085)455751
Klein Zwitserland – Renkum
Tel : (08373)12221
Rijnhotel – Arnhem
Tel : (085)434642
RESTAURANT : Wolfheze – Wolfheze
Tel : (085)337852

The 'Rosendaelsche' golf club is the oldest Dutch golf course, having been founded in 1895. It is an attractive golf course, venue for the 1984 Dutch Open, which is laid out on splendid gently rolling woodland with its narrow fairways running between beautiful trees and heather. *SSS 72*

GF $$ — R S
1895 F. Pennink
18 L 6057 P 72

Required : Club Membership Card
Best days : Weekdays

HOLE	LENGTH MEDAL-TEE	PAR	STROKE INDEX
1	356	4	9
2	384	4	5
3	339	4	7
4	396	4	1
5	463	5	11
6	372	4	3
7	147	3	17
8	486	5	13
9	147	3	15
TOTAL	3090	36	TOTAL

HOLE	LENGTH MEDAL-TEE	PAR	STROKE INDEX
10	350	4	10
11	369	4	4
12	161	3	16
13	279	4	8
14	407	4	2
15	439	5	12
16	129	3	18
17	469	5	14
18	364	4	6
TOTAL	2967	36	TOTAL

SINT-NICOLAASGA

TEL : (05138)99850
LOCATION : 10 km Joure/30 km S. Leeuwarden/20 km Sneek
ADDRESS : Legemeersterweg 16-18-8527 DS Legemeer
HOTEL :
De Wielen - Langwee
Tel : (05138)99185
Wijnberg - Sneek
Tel : (05150)12421
Bonnema - Sneek
Tel : (05150)13175

Built in the north of Holland in the very heart of picturesque "Friesland" an area with many lakes where sailing is predominant, this new course is harmoniously integrated into the tranquil "Friesian" landscape. The holes run through parkland alternating with open countryside. A first class golf hotel is scheduled for 1992. *SSS 70*

GF $

1990

18

—

A. Rijks, P. Rohn

L 5742 P 72

S

R

Required : Handicap Certificate
Best days : Weekdays

HOLE	LENGTH MEDAL-TEE	PAR	STROKE INDEX
1	326	4	15
2	143	3	11
3	341	4	5
4	376	4	1
5	350	4	9
6	439	5	3
7	443	5	7
8	140	3	13
9	314	4	17
TOTAL	2872	36	TOTAL

HOLE	LENGTH MEDAL-TEE	PAR	STROKE INDEX
10	121	3	14
11	450	5	16
12	360	4	4
13	280	4	18
14	325	4	10
15	376	4	2
16	144	3	12
17	339	4	6
18	475	5	8
TOTAL	2870	36	TOTAL

SPAARNWOUDE

TEL : (023)382708
LOCATION : On Road North Sea Canal
ADDRESS : Recreatiegebied Spaarnwoude – Het Hoge Land 8 – 1981 LT Velsen
HOTEL :
Lion d'Or – Haarlem
Tel : (023)321750
Crest – Amsterdam
Tel : (020)462300
Memphis – Amsterdam
Tel : (020)733141
RESTAURANT : Waterland – Velsen
Tel : (023)23250

Spaarnwoude is a public golf course featuring an 18 hole course, a short 9 hole par 3 course and a pitch and putt course of 11 holes, set on mostly flat terrain with young trees and shrubs landscaping the fairways. Numerous artificial lakes separate the holes and serve a hazards. There are several cycle tracks crossing the course. *SSS 69*

GF $

1977

27

—

F. Pennink

L 5469 P 70

S

R

Required : Handicap Certificate
Best days : Weekdays

HOLE	LENGTH MEDAL-TEE	PAR	STROKE INDEX
1	456	5	11
2	198	3	13
3	328	4	1
4	340	4	3
5	183	3	15
6	443	5	5
7	287	4	7
8	301	4	9
9	141	3	17
TOTAL	2677	35	TOTAL

HOLE	LENGTH MEDAL-TEE	PAR	STROKE INDEX
10	403	4	2
11	351	4	8
12	461	5	6
13	140	3	16
14	319	4	12
15	306	4	14
16	299	4	10
17	371	4	4
18	142	3	18
TOTAL	2792	35	TOTAL

ZEEGERSLOOT

TEL : (01720)74567
LOCATION : 30 km Amsterdam, Den Haag Rotterdam, Utrecht
ADDRESS : Kromme Aarweg 5 - 2403 NB Alphen aan den Rijn
HOTEL :
Toor - Alphen a/d Rijn
Tel : (01720)76966
RESTAURANT : De Landerije - Alphen a/d Rijn
Tel : (01720)76880

About 30 km from a number of Holland's main cities such as Amsterdam, The Hague, Rotterdam and Utrecht, this course extends over flat open polder landscape. Numerous canals are a persistant hazard on a number of holes. There is a 9 hole par 3 course built on gently rolling parkland.

GF $

1905/1989

18

—

D. van Heel

L 5063 P 69

S

R

Required : Handicap Certificate
Best days : Weekdays

HOLE	LENGTH MEDAL-TEE	PAR	STROKE INDEX
1	312	4	5
2	395	4	1
3	107	3	17
4	183	3	3
5	466	5	9
6	244	4	15
7	108	3	13
8	161	3	7
9	454	5	11
TOTAL	2430	34	TOTAL

HOLE	LENGTH MEDAL-TEE	PAR	STROKE INDEX
10	349	4	2
11	160	3	12
12	452	5	14
13	322	4	6
14	170	3	8
15	339	4	4
16	273	4	10
17	128	3	18
18	440	5	16
TOTAL	2633	35	TOTAL

ZEEWOLDE

TEL : (03242)2103
LOCATION : 15 km Harderwijk
ADDRESS : Golflaan-Zeewolde-Flevoland
HOTEL :
Koningshof-Harderwijk
Tel : (03410)22555
Lelystad-Lelystad
Tel : (03200)42444
RESTAURANT : Rivendal-Almere
Tel : (03240)19000

Located on the Flevoland polder, Zeewolde has a varied character. Its 18 holes run through partly wooded and partly open polder landscape. It features undulating greens defended by bunkers and ponds. There is a short 9 hole course which is ideal for beginners. *SSS 71*

GF $

1986

18

—

F. Pennink, D. Steel

L 5954 P 71

S

R

Required : Handicap Certificate
Best days : Weekdays

HOLE	LENGTH MEDAL-TEE	PAR	STROKE INDEX
1	326	4	13
2	363	4	11
3	246	4	15
4	170	3	7
5	460	5	5
6	431	4	1
7	129	3	17
8	362	4	9
9	479	5	3
TOTAL	2966	36	TOTAL

HOLE	LENGTH MEDAL-TEE	PAR	STROKE INDEX
10	345	4	4
11	407	4	2
12	222	3	6
13	378	4	10
14	288	4	18
15	467	5	14
16	156	3	16
17	303	4	12
18	422	4	8
TOTAL	2988	35	TOTAL

Car Rental

Reservation/Information telephone number :

Country code : 47

Telephone number : 2/700400

Headquarters address :

INTERRENT - EUROPCAR NORGE A/S
P.O. Box 62, 1473 Skarer
Tel. : (47) 2/700555
Telex : 19139
Fax : (47) 2700756

---

12 GOLF COURSES, 7 000 PLAYERS

★★★ Great golf course
★★ Very good golf course
$ 30-100 Nkr
★ Recommended golf course
☼ Holiday golf course
$ $ around 200 Nkr

TOWN	GOLF COURSE		TEL	MAP REF.
Bergen	Bergen		(05) 182077	•
Drammen	Kjekstad		(02) 855850	•
Hamar	Hedmark		(065) 396117	•
Kolbotn	Oppegaard *(ext. 18 h.)*		(02) 8148450	•
Kristiansand	Kristiansand		(042) 45863	•
Oslo	Oslo	★★★	(02) 504402	2
Sarpsborg	Borregaard		(031) 57401	•
	Skjeberg		(09) 166440	
Skien	Grenland			•
Stabekk	Baerum			•
Stavanger	Stavanger	★	(04) 557025	1
Trondheim	Trondheim		(07) 531855	•
Tønsberg	Vestfold		(033) 65105	3

NEW GOLF COURSES (18 HOLES OR MORE) TO OPEN SOON

Arendal Golflklubb
4801 Arendal
Tel. : (041) 88101

Baerum Golflklubb
1310 Blommenholm
Tel. : (2) 148480

Kjekstad Golflklubb
3440 Røyken
Tel. : (02) 855850

Onsoy Golflklubb
1601 Frerikstad
Tel. : (09) 333033

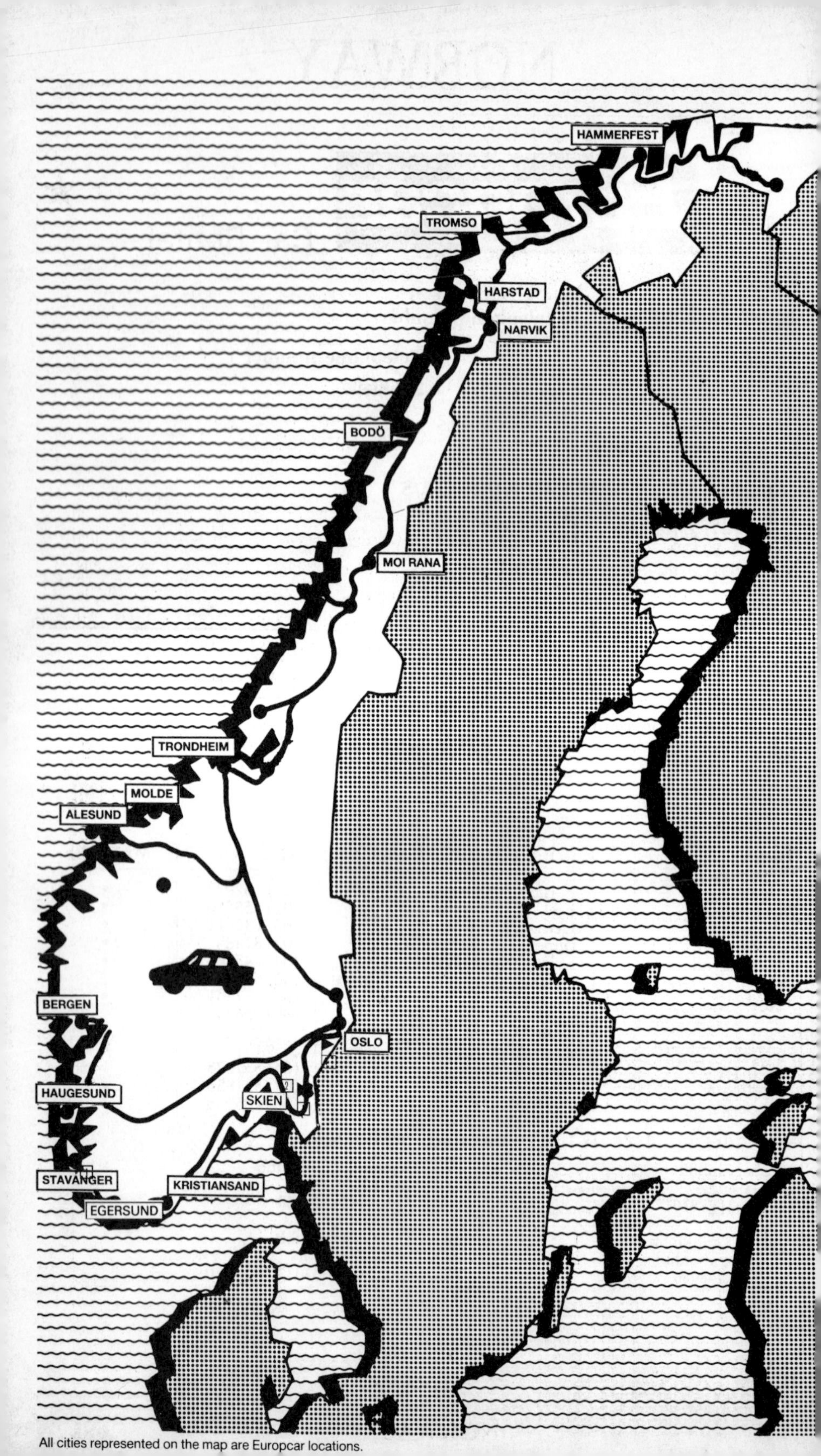

All cities represented on the map are Europcar locations.

OSLO

TEL : (02)50 44 02
LOCATION : 8 km Oslo
ADDRESS : Bogstad - 0757 Oslo 7
HOTEL :
Holmenkollen Park - Oslo
Tel : (02)146090
Oslo Plaza Tower - Oslo
Tel : (02)423660
SAS Scandinavia - Oslo
Tel : (02)113000
RESTAURANT : Theatercaféen - Oslo
Tel : (02)419060

Norway's most important club lies in the western suburbs of Oslo, quietly laid out on the shores of the scenic Bogstad Lake on gently rolling parkland and within a typical Norwegian forest. The championship course is rather long with several elevated greens, dog-leg holes and out of bounds. The 16th hole, named the 'Water Hole' is very picturesque, going across the lake. The Holmenkollen Park Hotel is 3km from the course, built high up with a panoramic view over the course, the lake and the forest.

GF $$ — Weekends until 13h — R S
1924 — —
18 — L 5997 P 72

Required : Handicap Certificate
Best days : Fridays

HOLE	LENGTH MEDAL-TEE	PAR	STROKE INDEX
1	340	4	13
2	436	5	5
3	184	3	15
4	378	4	1
5	340	4	9
6	362	4	7
7	326	4	11
8	148	3	17
9	528	5	3
TOTAL	3042	36	TOTAL

HOLE	LENGTH MEDAL-TEE	PAR	STROKE INDEX
10	510	5	2
11	151	3	18
12	362	4	4
13	344	4	10
14	326	4	12
15	464	5	6
16	166	3	16
17	338	4	8
18	294	4	14
TOTAL	2955	36	TOTAL

SKJEBERG

TEL : (09)166440/166310
LOCATION : 10 km Sarpsborg/100 km S. Oslo
ADDRESS : P.B. 149 - 1742 Klavestadhangen
HOTEL :
Saga - Sarpsborg
Tel : (09)154044

This sporty course is just 30 minutes drive from the Swedish border and 100 km south of Oslo. The holes are scenically laid out along the natural lines of the land near the picturesque lake Isejœn.

GF $

1986

18

October to mid May

J. Sederholm

L 5569 P 71

S

R

Required : Handicap Certificate
Best days : Weekdays

HOLE	LENGTH MEDAL-TEE	PAR	STROKE INDEX
1	343	4	18
2	171	3	9
3	274	4	5
4	272	4	13
5	133	3	17
6	367	4	3
7	112	3	10
8	287	4	15
9	435	5	11
TOTAL	2394	34	TOTAL

HOLE	LENGTH MEDAL-TEE	PAR	STROKE INDEX
10	361	4	6
11	184	3	14
12	343	4	8
13	404	4	2
14	450	5	1
15	285	4	16
16	333	4	4
17	449	5	7
18	366	4	12
TOTAL	3175	37	TOTAL

STAVANGER

★

TEL : (04)55 70 25/55 54 31
LOCATION : 3 km W. Stavanger
ADDRESS : Longebakke 45 – 4042 Hafrsfjord
HOTEL :
KNA – Stavanger
Tel : (04)528500
Royal – Stavanger
Tel : (04)567000
Atlantic – Stavanger
Tel : (04)527520

A picturesque lakeside course set along the shores of the Great Stokka Lake and carved out of rugged countryside of boulders, scrub, trees and marshland. Though fairly short, the course is a real test of golf including an unfriendly rough which requires accurate play on most holes. The club hosted the European Ladies Team Championship in 1985. It boasts a welcoming clubhouse, a genuine 'Jaer-House' which is a type of local building.
SSS 69

GF $ — — R S
1956 — F. Smith
18 — L 5333 P 69

Required : Handicap Certificate
Best days : Weekdays

HOLE	LENGTH MEDAL-TEE	PAR	STROKE INDEX
1	296	4	13
2	280	4	15
3	162	3	11
4	363	4	1
5	126	3	17
6	442	5	9
7	313	4	7
8	191	3	5
9	382	4	3
TOTAL	2555	34	TOTAL

HOLE	LENGTH MEDAL-TEE	PAR	STROKE INDEX
10	175	3	16
11	358	4	2
12	303	4	14
13	346	4	6
14	371	4	4
15	288	4	12
16	319	4	10
17	166	3	18
18	452	5	8
TOTAL	2778	35	TOTAL

VESTFOLD

TEL : (033)65105
LOCATION : 8 km Tønsberg
ADDRESS : Box 64 – 3101 Tønsberg
HOTEL :
Klubben – Tønsberg
Tel : (033)15111
Grand – Tønsberg
Tel : (033)12203
Maritim – Tønsberg
Tel : (033)17100

Situated in the southern part of Norway, the club was started in 1958 and was slowly expanded to the present 18 holes. This relatively short course is rather hilly with most of its narrow fairways separated by woodland. There is one water hazard on the 17th hole. *SSS 72*

GF $ — October to May — S

1958 — F. Pennink, J. Sederholm — 

18 — L 5860 P 73 — 

Required : Handicap Certificate
Best days : Mondays, Thursdays, Fridays, Sundays

HOLE	LENGTH MEDAL-TEE	PAR	STROKE INDEX
1	285	4	11
2	440	5	3
3	135	3	17
4	340	4	5
5	280	4	13
6	455	5	9
7	130	3	15
8	454	5	7
9	376	4	1
TOTAL	2895	37	TOTAL

HOLE	LENGTH MEDAL-TEE	PAR	STROKE INDEX
10	135	3	18
11	305	4	14
12	465	5	10
13	315	4	8
14	360	4	4
15	350	4	6
16	490	5	12
17	175	3	16
18	370	4	2
TOTAL	2965	36	TOTAL

PORTUGAL

Car Rental

Reservation/Information telephone number :

Country code : **351**

Telephone number : **1/9422322**

Headquarters address :

EUROPCAR INTERNACIONAL - ALUGUER DE AUTOMOVEIS LDA
Quinta da Francelha, Lote 7
Edificio Europcar - Prior Velho - 2685 SAVACEM
Tel. : (351) 1/9424024
Telex : 63260
Fax : (351) 1/9424543

23 GOLF COURSES, 4 500 PLAYERS

★★★ Great golf course
★★ Very good golf course
$ 800-5000 Esc.
★ Recommended golf course
☼ Holiday golf course
$ $ more than 5500 Esc.

TOWN	GOLF COURSE	TEL	MAP REF.
Estoril/Cascais	Estoril ★★ ☼	(01) 2681376	4
	Estoril Sol	(01) 9232461	•
	Quinta da Marinha ☼	(01) 289881	2
Lisbon	Club de Campo de Portugal ★	(01) 2263244	12
	Lisbon Sports Club	(01) 4310077	3
Porto	Estela ★ ☼	(052) 685567	14
	Miramar	(02) 7622067	•
	Oporto ☼	(02) 722008	1
Setubal	Troia ★ ☼	(065) 44151	5
Vidago	Vidago	(076) 97106	•
Vimeiro	Vimeiro	(061) 98157	•
AZORES			
Sao Miguel Island	Sao Miguel Achada *(ext. 18 h.)*	(096) 31925	•
Terceira Island	Terceira Ilha ☼	(095) 25847	I
MADEIRA			
Santa Cruz	Santa da Serra *(ext. 27 h.)*	(091) 55345	•
ALGARVE			
Almansil	Quinta do Lago ★★★ ☼	(089) 94529	10
	San Lorenzo ★ ☼	(089) 96534	10
Budens	Parque da Floresta ☼	(082) 65333	13
Lagos	Palmares ★★ ☼	(082) 62961	6
Loulé	Vale do Lobo ☼	(089) 94444	10
Portimao	Penina ★★ ☼	(082) 22051	7
Vilamoura	Vilamoura Um ☼	(089) 313652	9
	Vilamoura Dois ★★★ ☼	(089) 315562	11
	Vilamoura Três ☼	(089) 880724	15

NEW GOLF COURSES (18 HOLES OR MORE) TO OPEN SOON

Carvoeira Golf Club
8401 Lagoa
Tel. : (082) 53294

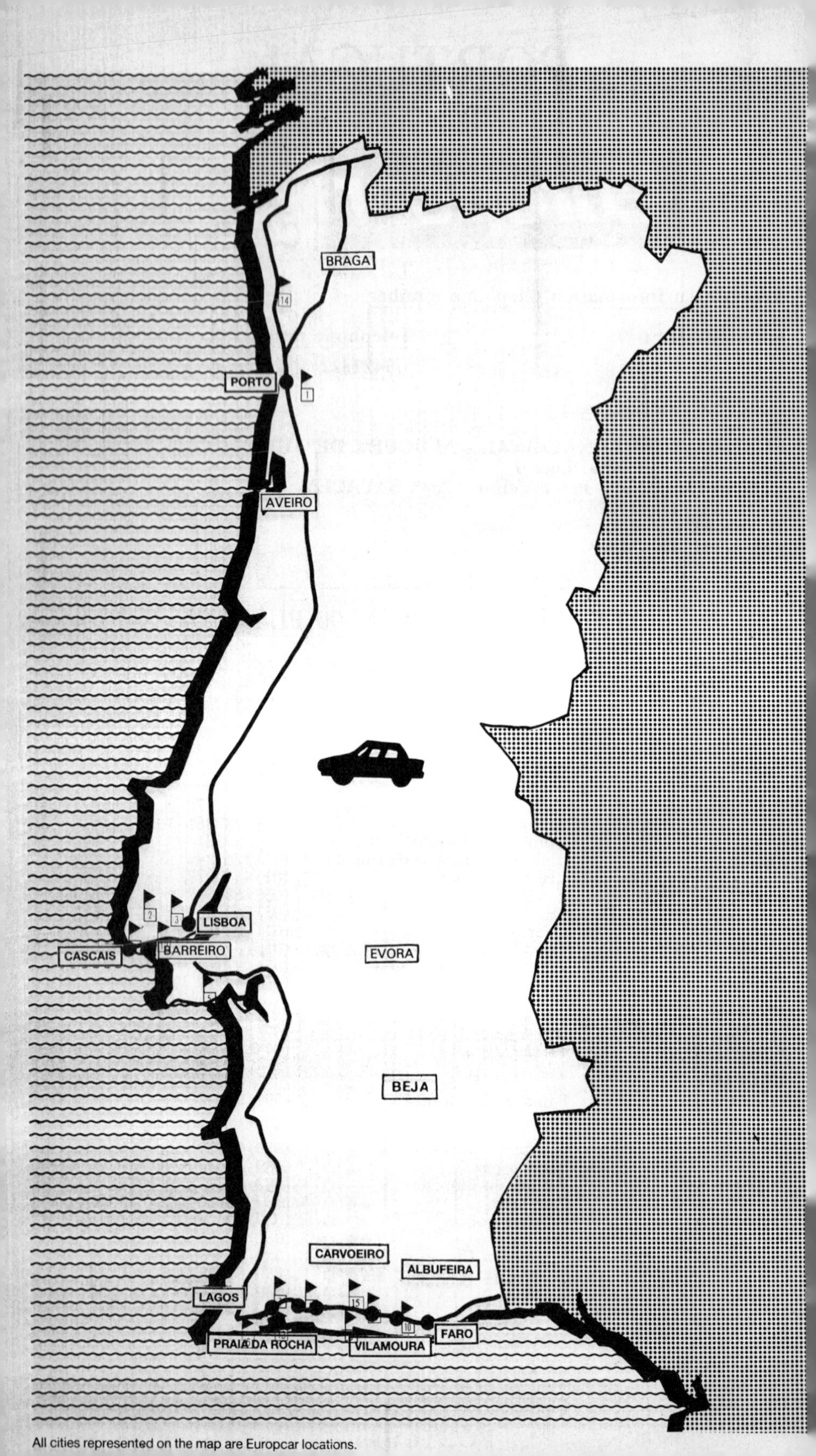

All cities represented on the map are Europcar locations.

CLUB DE CAMPO DE PORTUGAL (Portugal Country Club)

★

TEL : (01)2263244
LOCATION : 23 km S. Lisbon E 4
ADDRESS : Herdade de Aroeira – Fonte da Telha – 2825 Monte da Caparica
HOTEL :
Do Mar – Sesimbra
Tel : (01)2233326
Espadarte – Sesimbra
Tel : (01)2233189
RESTAURANT : Ribamar – Sesimbra
Tel : (01)2233107

A challenging and peacefully situated inland course not far from the Portuguese capital, set in gently rolling countryside near the Atlantic Ocean. The course, densely wooded with avenues of pines, features several strategically placed lakes affecting play on five holes. It belongs to a luxury residential tourist complex with a tennis club, a riding center and a rustic clubhouse. *SSS 72*

GF $ — 1972 — F. Pennink — 18 — L 6040 P 72 — S — R

Required : Handicap Certificate
Best days : Any day

HOLE	LENGTH MEDAL-TEE	PAR	STROKE INDEX
1	485	5	11
2	398	4	1
3	382	4	5
4	162	3	17
5	354	4	9
6	319	4	15
7	376	4	7
8	190	3	3
9	464	5	5
TOTAL	3130	36	TOTAL

HOLE	LENGTH MEDAL-TEE	PAR	STROKE INDEX
10	482	5	4
11	362	4	2
12	345	4	12
13	345	4	6
14	128	3	18
15	461	5	14
16	144	3	16
17	304	4	10
18	339	4	8
TOTAL	2910	36	TOTAL

ESTELA

TEL : (052)685567
LOCATION : 40 km N. Oporto between Póvoa and Ofir
ADDRESS : Rio Alte - 4490 Póvoa de Varzim
HOTEL :
St-André - Póvoa
Tel : (052)681881
Ofir - Fào
Tel : (053)961383
Vermar - Póvoa
Tel : (052)68341

One of Portugal's newest championship layouts lies in the heart of Costa Verde in the northern part of the country. It is a fine seaside course, set on open 'links' landscape, with its 18 holes hugging 3km of the Atlantic coast line. Most of the greens on this golf links are on elevated sites giving fine views of the sea and the mountains. There is a modern and well equipped clubhouse with a restaurant serving good Portuguese cuisine. *SSS 73*

GF $

1989

18

—

D. Sottomayor

L 5863 P 72

Required : Handicap Certificate
Best days : Any day

HOLE	LENGTH MEDAL-TEE	PAR	STROKE INDEX
1	432	5	6
2	133	3	18
3	397	4	1
4	162	3	9
5	375	4	3
6	369	4	4
7	464	5	8
8	298	4	14
9	346	4	11
TOTAL	2976	36	TOTAL

HOLE	LENGTH MEDAL-TEE	PAR	STROKE INDEX
10	351	4	12
11	322	4	15
12	159	3	17
13	447	5	10
14	338	4	7
15	460	5	2
16	333	4	13
17	135	3	16
18	342	4	5
TOTAL	2887	36	TOTAL

ESTORIL PALACIO

TEL : (01)2681376/2680176
LOCATION : 3 km E. Cascais/2 km Estoril
ADDRESS : Av. da República – 2765 Estoril
HOTEL :
Estoril Palacio – Estoril
Tel : (01)2680400
Atlantico – Monte Estoril
Tel : (01)2680270
Estoril Anka – Estoril
Tel : (01)2681811
RESTAURANT : Casa de Cha Oitavos – Cascais
Tel : (01)289277

Located near the legendary resort of Estoril, the Estoril Palacio golf course is scenically set in the foothills of the Sintra mountains. An international championship course, being the traditional site of, the Portuguese Amateur Championship, it runs on rolling ground between pines, eucalyptus and mimosas with lovely views out to the Atlantic. There is an elegant clubhouse with swimming pool overlooking the 18th green. The Estoril golf club is administered by the luxurious and stylish Palacio hotel. *SSS 68*

GF $

1945

27

—

E. Mackenzie Ross

L 5210 P 69, 2350 P 34

Required : Handicap Certificate
Best days : Weekdays only

HOLE	LENGTH MEDAL-TEE	PAR	STROKE INDEX
1	352	4	6
2	143	3	18
3	292	4	8
4	156	3	15
5	473	5	4
6	243	4	11
7	383	4	1
8	197	3	13
9	156	3	16
TOTAL	2395	33	TOTAL

HOLE	LENGTH MEDAL-TEE	PAR	STROKE INDEX
10	353	4	3
11	463	5	10
12	384	4	2
13	250	4	17
14	362	4	5
15	298	4	9
16	197	3	7
17	258	4	12
18	250	4	14
TOTAL	2815	36	TOTAL

LISBON SPORTS CLUB

TEL : (01)4310077
LOCATION : 25 km Lisbon N 117/4 km Belas
ADDRESS : Casal da Carregueira – Belas – 2745 Queluz
HOTEL :
York House – Lisbon
Tel : (01)662544
Principe Real – Lisbon
Tel : (01)360116
Tivoli Jardin – Lisbon
Tel : (01)539971
RESTAURANT : Cozinha Velha – Queluz
Tel : (01)950232

Located on the Belas-Vale de Lobo road north of Belas, the course being one of the oldest in Portugal, is set in quiet and pleasant countryside, surrounded by wooded green hills. There is a fine colonial style clubhouse with facilities including a swimming pool and several tennis courts. *SSS 68*

GF $

1920/1960

18

Wednesdays, Weekends

F. Hawtree

L 5216 y P 68

S

R

Required : Handicap Certificate
Best days : Mondays, Tuesdays, Thursdays, Fridays

HOLE	LENGTH MEDAL-TEE	PAR	STROKE INDEX
1	170	3	14
2	398	4	4
3	172	3	10
4	328	4	6
5	438	5	12
6	284	4	8
7	375	4	2
8	140	3	16
9	274	4	18
TOTAL	2579	34	TOTAL

HOLE	LENGTH MEDAL-TEE	PAR	STROKE INDEX
10	271	4	11
11	131	3	17
12	461	5	13
13	154	3	15
14	423	4	1
15	370	4	5
16	172	3	9
17	328	4	3
18	327	4	7
TOTAL	2637	34	TOTAL

OPORTO

TEL : (02)722008
LOCATION : 17 km Porto N 107
ADDRESS : Lugar do Sisto - Paramos - Silvade - 4500 Espinho
HOTEL :
Praia Golf - Espinho
Tel : (02)720630
Méridien - Porto
Tel : (02)668863
Solverde - Praia da Granja
Tel : (02)726111
RESTAURANT : Buiamar - Espinho
Tel : (02)725415

One of the oldest clubs in continental Europe dating back to 1890, the Oporto Golf Club was established by British port wine producers. It is laid out by the sea amid sand dunes and spruces near the seaside resort of Espinho 17 km south of Oporto. The Praia Golf hotel is nearby the course. *SSS 68*

GF $ — Mondays —  S

1890 — Sheffington/Pennink/Kendall — 

18 — L 5376 P 71 — 

Required : Handicap Certificate
Best days : Weekdays

HOLE	LENGTH MEDAL-TEE	PAR	STROKE INDEX
1	271	4	8
2	248	4	16
3	160	3	10
4	385	4	1
5	294	4	12
6	251	4	14
7	384	4	3
8	179	3	6
9	145	5	18
TOTAL	2617	35	TOTAL

HOLE	LENGTH MEDAL-TEE	PAR	STROKE INDEX
10	305	4	5
11	484	5	2
12	359	4	4
13	329	4	9
14	162	3	11
15	288	4	15
16	104	3	17
17	305	4	7
18	423	5	13
TOTAL	2759	36	TOTAL

PALMARES

TEL : (082)62961
LOCATION : 3 km Lagos
ADDRESS : Meia Praia – 8600 Lagos – Algarve
HOTEL :
De Lagos – Lagos
Tel : (082)62011
Meia Praia – Lagos
Tel : (082)60951
Golfinho – Lagos
Tel : (082)62081
RESTAURANT : Dom Sebastiao – Lagos
Tel : (082)62795

The Palmares championship golf course is situated in the western Algarve and is one of Portugal's finest, offering superb views of the Bay of Lagos and the distant Monchique mountains. There are five real 'links' holes, set on sand dunes along the beach. The remaining 13 holes are laid out among rolling hills covered by fig and almond trees. The clubhouse between the 9th and 10th holes overlooks about 25km of coastline. *SSS 72*

GF $

1975

18

—

F. Pennink

L 5614 P 71

S

R

Required : Handicap Certificate
Best days : Any day

HOLE	LENGTH MEDAL-TEE	PAR	STROKE INDEX
1	403	4	4
2	297	4	13
3	279	4	7
4	133	3	15
5	515	5	1
6	294	4	9
7	450	5	11
8	131	3	17
9	303	4	6
TOTAL	2805	36	TOTAL

HOLE	LENGTH MEDAL-TEE	PAR	STROKE INDEX
10	156	3	14
11	260	4	18
12	372	4	3
13	364	4	8
14	340	4	5
15	192	3	12
16	370	4	2
17	447	5	16
18	308	4	10
TOTAL	2809	35	TOTAL

PARQUE DA FLORESTA

✡★

TEL : (082)65333/4/5
LOCATION : 16 km W. Lagos, near Budens
ADDRESS : Vale do Poço-8650 Vila do Bispo-Algarve
HOTEL :
Lagos-Lagos
Tel : (082)62011
Golfinho-Lagos
Tel : (082)62081
RESTAURANT : Alpendre-Lagos
Tel : (082)62705

The golf course is the centrepiece of an exclusive residential leisure complex. The spectacular Parque da Floresta course is situated in gently rolling hills above the fishing village of Salema in Western Algarve. No two holes are alike : they run through valleys, vineyards, ravines filled with eucalyptus trees, and are flanked by olive, palm and pine trees. A scenic lake serves as a hazard on the 11th and 17th holes. There is an attractive Portuguese style clubhouse from which there are spectacular mountain and sea views. Leisure facilities will include a swimming pool complex, a fitness centre, squash and tennis courts. *SSS 72*

GF $  — 

 1987 P. Gancedo 

18 L 5888 P 72 

Required : None
Best days : Any day

HOLE	LENGTH MEDAL-TEE	PAR	STROKE INDEX
1	513	5	5
2	340	4	9
3	142	3	11
4	438	5	3
5	110	3	15
6	362	4	7
7	150	3	17
8	297	4	13
9	525	5	1
TOTAL	2877	36	TOTAL

HOLE	LENGTH MEDAL-TEE	PAR	STROKE INDEX
10	443	5	16
11	148	3	14
12	400	4	2
13	354	4	10
14	518	5	4
15	159	3	12
16	281	4	18
17	374	4	6
18	334	4	8
TOTAL	3011	36	TOTAL

PENINA

TEL : (082)22051
LOCATION : 5 km Portimao/12 km Lagos
ADDRESS : Penina Golf Hotel – Penina
Portimao – Algarve
HOTEL : HR
Penina Golf
Tel : (082)22051
Algarve – Portimao
Tel : (082)24001
Globo – Portimao
Tel : (082)22151

The Penina golf course is undoubtedly the finest achievement of Henry Cotton, three times British Open Champion, who used to be its resident consultant. Set in the centre of the Algarve, it is one of the longest and most testing courses in Portugal. Laid out on flat terrain and surrounded by quick-growing bushes and trees, there are numerous lakes, canals and bunkers, serving as hazards. One feature of the courses is the superb large greens. The main championship layout, the South course, has hosted various European championships, the World Team championship in 1976 and the Portuguese Open five times. In the middle of the courses stands the aristocratic and luxurious five star Penina Hotel (a Trusthouse Forte member) with swimming pool, tennis courts, bowling green, croquet lawn and riding paddock. *SSS 72*

GF $$ — —

1966 — H. Cotton

36 — L 6054 P 73, 3268 P 35, 1851 P 30

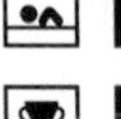

Required : Handicap Certificate
Best days : Any day

HOLE	LENGTH MEDAL-TEE	PAR	STROKE INDEX
1	392	4	6
2	384	4	1
3	286	4	12
4	359	4	5
5	443	5	10
6	164	3	18
7	254	4	14
8	166	3	17
9	379	4	3
TOTAL	2827	35	TOTAL

HOLE	LENGTH MEDAL-TEE	PAR	STROKE INDEX
10	482	5	7
11	474	5	9
12	375	4	2
13	171	3	13
14	375	4	4
15	302	4	15
16	176	3	16
17	437	5	8
18	435	5	11
TOTAL	3227	38	TOTAL

QUINTA DA MARINHA

TEL : (01)289881
LOCATION : 3 km Cascais/30 km W. Lisboa
ADDRESS : Casa 36 – 2750 Cascais
HOTEL : HΓ
Golf Cottages
Tel : (01)299881
Casa da Pergola – Cascais
Tel : (01)2840040
Do Guincho – Cascais
Tel : (01)2850491

Created by master architect Robert Trent Jones, the golf course is located on the Guincho Coast facing the Atlantic and backed by the Sintra Mountains. The fairways, lined by umbrella pines, are laid out on sandy pastures with rocks. Among its tricky holes is the 10th, almost entirely encircled by water. The club provides other sports facilities including six tennis courts, two swimming pools, and various water sports. There are numerous cottages for rental. *SSS 71*

GF $

1984

18

—

R. Trent Jones

 5606 P 71

Required : Handicap Certificate
Best days : Any day

HOLE	LENGTH MEDAL-TEE	PAR	STROKE INDEX
1	491	5	5
2	123	3	16
3	500	5	7
4	340	4	9
5	137	3	12
6	480	5	4
7	141	3	18
8	355	4	1
9	138	3	15
TOTAL	2705	35	TOTAL

HOLE	LENGTH MEDAL-TEE	PAR	STROKE INDEX
10	467	5	3
11	529	5	6
12	397	4	2
13	339	4	8
14	130	3	11
15	295	4	13
16	121	3	17
17	315	4	10
18	308	4	14
TOTAL	2901	36	TOTAL

QUINTA DO LAGO

TEL : (089)94782/94529
LOCATION : 10 km S Almansil / 20 km Faro
ADDRESS : Almansil – 8100 Loulé – Algarve
HOTEL : HR
Quinta do Lago
Tel : (089)94782/94529
Dona Filipa – Almansil
Tel : (089)94141
La Reserve – Faro
Tel : (089)91474

Quinta do Lago is one of the challenging golf developments in the Algarve and is considered as one of Europe's finest championship courses. It is part of a large and luxurious estate by the sea, laid out on undulating densely wooded land and bordering a scenic lagoon. Its fairways are lined by umbrella pines and meander through valleys covered with wild flowers. As there are three separate and interchangeable loops of nine holes, the golfer has the choice between three different 18 hole courses. Facilities include a riding school, tennis courts, a sailing and windsurfing centre. The Quinta do Lago golf club has become the permanent site of the Portuguese Open. *SSS 72*

GF $$

1974

27

—

W. Mitchell, J. Lee

L 2860 P 36, 2925 P 36, 2945 P 36

R S

Required : None
Best days : Any day

HOLE	LENGTH MEDAL-TEE	PAR	STROKE INDEX	HOLE	LENGTH MEDAL-TEE	PAR	STROKE INDEX	HOLE	LENGTH MEDAL-TEE	PAR	STROKE INDEX
1	340	4	6	1	345	4	5	1	375	4	4
2	145	3	9	2	470	5	1	2	160	3	9
3	480	5	1	3	350	4	3	3	425	5	2
4	350	4	3	4	135	3	9	4	285	4	7
5	320	4	5	5	480	5	2	5	350	4	5
6	335	4	4	6	315	4	7	6	160	3	8
7	130	3	8	7	160	3	8	7	330	4	6
8	320	4	7	8	350	4	4	8	490	5	1
9	440	5	2	9	320	4	6	9	370	4	3
TOTAL	2860	36	TOTAL	TOTAL	2925	36	TOTAL	TOTAL	2945	36	TOTAL

TEL : (089)96534/96522
LOCATION : 10 km s. Almansil 20 km Faro
ADDRESS : Almansil – 8100 Loulé – Algarve
HOTEL :
Dona Filipa – Vale do Lobo
Tel : (089)94141
La Réserve – Faro
Tel : (089)90474
RESTAURANT : Taverna Paulina – Quinta do Lago
Tel : (089)96767

The recently opened San Lorenzo golf course, a golfing development of the Trusthouse Forte group, lies in the unspoilt south east corner of the renowned Quinta do Lago Estate in Portugal's Algarve. The holes wind their way through gently undulating pine woodland. Some of them border the Ria Formosa Estuary (the 6th and 7th), a wintering ground for birds, or run alongside scenic salt water lagoons (the 8th, 10th, 17th and 18th) with beaches and the Atlantic Ocean in the background. Designed by the American architect Joseph Lee, San Lorenzo will without doubt become a spectacular golf venue in the Algarve. A luxury hotel is planned in the near future. *SSS 73*

GF $$ — S

1988 J. Lee

18 L 6238 P 72 R

Required : Handicap Certificate
Best days : Any day

HOLE	LENGTH MEDAL-TEE	PAR	STROKE INDEX
1	494	5	7
2	162	3	15
3	334	4	13
4	339	4	5
5	129	3	17
6	386	4	1
7	345	4	11
8	525	5	3
9	366	4	9
TOTAL	3080	36	TOTAL

HOLE	LENGTH MEDAL-TEE	PAR	STROKE INDEX
10	519	5	12
11	350	4	14
12	395	4	2
13	359	4	8
14	157	3	18
15	473	5	6
16	190	3	16
17	344	4	10
18	371	4	4
TOTAL	3158	36	TOTAL

TEL : (095)25847
LOCATION : 13,5 km Angra do Heroismo
ADDRESS : Terceira – 9760 Praia da Vitória-Azores
HOTEL :
Residential Cruzeiro – Angra do Heroismo
Tel : (095)24071
RESTAURANT : Beira Mar – Praia da Vitória
Tel : (095)53135

The Terceira golf course is situated in an attractive part of the island of Terceira, a few kilometres from Angra do Heroismo and Praia da Vitoria. The 18 holes run through rolling countryside landscaped among tall pine trees and backed by low wooded hills. Several small lakes and ditches serve as hazards. *SSS 70*

GF $

1954

18

—

—

L 6290 P 72

S

R

Required : None
Best days : Any day

HOLE	LENGTH MEDAL-TEE	PAR	STROKE INDEX
1	292	4	15
2	159	3	13
3	511	5	7
4	293	4	17
5	370	4	1
6	329	4	5
7	489	5	3
8	366	4	11
9	407	4	9
TOTAL	3216	37	TOTAL

HOLE	LENGTH MEDAL-TEE	PAR	STROKE INDEX
10	260	4	18
11	353	4	16
12	435	4	4
13	415	4	2
14	206	3	10
15	398	4	6
16	346	4	12
17	501	5	8
18	160	3	14
TOTAL	3074	35	TOTAL

TROIA

TEL : (065)44151/44236
LOCATION : 50 km S. Lisboa, on peninsula
ADDRESS : Torralta Troia – 2900 Setubal
HOTEL :
Rosamar – Troia
Tel : (065)44151
Esperance – Setùbal
Tel : (065)25151
Pousada de Sao Filipe – Setùbal
Tel : (065)23844

Set in natural surroundings on the Troia peninsula, this is a first class seaside course stretching out between sandy dunes and pine forest on the shores of the Atlantic Ocean. The course is part of a tourist development estate, which features the four star Aparthotel Rosamar, swimming pools, a riding center, tennis courts, water sports and sandy beaches.
SSS 74

GF $
1979
18

—
R. Trent Jones
L 6338 P 72

Required : Handicap Certificate
Best days : Any day

HOLE	LENGTH MEDAL-TEE	PAR	STROKE INDEX
1	480	5	3
2	191	3	15
3	361	4	11
4	144	3	17
5	401	4	7
6	416	4	5
7	517	5	1
8	303	4	13
9	374	4	9
TOTAL	3187	36	TOTAL

HOLE	LENGTH MEDAL-TEE	PAR	STROKE INDEX
10	310	4	14
11	178	3	16
12	359	4	12
13	405	4	8
14	443	5	4
15	410	4	6
16	396	4	10
17	173	3	18
18	477	5	2
TOTAL	3151	36	TOTAL

VALE DO LOBO

TEL : (089)94444
LOCATION : 6 km Almansil/20 km Faro
ADDRESS : Vale do Lobo – Almansil – 8100 Loulé – Algarve
HOTEL :
Doña Filipa – Vale do Lobo
Tel : (089)94141
Eva – Faro
Tel : (089)25054
La Reserve – Faro
Tel : (089)91474

Located in the Vale do Lobo(Valley of the Wolf), this is a pleasant and testing championship layout set in undulating country overlooking the white sandy beaches, and the ocean. The course consists of 3 loops of nine holes. The fairways are lined with fig and pine trees and meander their way inland through olive, orange and pomegrate orchards. It features one of the world's most photographed holes, the famous 7th, played across three red cliffs. The course belongs to the exclusive Vale do Lobo estate with luxury villas for rent, a tennis centre and the de luxe Dona Filipa Hotel, a member of the Trusthouse Forte chain.

GF $$

1966

27

—

H. Cotton

L 3334 P 36, 3207 P 36, 2927 P 35

S

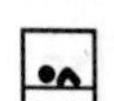

Required : Handicap Certificate
Best days : Any day

HOLE	LENGTH MEDAL-TEE	PAR	STROKE INDEX	HOLE	LENGTH MEDAL-TEE	PAR	STROKE INDEX	HOLE	LENGTH MEDAL-TEE	PAR	STROKE INDEX
1	487	5	4	1	477	5	4	1	300	4	6
2	327	4	8	2	444	4	1	2	209	3	7
3	419	4	7	3	346	4	6	3	367	4	5
4	409	4	1	4	172	3	9	4	524	5	1
5	402	4	3	5	378	4	5	5	373	4	4
6	327	4	9	6	199	3	7	6	161	3	8
7	218	3	5	7	567	5	2	7	444	5	2
8	400	4	2	8	151	3	8	8	154	3	9
9	345	4	6	9	473	5	3	9	395	4	3
TOTAL	3334	36	TOTAL	TOTAL	3207	36	TOTAL	TOTAL	2927	35	TOTAL

VILAMOURA UM

TEL : (089)313652
LOCATION : 30 km W. Faro
ADDRESS : Vilamoura – 8125 Quarteira – Algarve
HOTEL : HR
Vilamoura Golf – Vilamoura
Tel : (089)312321
Atlantis – Vilamoura
Tel : (089)889977
Dom Pedro – Vilamoura
Tel : (089)889650

This beautiful and testing course ranks among the world's best. It is laid out over a small hill with fine views of the coast and the sea. The lush fairways, carved through umbrella pines, are undulating and quite narrow demanding accurate shots. Opened in 1969, it was the venue for the 1976 Ladies' World Amateur Team Championship, the 1973 and 1976 Portuguese Open. The Vilamoura Golf Hotel is within walking distance of the course.
SSS 72

GF $$ — RP S

1969 F. Pennink

18 L 5955 P 73

Required : Handicap Certificate
Best days : Any day

HOLE	LENGTH MEDAL-TEE	PAR	STROKE INDEX
1	266	4	17
2	442	5	5
3	322	4	9
4	144	3	15
5	336	4	3
6	207	3	11
7	354	4	7
8	404	4	1
9	262	4	13
TOTAL	2737	35	TOTAL

HOLE	LENGTH MEDAL-TEE	PAR	STROKE INDEX
10	140	3	18
11	380	4	4
12	483	5	12
13	340	4	16
14	442	5	8
15	141	3	14
16	509	5	2
17	337	4	6
18	446	5	10
TOTAL	3218	38	TOTAL

VILAMOURA DOIS

✡

TEL : (089)315562
LOCATION : 30 km W Faro
ADDRESS : Vilamoura – 8125 Quarteira – Algarve
HOTEL :
Dom Pedro – Vilamoura
Tel : (089)889650
Atlantis – Vilamoura
Tel : (089)889977
Dom Pedro Portobelo – Vilamoura
Tel : (089)889603

The course (former Dom Pedro Golfclub) has been rebuilt with 9 new holes designed by Trent Jones. This inland course is sited near the sea with its fairways lined by the local umbrella pines. The first nine holes are on open and fairly flat land overlooking the Ocean, and the last nine holes are laid out in an area of small pine trees. *SSS 71*

GF $

1976

18

—

F. Pennink, R. Trent Jones

L 5866 P 72

S

R

Required : Handicap Certificate
Best days : Any day

HOLE	LENGTH MEDAL-TEE	PAR	STROKE INDEX
1	469	5	14
2	374	4	4
3	435	5	10
4	318	4	8
5	135	3	18
6	382	4	2
7	352	4	6
8	131	3	12
9	331	4	16
TOTAL	2927	36	TOTAL

HOLE	LENGTH MEDAL-TEE	PAR	STROKE INDEX
10	306	4	5
11	324	4	11
12	178	3	13
13	508	5	1
14	137	3	17
15	285	4	15
16	331	4	9
17	492	5	3
18	378	4	7
TOTAL	2939	36	TOTAL

VILAMOURA TRES

TEL : (089)880724
LOCATION : 35 km W. Faro
ADDRESS : Vilamoura - 8125 Quarteira - Algarve
HOTEL :
do Golfe - Vilamoura
Tel : (089)312321
Atlantis - Vilamoura
Tel : (089)88997
Atlantis - Vilamoura
Tel : (089)88997
Dom Pedro - Vilamoura
Tel : (089)889650

This is one of the recent challenging golfing venues set deep in the heart of the Algarve next to the widely known "Vilamoura I and Vilamoura II" courses. The famous architect Joseph Lee designed the three sporty american style loops of nine holes (Pinhal, Lago and Marina) set up along the coast and spread out over flat and lush countryside with 8 small but strategic lakes affecting play on 13 fairways.

GF $

1990

27

—

J. Lee

L 2816 P 36, 2760 P 36, 2966 P 36

R S

Required : Handicap Certificate
Best days : Any day

HOLE	LENGTH MEDAL-TEE	PAR	STROKE INDEX	HOLE	LENGTH MEDAL-TEE	PAR	STROKE INDEX	HOLE	LENGTH MEDAL-TEE	PAR	STROKE INDEX
1	328	4	4	1	453	5	7	1	437	5	
2	450	5	8	2	119	3	8	2	356	4	
3	290	4	9	3	342	4	2	3	145	3	
4	146	3	5	4	145	3	3	4	386	4	
5	316	4	6	5	298	4	5	5	324	4	
6	113	3	7	6	280	4	9	6	482	5	
7	360	4	2	7	303	4	6	7	336	4	
8	433	5	3	8	456	5	4	8	140	3	
9	380	4	1	9	364	4	1	9	360	4	
TOTAL	2816	36	TOTAL	TOTAL	2760	36	TOTAL	TOTAL	2966	36	TOTAL

Car Rental

Reservation/Information telephone number :

Country code :
34

Telephone number :
1/5971500

Headquarters address :

EUROPCAR IB S.A.
General Yague, Nr 6 bis
Madrid 28020
Tel. : (34) 1/5971500
Telex : 43087
Fax : (34) 1/5971706

117 GOLF COURSES, 50 000 PLAYERS

★★★ Great golf course
★★ Very good golf course
$ 1500-5000 Ptas
★ Recommended golf course
☼ Holiday golf course
$ $ more than 8000 Ptas

TOWN	GOLF COURSE		TEL	MAP REF.
Alcalá de Henares	Valdelaguila		(91) 8859659	•
Algorta	Real Sociedad Neguri	★★★	(94) 4690200	4
Almeria	Almerimar	☼	(951) 480234	32
	Playa Serena	☼	(951) 322055	33
Altea	Don Cayo		(965) 848046	•
Bagur	Pals	★★	(972) 636006	9
Barcelona	El Prat	★★★ ☼	(93) 3790278	13
	San Cugat	☼	(93) 6743908	8
	Vallromanas		(93) 5680362	12
Bilbao	La Bilbaina-Laukariz		(94) 6740858	5
Calpe	Ifach			•
Calvi	Bendinat		(971) 405200	•
Cartagena	La Manga	★★★ ☼	(968) 564511	41
Castellón de la Plana	Costa de Azahar		(964) 227064	•
	Mediterráneo	☼	(964) 321227	43
Chiclana	Chiclana			•
Córdoba	Los Villares		(957) 350208	27
Denia	Oliva Nova	☼	(965) 780650	50
El Escorial	Herrería		(91) 8905111	15
Estepona	Atalaya Park	☼	(952) 781894	35
	El Paraiso	☼	(952) 783000	37
Fuengirola	Mijas	★★ ☼	(952) 476843	28
Gijón	Castiello		(985) 366313	2
Granada	Los Moriscos *(ext. to 18 holes)*		(958) 600412	•
Huelva	Bellavista		(955) 318083	•
Javea	Javea		(965) 792584	•
La Coruña	La Coruña	★	(981) 285200	1
La Toja	La Toja		(986) 730726	•
Madrid	Barberán		(91) 2188505	•
	Club de Campo	★★★	(91) 3572132	20
	La Moraleja	★	(91) 6500700	16
	La Puerta de Hierro	★★★	(91) 3161745	17

TOWN	GOLF COURSE		TEL	MAP REF.
Madrid	Las Encinas de Boadilla		(91) 6331100	•
	Lomas Bosque	★	(91) 6162170	19
	Nuevo Club de Madrid		(91) 6300820	18
	Real Automovil Club de España	★★	(91) 6570011	21
	Somosaguas		(91) 2121647	•
Málaga	El Candado		(952) 294666	•
	Guadalhorce		(952) 243682	51
	La Duquesa	✡	(952) 890425	44
	Málaga	✡	(952) 381120	39
Marbella	Aloha	★★ ✡	(952) 812388/89	36
	Guadalmina	✡	(952) 781377	38
	La Quinta	★ ✡	(952) 783462	49
	Las Brisas	★★★ ✡	(952) 810875	42
	Los Naranjas	★★★ ✡	(952) 815206	42
	Rio Real	★ ✡	(952) 773776	34
Miraflores de la Sierra	Miraflores		(952) 8444471	•
Mataró	Llavaneras		(93) 7926050	•
Mojacár	Cortijo Grande	✡	(951) 479164	31
Motril	Los Moriscos		(958) 600412	•
Nerja	Nerja		(952) 520208	•
Oviedo	La Barganiza		(985) 742468	•
Pamplona	Ulzama		(948) 305162	•
Playa de Aro	Mas Nou	✡	(972) 818220	52
Pozoblanco	Pozoblanco		(957) 100239	•
Puerto de Santa Maria	Vista Hermosa		(956) 850011	•
Puigcerda	Cerdaña	★	(972) 881338	7
Rincon de la Victoria	Anoreta	✡	(952) 404000	53
San Feliú de Guixols	Costa Brava	✡	(972) 837150	10
San Sebastian	San Sebastian	★	(943) 616845	6
Santander	Mataleñas		(942) 311741	•
	Pedreña	★★	(942) 500001	3
Santiago de Compostela	Santiago		(981) 592400	•
Sevilla	Pineda de Sevilla		(954) 611400	•
Sitges	Terramar	✡	(93) 8940580	11
Sotogrande	Sotogrande	★★★ ✡	(956) 792050/51	30
	Valderrama	★★★ ✡	(956) 792775	40
Vitoria	Larrabea		(945) 131131	
Tarragona	Costa Dorado		(977) 653361	•
Torremolinos	Torrequebrada	★★ ✡	(952) 442742	29
Torrevieja	Villa Martin	✡	(965) 6760350	26
Valencia	Bosque	✡	(96) 2511011	45
	El Saler	★★★ ✡	(96) 1611186	46
	Escorpion	✡	(96) 1601211	47
	Manises		(96) 3790850	•
Vigo	Real Aero Club de Vigo		(986) 242493	•
Zaragoza	La Peñaza		(976) 342800	48
	Aero Club de Zaragoza		(976) 214378	•
Zarauz	Zarauz		(943) 830145	•
BALEARES				
MALLORCA				
Cala d'Or	Vall d'Or		(971) 576099	•
Canyamel	Canyamel	✡	(971) 564457	I
Palma	Bendinat	✡	(971) 405200	•
	Poniente	✡	(971) 680148	I
	Santa Ponsa	✡	(971) 690211	I
	Son Vida	✡	(971) 791210	I
Pollensa	Pollensa	✡	(971) 533216	I
Son Servera	Son Servera	✡	(971) 567802	I
MENORCA				
Mahon	Menorca	✡	(971) 363700	•
	Son Parc	✡	(971) 368806	•

TOWN	GOLF COURSE		TEL	MAP REF.
IBIZA				
Santa Eulalia	Roca Llisa	✡	(971) 313718	•
CANARY ISLANDS				
GRAN CANARIA				
Las Palmas	Las Palmas	✡	(928) 351050	I
Maspalomas	Maspalomas	✡	(928) 762581	I
TENERIFE				
San Miguel	Del Sur	✡	(922) 704555	I
Santa Cruz	Tenerife	✡	(922) 250240	I
LANZAROTE				
Arrecife	Costa Teguise	✡	(928) 813512	I

NEW GOLF COURSES (18 HOLES OR MORE) TO OPEN SOON

Bendinat
Calvia-Mallorca
Tel. : (971) 405200

Caldes
80140 Caldes de Motbui
Tel. : (93) 8651897

Masia Bach
08006 Barcelona
Tel. : (93) 2381324

Roca Viva
Capdepera – Mallorca
Tel. : (971) 565875

Quesada
03170 Rojales
Tel. : (96) 5722179

Salamanca
37170 Zarapicos
Tel. : (923) 313174

Ibiza
07800 Ibiza
Tel. : (971) 315003

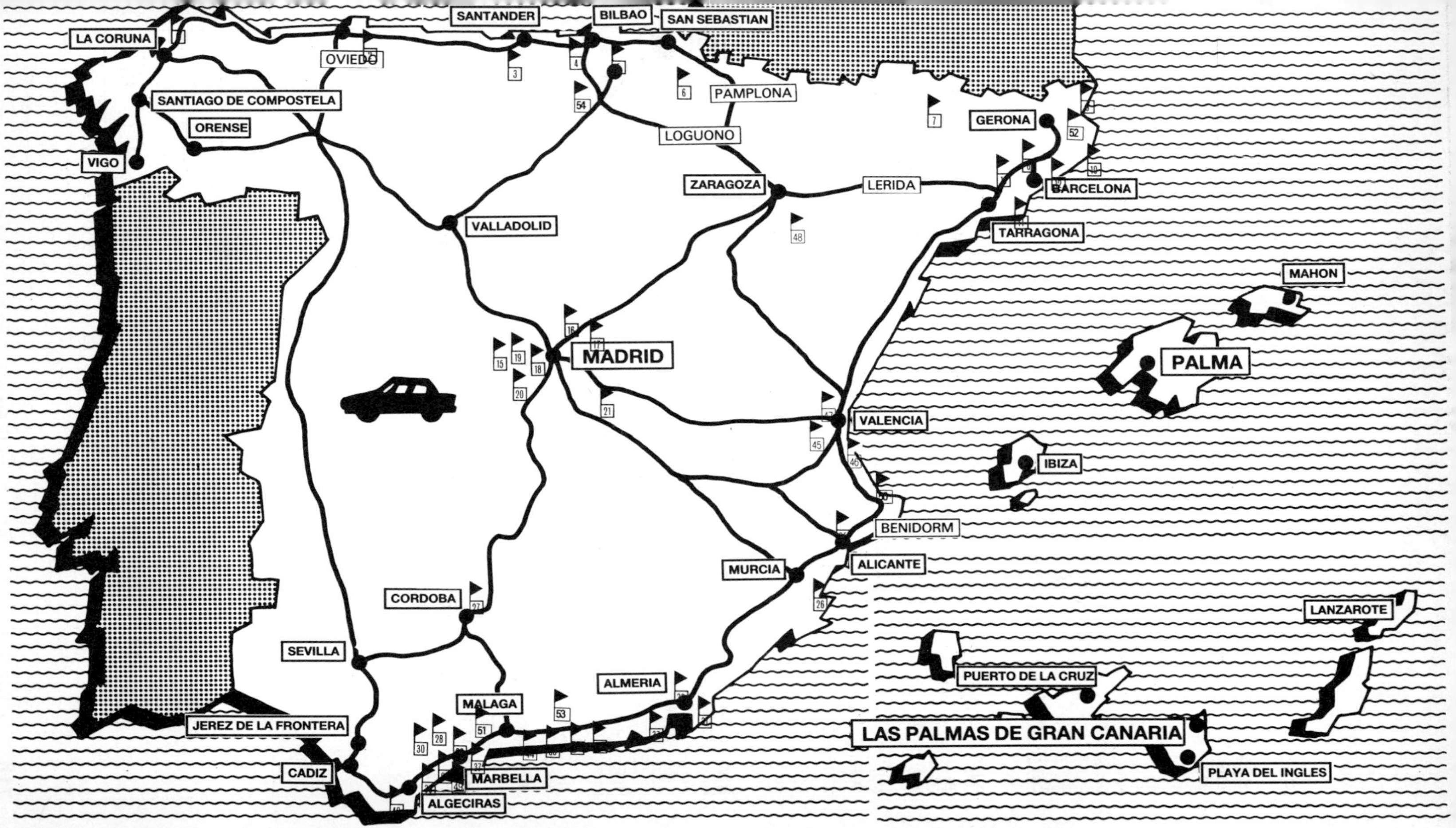

LA CORUNA
OVIEDO
SANTANDER
BILBAO
SAN SEBASTIAN
SANTIAGO DE COMPOSTELA
ORENSE
VIGO
PAMPLONA
LOGUONO
GERONA
BARCELONA
ZARAGOZA
LERIDA
TARRAGONA
VALLADOLID
MAHON
MADRID
PALMA
VALENCIA
IBIZA
BENIDORM
ALICANTE
MURCIA
CORDOBA
SEVILLA
LANZAROTE
ALMERIA
PUERTO DE LA CRUZ
MALAGA
JEREZ DE LA FRONTERA
LAS PALMAS DE GRAN CANARIA
CADIZ
MARBELLA
ALGECIRAS
PLAYA DEL INGLES

All cities represented on the map are Europcar locations.

ALMERIMAR

TEL : (951)480234
LOCATION : 35 km Almeria N 340
ADDRESS : El Ejido – Almeria
HOTEL : HP
Golf Hotel
Tel : (951)480234
Grandhotel Almeria – Almeria
Tel : (951)238011
Torreluz IV – Almeria
Tel : (951)234799

This fine holiday golf course, designed by Ron Kirby and the famous golf champion Gary Player, is set on the Costa del Sol. It lies parallel to the sea on fairly undulating land alongside sandy beaches and is backed by distant mountains. There are difficult water hazards on more than six holes, including an island green on the 12th hole. The course belongs to a vast residential complex with a 38-room Golf Hotel, two restaurants, a swimming pool and several tennis courts. *SSS 72*

GF $

1976

18

—

R. Kirby, G. Player

L 6111 P 72

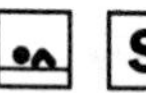

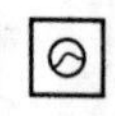

Required : None
Best days : Any day

HOLE	LENGTH MEDAL-TEE	PAR	STROKE INDEX
1	484	5	5
2	393	4	1
3	182	3	15
4	360	4	7
5	350	4	9
6	340	4	13
7	334	4	11
8	139	3	17
9	477	5	3
TOTAL	3059	36	TOTAL

HOLE	LENGTH MEDAL-TEE	PAR	STROKE INDEX
10	351	4	12
11	467	5	8
12	172	3	14
13	384	4	2
14	493	5	6
15	308	4	16
16	354	4	10
17	138	3	18
18	385	4	4
TOTAL	3052	36	TOTAL

ALOHA

TEL : (952)812388/89
LOCATION : 8 km Marbella N 340/E 26
ADDRESS : Urbanización Aloha – Marbella – Málaga
HOTEL :
Melia Don Pepe – Marbella
Tel : (952)770300
Estrella del Mar – Marbella
Tel : (952)830363
Las Fuentes des Rodeo – Marbella
Tel : (952)814017
RESTAURANT : La Hacienda – Marbella
Tel : (952)831116

Located on the sunny Costa del Sol, the Aloha golf course is a challenging and testing championship course masterminded by the famous Spanish golf architect Javier Arana. Not far from the sea front, it is laid out on rugged countryside following the gentle undulations of an Andalucian river valley. The fairways require great accuracy being landscaped amongst tall pines and eucalyptus. Water affects play on four of the holes. The fine clubhouse, with tennis courts and swimming pool, dominates the course.
SSS 72

GF $$

1975

18

—

J. Arana

L 6261 P 72

Required : Handicap Certificate
Best days : Any day

HOLE	LENGTH MEDAL-TEE	PAR	STROKE INDEX
1	545	5	2
2	331	4	10
3	305	4	16
4	207	3	12
5	450	5	6
6	365	4	4
7	309	4	14
8	178	3	18
9	314	4	8
TOTAL	3004	36	TOTAL

HOLE	LENGTH MEDAL-TEE	PAR	STROKE INDEX
10	513	5	5
11	353	4	7
12	377	4	1
13	196	3	13
14	337	4	17
15	365	4	9
16	481	5	11
17	225	3	15
18	410	4	3
TOTAL	3257	36	TOTAL

ANORETA

TEL : (952)404000
LOCATION : 12 km E. Málaga N. 340
ADDRESS : Avenida del Golf - 29730
Rincon de la Victoria - Málaga
HOTEL :
Rinconsol - Rincon de la Victoria
Tel : (952)401100
Balcon de Europa - Rincon de la Victoria
Tel : (952)520800
Monica - Rincon de la Victoria
Tel : (952)521100

The Spanish golf champion Jose Maria Canizares designed this new golf development which is set in the heart of the eastern Costa del Sol at about 12 km from Málaga. Only 500m from the sea shore, its 18 holes run over uneven open terrain. Seven large lakes serve as hazards. The golf course is part of a vast real estate complex which boasts an impressive clubhouse, tennis courts and swimming pools. A hotel is due to open soon. *SSS 70*

GF $

1990

18

—

J.M. Cañizares

L 5696 P 74

Required : None
Best days : Any days

HOLE	LENGTH MEDAL-TEE	PAR	STROKE INDEX
1	272	4	15
2	450	5	7
3	323	4	9
4	357	4	1
5	264	4	13
6	240	4	17
7	500	5	3
8	168	3	5
9	274	4	11
TOTAL	2848	37	TOTAL

HOLE	LENGTH MEDAL-TEE	PAR	STROKE INDEX
10	272	4	15
11	450	5	7
12	323	4	9
13	357	4	1
14	264	4	13
15	240	4	17
16	500	5	3
17	168	3	5
18	274	4	11
TOTAL	2848	37	TOTAL

ATALAYA PARK

TEL : (952)781894
LOCATION : 13 km Marbella
ADDRESS : Hotel Atalaya Park – Estepona – Málaga
HOTEL : H
Atalaya Park
Tel : (952)781300
Santa Marta – Estepona
Tel : (952)780716
Stakis – Estepona
Tel : (952)783000

An attractive golf course with a varied layout, designed by Bernard von Limburger. Set on undulating open parkland, with the Sierra Bermeja mountains in the background, the course counts around 60 well-placed bunkers, various out of bounds, streams crossing three fairways and two doglegs. The greens are of excellent quality. There is a superb clubhouse with panoramic views of the course. The course belongs to a vast holiday complex including the luxurious Atalaya Park Hotel set by the sea in tropical gardens. *SSS 72*

 $

1967

18

—

 B. v. Limburger

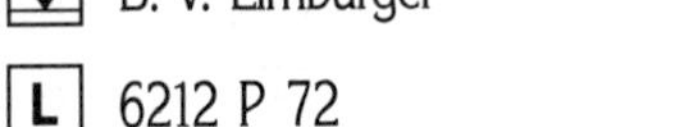

L 6212 P 72

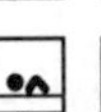

Required : Handicap Certificate
Best days : Any day

HOLE	LENGTH MEDAL-TEE	PAR	STROKE INDEX
1	389	4	13
2	154	3	11
3	414	4	1
4	348	4	7
5	541	5	3
6	319	4	9
7	194	3	17
8	460	5	5
9	321	4	15
TOTAL	3140	36	TOTAL

HOLE	LENGTH MEDAL-TEE	PAR	STROKE INDEX
10	348	4	6
11	482	5	8
12	174	3	14
13	393	4	4
14	356	4	10
15	340	4	16
16	143	3	18
17	522	5	2
18	314	4	12
TOTAL	3072	36	TOTAL

BARGANIZA

TEL : (985)742468
LOCATION : 12 km Oviedo N 634
14 km Gijon
ADDRESS : Apartado 277 - 33080 Oviedo
HOTEL :
Reconquista - Oviedo
Tel : (985)241100
Principe de Asturias - Oviedo
Tel : (985)367111
RESTAURANT : Del Arco - Oviedo
Tel : (985)255533

The recently extended Barganiza course lies between the historical cities of Gijon and Oviedo in the province of Asturias. Blending into fairly flat and open countryside it has several water hazards affecting play. The club boasts a rustic clubhouse with a small chalet reserved for children. Facilities include a swimming pool and tennis courts.

GF $ — 1982 — 18

— G. de la Cruz/M. Martiner — L 5298 P 70

S

R

Required : Handicap Certificate
Best days : Any day

HOLE	LENGTH MEDAL-TEE	PAR	STROKE INDEX
1	443	5	15
2	115	3	13
3	365	4	3
4	134	3	7
5	352	4	1
6	338	4	9
7	318	4	5
8	448	5	17
9	132	3	11
TOTAL	2645	35	TOTAL

HOLE	LENGTH MEDAL-TEE	PAR	STROKE INDEX
10	365	4	2
11	360	4	4
12	168	3	6
13	282	4	8
14	330	4	18
15	258	4	16
16	116	3	14
17	451	5	12
18	323	4	10
TOTAL	2653	35	TOTAL

BOSQUE

TEL : (96)2511011
LOCATION : 25 km Valencia N 111
ADDRESS : Carretera Godelleta - km 400 - 46370 Chiva (Valencia)
HOTEL :
La Carreta - Chiva
Tel : (96)2511100
Astoria - Valencia
Tel : (96)3526737
Reina Victoria - Valencia
Tel : (96)3520487
RESTAURANT : El Condestable - Valencia
Tel : (96)3699250

The Bosque course lies 25km inland from Valencia. Its 18 holes wind through flat open countryside following the gentle undulations of the terrain. Designed by Robert Trent Jones in 1975 and reopened in 1989, the course has several water hazards and features fine large bunkers. *SSS 72*

 $

 —

 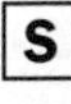

1975/1989

R. Trent Jones

L 5826 P 72

Required : None
Best days : Any day

HOLE	LENGTH MEDAL-TEE	PAR	STROKE INDEX
1	320	4	13
2	352	4	7
3	463	5	3
4	158	3	17
5	327	4	9
6	327	4	11
7	476	5	1
8	166	3	15
9	401	4	5
TOTAL	2990	36	TOTAL

HOLE	LENGTH MEDAL-TEE	PAR	STROKE INDEX
10	334	4	8
11	435	5	4
12	138	3	16
13	319	4	10
14	142	3	18
15	467	5	2
16	300	4	14
17	382	4	6
18	319	4	12
TOTAL	2836	36	TOTAL

CANYAMEL

TEL : (971)564457
LOCATION : 60 km Palma, on carretera de las Cuevas de Arta
ADDRESS : Urb. Canyamel-Casa del Guarda Ctra de Cuevas– 7580 Capdepera (Mallorca)
HOTEL :
Canyamel Park - Canyamel
Tel : (971)565511
Mayurca - Canyamel
Tel : (971)565361
RESTAURANT : Hostal Cuevas - Canyamel Beach

Set in a beautiful rolling, sheltered valley called Canyamel, once occupied by almond groves, Pepé Gancedo's latest creation promises to become a prestigious golfing venue in Mallorca. This course, flanked by wooded hills, has the river Torrente meandering alongside. The first nine holes run parallel to an almond grove through hazardous landscape and offer fine views of the surrounding landscape and the sea. The last nine are totally flat. Ponds affect play on the 8th,13th and 17th holes. The modern clubhouse is built on an elevated site. The golf club is part of a real estate development.

GF $$
1988
18

—
P. Gancedo
L 5813 P 72

S
R

Required : Handicap Certificate
Best days : Any day

HOLE	LENGTH MEDAL-TEE	PAR	STROKE INDEX
1	319	4	10
2	347	4	6
3	291	4	12
4	463	5	14
5	103	3	18
6	316	4	16
7	459	5	2
8	180	3	4
9	383	4	8
TOTAL	2861	36	TOTAL

HOLE	LENGTH MEDAL-TEE	PAR	STROKE INDEX
10	348	4	9
11	320	4	15
12	329	4	7
13	432	5	3
14	124	3	17
15	479	5	5
16	350	4	11
17	424	4	1
18	146	3	13
TOTAL	2952	36	TOTAL

CASTIELLO

TEL : (985)366313
LOCATION : 5 km SE Gijón
ADDRESS : Apartado 161 – Gijón
HOTEL :
Principe de Asturias – Gijón
Tel : (985)367111
Hernan Cortes – Gijon
Tel : (985)346000
Parador El Molino Viejo – Gijon
Tel : (985)370511
RESTAURANT : Los Hórreos – Gijón
Tel : (985)330898

Founded in 1958, the golf course has been extended to 18 holes. Castiello is an inland course situated in 'Asturias' with its short holes laid out on gently rolling terrain landscaped amongst tall trees. *SSS 67*

GF $ — Mondays during winter — RF S 

1958 — V. Cruz 

18 — L 4277 P 68 

Required : None
Best days : Any day

HOLE	LENGTH MEDAL-TEE	PAR	STROKE INDEX
1	389	5	7
2	147	3	10
3	243	4	13
4	169	3	6
5	288	4	4
6	88	3	18
7	352	4	2
8	99	3	15
9	244	4	11
TOTAL	2019	35	TOTAL

HOLE	LENGTH MEDAL-TEE	PAR	STROKE INDEX
10	93	3	17
11	259	4	16
12	296	4	1
13	411	5	5
14	292	4	3
15	150	3	9
16	242	4	12
17	300	4	8
18	215	4	14
TOTAL	2258	33	TOTAL

CERDANA

★

TEL : (972)881338
LOCATION : 1 km Puigcerdá
ADDRESS : Chalet de Golf – Apartado 63 – Puigcerdá
HOTEL : Hr
Chalet de Golf
Tel : (972)880962
Del Lago – Puigcerda
Tel : (972)881000
Maria Victoria – Puigcerda
Tel : (972)880300

Scenically laid out in undulating lush countryside 1100m above sea level, the Cerdana golf course has an attractive layout incorporating a setting of water obstacles and mature trees. There is an elegant clubhouse. The Chalet del Golf with 16 bedrooms, is adjacent to the course, and is built in rustic style. *SSS 70*

GF $$ — 1929 — 18

— — J. Arana — L 5570 P 71

S — R —

Required : Handicap Certificate
Best days : Any day

HOLE	LENGTH MEDAL-TEE	PAR	STROKE INDEX
1	466	5	
2	174	3	
3	427	5	
4	189	3	
5	317	4	
6	466	5	
7	323	4	
8	134	3	
9	369	4	
TOTAL	2865	36	TOTAL

HOLE	LENGTH MEDAL-TEE	PAR	STROKE INDEX
10	358	4	
11	300	4	
12	386	4	
13	326	4	
14	147	3	
15	464	5	
16	333	4	
17	179	3	
18	411	4	
TOTAL	2904	35	TOTAL

CLUB DE CAMPO

TEL : (91)3572132/4490726
LOCATION : 4 km Madrid in Casa de Campo and Monte de El Pardo
ADDRESS : Carretera de Castilla – km 2 – 28040 Madrid
HOTEL :
Florida Norte – Madrid Moncloa
Tel : (91)2416190
Melia – Madrid Moncloa
Tel : (91)2418200
Principe Pio – Madrid Moncloa
Tel : (91)2470800
RESTAURANT : Café Viena – Madrid
Tel : (91)2481591

One of Spain's noblest golf clubs lies inside a vast park called 'Casa de Campo', on the outskirts of Madrid. A classical and testing championship course set on undulating terrain with very long holes, lush fairways bordered by stately trees, large bunkers and well-defended greens. It includes a stream crossing the 6th (a difficult dogleg) and the 4th (a hole featuring a steep drop). Belonging to Europe's finest golf courses, the club hosted the 1965 World Cup, the Women's World Championship in 1970 and the Spanish Open numerous times. The impressive clubhouse with tennis courts and swimming pool, has panoramic views of Madrid. *SSS 74*

GF $$
1932
27

—
J. Arana
L 6331 P 72, 2761 P 35

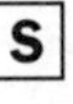

Required : Handicap Certificate
Best days : Weekdays only

HOLE	LENGTH MEDAL-TEE	PAR	STROKE INDEX
1	428	4	7
2	403	4	5
3	198	3	15
4	466	5	3
5	370	4	11
6	404	4	1
7	492	5	13
8	340	4	9
9	155	3	17
TOTAL	3262	36	TOTAL

HOLE	LENGTH MEDAL-TEE	PAR	STROKE INDEX
10	368	4	4
11	196	3	8
12	436	5	16
13	411	4	6
14	505	5	2
15	348	4	10
16	339	4	14
17	138	3	18
18	320	4	12
TOTAL	3108	36	TOTAL

COSTA BRAVA

TEL : (972)837150
LOCATION : 4 km San Feliú de Guixols C 250
ADDRESS : La Masia – Santa Cristina de Aro-Gerona
HOTEL : HP
Costa Brava Golf
Tel : (972)837052
Caleta Park – San Feliu de Guixols
Tel : (972)320012
Murla Park – San Feliu de Guixols
Tel : (972)320450
RESTAURANT : Eldorado Petit – San Feliú de Guixols
Tel : (972)321818

Set in fine natural surroundings, the first nine holes are carved out of a pine forest alongside the Ridaura Valley, the last nine going down to a river. Most of the holes are undulating with narrow fairways bordered by olive, pine and cork trees. The course is cunningly bunkered. There is a confortable 'old finca' style clubhouse. The Costa Brava Golfhotel, with 90 bedrooms, is adjacent to the golf club. *SSS 68*

GF $$

1968

18

Wed. from Oct. to May

Hamilton Stutt

L 5337 P 70

S

R

Required : Handicap Certificate
Best days : Weekdays

HOLE	LENGTH MEDAL-TEE	PAR	STROKE INDEX
1	272	4	5
2	305	4	3
3	130	3	17
4	437	5	9
5	174	3	7
6	395	4	1
7	298	4	15
8	120	3	13
9	286	4	11
TOTAL	2417	34	TOTAL

HOLE	LENGTH MEDAL-TEE	PAR	STROKE INDEX
10	354	4	8
11	447	5	12
12	198	3	6
13	445	5	18
14	490	5	10
15	167	3	14
16	330	4	2
17	126	3	6
18	363	4	4
TOTAL	2920	36	TOTAL

DEL SUR

TEL : (922)704555
LOCATION : 3 km Airport Tenerife Sur
ADDRESS : Urbanizacion El Guincho-San Miguel de Abona-Tenerife-Islas Canarias
HOTEL : HP
Tenerife Oasis
Tel : (922)704555

The new Del Sur golf course, part of Tenerife's premier leisure resort, is a fine natural course providing excellent holiday golf. Set alongside the Atlantic Ocean in an open rocky and volcanic landscape, its 27 holes are guarded by a large variety of cacti. There is an elegant 'hacienda' style clubhouse with a large area reserved for other sports activities such as tennis, squash, and bowling. There are also swimming pools and a golf school. In the grounds surrounding the course are many villas, appartments and the five star Tenerife Oasis hotel.

GF $

1987

27

—

P. Gancedo

L 5511 P 71, 2929 P 36

Required : Handicap Certificate
Best days : Any day

HOLE	LENGTH MEDAL-TEE	PAR	STROKE INDEX	HOLE	LENGTH MEDAL-TEE	PAR	STROKE INDEX	HOLE	LENGTH MEDAL-TEE	PAR	STROKE INDEX
1	440	5	12	10	340	4	6	1	356	4	
2	130	3	16	11	177	3	9	2	195	3	
3	415	4	1	12	445	5	14	3	388	4	
4	300	4	5	13	307	4	7	4	271	4	
5	437	5	8	14	240	4	18	5	493	5	
6	300	4	17	15	346	4	4	6	134	3	
7	350	4	3	16	365	4	2	7	279	4	
8	177	3	13	17	240	4	11	8	307	4	
9	360	4	10	18	142	3	15	9	506	5	
TOTAL	2909	36	TOTAL	TOTAL	2602	35	TOTAL	TOTAL	2929	36	TOTAL

EL PARAISO

TEL : (952)784712/784716
LOCATION : 14 km Marbella N 340
ADDRESS : Carretera de Cádiz – km 167 – Estepona – Málaga
HOTEL : HR
El Paraiso
Tel : (952)784716
Stakis – Estepona
Tel : (952)78300

Set in a sweeping valley and backed by distant mountains, this is a fine holiday course lying on the Costa del Sol. The course is landscaped among date palms with well-placed sandy bunkers and water hazards. The clubhouse and 200 room luxurious Golf Hotel are scenically situated on a hill overlooking the course. *SSS 71*

GF $
1974
18

—
R. Kirby, G. Player
L 6382 P 70

S
R

Required : Club Membership Card
Best days : Tuesdays and Thursdays

HOLE	LENGTH MEDAL-TEE	PAR	STROKE INDEX
1	443	4	7
2	196	3	15
3	424	4	5
4	352	4	11
5	402	4	3
6	343	4	13
7	433	4	1
8	148	3	17
9	510	5	9
TOTAL	3251	35	TOTAL

HOLE	LENGTH MEDAL-TEE	PAR	STROKE INDEX
10	462	4	4
11	374	4	12
12	192	3	16
13	478	5	10
14	170	3	18
15	363	4	8
16	393	4	2
17	319	4	14
18	380	4	6
TOTAL	3131	35	TOTAL

EL PRAT

TEL : (93)3790278
LOCATION : 15 km Barcelona C 246
ADDRESS : Prat de Llobregat – (Barcelona)
HOTEL :
Mediterraneo – Castelldefels
Tel : (93)6652100
Grand Hotel Don Jaime – Torre Barona
Tel : (93)6651300
Luna – Castelldefels
Tel : (93)6652150
RESTAURANT : Las Botas – Castelldefels
Tel : (93)6651824

One of Javier Arana's masterpieces is the El Prat golf course, being one of the world's greatest courses. It lies on a flat coastal stretch, some 15km south of Barcelona, and consists of three demanding nine hole loops. Ingeniously laid out, the first nine holes start from the sea and move inland to open country. The last holes turn back to the club house along the shore. Most of the fairways are lined by strategic umbrella pines. Staging many prestigious tournaments, the club boasts a modern clubhouse near the sea with a large swimming pool, sandy beaches, and a children's playground with paddle pool. *SSS 72, 73*

GF $$

1954

27

—

J. Arana

L 5992 P 73, 5690 P 72, 5761 P 72

Required : Handicap Certificate
Best days : Weekdays

HOLE	LENGTH MEDAL-TEE	PAR	STROKE INDEX	HOLE	LENGTH MEDAL-TEE	PAR	STROKE INDEX	HOLE	LENGTH MEDAL-TEE	PAR	STROKE INDEX
1	330	4	6	1	450	5	5	1	340	4	6
2	240	4	18	2	130	3	18	2	245	4	18
3	140	3	16	3	445	5	10	3	142	3	16
4	271	4	14	4	315	4	12	4	275	4	14
5	460	5	8	5	340	4	6	5	345	4	2
6	365	4	2	6	460	5	8	6	190	3	8
7	170	3	12	7	365	4	2	7	354	4	4
8	310	4	10	8	170	3	14	8	335	4	10
9	351	4	4	9	310	4	16	9	440	5	2
TOTAL	2637	35	TOTAL	TOTAL	2985	37	TOTAL	TOTAL	2666	35	TOTAL

EL SALER

TEL : (96)1611186
LOCATION : 18 km Valencia
ADDRESS : Parador de Turismo Luis Vives – El Saler – Valencia
HOTEL : HR
Parador Nacional Luis Vives
Tel : (96)1611186
Sidi Saler – El Saler
Tel : (96)1610411

Masterminded by the late Javier Arana, considered as being one of Europe's finest golf architects, this is a first class golf course being one of the best in Spain. Set on the shores of the Mediterranean Sea amongst tall pines on a gently rolling terrain, the golf course has a most interesting layout with excellent greens. The 58-room Luis Vives Parador (state-owned hotel) lies in the middle of the course with beaches, swimming pool and tennis courts. *SSS 75*

GF $

1968

18

—

J. Arana

L 6510 P 72

S

R

Required : Handicap Certificate
Best days : Any day by prior arrangement

HOLE	LENGTH MEDAL-TEE	PAR	STROKE INDEX
1	400	4	
2	375	4	
3	485	5	
4	190	3	
5	490	5	
6	400	4	
7	340	4	
8	360	4	
9	150	3	
TOTAL	3190	36	TOTAL

HOLE	LENGTH MEDAL-TEE	PAR	STROKE INDEX
10	375	4	
11	515	5	
12	200	3	
13	330	4	
14	385	4	
15	525	5	
16	400	4	
17	180	3	
18	410	4	
TOTAL	3320	36	TOTAL

ESCORPION

TEL : (96)1601211
LOCATION : 19 km Valencia
ADDRESS : Apartado 1 – Betera – Valencia
HOTEL :
Monte Picayo – Puzul
Tel : (96)1420100
Reina Victoria – Valencia
Tel : (96)3520487
Rey Don Jaime – Valencia
Tel : (96)3607300
RESTAURANT : El Condestable – Valencia
Tel : (96)3699250

The course is of championship standard and lies on flat open countryside, against a mountain backcloth. Many holes are lined by mature pine-trees and large ponds present an obstacle on more than seven of them. *SSS 72*

GF $

1975

18

—

R. Kirby

L 6106 P 72

Required : Handicap Certificate
Best days : Any day

HOLE	LENGTH MEDAL-TEE	PAR	STROKE INDEX
1	377	4	5
2	326	4	9
3	146	3	17
4	360	4	15
5	373	4	7
6	333	4	13
7	484	5	3
8	189	3	11
9	536	5	1
TOTAL	3124	36	TOTAL

HOLE	LENGTH MEDAL-TEE	PAR	STROKE INDEX
10	466	5	10
11	311	4	16
12	350	4	2
13	390	4	4
14	353	4	8
15	140	3	18
16	363	4	6
17	170	3	12
18	439	5	14
TOTAL	2982	36	TOTAL

GUADALHORCE

TEL : (952)243682
LOCATION : 5 km Málaga/10 km Torremolinos
ADDRESS : Carretera de Cartama - km 7
29590 Campanillas
HOTEL :
Cervantes - Torremolinos
Tel : (952)384033
Castillo de Santa Clara - Torremolinos
Tel : (952)383155
Don Pablo - Torremolinos
Tel : (952)383888

The Finnish architect Kosti Kuronen designed this new championship course standing between Málaga and Torremolinos on the Costa del Sol. Named after the river "Guadalhorce" with some of the holes running along its borders, the course has been divided into two distinct rounds. The outgoing part (holes 1-9) is a scottish type rolling course with large greens, whereas the incoming part is american style with a number of water hazards. The clubhouse with its charming patio is an old andalucian manor house. Other facilities include a 9 hole par 3 course, paddle tennis courts, a swimming pool and a finnish sauna.

GF $

1989

18

—

K. Kuronen

L 5916 P 72

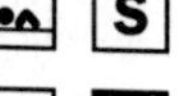

Required : Handicap Certificate
Best days : Any days

HOLE	LENGTH MEDAL-TEE	PAR	STROKE INDEX
1	295	4	12
2	125	3	18
3	346	4	8
4	435	5	10
5	157	3	16
6	330	4	14
7	449	5	6
8	390	4	2
9	355	4	4
TOTAL	2882	36	TOTAL

HOLE	LENGTH MEDAL-TEE	PAR	STROKE INDEX
10	510	5	5
11	400	4	1
12	463	5	9
13	162	3	13
14	335	4	11
15	339	4	7
16	300	4	17
17	150	3	15
18	375	4	3
TOTAL	3034	36	TOTAL

GUADALMINA

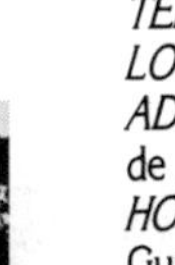

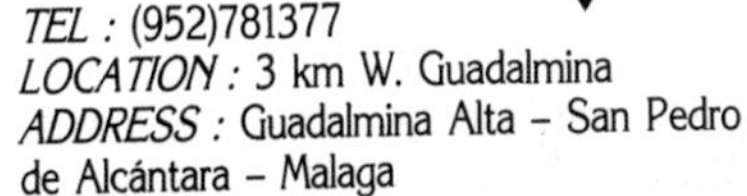

TEL : (952)781377
LOCATION : 3 km W. Guadalmina
ADDRESS : Guadalmina Alta – San Pedro de Alcántara – Malaga
HOTEL :
Guadalmina
Tel : (952)781400

The Guadalmina golf club was the first golf course on the Costa del Sol. There are two 18 hole courses, both ideal for holiday golf, laid out on rolling terrain in the wooded foothills of the Sierra Blanca mountains. Both courses are bordered by the sea and the Guadalmina river with panoramic views over the Mediterranean to Gibraltar. There is an elegant clubhouse with two tennis courts and a swimming pool. The Andalucian style Guadalmina Golf Hotel is adjacent to the course. Facilities include beaches, two swimming pools, children's playground, tennis and horse-riding. *SSS 70*

GF $

1959/1973

36

—

J. Arana, F. Nardi

L 5910 P 72, 5735 P 72

Required : Handicap Certificate
Best days : Any day

Campo Sur

HOLE	LENGTH MEDAL-TEE	PAR	STROKE INDEX
1	360	4	9
2	370	4	5
3	165	3	17
4	315	4	15
5	400	4	3
6	355	4	7
7	535	5	1
8	170	3	13
9	355	4	11
TOTAL	3025	35	TOTAL

HOLE	LENGTH MEDAL-TEE	PAR	STROKE INDEX
10	125	3	18
11	300	4	12
12	295	4	14
13	360	4	8
14	440	5	6
15	145	3	16
16	315	4	10
17	465	5	2
18	440	5	4
TOTAL	2885	37	TOTAL

Campo Norte

HOLE	LENGTH MEDAL-TEE	PAR	STROKE INDEX
1	330	4	13
2	150	3	17
3	340	4	9
4	440	5	3
5	545	5	1
6	150	3	15
7	365	4	5
8	305	4	7
9	320	4	11
TOTAL	2945	36	TOTAL

HOLE	LENGTH MEDAL-TEE	PAR	STROKE INDEX
10	535	5	2
11	125	3	18
12	450	5	4
13	285	4	12
14	125	3	16
15	330	4	8
16	360	4	6
17	260	4	14
18	320	4	10
TOTAL	2790	36	TOTAL

HERRERIA

TEL : (91)8905111
LOCATION : 3 km El Escorial
ADDRESS : San Lorenzo de El Escorial – Madrid
HOTEL :
Victoria Palace – El Escorial
Tel : (91)8901511
Hostal Christina – El Escorial
Tel : (91)8901961
Miranda y Suizo – El Escorial
Tel : (91)8904711
RESTAURANT : Meson La Cueva – El Escorial
Tel : (91)8901516

The setting of the Herreria golf club is unique, nestling in the foothills of luxuriant mountains at over 1000 m above sea level, near the historical village of 'El Escorial', home of King Felipe II. The course lies in front of the world famous Monastery of San Lorenzo del Escorial which dates back to the 16th century. A pleasant course with lush fairways following the slopes of the hills. *SSS 72*

GF $

1968

18

—

A. Lucena

L 6015 P 72

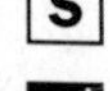

Required : Handicap Certificate
Best days : Weekdays

HOLE	LENGTH MEDAL-TEE	PAR	STROKE INDEX
1	345	4	10
2	499	5	1
3	175	3	16
4	343	4	8
5	335	4	14
6	312	4	6
7	149	3	18
8	486	5	4
9	347	4	12
TOTAL	2991	36	TOTAL

HOLE	LENGTH MEDAL-TEE	PAR	STROKE INDEX
10	160	3	3
11	478	5	2
12	359	4	13
13	179	3	7
14	320	4	9
15	446	5	11
16	323	4	17
17	361	4	15
18	388	4	5
TOTAL	3014	36	TOTAL

LA CORUNA

TEL : (981)285200
LOCATION : 7 km La Coruña N 550/E 50, in Arteijo
ADDRESS : Apartado 737 – La Coruña
HOTEL :
Finisterre – La Coruña
Tel : (981)205400
Atlantico – La Coruña
Tel : (981)226500
Ciudad de La Coruna – La Coruña
Tel : (981)211100
RESTAURANT : El Gallo de Oro – Arteijo
Tel : (981)600410

A prestigious golf club located in a region called 'Galicia', famous for its fertile ground and luxuriant woods. It borders the Bay of Biscay and is laid out on rolling lush countryside with its fairways tree-lined by pines. There is an attractive club house with tennis courts and a swimming pool. The nearby Finisterre Hotel is scenically situated overlooking the bay. *SSS 72*

 $

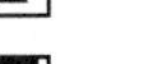 —

1962

A. Lucena

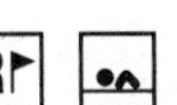 

18

L 6037 P 72

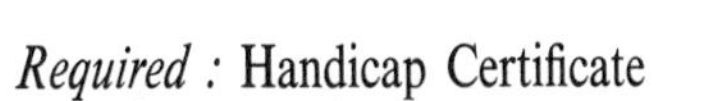
Required : Handicap Certificate
Best days : Weekdays

HOLE	LENGTH MEDAL-TEE	PAR	STROKE INDEX
1	133	3	
2	444	5	
3	304	4	
4	427	4	
5	321	4	
6	501	5	
7	163	3	
8	369	4	
9	432	4	
TOTAL	3094	36	TOTAL

HOLE	LENGTH MEDAL-TEE	PAR	STROKE INDEX
10	384	4	
11	153	3	
12	313	4	
13	492	5	
14	161	3	
15	280	4	
16	381	4	
17	479	5	
18	300	4	
TOTAL	2943	36	TOTAL

LA DUQUESA

TEL : (952)890425/6
LOCATION : 10 km Estepona
ADDRESS : Urbanizacion El Hacho – Manilva – Malaga
HOTEL :
Stakis – Estepona
Tel : (952)783000
Atalaya Park – Estepona
Tel : (952)781300

The latest creation of master architect Robert Trent Jones, inaugurated in 1987 on the Costa del Sol. A most promising championship layout set near sandy beaches and following the undulating slopes of the hills overlooking the new harbour and the new holiday complex of Puerto de la Duquesa. Backed by the Sierra Morena mountains, the holes cut through rugged terrain with flowering shrubs, gorse-covered hills and rocky outcrops. Many holes have elevated tees and testing, well-bunkered greens. There are scenic views of the sea and Morocco. The clubhouse is a magnificent Andalucian style building including 96 apartments, gymnasium, sauna, jacuzzis, indoor and outdoor swimming pools. Other sports facilities include a bowling green, and several tennis and squash courts. *SSS 70*

GF $$
1987
18

—
R. Trent Jones
L 5672 P 72

S
R

Required : Handicap Certificate
Best days : Any day

HOLE	LENGTH MEDAL-TEE	PAR	STROKE INDEX
1	314	4	15
2	301	4	9
3	132	3	11
4	357	4	1
5	162	3	5
6	353	4	3
7	474	5	7
8	295	4	17
9	481	5	13
TOTAL	2869	36	TOTAL

HOLE	LENGTH MEDAL-TEE	PAR	STROKE INDEX
10	479	5	4
11	156	3	12
12	319	4	6
13	307	4	14
14	471	5	2
15	146	3	8
16	331	4	18
17	108	3	16
18	486	5	10
TOTAL	2803	36	TOTAL

LA MANGA

TEL : (968)564511
LOCATION : 30 km Cartagena
ADDRESS : Los Belones – Cartagena-Murcia
HOTEL : HR
La Manga Club – Los Bellones
Tel : (968)564511
Doblemar Casino – La Manga del Mar Menor
Tel : (968)563914
Dos Mares – La Manga del Mar Menor
Tel : (968)563093
RESTAURANT : Tropical – La Manga del Mar Menor
Tel : (968)563345

Without doubt one of the world's great courses and brainchild of the American architect Robert Dean Putman. Set on the Costa Blanca and overlooking the Bay of Mar Menor, the course has thousands of date palms. It is backed by distant low mountains. Both courses are testing with large bunkers, numerous impressive lakes and deep ravines called 'barancas', serving as hazards. A very noble golf club with a world famous touring pro: Severiano Ballesteros. The La Manga Clubhotel with 47 bedrooms looks down upon the golf course. Facilities include tennis courts, horse-riding, swimming pool, cycling, windsurfing, and a children's playground. *SSS 72/73*

GF $$
1971
36

—
P. Putman
L 5573 P 71, 5925 P 72

Required : Handicap Certificate
Best days : Weekdays only

North Course

HOLE	LENGTH MEDAL-TEE	PAR	STROKE INDEX
1	332	4	11
2	109	3	17
3	441	5	3
4	178	3	13
5	355	4	7
6	473	5	1
7	378	4	5
8	150	3	15
9	309	4	9
TOTAL	2725	35	TOTAL

HOLE	LENGTH MEDAL-TEE	PAR	STROKE INDEX
10	282	4	14
11	464	5	10
12	146	3	18
13	318	4	4
14	291	4	2
15	486	5	8
16	169	3	16
17	323	4	12
18	369	4	6
TOTAL	2848	36	TOTAL

South Course

HOLE	LENGTH MEDAL-TEE	PAR	STROKE INDEX
1	341	4	14
2	328	4	12
3	455	5	6
4	373	4	4
5	182	3	18
6	341	4	10
7	355	4	8
8	173	3	16
9	523	5	2
TOTAL	3071	36	TOTAL

HOLE	LENGTH MEDAL-TEE	PAR	STROKE INDEX
10	323	4	11
11	337	4	7
12	119	3	17
13	477	5	5
14	314	4	9
15	378	4	1
16	291	4	13
17	169	3	15
18	446	5	3
TOTAL	2854	36	TOTAL

LA MORALEJA

★

TEL : (91)6500700
LOCATION : 11 km Madrid E 25/N 1
ADDRESS : Alcobendas – 28409 Madrid
HOTEL :
Pamplona – San Sebastian de los Reyes
Tel : (91)6529777
Castellana – Madrid
Tel : (91)4100200
Monte Real – Madrid Puerto de Hierro
Tel : (91)2162140
RESTAURANT : Meson Tejas Verdes – San Sebastian de los Reyes
Tel : (91)6527307

Scenically laid out in a fine parkland setting with lush fairways lined by mature trees, the championship course was designed by Jack Nicklaus in 1976. It staged the Spanish Open in 1986. The golf club is very private and only permits visiting golfers who are introduced by a member. *SSS 72*

GF $$ — R S
1976 — J. Nicklaus
18 — L 6016 P 72

Required : Special Introduction by a member
Best days : —

HOLE	LENGTH MEDAL-TEE	PAR	STROKE INDEX
1	362	4	
2	176	3	
3	284	4	
4	195	3	
5	354	4	
6	472	5	
7	420	4	
8	376	4	
9	475	5	
TOTAL	3114	36	TOTAL

HOLE	LENGTH MEDAL-TEE	PAR	STROKE INDEX
10	391	4	
11	388	4	
12	486	5	
13	308	4	
14	288	4	
15	160	3	
16	287	4	
17	150	3	
18	444	5	
TOTAL	2902	36	TOTAL

LA PENAZA

TEL : (976)342800/342804
LOCATION : 15 km Zaragoza N 11
ADDRESS : Carretera de Madrid – km 307 – Apartado 3039 – 50080 Zaragoza
HOTEL :
Oriente – Zaragoza
Tel : (976)221960
Goya – Zaragoza
Tel : (976)229331
Palafox – Zaragoza
Tel : (976)237700
RESTAURANT : Costa Vasca – Zaragoza
Tel : (976)217339

Located midway between Madrid and Barcelona, La Penaza is an inland course with gently rolling fairways landscaped amongst trees. There is an attractive clubhouse with a swimming pool, various tennis courts and a children's playground. *SSS 72*

GF $

1973

18

—

F. Hawtree

L 6161 P 72

S

Required : Handicap Certificate
Best days : Weekdays only

HOLE	LENGTH MEDAL-TEE	PAR	STROKE INDEX
1	315	4	17
2	308	4	10
3	162	3	18
4	358	4	4
5	488	5	11
6	173	3	8
7	483	5	6
8	330	4	14
9	402	4	1
TOTAL	3019	36	TOTAL

HOLE	LENGTH MEDAL-TEE	PAR	STROKE INDEX
10	326	4	15
11	482	5	16
12	190	3	12
13	365	4	5
14	364	4	2
15	191	3	7
16	469	5	9
17	398	4	3
18	357	4	13
TOTAL	3142	36	TOTAL

LA PUERTA DE HIERRO

TEL : (91)3161745
LOCATION : 4 km Madrid
ADDRESS : 28035 Madrid
HOTEL :
Monte Real – Ciudad Puerta de Hierro
Tel : (91)2162140
Florida Norte – Madrid (Moncloa)
Tel : (91)2416190
Principe Pio – Madrid (Moncloa)
Tel : (91)2470800
RESTAURANT : Zalacain – Madrid
Tel : (91)2614840

This prestigious and exclusive golf club lies in the outskirts of Madrid in the Ciudad Puerta de Hierro near the University complex. One of Spain's oldest clubs, having been founded in 1904, its thirty-six holes meander their way through fine rolling parkland. Water affects play on several holes. There is an imposing clubhouse, built high up and with extensive views. *SSS 73/68*

GF $$
 1904

Weekends
J. Harris, T. Simpson
L 6339 P 73, 5123 P 67

Required : Introduction letter, Handicap Certificate
Best days : Weekdays only

HOLE	LENGTH MEDAL-TEE	PAR	STROKE INDEX
1			
2			
3			
4			
5			
6			
7			
8			
9			
TOTAL			

HOLE	LENGTH MEDAL-TEE	PAR	STROKE INDEX
10			
11			
12			
13			
14			
15			
16			
17			
18			
TOTAL			

LA QUINTA

TEL : (952)783462
LOCATION : 11 km Marbella to Ronda (km 3,5 carretera de Ronda)
ADDRESS : Nueva Andalucia
Marbella-Malaga
HOTEL :
del Golf - Marbella
Tel : (952)811750
Puente Romano - Marbella
Tel : (952)770100
RESTAURANT : Michels - Puerto Banus

Designed by Spains's famous golf champion Antonio Garrido, this new Marbella golf venue (called already «Little Augusta») promises to become one of the leading courses on the Costa del Sol. Located near the famous resort of Puerto Banus not far from the sea, this American style course is sheltered by mountains and is laid out on hilly landscape featuring tricky water hazards, deep sandy bunkers and fast greens. Course facilities include a fine restaurant, paddle tennis facilities, a swimming pool and a childrens' playground.

GF $$ — S

1989 A. Garrido

18 L 5277 P 71

Required : Handicap Certificate
Best days : Weekdays

HOLE	LENGTH MEDAL-TEE	PAR	STROKE INDEX
1	464	5	4
2	316	4	8
3	162	3	12
4	325	4	2
5	105	3	18
6	256	4	10
7	294	4	14
8	148	3	16
9	451	5	6
TOTAL	2521	35	TOTAL

HOLE	LENGTH MEDAL-TEE	PAR	STROKE INDEX
10	264	4	11
11	120	3	17
12	448	5	7
13	325	4	9
14	359	4	1
15	463	5	5
16	160	3	13
17	379	4	3
18	238	4	15
TOTAL	2756	36	TOTAL

LARRABEA

TEL : (945)131131
LOCATION : 15 km Vitoria - Gasteiz/40 km Bilbao
ADDRESS : General Alava 10 - 01005 Vitoria
HOTEL :
General Alava - Vitoria
Tel : (945)222200
Parador Nacional de Argómaniz - Argómaniz
Tel : (945)242200
Canciller Ayala - Vitoria
Tel : (945)220800

The Larrabea course is a pleasant addition to the existing golf courses in the Basque country. It is laid out along the natural lines of the land in flat, lush countryside at the foot of the Albertia mountain amidst sweeping valleys, fields, forests and grasslands. Rows of trees, lakes and streams serve as hazards. Facilities will include a comfortable clubhouse, tennis and squash courts, and a swimming pool.

GF $
1989
18
Mondays
P. Gancedo
L 6050 P 72
S
R

Required : Handicap Certificate
Best days : Any day

HOLE	LENGTH MEDAL-TEE	PAR	STROKE INDEX
1	400	4	
2	320	4	
3	140	3	
4	535	5	
5	150	3	
6	500	5	
7	350	4	
8	280	4	
9	345	4	
TOTAL	3020	36	TOTAL

HOLE	LENGTH MEDAL-TEE	PAR	STROKE INDEX
10	310	4	
11	350	4	
12	160	3	
13	520	5	
14	315	4	
15	150	3	
16	340	4	
17	495	5	
18	400	4	
TOTAL	3040	36	TOTAL

LAS BRISAS (Nuevo Andalucia)

TEL : (952)810875/815518
LOCATION : 10 km Marbella to Cádiz (km 181)
ADDRESS : Apartado 147 – Nueva Andalucia (Málaga)
HOTEL : HP
Golf Plaza
Tel : (952)811750
Rincon Andaluz – Marbella
Tel : (952)811517
El Fuerte – Marbella
Tel : (952)771500

One of the finest golf courses in the world and one of the top Costa del Sol clubs, scene of many international tournaments such as the 1989 World Cup. The course is considered being a masterpiece bearing all the hallmarks of Robert Trent Jones. The layout is fascinating, running alongside a valley with a river meandering its way through the holes. Backed by the La Concha mountain of the Sierra Bianca chain, it is set amidst flowering shrubs and tropical trees. The fairways are long and wide with enormous sand bunkers and strategic water hazards. The greens are fast and sloping. The luxury Golf Plaza Hotel is adjacent to the course. *SSS 73*

GF $$ — —
1968 — R. Trent Jones — S 
18 — L 6198 P 72 — 

Required : Handicap Certificate
Best days : Any day after 12 h 30

HOLE	LENGTH MEDAL-TEE	PAR	STROKE INDEX
1	365	4	
2	385	4	
3	451	5	
4	185	3	
5	530	5	
6	350	4	
7	155	3	
8	461	5	
9	325	4	
TOTAL	3207	37	TOTAL

HOLE	LENGTH MEDAL-TEE	PAR	STROKE INDEX
10	368	4	
11	190	3	
12	468	5	
13	350	4	
14	360	4	
15	390	4	
16	205	3	
17	295	4	
18	365	4	
TOTAL	2991	35	TOTAL

LAS PALMAS

TEL : (928)351050
LOCATION : In Bandama, 14 km Las Palmas
ADDRESS : Apartado 183 – Las Palmas de Gran Canaria – Islas Canarias
HOTEL :
Santa Catalina – Las Palmas
Tel : (928)243040
Imperial Playa – Las Palmas
Tel : (928)264854
Los Bardinos – Las Palmas
Tel : (928)266100
RESTAURANT : Acuario – Las Palmas
Tel : (928)273432

Located on the island of Gran Canaria, this is a pleasant holiday course set amidst red rocky mountains on open terrain with olive trees scattered over the fairways. Having been founded in 1891, the Las Palmas golf club is the oldest on the Spanish peninsula, and will celebrate its centenary in 1991 by organizing the Spanish Open. *SSS 69*

GF $

1891

18

—

A. Mackenzie

L 5510 P 71

Required : Handicap Certificate
Best days : Any day

HOLE	LENGTH MEDAL-TEE	PAR	STROKE INDEX
1	225	4	18
2	336	4	5
3	124	3	15
4	320	4	7
5	430	4	2
6	277	4	13
7	306	4	9
8	155	3	11
9	462	5	4
TOTAL	2635	35	TOTAL

HOLE	LENGTH MEDAL-TEE	PAR	STROKE INDEX
10	158	3	16
11	394	4	3
12	274	4	17
13	283	4	10
14	364	4	1
15	184	3	14
16	426	5	8
17	295	4	12
18	497	5	6
TOTAL	2875	36	TOTAL

LAUKARIZ (La Bilbaina)

TEL : (94)6740858/62
LOCATION : 14 km NE Bilbao
ADDRESS : Laukáriz – Munguia – Vizcaya
HOTEL :
Villa de Bilbao – Bilbao
Tel : (94)4416000
Aranzazu – Bilbao
Tel : (94)4413100
Erulla – Bilbao
Tel : (94)4438900
RESTAURANT : Guria – Bilbao
Tel : (94)4410543

The city of Bilbao has two fine golf clubs nearby, one being the Bilbaina/Laukariz golf course 14km from the city. A pleasant inland course laid out amongst pine forest, with several ponds bordering the holes. Facilities include a fitness club, 2 swimming pools, a children's playground and numerous tennis courts. *SSS 74*

GF $

1976

18

—

P. Putman

L 6112 P 72

Required : Handicap Certificate
Best days : Mondays to Fridays

HOLE	LENGTH MEDAL-TEE	PAR	STROKE INDEX
1	374	4	13
2	372	4	7
3	134	3	18
4	334	4	11
5	361	4	3
6	470	5	5
7	177	3	10
8	359	4	16
9	509	5	1
TOTAL	3090	36	TOTAL

HOLE	LENGTH MEDAL-TEE	PAR	STROKE INDEX
10	499	5	2
11	179	3	15
12	387	4	8
13	352	4	9
14	272	4	17
15	181	3	14
16	296	4	12
17	468	5	4
18	388	4	6
TOTAL	3022	36	TOTAL

LOMAS-BOSQUE

★

TEL : (91)6162170
LOCATION : 18 km Madrid N 5/E 4
ADDRESS : Urbanización El Bosque – Villaviciosa de Odon – Madrid
HOTEL :
Princesa – Madrid (Moncloa)
Tel : (91)2423500
Emperador – Madrid Centro
Tel : (91)2472800
Suecia – Madrid Centro
Tel : (91)2316900
RESTAURANT : La Cañada – Boadillo del Monte
Tel : (91)6551283

The golf course is set within splendid natural grounds alongside the river 'Guadarrama' and bordering a large natural lake, which serves as a hazard for at least six holes. The pleasant clubhouse lies near the lake. Other facilities include two swimming pools, and a children's playground with paddle pool. *SSS 72*

GF $

1973

18

—

R.D. Putman

L 5829 P 72

S

Required : Handicap Certificate
Best days : Weekdays

HOLE	LENGTH MEDAL-TEE	PAR	STROKE INDEX
1	468	5	1
2	75	3	18
3	394	4	3
4	350	4	6
5	145	3	13
6	301	4	9
7	435	5	12
8	281	4	14
9	276	4	16
TOTAL	2725	36	TOTAL

HOLE	LENGTH MEDAL-TEE	PAR	STROKE INDEX
10	368	4	2
11	371	4	5
12	364	4	7
13	364	4	8
14	152	3	17
15	384	4	4
16	514	5	10
17	151	3	15
18	436	5	11
TOTAL	3104	36	TOTAL

LOS NARANJOS (Nueva Andalucia)

TEL : (952)815206/811428
LOCATION : 7 km Marbella to Cádiz (km 174)
ADDRESS : Apartado 64 – Nueva Andalucia (Málaga)
HOTEL :
Golf Plaza
Tel : (952)811750
El Fuerte
Tel : (952)771500
Don Pepe – Marbella
Tel : (952)770300

Built in 1977 by Robert Trent Jones, the club is adjacent to the Las Brisas course and claims to be the longest Spanish course. Its first nine holes wind through groves of orange trees. The second nine run over undulating and open countryside with large areas of huge bunkers. Mature pines and several lakes serve as hazards. There is a fine Andalucian style clubhouse. *SSS 72*

GF $$

1977

18

—

R. Trent Jones

L 6033 P 72

S

Required : Handicap Certificate
Best days : Any day after 14 h

HOLE	LENGTH MEDAL-TEE	PAR	STROKE INDEX
1	360	4	7
2	344	4	8
3	150	3	7
4	347	4	9
5	488	5	3
6	318	4	15
7	342	4	11
8	158	3	18
9	504	5	2
TOTAL	3011	36	TOTAL

HOLE	LENGTH MEDAL-TEE	PAR	STROKE INDEX
10	307	4	12
11	524	5	4
12	327	4	13
13	168	3	14
14	444	5	1
15	364	4	5
16	325	4	16
17	185	3	10
18	378	4	6
TOTAL	3022	36	TOTAL

LOS VILLARES

TEL : (957)350208
LOCATION : 9 km N. Córdoba
ADDRESS : Avda Generalisimo 1 – Apdo 463 – Córdoba
HOTEL :
Melia Córdoba – Córdoba
Tel : (957)298066
Adarve – Córdoba
Tel : (957)481102
Parador de la Arruzafa – Córdoba
Tel : (957)275900
RESTAURANT : Caballo Rojo – Córdoba
Tel : (957)475375

Situated close to the Moorish city of Córdoba, the golf course is set on undulating dry countryside with low hills in the background. Strategically placed olive trees serve as hazards on many holes. *SSS 73*

GF $

1976

18

—

Progolf

L 6050 P 71

Required : Handicap Certificate
Best days : Any day

HOLE	LENGTH MEDAL-TEE	PAR	STROKE INDEX
1	360	4	
2	440	5	
3	375	4	
4	495	5	
5	160	3	
6	300	4	
7	365	4	
8	355	4	
9	155	3	
TOTAL	3005	36	TOTAL

HOLE	LENGTH MEDAL-TEE	PAR	STROKE INDEX
10	325	4	
11	280	4	
12	180	3	
13	395	4	
14	495	4	
15	180	3	
16	360	4	
17	530	5	
18	300	4	
TOTAL	3045	35	TOTAL

MÁLAGA

TEL : (952)381120/381255
LOCATION : 9 km Málaga N 340 / E 26
ADDRESS : Apartado 324 – Málaga
HOTEL :
Parador Nacional del Golf
Tel : (952)381255
Al-Andalus – Torremolinos
Tel : (952)381200
Pez Espada – Torremolinos
Tel : (952)380300

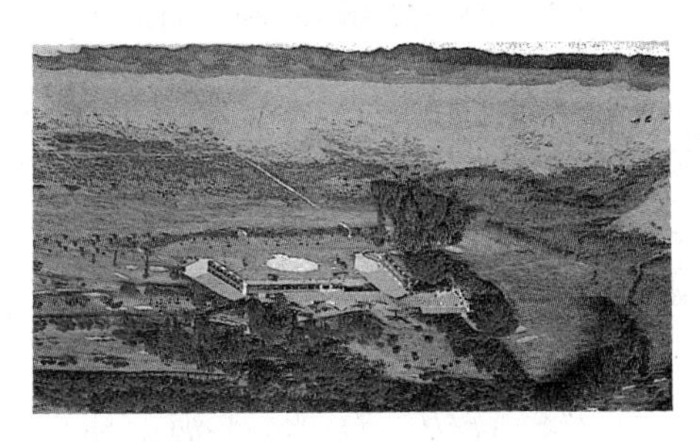

This fine holiday golf course is scenically set on the Costa del Sol in peaceful surroundings amongst palms, eucalyptus, mimosas, oleanders, banana trees, yucca and willows. The course is bordered on two sides by the sea and a river. The Parador Nacional (picturesque state-owned hotel) with swimming pool lies in the middle of the course. *SSS 73*

GF $

1925

18

 Sundays

 T. Simpson

L 6249 P 72

Required : Handicap Certificate
Best days : Weekdays

HOLE	LENGTH MEDAL-TEE	PAR	STROKE INDEX
1	451	5	6
2	350	4	11
3	289	4	14
4	415	4	2
5	386	4	4
6	179	3	17
7	363	4	9
8	353	4	13
9	190	3	16
TOTAL	2976	35	TOTAL

HOLE	LENGTH MEDAL-TEE	PAR	STROKE INDEX
10	380	4	10
11	199	3	15
12	500	5	3
13	167	3	18
14	453	5	7
15	387	4	8
16	458	5	5
17	333	4	12
18	396	4	1
TOTAL	3273	37	TOTAL

MAS NOU

TEL : (972)818220
LOCATION : 30 km Gerona/150 km Barcelona
ADDRESS : Urbanizacion Mas Nou - 17250 La Playa de Aro
HOTEL :
Mas de Torrent - Torrent
Tel : (972)303292
Hostal de la Gavina - S'Agaró
Tel : (972)321100
Guitart - Playa de Aro
Tel : (972)7220
RESTAURANT : Mas Nou - Playa de Aro
Tel : (972)817853

This is a thrilling and most enjoyable championship course near the popular holiday resort of Playa de Aro. Set inland on scenic countryside not far from the sea, the sporty holes are found in a pleasant setting of trees, lakes and rolling green hills. Facilities include a smart restaurant, tennis courts and a fine swimming pool. A hotel is planned for the near future. *SSS 72*

GF $

1989

18

—

R. Espinoza

L 5978 P 72

Required : Handicap Certificate
Best days : Weekdays

HOLE	LENGTH MEDAL-TEE	PAR	STROKE INDEX
1	355	4	9
2	363	4	1
3	167	3	17
4	466	5	11
5	164	3	15
6	358	4	3
7	283	4	13
8	504	5	7
9	350	4	5
TOTAL	3010	36	TOTAL

HOLE	LENGTH MEDAL-TEE	PAR	STROKE INDEX
10	306	4	12
11	189	3	14
12	339	4	6
13	473	5	4
14	160	3	18
15	372	4	2
16	352	4	8
17	471	5	10
18	306	4	16
TOTAL	2968	36	TOTAL

MASPALOMAS

TEL : (928)762581
LOCATION : 5 km S. Maspalomas
ADDRESS : Avda de Africa, s/n Maspalomas – Gran Canaria
HOTEL :
Maspalomas Oasis – Maspalomas
Tel : (928)760170
Palm Beach – Maspalomas
Tel : (928)762920
RESTAURANT : San Augustin Beach Club – San Augustin
Tel : (928)760400

A fine holiday courses located on the Gran Canaria Island. Separated from the sea by white sandy dunes, the course is laid out on relatively flat open ground with palm trees dotted around the holes. The club boasts a two-floor driving range.

GF $ — RP S

1968 — M. Mackenzie Ross

18 — L 6036 P 72

Required : None
Best days : Any day

HOLE	LENGTH MEDAL-TEE	PAR	STROKE INDEX
1	345	4	11
2	343	4	1
3	130	3	18
4	441	5	13
5	313	4	15
6	365	4	7
7	485	5	5
8	205	3	3
9	361	4	9
TOTAL	2988	36	TOTAL

HOLE	LENGTH MEDAL-TEE	PAR	STROKE INDEX
10	365	4	8
11	435	5	16
12	205	3	4
13	355	4	10
14	370	4	2
15	325	4	17
16	165	3	14
17	390	4	12
18	438	5	6
TOTAL	3048	37	TOTAL

MEDITERRANEO

TEL : (964)321227
LOCATION : 3,5 km N. Castellón de la Plana
ADDRESS : Urbanización la Coma – Borriol Castellón
HOTEL :
Mindoro – Castellón de la Plana
Tel : (964)222300
Real – Castellon de la Plana
Tel : (964)211944
Turcosa – El Grao de Castellón
Tel : (964)222150
RESTAURANT : Nina y Angelo – Castellón de la Plana
Tel : (964)239292

The Mediterraneo golf course belongs to a vast urbanization complex including various sport and leisure facilities such as nine tennis courts, two swimming pools, and a children's playground. The course itself lies on open ground, with a fine setting of lakes serving as hazards. The holes are landscaped amongst palm and olive trees and backed by luxuriant wooded hills. *SSS 72*

GF $

1978

18

—

R. Espinosa, Ibergolf

L 6042 P 72

Required : Handicap Certificate
Best days : Weekdays

HOLE	LENGTH MEDAL-TEE	PAR	STROKE INDEX
1	335	4	11
2	198	3	15
3	361	4	5
4	515	5	1
5	343	4	9
6	170	3	17
7	302	4	13
8	483	5	3
9	370	4	7
TOTAL	3077	36	TOTAL

HOLE	LENGTH MEDAL-TEE	PAR	STROKE INDEX
10	310	4	8
11	298	4	16
12	189	3	12
13	539	5	2
14	312	4	14
15	356	4	6
16	170	3	18
17	469	5	4
18	322	4	10
TOTAL	2965	36	TOTAL

MIJAS

TEL : (952)476843
LOCATION : 3 km N. Fuengirola
ADDRESS : Camino Viejo de Coin – km 3 – Mijas Costa – Apartado 138 – Fuengirola – Málaga
HOTEL : HF
Byblos Andaluz
Tel : (952)473050
Mijas – Mijas
Tel : (952)485800
Florida – Fuengirola
Tel : (952)476100

The golf club lies in the Mijas Valley near the picturesque village of Mijas, about 3km inland from Fuengirola. There are two 18 hole courses bearing the same characteristics. Set on fairly rolling land, they have a spacious layout with generous fairways and large sand bunkers. Both incorporate a fine setting of water hazards. An attractive feature is the charming clubhouse, a former old Andalucian ranch house, lying between the two courses. The tasteful Byblos Andaluz Hotel with 135 rooms, 3 swimming pools, 5 tennis courts, a riding centre and a famous thalasotherapy centre, overlooks the first hole of the Los Olivos course. Hotel Mijas, a charming hacienda-style hotel, is built at 400 m above sea level, overlooking the Costa del Sol and the sea. *SSS 70/72*

GF $$

1976

36

—

R. Trent Jones

L 5545 P 72, 5975 P 71

S

Required : Handicap Certificate
Best days : Any day

Los Olivos

HOLE	LENGTH MEDAL-TEE	PAR	STROKE INDEX
1	300	4	15
2	332	4	5
3	147	3	13
4	307	4	9
5	108	3	17
6	498	5	1
7	308	4	11
8	148	3	7
9	501	5	3
TOTAL	2649	35	TOTAL

HOLE	LENGTH MEDAL-TEE	PAR	STROKE INDEX
10	510	5	2
11	331	4	12
12	338	4	6
13	286	4	10
14	126	3	16
15	435	5	4
16	118	3	18
17	317	4	14
18	435	5	8
TOTAL	2896	37	TOTAL

Los Lagos

HOLE	LENGTH MEDAL-TEE	PAR	STROKE INDEX
1	504	5	9
2	146	3	17
3	333	4	15
4	382	4	5
5	473	5	1
6	386	4	3
7	378	4	11
8	191	3	7
9	352	4	13
TOTAL	3145	36	TOTAL

HOLE	LENGTH MEDAL-TEE	PAR	STROKE INDEX
10	387	4	4
11	150	3	12
12	344	4	8
13	491	5	2
14	299	4	18
15	149	3	14
16	337	4	6
17	341	4	16
18	332	4	10
TOTAL	2830	35	TOTAL

NUEVO CLUB DE MADRID

TEL : (91)6300820
LOCATION : 26 km Madrid A 6
ADDRESS : Las Matas – Madrid
HOTEL :
Monte Real – Ciudad Puerta de Hierro
Tel : (91)2162140
Melia Madrid – Madrid Moncloa
Tel : (91)2418200
Tirol Melia – Madrid Moncloa
Tel : (91)2481900
RESTAURANT : Portonovo – Aravaca
Tel : (91)2070173

A popular golf course laid out in the foothills surrounding the Spanish capital. Founded in 1972, the course lies on undulating countryside with its holes landscaped amongst mature trees. The clubhouse is modern and equipped with a swimming pool and tennis courts.

GF $
1972
18

—
A.I.D.E.S.A.
L 5657 P 72

S
R

Required : Handicap Certificate
Best days : Weekdays

HOLE	LENGTH MEDAL-TEE	PAR	STROKE INDEX
1	377	4	
2	368	5	
3	198	3	
4	404	5	
5	276	4	
6	264	4	
7	194	3	
8	387	4	
9	355	4	
TOTAL	2823	36	TOTAL

HOLE	LENGTH MEDAL-TEE	PAR	STROKE INDEX
10	450	5	
11	171	3	
12	407	4	
13	458	5	
14	295	4	
15	311	4	
16	141	3	
17	324	4	
18	277	4	
TOTAL	2834	36	TOTAL

OLIVA NOVA

✡

TEL : (965)780650
LOCATION : 90 km Alicante, exit 61 of A7
ADDRESS : Marquès de Campo 50 - 03700 Denia
HOTEL :
Costa Blanca - Denia
Tel : (965)780336
Los Angeles - Denia
Tel : (965)780458

Laid out in the heart of the Costa Blanca midway between Alicante and Valencia, the Oliva Nova course was designed by Spain's most famous sportsman and golfer Severiano Ballesteros. The course is peacefully situated on flat landscape along the coast amidst rising dunes, sandy beaches and scenic lakes with an individual setting for each of the holes. Part of a luxurious real estate complex, a hotel will open soon.

GF $ — —  

1990 — S. Ballesteros —  S

18 — L 6035 P 72 — 

Required : Handicap Certificate
Best days : Any day

HOLE	LENGTH MEDAL-TEE	PAR	STROKE INDEX
1	510	5	
2	385	4	
3	180	3	
4	365	4	
5	275	4	
6	200	3	
7	395	4	
8	470	5	
9	410	4	
TOTAL	3190	36	TOTAL

HOLE	LENGTH MEDAL-TEE	PAR	STROKE INDEX
10	410	4	
11	200	3	
12	490	5	
13	395	4	
14	345	4	
15	320	4	
16	150	3	
17	430	4	
18	515	5	
TOTAL	3255	36	TOTAL

PALS

TEL : (972)636006
LOCATION : 7 km Bagur
ADDRESS : Playa de Pals – Gerona – Costa Brava
HOTEL :
Aigua Blava – Bagur
Tel : (972)622058
Bonaiga – Bagur
Tel : (972)622050
Parador de la Costa Brava – Bagur
Tel : (972)622162
RESTAURANT : Mas Comangau – Bagur
Tel : (972)623210

Set within a peaceful and splendid landscape near the sea on the Costa Brava, this is an excellent golf course with plenty of variety. It is laid out on wooded parkland with each hole separated by umbrella pines. The rustic clubhouse with swimming pool and private beach, has a fine terrace overlooking the course and distant hills. The Aigua Blava Hotel is situated 4km from the course. *SSS 74*

GF $

1966

18

Tuesdays

F.W. Hawtree

L 5940 P 73

Required : Handicap Certificate
Best days : Weekdays

HOLE	LENGTH MEDAL-TEE	PAR	STROKE INDEX
1	281	4	14
2	305	4	6
3	300	4	12
4	359	4	2
5	465	5	4
6	151	3	18
7	357	4	8
8	472	5	10
9	140	3	16
TOTAL	2830	36	TOTAL

HOLE	LENGTH MEDAL-TEE	PAR	STROKE INDEX
10	320	4	5
11	124	3	17
12	387	4	1
13	349	4	9
14	455	5	13
15	175	3	15
16	492	5	11
17	361	4	3
18	447	5	7
TOTAL	3110	37	TOTAL

PEDRENA

TEL : (942)500001
LOCATION : 24 km Santander
ADDRESS : Apartado 233 – Santander
HOTEL :
Bahia – Santander
Tel : (942)221700
Real – El Sardinero
Tel : (942)272550
Santemar – El Sardinero
Tel : (942)272900
RESTAURANT : El Molino de Puente Arce – Puente Arce
Tel : (942)574052

The splendid Pedrena golf club is scenically situated on a peninsula in the middle of a bay with panoramic views over the city of Santander. The course is bordered on three sides by water, and many of the holes are separated by dense pine forest. It is the birthplace of the famous champion Severiano Ballesteros, who started his career as a young caddy at La Pedrena, and is now an honorary member of the club. *SSS 69*

GF $$ — S

1928 — H. Colt, J. Allison, M. Morrison

18 — L 5478 P 70 — R

Required : Club Membership Card, Handicap Certificate
Best days : Weekdays from September to July 15th

HOLE	LENGTH MEDAL-TEE	PAR	STROKE INDEX
1	307	4	13
2	181	3	9
3	341	4	7
4	373	4	1
5	272	4	17
6	376	4	3
7	145	3	11
8	330	4	5
9	435	5	15
TOTAL	2760	35	TOTAL

HOLE	LENGTH MEDAL-TEE	PAR	STROKE INDEX
10	171	3	4
11	445	5	14
12	147	3	16
13	348	4	2
14	290	4	18
15	205	3	8
16	446	5	6
17	340	4	12
18	326	4	10
TOTAL	2718	35	TOTAL

PLAYA SERENA

TEL : (951)333055
LOCATION : 25 km Almeria N 340
ADDRESS : Urbanización Playa Serena – Roquetas de Mar-Almeria
HOTEL :
Sabinal – Roquetas de Mar
Golf Hotel Almerimar – El Ejido
Tel : (951)480950
Torreluz IV – Almeria
Tel : (951)234799
RESTAURANT : Club de Mar – Almeria
Tel : (951)235048

A fine and flat seaside course, ideal for holiday golf, set on the coast of Almeria and backed by red coloured mountains. The holes are laid out amidst sandy beaches with six lakes serving as resting places for migrating birds. *SSS 72*

GF $ — —

1979 — A. Gallardo, P. Allis

18 — L 5905 P 72

Required : Handicap Certificate
Best days : Weekdays

HOLE	LENGTH MEDAL-TEE	PAR	STROKE INDEX
1	339	4	15
2	173	3	13
3	449	5	5
4	410	4	1
5	345	4	7
6	330	4	17
7	511	5	3
8	167	3	9
9	379	4	11
TOTAL	3103	36	TOTAL

HOLE	LENGTH MEDAL-TEE	PAR	STROKE INDEX
10	291	4	8
11	130	3	12
12	411	4	2
13	435	5	4
14	496	5	6
15	315	4	16
16	399	4	14
17	171	3	10
18	319	4	18
TOTAL	2802	36	TOTAL

PONIENTE

TEL : (971)680148
LOCATION : 16 km Palma/2 km Magaluf
ADDRESS : Crta. Cala Figuera – Costa de Calvia-Palma de Mallorca
HOTEL :
Atlantic – Magalluf
Tel : (971)680208
Coral Playa – Magalluf
Tel : (971)680562
Punta Negra – Palma Nova
Tel : (971)680762
RESTAURANT : C'an Jaume – Magalluf
Tel : (971)680382

Located on the island of Palma de Mallorca, 16 km south-west of Palma, this is an attractive golf course set on relatively hilly countryside. The wide fairways are lush and are bordered by majestic pines and wild flowers with ponds serving as hazards. Set near the sea, the course is surrounded by wooded hills. *SSS 72*

GF $
1977
18
—
J.D. Harris
L 6430 P 72
S
R

Required : Handicap Certificate
Best days : Any day

HOLE	LENGTH MEDAL-TEE	PAR	STROKE INDEX
1	405	4	10
2	535	5	14
3	390	4	2
4	370	4	8
5	440	5	18
6	180	3	12
7	330	4	6
8	375	4	4
9	190	3	16
TOTAL	3215	36	TOTAL

HOLE	LENGTH MEDAL-TEE	PAR	STROKE INDEX
10	400	4	1
11	510	5	11
12	210	3	3
13	375	4	9
14	340	4	13
15	160	3	17
16	350	4	5
17	380	4	7
18	490	5	15
TOTAL	3215	36	TOTAL

REAL AUTOMOVIL CLUB DE ESPANA

★★

TEL : (91)6570011/4473200
LOCATION : 28 km Madrid E 25
ADDRESS : José Abascal 10 – Madrid 28003
HOTEL :
Pamplona – Fuencarral
Tel : (91)6529777
Mindanao – Madrid Chambéri
Tel : (91)4495500
Tryp Palacio – Madrid Chambéri
Tel : (91)4425100
RESTAURANT : Meson Tejas Verdes – Fuencarral
Tel : (91)6527307

The R.A.C.E. lies 28km from the Spanish capital on the motorway to Burgos. It is one of Madrid's exclusive social clubs, counting many members. Among its facilities is a fine championship golf course, set on rolling lush countryside with stately trees flanking the holes. The course is of excellent quality and has been the scene of many national championships. It is equipped with a swimming pool, various tennis courts and a children's playground. *SSS 72*

GF $$

1967

18

Mondays

J. Arana

L 6046 P 72

R S

Required : Handicap Certificate, Club Membership Card
Best days : Weekdays

HOLE	LENGTH MEDAL-TEE	PAR	STROKE INDEX
1	450	5	9
2	375	4	14
3	183	3	8
4	351	4	6
5	488	5	3
6	346	4	1
7	327	4	12
8	309	4	16
9	149	3	18
TOTAL	2978	36	TOTAL

HOLE	LENGTH MEDAL-TEE	PAR	STROKE INDEX
10	342	4	15
11	465	5	11
12	375	4	4
13	206	3	7
14	447	5	10
15	390	4	5
16	343	4	2
17	169	3	13
18	331	4	17
TOTAL	3068	36	TOTAL

REAL SOCIEDAD NEGURI

TEL : (94)4690200
LOCATION : 2 km NW Algorta, 17 km Bilbao
ADDRESS : Apartado 9 – Algorta – Vizcaya
HOTEL :
Los Tamarises – Algorta
Tel : (94)4690050
Aranzazu – Bilbao
Tel : (94)4413100
Villa de Bilbao – Bilbao
Tel : (94)4690200
RESTAURANT : Jolastoki – Neguri
Tel : (94)4693031

Brainchild of Spain's most famous architect Javier Arana, who used to be a member of the club, the Neguri golf course, also called 'La Galea', is one of the most renowned in Spain and one of the leading courses in Europe. It lies in Basque country near the city of Bilbao within an estate called 'La Galea'. Bordering the Bay of Biscay, the long holes with lush fairways and deep bunkers, are flanked by tall pine trees. Each one has its own distinctive challenge, including the longest and most toughest of the course, the 13th with a double dogleg. Having hosted the Spanish Open and other important tournaments many times, the club has a fine modern clubhouse with swimming pool, children's playground and tennis courts. *SSS 72*

GF $ — —  

1911 — J. Arana —  

18 — L 6104 P 72

Required : Club Membership Card
Best days : Weekdays

HOLE	LENGTH MEDAL-TEE	PAR	STROKE INDEX
1	405	4	8
2	125	3	18
3	395	4	4
4	294	4	14
5	466	5	2
6	194	3	12
7	393	4	6
8	335	4	10
9	311	4	16
TOTAL	2918	35	TOTAL

HOLE	LENGTH MEDAL-TEE	PAR	STROKE INDEX
10	501	5	3
11	283	4	15
12	376	4	7
13	515	5	1
14	184	3	13
15	329	4	11
16	352	4	9
17	147	3	17
18	499	5	5
TOTAL	3186	37	TOTAL

RIO REAL

TEL : (952)773776
LOCATION : 5 km Marbella N 340/E 26
ADDRESS : Apartado 82 – Marbella-Málaga
HOTEL :
Los Monteros – Marbella
Tel : (952)771700
Don Carlos – Marbella
Tel : (952)831140
Incosol-Marbella – Marbella
Tel : (952)773700

One of the most popular courses on the Costa del Sol, linked to the elegant 'Los Monteros' Hotel. The course, set alongside the sea, follows the gentle undulations of a scenic valley. It constitutes a demanding test for golfers with the Rio Real river cutting the course in two, and meandering its way to the beach through at least six holes. There is a remarkable hacienda-style clubhouse with heated pool, overlooking the course and the sea. Weekly golf tournaments are organized during summer for golfers staying at the prestigious Los Monteros Hotel. Undoubtedly one of the best and most elegant hotels in Spain, it is set in tropical gardens near the sea, with a beach club, indoor and outdoor pools, gymnasium, sauna, tennis and squash courts, riding school, water sports facilities and children's playground. *SSS 72*

GF $$

1965

18

—

J. Arana

L 5730 P 72

R S

Required : Handicap Certificate
Best days : Any day

HOLE	LENGTH MEDAL-TEE	PAR	STROKE INDEX
1	274	4	14
2	338	4	12
3	129	3	17
4	379	4	8
5	349	4	10
6	159	3	15
7	417	5	2
8	376	4	6
9	430	5	4
TOTAL	2851	36	TOTAL

HOLE	LENGTH MEDAL-TEE	PAR	STROKE INDEX
10	318	4	7
11	323	4	9
12	479	5	1
13	148	3	16
14	382	4	5
15	472	5	3
16	295	4	11
17	132	3	18
18	330	4	13
TOTAL	2879	36	TOTAL

SAN CUGAT

TEL : (93)6743908/58
LOCATION : 20 km Barcelona
ADDRESS : Calle Villá – San Cugat del Valles
HOTEL :
Bellaterra – San Cugat del Valles
Tel : (93)6926054
Colon – Barcelona
Tel : (93)3011404
Gran Derby – Barcelona
Tel : (93)3223215
RESTAURANT : Rossinyol – Valldoreix
Tel : (93)6742300

Set on the Costa Brava, this is a pleasant densely wooded course with its fairways bordered by mature pines and palm trees. The clubhouse is built in Andalucian style and boasts a swimming pool. *SSS 68*

GF $

1919

18

Mondays

 —

L 5139 P 69

S

Required : Handicap Certificate
Best days : Weekdays

HOLE	LENGTH MEDAL-TEE	PAR	STROKE INDEX
1	323	4	8
2	327	4	16
3	163	3	14
4	455	5	2
5	298	4	12
6	303	4	10
7	251	4	18
8	319	4	6
9	340	4	4
TOTAL	2779	36	TOTAL

HOLE	LENGTH MEDAL-TEE	PAR	STROKE INDEX
10	159	3	13
11	276	4	9
12	172	3	15
13	300	4	11
14	123	3	17
15	337	4	3
16	294	4	5
17	182	3	7
18	517	5	1
TOTAL	2360	33	TOTAL

SAN-SEBASTIAN

★

TEL : (943)616845
LOCATION : 14 km San-Sebastian/
3 km Irun
ADDRESS : Apartado 6 – 20280 Hondarribi
HOTEL :
Residencia Jaurequi – Fuenterrabia
Tel : (943)641400
Pampinot – Fuentarrabia
Tel : (943)640600
Parador El Emperador – Fuentarrabia
Tel : (943)642140
RESTAURANT : Rámon Rotéta –
Fuenterrabia
Tel : (943)641693

Laid out in the verdant Basque country near the seaside resort of Fuenterrabia, the course follows the gentle undulations of the lush foothills of the Jaizquibel mountains in the Pyrenees. Spain's most recent golf prodigy José Maria Olazabal began his career here, being the son of the greenkeeper and is now an honorary member of the club. *SSS 71*

GF $ — 1910 — 18

— P. Hirigoyen — L 5739 P 72

R S

Required : Handicap Certificate
Best days : Weekdays only

HOLE	LENGTH MEDAL-TEE	PAR	STROKE INDEX
1	336	4	8
2	331	4	11
3	448	5	3
4	144	3	15
5	393	4	4
6	235	4	17
7	404	4	1
8	153	3	16
9	435	5	2
TOTAL	2879	36	TOTAL

HOLE	LENGTH MEDAL-TEE	PAR	STROKE INDEX
10	243	4	18
11	435	5	5
12	128	3	12
13	403	4	2
14	326	4	9
15	336	4	14
16	454	5	13
17	370	4	7
18	165	3	6
TOTAL	2860	36	TOTAL

SANTA PONSA

TEL : (971)690211/690800
LOCATION : 2 km Santa Ponsa
ADDRESS : Santa Ponsa-Calvia – Mallorca
HOTEL :
Santa Ponsa
Tel : (971)690211
Galatzo – Paguera
Tel : (971)690861
Villamil – Paguera
Tel : (971)686050

The course was designed by Folco Nardi and redesigned by the famous Spanish amateur golf champion, Pepé Gancedo. A fine holiday golf course on Majorca set near the sea front of the scenic Bay of Santa Ponsa. Laid out on rolling countryside and surrounded by low wooded hills, the course has an attractive layout. It features one of the longest holes in the world, the 590m 10th (from champ. tee). The pleasant clubhouse is built high up overlooking the course and the Bay. The Santa Ponsa Hotel with 18 bedrooms is situated close to the course. *SSS 72*

GF $

1976

18

—

F. Nardi, P. Gancedo

L 6170 P 72

R S

Required : Handicap Certificate
Best days : Any day

HOLE	LENGTH MEDAL-TEE	PAR	STROKE INDEX
1	390	4	8
2	500	5	2
3	150	3	18
4	400	4	6
5	300	4	12
6	440	5	4
7	160	3	16
8	350	4	14
9	380	4	10
TOTAL	3070	36	TOTAL

HOLE	LENGTH MEDAL-TEE	PAR	STROKE INDEX
10	560	5	1
11	340	4	15
12	200	3	9
13	440	5	3
14	350	4	11
15	150	3	17
16	370	4	7
17	300	4	13
18	390	4	5
TOTAL	3100	36	TOTAL

SON VIDA

TEL : (971)791210
LOCATION : 5 km NW. Palma
ADDRESS : Urbanizacion Son Vida – Palma 13 – 07013 Palma de Mallorca
HOTEL : HP
Son Vida Sheraton
Tel : (971)790000
Maricel – C'as Catala
Tel : (971)402712
Valparaiso Palace – La Bonanova
Tel : (971)400411
RESTAURANT : El Pato – Palma
Tel : (971)791210

Five kilometres from Palma de Mallorca, the golf course is situated within Mallorca's most exclusive estate 'Son Vida'. Though rather short, it demands accuracy from tee to green. Many of the fairways are narrow with doglegs, strategic trees and bunkers. There are two water hazards on the 16th and 18th holes. The world famous Son Vida Hotel (Sheraton member), a castle dating back to the 13th century, stands in tropical gardens on high ground overlooking the Palma Bay. The hotel with 175 rooms is sumptuously decorated, and equipped with swimming pools, riding school and tennis courts. The new 4 star Arabella Golf Hotel will be ready in 1991. *SSS 68*

GF $ — 1964 — F. Hawtree — 18 — L 5705 P 72

S — RP

Required : Handicap Certificate
Best days : Any day

HOLE	LENGTH MEDAL-TEE	PAR	STROKE INDEX
1	264	4	13
2	354	4	5
3	369	4	1
4	147	3	17
5	368	4	7
6	457	5	3
7	307	4	9
8	133	3	15
9	312	4	11
TOTAL	2705	35	TOTAL

HOLE	LENGTH MEDAL-TEE	PAR	STROKE INDEX
10	273	4	12
11	493	5	2
12	142	3	16
13	507	5	10
14	288	4	14
15	324	4	8
16	133	3	18
17	375	4	4
18	465	5	6
TOTAL	3000	37	TOTAL

SOTOGRANDE-OLD COURSE

TEL : (956)792050/51
LOCATION : 30 km Gibraltar
ADDRESS : Apartado 14 – Sotogrande – Cádiz
HOTEL : HP
Sotogrande
Tel : (956)792100/792050

The Old Course counts among the world's greatest golf courses attracting golfers worldwide. Designed by Robert Trent Jones, it is set on a splendid natural landscape near the sea, backed by the Bermeja mountains and overlooking the Rock of Gibraltar to the African coastline. It has a spectacular and challenging layout incorporating long dogleg holes, enormous bunkers and picturesque water hazards. Most of the fast greens are elevated and well-defended. Pine, cork and olive trees are strategically scattered over the course. The Sotogrande Club Hotel, the fine clubhouse and the elegant beach club are situated on the course only 250m from the sea. *SSS 74*

GF $$ — 1964 — 27

— R. Trent Jones — L 6298 P 72, 1299 P 29

S — RP

Required : Handicap Certificate
Best days : Any day

HOLE	LENGTH MEDAL-TEE	PAR	STROKE INDEX
1	360	4	7
2	482	5	1
3	310	4	17
4	209	3	13
5	330	4	11
6	473	5	3
7	386	4	5
8	185	3	15
9	332	4	9
TOTAL	3067	36	TOTAL

HOLE	LENGTH MEDAL-TEE	PAR	STROKE INDEX
10	414	4	4
11	332	4	14
12	538	5	2
13	190	3	16
14	460	5	10
15	390	4	6
16	355	4	12
17	154	3	18
18	398	4	8
TOTAL	3231	36	TOTAL

SOTOGRANDE-VALDERRAMA

★★★

TEL : (956)792775/792750
LOCATION : 30 km Gibraltar
ADDRESS : Apartado 1 – Sotogrande – Cádiz
HOTEL :
Sotogrande – Sotogrande
Tel : (956)792050/792100

The former Las Aves golf club is the newer of the two Sotogrande championship courses, having been founded in 1975. Its holes, set on rolling terrain, cut through strategically placed cork trees backed by low and well-wooded hills. The fairways are quite narrow and cunningly bunkered. Feature holes include the 14th with its double greens protected by a lake and a waterfall with a stream to the right of the green. Many more changes to the course are taking place under the guidance of Robert Trent Jones and the club is now the 'Home' of the Volvo Masters. There is a spacious clubhouse. *SSS 72*

GF $$

1975

18

—

R. Trent Jones

L 5974 P 72

S

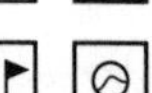

Required : Handicap Certificate
Best days : Any day

HOLE	LENGTH MEDAL-TEE	PAR	STROKE INDEX
1	337	4	7
2	355	4	9
3	141	3	17
4	490	5	3
5	330	4	13
6	139	3	5
7	445	5	15
8	293	4	11
9	400	4	1
TOTAL	2930	36	TOTAL

HOLE	LENGTH MEDAL-TEE	PAR	STROKE INDEX
10	346	4	14
11	484	5	18
12	188	3	2
13	340	4	12
14	314	4	10
15	184	3	16
16	354	4	8
17	491	5	16
18	397	4	4
TOTAL	3098	36	TOTAL

TENERIFE

TEL : (922)251048/251236
LOCATION : 7 km W. La Laguna
ADDRESS : Apartado 125 – La Laguna – Tenerife – Islas Canarias
HOTEL :
Mencey – Santa Cruz de Tenerife
Tel : (922)276700
Botanico – Puerto de la Cruz
Tel : (922)381400
Colon Rambla – Santa Cruz de Tenerife
Tel : (922)272550
RESTAURANT : La Riviera – Santa Cruz de Tenerife
Tel : (922)275812

A pleasant short golf course picturesquely set on undulating ground within an orange grove on the island of Tenerife, part of the Canary Islands. It is ideal for holiday golf with several first-class hotels nearby. *SSS 68*

GF $

1932

18

—

A. Alberto, A. Lucena, J. Laynez, A. Yanez

L 5151 P 68

R S

Required : Handicap Certificate
Best days : Weekdays only

HOLE	LENGTH MEDAL-TEE	PAR	STROKE INDEX
1	201	3	9
2	381	4	5
3	227	3	3
4	306	4	11
5	267	4	17
6	372	4	1
7	453	4	13
8	228	5	7
9	313	3	15
TOTAL	2748	34	TOTAL

HOLE	LENGTH MEDAL-TEE	PAR	STROKE INDEX
10	180	3	14
11	339	4	16
12	443	5	2
13	182	3	10
14	135	3	18
15	328	4	8
16	193	3	4
17	349	4	6
18	500	5	12
TOTAL	2649	34	TOTAL

TERRAMAR

TEL : (93)8940580/8942043
LOCATION : In Sitges, 37 km Barcelona
ADDRESS : Apartado 6 – Sitges – Barcelona
HOTEL :
Terramar – Sitges
Tel : (93)8940050
Calipolis – Sitges
Tel : (93)8941500
Romantic y la Renaixença – Sitges
Tel : (93)8940643
RESTAURANT : El Greco – Sitges
Tel : (93)8942906

Located in the popular seaside resort of Sitges on the Costa Brava, this is a fine holiday golf course set on a typical Mediterranean landscape among pine and cork trees, bordering the sea. The course is cut in two by a river, thus separating the first five holes from the others. The only water hazard on the course is a small lake near the green of the 11th hole. There is a Catalan style clubhouse with tennis courts. *SSS 69*

GF $
1922
18
—
F. Hawtree
L 5486 P 70

Required : Handicap Certificate
Best days : Weekdays

HOLE	LENGTH MEDAL-TEE	PAR	STROKE INDEX
1	350	4	3
2	435	5	11
3	240	4	13
4	300	4	7
5	167	3	15
6	390	4	1
7	159	3	17
8	460	5	9
9	370	4	5
TOTAL	2871	36	TOTAL

HOLE	LENGTH MEDAL-TEE	PAR	STROKE INDEX
10	360	4	8
11	340	4	12
12	332	4	4
13	149	3	18
14	281	4	14
15	315	4	6
16	148	3	16
17	365	4	2
18	325	4	10
TOTAL	2615	34	TOTAL

TORREQUEBRADA

TEL : (952)442742
LOCATION : 10 km Torremolinos
N 340/E 26
ADDRESS : Apartado 67 – 29630
Benalmadena-Málaga
HOTEL :
Hacienda Torrequebrada – Benalmadena
Tel : (952)442740
Los Patos – Benalmadena Costa
Tel : (952)441990
Riviera – Benalmadena Costa
Tel : (952)441240
RESTAURANT : El Molino de la Torre – Torremolinos *Tel :* (952)387756

Designed by Spain's most famous amateur champion, Pepé Gancedo, this is a sporting and spectacular inland course requiring a great deal of accuracy. Spectacularly set on the Costa del Sol with the fairways cutting along rugged valleys, it has mountains on one side and the sea on the other. Strategically placed lakes, cork and pine trees serve as hazards. There is a spacious and modern clubhouse with a swimming pool, tennis and squash courts. *SSS 70*

GF $$

1976

18

—

P. Gancedo

L 5473 P 72

  S

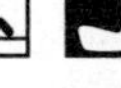

Required : Handicap Certificate
Best days : Any day

HOLE	LENGTH MEDAL-TEE	PAR	STROKE INDEX
1	439	5	9
2	307	4	6
3	78	3	18
4	285	4	12
5	331	4	15
6	471	5	4
7	291	4	13
8	335	4	3
9	131	3	17
TOTAL	2668	36	TOTAL

HOLE	LENGTH MEDAL-TEE	PAR	STROKE INDEX
10	361	4	2
11	141	3	14
12	435	5	5
13	128	3	16
14	436	5	7
15	306	4	10
16	358	4	1
17	337	4	8
18	303	4	11
TOTAL	2805	36	TOTAL

VALLROMANAS

TEL : (93)5680362
LOCATION : 25 km Barcelona A 19
ADDRESS : Apartado 43 – Montornes del Valles-Barcelona 6
HOTEL :
Grand Derby – Barcelona
Tel : (93)3223215
Diplomatic – Barcelona
Tel : (93)3173100
Majestic – Barcelona
Tel : (93)2154512
RESTAURANT : Jaume de Provença – Barcelona
Tel : (93)2300029

A fine golf course with an attractive layout, set inland on the Costa Brava and backed by wooded hills. There is a fine Catalan style clubhouse equipped with sauna, gymnasium, a large swimming pool and four tennis courts. *SSS 71*

GF $ — Tuesdays — S
1969 — F. Hawtree
18 — L 5878 P 72 — R

Required : Handicap Certificate
Best days : Weekdays

HOLE	LENGTH MEDAL-TEE	PAR	STROKE INDEX
1	339	4	6
2	159	3	18
3	332	4	4
4	487	5	12
5	300	4	14
6	323	4	10
7	162	3	16
8	325	4	2
9	451	5	8
TOTAL	2878	36	TOTAL

HOLE	LENGTH MEDAL-TEE	PAR	STROKE INDEX
10	401	4	1
11	474	5	7
12	165	3	17
13	265	4	11
14	328	4	13
15	333	4	5
16	497	5	9
17	174	3	15
18	363	4	3
TOTAL	3000	36	TOTAL

VILLA MARTIN

TEL : (965)6760350
LOCATION : 8 km Torrevieja
ADDRESS : Apartado 35 – Torrevieja-Alicante
HOTEL :
La Zenia – Torrevieja
Tel : (965)320200
Montepiedra – Dehesa de Campoamor
Tel : (96)5320300
Torrejoven – Torrevieja
Tel : (96)5714052
RESTAURANT : Miramar – Torrevieja
Tel : (965)710765

Located in the popular holiday region of Alicante, the golf lies alongside the sea on fairly undulating countryside. Many of the fairways are lined with palm, cork and pine trees. Among its feature holes is the short 9th with a pond cutting the hole in two parts. *SSS 72*

GF $

1972

18

—

Ibergolf

L 6132 P 72

S

R

Required : Handicap Certificate
Best days : Weekdays

HOLE	LENGTH MEDAL-TEE	PAR	STROKE INDEX
1	480	5	4
2	355	4	6
3	340	4	8
4	331	4	12
5	460	5	2
6	183	3	10
7	303	4	16
8	328	4	14
9	147	3	18
TOTAL	2927	36	TOTAL

HOLE	LENGTH MEDAL-TEE	PAR	STROKE INDEX
10	315	4	11
11	445	5	7
12	380	4	3
13	180	3	15
14	515	5	1
15	315	4	17
16	370	4	9
17	210	3	13
18	380	4	5
TOTAL	3110	36	TOTAL

Car Rental

Reservation/Information telephone number :

Country code :
46

Telephone number :
8/6795280

Headquarters address :

EUROPCAR - EUROPEISK BILUTHYRNING
P.O. box 7545, 10393 Stockholm
Tel. : (46) 8/6137200
Telex : 11565
Fax : (46) 8/6114360

210 GOLF COURSES, 260 000 PLAYERS

★★★ Great golf course
★★ Very good golf course
$ 100-150 SEK
★ Recommended golf course
☼ Holiday golf course
$ $ more than 200 SEK

TOWN	GOLF COURSE		TEL	MAP REF.
Abbekas	Abbekias		(0411) 33490	•
Alfta	Alfta-Edsbyns		(0271) 11626	•
Ålingsas	Ålingsas		(0322) 52421	119
Ålmhult	Ålmhult		(0476) 14135	•
Almunge	Almunge		(0175) 73280	•
Alvkarleby	Alvkarleby		(026) 72757	•
Åmal	Forsbacka		(0532) 43055	25
Ängelholm	Ängelholm		(0431) 30260	102
Arvika	Arvika		(0570) 54133	•
Åskersund	Åskersund		(0583) 34442	•
Åtvidaberg	Åtvidaberg	★	(0120) 11425	4
Avesta	Avesta		(0226) 10866	•
Båstad	Båstad	★★	(0431) 73136	6
	Bjäre		(0431) 61053	6
	Okagardens		(0431) 61313	•
Björkliden	Björkliden		(0980) 40040	•
Boden	Boden		(0921) 61071	•
Bollnäs	Bollnäs		(0278) 50540	•
	Söraker		(0278) 13450	•
Borås	Borås	★	(033) 50142	10
	Hulta	★	(033) 88180	33
Borgholm	Öland		(0485) 11200	•
Borlänge	Falun-Borlänge		(023) 31015	22
Bro	Bro-Balsta		(0758) 41300	108
Deje	Forshaga		(0552) 11440	•
Eksjö	Eksjö		(0381) 13525	16
Emmaboda	Emmaboda		(0471) 20505	•
Enköping	Enköping		(0171) 20830	109
Eskilstuna	Eskilstuna		(016) 142629	17
	Torshälla		(016) 358722	•
Eslöv	Eslöv		(0413) 18610	18
Fagersta	Fagersta		(0223) 54060	•

TOWN	GOLF COURSE		TEL	MAP REF.
Falkenberg	Falkenberg	★	(0346) 50287	19
Falköping	Falköping		(0515) 31270	20
Falsterbo	Falsterbo	★★★ ☼	(040) 475078	21
	Flommens	★★ ☼	(040) 475016	24
	Ljunghusen	★★ ☼	(040) 450384	50
Filipstad	Saxå		(0590) 13827	•
Finspang	Finspang		(0122) 13940	•
Fiskebäckskil	Skaftö		(0523) 22544	•
Fjällbacka	Fjällbacka	☼	(0525) 31150	23
Flen	Flens		(0157) 10204	•
Gällivare	Gällivare		(0970) 10660	•
Gävle	Gävle		(026) 113163	26
Gislaved	Isaberg	☼	(0370) 36330	35
Göteborg	Albatross	★ ☼	(031) 551901	2
	Delsjö	★ ☼	(031) 406959	13
	Göteborg	★★ ☼	(031) 282444	27
	Oijared	★ ☼	(0302) 30604	57
	Stora Lundby		(0302) 44200	101
Gullspang	Ribbingsfors		(0551) 21225	•
Hagfors	Uddeholm		(0563) 60335	86
Halmstad	Bäckavattnet		(035) 44271	103
	Halmstad	★★★	(035) 30077	29
	Ringenäs		(035) 59050	123
Handen	Haninge		(0750) 32240	110
Härnösand	Härnösand		(0611) 66169	121
Helsingborg	Helsingborg		(042) 236147	•
	Rya	☼	(042) 220182	66
	Söderåsen		(042) 73337	70
	Vasatorps	★	(042) 235058	92
Hjo	Hökensas		(0503) 16059	31
Hofors	Hofors		(0290) 85125	•
Hok	Hooks	☼	(0393) 21420	32
Höör	Bosjökloster		(0413) 25858	11
Hudiksvall	Hudiksvall		(0650) 15930	•
Jönköping	A6		(036) 175060	125
	Jönköping	★★	(036) 76567	36
Kalmar	Kalmar	★	(0480) 72111	37
Karlshamn	Karlshamn		(0454) 50085	38
Karlskoga	Karlskoga		(0586) 28597	39
Karlskrona	Carlskrona		(0455) 35251	12
Karlstad	Karlstad	★	(054) 36406	40
Katrineholm	Katrineholm		(0150) 39012/11	41
Kil	Kils		(0554) 12701	•
Kinna	Marks		(0320) 14220	99
Klövsjö	Klövsjö Vemdalen		(0682) 21434	•
Köping	Korlöt		(0221) 81090	112
Kopparberg	Stjernfors		(0580) 41048	•
Kristianstad	Kristianstad	★	(044) 240656	42
	Ö. Göinge		(044) 60060	•
	Skepparslöv		(044) 229031	111
Kristinehamn	Kristinehamn		(0550) 82310	•
Kungälv	Gullbringa	☼	(0303) 27161	28
	Lysegarden	★★	(0303) 23426	53
Kungsbacka	Forsgarden		(0300) 13649	126
	Kungsbacka	★	(031) 936277	43
Laholm	Laholm		(0430) 30601	44
	Slite		(0498) 26071	•
Landskrona	Landskrona	★★	(0418) 19528	45
Leksand	Leksand		(0247) 10922	100
Lidköping	Lidköping	★★	(0510) 46122	47
Lindesberg	Linde		(0581) 13960	114
Linköping	Landeryd		(013) 151504	127
	Linköping	★	(013) 120646	49
Ljungby	Lagan	★	(0372) 30450	106
Ljungskile	Lyckorna	★	(0522) 20176	52
Ljusdal	Ljusdal *(ext. to 18 h.)*		(0651) 14366	•
Ljusnedal	Härjedalsfjällen		(0684) 21100	120
Ludvika	Hagge		(0240) 28087	•
Luleå	Luleå		(0920) 56174	122
Lund	Lunds Akademisca	★★	(046) 99005	51
Malmö	Barsebäck	★★ ☼	(046) 776230	5
	Bokskogen	★★ ☼	(040) 481004	9

TOWN	GOLF COURSE		TEL	MAP REF.
	Hylliekroken		(040) 160262	•
	Malmö	✡	(040) 292535	115
Mardaklev	Atradalens		(0325) 50280	•
Mariestad	Mariestad		(0501) 17383	105
Mjölby	Mjölby		(0142) 12570	•
Mölle	Mölle	★	(042) 47012	54
Mora	Mora	✡	(0250) 10182	116
Motala	Motala	✡	(0141) 50856	55
Norrköping	Norrköping		(011) 35235	56
Norrtalje	Roslagens		(0176) 37194	65
Nybro	Nybro		(0480) 55044	•
Nyköping	Årila	★★	(0155) 14967	3
Nynäshamn	Körunda	✡	(0752) 38666	104
Örebro	Örebro	★	(019) 91065	58
	Mosjö		(019) 225780	129
Örnsköldsvik	Öviks Puttom		(0660) 64070	61
Oskarhamn	Oskarhamn		(0491) 94033	•
Östersund	Östersund	✡	(063) 43001	60
Partille	Partille		(031) 987004	113
Perstorp	Perstorp		(0435) 35411	62
Piteå	Piteå		(0911) 14990	•
Rättvik	Rättviks	✡	(0248) 10773	63
Ronneby	Ronneby		(0457) 13212	•
Rydö	Rydö		(0345) 21046	•
Säffle	Billerud		(0555) 91313	7
Sala	Sala		(0224) 53077	124
Sälen	Sälens		(0280) 33700	•
Sandviken	Högbo		(026) 45015	30
Sigtuna	Sigtunabygden		(0760) 54012	68
Simrishamn	Österlens	✡	(0414) 24230	59
Skellefteå	Skellefteå	★★★	(0910) 79333	69
Skövde	Billingen		(0511) 80291	8
Slite	Slite		(0498) 26071	•
Söderhamn	Söderhamn		(0270) 51300	71
Söderköping	Söderköping		(011) 70579	107
Södertalje	Södertalje		(0755) 38240	72
Sollefteå	Sollefteå-Långsele	★	(0620) 21477	75
Sölvesborg	Sölvesborg		(0456) 70650	130
St.Ibb	St.Ibb		(046) 776320	•
Stånga	När		(0497) 92131	•
Stockholm & Suburbs	Ågesta		(08) 645641	1
	Björkhagen		(08) 7730431	•
	Djursholm	★	(08) 7551598	14
	Drottningholm	★★★	(08) 7590311	15
	Ingäro		(0766) 28244	34
	Lidingö	★	(08) 7657911	46
	Lindö		(0762) 72260	48
	Osteraker		(0764) 85190	131
	Saltsjöbaden	★	(08) 7170125	67
	Sollentuna		(08) 7543625	74
	Stockholm	★★	(08) 7550031	77
	Täby		(0762) 23261	79
	Ullna	★★★	(0762) 26106	87
	Viksjö		(0758) 16708	95
	Wermdö	★★	(0766) 20849	97
Strängnäs	Strängnäs		(0152) 14731	78
Strömstad	Strömstad		(0526) 11788	•
Sundsvall	Sundsvall	✡	(060) 561030	75
	Timra		(060) 570153	128
Sunne	Sunne		(0565) 60300	•
Töreboda	Töreboda		(0506) 16240	•
Torekov	Torekovs	✡	(0431) 63572	81
Torshälla	Nyby Bruks		(016) 358722	•
Tranås	Tranås		(0140) 11661	83
Trelleborg	Bedinge		(0410) 25514	•
	Trelleborg	✡	(0410) 30460	84
Trollhättans	Ekarna		(0514) 11450	•
	Trollhättan	★	(0520) 41000	85
Trosa	Trosa-Vagnhärad		(0156) 16020	•
Tyringe	Hässleholm		(0451) 53111	117
Uddevalla	Torreby		(0524) 21109	82
Ulricehamn	Ulricehamn		(0321) 10021	88

TOWN	GOLF COURSE		TEL	MAP REF.
Umeå	Umeå		(090) 41071	•
Upsala	Kabo		(018) 696667	•
	Upsala	★★	(018) 461270	89
Vadstena	Vadstena		(0143) 12440	•
Vänersborg	Onsjö		(0521) 64149	118
Vara Bjertorp	Vara Bjertorp		(0512) 20261	132
Varberg	Varberg		(0340) 37470	90
Värnamo	Värnamo		(0370) 23123	91
Västerås	Angsö		(0171) 41012	93
	Frösaker		(021) 25024	93
	Västerås		(021) 357543	93
Västervik	Västervik		(0490) 19417	•
Växjö	Växjö		(0470) 21539	94
Veberod	Romeleåsens		(046) 82012	69
Vetlanda	Vetlanda		(0383) 18310	•
Vimmerby	Tobo	✡	(0492) 30346	80
Vingåker	Vingåker		(0151) 13136	•
Visby	Gotska		(0498) 15545	•
	Visby	✡	(0498) 45058	96
Vittsjö	Vittsjö		(0451) 22635	98
Ystad	Ystad	✡	(0411) 50350	84

NEW GOLF COURSES (18 HOLES OR MORE) TO OPEN SOON

Arvika Golfklubb
67101 Arvika 1
Tel. : (0570)54133

Askersunds Golfklubb
69603 Ammeberg
Tel. : (0583)34442

Botkyrka Golfklubb
14032 Grödinge
Tel. : (0753)29080

Gränna Golfklubb
56300 Gränna
Tel. : (0390)11347

Haverdals Golfklubb
31040 Harplinge
Tel. : (035) 50224

Kumla Golfklubb
69200 Kumla
Tel. : (019)77370

Lidhem Golfklubb
36014 Väckelsang
Tel. : (0470) 33660

Mölndals Golfklubb
43124 Mölndal
Tel. : (031)994900

Nybro Golfklubb
38200 Nybro
Tel. : (0480)55044

Olands Golfklubb
38700 Borgholm
Tel. : (0485) 11200

Orust Golfklubb
44080 Ellös
Tel. : (0304)53170

Ringenäs Golfklubb
30591 Halmstad
Tel. : (035) 59050

Ronneby Golfklubb
37201 Ronneby
Tel. : (0457)13212

Sala Golfklubb
73300 Sala
Tel. : (0224)53077

Säters Golfklubb
78300 Säters
Tel. : (0225) 50030

Skogaby Golfklubb
31293 Laholm
Tel. : (0430) 60078

Strömstad Golfklubb
45201 Strömstad
Tel. : (0526)11788

Uddeholms Golfklubb
68303 Rada
Tel. : (0563) 60335

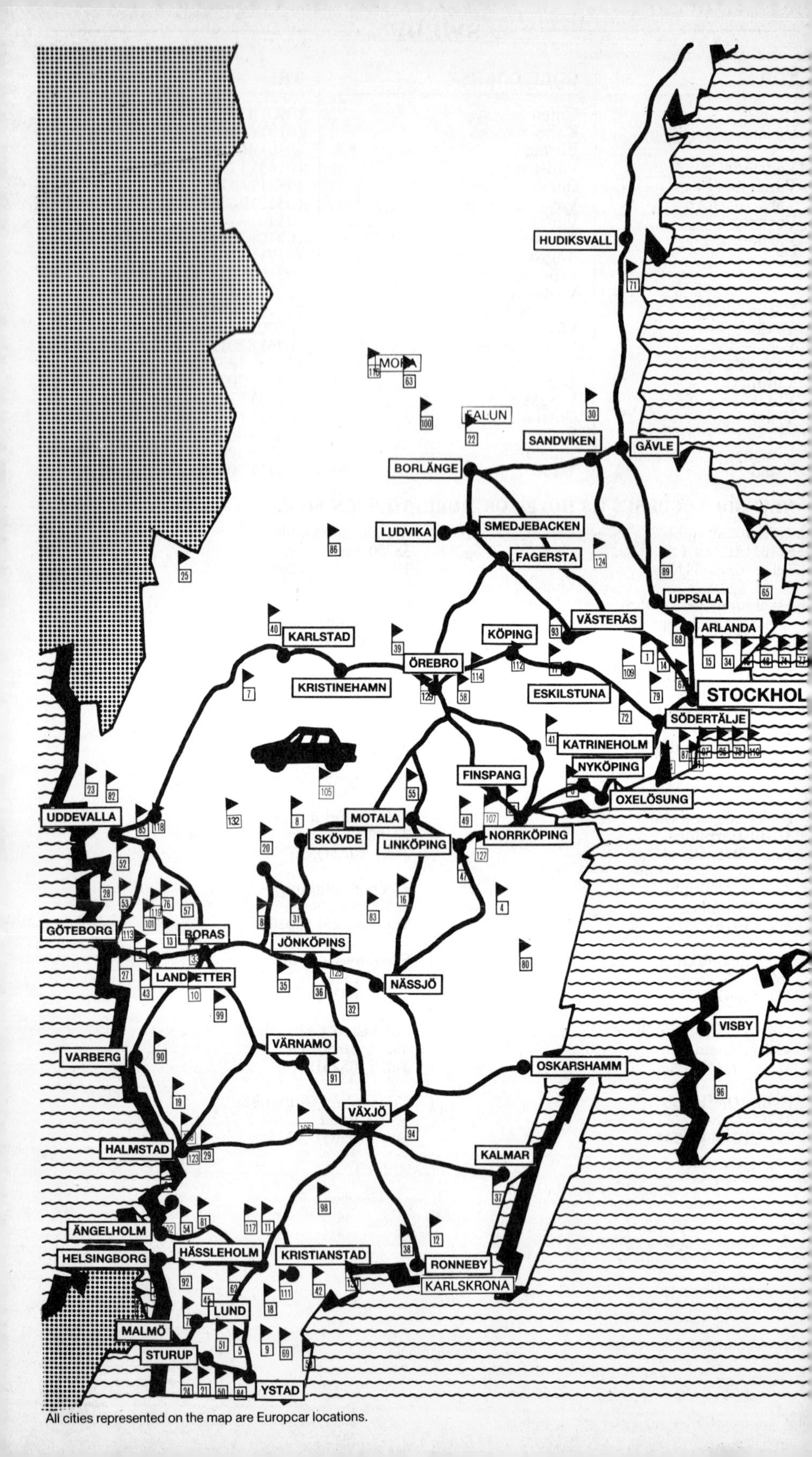

All cities represented on the map are Europcar locations.

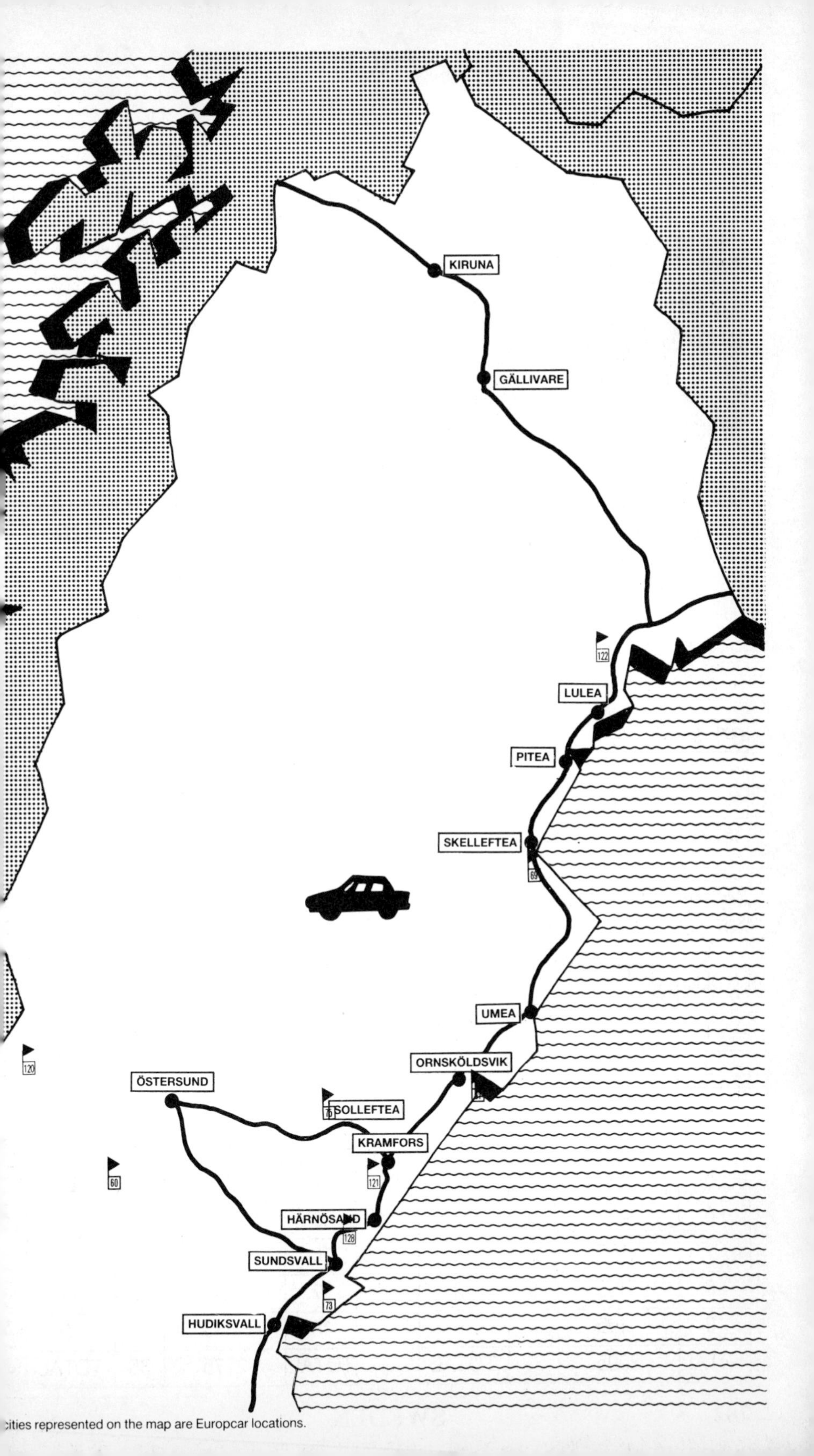

cities represented on the map are Europcar locations.

A6

TEL : (036)175606
LOCATION : 2 km Jönköping A 6
ADDRESS : Box 11025– 55011 Jönköping
HOTEL :
John Bauer - Jönköping
Tel : (036)100500
Klosterkungen - Jönköping
Tel : (036)100800
Concept - Huskvarna
Tel : (036)132810

Situated in unspoilt hilly countryside in Eastern Sweden, this popular course with its sloping fairways runs through forests over ravines and features large Scottish style greens. Another nine holes are planned for 1991.

GF $

1989

18

December to April

P. Nordvall

L 5770 P 72

S

R

Required : Handicap Certificate
Best days : Mondays, Wednesdays and Fridays

HOLE	LENGTH MEDAL-TEE	PAR	STROKE INDEX
1	440	5	12
2	270	4	8
3	365	4	4
4	310	4	16
5	135	3	18
6	430	5	10
7	155	3	14
8	495	5	2
9	395	4	6
TOTAL	2995	37	TOTAL

HOLE	LENGTH MEDAL-TEE	PAR	STROKE INDEX
10	140	3	13
11	350	4	7
12	325	4	3
13	130	3	17
14	350	4	11
15	565	5	1
16	335	4	5
17	135	3	15
18	445	5	9
TOTAL	2775	35	TOTAL

AGESTA

TEL : (08)6045641
LOCATION : 3 km Farsta
ADDRESS : Agesta – 12352 Farsta
HOTEL :
Agesta Kursgard – Agesta
Tel : (08)940425
Sjofarts – Stockholm
Tel : (08)226960

Situated in the Stockholm region, the course is laid out on gently rolling countryside, with its fairways meandering through meadows and luxuriant woodland. There is an easy nine hole course, ideal for beginners. *SSS 72*

GF $ — November to May — R S

1958 — J. Sederholm 

27 — L 5705 P 72, 3660 P 36 

Required : Handicap Certificate
Best days : Weekdays

HOLE	LENGTH MEDAL-TEE	PAR	STROKE INDEX
1	285	4	15
2	300	4	9
3	130	3	17
4	495	5	3
5	175	3	13
6	350	4	1
7	310	4	5
8	470	5	7
9	310	4	11
TOTAL	2825	36	TOTAL

HOLE	LENGTH MEDAL-TEE	PAR	STROKE INDEX
10	430	5	10
11	160	3	14
12	310	4	8
13	380	4	2
14	440	5	6
15	330	4	16
16	335	4	4
17	135	3	18
18	360	4	12
TOTAL	2880	36	TOTAL

ALBATROSS

★

TEL : (031)551901
LOCATION : 9 km Göteborg E 6
ADDRESS : Lillhagsvägen – 42250 Hisings Backa
HOTEL :
Stenungsbaden – Stenungsund
Tel : (0303)83100
Scandic – Göteborg
Tel : (031)520060
Ramada – Göteborg
Tel : (031)222420
RESTAURANT : Fars Hat – Kungalv
Tel : (0303)10970

Located in the western part of Sweden near the coast, the Albatross championship course is a fine undulating parkland course with numerous small ponds and streams serving as hazards on about eleven holes. *SSS 72*

GF $$

1973

18

—

L. Andreasson

L 5785 P 72

S

R

Required : Handicap Certificate
Best days : Tuesdays, Wednesdays

HOLE	LENGTH MEDAL-TEE	PAR	STROKE INDEX
1	390	4	3
2	360	4	1
3	455	5	13
4	125	3	15
5	330	4	11
6	340	4	5
7	440	5	17
8	180	3	7
9	305	4	9
TOTAL	2925	36	TOTAL

HOLE	LENGTH MEDAL-TEE	PAR	STROKE INDEX
10	125	3	18
11	465	5	12
12	120	3	16
13	280	4	10
14	285	4	14
15	370	4	6
16	365	4	2
17	475	5	8
18	375	4	4
TOTAL	2860	36	TOTAL

ALINGSÅS

TEL : (0322)52421
LOCATION : 5 km Alingsås rd 180
ADDRESS : Hjälmared 4050-44195 Alingsås
HOTEL :
Scandic-Alingsås
Tel : (0322)14000

The Alingsås golf course, inaugurated in 1988, lies in the western part of Sweden, not far from Göteborg, in a fine holiday area boasting some of Sweden's finest golf courses. It is set in flat countryside amidst trees, with water affecting play on several holes. An attractive feature is the local style clubhouse. *SSS 71*

GF $ | November to April | S
1988 | J. Sederholm
18 | L 5600 P 71 | R

Required : Handicap Certificate
Best days : Weekdays

HOLE	LENGTH MEDAL-TEE	PAR	STROKE INDEX
1	485	5	5
2	355	4	3
3	155	3	11
4	500	5	1
5	315	4	13
6	185	3	15
7	265	4	17
8	310	4	9
9	335	4	7
TOTAL	2905	36	TOTAL

HOLE	LENGTH MEDAL-TEE	PAR	STROKE INDEX
10	340	4	6
11	520	5	2
12	305	4	14
13	165	3	12
14	310	4	8
15	160	3	16
16	290	4	10
17	140	3	18
18	465	5	4
TOTAL	2695	35	TOTAL

ÄNGELHOLM

TEL : (0431)30260
LOCATION : 10 km Ängelholm
ADDRESS : Box 1117 – 26222 Ängelholm
HOTEL :
Klitterbyn – Ängelholm
Tel : (0431)17180
Continental – Ängelholm
Tel : (0431)12700
Lilton – Ängelholm
Tel : (0431)82400.
RESTAURANT : Paletten – Ängelholm
Tel : (0431)82280

Founded in 1973, the course has been recently extended to 18 holes. It is a thickly wooded course, not far from the sea, laid out on fairly undulating terrain with strategic water hazards on more than fourteen holes. *SSS 72*

GF $ — December to March — S

1973 — J. Sederholm

18 — L 5760 P 72 — R

Required : Handicap Certificate
Best days : Weekdays

HOLE	LENGTH MEDAL-TEE	PAR	STROKE INDEX
1	445	5	9
2	310	4	17
3	440	5	15
4	175	3	3
5	330	4	5
6	340	4	7
7	350	4	1
8	160	3	11
9	445	5	13
TOTAL	2995	37	TOTAL

HOLE	LENGTH MEDAL-TEE	PAR	STROKE INDEX
10	365	4	2
11	355	4	4
12	160	3	12
13	495	5	6
14	140	3	16
15	330	4	14
16	450	5	10
17	135	3	18
18	335	4	8
TOTAL	2765	35	TOTAL

ÄNGSÖ

TEL : (0171)41012
LOCATION : 15 km E. Västeräs
ADDRESS : Skultunavägen 7-72217
Västeräs
HOTEL :
Park-Västeräs
Tel : (021)110120
Stads-Västeräs
Tel : (021)180420
Scandic-Västeräs
Tel : (021)180280

Extended to 18 holes, this golf course is located in Central Sweden near the scenic lake Angsösund and is laid out in flat parkland with the holes separated from each other by tall pine trees. Streams and creeks serve as water traps on most of the holes. *SSS 72*

GF $ — November to April 

1979  — 

18 — L 5825 P 72 

Required : Handicap Certificate
Best days : Any day

HOLE	LENGTH MEDAL-TEE	PAR	STROKE INDEX
1	345	4	13
2	330	4	5
3	170	3	15
4	315	4	7
5	460	5	3
6	305	4	9
7	522	5	1
8	335	4	17
9	125	3	11
TOTAL	2907	36	TOTAL

HOLE	LENGTH MEDAL-TEE	PAR	STROKE INDEX
10	510	5	2
11	300	4	18
12	160	3	16
13	440	5	10
14	330	4	6
15	145	3	8
16	323	4	14
17	345	4	4
18	365	4	12
TOTAL	2918	36	TOTAL

ÄRILA

★★

TEL : (0155)14967
LOCATION : 5 km Nyköping to Nävekvarn
ADDRESS : Nikolai – 61190 Nyköping
HOTEL :
Scandic – Nyköping
Tel : (0155)89000
Ankaret – Oxelösund
Tel : (0155)33020
Kompaniet – Nyköping
Tel : (0155)88020

Designed by two Swedish architects Nils Skold and Sune Linde, this fine championship layout is set on fairly undulating parkland, located in the eastern part of Sweden. Water mainly ditches, affects play on several holes. *SSS 72*

GF $

1951

18

November to May

N. Skold, S. Linde

L 6220 P 72

R S

Required : Handicap Certificate
Best days : Tuesdays, Fridays

HOLE	LENGTH MEDAL-TEE	PAR	STROKE INDEX
1	360	4	5
2	485	5	11
3	150	3	17
4	490	5	3
5	360	4	7
6	130	3	15
7	365	4	1
8	300	4	13
9	370	4	9
TOTAL	3010	36	TOTAL

HOLE	LENGTH MEDAL-TEE	PAR	STROKE INDEX
10	130	3	18
11	485	5	8
12	415	4	2
13	155	3	16
14	395	4	12
15	460	5	14
16	405	4	4
17	345	4	10
18	375	4	6
TOTAL	3165	36	TOTAL

ATVIDABERG

★

TEL : (0120)11425
LOCATION : 2 km Atvidaberg
ADDRESS : Stenhusgatan 25 A – 59700 Atvidaberg
HOTEL : HR
Trädgardshotellet
Tel : (0120)12800
Stallet – Atvidaberg
Tel : (0120)11940

This attractive traditional inland course is picturesquely laid out on rolling landscape partly running parallel to lake 'Bysjön'. Many of the fairways are lined by majestic oak trees. The charming Trädgardshotellet, a 'Relais and Châteaux' hotel, lies between the 1st and 18th hole, overlooking the lake. *SSS 72*

GF $$
1953
18

November to April
D. Brazier
L 5895 P 72

S
RP

Required : Handicap Certificate
Best days : Weekdays

HOLE	LENGTH MEDAL-TEE	PAR	STROKE INDEX
1	330	4	13
2	530	5	1
3	315	4	15
4	490	5	3
5	170	3	11
6	330	4	9
7	340	4	7
8	165	3	17
9	350	4	5
TOTAL	3020	36	TOTAL

HOLE	LENGTH MEDAL-TEE	PAR	STROKE INDEX
10	380	4	10
11	465	5	4
12	130	3	16
13	350	4	2
14	245	4	6
15	345	4	6
16	170	3	14
17	445	5	12
18	345	4	8
TOTAL	2875	36	TOTAL

BÄCKAVATTNETS

TEL : (035)44271
LOCATION : 13 km Halmstad R 25
ADDRESS : Box 173 – 30103 Halmstad
HOTEL :
Hallandia – Halmstad
Tel : (035)118800
Amadeus – Halmstad
Tel : (035)109770
Tallhojdens – Simlangsdalen
Tel : (035)70245
RESTAURANT : Martensson – Halmstad
Tel : (035)118070

The golf club is situated on Sweden's West Coast, not far from the seaside resort of Halmstad. Recently extended to 18 holes, the course is set on undulating woodland with several water hazards.

GF $

1980

18

November to April

A. Persson

L 5770 P 72

S

R

Required : Handicap Certificate
Best days : Weekdays

HOLE	LENGTH MEDAL-TEE	PAR	STROKE INDEX
1	450	5	13
2	375	4	7
3	325	4	9
4	450	5	11
5	475	5	3
6	135	3	15
7	365	4	5
8	350	4	1
9	130	3	17
TOTAL	3055	37	TOTAL

HOLE	LENGTH MEDAL-TEE	PAR	STROKE INDEX
10	320	4	12
11	360	4	8
12	330	4	14
13	340	4	2
14	320	4	10
15	125	3	18
16	460	5	4
17	315	4	6
18	145	3	16
TOTAL	2715	35	TOTAL

BARSEBÄCK

TEL : (046)776230
LOCATION : 14 km Landskrona
ADDRESS : Box 274-24022 Löddeköpinge
HOTEL : HP
Järavallen Country Club
Tel : (046)775803/775510
Chaplin – Landskrona
Tel : (0418)16335
Kronan – Landskrona
Tel : (0418)16225

One of the finest holiday courses in the southern part of Sweden is the Barsebäck golf course, designed by Thure Bruce and Donald Steel on typical Swedish landscape. It has a varied and entertaining layout and is set on the 'Oresund'(connecting the Baltic with the North Sea) with its 36 holes winding through woodland and parkland. The Järavallens Conference & Country Club Hotel with villas for rent, is adjacent to the course with tennis courts and a swimming pool. *SSS 72*

GF $$

December to March

 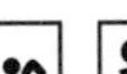 

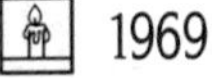
1969

T. Bruce, D. Steel

36

L 5900 P 72, 2860 P 36

Required : Handicap Certificate
Best days : Weekdays

HOLE	LENGTH MEDAL-TEE	PAR	STROKE INDEX
1	300	4	15
2	125	3	17
3	345	4	5
4	465	5	11
5	160	3	13
6	315	4	9
7	370	4	1
8	500	5	3
9	345	4	7
TOTAL	2925	36	TOTAL

HOLE	LENGTH MEDAL-TEE	PAR	STROKE INDEX
10	340	4	6
11	145	3	18
12	485	5	14
13	370	4	2
14	350	4	12
15	135	3	16
16	475	5	8
17	350	4	4
18	325	4	10
TOTAL	2975	36	TOTAL

BASTAD

TEL : (0431)73136
LOCATION : 4 km Bastad
ADDRESS : Box 1037 – 26901 Bastad
HOTEL :
Bastad – Bastad
Tel : (0431)72090
Borgen – Bastad
Tel : (0431)75080
Skansen – Bastad
Tel : (0431)72050
RESTAURANT : Havsbad – Bastad
Tel : (0431)71030

This beautiful course is one of the best inland courses in Sweden. Laid out on rolling parkland with mature trees flanking many of the fairways, the course is of championship standard and attracts many visitors in summer. Another 18 hole course is due to open in 1991. There is a stylish clubhouse. *SSS 71*

GF $$
1930
18

November to April
F. Hawtree, M. Taylor
L 5612 P 71

S

Required : Handicap Certificate
Best days : Weekdays (very busy in July)

HOLE	LENGTH MEDAL-TEE	PAR	STROKE INDEX
1	448	5	9
2	277	4	15
3	345	4	5
4	136	3	7
5	305	4	7
6	372	4	1
7	140	3	17
8	476	5	3
9	159	3	11
TOTAL	2658	35	TOTAL

HOLE	LENGTH MEDAL-TEE	PAR	STROKE INDEX
10	395	4	2
11	340	4	10
12	144	3	16
13	524	5	4
14	165	3	8
15	453	5	12
16	275	4	18
17	168	3	14
18	490	5	6
TOTAL	2954	36	TOTAL

BILLERUD

TEL : (0555)91313
LOCATION : 15 km Säffle rd 45 to Karlstad
ADDRESS : Box 192 – 66100 Säffle
HOTEL :
Bruks – Grums
Tel : (0555)10350
RESTAURANT : Pizzeria Serone – Säffle
Tel : (0533)16925

Located in Central Sweden not far from the Norwegian borders, the course is set beside water on undulating countryside with its fairways winding through luxuriant woodland. Several ponds serve as hazards. *SSS 72*

GF $

 November to May

S

 1961

N. Skold, D. Brazier

R

18

L 5874 P 72

Required : Handicap Certificate
Best days : Weekdays

HOLE	LENGTH MEDAL-TEE	PAR	STROKE INDEX
1	500	5	
2	143	3	
3	304	4	
4	343	4	
5	352	4	
6	158	3	
7	314	4	
8	477	5	
9	401	4	
TOTAL	2992	36	TOTAL

HOLE	LENGTH MEDAL-TEE	PAR	STROKE INDEX
10	340	4	
11	290	4	
12	144	3	
13	509	5	
14	312	4	
15	323	4	
16	464	5	
17	154	3	
18	346	4	
TOTAL	2882	36	TOTAL

BILLINGENS

TEL : (0511)80291
LOCATION : 20 km Skövde
ADDRESS : St-Kulhult – 54017 Lerdala
HOTEL :
Billingehus – Skövde
Tel : (0500)83000
Prisma – Skövde
Tel : (0500)88000
Vasterhojdsgarden – Skövde
Tel : (0500)13832
RESTAURANT : Hemgarden – Skövde
Tel : (0500)13832

This inland course is laid out on rolling, mostly open terrain with parts of it encircled by small woods. The average golfer won't find this rather short course too much of a test. *SSS 71*

GF $ | November to April | S
1948 | — | R
18 | L 5605 P 71

Required : Handicap Certificate
Best days : Weekdays

HOLE	LENGTH MEDAL-TEE	PAR	STROKE INDEX
1	290	4	15
2	170	3	5
3	440	5	17
4	360	4	7
5	170	3	13
6	350	4	3
7	370	4	1
8	340	4	9
9	460	5	11
TOTAL	2950	36	TOTAL

HOLE	LENGTH MEDAL-TEE	PAR	STROKE INDEX
10	155	3	10
11	450	5	8
12	145	3	16
13	360	4	2
14	320	4	6
15	350	4	4
16	135	3	14
17	300	4	12
18	440	5	18
TOTAL	2655	35	TOTAL

BJÄRE

TEL : (0431)61053
LOCATION : 5 km Båstad
ADDRESS : Salomonhög 3086 - 26900 Båstad
HOTEL :
Borgen - Båstad
Tel : (0431)75080
Hallands Rasta - Båstad
Tel : (0431)74270
Riviera - Båstad
Tel : (0431)76000

This welcoming golf course runs alongside a lake and follows the natural and sweeping undulations of the landscape. Mature trees and several ponds serve as obstacles. The club boasts a cosy and comfortable clubhouse which has an excellent restaurant. *SSS 71*

GF $ — November to April — S
1990 — S. Linde
18 — L 5543 P 71 — R

Required : Handicap Certificate
Best days : Any day

HOLE	LENGTH MEDAL-TEE	PAR	STROKE INDEX
1			
2			
3			
4			
5			
6			
7			
8			
9			7
TOTAL			TOTAL

HOLE	LENGTH MEDAL-TEE	PAR	STROKE INDEX
10			
11			
12			
13			
14			
15			
16			
17			
18			
TOTAL			TOTAL

BOKSKOGENS

★★

TEL : (040)481004
LOCATION : 15 km Malmö
ADDRESS : Box 30 – 230 40 Bara
HOTEL :
Alexandra – Malmö
Tel : (040)180900
Kramer – Malmö
Tel : (040)70120
Scandic – Malmö
Tel : (040)180120
RESTAURANT : Teater – Malmö
Tel : (040)77010

Designed by Anders Amilon, this fine championship course lies at the edge of a picturesque lake called the Yddinggesjön. Set in natural surroundings amongst beautiful beeches ('Bokskogen' in Swedish), the club has hosted the Scandinavian Open twice. Its long fairways run through flat woodland and parkland with several water hazards crossing the course. There is a fine farmhouse style clubhouse. *SSS 73*

GF $

1963

27

December to April

A. Amilon

L 5992 P 72

Required : Handicap Certificate
Best days : Weekdays except Thursdays

HOLE	LENGTH MEDAL-TEE	PAR	STROKE INDEX
1	334	4	17
2	176	3	3
3	340	4	15
4	341	4	9
5	454	5	13
6	136	3	11
7	336	4	5
8	361	4	1
9	494	5	7
TOTAL	2972	36	TOTAL

HOLE	LENGTH MEDAL-TEE	PAR	STROKE INDEX
10	125	3	18
11	402	4	2
12	476	5	14
13	353	4	12
14	350	4	8
15	143	3	16
16	349	4	10
17	350	4	4
18	472	5	6
TOTAL	3020	36	TOTAL

BORAS

★

TEL : (033)50142
LOCATION : 6 km Boras
ADDRESS : Ostra Vik – 50595 Boras
HOTEL :
Grand Hotel – Boras
Tel : (033)108200
Boras – Boras
Tel : (033)117020
Scandic – Boras
Tel : (033)157000

A typical inland course of medium difficulty with many of its narrow fairways running through dense woodland. There are several water hazards such as a lake between the 2nd and 3rd fairway, and streams crossing the green and the fairway of the 14th hole. *SSS 72*

GF $

November to April

1933

 D. Brazier

18

L 5835 P 72

Required : Handicap Certificate
Best days : Weekdays

HOLE	LENGTH MEDAL-TEE	PAR	STROKE INDEX
1	460	5	5
2	425	5	9
3	300	4	13
4	360	4	1
5	140	3	17
6	350	4	3
7	150	3	15
8	325	4	11
9	325	4	7
TOTAL	2855	36	TOTAL

HOLE	LENGTH MEDAL-TEE	PAR	STROKE INDEX
10	135	3	18
11	365	4	2
12	355	4	8
13	360	4	4
14	450	5	12
15	190	3	10
16	510	5	6
17	150	3	16
18	465	5	14
TOTAL	2980	36	TOTAL

BOSJÖKLOSTER

TEL : (0413)25858
LOCATION : 5 km Höör
ADDRESS : 243 95 Höör
HOTEL :
Frostavallen – Höör
Tel : (0413)22060
Granliden – Höör
Tel : (0415)51009
Höörs Gästgifvaregård – Höör
Tel : (0413)22010
RESTAURANT : Ringsjo Wardshus – Höör
Tel : (0413)33223

Laid out by the well-known architect Douglas Brazier, this is a golf course of excellent quality, set on rolling and open parkland with fine large greens, well-defended by bunkers. There are several small and strategically placed water hazards. *SSS 72*

GF $

1974

18

November to April

D. Brazier

L 5890 P 72

S

R

Required : Handicap Certificate
Best days : Weekdays

HOLE	LENGTH MEDAL-TEE	PAR	STROKE INDEX
1	445	5	9
2	335	4	3
3	145	3	17
4	350	4	5
5	435	5	13
6	330	4	11
7	360	4	1
8	150	3	15
9	335	4	7
TOTAL	2885	36	TOTAL

HOLE	LENGTH MEDAL-TEE	PAR	STROKE INDEX
10	305	4	10
11	500	5	4
12	135	3	18
13	340	4	2
14	365	4	14
15	190	3	12
16	450	5	16
17	370	4	8
18	350	4	6
TOTAL	3005	36	TOTAL

BRO-BALSTA

TEL : (0758)41300
LOCATION : 40 km Stockholm on E 18 to Bro
ADDRESS : Box 96 – 19700 Bro
HOTEL :
Lejondals Slott-Bro
Tel : (0758)48000
Thoresta Herrgård-Bro
Tel : (0758)42600

Opened in 1984, the course was designed by Peter Nordwall. It is laid out in rolling parkland, and is of the classic British style with deep, beautifully contoured bunkers and large, undulating greens. Numerous small ponds serve as hazards. There is a short 9 hole course. *SSS 73*

GF $

1978

18

November to April

P. Nordwall

L 5865 P 73

S

R

Required : Handicap Certificate
Best days : Weekdays

HOLE	LENGTH MEDAL-TEE	PAR	STROKE INDEX
1	440	5	10
2	300	4	8
3	110	3	18
4	360	4	4
5	265	4	12
6	450	5	6
7	150	3	16
8	380	4	2
9	465	5	14
TOTAL	2920	37	TOTAL

HOLE	LENGTH MEDAL-TEE	PAR	STROKE INDEX
10	330	4	5
11	395	4	3
12	330	4	9
13	115	3	17
14	510	5	7
15	360	4	1
16	135	3	15
17	445	5	13
18	325	4	11
TOTAL	2945	36	TOTAL

CARLSKRONA

TEL : (0455)35123
LOCATION : 15 km Karlskrona
ADDRESS : Almö – 370 24 Nättraby
HOTEL :
Stadshotellet – Karlskrona
Tel : (0455)19250
Carlskrona – Karlskrona
Tel : (0455)19630
Ja-Karlskrona
Tel : (0455)27000
RESTAURANT : Wenström – Karlskrona
Tel : (0455)81415

Although situated near the sea, the course is of the parkland type laid out on flat terrain with fine views over the Baltic Sea. There are several water holes such as the 7th and 18th with carries over the water, demanding accurate play. *SSS 70*

GF $

1949

18

November to April

A. Amilon, J. Sederholm

L 5525 P 70

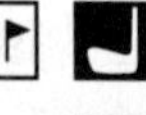

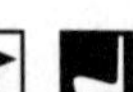

Required : Handicap Certificate
Best days : Weekdays

HOLE	LENGTH MEDAL-TEE	PAR	STROKE INDEX
1	190	3	13
2	460	5	9
3	155	3	15
4	460	5	5
5	155	3	17
6	360	4	1
7	330	4	7
8	375	4	3
9	445	5	11
TOTAL	2930	36	TOTAL

HOLE	LENGTH MEDAL-TEE	PAR	STROKE INDEX
10	135	3	16
11	325	4	6
12	380	4	2
13	285	4	14
14	315	4	10
15	115	3	18
16	325	4	12
17	370	4	4
18	345	4	8
TOTAL	2595	34	TOTAL

DELSJÖ

★

TEL : (031)406959
LOCATION : 3 km Göteborg
ADDRESS : Kallebäck - 41276 Göteborg
HOTEL :
Gothia - Göteborg
Tel : (031)409300
Kung Karl - Göteborg
Tel : (031)172835
Tidbloms - Göteborg
Tel : (031)192070
RESTAURANT : Gösta's - Göteborg
Tel : (031)161183

Delsjö is a luxuriant wooded inland course of the parkland type situated near the seaside resort of Göteborg, Sweden's second city. There are undulating fairways landscaped among tall trees. The course is of excellent quality. *SSS 71*

GF $ — November to April — 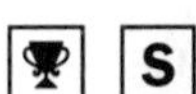

1962 — J. Tobiasson — 

18 — L 5875 P 71 — R

Required : Handicap Certificate
Best days : Mondays, Fridays

HOLE	LENGTH MEDAL-TEE	PAR	STROKE INDEX
1	170	3	15
2	460	5	9
3	340	4	3
4	195	3	7
5	185	3	13
6	365	4	1
7	325	4	17
8	325	4	11
9	490	5	5
TOTAL	2855	35	TOTAL

HOLE	LENGTH MEDAL-TEE	PAR	STROKE INDEX
10	365	4	8
11	470	5	4
12	350	4	10
13	175	3	14
14	315	4	16
15	360	4	2
16	345	4	6
17	145	3	18
18	495	5	12
TOTAL	3020	36	TOTAL

DJURSHOLM

★

TEL : (08)7551598/7551477
LOCATION : 10 km Stockholm
ADDRESS : Hagbardsv 1 –
182 63 Djursholm
HOTEL :
Anglais – Stockholm
Tel : (08)249900
Diplomat – Stockholm
Tel : (08)6635800
Tegnerlunden – Stockholm
Tel : (08)349780
RESTAURANT : La Riche – Stockholm
Tel : (08)236840

A technically demanding inland course set on rolling countryside near the capital. It presents a number of obstacles such as strategic trees, ponds and many well-bunkered greens. There is an attractive mansion style clubhouse overlooking the course. *SSS 73*

GF $$ | November to May | S
1931 | N. Skold
27 | L 5920 P 71 | R

Required : Handicap Certificate
Best days : Weekdays

HOLE	LENGTH MEDAL-TEE	PAR	STROKE INDEX
1	335	4	13
2	380	4	5
3	315	4	15
4	460	5	9
5	365	4	3
6	180	3	11
7	505	5	7
8	140	3	17
9	380	4	1
TOTAL	3060	36	TOTAL

HOLE	LENGTH MEDAL-TEE	PAR	STROKE INDEX
10	295	4	18
11	160	3	10
12	480	5	4
13	345	4	12
14	350	4	2
15	200	3	8
16	350	4	14
17	340	4	6
18	340	4	16
TOTAL	2860	35	TOTAL

DROTTNINGHOLMS

TEL : (08)7590085
LOCATION : 13 km Stockholm
ADDRESS : 170 11 Drottningholm
HOTEL :
Birger Jarl – Stockholm
Tel : (08)151020
Aston – Stockholm
Tel : (08)440690
Oden – Stockholm
Tel : (08)349340
RESTAURANT : Wedholms Fisk – Stockholm
Tel : (08)104874

Located 13 km from Stockholm near Drottningholm castle, home of the Swedish Royal family, the golf course is of championship standard, and has hosted most of the important professional tournaments during the seventies. Set on gently undulating terrain, the first nine holes run through woodland, while the last nine lie in open country with wide fairways. The club featured the 1988 Ladies Team World Championships. *SSS 72*

GF $$ — November to April — R S

1958 — N. Skold, R. Sundblum 

18 — L 5825 P 72

Required : Handicap Certificate
Best days : Weekdays with booking in advance

HOLE	LENGTH MEDAL-TEE	PAR	STROKE INDEX
1	345	4	7
2	340	4	5
3	345	4	9
4	405	5	13
5	155	3	15
6	445	5	11
7	495	5	3
8	140	3	17
9	340	4	1
TOTAL	3010	37	TOTAL

HOLE	LENGTH MEDAL-TEE	PAR	STROKE INDEX
10	385	4	4
11	330	4	16
12	130	3	18
13	310	4	12
14	360	4	2
15	480	5	6
16	145	3	14
17	500	5	8
18	175	3	10
TOTAL	2815	35	TOTAL

EKSJÖ

TEL : (0381)13525
LOCATION : 6 km Eksjö rd 33
ADDRESS : Skedhult - 57500 Eksjö
HOTEL :
Ullinge Wärdshus - Eksjö
Tel : (0381)81060
Eken - Eksjö
Tel : (0381)10996
Högland - Nässjö
Tel : (0380)13100

An undulating golf course situated in the eastern part of Sweden laid out on open land flanked by woods, with fairways separated by mature trees. Two large and picturesque lakes serve as hazards on several of the holes. *SSS 72*

GF $ — November to May — S

1938 — A. Amilon

18 — L 5870 P 72 — R

Required : Handicap Certificate
Best days : Weekdays except Fridays

HOLE	LENGTH MEDAL-TEE	PAR	STROKE INDEX
1	345	4	9
2	500	5	1
3	165	3	15
4	365	4	3
5	350	4	7
6	330	4	13
7	145	3	17
8	450	5	11
9	345	4	5
TOTAL	2995	36	TOTAL

HOLE	LENGTH MEDAL-TEE	PAR	STROKE INDEX
10	340	4	6
11	120	3	14
12	345	4	2
13	510	5	4
14	355	4	10
15	330	4	16
16	120	3	18
17	465	5	8
18	290	4	12
TOTAL	2875	36	TOTAL

ENKÖPING

TEL : (0171)20830
LOCATION : 2 km Enköping
ADDRESS : Box 206 – 19902 Enköping
HOTEL :
Stadshotellet – Enköping
Tel : (071)20010
Park Astoria – Enköping
Tel : (0171)38420
Arribergns Herrgard – Örsundsbro
Tel : (0171)63012

Located in Central Sweden, the course has been extended to 18 holes. Designed by the famous Swedish architect Nils Skold, Enköping is a typical parkland course of medium difficulty. *SSS 72*

GF $

November to May

S

1970

N. Skold

R

18

L 5775 P 71

Required : Handicap Certificate
Best days : Weekdays

HOLE	LENGTH MEDAL-TEE	PAR	STROKE INDEX
1	300	4	
2	160	3	
3	490	5	
4	160	3	
5	440	5	
6	190	3	
7	300	4	
8	300	4	
9	385	4	
TOTAL	2725	35	TOTAL

HOLE	LENGTH MEDAL-TEE	PAR	STROKE INDEX
10	355	4	
11	420	4	
12	440	5	
13	170	3	
14	465	5	
15	370	4	
16	140	3	
17	390	4	
18	300	4	
TOTAL	3050	36	TOTAL

ESKILSTUNA

TEL : (016)142629
LOCATION : 4 km Eskilstuna
ADDRESS : Strängnäsvägen – 63349 Eskilstuna
HOTEL : Hr
Country – Eskilstuna
Tel : (016)110410
Sweden – Eskiltuna
Tel : (016)137690

A parkland course set on flat countryside with small greens and meandering streams serving as hazards. Most of the fairways are separated from each other by mature trees. The Country Hotel is almost adjacent to the course. *SSS 70*

GF $

November to May

 1951

D. Brazier

18

L 5590 P 70

Required : Handicap Certificate
Best days : Weekdays except Wednesdays

HOLE	LENGTH MEDAL-TEE	PAR	STROKE INDEX
1	350	4	5
2	150	3	15
3	475	5	3
4	325	4	13
5	145	3	11
6	300	4	7
7	190	3	9
8	460	5	17
9	370	4	1
TOTAL	2765	35	TOTAL

HOLE	LENGTH MEDAL-TEE	PAR	STROKE INDEX
10	405	4	2
11	190	3	6
12	285	4	18
13	340	4	12
14	360	4	4
15	335	4	10
16	115	3	16
17	440	5	14
18	355	4	8
TOTAL	2825	35	TOTAL

ESLÖVS

TEL : (0413)18610
LOCATION : 3 km Eslöv
ADDRESS : Box 150 – 241 22 Eslöv
HOTEL :
City – Eslöv
Tel : (0413)16010
Sten Stensson Sten – Eslöv
Tel : (0413)16010
Höörs Gastgivarengard - Höör
Tel : (0413)22010

Set within a typical south Swedish landscape, this is a gently undulating parkland course laid out alongside a stream which meanders its way through at least seven holes. Eslövs provides enjoyable golf for the average player. *SSS 71*

GF $

December to April

S

1966

T. Bruce, A. Amilon

18

L 5670 P 70

R

Required : Handicap Certificate
Best days : Weekdays

HOLE	LENGTH MEDAL-TEE	PAR	STROKE INDEX
1	505	5	7
2	125	3	17
3	490	5	3
4	165	3	15
5	350	4	9
6	385	4	5
7	150	3	11
8	375	4	1
9	310	4	13
TOTAL	2855	35	TOTAL

HOLE	LENGTH MEDAL-TEE	PAR	STROKE INDEX
10	145	3	16
11	475	5	4
12	345	4	10
13	150	3	18
14	375	4	8
15	360	4	2
16	320	4	14
17	330	4	6
18	315	4	12
TOTAL	2815	35	TOTAL

FALKENBERG

★

TEL : (0346)50287
LOCATION : 5 km S Falkenberg E 6
ADDRESS : Golfvägen –
31175 Falkenberg
HOTEL :
Skrea – Falkenberg
Tel : (0346)50170
Grand – Falkenberg
Tel : (0346)14450
Vita Hästen – Falkenberg
Tel : (0346)80020

Situated near the seaside resort of Falkenberg on Sweden's West Coast, the course is of championship standard, and was laid out by Jan Sederholm on flat parkland. There are three loops of nine holes that are combined to form one 18 hole combination and one 9 hole course. The Skrea motel is situated 500 m from the golf club. *SSS 72*

GF $

1961

27

November to April

J. Sederholm

L 2928 P 36, 2821 P 35,
2795 P 36

R S

Required : Handicap Certificate
Best days : Weekdays

HOLE	LENGTH MEDAL-TEE	PAR	STROKE INDEX	HOLE	LENGTH MEDAL-TEE	PAR	STROKE INDEX	HOLE	LENGTH MEDAL-TEE	PAR	STROKE INDEX
1	148	3	6	1	319	4	8	1	330	4	8
2	399	4	2	2	350	4	1	2	165	3	5
3	360	4	1	3	470	5	4	3	445	5	3
4	335	4	3	4	335	4	7	4	325	4	7
5	352	4	5	5	335	4	3	5	135	3	9
6	119	3	9	6	350	4	2	6	455	5	2
7	288	4	8	7	162	3	9	7	275	4	6
8	437	5	7	8	340	4	5	8	310	4	4
9	490	5	4	9	160	3	6	9	355	4	1
TOTAL	2928	36	TOTAL	TOTAL	2821	35	TOTAL	TOTAL	2795	36	TOTAL

FALKÖPING

TEL : (0515)31270
LOCATION : 8 km Falköping
ADDRESS : Box 99 – 521 01 Falköping 1
HOTEL :
Guldhatten – Falköping
Tel : (0515)13000
St Olof – Falköping
Tel : (0515)10728
Rantens – Falköping
Tel : (0515)13030
RESTAURANT : Rantens – Falköping
Tel : (0515)13030

This parkland course set in pleasant surroundings, has a very attractive layout. It lies on rolling and lush countryside with mature trees bordering the fairways. The clubhouse is built high up and overlooks the course. *SSS 72*

GF $ | November to May | S
1965 | N. Skold |
18 | L 5835 P 72 | R

Required : Handicap Certificate
Best days : Weekdays

HOLE	LENGTH MEDAL-TEE	PAR	STROKE INDEX
1	450	5	11
2	380	4	3
3	190	3	7
4	320	4	17
5	380	4	1
6	430	5	5
7	150	3	15
8	325	4	9
9	325	4	13
TOTAL	2950	36	TOTAL

HOLE	LENGTH MEDAL-TEE	PAR	STROKE INDEX
10	355	4	4
11	485	5	12
12	370	4	2
13	335	4	14
14	140	3	18
15	300	4	10
16	130	3	16
17	465	5	8
18	305	4	6
TOTAL	2885	36	TOTAL

FALSTERBO

TEL : (040)475078/470078
LOCATION : 35 km Malmö E 6
ADDRESS : Box 71 – 23011 Falsterbo
HOTEL :
Falsterbo Inn – Falsterbo
Tel : (040)470015
Gässlingen – Skanör
Tel : (040)473035
Villa Paradiset – Falsterbo
Tel : (040)470800
RESTAURANT : Kaptensgarden – Falsterbo
Tel : (040)470750

Laid out on a peninsula, flanked by the Baltic sea and the Oresund, this is a memorable course rating among the best courses in the world. A true links often compared with Portmarnock in layout, Falsterbo is also the oldest golf course in Sweden having been founded in 1909. Though rather short, all the holes have great character and variety, demanding accuracy from tee to green. A links-player feels at home at Falsterbo with its fine natural bunkers (92), its sandy soil, its fast running greens, its prevailing wind, its many natural water hazards, and its strategic hillocks. One of the feature holes is the famous 11th, a treacherous water hole. The clubhouse is scenically situated bordering the Baltic. *SSS 72*

GF $$ — — S
1909 — G. Bauer — R

18 — L 5895 P 71

Required : Handicap Certificate
Best days : Weekdays (very crowded in June, July and August)

HOLE	LENGTH MEDAL-TEE	PAR	STROKE INDEX
1	400	4	7
2	160	3	17
3	480	5	11
4	360	4	1
5	350	4	5
6	155	3	15
7	295	4	9
8	175	3	13
9	380	4	3
TOTAL	2755	34	TOTAL

HOLE	LENGTH MEDAL-TEE	PAR	STROKE INDEX
10	360	4	8
11	130	3	18
12	355	4	2
13	515	5	12
14	200	3	6
15	440	5	14
16	340	4	4
17	345	4	10
18	455	5	16
TOTAL	3140	37	TOTAL

FALUN-BORLÄNGE

TEL : (023)31015/31241
LOCATION : 8 km Borlänge
ADDRESS : Box 40 – 791 21 Falun
HOTEL :
Galaxen – Borlänge
Tel : (0243)80010
Gustaf Wasa – Borlänge
Tel : (0243)81000
Scandic – Borlänge
Tel : (0243)28120
RESTAURANT : Vardhuset – Borlänge
Tel : (0243)31010

Set in Central Sweden, this is a picturesque parkland course laid out on gently rolling countryside amid trees, ponds and streams. The style of the clubhouse is typical of the area.

GF $ — November to May — R 

1977 — N. Skold 

18 — L 5745 P 72 

Required : Handicap Certificate
Best days : Tuesdays to Fridays

HOLE	LENGTH MEDAL-TEE	PAR	STROKE INDEX
1	350	4	5
2	450	5	13
3	130	3	15
4	360	4	1
5	330	4	11
6	450	5	9
7	350	4	3
8	150	3	17
9	330	4	7
TOTAL	2900	36	TOTAL

HOLE	LENGTH MEDAL-TEE	PAR	STROKE INDEX
10	445	5	10
11	365	4	4
12	300	4	12
13	245	4	18
14	135	3	14
15	340	4	6
16	170	3	16
17	370	4	2
18	475	5	8
TOTAL	2845	36	TOTAL

FINSPÅNG

TEL : (0122)13940
LOCATION : 2 km Finspång/25 km Norrköping
ADDRESS : Viberga Gård - 61200 Finspång
HOTEL :
De Geer - Finspång
Tel : (0122)13150
Lottas Krog - Finspång
Tel : (0122)10833

Recently extended to 18 holes, the course is set on the east coast of Sweden with its holes running through partly hilly and flat wooded landscape. Water affects play on five holes. *SSS 72*

GF $ — October to April — S

1965 — S. Linde — 

18 — L 5800 P 72 — 

Required : None
Best days : Weekdays

HOLE	LENGTH MEDAL-TEE	PAR	STROKE INDEX
1	330	4	9
2	345	4	7
3	330	4	15
4	500	5	1
5	175	3	11
6	335	4	5
7	510	5	3
8	130	3	17
9	290	4	13
TOTAL	2945	36	TOTAL

HOLE	LENGTH MEDAL-TEE	PAR	STROKE INDEX
10	340	4	4
11	435	5	16
12	165	3	12
13	335	4	6
14	455	5	10
15	310	4	14
16	125	3	18
17	335	4	8
18	360	4	2
TOTAL	2860	36	TOTAL

FJÄLLBACKA

TEL : (0525)31150
LOCATION : 2 km N. Fjällbacka
ADDRESS : Morhult 368 –
450 71 Fjällbacka
HOTEL :
Tanumshede Gästgivaregard – Tanumshede
Tel : (0525)29010
Kung Rane – Dingle
Tel : (0524)43040
Stora – Fjällbacka
Tel : (0525)31003
RESTAURANT : Grönalids – Fjällbacka
Tel : (0525)31041

Located near the seaside resort of Fjällbacka on the popular West Coast, this course has a varied layout, with holes running through open, and at the same time undulating, land. Six of the fairways are encircled by water. *SSS 72*

GF $

November to April

1966

E. Röhss

18

L 5850 P 72

Required : Handicap Certificate
Best days : Any day

HOLE	LENGTH MEDAL-TEE	PAR	STROKE INDEX
1	300	4	13
2	360	4	5
3	125	3	17
4	525	5	3
5	355	4	11
6	465	5	9
7	370	4	1
8	130	3	15
9	480	5	7
TOTAL	3110	37	TOTAL

HOLE	LENGTH MEDAL-TEE	PAR	STROKE INDEX
10	305	4	12
11	345	4	8
12	310	4	14
13	170	3	16
14	330	4	2
15	475	5	4
16	155	3	18
17	320	4	10
18	330	4	6
TOTAL	2740	35	TOTAL

FLOMMENS

TEL : (040)475016/475017
LOCATION : 35 km Malmö E 6
ADDRESS : Box 49 – 230 11 Falsterbo
HOTEL :
Villa Astrid – Falsterbo
Tel : (040)470116
Dannegarden – Trelleborg
Tel : (0410)11120
Gässlingen – Skanör
Tel : (040)473035
RESTAURANT : Villa Paradiset – Falsterbo
Tel : (040)470800

Set on the 'Falsterbonäset' peninsula, the Swedish golfers' paradise, this is another challenging links well worth a visit. Laid out on flat terrain, there are numerous strategically placed water hazards. The peninsula is ideal for holiday golf with many other sports and leisure activities such as sailing, windsurfing, cycling, horse-riding, tennis etc..
SSS 72

GF $

1935

18

—

S. Kristersson, S. Bergendorff

L 5725 P 72

S

R

Required : Handicap Certificate
Best days : Weekdays

HOLE	LENGTH MEDAL-TEE	PAR	STROKE INDEX
1	130	3	13
2	365	4	1
3	455	5	15
4	375	4	3
5	465	5	7
6	305	4	11
7	145	3	17
8	345	4	9
9	345	4	5
TOTAL	2930	36	TOTAL

HOLE	LENGTH MEDAL-TEE	PAR	STROKE INDEX
10	160	3	8
11	280	4	16
12	450	5	6
13	360	4	2
14	160	3	14
15	460	5	4
16	435	5	12
17	130	3	18
18	360	4	10
TOTAL	2795	36	TOTAL

FORSBACKA

TEL : (0532)43055
LOCATION : 7 km Amal
ADDRESS : Box 136 – 662 00 Amal
HOTEL :
Stadt Amal – Amal
Tel : (0532)12020
Dalia – Bengtfors
Tel : (0531)11650
Svaneholms – Svansborg
Tel : (0532)30430

Set on the West Coast, Forsbacka is an inland course with several holes running through lush woodland and others laid out over typical Swedish parkland. It features several sporting water holes. *SSS 72*

GF $

November to May

R S

1970

N. Skold

18

L 5856 P 72

Required : Handicap Certificate
Best days : Weekdays

HOLE	LENGTH MEDAL-TEE	PAR	STROKE INDEX
1	280	4	
2	338	4	
3	306	4	
4	539	5	
5	150	3	
6	353	4	
7	483	5	
8	131	3	
9	282	4	
TOTAL	2862	36	TOTAL

HOLE	LENGTH MEDAL-TEE	PAR	STROKE INDEX
10	286	4	
11	465	5	
12	165	3	
13	518	5	
14	374	4	
15	186	3	
16	347	4	
17	349	4	
18	304	4	
TOTAL	2994	36	TOTAL

FORSGÅRDENS

TEL : (0300)13649
LOCATION : 27 km S. Göteborg, in Kungsbacka
ADDRESS : Gamla Forsvägen 1
43447 Kungsbacka
HOTEL :
Halland - Kungsbacka
Tel : (0300)11530
Sommarro - Kungsbacka
Tel : (0300)27268

Created by Sweden's illustrous golf architect Sune Linde, the course lies in a fine holiday region not far from the sea. It is laid out on flat and fairly wooded landscape and has a river flowing through some of the holes. A comfortable clubhouse is scheduled soon. *SSS 72*

GF $

1989

18

November to April

S. Linde

L 5740 P 72

S

R

Required : Handicap Certificate
Best days : Weekdays

HOLE	LENGTH MEDAL-TEE	PAR	STROKE INDEX
1	350	4	7
2	160	3	13
3	315	4	9
4	480	5	3
5	115	3	17
6	280	4	15
7	300	4	11
8	445	5	5
9	380	4	1
TOTAL	2825	36	TOTAL

HOLE	LENGTH MEDAL-TEE	PAR	STROKE INDEX
10	305	4	12
11	160	3	16
12	325	4	14
13	330	4	4
14	475	5	10
15	355	4	6
16	460	5	8
17	135	3	18
18	370	4	2
TOTAL	2915	36	TOTAL

FRÖSAKER

TEL : (021)25024
LOCATION : 20 km E. Västerås
ADDRESS : Frösåker Gård - 72597 Västerås
HOTEL :
Aros - Västerås
Tel : (021)101010
Stads - Västerås
Tel : (021)180420
Park - Västerås
Tel : (021)110120

Sune Linde designed this challenging new course which is found in beautiful unspoiled landscape. It features lush holes flanked by mature trees, scenic rivers and lakes. The course lies in a cove of Lake Mälaren close to the town of Västeras in Central Sweden.
SSS 73

GF $ — October to May — S
1989 — S. Linde
18 — L 5825 P 72

Required : None
Best days : Weekdays

HOLE	LENGTH MEDAL-TEE	PAR	STROKE INDEX
1	475	5	13
2	325	4	9
3	335	4	7
4	310	4	17
5	160	3	11
6	475	5	3
7	130	3	15
8	375	4	1
9	340	4	5
TOTAL	2925	36	TOTAL

HOLE	LENGTH MEDAL-TEE	PAR	STROKE INDEX
10	325	4	6
11	140	3	18
12	350	4	12
13	460	5	10
14	150	3	14
15	305	4	16
16	490	5	8
17	335	4	2
18	345	4	4
TOTAL	2900	36	TOTAL

GÄVLE

TEL : (026)113163
LOCATION : 3 km Gävle E 4
ADDRESS : Bönavägen 23 – 805 95 Gävle
HOTEL :
Scandic – Gävle
Tel : (026)188060
Aveny – Gävle
Tel : (026)115590
Gävle – Gävle
Tel : (026)115470
RESTAURANT : Norrtulls – Gävle
Tel : (026)127754

Situated in Central Sweden, Gävle is a popular inland course featuring several strategic water hazards. Relatively flat with some undulations, the holes run through woodland and meadowland. *SSS 72*

GF $

1947

27

November to May

N. Skold

L 5735 P 72

S

R

Required : Handicap Certificate
Best days : Weekdays

HOLE	LENGTH MEDAL-TEE	PAR	STROKE INDEX
1	435	5	7
2	180	3	9
3	330	4	5
4	165	3	17
5	310	4	1
6	450	5	13
7	320	4	15
8	165	3	11
9	450	5	3
TOTAL	2805	36	TOTAL

HOLE	LENGTH MEDAL-TEE	PAR	STROKE INDEX
10	355	4	6
11	330	4	12
12	280	4	16
13	440	5	10
14	375	4	2
15	150	3	8
16	515	5	4
17	140	3	14
18	345	4	8
TOTAL	2930	36	TOTAL

GÖTEBORGS

TEL : (031)282444
LOCATION : 10 km Göteborg
ADDRESS : Box 2056 – 43602 Hovas
HOTEL :
Europa – Göteborg
Tel : (031)801280
Lilton – Göteborg
Tel : (031)828808
Windsor – Göteborg
Tel : (031)176540
RESTAURANT : Johanna – Göteborg
Tel : (031)112250

Göteborg golf club, set alongside the sea, is one of Sweden's oldest golf clubs dating back to 1902. The championship course is a challenge from beginning to end with some of the holes lined with rocks. Laid out on undulating parkland, most of the fairways are landscaped with mature trees. *SSS 69*

GF $$

1902

18

—

V. Zetterberg, A. Perssony

L 5205 P 70

S

R

Required : Handicap Certificate
Best days : Tuesdays, Thursdays, Fridays

HOLE	LENGTH MEDAL-TEE	PAR	STROKE INDEX
1	195	3	9
2	295	4	13
3	425	5	3
4	110	3	17
5	340	4	5
6	355	4	1
7	115	3	15
8	295	4	11
9	350	4	7
TOTAL	2480	34	TOTAL

HOLE	LENGTH MEDAL-TEE	PAR	STROKE INDEX
10	465	5	6
11	425	5	12
12	370	4	2
13	140	3	14
14	240	4	18
15	280	4	8
16	350	4	4
17	175	3	10
18	280	4	16
TOTAL	2725	36	TOTAL

GULLBRINGA

TEL : (0303)27161/27872
LOCATION : 14 km Kungälv
ADDRESS : Gullbringa Sateri – 44290 Kungälv
HOTEL :
Fars Hatt – Kungälv
Tel : (0303)10970
Golf Scandic – Hisings Backa
Tel : (031)520060
Ramada – Göteborg
Tel : (031)222420
RESTAURANT : Stenungsbaden – Stenungson
Tel : (0303)83100

A testing inland course set on varying terrain located 12km from the sea front. The club is part of the Gullbringa Country Club with sports facilities such as a swimming pool, various tennis courts and riding stables.

GF $

1967

18

December to April

D. Brazier

L 5490 P 72

S R

Required : Handicap Certificate
Best days : Weekdays

HOLE	LENGTH MEDAL-TEE	PAR	STROKE INDEX
1	360	4	3
2	420	5	17
3	320	4	5
4	125	3	11
5	365	4	1
6	180	3	9
7	265	4	15
8	325	4	13
9	430	5	7
TOTAL	2790	36	TOTAL

HOLE	LENGTH MEDAL-TEE	PAR	STROKE INDEX
10	180	3	8
11	335	4	4
12	150	3	16
13	255	4	18
14	450	5	2
15	440	5	10
16	430	5	14
17	150	3	12
18	310	4	6
TOTAL	2700	36	TOTAL

HALMSTAD

TEL : (035)30077
LOCATION : 9 km Halmstad
ADDRESS : Golfbanevagen –
302 73 Halmstad
HOTEL : HR
Nya Tylösand
Tel : (035)30500
Amadeus – Halmstad
Tel : (035)109770
Strandgarden – Tylösand
Tel : (035)30745

A popular inland course located bewteen Malmö and Göteborg on the West Coast, near the scenic town of Tylosand. Often compared with Wentworth in layout, the championship course is interesting and challenging. Set on sandy soil, the heavily bunkered holes run through pine forest. Undoubtedly one of Scandinavia's best courses, featuring several excellent dogleg holes such as the 6th, 8th, 9th and 10th. There is a friendly and comfortable clubhouse with accomodation for golfers. Every year in August, the Halmstad Golf Club organizes the 'Tylosands Week' welcoming visitors. The Nya hotel is adjacent to the course.
SSS 73/72

GF $$

1938

36

 November to April

R. Sundblom, F. Pennink

L Southern Course 5720 P 72,
Northern Course 5980 P 72

R S

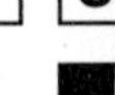

Required : Handicap Certificate
Best days : Weekdays

HOLE	LENGTH MEDAL-TEE	PAR	STROKE INDEX
1	340	4	5
2	455	5	17
3	320	4	11
4	155	3	15
5	535	5	1
6	320	4	9
7	180	3	13
8	355	4	7
9	395	4	3
TOTAL	3055	36	TOTAL

HOLE	LENGTH MEDAL-TEE	PAR	STROKE INDEX
10	330	4	6
11	440	5	18
12	385	4	12
13	145	3	10
14	505	5	4
15	300	4	16
16	165	3	8
17	315	4	14
18	340	4	12
TOTAL	2925	36	TOTAL

HANINGE

TEL : (0750)32240
LOCATION : 30 km S. Stockholm
ADDRESS : Arsta Slott – 13691 Haninge
HOTEL :
Najaden – Handen
Tel : (08)7457400
Smadalarö – Dalarö
Tel : (0750)53200

Haninge is one of Sweden's newest championship layouts, designed by Jan Sederholm in 1985. Situated 30km south of Stockholm around the 'Arsta Slott', a 17th century palace, it is an undulating parkland course with numerous ponds bordering the fairways. The Clubhouse is housed in one of the wings of the scenic castle. *SSS 73*

GF $$
1985
27
December to March
J. Sederholm
L 5930 P 73
S
R

Required : Handicap Certificate
Best days : Weekdays

HOLE	LENGTH MEDAL-TEE	PAR	STROKE INDEX
1	440	5	11
2	135	3	15
3	335	4	9
4	330	4	7
5	480	5	1
6	290	4	13
7	345	4	5
8	120	3	17
9	355	4	3
TOTAL	2830	36	TOTAL

HOLE	LENGTH MEDAL-TEE	PAR	STROKE INDEX
10	365	4	2
11	485	5	6
12	160	3	12
13	460	5	14
14	315	4	16
15	340	4	8
16	140	3	18
17	370	4	4
18	465	5	10
TOTAL	3100	37	TOTAL

HÄRJEDALSFJÄLLENS

TEL : (0684)21100
LOCATION : 5 km Funäsdalen, in Ljusnedal
ADDRESS : Vintergatan 5-84095
Funäsdalen
HOTEL : HP
Gyllene Bocken
Tel : (0684)21090
Eriksgardens Fjäll-Funäsdalen
Tel : (0684)21006
Sörmons Stugby-Ljusnedal
Tel : (0684)21511

Extended to 18 holes in 1988, the golf course is beautifully laid out amongst snow clad mountain scenery not far from the Norwegian border. The course, set in hilly and fairly wooded landscape, runs alongside a lake called the Ljusnedalssjön. The Gyllene Bocken hotel with 22 rooms is situated on the golf course. *SSS 72.*

GF $

1972

18

October to June

 S. Linde

 5540 P 72

Required : Green Card
Best days : Weekdays

HOLE	LENGTH MEDAL-TEE	PAR	STROKE INDEX
1	435	5	11
2	390	4	1
3	155	3	15
4	440	5	7
5	320	4	9
6	270	4	13
7	350	4	5
8	130	3	17
9	350	4	3
TOTAL	2840	36	TOTAL

HOLE	LENGTH MEDAL-TEE	PAR	STROKE INDEX
10	350	4	2
11	470	5	4
12	320	4	6
13	240	4	14
14	460	5	8
15	130	3	16
16	305	4	12
17	140	3	18
18	285	4	10
TOTAL	2700	36	TOTAL

HÄRNOSÄND

TEL : (0611)66169
LOCATION : 16 km N. Härnosänd to Hemsö
ADDRESS : Box 52-87122 Härnosänd
HOTEL :
Stads-Härnosänd
Tel : (0611)10510
Royal-Härnosänd
Tel : (0611)20455
Scandic-Härnosänd
Tel : (0611)19560

The club lies in the northern part of Southern Norrland, on the peninsula Vägnön with the Bothnia Sea one side and the river Ångermanälven on the other side. The scenic location is partly flanked by distant mountains. The 18 holes wind through undulating park and wooded countryside. The course is at its best in august and september. *SSS 69*

GF $

1957

18

December to May

N. Skold

L 5385 P 70

R S

Required : None
Best days : Weekdays

HOLE	LENGTH MEDAL-TEE	PAR	STROKE INDEX
1	135	3	13
2	335	4	11
3	355	4	1
4	345	4	5
5	125	3	17
6	485	5	7
7	325	4	9
8	280	4	15
9	335	4	3
TOTAL	2720	35	TOTAL

HOLE	LENGTH MEDAL-TEE	PAR	STROKE INDEX
10	350	4	2
11	410	5	12
12	320	4	16
13	180	3	8
14	360	4	4
15	95	3	18
16	330	4	8
17	180	3	10
18	320	4	14
TOTAL	2545	34	TOTAL

HÄSSLEHOLMS

TEL : (0451)53111
LOCATION : 6 km Tyringe, at Skyrup
ADDRESS : Skyrup – 28200 Tyringe
HOTEL : HP
Skyrupsgarden
Tel : (0451)53055
Kurhotellet – Tyringe
Tel : (0451)50910

A pleasant parkland course, of medium difficulty, set on flat terrain with several picturesque ponds and lakes serving as hazards. There is the Kurhotellet hotel near the course open from May to October and the Skyrupsgarden hotel within walking distance. *SSS 72*

GF $ — November to May  

1977 — J. Sederholm, B. Jensen 

18 — L 5830 P 72 — RP

Required : Handicap Certificate
Best days : Any day

HOLE	LENGTH MEDAL-TEE	PAR	STROKE INDEX
1	300	4	13
2	345	4	3
3	130	3	17
4	450	5	9
5	335	4	5
6	450	5	7
7	390	4	1
8	165	3	11
9	310	4	15
TOTAL	2875	36	TOTAL

HOLE	LENGTH MEDAL-TEE	PAR	STROKE INDEX
10	475	5	10
11	150	3	18
12	375	4	2
13	365	4	4
14	135	3	14
15	320	4	8
16	315	4	16
17	360	4	6
18	460	5	12
TOTAL	2955	36	TOTAL

HÖGBO

TEL : (026)45015
LOCATION : 5 km N. Sandviken Rd 272
ADDRESS : Daniel Tilas Väg 4 –
811 92 Sandviken
HOTEL :
Eos Car – Sandviken
Tel : (025)259900
Forsbacka Wärdshus – Forsbacka
Tel : (026)35170
Princess – Sandviken
Tel : (026)254050
RESTAURANT : Lindangen – Sandviken
Tel : (025)253157

The course runs partly over lush woodland, and partly over parkland. Many of its 18 holes are laid out alongside a stream which meanders its way through the fairways. *SSS 71*

GF $ — November to May — S

1962 — N. Skold — 

18 — L 5680 P 71 — R

Required : Handicap Certificate
Best days : Weekdays

HOLE	LENGTH MEDAL-TEE	PAR	STROKE INDEX
1	280	4	13
2	390	4	1
3	355	4	3
4	505	5	7
5	125	3	15
6	285	4	11
7	140	3	17
8	310	4	9
9	495	5	5
TOTAL	2885	36	TOTAL

HOLE	LENGTH MEDAL-TEE	PAR	STROKE INDEX
10	345	4	8
11	365	4	4
12	175	3	12
13	392	4	2
14	325	4	14
15	312	4	10
16	465	5	6
17	148	3	16
18	268	4	18
TOTAL	2795	35	TOTAL

HÖKENSAS

TEL : (0503)16059
LOCATION : 8 km S. Hjo Rd 195
ADDRESS : Lindgatan 4 – 544 00 Hjo
HOTEL :
Bellevue – Hjo
Tel : (0503)12000
Vättersro – Hjo
Tel : (0502)50350
Västerhöjdsgarden – Skövde
Tel : (0500)13832
RESTAURANT : Stora – Tidaholm
Tel : (0502)10378

Laid out on partly undulating countryside in West Sweden, the course is landscaped by mature trees and incorporates several water hazards. *SSS 71*

GF $ — November to April — S

1962 — —

18 — L 5540 P 71 — R

Required : Handicap Certificate
Best days : Tuesdays to Thursdays inc.

HOLE	LENGTH MEDAL-TEE	PAR	STROKE INDEX
1	445	5	13
2	320	4	9
3	175	3	3
4	400	4	1
5	140	3	17
6	270	4	11
7	320	4	15
8	320	4	7
9	310	4	5
TOTAL	2700	35	TOTAL

HOLE	LENGTH MEDAL-TEE	PAR	STROKE INDEX
10	165	3	14
11	475	5	8
12	450	5	10
13	145	3	18
14	355	4	2
15	150	3	12
16	380	4	4
17	450	5	6
18	270	4	16
TOTAL	2840	36	TOTAL

HOOKS

TEL : (0393)21420
LOCATION : 30 km Jönköping N 30
ADDRESS : 56013 Hok
HOTEL : Hr
Herrgard Hooks
Tel : (0393)21080

This pleasant inland course is peacefully situated with numerous lakes and ponds serving as hazards. The course belongs to Hooks Herrgard, an attractive hotel with 80 rooms. There is a private swimming pool and several tennis courts. *SSS 72*

GF $

October to May

1934

T. Bruce, S. Edberg

18

L 5748 P 72

Required : Handicap Certificate
Best days : Any day

HOLE	LENGTH MEDAL-TEE	PAR	STROKE INDEX
1	320	4	7
2	342	4	13
3	437	5	3
4	318	4	9
5	268	4	11
6	134	3	17
7	346	4	1
8	313	4	15
9	508	5	5
TOTAL	2986	37	TOTAL

HOLE	LENGTH MEDAL-TEE	PAR	STROKE INDEX
10	364	4	12
11	326	4	10
12	144	3	8
13	322	4	4
14	443	5	14
15	324	4	18
16	381	4	2
17	134	3	16
18	324	4	6
TOTAL	2762	35	TOTAL

HULTA

★

TEL : (033)88180
LOCATION : 25 km Boras / 3 km Bollebygd
ADDRESS : Box 54 – 517 01 Bollebygd
HOTEL :
Hindas – Hindas
Tel : (0301)11050
Hindasgarden – Hindas
Tel : (0301)10530
Grand – Boras
Tel : (033)108200
RESTAURANT : Asengard – Dannike
Tel : (033)81146

Located between Boras and Göteborg, this is a fine and sporting inland course set on gently rolling open land and flanked by forest. Among its many water hazards is a stream cutting the course in two. The club boasts an stately and well-appointed clubhouse. *SSS 73*

GF $

1972

18

November to May

J. Sederholm

L 5915 P 72

R 

Required : Handicap Certificate
Best days : Weekdays

HOLE	LENGTH MEDAL-TEE	PAR	STROKE INDEX
1	375	4	5
2	340	4	3
3	135	3	15
4	360	4	9
5	315	4	13
6	140	3	11
7	445	5	11
8	365	4	7
9	335	4	1
TOTAL	2810	35	TOTAL

HOLE	LENGTH MEDAL-TEE	PAR	STROKE INDEX
10	445	5	8
11	340	4	4
12	500	5	10
13	370	4	2
14	305	4	18
15	160	3	16
16	315	4	14
17	170	3	12
18	500	5	6
TOTAL	3105	37	TOTAL

INGARÖ

TEL : (0766)28244
LOCATION : 32 km Stockholm
ADDRESS : Fogelvik – 13035 Ingarö
HOTEL :
Diplomat – Stockholm
Tel : (08)635800
Aston – Stockholm
Tel : (08)440690
RESTAURANT : Erik's – Stockholm
Tel : (08)606060

This pleasant course is situated on the island of Ingaro in the archipelago of Stockholm 25 minutes by car from the city. The 5th, 6th and 7th holes are set on the shores of a bay bordering the Baltic sea. *SSS 71*

GF $

1962

18

November to May

N. Skold

L 5603 P 71

S

R

Required : Handicap Certificate
Best days : Weekdays

HOLE	LENGTH MEDAL-TEE	PAR	STROKE INDEX
1	259	4	15
2	264	4	13
3	370	4	5
4	181	3	11
5	525	5	3
6	178	3	17
7	433	5	7
8	413	4	1
9	266	4	9
TOTAL	2889	36	TOTAL

HOLE	LENGTH MEDAL-TEE	PAR	STROKE INDEX
10	495	5	8
11	151	3	16
12	350	4	4
13	344	4	10
14	346	4	2
15	138	3	18
16	468	5	6
17	183	3	12
18	239	4	14
TOTAL	2714	35	TOTAL

ISABERGS

TEL : (0370)36330
LOCATION : 18 km Gislaved
ADDRESS : Box 40 – 332 00 Gislaved
HOTEL :
Hestravikens Vardshus – Hestra
Tel : (0370)36370
Nissastigen – Gislaved
Tel : (0371)11540
RESTAURANT : Isaberg Stugby – Hestra
Tel : (0370)35700

Scenically laid out in natural surroundings on the shores of Lake Hammar (Hammarsjön) and along the Nissan river, this is a well-wooded inland course set on undulating land. The course is cut in two by the river 'Nissan' serving as a hazard on several holes.
SSS 72

GF $

1968

18

October to May

 A. Amilon, T. Bruce, M. Edenberg

 5690 P 72

Required : Handicap Certificate
Best days : Weekdays

HOLE	LENGTH MEDAL-TEE	PAR	STROKE INDEX
1	490	5	3
2	265	4	15
3	505	5	5
4	310	4	11
5	300	4	13
6	130	3	17
7	350	4	1
8	175	3	7
9	310	4	9
TOTAL	2835	36	TOTAL

HOLE	LENGTH MEDAL-TEE	PAR	STROKE INDEX
10	325	4	8
11	305	4	10
12	125	3	18
13	315	4	6
14	510	5	2
15	320	4	14
16	145	3	16
17	450	5	12
18	360	4	4
TOTAL	2855	36	TOTAL

JÖNKÖPINGS

★★

TEL : (036)76567
LOCATION : 3 km Jönköping E 4
ADDRESS : Kettilstorp – 55267 Jönköping
HOTEL :
Stora – Jönköping
Tel : (036)119300
Klosterkungen – Jönköping
Tel : (036)100800
Savoy – Jönköping
Tel : (036)119480
RESTAURANT : Hablahester – Mullsjö
Tel : (0392)12320

Designed by the well-known Swedish architect Nils Skold, this hilly championship course flows over a lush parkland landscape set in the east of Sweden. Several of the holes are laid out alongside a stream. *SSS 70*

GF $ — December to April  S

1930 — N. Skold 

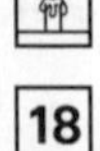 18 —  L 5555 P 70

Required : Handicap Certificate
Best days : Weekdays

HOLE	LENGTH MEDAL-TEE	PAR	STROKE INDEX
1	445	5	11
2	370	4	3
3	345	4	7
4	315	4	17
5	155	3	13
6	385	4	1
7	330	4	9
8	145	3	15
9	375	4	5
TOTAL	2865	35	TOTAL

HOLE	LENGTH MEDAL-TEE	PAR	STROKE INDEX
10	145	3	14
11	155	3	10
12	515	5	2
13	295	4	6
14	450	5	18
15	265	4	16
16	190	3	12
17	305	4	8
18	370	4	4
TOTAL	2690	35	TOTAL

KALMAR

★

TEL : (0480)72111
LOCATION : 10 km Kalmar E 66
ADDRESS : Box 278 – 391 23 Kalmar 1
HOTEL :
Kalmarsund – Kalmar
Tel : (0480)18100
Packhuset – Kalmar
Tel : (0480)57000
Slotts – Kalmar
Tel : (0480)88260
RESTAURANT : Stadspark – Kalmar
Tel : (0480)10085

Kalmar is a well-wooded parkland course running over flat countryside. It features various water hazards, such as strategically placed ditches before the greens of the 6th and 13th holes. *SSS 72*

GF $

 November to April

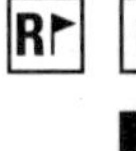

1974

 R. Sundblom

18

L 6130 P 72

Required : Handicap Certificate
Best days : Any days except Saturdays

HOLE	LENGTH MEDAL-TEE	PAR	STROKE INDEX
1	155	3	15
2	345	4	13
3	410	4	5
4	340	4	9
5	400	4	1
6	160	3	11
7	460	5	17
8	530	5	3
9	365	4	7
TOTAL	3165	36	TOTAL

HOLE	LENGTH MEDAL-TEE	PAR	STROKE INDEX
10	335	4	16
11	325	4	14
12	485	5	4
13	185	3	10
14	500	5	2
15	350	4	6
16	170	3	18
17	290	4	8
18	325	4	12
TOTAL	2965	36	TOTAL

KARLSHAMNS

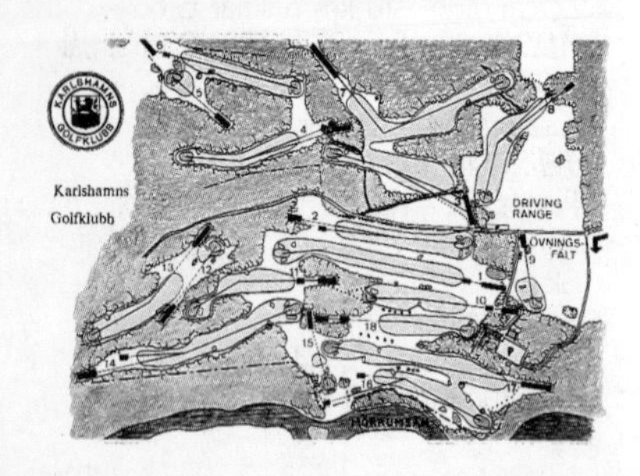

TEL : (0454)50085
LOCATION : 10 km Karlshamn, in Morrum
ADDRESS : Box 188 –
37423 Karlshamn
HOTEL :
Fiske och Golf – Morrum
Tel : (0454)50044
Carlshamn – Karlshamn
Tel : (0454)89000
Scandic – Karlshamn
Tel : (0454)16660

Set in the south of Sweden, the Karlshamn is a testing inland course demanding a great deal of accuracy. Laid out on undulating countryside and landscaped among dense forest, it lies on the edge of the river 'Mörrumsan'. The pleasant 'Fiske och Golf' hotel is situated 1 km from the golf club. *SSS 72*

GF $ — December to April — S

1963 — D. Brazier

18 — L 5861 P 72 — R

Required : Handicap Certificate
Best days : Weekdays except Thursdays

HOLE	LENGTH MEDAL-TEE	PAR	STROKE INDEX
1	475	5	9
2	361	4	3
3	334	4	11
4	351	4	1
5	150	3	15
6	343	4	7
7	509	5	5
8	309	4	13
9	138	3	17
TOTAL	2970	36	TOTAL

HOLE	LENGTH MEDAL-TEE	PAR	STROKE INDEX
10	305	4	8
11	299	4	10
12	182	3	6
13	333	4	4
14	456	5	12
15	163	3	16
16	376	4	2
17	458	5	18
18	319	4	14
TOTAL	2891	36	TOTAL

KARLSKOGA

TEL : (0586)28597
LOCATION : 5 km Karlskoga E 18
ADDRESS : Valasen – 691 91 Karlskoga
HOTEL :
Scandic – Karlskoga
Tel : (0586)50460
Grythyttans – Grythyttan
Tel : (0591)14310

Karlskoga was designed by three well-known Scandinavian architects. It is a relatively flat parkland course with mature trees flanking the fairways. Water affects play on several holes. *SSS 72*

GF $

1975

18

December to April

N. Skold, N. Cederholm, B. Engdahl

L 5730 P 72

R S

Required : Handicap Certificate
Best days : Wednesdays, Thursdays and Fridays

HOLE	LENGTH MEDAL-TEE	PAR	STROKE INDEX
1	495	5	5
2	305	4	17
3	365	4	1
4	500	5	3
5	180	3	11
6	355	4	9
7	140	3	15
8	240	4	13
9	340	4	7
TOTAL	2920	36	TOTAL

HOLE	LENGTH MEDAL-TEE	PAR	STROKE INDEX
10	455	5	4
11	140	3	12
12	300	4	8
13	435	5	14
14	385	4	2
15	310	4	18
16	125	3	16
17	320	4	10
18	340	4	6
TOTAL	2810	36	TOTAL

KARLSTAD

★

TEL : (054)36353
LOCATION : 12 km Karlstad E 18
ADDRESS : Box 294 – 651 07 Karlstad 1
HOTEL :
Gustaf Fröding – Karlstad
Tel : (054)131010
Sara-Karlstad
Tel : (054)102220
Stads – Karlstad
Tel : (054)115220
RESTAURANT : Stekhuset – Karlstad
Tel : (054)163080

This very popular championship golf course, bearing all the caracteristics of its architect Nils Skold, has an interesting and varied layout. Not very hilly, most holes have tight fairways running through avenues of mature trees with ponds and ditches serving as hazards. *SSS 72*

GF $

1957

27

November to May

N. Skold

L 5955 P 72

R S

Required : Handicap Certificate
Best days : Weekdays

HOLE	LENGTH MEDAL-TEE	PAR	STROKE INDEX
1	520	5	2
2	170	3	6
3	335	4	4
4	460	5	7
5	350	4	5
6	410	4	1
7	150	3	9
8	350	4	3
9	295	4	8
TOTAL	3040	36	TOTAL

HOLE	LENGTH MEDAL-TEE	PAR	STROKE INDEX
10	435	5	8
11	175	3	4
12	375	4	1
13	325	4	3
14	140	3	9
15	460	5	5
16	325	4	7
17	355	4	2
18	325	4	6
TOTAL	2915	36	TOTAL

KATRINEHOLMS

TEL : (0150)39012/11
LOCATION : 7 km W. Katrineholm
ADDRESS : Box 74 –
641 21 Katrineholm
HOTEL :
Excelsior – Katrineholm
Tel : (0150)10922
Focus – Katrineholm
Tel : (0150)13050
Stads – Katrineholm
Tel : (0150)50440
RESTAURANT : Stortugan – Katrineholm
Tel : (0150)10212

Laid out in typical Sörmland countryside, the course has a parkland character and is of medium difficulty. Several holes run alongside the scenic 'Stensjön'lake. The club boasts a fine mansion style clubhouse. *SSS 72*

GF $

1959

18

November to May

N. Skold, I. Ringstrom

L 5850 P 72

S

R

Required : Handicap Certificate
Best days : Weekdays

HOLE	LENGTH MEDAL-TEE	PAR	STROKE INDEX
1	470	5	9
2	155	3	15
3	355	4	3
4	505	5	7
5	340	4	11
6	525	5	1
7	155	3	17
8	340	4	13
9	330	4	5
TOTAL	3175	37	TOTAL

HOLE	LENGTH MEDAL-TEE	PAR	STROKE INDEX
10	310	4	12
11	345	4	2
12	120	3	18
13	300	4	10
14	300	4	14
15	320	4	6
16	160	3	16
17	435	5	8
18	385	4	4
TOTAL	2675	35	TOTAL

KORSLÖTS

TEL : (0221)81090
LOCATION : 5 km N. Köping Rd 250
ADDRESS : Box 278 – 73126 Köping
HOTEL :
Scheele – Köping
Tel : (0221)18120

Located in Central Sweden, the course was recently extended to 18 holes. It is an undulating parkland course which runs through avenues of tall pine trees, featuring wide and generous fairways. *SSS 71*

GF $

1963

18

November to April

D. Brazier, P. Nordvall, J. Sederholm

L 5621 P 71

S

R

Required : Handicap Certificate
Best days : Any day

HOLE	LENGTH MEDAL-TEE	PAR	STROKE INDEX
1	322	4	
2	326	4	
3	135	3	
4	292	4	
5	465	5	
6	146	3	
7	350	4	
8	442	5	
9	147	3	
TOTAL	2625	35	TOTAL

HOLE	LENGTH MEDAL-TEE	PAR	STROKE INDEX
10	325	4	
11	450	5	
12	170	3	
13	446	5	
14	335	4	
15	345	4	
16	380	4	
17	160	3	
18	365	4	
TOTAL	2990	36	TOTAL

KÖRUNDA-NYNÄSHAMNS

KÖRUNDA GOLFKLUBB, NYNÄSHAMN

TEL : (0752)38666
LOCATION : 50 km Stockholm Rd 73
ADDRESS : Box 4 – 14800 Ösmo
HOTEL :
Körunda Golf – Ösmo
Tel : (0752)39030
Nynäs – Nynäshamn
Tel : (0752)11120
Trehörningen – Nynäshamn
Tel : (0752)12024

Scenically situated amidst a forest of pine trees and picturesque lakes, the scenery of the landscape is typically Swedish. The course lies on flat countryside with its holes winding through lush parkland and woodland. *SSS 72*

GF $

1977

18

November to May

A. Persson

L 5700 P 72

S

R

Required : Handicap Certificate
Best days : Weekdays

HOLE	LENGTH MEDAL-TEE	PAR	STROKE INDEX
1	280	4	13
2	455	5	7
3	335	4	11
4	480	5	1
5	95	3	17
6	350	4	5
7	365	4	9
8	155	3	15
9	380	4	3
TOTAL	2895	36	TOTAL

HOLE	LENGTH MEDAL-TEE	PAR	STROKE INDEX
10	485	5	10
11	345	4	2
12	310	4	14
13	325	4	4
14	125	3	16
15	325	4	8
16	310	4	6
17	130	3	18
18	450	5	12
TOTAL	2805	36	TOTAL

KRISTIANSTAD

★

TEL : (044)240656
LOCATION : 15 km Kristianstad
ADDRESS : Box 41 - 296 00 Ahus
HOTEL :
Slafen - Ahus
Tel : (044)248301
Grand - Kristianstad
Tel : (044)103600
Kastanjelund - Yngsjö
Tel : (044)232533
RESTAURANT : Ahus Gastgivareyard
Tel : (044)240025

Situated not far from the sea front, the Kristianstad course is laid out on flat terrain with fairways running through heather and woodland. There is only one water hazard which is a pond on the 14th fairway. The club lies in Ahus, a fine seaside resort on the Baltic. The Slafen hotel lies within walking distance from the course. *SSS 72*

GF $ — December to March — R S

1924 — D. Brazier, S. Linde

27 — L 5852 P 72, 2945 P 36

Required : Handicap Certificate
Best days : Any day

HOLE	LENGTH MEDAL-TEE	PAR	STROKE INDEX
1	452	5	7
2	357	4	3
3	196	3	7
4	342	4	1
5	318	4	15
6	184	3	11
7	309	4	13
8	471	5	9
9	359	4	5
TOTAL	2988	36	TOTAL

HOLE	LENGTH MEDAL-TEE	PAR	STROKE INDEX
10	452	5	18
11	137	3	12
12	380	4	2
13	285	4	10
14	138	3	14
15	300	4	16
16	334	4	6
17	350	4	8
18	488	5	4
TOTAL	2864	36	TOTAL

KUNGSBACKA

★

TEL : (031)936277
LOCATION : 3 km N. Kungsbacka
ADDRESS : Hamra Gard – Pl. 515
– 43040 Saro
HOTEL :
Halland – Kungsbacka
Tel : (0300)11530
Halland – Kungsbacka
Tel : (0300)11530
RESTAURANT : Blomstermala – Saro
Tel : (031)705302

Kungsbacka is a championship course of the seaside type set on the borders of the Kattegatt with some of its fairways laid out in rolling parkland. There are several water hazards. Hotel Halland is near the golf club. *SSS 72*

GF $

1974

18

 November to April

 F. Pennink

L 6120 P 72

 S

Required : Handicap Certificate
Best days : Mondays

HOLE	LENGTH MEDAL-TEE	PAR	STROKE INDEX
1	130	3	17
2	370	4	9
3	525	5	7
4	315	4	15
5	395	4	1
6	485	5	3
7	190	3	13
8	405	4	5
9	405	4	11
TOTAL	3220	36	TOTAL

HOLE	LENGTH MEDAL-TEE	PAR	STROKE INDEX
10	350	4	8
11	435	4	2
12	490	5	6
13	130	3	16
14	240	4	12
15	255	4	14
16	490	5	4
17	365	4	10
18	145	3	18
TOTAL	2900	36	TOTAL

LAGAN

★

TEL : (0372)30450
LOCATION : 10 km N. Ljungby E 4
ADDRESS : Box 63 – 340 14 Lagan
HOTEL :
Scandic – Lagan
Tel : (0372)35200
Linnéa – Ljungby
Tel : (0372)82881
Terraza – Ljungby
Tel : (0372)13560
RESTAURANT : Terraza – Ljungby
Tel : (0372)13560

An undulating parkland course with a few well-placed water hazards and bunkers. Its toughest hole is the 15th, a left hand dogleg. The 17th hole features a green on top of a hill and the 18th is an excellent finishing hole, commanding fine views of the surrounding area. *SSS 71*

GF $ — November to May — S

1966 — A. Amilon, A. Persson — R

18 — L 5580 P 71

Required : Handicap Certificate
Best days : Weekdays

HOLE	LENGTH MEDAL-TEE	PAR	STROKE INDEX
1	310	4	11
2	335	4	3
3	320	4	7
4	175	3	13
5	460	5	1
6	120	3	17
7	335	4	5
8	330	4	9
9	145	3	15
TOTAL	2530	34	TOTAL

HOLE	LENGTH MEDAL-TEE	PAR	STROKE INDEX
10	320	4	12
11	335	4	8
12	280	4	18
13	150	3	16
14	440	5	14
15	370	4	2
16	475	5	4
17	320	4	6
18	360	4	10
TOTAL	3050	37	TOTAL

LAHOLMS

TEL : (0430)30601
LOCATION : 10 km Laholm Rd 24
ADDRESS : Krokusvagen 8 –
312 00 Laholm
HOTEL :
Laholms Stad – Laholm
Tel : (0430)12830
Standard – Laholm
Tel : (0430)13318
RESTAURANT : Gröna Hästen – Laholm
Tel : (0430)10057

Situated in the western part of Sweden, this is a gently rolling parkland course featuring several attractive tree-lined holes. Laholm is a fine test for the average golfer. *SSS 70*

GF $

1964

18

November to May

J. Sederholm

L 5725 P 70

S

R

Required : Handicap Certificate
Best days : Weekdays

HOLE	LENGTH MEDAL-TEE	PAR	STROKE INDEX
1	470	5	
2	150	3	
3	390	4	
4	130	3	
5	330	4	
6	310	4	
7	180	3	
8	360	4	
9	490	5	
TOTAL	2810	35	TOTAL

HOLE	LENGTH MEDAL-TEE	PAR	STROKE INDEX
10	175	3	
11	365	4	
12	380	4	
13	450	5	
14	380	4	
15	200	3	
16	355	4	
17	160	3	
18	450	5	
TOTAL	2915	35	TOTAL

LANDERYD

TEL : (03)150493
LOCATION : 10 km SE Linköping off E4
ADDRESS : Box 11040 - 58011 Linköping
HOTEL :
Frimurare - Linköping
Tel : (013)129180
Ekoxen - Linköping
Tel : (013)141670

Designed by the Californian Ronald Fream, former assistant of Trent Jones Sr,the course which is part of a 36 holes project, threads its way through open landscape flanked by forest. It is set on both hilly and flat ground with water hazards affecting play on most of the holes. It features a cosy and local style clubhouse. *SSS 72*

GF $

1989

18

November to April

R. Fream

L 5700 P 72

R S

Required : Handicap Certificate
Best days : Any day

HOLE	LENGTH MEDAL-TEE	PAR	STROKE INDEX
1	330	4	9
2	305	4	11
3	150	3	17
4	380	4	1
5	440	5	5
6	370	4	7
7	165	3	15
8	290	4	13
9	460	5	3
TOTAL	2890	36	TOTAL

HOLE	LENGTH MEDAL-TEE	PAR	STROKE INDEX
10	350	4	2
11	130	3	16
12	440	5	10
13	420	5	4
14	340	4	12
15	160	3	14
16	480	5	6
17	125	3	18
18	365	4	8
TOTAL	2810	36	TOTAL

LANDSKRONA

★★

TEL : (0418)19528
LOCATION : 4 km Landskrona E 6
ADDRESS : Erikstorp – 261 61 Landskrona
HOTEL :
Örenas Slott – Landskrona
Tel : (0418)70250
Chaplin – Landskrona
Tel : (0418)16335
Kronan – Landskrona
Tel : (0418)16225
RESTAURANT : Erikstorps Kungsgard – Landskrona

A first class seaside course bordering the Oresund and ideal for holiday golf. Set on flat terrain, tall trees are scattered all over the course giving it a parkland character. There are some fine views overlooking the sea. A short 18 hole course has been opened in 1988. The Örenas Slott Hotel is 7km from the course. *SSS 71/62*

GF $ — November to May — R S

1960 —  T. Bruce, A. Persson — 

36 —  L 5820 P 71, 3990 P 61

Required : Handicap Certificate
Best days : Any day by prior arrangement only

HOLE	LENGTH MEDAL-TEE	PAR	STROKE INDEX
1	355	4	7
2	130	3	17
3	360	4	3
4	340	4	5
5	460	5	11
6	265	4	13
7	160	3	15
8	350	4	9
9	520	5	7
TOTAL	2940	36	TOTAL

HOLE	LENGTH MEDAL-TEE	PAR	STROKE INDEX
10	385	4	2
11	315	4	14
12	175	3	6
13	475	5	12
14	135	3	16
15	475	5	8
16	380	4	10
17	380	4	4
18	160	3	8
TOTAL	2880	35	TOTAL

LEKSAND

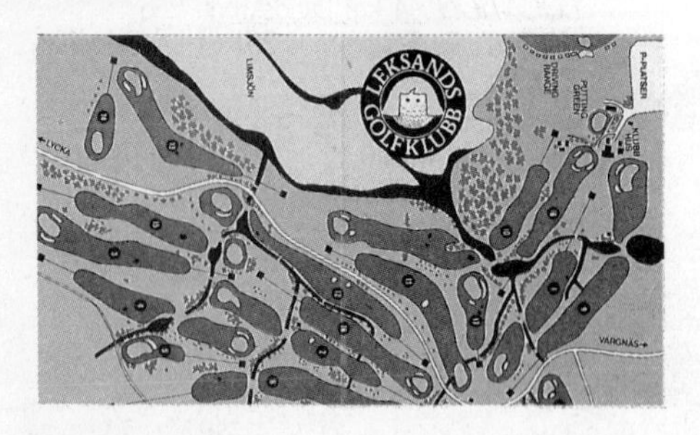

TEL : (0247)10922/14204
LOCATION : 3 km Leksand
ADDRESS : Box 25 – 79301 Leksand
HOTEL :
Dalecarlia – Tällberg
Tel : (0247)50255
Green – Tällberg
Tel : (0247)50250
Langbergs – Tällberg
Tel : (0247)50290

Set in the middle of Central Sweden, the Leksand course is picturesquely laid out on the borders of a lake called 'Limsjön'. The course is flat with numerous streams separating the holes from each other. The modern Dalecarlia hotel, nearby the golf club, has a swimming pool and several tennis courts. *SSS 72*

GF $

1977

18

November to May

N. Skold

L 5693 P 72

S

R

Required : None
Best days : Any day

HOLE	LENGTH MEDAL-TEE	PAR	STROKE INDEX
1	350	4	11
2	371	4	3
3	307	4	13
4	356	4	5
5	180	3	9
6	490	5	1
7	286	4	15
8	138	3	17
9	453	5	7
TOTAL	2931	36	TOTAL

HOLE	LENGTH MEDAL-TEE	PAR	STROKE INDEX
10	451	5	4
11	326	4	16
12	449	5	2
13	315	4	8
14	160	3	12
15	329	4	10
16	343	4	6
17	114	3	18
18	275	4	14
TOTAL	2762	36	TOTAL

LIDINGÖ

★

TEL : (08)7657911
LOCATION : 7 km Stockholm/2 km Lidingö
ADDRESS : Box 35 – 181 21 Lidingö 1
HOTEL :
Lidingöhus – Lidingö
Tel : (08)7679120
Oden – Stockholm
Tel : (08)349340

This fine inland course in the Stockholm region is worth a visit. Laid out in unspoilt sweeping landscape with beautiful trees bordering the fairways, the club has hosted many international tournaments. There are no water hazards. *SSS 71*

GF $$ — November to April — R S
1933 — —
18 — L 5672 P 71

Required : Handicap Certificate
Best days : Weekdays; Weekends after 13 h only

HOLE	LENGTH MEDAL-TEE	PAR	STROKE INDEX
1	255	4	17
2	479	5	5
3	170	3	11
4	520	5	1
5	276	4	13
6	177	3	9
7	325	4	3
8	325	4	7
9	145	3	15
TOTAL	2672	35	TOTAL

HOLE	LENGTH MEDAL-TEE	PAR	STROKE INDEX
10	445	5	14
11	137	3	18
12	485	5	4
13	338	4	10
14	314	4	12
15	347	4	6
16	175	3	16
17	414	4	2
18	345	4	8
TOTAL	3000	36	TOTAL

LIDKÖPINGS

★★

TEL : (0510)46144
LOCATION : 5 km Lidköping E 3
ADDRESS : Box 2029 –
531 02 Lidköping
HOTEL :
Stads – Lidköping
Tel : (0510)22085
Göta – Götene
Tel : (0511)50790
RESTAURANT : Edward – Lidköping
Tel : (0510)22100

Situated between Lidköping and Götene, the Lidköping championship course is laid out on flat woodland and partly on parkland. It has an entertaining layout and features several tricky, well-contrived dogleg holes, requiring a great deal of accuracy. *SSS 70*

GF $ — November to May 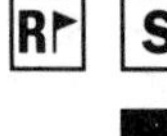 

1967 — D. Brazier  

18 — L 5565 P 70

Required : Handicap Certificate
Best days : Mondays to Saturdays inc.

HOLE	LENGTH MEDAL-TEE	PAR	STROKE INDEX
1	485	5	11
2	285	4	13
3	315	4	9
4	385	4	1
5	355	4	3
6	335	4	7
7	160	3	15
8	505	5	5
9	145	3	17
TOTAL	2970	36	TOTAL

HOLE	LENGTH MEDAL-TEE	PAR	STROKE INDEX
10	175	3	12
11	310	4	14
12	330	4	4
13	485	5	6
14	345	4	2
15	130	3	18
16	340	4	8
17	320	4	10
18	320	3	16
TOTAL	2595	34	TOTAL

LINDE

TEL : (0581)13960/15917
LOCATION : 1 km Lindesberg/42 km Orebro E 3 – E 18
ADDRESS : Dalkarlshyttan – 71131 Lindesberg
HOTEL :
Lindesberg Stads – Lindesberg
Tel : (0581)12450

One of the recent 18 hole courses designed by Jan Sederholm in 1984. The fairways meander their way through scenic undulating woodland. The first nine holes are practically encircled by picturesque lakes. *SSS 71*

GF $

October to May

S

1984

J. Sederholm

R

18

L 5585 P 71

Required : Handicap Certificate
Best days : Any day

HOLE	LENGTH MEDAL-TEE	PAR	STROKE INDEX
1	456	5	5
2	145	3	13
3	435	5	3
4	155	3	17
5	459	5	1
6	294	4	11
7	160	3	15
8	342	4	9
9	346	4	7
TOTAL	2792	36	TOTAL

HOLE	LENGTH MEDAL-TEE	PAR	STROKE INDEX
10	151	3	16
11	330	4	8
12	325	4	10
13	333	4	6
14	452	5	14
15	123	3	18
16	369	4	4
17	335	4	12
18	394	4	2
TOTAL	2812	35	TOTAL

LINDÖ

TEL : (0762)72260
LOCATION : 2,5 km Vallentuna, 20 km Stockholm E 4
ADDRESS : 18692 Vallentuna
HOTEL :
Scandic Täby – Täby
Tel : (08)7680580
RESTAURANT : Coq Blanc – Stockholm
Tel : (08)116153

Located near Stockholm, this is a good inland course with a wealth of water hazards. Almost every hole is surrounded by scenic streams and lakes. The modern sports complex boasts a swimming pool and several tennis courts. *SSS 72*

GF $

1978

27

October to May

A. Persson

L 5740 P 72, 2930 P 35

S

R

Required : Handicap Certificate
Best days : Any day

HOLE	LENGTH MEDAL-TEE	PAR	STROKE INDEX
1	350	4	7
2	335	4	11
3	120	3	17
4	490	5	1
5	170	3	5
6	315	4	9
7	360	4	3
8	300	4	15
9	435	5	13
TOTAL	2875	36	TOTAL

HOLE	LENGTH MEDAL-TEE	PAR	STROKE INDEX
10	345	4	10
11	105	3	18
12	350	4	8
13	360	4	6
14	435	5	16
15	320	4	12
16	350	4	2
17	130	3	14
18	470	5	4
TOTAL	2865	36	TOTAL

LINKÖPINGS

TEL : (013)120646
LOCATION : 5 km Linköping
ADDRESS : Kalmarvägen –
580 10 Linköping
HOTEL :
Stads – Linköping
Tel : (013)22085
Brask – Linköping
Tel : (013)130200
Stora – Linköping
Tel : (013)129630
RESTAURANT : Brannebrona Vardshus –
Gotene
Tel : (013)53180

Set in the middle of the eastern part of Sweden, the golf club lies not far from the Linköping University and is a relatively flat parkland course with stately trees bordering the fairways. Most of the greens are cunningly bunkered, and water affects play on two holes. *SSS 71*

GF $ | November to April | S
1967 | D. Brazier, R. Sundquist
18 | L 5675 P 71 | R

Required : Handicap Certificate
Best days : Weekdays before 16 h

HOLE	LENGTH MEDAL-TEE	PAR	STROKE INDEX
1	310	4	11
2	350	4	3
3	130	3	17
4	450	5	9
5	150	3	15
6	500	5	5
7	150	3	13
8	310	4	7
9	330	4	1
TOTAL	2680	35	TOTAL

HOLE	LENGTH MEDAL-TEE	PAR	STROKE INDEX
10	480	5	14
11	160	3	16
12	300	4	10
13	360	4	2
14	510	5	8
15	350	4	6
16	135	3	18
17	320	4	12
18	380	4	4
TOTAL	2995	36	TOTAL

LJUNGHUSENS

✡★★

TEL : (040)450384
LOCATION : 30 km W. Malmö E 6
ADDRESS : Kinells Vag –
236 00 Höllviken
HOTEL :
Villa Paradiset – Falsterbo
Tel : (040)470800
Gässlingen – Skanör
Tel : (040)473035
RESTAURANT : Kaptensgarden – Falsterbo
Tel : (040)470750

Situated on the scenic shores of the peninsula Falsterbonäset out in the Baltic, the Ljunghusens course is ideal for holiday golf. The course's Swedish name means 'houses on the heather', as almost every hole is encircled by heather. A flat, testing seaside course with several tough holes, especially when the wind is blowing. There are a great number of small ponds spread over the course, serving as hazards. The clubhouse is comfortable with fine views over the course and the sea. Several cottages for 2-6 persons are available near the club. *SSS 73*

GF $$

1932

27

—

D. Brazier

L 2840 P 35, 3055 P 37, 2615 P 35

Required : Handicap Certificate
Best days : Weekdays

HOLE	LENGTH MEDAL-TEE	PAR	STROKE INDEX	HOLE	LENGTH MEDAL-TEE	PAR	STROKE INDEX	HOLE	LENGTH MEDAL-TEE	PAR	STROKE INDEX
1	310	4	7	1	380	4	2	1	425	5	9
2	400	4	2	2	175	3	5	2	345	4	2
3	335	4	5	3	475	5	7	3	175	3	4
4	150	3	6	4	355	4	1	4	450	5	6
5	355	4	3	5	435	5	9	5	360	4	1
6	445	5	9	6	340	4	4	6	240	4	7
7	350	4	4	7	155	3	8	7	135	3	5
8	365	4	1	8	285	4	3	8	340	4	3
9	130	3	8	9	455	5	6	9	145	3	8
TOTAL	2840	35	TOTAL	TOTAL	3055	37	TOTAL	TOTAL	2615	35	TOTAL

LULEA

TEL : (0920)56174
LOCATION : 11 km N. Lulea E. 4
ADDRESS : Box 314-95125 Lulea
HOTEL :
Lulea-Lulea
Tel : (0920)94000
Aveny-Lulea
Tel : (0920)21820
RESTAURANT : Max-Lulea
Tel : (0920)20220

Lulea is the most northern 18 hole golf course in the world. It is a combined parkland and woodland course spaciously laid out in flat landscape with plenty of room between the fairways. Several well placed lakes demand accuracy on five holes. During the middle of the summer one can play golf here by day and night. The club boasts a charming clubhouse built at the turn of the century. *SSS 72*

GF $

 October to May

S

1955

 N. Skold

18

L 5675 P 72

R

Required : Handicap Certificate
Best days : Weekdays

HOLE	LENGTH MEDAL-TEE	PAR	STROKE INDEX
1	310	4	11
2	125	3	17
3	335	4	5
4	350	4	3
5	485	5	1
6	135	3	15
7	275	4	13
8	460	5	7
9	305	4	9
TOTAL	2780	36	TOTAL

HOLE	LENGTH MEDAL-TEE	PAR	STROKE INDEX
10	310	4	16
11	175	3	12
12	315	4	10
13	355	4	6
14	465	5	2
15	145	3	18
16	460	5	8
17	310	4	14
18	360	4	4
TOTAL	2895	36	TOTAL

LUNDS AKADEMISKA

TEL : (046)99005
LOCATION : 5 km E. Lund
ADDRESS : Kungsmarken – 225 90 Lund
HOTEL :
Grand – Lund
Tel : (046)117010
Concordia – Lund
Tel : (046)135050
Sparta – Lund
Tel : (046)124080
RESTAURANT : Lundia – Lund
Tel : (046)124140

Located not far from the Swedish South Coast, Lunds Akademiska golf club belongs to the well-known University of Lund. An attractive parkland course with wide and generous fairways laid out on gently rolling countryside. A lake, the 'Glomsjön', lies in the middle of the course with a stream, the 'Glomsbäcken' meandering its way through several holes. The course is of championship standard and one of Sweden's finest golf courses. *SSS 72*

GF $ — November to April — R S

1936 — S. Bostrom, J. Morrisson

18 — L 5785 P 72

Required : Handicap Certificate
Best days : Weekdays

HOLE	LENGTH MEDAL-TEE	PAR	STROKE INDEX
1	320	4	12
2	125	3	16
3	320	4	6
4	430	5	18
5	315	4	4
6	170	3	10
7	410	4	2
8	340	4	8
9	490	5	14
TOTAL	2920	36	TOTAL

HOLE	LENGTH MEDAL-TEE	PAR	STROKE INDEX
10	470	5	11
11	325	4	3
12	410	5	17
13	145	3	15
14	410	4	1
15	295	4	13
16	180	3	7
17	340	4	5
18	380	4	9
TOTAL	2955	36	TOTAL

LYCKORNA

★

TEL : (0522)20176
LOCATION : 2 km Lyckorna/Ljungskile E 6
ADDRESS : Box 66 – 45900 Ljungskile
HOTEL :
Sarla – Ljungskile
Tel : (0522)20431
RESTAURANT : Stenungsbaden – Stenungsund
Tel : (0303)83100

Located on Sweden's West Coast, this is a very picturesque undulating course laid out partly around a scenic lake in a setting of luxuriant pine wood. The Sarla hotel is situated 1 km from the Lyckorna golf club. *SSS 72*

GF $ — November to April — S

1967 —  A. Amilon —   

18 — L 5845 P 72 — 

Required : Handicap Certificate
Best days : Weekdays

HOLE	LENGTH MEDAL-TEE	PAR	STROKE INDEX
1	285	4	16
2	430	5	12
3	285	4	6
4	155	3	14
5	325	4	4
6	345	4	10
7	395	4	2
8	465	5	8
9	120	3	18
TOTAL	2805	36	TOTAL

HOLE	LENGTH MEDAL-TEE	PAR	STROKE INDEX
10	350	4	1
11	475	5	5
12	150	3	13
13	325	4	9
14	330	4	15
15	340	4	11
16	510	5	3
17	165	3	17
18	370	4	7
TOTAL	3015	36	TOTAL

LYSEGARDENS

TEL : (0303)23426
LOCATION : 9 km Kungälv
ADDRESS : Box 82 – 442 21 Kungälv
HOTEL :
Fars Hatt – Kungälv
Tel : (0303)10970
Thorskog Slott – Lilla Edet
Tel : (0520)61000
RESTAURANT : Stigs – Backadal
Tel : (031)522281

One of Sweden's finest inland courses is the Lysegarden championship layout which has plenty of interest and variety. Some of its holes cut into dense woodland, others are laid out in rolling open countryside. There are many water hazards such as an artificial lake (filled with trout), causing problems on six of the last nine holes. Its feature hole is the 13th, a difficult dogleg hole with its fairway and green flanked by a ravine and a waterfall.
SSS 71

GF $

1966

27

November to April

E. Röhss, A. Engström

L 5944 P 71

S

R

Required : Handicap Certificate
Best days : Weekdays

HOLE	LENGTH MEDAL-TEE	PAR	STROKE INDEX
1	150	3	15
2	325	4	5
3	300	4	7
4	144	3	17
5	515	5	9
6	345	4	3
7	320	4	13
8	310	4	11
9	550	5	1
TOTAL	2959	36	TOTAL

HOLE	LENGTH MEDAL-TEE	PAR	STROKE INDEX
10	355	4	12
11	215	3	8
12	510	5	10
13	365	4	2
14	365	4	14
15	155	3	16
16	550	5	4
17	150	3	18
18	320	4	6
TOTAL	2985	35	TOTAL

MALMÖ

TEL : (040)292535
LOCATION : In Malmö Segeväng
ADDRESS : Box 21068-Segesvängen
– 20021 Malmö
HOTEL : HP
Scandic
Tel : (040)180120
Kramer – Malmö
Tel : (040)70120
Strand – Malmö
Tel : (040)162030

A pleasant 18 hole course designed by the famous Swedish golf architect Jan Sederholm in the popular seaside resort of Malmö, Sweden's third biggest town. Located inland, the course is flat and rather windy with several natural hazards, such as lakes and streams crossing fairways and greens. One of its most attractive holes is the 6th with an island green. The Scandic Hotel is situated 300m from the first tee. *SSS 71*

GF $

—

 S

1981

J. Sederholm

18

L 5630 P 72

Required : Handicap Certificate
Best days : Mondays, Thursdays and Fridays

HOLE	LENGTH MEDAL-TEE	PAR	STROKE INDEX
1	325	4	
2	340	4	
3	335	4	
4	440	5	
5	355	5	
6	140	3	
7	275	4	
8	140	3	
9	320	4	
TOTAL	2670	36	TOTAL

HOLE	LENGTH MEDAL-TEE	PAR	STROKE INDEX
10	360	4	
11	280	4	
12	355	4	
13	135	3	
14	505	5	
15	375	4	
16	330	4	
17	165	3	
18	455	5	
TOTAL	2960	36	TOTAL

MARIESTADS

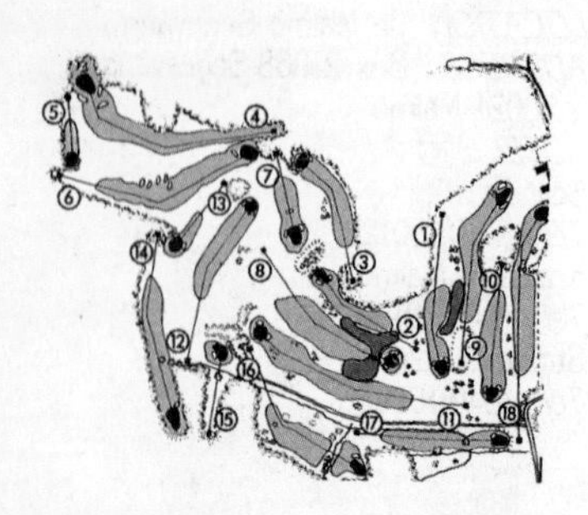

TEL : (0501)17383
LOCATION : 2 km Mariestad E 3
ADDRESS : Box 299 – 542 01 Mariestad
HOTEL :
Stadshotellet – Mariestad
Tel : (0501)13990
Vänerport – Mariestad
Tel : (0501)11111
RESTAURANT : Stekhuset – Hövdingen
Tel : (0501)19900

Set in West Sweden, Mariestad is laid out near a large lake in a flat parkland setting featuring several sporting water holes. *SSS 72*

GF $

1980

18

 November to April

 S. Meistedt

L 5930 P 72

 S

Required : Handicap Certificate
Best days : Any day

HOLE	LENGTH MEDAL-TEE	PAR	STROKE INDEX
1	335	4	5
2	320	4	7
3	315	4	13
4	435	5	17
5	130	3	15
6	405	4	1
7	195	3	9
8	460	5	11
9	350	4	3
TOTAL	2945	36	TOTAL

HOLE	LENGTH MEDAL-TEE	PAR	STROKE INDEX
10	305	4	18
11	490	5	10
12	360	4	6
13	155	3	16
14	360	4	2
15	160	3	14
16	360	4	4
17	310	4	8
18	485	5	12
TOTAL	2985	36	TOTAL

MARKS

TEL : (0320)14220
LOCATION : 2 km Kinna RV 41
ADDRESS : Brättingstorpsvägen 28 – 511 00 Kinna
HOTEL :
Kinna – Kinna
Tel : (0320)14300

Marks is a pleasant undulating parkland course, not too difficult for the average golfer. Recently moved up to 18 holes, it is located near the city of Kinna on Sweden's west coast. *SSS 69*

GF $ — November to May — S

1962 — J. Sederholm — R

18 — L 5155 P 69

Required : Handicap Certificate
Best days : Weekdays

HOLE	LENGTH MEDAL-TEE	PAR	STROKE INDEX
1	260	4	17
2	320	4	9
3	140	3	15
4	345	4	1
5	435	5	3
6	145	3	11
7	315	4	7
8	300	4	13
9	175	3	5
TOTAL	2435	34	TOTAL

HOLE	LENGTH MEDAL-TEE	PAR	STROKE INDEX
10	345	4	8
11	355	4	2
12	305	4	10
13	255	4	16
14	135	3	14
15	500	5	6
16	315	4	12
17	140	3	18
18	370	4	4
TOTAL	2720	35	TOTAL

MÖLLE

TEL : (042)47520
LOCATION : 3 km Mölle
ADDRESS : Kullagarden – 26042 Mölle
HOTEL :
Grand – Mölle
Tel : (042)47280
Rusthallargarden – Arild
Tel : (042)46275
RESTAURANT : Kullagardens Wärdshus – Mölle
Tel : (042)47148

Set in fine natural surroundings amid hills, north of Rya, near the picturesque village of Mölle, the course lies in the middle of a nature reserve on excellent turfland. One of Sweden's most interesting courses, it features various tees perched on steep cliffs overlooking rocky shores. The only problem on this course is presented by the continuous ups and downs of the terrain. *SSS 70*

GF $$

1943

18

December to April

T. Bruce

L 5640 P 70

S

Required : Handicap Certificate
Best days : Weekdays

HOLE	LENGTH MEDAL-TEE	PAR	STROKE INDEX
1	325	4	8
2	160	3	14
3	330	4	4
4	160	3	16
5	330	4	10
6	470	5	2
7	160	3	18
8	360	4	6
9	320	4	12
TOTAL	2615	34	TOTAL

HOLE	LENGTH MEDAL-TEE	PAR	STROKE INDEX
10	365	4	3
11	145	3	17
12	360	4	7
13	415	4	11
14	460	5	1
15	290	4	13
16	360	4	9
17	435	5	5
18	195	3	15
TOTAL	3025	36	TOTAL

MORA

TEL : (0250)10182
LOCATION : 1 km Mora
ADDRESS : Box 264 – 79201 Mora
HOTEL :
Scandic – Mora
Tel : (0250)15070
Ljustret – Mora
Tel : (0250)17800
Siljan – Mora
Tel : (0250)13000

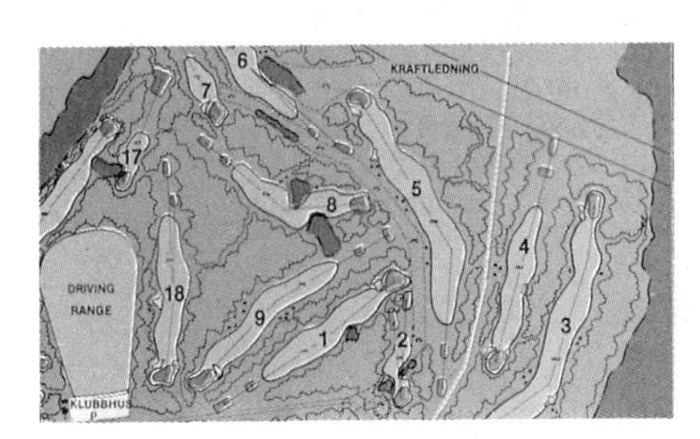

Peacefully located in central Sweden on the borders of a lake called the 'Osterdalalven', the course is flanked by water on three sides. Laid out in dense woodland, this pleasant course is ideal for holiday golf being near the resort of Mora which offers many other sports and leisure facilities like sailing, tennis, trekking, riding, etc.. *SSS 72*

GF $ — November to March — S
1985 — S. Linde
18 — L 5630 P 72 — R

Required : Handicap Certificate
Best days : Any day

HOLE	LENGTH MEDAL-TEE	PAR	STROKE INDEX
1	310	4	11
2	140	3	15
3	465	5	5
4	330	4	3
5	445	5	9
6	355	4	1
7	175	3	13
8	280	4	17
9	310	4	7
TOTAL	2810	36	TOTAL

HOLE	LENGTH MEDAL-TEE	PAR	STROKE INDEX
10	305	4	10
11	495	5	2
12	360	4	4
13	125	3	18
14	355	4	6
15	290	4	16
16	435	5	14
17	155	3	8
18	300	4	12
TOTAL	2820	36	TOTAL

MOSJÖ

TEL : (019)225780
LOCATION : 10 km S. Örebro
ADDRESS : Mosjö Gard - 70594 Örebro
HOTEL :
Good Morning - Örebro
Tel : (019)170707
Grand - Örebro
Tel : (019)150200
Grev Rosen - Örebro
Tel : (019)130240

An attractive and scenic layout with lots of variety, this scottish style course runs on flat terain with hillocks and lots of water. Each hole is guarded by at least one or two ponds which makes this venue a fine test of golf. *SSS 74*

GF $ — November to May 

1988 — A. Pehrsson 

18 — L 6225 P72 

Required : None
Best days : Any days

HOLE	LENGTH MEDAL-TEE	PAR	STROKE INDEX
1	495	5	8
2	340	4	4
3	345	4	12
4	170	3	16
5	320	4	10
6	335	4	2
7	365	4	6
8	155	3	18
9	465	5	14
TOTAL	2990	36	TOTAL

HOLE	LENGTH MEDAL-TEE	PAR	STROKE INDEX
10	360	4	13
11	385	4	5
12	165	3	15
13	530	5	1
14	370	4	7
15	380	4	13
16	180	3	17
17	485	5	9
18	380	4	11
TOTAL	3235	36	TOTAL

MOTALA

TEL : (0141)50840
LOCATION : 5 km Motala R 50, in Tuddarp
ADDRESS : Box 264 – 591 23 Motala
HOTEL :
Stads – Motala
Tel : (0141)16400
Palace – Motala
Tel : (0141)16660
RESTAURANT : Baltzar – Motala
Tel : (0141)54330

Not far from the holiday resort of Motala set along a scenic lake, the golf course is laid out in typical Swedish undulating countryside with numerous small water hazards. There is an attractive clubhouse overlooking the course. *SSS 72*

GF $ — November to May — S

1966 — D. Brazier, N. Skold, J. Sederholm — 

18 — L 5855 P 72 — 

Required : Handicap Certificate
Best days : Weekdays

HOLE	LENGTH MEDAL-TEE	PAR	STROKE INDEX
1	450	5	13
2	315	4	3
3	155	3	15
4	480	5	11
5	355	4	7
6	170	3	17
7	345	4	1
8	355	4	5
9	435	5	9
TOTAL	3060	37	TOTAL

HOLE	LENGTH MEDAL-TEE	PAR	STROKE INDEX
10	315	4	14
11	435	5	12
12	335	4	10
13	145	3	16
14	345	4	2
15	140	3	18
16	370	4	4
17	335	4	8
18	375	4	6
TOTAL	2795	35	TOTAL

NORRKÖPINGS

TEL : (011)35235
LOCATION : 8 km. Norrköping E 4
ADDRESS : Klinga - 60002 Norrköping
HOTEL :
Standard - Norrköping
Tel : (011)129220
Princess - Norrköping
Tel : (011)197220
Scandic - Norrköping
Tel : (011)170020
RESTAURANT : Peter's Pub - Norrköping
Tel : (011)183130

One of the oldest golf clubs in Sweden, having been founded in 1928. Located in the middle of eastern Sweden, this inland course lies on rolling terrain and is partly flanked by dense forest. *SSS 73*

GF — October to April — S

1928 — N. Skold — 

18 — L 5930 P 73 — 

Required : Handicap Certificate
Best days : Any day except Saturdays

HOLE	LENGTH MEDAL-TEE	PAR	STROKE INDEX
1	465	5	5
2	300	4	11
3	310	4	9
4	135	3	17
5	320	4	3
6	310	4	13
7	335	4	7
8	440	5	15
9	360	4	1
TOTAL	2975	37	TOTAL

HOLE	LENGTH MEDAL-TEE	PAR	STROKE INDEX
10	395	4	4
11	325	4	6
12	150	3	18
13	320	4	10
14	495	5	12
15	330	4	2
16	450	5	16
17	160	3	14
18	330	4	8
TOTAL	2955	36	TOTAL

ÖIJAREDS

★

TEL : (0302)30604
LOCATION : 24 km Alingsas/33 km Göteborg E3
ADDRESS : Pl. 1082 – 448 00 Floda
HOTEL :
Parkaden – Alingsas
Tel : (0322)17020
RESTAURANT : Scandic – Alingsas
Tel : (0322)14000

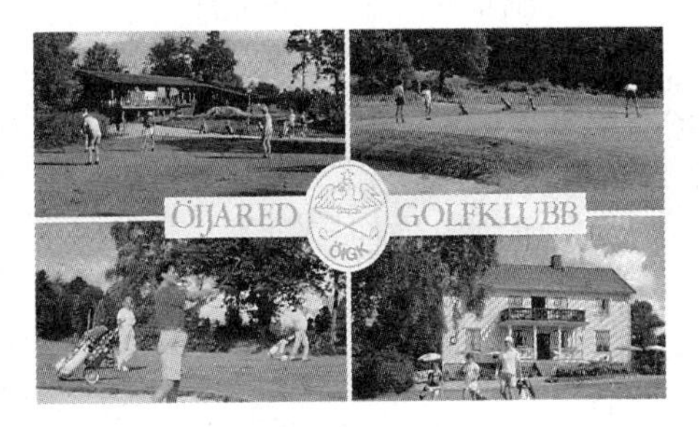

The Old Course is designed by Eric Röhss and Douglas Brazier. Set on gently undulating woodland, it has an attractive layout of championship standard with its fairways cutting through dense forest. The New Course, designed by Anders Amilon, is of the parkland type with a fine setting of trees and a lake on the 9th hole. The country club forms with their new built 18 hole course and a 9 hole iron course the largest golfing facilities in Continental Europe with its 63 holes. *SSS 71/71*

GF $$

1958

36

November to April

E. Röhss, D. Brazier, A. Amilon

L 5655 P 71, 5870 P 72

S

R

Required : Handicap Certificate, Club Membership Card
Best days : Weekdays; Weekends after 15 h

Old Course

HOLE	LENGTH MEDAL-TEE	PAR	STROKE INDEX
1	460	4	9
2	355	3	3
3	140	4	15
4	285	4	13
5	390	4	1
6	355	4	7
7	330	4	11
8	365	4	5
9	455	5	14
TOTAL	3135	37	TOTAL

HOLE	LENGTH MEDAL-TEE	PAR	STROKE INDEX
10	475	5	10
11	110	3	18
12	350	4	6
13	280	4	12
14	350	4	4
15	150	3	16
16	350	4	2
17	335	4	8
18	120	3	17
TOTAL	2520	34	TOTAL

New Course

HOLE	LENGTH MEDAL-TEE	PAR	STROKE INDEX
1	330	4	3
2	375	4	1
3	325	4	15
4	190	3	13
5	475	5	8
6	345	4	2
7	355	4	4
8	350	4	14
9	175	3	12
TOTAL	2920	35	TOTAL

HOLE	LENGTH MEDAL-TEE	PAR	STROKE INDEX
10	460	5	6
11	145	3	18
12	435	5	10
13	290	4	16
14	320	4	11
15	475	5	5
16	315	4	9
17	160	3	17
18	350	4	7
TOTAL	2950	37	TOTAL

ONSJÖ

TEL : (0521)64149
LOCATION : 3 km Vänersborg
ADDRESS : Box 100 –
46200 Vänersborg
HOTEL :
Scandic – Vänersborg
Tel : (0521)62120
Ronnums Herrgård – Vargön
Tel : (0521)23270

The Onsjö golf club is situated 3km from Vänersborg, at the entrance to Volvo Brandt, on varying terrain, partly open and partly wooded. The course has been extended to 18 holes in 1986. The first class Scandic hotel, with an indoor swimming pool, is nearby the club. *SSS 72*

GF $ — S

1974 —

18 L 5730 P 72 R

Required : Handicap Certificate
Best days : Any day

HOLE	LENGTH MEDAL-TEE	PAR	STROKE INDEX
1	325	4	5
2	320	4	9
3	145	3	17
4	450	5	7
5	400	4	1
6	320	4	11
7	150	3	13
8	310	4	3
9	330	4	15
TOTAL	2750	35	TOTAL

HOLE	LENGTH MEDAL-TEE	PAR	STROKE INDEX
10	475	5	4
11	320	4	10
12	425	5	14
13	150	3	16
14	310	4	12
15	120	3	18
16	360	4	2
17	470	5	6
18	350	4	8
TOTAL	2980	37	TOTAL

ÖREBRO

★

TEL : (019)91065
LOCATION : 22 km Örebro E 18
ADDRESS : 71015 Vintrosa
HOTEL : HF
Örebro Golf
Tel : (019)91065
Sanna Kroa – Vintrosa
Tel : (019)94414
Scandic – Örebro
Tel : (019)130480

This picturesque inland course is worth a visit as it has an entertaining layout. Set on rolling parkland amongst woodland, the course is scattered with old trees and includes several water hazards. The par 4 holes are of excellent quality. The Golfhotel has 7 rooms with 22 beds, and is equipped with a swimming pool. *SSS 72*

GF $

1938

18

 November to May

 N. Skold

L 5865 P 71

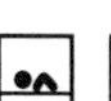 

RF

Required : Handicap Certificate
Best days : Weekdays except Wednesdays

HOLE	LENGTH MEDAL-TEE	PAR	STROKE INDEX
1	345	4	9
2	540	5	1
3	140	3	15
4	335	4	3
5	160	3	17
6	320	4	13
7	445	5	7
8	345	4	11
9	380	4	5
TOTAL	3010	36	TOTAL

HOLE	LENGTH MEDAL-TEE	PAR	STROKE INDEX
10	390	4	2
11	310	4	18
12	325	4	10
13	195	3	12
14	465	5	6
15	145	3	16
16	365	4	4
17	335	4	8
18	325	4	14
TOTAL	2855	35	TOTAL

ÖSTERÅKER

TEL : (0764)85190
LOCATION : 10 km SW Stockholm
E3/V.276
ADDRESS : Box 314 - 18424 - Åkersberga
HOTEL :
Stuva Wärdshus - Åkersberga
Tel : (0764)62524
Diplomat - Stockholm
Tel : (08)635800
Oden - Stockholm
Tel : (08)349340

At only 10 km from Stockholm, the new Österåker course with its 36 well designed holes will certainly become a popular golfing venue. Both courses (East and West) are built on flat landscape in the middle of Stockholm's archipelago. Many water hazards affect play throughout the course. *SSS 72*

GF $$ — November to March — S

1990 — J. Sederholm

36 — L 5801 P 72, 5856 P 72 — R

Required : Handicap Certificate
Best days : Weekdays

HOLE	LENGTH MEDAL-TEE	PAR	STROKE INDEX
1	473	5	10
2	294	4	18
3	264	4	6
4	151	3	14
5	375	4	2
6	444	5	4
7	143	3	12
8	344	4	8
9	326	4	16
TOTAL	2814	36	TOTAL

HOLE	LENGTH MEDAL-TEE	PAR	STROKE INDEX
10	317	4	17
11	382	4	1
12	354	4	5
13	475	5	9
14	152	3	15
15	349	4	3
16	321	4	11
17	158	3	7
18	479	5	13
TOTAL	2987	36	TOTAL

HOLE	LENGTH MEDAL-TEE	PAR	STROKE INDEX
1	338	4	4
2	326	4	12
3	451	5	8
4	381	4	6
5	149	3	16
6	342	4	10
7	335	4	14
8	134	3	18
9	485	5	2
TOTAL	2941	36	TOTAL

HOLE	LENGTH MEDAL-TEE	PAR	STROKE INDEX
10	446	5	11
11	331	4	15
12	511	5	3
13	150	3	9
14	348	4	5
15	288	4	7
16	285	4	17
17	130	3	13
18	400	4	1
TOTAL	2889	36	TOTAL

ÖSTERLENS

TEL : (0414)24230
LOCATION : 10 km N. Simrishamn
ADDRESS : Lilla Vik –
272 00 Simrishamn
HOTEL : HR
Lilla Vik
Tel : (0414)24280
Kockska Gården – Simrishamn
Tel : (0414)11755

A fine seaside course bordering the Baltic coast and ideal for holiday golf. Set on mostly open terrain, the course is separated from the sea by large trees. The course is part of a holiday complex including a hotel, several cottages for rent, and equipped with a swimming pool and tennis courts. *SSS 72*

GF $

 —

1945

 T. Nordstrom

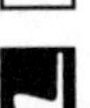

18

L 5815 P 72

Required : Handicap Certificate
Best days : Weekdays

HOLE	LENGTH MEDAL-TEE	PAR	STROKE INDEX
1	475	5	11
2	295	4	3
3	140	3	17
4	300	4	9
5	155	3	15
6	440	5	5
7	340	4	1
8	170	3	7
9	285	4	13
TOTAL	2600	35	TOTAL

HOLE	LENGTH MEDAL-TEE	PAR	STROKE INDEX
10	340	4	6
11	500	5	12
12	150	3	18
13	480	5	8
14	340	4	16
15	315	4	2
16	345	4	10
17	380	4	4
18	365	4	14
TOTAL	3215	37	TOTAL

ÖSTERSUND-FRÖSÖ

✡

TEL : (063)43001
LOCATION : 6 km Östersund
ADDRESS : Fritzhemsgatan 49 – 832 00 Frösön
HOTEL :
Frösö Wardshus – Frösön
Tel : (063)43163
Zäta – Östersund
Tel : (063)117860
RESTAURANT : Scandic – Östersund
Tel : (063)127560

The course lies in a region called the 'Southern Norrland' in the north of Sweden, located where the sun never sets in summer. It is scenically laid out within a splendid natural landscape amongst lakes in a parkland setting and backed by distant hills. *SSS 73*

GF $

1947

18

November to May

N. Skold

L 5130 P 73

S

R

Required : Handicap Certificate
Best days : Mondays to Thursdays inc.

HOLE	LENGTH MEDAL-TEE	PAR	STROKE INDEX
1	435	5	13
2	280	4	5
3	440	5	7
4	125	3	17
5	300	4	3
6	290	4	1
7	135	3	15
8	375	5	9
9	250	4	11
TOTAL	2630	37	TOTAL

HOLE	LENGTH MEDAL-TEE	PAR	STROKE INDEX
10	290	4	4
11	315	4	2
12	410	5	10
13	240	4	18
14	130	3	14
15	390	5	6
16	310	4	12
17	140	3	16
18	275	4	8
TOTAL	2500	36	TOTAL

ÖVIKS PUTTOM

TEL : (0660)64070/62488
LOCATION : 13 km N. Örnsköldsvik E 4
ADDRESS : Idrottens Hus –
89132 Örnsköldsvik
HOTEL :
Scandic – Örnsköldsvik
Tel : (0660)82870
Sara – Örnsköldsvik
Tel : (0660)10110

During summer, one can play golf around the clock at the Öviks Puttom golf course, situated in the northern part of Sweden. Designed by Nils Skold, the course is constructed in the form of a four-leaf clover on undulating terrain. A feature of the course are two large lakes, the Lill-Rössjön and the Stor-Rössjön, serving as hazards. *SSS 72*

GF $ — October to June — R S
1967 — N. Skold
18 — L 5025 P 72

Required : None
Best days : Any day

HOLE	LENGTH MEDAL-TEE	PAR	STROKE INDEX
1	265	4	15
2	285	4	5
3	120	3	17
4	380	5	3
5	135	3	11
6	285	4	7
7	290	4	1
8	275	4	13
9	405	5	9
TOTAL	2440	36	TOTAL

HOLE	LENGTH MEDAL-TEE	PAR	STROKE INDEX
10	330	4	2
11	330	4	6
12	95	3	18
13	385	5	8
14	405	5	10
15	135	3	14
16	260	4	12
17	340	4	4
18	305	4	16
TOTAL	2585	36	TOTAL

PARTILLE

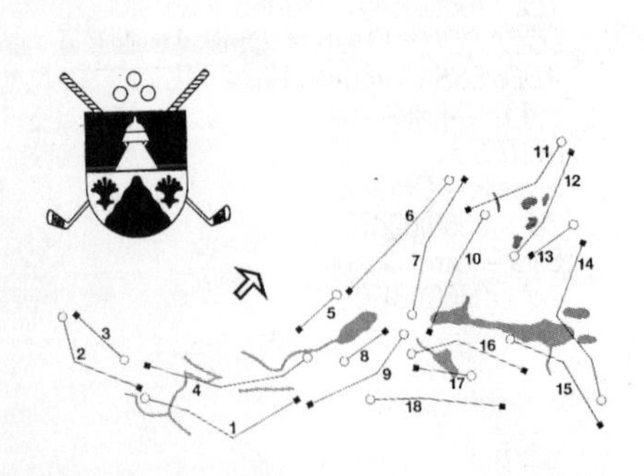

TEL : (031)987004
LOCATION : 8 km Partille
ADDRESS : Öjersjö – Box 234 – 433 50 Partille
HOTEL :
Partille-Partille
Tel : (031)440760
Örgryte – Göteborg
Tel : (031)197620
Tidbloms – Göteborg
Tel : (031)192070

Inaugurated in 1986, Partille is a sporting golf course designed by Jan Sederholm. It is set in undulating countryside near Göteborg with its fairways running through woodland and parkland. Streams and ponds serve as hazards on many holes. *SSS 70*

GF $ — S

1986 J. Sederholm R

18 L 5530 P 70

Required : Handicap Certificate
Best days : Any day

HOLE	LENGTH MEDAL-TEE	PAR	STROKE INDEX
1	430	5	15
2	315	4	3
3	150	3	13
4	455	5	5
5	100	3	11
6	395	4	1
7	390	4	7
8	125	3	17
9	330	4	9
TOTAL	2690	35	TOTAL

HOLE	LENGTH MEDAL-TEE	PAR	STROKE INDEX
10	290	4	16
11	370	4	2
12	325	4	14
13	175	3	10
14	480	5	6
15	375	4	4
16	285	4	12
17	165	3	8
18	375	4	18
TOTAL	2840	35	TOTAL

PERSTORPS

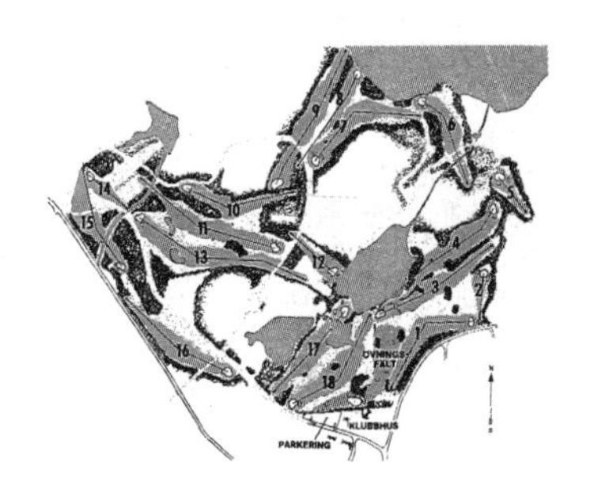

TEL : (0435)35411
LOCATION : 1 km Perstorp Rd 21
ADDRESS : Box 87 – 284 00 Perstorp
HOTEL :
Gästgivaren – Klippan
Tel : (0435)12010
Perstorp – Perstorp
Tel : (0435)34040

Situated in southern Sweden, Perstorp is a parkland course having undulating fairways. Several holes are laid out alongside large lakes, and picturesque streams serve as hazards.
SSS 71

GF $ | November to April | S

1963 | N. Amilon, A.Persson | 

18 | L 5675 P 71 | R

Required : Handicap Certificate
Best days : Weekdays

HOLE	LENGTH MEDAL-TEE	PAR	STROKE INDEX
1	300	4	13
2	125	3	15
3	370	4	7
4	450	5	9
5	130	3	11
6	330	4	5
7	380	4	3
8	275	4	17
9	370	4	1
TOTAL	2730	35	TOTAL

HOLE	LENGTH MEDAL-TEE	PAR	STROKE INDEX
10	315	4	18
11	485	5	8
12	170	3	10
13	525	5	2
14	155	3	4
15	330	4	4
16	350	4	6
17	300	4	12
18	315	4	14
TOTAL	2945	36	TOTAL

RÄTTVIKS

✡

TEL : (0248)10773
LOCATION : 1 km N. Rättvik Rd 70
ADDRESS : Fack 29 – 795 00 Rättvik
HOTEL :
Lerdalshöjden – Rättvik
Tel : (0248)11150
Siljanshill – Rättvik
Tel : (0248)13350
Stiftsgarden – Rättvik
Tel : (0248)11020
RESTAURANT : Lustigsgarden – Rättvik
Tel : (0248)10039

Set in a charming natural landscape, the course is near the holiday resort of Rättvik, with its well-known entertainment park, lake and beaches, riding stables, swimming pools, and many other leisure activities. The course is undulating and densely wooded with high, centuries-old Dalecarlien pines bordering the holes. It is part of the golf village which has well-equipped cottages for rent. *SSS 69*

GF $ — November to May 

1954 — T. Bruce 

18 — L 5309 P 70 — R

Required : Handicap Certificate
Best days : Any day

HOLE	LENGTH MEDAL-TEE	PAR	STROKE INDEX
1	284	4	11
2	117	3	13
3	349	4	1
4	150	3	15
5	318	4	5
6	454	5	7
7	364	4	3
8	435	5	9
9	133	3	17
TOTAL	2604	35	TOTAL

HOLE	LENGTH MEDAL-TEE	PAR	STROKE INDEX
10	338	4	10
11	169	3	8
12	491	5	2
13	112	3	18
14	270	4	16
15	164	3	14
16	368	4	4
17	476	5	6
18	317	4	12
TOTAL	2705	35	TOTAL

RINGENÄS

TEL : (035)59050
LOCATION : 10 km NW Halmstad
ADDRESS : Strandlida-30591 Halmstad
HOTEL :
Amadeus-Halmstad
Tel : (035)109770
Norre Park-Halmstad
Tel : (035)118555
Strandgarden-Halmstad
Tel : (035)30745
RESTAURANT : Krögar Anders-Halmstad
Tel : (035)59450

The Ringenäs golf club is situated near the fine seaside resort of Halmstad on Sweden's popular West Coast. Its 27 holes are laid alongside the Ostersund sea front on partly flat and sometimes rolling landscape. It features spacious fairways with few trees and it is well bunkered with lakes serving as hazards.

GF $

 1986

27

December to March

S. Lunde

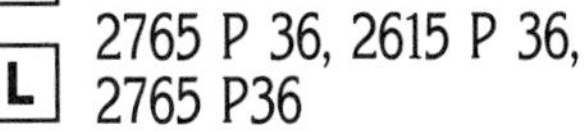
L 2765 P 36, 2615 P 36, 2765 P36

Required : Handicap Certificate
Best days : Weekdays

HOLE	LENGTH MEDAL-TEE	PAR	STROKE INDEX	HOLE	LENGTH MEDAL-TEE	PAR	STROKE INDEX	HOLE	LENGTH MEDAL-TEE	PAR	STROKE INDEX
1	305	4	7	1	340	4	7	1	440	5	4
2	470	5	4	2	160	3	4	2	340	4	1
3	300	4	6	3	430	5	8	3	290	4	5
4	325	4	3	4	145	3	6	4	160	3	6
5	150	3	9	5	385	4	1	5	290	4	8
6	320	4	2	6	265	4	5	6	300	4	9
7	450	5	1	7	470	5	2	7	175	3	3
8	320	4	8	8	320	4	3	8	330	4	2
9	125	3	5	9	100	3	9	9	440	5	7
TOTAL	2765	36	TOTAL	TOTAL	2615	35	TOTAL	TOTAL	2765	36	TOTAL

ROMELEASENS

TEL : (046)82012
LOCATION : 7 km Veberöd Rd 12
ADDRESS : Kvarnbrodda – 24014 Veberöd
HOTEL :
Jorgen – Malmö
Tel : (040)77300
Kramer – Malmö
Tel : (040)70120
Strand – Malmö
Tel : (040)162030
RESTAURANT : Kramer – Malmö
Tel : (040)70120

Situated between Veberöd and Skurup, not far from the city of Malmö, this is a wooded inland course of medium difficulty set in rolling countryside. Water affects play on seven holes. *SSS 72*

GF $

1969

18

December to April

D. Brazier

L 5830 P 72

S

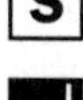

Required : Handicap Certificate
Best days : Weekdays except Wednesdays

HOLE	LENGTH MEDAL-TEE	PAR	STROKE INDEX
1	320	4	7
2	140	3	17
3	325	4	5
4	435	5	11
5	355	4	3
6	330	4	9
7	450	5	1
8	320	4	13
9	160	3	15
TOTAL	2835	36	TOTAL

HOLE	LENGTH MEDAL-TEE	PAR	STROKE INDEX
10	415	4	2
11	485	5	14
12	125	3	14
13	255	4	18
14	390	4	6
15	340	4	4
16	380	4	8
17	140	3	16
18	465	5	10
TOTAL	2995	36	TOTAL

ROSLAGENS

TEL : (0176)37194
LOCATION : 7 km Norrtälje
ADDRESS : Box 110 – 761 88 Norrtälje
HOTEL :
Roslagen – Norrtälje
Tel : (0176)17180
Havsbaden – Grisslehamn
Tel : (01765)30021
Norrtälje – Norrtälje
Tel : (0176)17000
RESTAURANT : Grisslehamns – Grisslehamn
Tel : (0175)30021

Located in Central Sweden, near the holiday resort of Norrtälje, Roslagens is a quite testing golf course with its 27 holes set in attractive undulating woodland and parkland with several narrow fairways running through pine forest. *SSS 72*

GF $ | October to May | S

1965 | T. Oxenstierna

27 | L 5650 P 72 | R

Required : Handicap Certificate
Best days : Mondays, Thursdays

HOLE	LENGTH MEDAL-TEE	PAR	STROKE INDEX
1	340	4	9
2	435	5	13
3	135	3	17
4	335	4	5
5	295	4	11
6	460	5	7
7	160	3	15
8	475	5	3
9	340	4	1
TOTAL	2975	37	TOTAL

HOLE	LENGTH MEDAL-TEE	PAR	STROKE INDEX
10	340	4	8
11	275	4	14
12	150	3	10
13	490	5	2
14	435	5	12
15	170	3	4
16	330	4	4
17	120	3	18
18	365	4	6
TOTAL	2675	35	TOTAL

RYA

✡

TEL : (042)220182
LOCATION : 10 km Helsingborg
ADDRESS : Rya 5500 –
255 90 Helsingborg
HOTEL :
Grand Hotel – Helsingborg
Tel : (042)120170
Kärnan – Helsingborg
Tel : (042)120820
Mollberg – Helsingborg
Tel : (042)120270
RESTAURANT : Ramlosa Wardhus –
Helsingborg
Tel : (042)296257

Bordering the Oresund, linking the Baltic with the North Sea, the course has a seaside character with several holes running inland. Open all year, it is very pleasant with excellent views of the coastline and across the sea to Denmark. *SSS 72*

GF $$

1934

18

—

N. Amilon, J. Sederholm

L 5691 P 72

S

Required : Handicap Certificate
Best days : Mondays, Thursdays, Fridays

HOLE	LENGTH MEDAL-TEE	PAR	STROKE INDEX
1	440	5	16
2	131	3	15
3	361	4	3
4	138	3	12
5	431	5	18
6	161	3	7
7	386	4	1
8	441	5	13
9	336	4	4
TOTAL	2825	36	TOTAL

HOLE	LENGTH MEDAL-TEE	PAR	STROKE INDEX
10	331	4	11
11	465	5	8
12	317	4	10
13	357	4	5
14	170	3	6
15	432	5	7
16	151	3	14
17	370	4	2
18	350	4	9
TOTAL	2943	36	TOTAL

SALA

TEL : (0224)53077
LOCATION : 9 km E. Sala
ADDRESS : Box 16-73300 Sala
HOTEL :
Sala Stads-Sala
Tel : (0224)13030
RESTAURANT : Lilla Bla-Sala
Tel : (0224)17418

Sala, just one hour's drive from Stockholm, is a relatively flat course with some undulations. The holes run through luxuriant woodland and old farmland. The course has grass tees and features a spectacular double-green. Water comes into play on four holes. *SSS 71*

GF $

 1970

18

October to April

—

L 5570 P 71

R S

Required : Handicap Certificate
Best days : Any day

HOLE	LENGTH MEDAL-TEE	PAR	STROKE INDEX
1	320	4	16
2	125	3	18
3	490	5	4
4	145	3	14
5	445	5	10
6	325	4	2
7	300	4	8
8	165	3	12
9	315	4	6
TOTAL	2630	35	TOTAL

HOLE	LENGTH MEDAL-TEE	PAR	STROKE INDEX
10	190	3	9
11	460	5	13
12	360	4	1
13	325	4	15
14	475	5	5
15	125	3	17
16	340	4	3
17	315	4	11
18	350	4	7
TOTAL	2940	36	TOTAL

SALTSJÖBADENS

★

TEL : (08)7170125
LOCATION : 15 km E. Stockholm
ADDRESS : Box 51 – Kvarntorpsvägen – 13301 Saltsjöbaden
HOTEL :
Grand-Saltsjöbaden
Tel : (08)7170020

Saltsjobadens is one of Sweden's oldest golf clubs, having been founded in 1929. Set within the scenic lake district around Stockholm, the 27 holes are laid out in peaceful wooded countryside with several holes laid out alongside the Lundsjön lake. *SSS 72*

GF $

1929

27

November to May

A. Björklund, D. Brazier

L 5680 P 72, 1805 P 31

R S

Required : Handicap Certificate
Best days : Weekdays only

HOLE	LENGTH MEDAL-TEE	PAR	STROKE INDEX
1	320	4	13
2	295	4	11
3	125	3	17
4	480	5	13
5	280	4	15
6	480	5	1
7	360	4	7
8	175	3	9
9	300	4	5
TOTAL	2815	36	TOTAL

HOLE	LENGTH MEDAL-TEE	PAR	STROKE INDEX
10	355	4	8
11	310	4	4
12	165	3	12
13	445	5	16
14	120	3	18
15	340	4	6
16	445	5	14
17	340	4	2
18	345	4	10
TOTAL	2865	36	TOTAL

SIGTUNABYGDENS

TEL : (0760)54012
LOCATION : 4 km N. Sigtuna
ADDRESS : Box 89 – 193 00 Sigtuna
HOTEL :
Star Arlandia – Stockholm Arlanda
Tel : (0760)61800
Motel Lindskrog – Stockholm Arlanda
Tel : (0760)60238
RESTAURANT : Stads – Sigtuna
Tel : (0760)50100

Sigtunabygdens is picturesquely situated on the borders of a lake in the Stockholm region. The course, of medium difficulty, is fairly undulating having tree-lined fairways and several water hazards. *SSS 72*

GF $

1961

18

November to May

N. Skold

L 5750 P 72

S

R

Required : Handicap Certificate
Best days : Any day

HOLE	LENGTH MEDAL-TEE	PAR	STROKE INDEX
1	315	4	6
2	455	5	18
3	305	4	14
4	175	3	8
5	320	4	12
6	465	5	2
7	140	3	16
8	310	4	4
9	295	4	10
TOTAL	2780	36	TOTAL

HOLE	LENGTH MEDAL-TEE	PAR	STROKE INDEX
10	325	4	9
11	370	4	3
12	145	3	17
13	335	4	7
14	160	3	15
15	360	4	11
16	335	4	5
17	495	5	1
18	435	5	13
TOTAL	2960	36	TOTAL

SKELLEFTEA

★★★

TEL : (0910)79333/15604
LOCATION : 5 km Skelleftea E 4
ADDRESS : Box 152 –
931 22 Skelleftea 1
HOTEL :
Malmia – Skelleftea
Tel : (0910)77300
Stads – Skelleftea
Tel : (0910)14140
Victoria – Skelleftea
Tel : (0910)17470

This excellent and beautiful course, one of Scandinavia's best, lies in the northern part of Sweden, the 'Northern Norrland', only 200km from the Artic Circle. Skelleftea is the most northerly championship course in the world, one can play golf here 24 hrs per day. Built on old farmland with typical Swedish red barns, high pine trees, and lots of water hazards such as the Rönnbäcken, a creek rich with trout, winding through the whole course. *SSS 72*

GF $ | November to April | R S
1968 | B. Carlsson, N. Skold
18 | L 5767 P 72

Required : Handicap Certificate
Best days : Weekdays

HOLE	LENGTH MEDAL-TEE	PAR	STROKE INDEX
1	310	4	11
2	484	5	3
3	313	4	9
4	156	3	15
5	441	5	13
6	309	4	7
7	152	3	17
8	329	4	1
9	351	4	5
TOTAL	2845	36	TOTAL

HOLE	LENGTH MEDAL-TEE	PAR	STROKE INDEX
10	466	5	2
11	362	4	6
12	346	4	12
13	143	3	16
14	335	4	8
15	120	3	18
16	500	5	4
17	310	4	14
18	340	4	10
TOTAL	2922	36	TOTAL

SKEPPARSLÖVS

TEL : (044)229031/229508
LOCATION : 7 km Kristianstad.
In Skepparslöv, near the church
ADDRESS : Uddarp-Skepparslöv –
29192 Kristianstad
HOTEL :
Grand-Kristianstad
Tel : (044)103600
Christian-Kristianstad
Tel : (044)126300
Turisten-Kristianstad
Tel : (044)126150

The Skepparslövs course, situated in Southern Sweden, is a typical parkland course set in undulating terrain with a stream meandering its way through several fairways. *SSS 71*

GF $

1986

18

November to March

R. Collijn

L 5831 P 72

S

R

Required : Handicap Certificate
Best days : Mondays to Thursdays inc.

HOLE	LENGTH MEDAL-TEE	PAR	STROKE INDEX
1	464	5	9
2	149	3	17
3	334	4	3
4	463	5	5
5	301	4	11
6	309	4	7
7	344	4	15
8	350	4	1
9	182	3	13
TOTAL	2896	36	TOTAL

HOLE	LENGTH MEDAL-TEE	PAR	STROKE INDEX
10	350	4	12
11	342	4	10
12	136	3	10
13	457	5	4
14	381	4	2
15	309	4	14
16	477	5	8
17	130	3	16
18	353	4	6
TOTAL	2935	36	TOTAL

SÖDERASENS

TEL : (042)73337
LOCATION : 2 km Billesholm
ADDRESS : Box 41 – 26050 Billesholm
HOTEL : HR
Söderasens Wärdshus
Tel : (042)72070
Stora Mörshög – Bjuv
Tel : (042)72610
Sir James – Söderasens
Tel : (042)119202

Designed by the Swedish architect Thure Bruce, this flat course is set on open countryside and is surrounded by parkland. It features difficult greens, demanding a great deal of accuracy. The Söderasens Wärdshus hotel with its 60 rooms is at 200 m from the club. *SSS 73*

GF $

1966

18

Mondays

T. Bruce

L 5920 P 73

S

RF

Required : None
Best days : Any day

HOLE	LENGTH MEDAL-TEE	PAR	STROKE INDEX
1	310	4	7
2	325	4	11
3	300	4	9
4	410	5	15
5	465	5	1
6	150	3	17
7	370	4	3
8	450	5	5
9	160	3	13
TOTAL	2940	37	TOTAL

HOLE	LENGTH MEDAL-TEE	PAR	STROKE INDEX
10	365	4	4
11	355	4	2
12	470	5	8
13	165	3	14
14	470	5	12
15	150	3	18
16	375	4	6
17	325	4	10
18	305	4	16
TOTAL	2980	36	TOTAL

SÖDERHAMNS

TEL : (0270)51300
LOCATION : 10 km Söderhamn
ADDRESS : Oxtorget 1c –
826 00 Söderhamn
HOTEL :
Stadshotellet – Söderhamn
Tel : (0270)11410
Scandic – Söderhamn
Tel : (0270)18020
RESTAURANT : Marden – Söderhamn
Tel : (0270)18000

The course lies in Southern Norrland, up in the north of Sweden, and is laid out in rolling parkland with wide and generous fairways landscaped by mature trees. *SSS 72*

GF $

1961

18

November to May

N. Skold

L 5825 P 72

S

Required : Handicap Certificate
Best days : Weekdays

HOLE	LENGTH MEDAL-TEE	PAR	STROKE INDEX
1	325	4	15
2	480	5	5
3	345	4	9
4	500	5	1
5	175	3	11
6	290	4	13
7	125	3	17
8	370	4	3
9	335	4	7
TOTAL	2945	36	TOTAL

HOLE	LENGTH MEDAL-TEE	PAR	STROKE INDEX
10	450	5	6
11	150	3	14
12	365	4	2
13	480	5	4
14	195	3	10
15	335	4	12
16	430	5	16
17	140	3	18
18	335	4	8
TOTAL	2880	36	TOTAL

SÖDERKÖPING

TEL : (011)70579/70714
LOCATION : 9 km Söderköping Rd 210
ADDRESS : Hylinge - 60590 Norrköping
HOTEL :
Söderköpings Brunn – Söderköping
Tel : (0121)10900

Founded in 1983 and designed by the Californian architect Ronald Fream, the course is situated in a typical Mid-Swedish landscape with ancient oak trees growing on soft rolling hills overlooking the Göta Kanal, the famous Swedish waterway. The course is of the 'American' type with tricky water hazards on several holes. *SSS 72*

GF $

1983

18

November to May

R. Fream

L 5650 P 72

 S

R

Required : None
Best days : Any day

HOLE	LENGTH MEDAL-TEE	PAR	STROKE INDEX
1	345	4	4
2	335	4	6
3	310	4	12
4	505	5	10
5	315	4	14
6	280	4	18
7	125	3	16
8	355	4	8
9	370	4	8
TOTAL	2940	36	TOTAL

HOLE	LENGTH MEDAL-TEE	PAR	STROKE INDEX
10	310	4	7
11	150	3	11
12	335	4	1
13	300	4	13
14	335	4	9
15	460	5	5
16	285	4	17
17	105	3	15
18	430	5	3
TOTAL	2710	36	TOTAL

SÖDERTÄLJE

TEL : (0755)38240
LOCATION : 3 km Södertälje
ADDRESS : Box 91.– 151 21 Södertälje
HOTEL :
Scandic – Södertälje
Tel : (0755)34260
Skogshöjd-Södertälje
Tel : (0755)32670
RESTAURANT : Stads – Södertälje
Tel : (0755)34000

A fine classical parkland course of medium difficulty with majestic trees flanking the gently rolling fairways. An attractive feature of the course is the stately clubhouse. *SSS 72*

GF $

1952

18

November to May

N. Skold

L 5855 P 72

S

R

Required : Handicap Certificate
Best days : Weekdays only

HOLE	LENGTH MEDAL-TEE	PAR	STROKE INDEX
1	290	4	7
2	140	3	17
3	330	4	15
4	355	4	3
5	490	5	13
6	145	3	11
7	375	4	1
8	345	4	9
9	335	4	5
TOTAL	2805	35	TOTAL

HOLE	LENGTH MEDAL-TEE	PAR	STROKE INDEX
10	350	4	8
11	310	4	4
12	455	5	18
13	130	3	16
14	460	5	14
15	310	4	6
16	165	3	10
17	380	4	2
18	490	5	12
TOTAL	3050	37	TOTAL

SOLLEFTEA-LANGSELE

TEL : (0620)21477
LOCATION : 4 km Langsele/15 km Solleftea Rd 87
ADDRESS : Box 213 – 881 01 Solleftea
HOTEL :
Hallstaberget – Solleftea
Tel : (0620)12320
City – Solleftea
Tel : (0620)16700
RESTAURANT : Appelberg – Solleftea
Tel : (0620)12130

The course lies on open ground in the middle of a dense pine forest and is backed by luxuriant wooded hills. In 1985, it was the venue for the Swedish National Championship.
SSS 72

GF $

1970

18

November to May

N. Skold

L 5765 P 72

Required : Handicap Certificate
Best days : Any day

HOLE	LENGTH MEDAL-TEE	PAR	STROKE INDEX
1	328	4	9
2	258	4	17
3	361	4	1
4	461	5	3
5	162	3	13
6	320	4	11
7	375	4	5
8	144	3	15
9	441	5	7
TOTAL	2850	36	TOTAL

HOLE	LENGTH MEDAL-TEE	PAR	STROKE INDEX
10	501	5	6
11	177	3	12
12	350	4	8
13	386	4	4
14	470	5	2
15	115	3	18
16	410	5	16
17	173	3	10
18	333	4	14
TOTAL	2915	36	TOTAL

SOLLENTUNA

TEL : (08)7543625
LOCATION : 20 km Stockholm E 4
ADDRESS : Skillingegården – 191 77 Sollentuna
HOTEL :
Welcome – Järfälla
Tel : (08)7602520
Star – Sollentuna
Tel : (08)920100
RESTAURANT : Chapeau Claque – Stockholm
Tel : (08)102524

Situated in the Stockholm region, Sollentuna is a flat parkland course designed by Nils Skold with water affecting play on seven holes. The toughest hole of the course is the finishing 18th hole, being uphill all the way. The Welcome hotel is situated 4 km from the golfclub. *SSS 72*

GF $$

1967

18

—

N. Skold

L 5910 P 72

S

Required : Handicap Certificate
Best days : Weekdays except Thursdays

HOLE	LENGTH MEDAL-TEE	PAR	STROKE INDEX
1	355	4	7
2	130	3	17
3	310	4	13
4	355	4	9
5	130	3	15
6	480	5	1
7	375	4	5
8	340	4	11
9	540	5	3
TOTAL	3015	36	TOTAL

HOLE	LENGTH MEDAL-TEE	PAR	STROKE INDEX
10	480	5	10
11	330	4	12
12	350	5	6
13	420	4	4
14	150	3	18
15	300	4	8
16	375	4	2
17	160	3	16
18	330	4	14
TOTAL	2895	36	TOTAL

SÖLVESBORG

TEL : (0456)70650
LOCATION : 3 km Sölvesborg
ADDRESS : Box 63 29401 Sölvesborg
HOTEL :
Hanöhus - Sölvesborg
Tel : (0456)52510

This friendly seaside course, bordering the Baltic Sea, winds its way through flat and tree-lined countryside, and has four lakes defending four of the holes. *SSS 72*

GF $

1990

18

November to March

—

L 5640 P 72

R S

Required : None
Best days : Weekdays

HOLE	LENGTH MEDAL-TEE	PAR	STROKE INDEX
1	335	4	5
2	125	3	17
3	450	5	7
4	370	4	11
5	155	3	15
6	300	4	13
7	330	4	3
8	330	4	11
9	455	5	9
TOTAL	2850	36	TOTAL

HOLE	LENGTH MEDAL-TEE	PAR	STROKE INDEX
10	340	4	4
11	140	3	16
12	330	4	10
13	430	5	8
14	125	3	18
15	360	4	2
16	305	4	12
17	455	5	6
18	305	4	14
TOTAL	2790	36	TOTAL

STOCKHOLMS

TEL : (08)7550031/7550753
LOCATION : 7 km Stockholm
ADDRESS : Kevingestrand 20 – 18231 Danderyd
HOTEL :
Diplomat – Stockholm
Tel : (08)635800
Aston – Stockholm
Tel : (08)440690
Oden – Stockholm
Tel : (08)349340
RESTAURANT : Le Riche – Stockholm
Tel : (08)236840

A classical and renowned championship golf course located in Kevinge, on the outskirts of Stockholm. Having been founded in 1904, the golf club is one of the oldest in Sweden. It is laid out in fine undulating parkland with stately trees bordering the fairways, and featuring two strategic water hazards. Parts of the course are flanked by the scenic 'Edsviken' lake. There is a well-appointed clubhouse. *SSS 71*

GF $$ — November to May — R S
1904 — J. Morrison, N. Skold
18 — L 5765 P 71

Required : Handicap Certificate
Best days : Weekdays except Wednesday afternoons

HOLE	LENGTH MEDAL-TEE	PAR	STROKE INDEX
1	340	4	7
2	405	4	5
3	380	4	1
4	165	3	11
5	450	5	13
6	315	4	9
7	335	4	3
8	315	4	15
9	120	3	17
TOTAL	2825	35	TOTAL

HOLE	LENGTH MEDAL-TEE	PAR	STROKE INDEX
10	515	5	4
11	285	4	10
12	175	3	12
13	490	5	6
14	140	3	18
15	380	4	2
16	160	3	16
17	460	5	8
18	335	4	14
TOTAL	2940	36	TOTAL

STORA LUNDBY

TEL : (0302)44200
LOCATION : 25 km Göteborg
ADDRESS : Pl. 4034 – 44006 Grabo
HOTEL :
Aspenäs Gard – Lerum
Windsor – Göteborg
Tel : (031)176540
Forum – Göteborg
Tel : (031)840080

Designed by Frank Pennink in 1983, Stora Lundby is a popular inland course with wide and generous fairways, easy from the forward tees but difficult from the back tees. *SSS 72*

GF $

1983

27

December to April

F. Pennink

L 5808 P 73

S

R

Required : None
Best days : Weekdays

HOLE	LENGTH MEDAL-TEE	PAR	STROKE INDEX
1	475	5	7
2	385	4	1
3	420	5	5
4	175	3	9
5	303	5	13
6	135	3	17
7	490	5	3
8	160	3	15
9	320	4	11
TOTAL	2863	37	TOTAL

HOLE	LENGTH MEDAL-TEE	PAR	STROKE INDEX
10	155	3	18
11	345	4	6
12	370	4	2
13	165	3	16
14	320	4	10
15	457	5	12
16	348	4	8
17	305	4	14
18	480	5	4
TOTAL	2945	36	TOTAL

STRÄNGNÄS

TEL : (0152)14731
LOCATION : 3 km Strängnäs E 3
ADDRESS : Bergvagen 17 –
64521 Strängnäs
HOTEL :
Rogge – Strängnäs
Tel : (0152)13450
O'Henrys – Strängnäs
Tel : (0152)18000
RESTAURANT : Wärdshus – Strängnäs
Tel : (0152)11200

Situated in the northern part of Sweden's East Coast, this is a friendly course of medium difficulty laid out in flat parkland. Most of the fairways are separated from each other by mature trees. *SSS 72*

GF $

1968

18

November to May

N. Skold

L 5790 P 72

S

R

Required : None
Best days : Weekdays

HOLE	LENGTH MEDAL-TEE	PAR	STROKE INDEX
1	325	4	11
2	345	4	1
3	335	4	5
4	290	4	13
5	125	3	17
6	325	4	7
7	490	5	3
8	160	3	15
9	460	5	9
TOTAL	2855	36	TOTAL

HOLE	LENGTH MEDAL-TEE	PAR	STROKE INDEX
10	350	4	6
11	270	4	18
12	170	3	16
13	375	4	2
14	445	5	8
15	190	3	12
16	380	4	4
17	445	5	10
18	310	4	14
TOTAL	2935	36	TOTAL

SUNDSVALLS

TEL : (060)561030/561056
LOCATION : 17 km Sundsvall E 4
ADDRESS : Golfvägen 5 – 86200 Kvissleby
HOTEL :
Golfhotel
Tel : (060)561030
Ankaret – Kvissleby
Tel : (060)514060
Scandic – Sundsvall
Tel : (060)566860

One can play golf under the Midnight Sun in Sundsvall which lies in an attractive English-type landscape alongside a scenic lake. The club's golf hotel can accomodate up to 16 guests. *SSS 72*

GF $

1952

18

October to May

—

L 5885 P 72

Required : Handicap Certificate
Best days : Weekdays

HOLE	LENGTH MEDAL-TEE	PAR	STROKE INDEX
1	345	4	7
2	170	3	11
3	345	4	5
4	480	5	9
5	455	5	15
6	370	4	3
7	290	4	17
8	160	3	13
9	370	4	1
TOTAL	2985	36	TOTAL

HOLE	LENGTH MEDAL-TEE	PAR	STROKE INDEX
10	335	4	4
11	450	5	16
12	305	4	10
13	320	4	14
14	325	4	2
15	130	3	18
16	295	4	12
17	340	4	8
18	400	4	6
TOTAL	2900	36	TOTAL

TÄBY

TEL : (0762)23261
LOCATION : 18 km Stockholm
ADDRESS : Skalhamragard –
183 64 Täby
HOTEL :
Scandic – Täby
Tel : (08)7680580
Scandic – Solna
Tel : (08)850360
RESTAURANT : Operakällaren – Stockholm
Tel : (08)110026

Scenically laid out amidst lakes in undulating well-wooded countryside with large pines bordering the fairways, this is a pleasant course with a wealth of strategically placed water hazards. *SSS 73*

GF $$
1968
18

November to May
N. Skold
L 5776 P 72

S
R

Required : Handicap Certificate
Best days : Wednesdays, Fridays

HOLE	LENGTH MEDAL-TEE	PAR	STROKE INDEX
1	432	5	13
2	344	4	11
3	343	4	1
4	135	3	17
5	362	4	5
6	446	5	7
7	153	3	15
8	376	4	3
9	309	4	9
TOTAL	2900	36	TOTAL

HOLE	LENGTH MEDAL-TEE	PAR	STROKE INDEX
10	370	4	10
11	336	4	8
12	465	5	2
13	313	4	12
14	164	3	16
15	290	4	14
16	341	4	4
17	151	3	18
18	446	5	6
TOTAL	2876	36	TOTAL

TIMRA

TEL : (060)570153
LOCATION : 25 km N. Sundsvall to Fagervik
ADDRESS : Box 140– 86100 Timra
HOTEL :
Baltic - Sundsvall
Tel : (060)15593
Scandic - Sundsvall
Tel : (060)566860

Located on flat and open terrain on the scenic East Coast of Sweden, bordering the Gulf of Bothnic, this very original course is full of water hazards. It is situated on the delta of the river «Indalstalven» with three delta arms flowing through seventeen holes.

GF $ — October to April  

1986 — S. Linde 

18 — L 5715 P 72 

Required : None
Best days : Weekdays

HOLE	LENGTH MEDAL-TEE	PAR	STROKE INDEX
1	325	4	7
2	305	4	13
3	465	5	9
4	355	4	3
5	150	3	15
6	365	4	1
7	430	5	11
8	135	3	17
9	320	4	5
TOTAL	2850	36	TOTAL

HOLE	LENGTH MEDAL-TEE	PAR	STROKE INDEX
10	465	5	10
11	305	4	14
12	160	3	16
13	345	4	2
14	350	4	4
15	115	3	18
16	305	4	12
17	480	5	6
18	340	4	8
TOTAL	2865	36	TOTAL

TOBO

TEL : (0492)30346
LOCATION : 3 km W. Storebro R 34
ADDRESS : Tobo Gard –
598 00 Vimmerby
HOTEL : HR
Fredensborg Herrgard
Tel : (0492)30600
Vimmerby Stads – Vimmerby
Tel : ((0492)12100

The course is peacefully set within splendid natural countryside in the middle of a pine forest on the borders of a scenic lake (Sjön Gissen). Among several water hazards, there is a stream winding through a part of the course. The typical Swedish-style hotel 'Fredensborg Herrgard' lies in the middle of the course. Ideal for holiday golf with leisure facilities such as fishing and rowing on the lake. *SSS 73*

GF $

1975

18

November to April

D. Brazier, B. Jensen

L 5690 P 72

 S

Required : Handicap Certificate
Best days : Any day

HOLE	LENGTH MEDAL-TEE	PAR	STROKE INDEX
1	285	4	16
2	480	5	4
3	100	3	18
4	295	4	8
5	310	4	12
6	305	4	6
7	150	3	10
8	260	4	14
9	520	5	2
TOTAL	2705	36	TOTAL

HOLE	LENGTH MEDAL-TEE	PAR	STROKE INDEX
10	310	4	13
11	160	3	17
12	520	5	1
13	380	4	3
14	320	4	15
15	455	5	11
16	315	4	5
17	350	4	9
18	175	3	7
TOTAL	2985	36	TOTAL

TOREKOVS

TEL : (0431)63355
LOCATION : 2 km Torekov
ADDRESS : Box 81 – 260 93 Torekov
HOTEL :
Kattegatt – Torekov
Tel : (0431)63002
Solsidan – Torekov
Tel : (0431)63360

Designed by Nils Skold, this is a flat seaside course laid out in Southern Sweden and bordering the Oresund, sometimes made difficult by the prevailing wind. It can be very busy in July. *SSS 72*

GF $

1924

18

December to March

N. Skold

L 5785 P 72

R S

Required : Handicap Certificate
Best days : Weekdays

HOLE	LENGTH MEDAL-TEE	PAR	STROKE INDEX
1	330	4	15
2	305	4	7
3	335	4	3
4	495	5	9
5	380	4	1
6	140	3	11
7	490	5	5
8	160	3	13
9	250	4	17
TOTAL	2885	36	TOTAL

HOLE	LENGTH MEDAL-TEE	PAR	STROKE INDEX
10	470	5	10
11	300	4	16
12	325	4	4
13	180	3	6
14	290	4	14
15	480	5	2
16	350	4	8
17	320	4	18
18	185	3	12
TOTAL	2900	36	TOTAL

TORREBY

TEL : (0524)21109
LOCATION : 30 km N. Uddevalla E 6
ADDRESS : Postlada Torreby –
455 00 Munkedal
HOTEL :
Atorp – Munkedal
Tel : (0523)12000
Bohusrasta – Munkedal
Tel : (0524)23210
Viking – Uddevalla
Tel : (0522)14550
RESTAURANT : Gastis – Hunnebostrand
Tel : (0523)50450

An entertaining parkland course on the West Coast, laid out on gently rolling countryside nearby the Färlevfjorden. An attractive feature is the clubhouse, a former château dating back several centuries. *SSS 72*

GF $ — December to April — S

1961 — D. Brazier — 

18 — L 5855 P 72 — R

Required : None
Best days : Any day

HOLE	LENGTH MEDAL-TEE	PAR	STROKE INDEX
1	405	4	5
2	335	4	7
3	395	4	3
4	440	5	11
5	145	3	17
6	330	4	9
7	300	4	15
8	455	5	13
9	400	4	1
TOTAL	3205	37	TOTAL

HOLE	LENGTH MEDAL-TEE	PAR	STROKE INDEX
10	115	3	18
11	500	5	6
12	160	3	4
13	340	4	2
14	450	5	12
15	300	4	14
16	130	3	16
17	320	4	8
18	335	4	10
TOTAL	2650	35	TOTAL

TRANAS

TEL : (0140)11661
LOCATION : 2 km Tranas
ADDRESS : N. Storgatan 130
57300 Tranas
HOTEL : Hr
Tranasbaden – Tranas
Tel : (0140)18025
Tranas Stad – Tranas
Tel : (0140)14160
RESTAURANT : Tranas Kuranstalt – Tranas
Tel : (0140)69100

Located near the health resort of Tranas, this is a gently undulating course in a woodland setting with a spacious layout. The fairways are landscaped by mature trees with water affecting play on several holes. The Tranasbaden hotel with 60 rooms lies within walking distance from the course. *SSS 72*

GF $
1951
18

November to April
N. Skold
L 5830 P 72

S
R

Required : None
Best days : Weekdays

HOLE	LENGTH MEDAL-TEE	PAR	STROKE INDEX
1	260	4	17
2	160	3	11
3	365	4	5
4	280	4	13
5	485	5	1
6	340	4	7
7	485	5	9
8	150	3	15
9	370	4	3
TOTAL	2895	36	TOTAL

HOLE	LENGTH MEDAL-TEE	PAR	STROKE INDEX
10	140	3	16
11	475	5	8
12	130	3	18
13	370	4	2
14	455	5	10
15	340	4	12
16	365	4	4
17	320	4	14
18	340	4	6
TOTAL	2935	36	TOTAL

TRELLEBORGS

✡

TEL : (0410)30460
LOCATION : 5 km Trelleborg E 6
ADDRESS : Maglarp – PL 401 – 231 93 Trelleborg
HOTEL :
Standard – Trelleborg
Tel : (0410)10438
Dannegarden – Trelleborg
Tel : (0410)11120
RESTAURANT : Stads – Trelleborg
Tel : (0410)15250

A flat seaside course, ideal for holiday golf, set on the Baltic coast not far from the Falsterbo Peninsula. There is a stream bordering the fairway of the 9th hole. *SSS 69*

GF $ | — | R S
1963 | — |
18 | L 5330 P 70 |

Required : Handicap Certificate
Best days : Weekdays

HOLE	LENGTH MEDAL-TEE	PAR	STROKE INDEX
1	460	5	4
2	120	3	15
3	330	4	7
4	365	4	3
5	295	4	17
6	160	3	13
7	305	4	9
8	175	3	11
9	470	5	1
TOTAL	2680	35	TOTAL

HOLE	LENGTH MEDAL-TEE	PAR	STROKE INDEX
10	120	3	16
11	415	4	2
12	330	4	8
13	135	3	18
14	500	5	4
15	140	3	12
16	235	4	14
17	325	4	6
18	450	5	10
TOTAL	2650	35	TOTAL

TROLLHÄTTANS

★

TEL : (0520)41000
LOCATION : 21 km Trollhättan
ADDRESS : Box 254 - 461 26 Trollhättan
HOTEL :
Bele - Trollhättan
Tel : (0520)12530
Kung Oscar - Trollhättan
Tel : (0520)30220
RESTAURANT : Drott - Trollhättan
Tel : (0520)10107

Designed by Sweden's celebrated golf architect Nils Skold, Trollhättan is a scenic and flat parkland course laid out on the borders of a lake with numerous ponds and streams serving as hazards. *SSS 72*

GF $

1963

18

November to April

N. Skold

L 5875 P 72

S

R

Required : Handicap Certificate
Best days : Weekdays

HOLE	LENGTH MEDAL-TEE	PAR	STROKE INDEX
1	340	4	5
2	335	4	15
3	325	4	9
4	330	4	11
5	175	3	13
6	350	4	7
7	370	4	1
8	145	3	17
9	480	5	3
TOTAL	2850	35	TOTAL

HOLE	LENGTH MEDAL-TEE	PAR	STROKE INDEX
10	495	5	2
11	155	3	18
12	295	4	8
13	345	4	4
14	435	5	12
15	300	4	16
16	145	3	14
17	375	4	6
18	480	5	10
TOTAL	3025	37	TOTAL

UDDEHOLMS

TEL : (0563)60335/60564
LOCATION : 14 km Hagfors
ADDRESS : Risäters Herrgard – 683 03 Rada
HOTEL :
Björns Wärdshus – Rada
Tel : (0563)60290
Risäters Herrgard – Rada
Tel : (0563)60025
Uddeholm – Uddeholm
Tel : (0563)23600

Situated in Central Sweden, not far from the Norwegian border, the course is set amidst picturesque lakes on fine undulating countryside with mature trees surrounding the holes. The Björns Wärdshus'hotel is situated nearby the golf club. *SSS 72*

GF $ | November to May | S

1965 | N. Skold

18 | L 5833 P 72 | R

Required : None
Best days : Any day

HOLE	LENGTH MEDAL-TEE	PAR	STROKE INDEX
1	342	4	9
2	349	4	3
3	328	4	11
4	344	4	13
5	105	3	17
6	315	4	15
7	358	4	5
8	475	5	1
9	348	4	7
TOTAL	2964	36	TOTAL

HOLE	LENGTH MEDAL-TEE	PAR	STROKE INDEX
10	302	4	16
11	441	5	8
12	392	4	4
13	174	3	10
14	359	4	6
15	475	5	2
16	130	3	18
17	307	4	12
18	289	4	14
TOTAL	2869	36	TOTAL

ULLNA

★★★

TEL : (0762)26075
LOCATION : 17 km Stockholm
ADDRESS : Rosenkälla –
18400 Åkersberga
HOTEL :
Vaxholm – Vaxholm
Tel : (0764)30150
Scandic – Väsby
Tel : (0760)93100

One of the most challenging courses in Sweden laid out in the Stockholm archipelago on the borders of the 'Ullansjön'. Designed by Sven Tumba, this is a testing and sometimes windy course with plenty of variety. Many of the fairways lie directly alongside the lake with scenic views overlooking the bay. The course incorporates strategic ponds and streams serving as hazards. Between 1983 and 1987 Ullna was the permanent venue for the Scandinavian Open. *SSS 72*

GF $$

1980

18

November to May

S. Tumba

L 5720 P 72

S

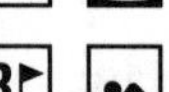

R

Required : Handicap Certificate
Best days : Weekdays

HOLE	LENGTH MEDAL-TEE	PAR	STROKE INDEX
1	440	5	5
2	285	4	15
3	125	3	17
4	430	5	3
5	170	3	11
6	310	4	7
7	335	4	1
8	320	4	9
9	300	4	13
TOTAL	2715	36	TOTAL

HOLE	LENGTH MEDAL-TEE	PAR	STROKE INDEX
10	365	4	10
11	340	4	12
12	160	3	16
13	465	5	6
14	535	5	4
15	270	4	18
16	145	3	14
17	370	4	2
18	355	4	8
TOTAL	3005	36	TOTAL

ULRICEHAMNS

TEL : (0321)10021
LOCATION : 2 km Ulricehamn
ADDRESS : Box 84 – 523 01 Ulricehamn
HOTEL :
Scandic – Ulricehamn
Tel : (0321)12040
RESTAURANT : Asengard – Dannike
Tel : (033)81146

An undulating inland course with several tight holes and well-placed trees scattered over the course, demanding accuracy from tee to green. There is a road dividing the course into two separate parts. *SSS 70*

GF $
1947
18
November to May
N. Skold
L 5402 P 70
S
R

Required : Handicap Certificate
Best days : Any day except Sundays

HOLE	LENGTH MEDAL-TEE	PAR	STROKE INDEX
1	150	3	17
2	361	4	7
3	331	4	9
4	175	3	13
5	451	5	3
6	316	4	11
7	358	4	1
8	303	4	15
9	325	4	5
TOTAL	2770	35	TOTAL

HOLE	LENGTH MEDAL-TEE	PAR	STROKE INDEX
10	161	3	16
11	326	4	10
12	262	4	12
13	467	5	2
14	123	3	18
15	335	4	8
16	346	4	8
17	300	4	14
18	312	4	6
TOTAL	2632	35	TOTAL

UPSALA

TEL : (018)461270
LOCATION : 7 km Upsala
ADDRESS : Hamö Gard – Box 12015 – 750 12 Upsala
HOTEL :
Uplandia – Upsala
Tel : (018)102160
Elit – Upsala
Tel : (018)130345
Sara Gillet – Upsala
Tel : (018)155360

One of Sweden's most interesting championship courses is the Upsala golf course laid out on gently rolling terrain in Central Sweden. The course features well-bunkered greens and several water hazards such as the creek on the long 13th hole. There are various fine uphill and downhill holes like the 18th with a beautiful view from the tee of the clubhouse. The Upsala golf club has been the venue for the Swedish International. *SSS 73*

GF $

1937

27

November to April

G. Paulsson

L 5914 P 72

Required : Handicap Certificate
Best days : Weekdays

HOLE	LENGTH MEDAL-TEE	PAR	STROKE INDEX
1	349	4	11
2	135	3	17
3	327	4	7
4	486	5	3
5	152	3	15
6	330	4	13
7	336	4	5
8	477	5	9
9	396	4	1
TOTAL	2988	36	TOTAL

HOLE	LENGTH MEDAL-TEE	PAR	STROKE INDEX
10	347	4	8
11	180	3	12
12	356	4	2
13	464	5	6
14	325	4	14
15	144	3	18
16	334	4	4
17	436	5	16
18	340	4	10
TOTAL	2926 ·	36	TOTAL

VARA BJERTORP

TEL : (0512)20261
LOCATION : 100 km N. Goteborg
E3/14 km Vara E3
ADDRESS : Bjertorp - 53500 Kränum
HOTEL :
Scandic - Vara
Tel : (0512)34135
Bjertorp - Vara
Tel : (0512)20390

This pleasant inland course lies in the western part of Sweden not far from the city of Lidköping and offers a varied layout. The holes run through attractive lush parkland. Several lakes serve as hazards. *SSS 73*

GF $ | November to April | S
1990 | J. Sederholm
18 | L 6005 P 72 | R

Required : None
Best days : Weekdays

HOLE	LENGTH MEDAL-TEE	PAR	STROKE INDEX
1	305	4	11
2	320	4	13
3	370	4	3
4	130	3	17
5	490	5	5
6	145	3	15
7	315	4	9
8	465	5	7
9	385	4	1
TOTAL	2925	36	TOTAL

HOLE	LENGTH MEDAL-TEE	PAR	STROKE INDEX
10	370	4	6
11	190	3	12
12	460	5	2
13	375	4	4
14	325	4	18
15	340	4	14
16	170	3	16
17	505	5	8
18	345	4	10
TOTAL	3080	36	TOTAL

VARBERGS

TEL : (0340)37470
LOCATION : 15 km Varberg
ADDRESS : Box 39 – 43200 Varberg
HOTEL :
Varberg – Varberg
Tel : (0340)16125
Akulla Friluftsgard – Rolfstorp
Tel : (0340)36057
Gästis – Varberg
Tel : (0340)18050
RESTAURANT : Sara – Varberg
Tel : (0340)16100

Located near the seaside resort of Varberg on Sweden's West Coast, the course lies inland on undulating, mostly open terrain with numerous ponds and a large lake serving as hazards. The clubhouse is modern and overlooks several holes. *SSS 73*

GF $

November to April

S

1950

N. Skold

18

L 5757 P 72

R

Required : Handicap Certificate
Best days : Weekdays

HOLE	LENGTH MEDAL-TEE	PAR	STROKE INDEX
1	466	5	13
2	355	4	3
3	170	3	11
4	435	5	15
5	345	4	9
6	330	4	5
7	130	3	17
8	360	4	1
9	367	4	7
TOTAL	2958	36	TOTAL

HOLE	LENGTH MEDAL-TEE	PAR	STROKE INDEX
10	337	4	6
11	357	4	2
12	127	3	18
13	440	5	12
14	150	3	16
15	275	4	14
16	342	4	8
17	435	5	4
18	336	4	10
TOTAL	2799	36	TOTAL

VÄRNAMO

TEL : (0370)23123
LOCATION : 8 km Värnamo
ADDRESS : Box 146 – 331 01 Värnamo
HOTEL :
Stads – Värnamo
Tel : (0370)11530
Tre Liljor – Värnamo
Tel : (0370)47300
Motel Finnveden – Värnamo
Tel : (0370)21090

The course lies in Eastern Sweden within a fine natural undulating landscape, bordered on one side by a scenic lake. Many of the fairways are separated from each other by lush woodland. One of its most attractive holes is the 12th with its tee on one side of the lake and its green on the other. *SSS 71*

GF $

1962

18

November to April

N. Skold

L 5588 P 72

S

R

Required : None
Best days : Any day

HOLE	LENGTH MEDAL-TEE	PAR	STROKE INDEX
1	448	5	15
2	359	4	1
3	348	4	7
4	440	5	9
5	125	3	13
6	302	4	5
7	290	4	17
8	302	4	3
9	140	3	11
TOTAL	2754	36	TOTAL

HOLE	LENGTH MEDAL-TEE	PAR	STROKE INDEX
10	328	4	18
11	155	3	16
12	263	4	8
13	442	5	2
14	172	3	10
15	493	5	4
16	284	4	14
17	382	4	6
18	315	4	12
TOTAL	2834	36	TOTAL

VASATORPS

★★

TEL : (042)235058
LOCATION : 7 km Helsingborg
ADDRESS : 25013 Helsingborg
HOTEL :
Scandic – Helsingborg
Tel : (042)151560
Bruks – Helsingborg
Tel : (042)119202
Horisont – Helsingborg
Tel : (042)149260
RESTAURANT : Ramlosa Wardhus – Helsingborg
Tel : (042)296257

Situated 7 km from the seaside resort of Helsingborg, the Vasatorp golf course is one of Sweden's leading courses. It consists of three loops of nine holes, laid out on undulating terrain in a parkland setting. There are several tight and testing dogleg holes with well-defended greens. Like most of the Swedish courses, water affects play on many holes, for example streams crossing the fairways and strategic ponds. The club has hosted the Scandinavian Open in 1978, 1979 and 1980. *SSS 72*

GF $$ — December to April  

 1973 —  T. Bruce 

27 — L  2940 P 36, 2950 P 36, 2925 P 36 

Required : Handicap Certificate
Best days : Weekdays

HOLE	LENGTH MEDAL-TEE	PAR	STROKE INDEX	HOLE	LENGTH MEDAL-TEE	PAR	STROKE INDEX	HOLE	LENGTH MEDAL-TEE	PAR	STROKE INDEX
1	465	5	5	1	355	4	3	1	355	4	4
2	300	4	8	2	500	5	1	2	140	3	9
3	380	4	1	3	330	4	6	3	370	4	3
4	330	4	3	4	140	3	9	4	450	5	5
5	165	3	7	5	460	5	2	5	375	4	1
6	315	4	6	6	335	4	5	6	340	4	6
7	335	4	2	7	160	3	7	7	460	5	2
8	150	3	9	8	300	4	8	8	145	3	8
9	500	5	4	9	370	4	4	9	290	4	7
TOTAL	2940	36	TOTAL	TOTAL	2950	36	TOTAL	TOTAL	2925	36	TOTAL

VÄSTERAS

TEL : (021)357543
LOCATION : 1 km Västeras E 18
ADDRESS : Bjärby – 72481 Västeras
HOTEL :
Park – Västeras
Tel : (021)110120
Astoria – Västeras
Tel : (021)110080
Herrgards – Surahammar
Tel : (0220)36220
RESTAURANT : Klippen – Västeras
Tel : (021)137650

Located in Central Sweden, Västeras is a pleasant parkland course bordered on one side by the Skerike road, and on the other by a stream. The course is not too testing for the average golfer. *SSS 69*

GF $

1949

18

 November to April

 R. Sundblom, N. Skold

L 5395 P 69

Required : Handicap Certificate
Best days : Weekdays

HOLE	LENGTH MEDAL-TEE	PAR	STROKE INDEX
1	165	3	9
2	330	4	15
3	470	5	11
4	170	3	7
5	380	4	1
6	350	4	3
7	435	5	13
8	160	3	17
9	350	4	5
TOTAL	2810	35	TOTAL

HOLE	LENGTH MEDAL-TEE	PAR	STROKE INDEX
10	130	3	18
11	310	4	14
12	385	4	4
13	360	4	2
14	175	3	10
15	470	5	6
16	280	4	12
17	145	3	16
18	330	4	8
TOTAL	2585	34	TOTAL

VÄXJÖ

TEL : (0470)21539
LOCATION : 2 km Växjö
ADDRESS : Augustivagen 14 – 35105 Växjö
HOTEL :
Sara Statt – Växjö
Tel : (0470)13400
Cardinal – Växjö
Tel : (0470)13430
Carisma – Växjö
Tel : (0470)10440
RESTAURANT : Scandic – Växjö
Tel : (0470)22070

Set in the middle of the East Coast of Sweden, Växjö is a testing inland course of championship standard laid out on varied flat countryside. Strategically placed trees demand accurate play on this difficult course. *SSS 72*

GF $

1960

18

December to April

D. Brazier

L 5860 P 72

R S

Required : Handicap Certificate
Best days : Weekdays

HOLE	LENGTH MEDAL-TEE	PAR	STROKE INDEX
1	400	4	3
2	120	3	17
3	320	4	7
4	390	4	1
5	440	5	15
6	195	3	5
7	470	5	13
8	310	4	9
9	290	4	11
TOTAL	2935	36	TOTAL

HOLE	LENGTH MEDAL-TEE	PAR	STROKE INDEX
10	160	3	14
11	345	4	8
12	445	5	16
13	305	4	10
14	480	5	2
15	130	3	18
16	320	4	12
17	360	4	4
18	380	4	6
TOTAL	2925	36	TOTAL

VIKSJÖ

TEL : (0758)16708
LOCATION : 3 km Jakobsberg E 18/18 km Stockholm
ADDRESS : Fjällens Gard – 175 45 Järfälla
HOTEL :
Welcome – Järfälla
Tel : (08)7602520
Diplomat – Stockholm
Tel : (08)635800

The course is laid out on flat open fields with several holes cutting through parkland. Several strategic streams meander their way through the course, requiring precision. Hotel Welcome is situated about 4 km from the Viksjö golf course. *SSS 73*

GF $ — November to May — S

1969 — N. Skold — 

18 — L 5930 P 73 — R

Required : Handicap Certificate
Best days : Thursdays, Fridays

HOLE	LENGTH MEDAL-TEE	PAR	STROKE INDEX
1	305	4	9
2	485	5	11
3	485	5	1
4	310	4	5
5	130	3	15
6	490	5	7
7	345	4	3
8	140	3	17
9	320	4	13
TOTAL	3010	37	TOTAL

HOLE	LENGTH MEDAL-TEE	PAR	STROKE INDEX
10	490	5	8
11	335	4	2
12	345	4	6
13	195	3	16
14	295	4	10
15	300	4	18
16	150	3	14
17	365	4	4
18	445	5	12
TOTAL	2920	36	TOTAL

VISBY

TEL : (0498)45058
LOCATION : 25 km S. Visby Rd 140
ADDRESS : Box 1038 – 621 21 Visby
HOTEL :
Toftagarden – Visby
Tel : (0498)65400
Smagarde – Visby
Tel : (0498)65006
Visby – Visby
Tel : (0498)11925
RESTAURANT : Hemse – Hemse
Tel : (0498)80151

The course is picturesquely situated on the tiny island of Gotland, out in the Baltic. Ideal for holiday golf, with short holes bordering the sea. The charming clubhouse is built high up on the rocks next to the lighthouse. The Toftagarden hotel is situated nearby and is equipped with a pitch and putt, tennis courts and windsurf facilities. *SSS 72*

GF $

1958

18

December to April

N. Skold, G. Hörnfeldt

L 5015 P 72

R S

Required : Handicap Certificate
Best days : Weekdays; in July and August booking in advance

HOLE	LENGTH MEDAL-TEE	PAR	STROKE INDEX
1	130	3	17
2	330	4	1
3	260	4	13
4	400	5	11
5	125	3	15
6	290	4	5
7	305	4	3
8	385	5	7
9	275	4	9
TOTAL	2500	36	TOTAL

HOLE	LENGTH MEDAL-TEE	PAR	STROKE INDEX
10	325	4	4
11	115	3	18
12	290	4	2
13	285	4	6
14	380	5	12
15	130	3	16
16	415	5	8
17	295	4	10
18	280	4	14
TOTAL	2515	36	TOTAL

WERMDÖ

TEL : (0766)20849
LOCATION : 30 km Stockholm
ADDRESS : Torpa – 139 00 Värmdö
HOTEL :
Djurö Vardshus – Djurhamn
Tel : (0766)51800
Sergel Plaza – Stockholm
Tel : (08)226600

One of Sweden's prestigious country clubs with a swimming pool, several tennis courts and a good golf course with plenty of variety. Set in the middle of the Stockholm archipelago in fine undulating countryside, there are several well-placed water hazards. Many of the fairways are flanked by majestic trees. The club has one of Sweden's most attractive clubhouses which overlooks the course. *SSS 72*

GF $$

1966

18

November to April

N. Skold

L 5625 P 72

 S

Required : Handicap Certificate
Best days : Tuesdays, Thursdays, Fridays

HOLE	LENGTH MEDAL-TEE	PAR	STROKE INDEX
1	340	4	9
2	280	4	5
3	440	5	13
4	380	4	1
5	145	3	15
6	310	4	7
7	305	4	3
8	120	3	17
9	330	4	11
TOTAL	2650	35	TOTAL

HOLE	LENGTH MEDAL-TEE	PAR	STROKE INDEX
10	440	5	10
11	160	3	14
12	345	4	2
13	300	4	6
14	170	3	16
15	280	4	18
16	450	5	8
17	500	5	4
18	330	4	12
TOTAL	2975	37	TOTAL

WITTSJÖ

TEL : (0451)22635
LOCATION : 2 km Vittsjö
ADDRESS : Ubbaltsgården – 280 22 Vittsjö
HOTEL :
Trobeck – Vittsjö
Tel : (0451)22940
Ibegarden – Vittsjö
Tel : (0451)22194
RESTAURANT : Värdshuset Vita Hasten – Vittsjö
Tel : (0451)27030

Densely wooded with stately trees bordering the fairways, the course is laid out in undulating countryside near the coast of Southern Sweden. There is an attractive Swedish style clubhouse. *SSS 70*

GF $

1962

18

November to April

A. Amilon, N. Skold

L 5310 P 70

S

R

Required : None
Best days : Weekdays

HOLE	LENGTH MEDAL-TEE	PAR	STROKE INDEX
1	305	4	11
2	195	3	9
3	300	4	7
4	320	4	15
5	130	3	17
6	540	5	1
7	280	4	5
8	175	3	13
9	395	4	3
TOTAL	2640	34	TOTAL

HOLE	LENGTH MEDAL-TEE	PAR	STROKE INDEX
10	305	4	8
11	435	5	12
12	320	4	4
13	300	4	14
14	110	3	18
15	430	5	2
16	305	4	6
17	130	3	16
18	335	4	10
TOTAL	2670	36	TOTAL

YSTAD

TEL : (0411)50350
LOCATION : 7 km E. Ystad to Simrishamn
ADDRESS : Box 162 – 27100 Ystad
HOTEL :
Ystads Saltsjöbad – Ystad
Tel : (0411)13630
Continental – Ystad
Tel : (0411)13700
Lagpris – Ystad
Tel : (0411)12954

Located near the seaside resort of Ystad on the popular south coast, Ystad is a typical seaside course with fairways running through heathland. Ideal for holiday golf with the fine Ystads hotel at only 6 km from the club. *SSS 72*

GF $

November to April

1931

 T. Bruce

RP

18

 5740 P 72

Required : Handciap Certificate
Best days : Mondays, Fridays

HOLE	LENGTH MEDAL-TEE	PAR	STROKE INDEX
1	140	3	15
2	330	4	9
3	315	4	1
4	330	4	11
5	470	5	3
6	325	4	17
7	435	5	7
8	165	3	13
9	340	4	5
TOTAL	2850	36	TOTAL

HOLE	LENGTH MEDAL-TEE	PAR	STROKE INDEX
10	470	5	12
11	155	3	14
12	375	4	2
13	350	4	10
14	330	4	6
15	110	3	18
16	450	5	16
17	340	4	4
18	310	4	8
TOTAL	2890	36	TOTAL

34 GOLF COURSES, 17 000 PLAYERS

★★★ Great golf course
★★ Very good golf course
$ 15-50 Sfr.
★ Recommended golf course
✡ Holiday golf course
$$ more than 50 Sfr.

TOWN	GOLF COURSE		TEL	MAP REF.
Arosa	Arosa		(081) 312215	•
Ascona	Patriziale Ascona	★★★ ✡	(093) 352132	21
Bad Ragaz	Bad Ragaz	★	(085) 91556	11
Bad Schinznach	Bad Schinznach		(056) 431226	•
Basel	Basel	★	89.68.50.91	1
Bern	Blumisberg		(037) 363438	10
Bürgenstock	Bürgenstock		(041) 612434	•
Crans-sur-Sierre	Crans-sur-Sierre	★★★ ✡	(027) 412168	19
Davos	Davos	✡	(081) 465634	14
Genève	Bonmont		(022) 692345	24
	Bossey (see France)	★★	50.43.75.25	25
	Domaine Imperial	★	(022) 644545	26
	Esery (see France)		50.36.58.70	
	Genève	★★★	(022) 7357540	16
Gstaad	Gstaad-Saanenland		(030) 42636	•
Interlaken	Interlaken	★	(036) 226022	12
Lausanne	Lausanne	★★	(021) 7841315	15
Lenzerheide	Lenzerheide-Valbella	✡	(081) 341316	13
Lindau (in W. Germany)	Bodensee (W. Germany)		(08389) 89190	27
Lucerne	Lucerne	✡	(041) 369787	9
Lugano	Lugano	✡	(091) 711557	22
Montreux	Montreux	★★★	(025) 264616	17
Neuchâtel	Neuchâtel		(038) 335550	2
Oberentfelden	Mitteland		(064) 438984	•
Riederalp	Riederalp		(028) 272932	•
St. Gallen	Ostschweizerischer		(071) 811856	6
St. Moritz	Engadine	✡	(082) 65226	23
Verbier	Verbier	✡	(026) 311566	20
Villars	Villars	✡	(025) 354214	18
Vulpera	Vulpera		(084) 99688	•
Zürich	Breitenloo		(01) 8366486	3
	Dolder		(01) 475045	•
	Hittnau		(01) 9502442	5
	Schönenberg		(01) 7881624	7
	Zürich	★★	(01) 9180050	4

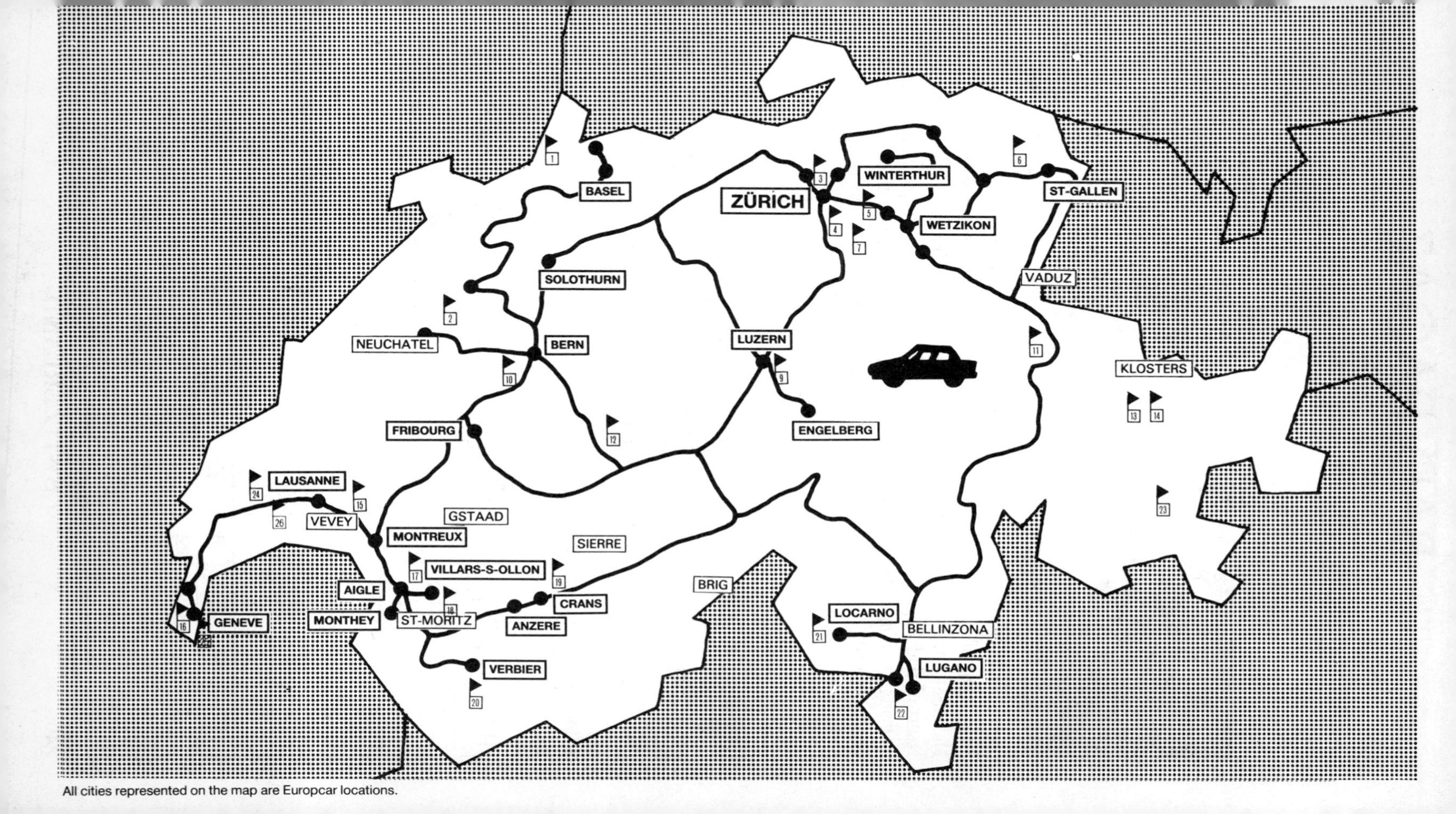

All cities represented on the map are Europcar locations.

BAD RAGAZ

TEL : (085)91556
LOCATION : 20 km Chur
ADDRESS : Hans-Albrechtstr. – 7310 Bad Ragaz
HOTEL :
Hof Ragaz – Bad Ragaz
Tel : (085)90131
Parkhotel – Bad Ragaz
Tel : (085)92244
Quellenhof – Bad Ragaz
Tel : (085)90111
RESTAURANT : Quellenhof Grill – Bad Ragaz
Tel : (085)90111

In a setting of scenic beauty among centuries old trees, this is one of Switzerland's oldest and most attractive golf courses. Laid out in the Alpine foothills near the famous spa resort of Bad Ragaz, the course is heavily wooded, and includes a picturesque lake and a small stream meandering its way through several holes. Every year in October, the club organizes a popular fortnight of competitions open to any golfer. There is a modern chalet style clubhouse. *SSS 70*

GF $

1895

18

November to April

—

L 5494 P 70

S

R

Required : Handicap Certificate
Best days : Weekdays only

HOLE	LENGTH MEDAL-TEE	PAR	STROKE INDEX
1	330	4	9
2	305	4	13
3	128	3	17
4	437	5	5
5	382	4	1
6	370	4	3
7	318	4	15
8	335	4	7
9	187	3	11
TOTAL	2792	35	TOTAL

HOLE	LENGTH MEDAL-TEE	PAR	STROKE INDEX
10	320	4	16
11	137	3	18
12	505	5	2
13	390	4	4
14	152	3	8
15	275	4	12
16	437	5	14
17	161	3	10
18	325	4	6
TOTAL	2702	35	TOTAL

BASEL

★

TEL : France : 89685091
LOCATION : 15 km Basel A 35
ADDRESS : 68220 Hagenthal-le-Bas – Ht Rhin – France
HOTEL :
Jenny – Hagenthal-le-Bas
Tel : France : 89685009
Drachen – Basel
Tel : (061)239090
Merian am Rhein – Basel
Tel : (061)6810000
RESTAURANT : Stucki – Basel
Tel : (061)358222

Though located in France in the picturesque Alsace region just over the Swiss/French border, the golf club is a member of both the Swiss and the French Golf Federation. It is a very attractive undulating inland course with several fairways laid out in woodland. Rather long, the course constitutes a fine test for the average player with various dog-leg holes, water hazards, elevated greens and narrow fairways. The course gives fine views over the Black Forest, the Jura and Vosges mountain chains. *SSS 71*

GF $ — Wed.; Nov. to March — S

1926 — B. von Limburger

18 — L 5938 P 72 — R

Required : Handicap Certificate, Club Membership Card
Best days : Tuesdays and Fridays

HOLE	LENGTH MEDAL-TEE	PAR	STROKE INDEX
1	305	4	16
2	437	5	8
3	193	3	12
4	385	4	2
5	359	4	10
6	490	5	4
7	127	3	18
8	331	4	6
9	299	4	14
TOTAL	2926	36	TOTAL

HOLE	LENGTH MEDAL-TEE	PAR	STROKE INDEX
10	438	5	15
11	175	3	11
12	328	4	7
13	367	4	1
14	372	4	5
15	292	4	13
16	159	3	17
17	384	4	3
18	497	5	9
TOTAL	3012	36	TOTAL

BLUMISBERG

TEL : (037)363438
LOCATION : 16 km Bern
ADDRESS : 3184 Wünnewil
HOTEL :
Goldener Adler – Bern
Tel : (031)221725
Bären – Bern
Tel : (031)223367
Wächter Mövenpick – Bern
Tel : (031)220866
RESTAURANT : Zum Rathaus – Bern
Tel : (031)226183

Situated 16 km from the Swiss capital, this popular course is set on partly wooded and rolling countryside at 600m above sea level with its layout following the natural undulations of the terrain. There is a pleasant farm style clubhouse. *SSS 73*

GF $ — November to March — R S
1959 — —
18 — L 5707 P 72

Required : Handicap Certificate, Club Membership Card
Best days : Weekdays only esp. Tuesdays and Fridays

HOLE	LENGTH MEDAL-TEE	PAR	STROKE INDEX
1	320	4	9
2	162	3	7
3	436	5	15
4	301	4	3
5	123	3	17
6	329	4	11
7	435	5	13
8	379	4	1
9	382	4	5
TOTAL	2867	36	TOTAL

HOLE	LENGTH MEDAL-TEE	PAR	STROKE INDEX
10	138	3	14
11	299	4	6
12	292	4	18
13	447	5	10
14	164	3	16
15	502	5	2
16	368	4	4
17	296	4	12
18	334	4	8
TOTAL	2840	36	TOTAL

BODENSEE

TEL : (08389)89190
LOCATION : 4 km Lindau
ADDRESS : Lampertsweiler 51-8995 Weissensberg (in West Germany)
HOTEL : HP
Golfhotel Bodensee
Tel : (08389)891-0
Bahnhof Post-Kreuzlingen
Tel : (072)727972
Schweizerhof-Kreuzlingen
Tel : (072)723840

This Swiss club is actually situated near Lindau, by the scenic Lake Constance in West Germany. At around 500m above sea level, the course, designed by Robert Trent Jones, is promising. The 18 holes run along a varied landscape through areas of woodland, streams, sloping terrain and natural lakes. It offers fine views over the Swiss and Austrian Alps. An exclusive 4 star hotel with full sports and leisure facilities such as fitness centre, and an indoor pool is fully operational. An originality of the Bodensee golf club is that it is one of the rare clubs with telephones on some of its fairways. *SSS 71*

GF $$ — Dec. to March — S
1986 — R. Trent Jones — RP
18 — L 5856 P 71

Required : Club Membership Card, Handicap Certificate
Best days : Weekdays

HOLE	LENGTH MEDAL-TEE	PAR	STROKE INDEX
1	338	4	9
2	156	3	17
3	306	4	13
4	207	3	7
5	503	5	1
6	288	4	11
7	360	4	5
8	342	4	3
9	313	4	15
TOTAL	2813	35	TOTAL

HOLE	LENGTH MEDAL-TEE	PAR	STROKE INDEX
10	332	4	8
11	339	4	10
12	374	4	12
13	471	5	2
14	169	3	16
15	380	4	14
16	505	5	4
17	128	3	18
18	345	4	16
TOTAL	3043	36	TOTAL

BONMONT

TEL : (022)692345
LOCATION : 30 km Genève
ADDRESS : Domaine de Bonmont – 1261 Chéserex
HOTEL :
du Lac – Coppet
Tel : (022)761521
Beau Rivage – Nyon
Tel : (022)613231
D'Orange – Coppet
Tel : (022)761037
RESTAURANT : Auberge de Chateauvieux – Satigny
Tel : (022)531445

One of the newest Swiss golf courses lies 30km from Geneva in Chéserex. This promising course was designed, like many other Swiss courses, by the English architect Donald Harradine. The course has a varied layout with numerous water hazards, presenting a great challenge to players. There is a magnificent clubhouse with several bedrooms, tennis courts, a riding centre, a fitness club, conference facilities and an indoor swimming pool. *SSS 71*

GF $$
1982
18

—
D. Harradine
L 5750 P 71

S
R

Required : Handicap Certificate
Best days : Weekdays only

HOLE	LENGTH MEDAL-TEE	PAR	STROKE INDEX
1	330	4	12
2	310	4	6
3	150	3	16
4	305	4	8
5	390	4	2
6	440	5	14
7	120	3	18
8	495	5	10
9	355	4	4
TOTAL	2895	36	TOTAL

HOLE	LENGTH MEDAL-TEE	PAR	STROKE INDEX
10	405	4	3
11	170	3	15
12	440	5	9
13	320	4	5
14	375	4	1
15	360	4	11
16	150	3	17
17	315	4	7
18	320	4	13
TOTAL	2855	35	TOTAL

BREITENLOO

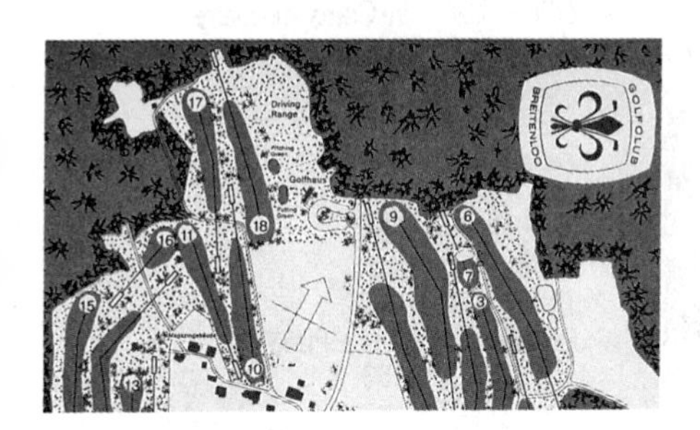

TEL : (01)8366486
LOCATION : 6 km Zürich Airport
ADDRESS : 8309 Oberwil
HOTEL :
Hilton – Kloten
Tel : (01)8103131
Altbach – Bassersdorf
Tel : (01)8366767
Welcome Inn – Kloten
Tel : (01)8140727
RESTAURANT : Braustube Hürlimann – Zürich
Tel : (01)2111770

One of the four 18-hole golf courses in the Zürich region is the Breitenloo championship lay-out, originally designed by Frank Pennink and redesigned by the Swiss based Donald Harradine. This inland course is surrounded by woodland and many of its fairways are tree-lined. *SSS 71*

GF $ — November to April — R S

1964 — F. Pennink, D. Harradine

18 — L 5745 P 72

Required : Handicap Certificate
Best days : Weekdays only

HOLE	LENGTH MEDAL-TEE	PAR	STROKE INDEX
1	460	5	11
2	145	3	15
3	400	4	7
4	355	4	1
5	150	3	13
6	470	5	5
7	125	3	17
8	335	4	3
9	445	5	9
TOTAL	2885	36	TOTAL

HOLE	LENGTH MEDAL-TEE	PAR	STROKE INDEX
10	345	4	2
11	285	4	18
12	470	5	10
13	175	3	6
14	310	4	16
15	465	5	8
16	145	3	12
17	330	4	4
18	335	4	14
TOTAL	2860	36	TOTAL

CRANS-SUR-SIERRE

TEL : (027)412168
LOCATION : In Crans-sur-Sierre
ADDRESS : 3963 Crans-sur-Sierre
HOTEL :
Golf– Crans
Tel : (027)414242
Des Alpes – Crans
Tel : (027)413754
Rhodania – Crans
Tel : (027)401141
RESTAURANT : Le Plaza-Crans
Tel : (027)412083

Famous as a top level ski resort in winter and as a high class golf resort in summer, the Crans golf course ranks among the world's great alpine courses. The course is long, varied and entertaining with magnificent views over the Rhone valley and the snow covered mountain peaks of the Berner Alps. It is a classic example of a mountain course with continuous ups and downs of the terrain. Every year the golf club hosts the popular Swiss Open, welcoming many great golf champions. There is a fine clubhouse with a terrace, featuring a swimming pool and a picturesque lake just below. *SSS 72*

GF $$
1907
27
November to May
M. Nicholson
L 5850 P 72
S
R

Required : Handicap Certificate
Best days : Any day

HOLE	LENGTH MEDAL-TEE	PAR	STROKE INDEX
1	470	5	11
2	380	4	5
3	150	3	15
4	440	4	3
5	295	4	7
6	285	4	9
7	275	4	17
8	160	3	13
9	540	5	1
TOTAL	2995	36	TOTAL

HOLE	LENGTH MEDAL-TEE	PAR	STROKE INDEX
10	365	4	10
11	185	3	8
12	350	4	12
13	155	3	6
14	450	5	2
15	455	5	16
16	280	4	14
17	305	4	18
18	310	4	4
TOTAL	2855	36	TOTAL

DAVOS

TEL : (081)465634/465271
LOCATION : In Davos
ADDRESS : 7270 Davos–Platz
HOTEL : HF
Golfhotel Waldhuus
Tel : (083)61131
Montana Sport – Davos Platz
Tel : (083)53444
Schweizerhof – Davos Platz
Tel : (083)21151
RESTAURANT : Berghaus Strelapass – Davos
Tel : (083)35260

A fine holiday course, at over 1500 m above sea level, wedged between mighty snow covered mountain peaks of the Swiss Alps near the popular resort of Davos. The course is bordered on one side by a river, and on the other side by a stream crossing the course. There is a picturesque chalet style clubhouse. Just several metres from the golf course is the first-class Waldhuus Hotel with tennis courts and a swimming pool. *SSS 67*

GF $ — November to May — RF S

1960 — D. Harradine

18 — L 5135 P 69

Required : Handicap Certificate
Best days : Any day

HOLE	LENGTH MEDAL-TEE	PAR	STROKE INDEX
1	390	4	1
2	125	3	17
3	440	5	9
4	135	3	15
5	340	4	13
6	450	5	3
7	150	3	11
8	380	4	5
9	180	3	7
TOTAL	2590	34	TOTAL

HOLE	LENGTH MEDAL-TEE	PAR	STROKE INDEX
10	360	4	2
11	270	4	14
12	280	4	12
13	325	4	10
14	130	3	16
15	340	4	4
16	265	4	8
17	115	3	18
18	460	5	6
TOTAL	2545	35	TOTAL

DOMAINE IMPERIAL

★

TEL : (022)644545
LOCATION : 30 km Genève, near Nyon
ADDRESS : 1196 Gland
HOTEL :
Beau Rivage-Nyon
Tel : (022)613231
Des Alpes-Nyon
Tel : (022)613231
Clos de Sadex-Nyon
Tel : (022)612831
RESTAURANT : Du Lac-Nyon
Tel : (022)614633

Le Domaine Imperial is a new and exclusive golf club laid out by Peter Dye on the borders of Lac Léman between Lausanne and Geneva. A challenging championship course featuring long holes flanked by majestic trees (holes 1 to 8) with the last nine running through open countryside. Fairways and greens are heavily bunkered and two lakes and one stream serve as hazards. The clubhouse, overlooking the lake, has been installed in the beautifully restored Villa Prangins, built in 1860 and former property of Prince de Napoléon.

GF $$ — Mon.; Dec. to March — R S
1987 — P. Dye
18 — L 5903 P 72

Required : Handicap Certificate
Best days : Weekdays till 12 h, with booking in advance

HOLE	LENGTH MEDAL-TEE	PAR	STROKE INDEX
1	469	5	9
2	148	3	17
3	356	4	5
4	507	5	3
5	147	3	13
6	359	4	1
7	316	4	15
8	338	4	11
9	369	4	7
TOTAL	3009	36	TOTAL

HOLE	LENGTH MEDAL-TEE	PAR	STROKE INDEX
10	360	4	6
11	399	4	2
12	115	3	14
13	452	5	12
14	306	4	16
15	109	3	18
16	437	5	8
17	373	4	4
18	343	4	10
TOTAL	2894	36	TOTAL

ENGADINE

TEL : (082)65226
LOCATION : 6 km St Moritz
ADDRESS : 7503 St Moritz Samedan
HOTEL :
Quadratscha – Samedan
Tel : (082)64257
Badrutt's Palace – St. Moritz
Tel : (082)21101
Neues Post – St. Moritz
Tel : (082)22121
RESTAURANT : Talvo – St Moritz
Tel : (082)34455

Situated 1750m above sea level, 6km from the famous ski resort St-Moritz, the Engadine golf course is one of Europe's highest 18 hole courses. Laid out amidst beautiful mountain scenery, the course is hilly with trees and several water hazards. Ideal for holiday golf with the Quadratscha Hotel equipped with tennis courts, a fitness room and a swimming pool nearby. *SSS 72*

GF $

October to June

S

1978

M. Verdieri

18

L 6350 P 72

R

Required : Handicap Certificate
Best days : Any day

HOLE	LENGTH MEDAL-TEE	PAR	STROKE INDEX
1	360	4	
2	500	5	
3	550	5	
4	325	4	
5	365	4	
6	405	4	
7	190	3	
8	390	4	
9	370	4	
TOTAL	3355	37	TOTAL

HOLE	LENGTH MEDAL-TEE	PAR	STROKE INDEX
10	210	3	
11	320	4	
12	395	4	
13	440	5	
14	385	4	
15	140	3	
16	375	4	
17	155	3	
18	475	5	
TOTAL	2995	35	TOTAL

GENEVE

TEL : (022)7357540
LOCATION : 4 km Genève
ADDRESS : 70 Route de la Capite – 1223 Cologny
HOTEL :
Hostellerie de la Vendée – Genève
Tel : (022)7920411
Du Midi – Genève
Tel : (022)7317800
Moga Hilton – Genève
Tel : (022)7319811
RESTAURANT : Auberge d'Hermance – Hermance
Tel : (022)7511368

This fine and traditional golf course redesigned by Robert Trent Jones is one of Europe's prestigious courses. Laid out on the Cologny plateau among centuries old trees only 6km from Geneva, with fine distant views over the Alps and Jura chain. It is a long and testing course including large bunkers, numerous dog-legs and water hazards (lake guarding the greens of the 16th and 17th holes). Undoubtedly the greatest Swiss golf course, it has hosted many important tournaments and was the venue for the World Team Championship in 1982. There is an imposing and luxurious clubhouse with outstanding facilities. *SSS 73*

GF $$ — Mondays — R S

1923/1973 — R. Trent Jones — 

18 — L 5955 P 72 — 

Required : Handicap Certificate, Club Membership Card
Best days : Weekdays only

HOLE	LENGTH MEDAL-TEE	PAR	STROKE INDEX
1	295	4	15
2	355	4	5
3	160	3	17
4	320	4	11
5	435	5	7
6	365	4	1
7	185	3	13
8	455	5	9
9	380	4	3
TOTAL	2950	36	TOTAL

HOLE	LENGTH MEDAL-TEE	PAR	STROKE INDEX
10	330	4	14
11	135	3	18
12	360	4	6
13	495	5	10
14	400	4	2
15	510	5	4
16	285	4	12
17	140	3	16
18	350	4	8
TOTAL	3005	36	TOTAL

HITTNAU

TEL : (01)9502442
LOCATION : 25 km Zürich, near Pfäffikon, in Dürstelen
ADDRESS : 8335 Hittnau
HOTEL :
Seerose – Pfäffikon
Tel : (01)9500101
Baur au Lac – Zürich
Tel : (01)2211650
Bellerive au Lac – Zürich
Tel : (01)2517010
RESTAURANT : Petermanns – Küsnacht
Tel : (01)9100715

The Hittnau golf course, at 800m above sea level, is charmingly landscaped and set amidst peaceful surroundings overlooking the lakes of Pfäffikon and Greifensee to the Alps of Glarus. The fairways are partly laid out in open fields and partly in thick pine forest. *SSS 70*

GF $ — November to March — 

1974 — — 

18 — L 5535 P 71 — 

Required : Handicap Certificate
Best days : Weekdays only

HOLE	LENGTH MEDAL-TEE	PAR	STROKE INDEX
1	260	4	15
2	365	4	5
3	380	4	1
4	120	3	17
5	350	4	3
6	360	4	9
7	335	4	7
8	330	4	11
9	200	3	13
TOTAL	2700	34	TOTAL

HOLE	LENGTH MEDAL-TEE	PAR	STROKE INDEX
10	490	5	2
11	250	4	18
12	330	4	4
13	155	3	12
14	325	4	8
15	155	3	6
16	315	4	10
17	380	5	14
18	435	5	16
TOTAL	2835	37	TOTAL

INTERLAKEN

★

TEL : (036)226022
LOCATION : 2 km Interlaken
ADDRESS : 3800 Interlaken
HOTEL :
Métropole – Interlaken
Tel : (036)212151
Landhotel Golf – Interlaken
Tel : (036)232131
Du Lac – Interlaken
Tel : (036)222922
RESTAURANT : Zum goldenen Anker – Interlaken
Tel : (036)221672

The course is set on the banks of the 'Thuner See' within splendid natural landscape, surrounded by mountains and bordering a nature reserve. There are numerous small ponds and streams meandering their way through the fairways. Both hotels, Métropole and Landhotel Golf are nearby the golf club. *SSS 72*

GF $ — November to April  

1965 — D. Harradine 

18 — L 5980 P 72 

Required : Handicap Certificate
Best days : Weekdays

HOLE	LENGTH MEDAL-TEE	PAR	STROKE INDEX
1	352	4	4
2	173	3	18
3	365	4	2
4	462	5	6
5	350	4	8
6	342	4	10
7	346	4	14
8	176	3	16
9	478	5	12
TOTAL	3044	36	TOTAL

HOLE	LENGTH MEDAL-TEE	PAR	STROKE INDEX
10	356	4	7
11	453	5	15
12	324	4	9
13	323	4	5
14	136	3	17
15	279	4	13
16	537	5	1
17	170	3	11
18	358	4	3
TOTAL	2936	36	TOTAL

LAUSANNE

TEL : (021)7841315/16117
LOCATION : 10 km Lausanne
ADDRESS : Le Châlet à Gobet – 1000 Lausanne 25
HOTEL :
Vert Bois – Châlet à Gobet
Tel : (021)7841121
Château d'Ouchy – Lausanne
Tel : (021)267451
Les Chevreuils – Châlet à Gobet
Tel : (021)7842021
RESTAURANT : La Grappe d'Or – Lausanne
Tel : (021)230760

Six kilometres north from Lausanne and 853m above sea level, the course is scenically laid out with fine views of Lac Leman and the Savoy Alps. The course itself is set on undulating country at the edge of the vast spruce forests of the Jorat. Originally designed by a keen local golfer Oscar Dolfuss, it was redesigned in 1960 by Donald Harradine and is now considered one of the best Swiss courses. There is a large and attractive mansion style clubhouse. *SSS 74*

GF $$ — November to April  

1921 — D. Harradine, O. Dolfuss 

18 — L 5900 P 72 

Required : Handicap certificate
Best days : Mondays to Fridays

HOLE	LENGTH MEDAL-TEE	PAR	STROKE INDEX
1	380	4	9
2	355	4	3
3	125	3	17
4	355	4	7
5	385	4	1
6	465	5	5
7	310	4	15
8	165	3	11
9	455	5	13
TOTAL	2995	36	TOTAL

HOLE	LENGTH MEDAL-TEE	PAR	STROKE INDEX
10	375	4	2
11	130	3	18
12	305	4	12
13	435	5	6
14	330	4	10
15	350	4	4
16	360	4	8
17	150	3	16
18	470	5	14
TOTAL	2905	36	TOTAL

LENZERHEIDE– VALBELLA

✡

TEL : (081)341316
LOCATION : 2 km Lenzerheide
ADDRESS : 7078 Lenzerheide
HOTEL :
Guarda Val Sporz – Lenzerheide
Tel : (081)342214
Schweizerhof – Lenzerheide
Tel : (081)340111
Valbella Inn – Valbella
Tel : (081)343636
RESTAURANT : Romana – Valbella
Tel : (081)341616

A fine mountain course 1500m above sea level, enclosed between snow clad peaks and laid out near the friendly alpine resort of Lenzerheide. Many of the gently rolling fairways of this short course are lined by pine trees. Hotel Guarda Val, near the course, is a Relais & Châteaux hotel. *SSS 69*

GF $

1952

18

November to May

—

L 5269 P 69

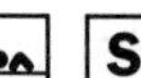

S

R

Required : Handicap Certificate
Best days : Weekdays

HOLE	LENGTH MEDAL-TEE	PAR	STROKE INDEX
1	380	4	3
2	165	3	11
3	410	4	1
4	155	3	13
5	266	4	17
6	285	4	7
7	418	5	15
8	189	3	5
9	165	3	9
TOTAL	2433	33	TOTAL

HOLE	LENGTH MEDAL-TEE	PAR	STROKE INDEX
10	466	5	8
11	255	4	18
12	170	3	16
13	378	4	2
14	135	3	14
15	436	5	4
16	356	4	6
17	485	5	12
18	155	3	10
TOTAL	2836	36	TOTAL

LUCERNE

TEL : (041)369787
LOCATION : 5 km Lucerne
ADDRESS : 6006 Lucerne/Dietschiberg
HOTEL :
Palace – Lucerne
Tel : (041)502222
Astoria – Lucerne
Tel : (041)244466
Schiller – Lucerne
Tel : (041)235155
RESTAURANT : Schwanen – Lucerne
Tel : (041)511177

Laid out in the foothills of the Alps with fine overall views, the Lucerne golf club is one of Switzerland's oldest clubs dating back to 1903. The course is not difficult, though rather hilly with many ups and downs. Ideal for holiday golf, several holes are tree-lined and there is one water hazard on the 15th fairway. Accomodation for golfers is available in the typical Swiss clubhouse. *SSS 69*

GF $
1903
18

December to March
—
L 5388 P 72

S
R

Required : Handicap Certificate
Best days : Weekdays only

HOLE	LENGTH MEDAL-TEE	PAR	STROKE INDEX
1	269	4	14
2	267	4	12
3	133	3	18
4	217	4	8
5	463	5	2
6	423	5	4
7	148	3	16
8	297	4	10
9	337	4	6
TOTAL	2554	36	TOTAL

HOLE	LENGTH MEDAL-TEE	PAR	STROKE INDEX
10	409	5	11
11	216	3	15
12	497	5	3
13	328	4	7
14	324	4	1
15	261	4	15
16	324	4	5
17	120	3	17
18	355	4	9
TOTAL	2834	36	TOTAL

LUGANO

TEL : (091)711557
LOCATION : 8 km Lugano
ADDRESS : 6983 Magliaso
HOTEL : HP
Villa Magliasina
Tel : (091)713471
Garderia – Caslano Lugano
Tel : (091)711716
Sporting Magliaso – Magliaso
Tel : (091)711135
RESTAURANT : Motto del Gallo – Taverne
Tel : (091)932871

An attractive golf course surrounded by hills decked with luxuriant woods, laid out on both sides of the scenic river 'Magliasina' in the Magliaso-Caslano area. The course winds in and out among lines of birch-trees, ancient oak-trees and colourful flowerbeds. Golfhotel Magliasina is situated on the golf course. *SSS 71*

GF $ — — RP S

1923 — —

18 L 5740 P 71

Required : Handicap Certificate
Best days : Weekdays

HOLE	LENGTH MEDAL-TEE	PAR	STROKE INDEX
1	340	4	3
2	340	4	13
3	185	3	11
4	440	5	17
5	360	4	5
6	160	3	15
7	435	5	7
8	175	3	9
9	405	4	1
TOTAL	2840	35	TOTAL

HOLE	LENGTH MEDAL-TEE	PAR	STROKE INDEX
10	515	5	2
11	110	3	18
12	350	4	6
13	435	5	14
14	280	4	16
15	315	4	12
16	385	4	4
17	155	3	10
18	355	4	8
TOTAL	2900	36	TOTAL

MONTREUX

TEL : (025)264616
LOCATION : 20 km Montreux
ADDRESS : Route d'Evian – 1860 Aigle
HOTEL :
Du Nord– Aigle
Tel : (025)261055
Eden au Lac – Montreux
Tel : (021)9635551
Hostellerie du Lac
Tel : (021)9633271
RESTAURANT : Château de Chillon – Montreux
Tel : (021)637664

One of the oldest and busiest clubs in Switzerland having been founded in 1902. The course was extended to 18 holes in 1964 and is one of Switzerland's most popular championship layouts. It is situated in the Rhône Valley at the foot of the vineyards of Yvorne and Aigle with the Alps in the background. The first-class Hotel Du Nord, with swimming pool, tennis courts and a children's playground, is nearby. *SSS 71*

GF $$ — R S
1902 D. Harradine 
18 L 5890 P 72

Required : Handicap Certificate
Best days : Weekdays; Weekends by prior arrangement

HOLE	LENGTH MEDAL-TEE	PAR	STROKE INDEX
1	445	5	7
2	150	3	15
3	350	4	1
4	345	4	5
5	300	4	17
6	320	4	13
7	485	5	3
8	190	3	11
9	320	4	9
TOTAL	2905	36	TOTAL

HOLE	LENGTH MEDAL-TEE	PAR	STROKE INDEX
10	335	4	8
11	330	4	18
12	140	3	16
13	355	4	4
14	170	3	14
15	490	5	6
16	375	4	2
17	440	5	12
18	350	4	10
TOTAL	2985	36	TOTAL

NEUCHÂTEL

TEL : (038)335550
LOCATION : 6 km Neuchâtel, route de Lignières
ADDRESS : 2072 Voëns-sur-Saint-Blaise
HOTEL :
Novotel – Neuchâtel
Tel : (038)335757
Beaulac – Neuchâtel
Tel : (038)258822
City – Neuchâtel
Tel : (038)255412
RESTAURANT : Au vieux Vapeur– Neuchâtel
Tel : (038)243400

Laid out in a parkland setting with fairways bordered by trees, this fairly undulating course includes one water hazard, a lake guarding the 9th fairway. There is a road dividing the course into separate parts. *SSS 70*

GF $ | November to April | S
1975 | — |
18 | L 5444 P 70 | R

Required : Handicap Certificate
Best days : Any day

HOLE	LENGTH MEDAL-TEE	PAR	STROKE INDEX
1	271	4	14
2	505	5	8
3	117	3	16
4	325	4	7
5	405	5	18
6	345	4	3
7	201	3	9
8	395	4	5
9	180	3	1
TOTAL	2744	35	TOTAL

HOLE	LENGTH MEDAL-TEE	PAR	STROKE INDEX
10	125	3	17
11	310	4	11
12	310	4	15
13	280	4	13
14	165	3	12
15	480	5	2
16	380	4	6
17	350	4	4
18	300	4	10
TOTAL	2700	35	TOTAL

OSTSCHWEIZERISCHER

TEL : (071)811856
LOCATION : 20 km St-Gallen
ADDRESS : 9246 Niederbüren
HOTEL : HR
Uzwil– Uzwil
Tel : (073)515151
Ochsen – Niederuzwil
Tel : (073)517255
Alte Herberge – Niederbüren
Tel : (071)812091
RESTAURANT : Rossli – Niederwil
Tel : (071)833847

Set on the banks of the river 'Thur', the course includes many water courses presenting a constant hazard on many of the fairways. The course, designed by the Swiss based golf architect Donald Harradine, is of championship standard and hosted the Swiss Senior and Swiss Interclubs championship.

GF $

December to March

R S

1948

D. Harradine

18

L 5631 P 72

Required : Handicap Certificate
Best days : Tuesdays, Thursdays, Fridays

HOLE	LENGTH MEDAL-TEE	PAR	STROKE INDEX
1	421	5	13
2	306	4	7
3	337	4	1
4	453	5	9
5	148	3	15
6	280	4	11
7	305	4	5
8	124	3	17
9	318	4	3
TOTAL	2692	36	TOTAL

HOLE	LENGTH MEDAL-TEE	PAR	STROKE INDEX
10	134	3	18
11	302	4	16
12	328	4	12
13	360	4	2
14	340	4	6
15	469	5	10
16	168	3	14
17	361	4	4
18	477	5	8
TOTAL	2939	36	TOTAL

PATRIZIALE ASCONA

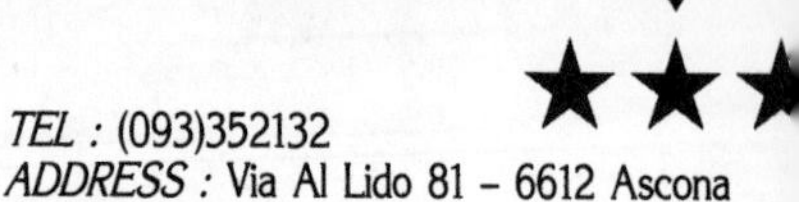

TEL : (093)352132
ADDRESS : Via Al Lido 81 – 6612 Ascona
HOTEL : HR
Giardino
Tel : (093)350101
Ascovilla – Ascona
Tel : (093)350252
Casa Berno – Ascona
Tel : (093)353232
RESTAURANT : Osteria Nostrana – Ascona
Tel : (093)355158

A beautiful inland course partly laid out on the banks of Lago Maggiore and backed by majestic mountains. The rather short course is flat and includes around 45 bunkers and a picturesque lake on the 17th hole. Scenically situated, the course is scattered with mature pines, birch trees and age-old chestnuts. The elegant and new Giardino Hotel is situated on the golf course. *SSS 71*

GF $$ — S
1928 J. Harris, C.K. Cotton
18 L 5893 P 71 R

Required : Handicap Certificate
Best days : Weekdays

HOLE	LENGTH MEDAL-TEE	PAR	STROKE INDEX
1	373	4	7
2	191	3	9
3	378	4	1
4	456	5	11
5	362	4	3
6	436	5	13
7	132	3	17
8	292	4	15
9	389	4	5
TOTAL	3009	36	TOTAL

HOLE	LENGTH MEDAL-TEE	PAR	STROKE INDEX
10	153	3	16
11	474	5	12
12	463	5	10
13	154	3	18
14	380	4	2
15	350	4	8
16	363	4	6
17	169	3	14
18	378	4	4
TOTAL	2884	35	TOTAL

SCHÖNENBERG

TEL : (01)7881624
LOCATION : 20 km Zürich
ADDRESS : 8821 Schönenberg
HOTEL :
Le Belvoir – Rüschlikon
Tel : (01)7240202
Du Lac – Wädenswill
Tel : (01)7800031
Schweizerhof – Wetzikon
Tel : (0101)9324440
RESTAURANT : Wirtschaft zum Letten – Wädenswill
Tel : (01)7808655

Schönenberg is a typical inland course, situated near the city of Zürich. An abundance of strategically placed trees demand precision. The course incorporates a fine setting of small ponds serving as hazards. *SSS 71*

GF $$

1964

18

November to April

—

L 5686 P 72

S

R

Required : Handicap Certificate, Club Membership Card
Best days : Weekdays only

HOLE	LENGTH MEDAL-TEE	PAR	STROKE INDEX
1	451	5	15
2	302	4	13
3	364	4	3
4	335	4	9
5	327	4	11
6	142	3	17
7	356	4	1
8	465	5	5
9	176	3	7
TOTAL	2918	36	TOTAL

HOLE	LENGTH MEDAL-TEE	PAR	STROKE INDEX
10	324	4	4
11	157	3	3
12	261	4	4
13	486	5	5
14	300	4	4
15	166	3	3
16	265	4	4
17	451	5	5
18	358	4	4
TOTAL	2768	36	TOTAL

VERBIER

✡

TEL : (026)311566/311995
LOCATION : In Verbier
ADDRESS : 1936 Verbier Valais
HOTEL :
Bristol – Verbier
Tel : (026)316577
de la Poste – Verbier
Tel : (026)316681
Les 4 Vallées – Verbier
Tel : (026)316066
RESTAURANT : Ecurie – Verbier
Tel : (026)312760

The popular Verbier golf course, 1500m above sea level, is laid out in the idyllic surroundings of the Valaisannes Alps. It is a short alpine course set on rolling slopes with sparse vegetation. A new and longer 18 hole par 70 course is under construction and will be operational in the summer of 1991. Ideal for holiday golf when staying in Verbier. *SSS 54/70*

GF $

1969/1990

36

October to June

P. Bagnoud, D. Harradine

L 2005 P 54, 5350 P70

S

R

Required : Handicap Certificate for the new course, none for the old course
Best days : Anyday

HOLE	LENGTH MEDAL-TEE	PAR	STROKE INDEX
1	95	3	3
2	140	3	1
3	150	3	9
4	110	3	5
5	100	3	13
6	95	3	7
7	80	3	11
8	80	3	17
9	70	3	15
TOTAL	920	27	TOTAL

HOLE	LENGTH MEDAL-TEE	PAR	STROKE INDEX
10	130	3	12
11	75	3	18
12	120	3	16
13	145	3	2
14	155	3	10
15	110	3	14
16	100	3	6
17	160	3	4
18	90	3	8
TOTAL	1085	27	TOTAL

HOLE	LENGTH MEDAL-TEE	PAR	STROKE INDEX
1	170	3	
2	450	5	
3	370	4	
4	130	3	
5	470	5	
6	440	5	
7	140	3	
8	290	4	
9	180	3	
TOTAL	2640	35	TOTAL

HOLE	LENGTH MEDAL-TEE	PAR	STROKE INDEX
10	330	4	
11	150	3	
12	470	5	
13	360	4	
14	370	4	
15	250	4	
16	240	4	
17	350	4	
18	190	3	
TOTAL	2710	35	TOTAL

VILLARS

TEL : (025)354214
LOCATION : 7 km Villars
ADDRESS : BP 152 – 1884 Villars
HOTEL :
Alpe Fleuri – Villars
Tel : (025)352494
Elite – Villars
Tel : (025)351341
Panorama – Villars
Tel : (025)362111
RESTAURANT : Marie-Louise – Villars
Tel : (025)352477

A pleasant and popular mountain course, scenically laid out amidst the towering snow clad peaks of the Alps. The only problems on this short course are presented by the continuous ups and downs of the terrain. There is a charming clubhouse, a former farmhouse, with a terrace overlooking the course, the forests and mountains. *SSS 61*

GF $

1980

18

 November to June

 D. Harradine

L 4093 P 64

Required : Handicap Certificate
Best days : Weekdays

HOLE	LENGTH MEDAL-TEE	PAR	STROKE INDEX
1	188	3	3
2	168	3	7
3	152	3	5
4	247	4	17
5	137	3	11
6	237	4	9
7	235	4	15
8	306	4	1
9	251	4	13
TOTAL	1921	32	TOTAL

HOLE	LENGTH MEDAL-TEE	PAR	STROKE INDEX
10	238	4	10
11	337	4	2
12	198	3	12
13	296	4	14
14	324	4	4
15	105	3	18
16	164	3	6
17	358	4	8
18	152	3	16
TOTAL	2172	32	TOTAL

ZÜRICH

★★

TEL : (01)9180050
LOCATION : 8 km S. Zürich/E. side Zürichsee
ADDRESS : 8126 Zumikon
HOTEL :
Waldhaus – Dolder Zürich
Tel : (01)2519360
Dolder Grand – Zürich
Tel : (01)2516231
Tiefenau – Zürich
Tel : (01)2512409
RESTAURANT : Zunfthans zur Waag – Zürich
Tel : (01)2110730

The original course was designed by the Briton Tom Williamson in 1931. Fifty years later Donald Harradine modified the course and nowadays the Zürich golf course is one of Switzerland's finest championship layouts. It is a typical inland course, with five dog-legs, five water hazards and around 45 bunkers. Laid out on undulating majestic parkland, there is an elegant mansion style clubhouse. *SSS 72*

GF $$ — November to April — S

1931 — D. Harradine, T. Williamson

18 — L 5860 P 72 — R

Required : Handicap Certificate
Best days : Tuesdays, Thursdays, Fridays

HOLE	LENGTH MEDAL-TEE	PAR	STROKE INDEX
1	335	4	11
2	350	4	7
3	475	5	15
4	160	3	13
5	270	4	17
6	520	5	3
7	170	3	9
8	385	4	1
9	360	4	5
TOTAL	3025	36	TOTAL

HOLE	LENGTH MEDAL-TEE	PAR	STROKE INDEX
10	275	4	18
11	320	4	10
12	470	5	14
13	345	4	2
14	140	3	16
15	325	4	8
16	340	4	4
17	170	3	6
18	450	5	12
TOTAL	2835	36	TOTAL

Reservation/Information telephone number :

Country code : 38

Telephone number : 71/202070

Headquarters address :

EUROPCAR - UNIS TOUR
Trscanska 7, 71000 Sarajevo
Tel. : (38) 71 202070
Telex : 41891
Fax : (38) 71 212382

1 GOLF COURSES, 500 PLAYERS

★★★ Great golf course
★★ Very good golf course
★ Recommended golf course
✡ Holiday golf course

TOWN	GOLF COURSE	TEL	MAP REF.
Bled	Bled	(064) 78282	1
Sežana	Lipica	(067) 73781	•

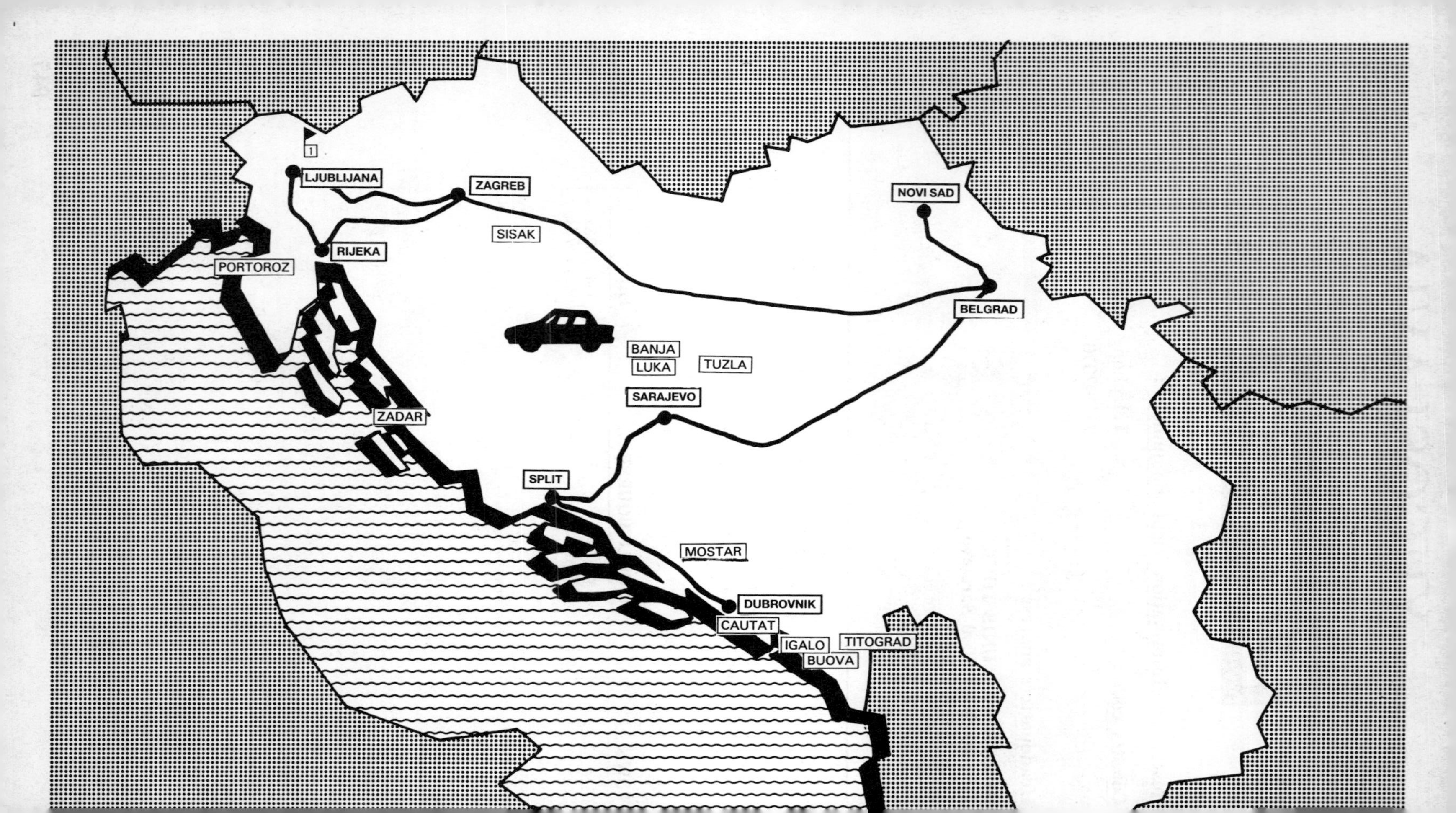

1
LJUBLJANA
ZAGREB
NOVI SAD
SISAK
RIJEKA
PORTOROZ
BELGRAD
BANJA
LUKA
TUZLA
SARAJEVO
ZADAR
SPLIT
MOSTAR
DUBROVNIK
CAUTAT
IGALO
TITOGRAD
BUOVA

BLED

TEL : (064)78282
LOCATION : 2,5 km Bled
ADDRESS : 64260 Bled
HOTEL : HR
Golf Hotel – Tel : (064)78282/77591
Vila Bled – Bled
Tel : (064)77320
RESTAURANT : Toplice – Bled
Tel : (064)77222

Picturesquely situated near the alpine summer resort of Bled, the course is set on a terrace-like stretch of land above the Sava valley at over 520m above sea level. The championship course is encircled by the majestic mountain tops of the Karavanke and Julian Alps. The clubhouse is a charming rustic building, sumptuously furnished, with several bedrooms. The Vila Bled, (member of the Relais & Chateaux chain) with 30 rooms, swimming pool, sauna and tennis courts, is at 3 km from the club bordering the lake Bled.

GF $ — November to April — R S
1974 — D. Harradine
18 — L 5960 P 73

Required : Handicap Certificate
Best days : Any day

HOLE	LENGTH MEDAL-TEE	PAR	STROKE INDEX
1	350	4	7
2	455	5	5
3	160	3	9
4	365	4	1
5	450	5	11
6	310	4	15
7	150	3	13
8	300	4	17
9	350	4	3
TOTAL	2890	36	TOTAL

HOLE	LENGTH MEDAL-TEE	PAR	STROKE INDEX
10	145	3	18
11	375	4	2
12	465	5	14
13	155	3	10
14	335	4	16
15	325	4	8
16	460	5	6
17	450	5	12
18	360	4	4
TOTAL	3070	37	TOTAL

OTHER COUNTRIES

Guadeloupe

Reservation/Information telephone number :

Country code :	**Telephone number :**
590	**266064**

Headquarters address :

EUROPCAR - SOCIÉTÉ NOUVELLE DE LOCATION
Z.I. De Jarry, Impasse Jacquard
B.P. 631
97122 Baie Mahault
Tel. : (590) 266064
Telex : 919964
Fax : (590) 266889

Martinique

Reservation/Information telephone number :

Country code :	**Telephone number :**
596	**512033**

Headquarters address :

EUROPCAR - MARTINIQUE AUTOMOBILES
Zone Industrielle de la Lézarde
B.P. 250
97285 Lamentin Cedex 2
Tel. : (596) 512033
Telex : 912168
Fax : (596) 51.62.39

Réunion

Reservation/Information telephone number :

Country code :	**Telephone number :**
262	**281010**

Headquarters address :

EUROPCAR RÉUNION
Gillot La Ferme
97438 Sainte-Marie
Tel. : (262) 281010
Telex : 916096
Fax : (262) 283636

Israël

Reservation/Information telephone number :

Country code :	Telephone number :
972	3/5705166

Headquarters address :

EUROPCAR – O.C. VEHICLES
Baruch Hirsch 27 – P/O Box 51320
Bnei Brak 51100
Tel. : (972) 3/5705166
Telex : 371585
Fax : (972) 3/5705170

Ivory Coast

Reservation/Information telephone number :

Country code :	Telephone number :
225	351135

Headquarters address :

EUROPCAR RENT A CAR – CI
07 BP 211
Abidjan 07
Tel. : (225) 351135
Telex : 214235 (in France)

Malta

Reservation/Information telephone number :

Country code :	Telephone number :
356	238580

Headquarters address :

EUROPCAR – JOHN'S GARAGE LTD
38 Villambrosa street, Hamrun
Tel. : (356) 238580
Telex : 989
Fax : (356) 221720

Car Rental

Morocco

Reservation/Information telephone number :

Country code :	Telephone number :
212	2/313737

Headquarters address :

EUROPCAR – S.P.T.T. S.A.
44, avenue des F.A.R.
Casablanca 01
Tel. : (212) 2/313737
Telex : 22990 – 22088
Fax : (212) 2/310360

Tunisia

Reservation/Information telephone number :

Country code :	Telephone number :
216	710028 717237

Headquarters address :

EUROPCAR STTA
B.P. 45
Aeroport Tunis-Carthage
Tunis
Tel. : (216) 1/710028
Telex : 13243 – 15328
Fax : (216) 1/712285

FRENCH OVERSEAS

TOWN	GOLF COURSE		TEL	MAP REF.
Guadeloupe	St-François	✡	(590) 844187	I
La Réunion	Bourbon (2 × 9)	✡	(262) 263339	I
Martinique	Les Trois-Ilets	★★ ✡	(596) 683281	I

ISRAEL

TOWN	GOLF COURSE		TEL	MAP REF.
Caesarea	Caesarea	✡	(063) 61174	1

IVORY COAST

TOWN	GOLF COURSE		TEL	MAP REF.
Abidjan	Abidjan	★★★ ✡	430845	2
Yamoussoukro	President	★★ ✡	640429	1

MALTA

TOWN	GOLF COURSE		TEL	MAP REF.
Malta	Marsa	✡	622914	1

MOROCCO

TOWN	GOLF COURSE		TEL	MAP REF.
Agadir	Agadir (18 h. under construction)			
Casablanca	Anfa			•
Marrakech	Marrakech	✡	(05) 447-05	2
Meknes	Royal Meknes			•
Mohammedia	Mohammedia	✡	(032) 2052	3
Rabat	Dar es Salam	★★★ ✡	(07) 55864	1
Tanger	Cabo Negro			•
	Tanger	✡		4

TUNISIA

TOWN	GOLF COURSE		TEL	MAP REF.
Hammamet	Hammamet	✡	(02) 82722	4
Monastir	Monastir-El Qortine	✡	(03) 61105	3
Sousse	Port el Kantaoui	★★ ✡	(03) 41755/56	2
Tunis	La Soukra	✡	(03) 903381	1

ISRAËL

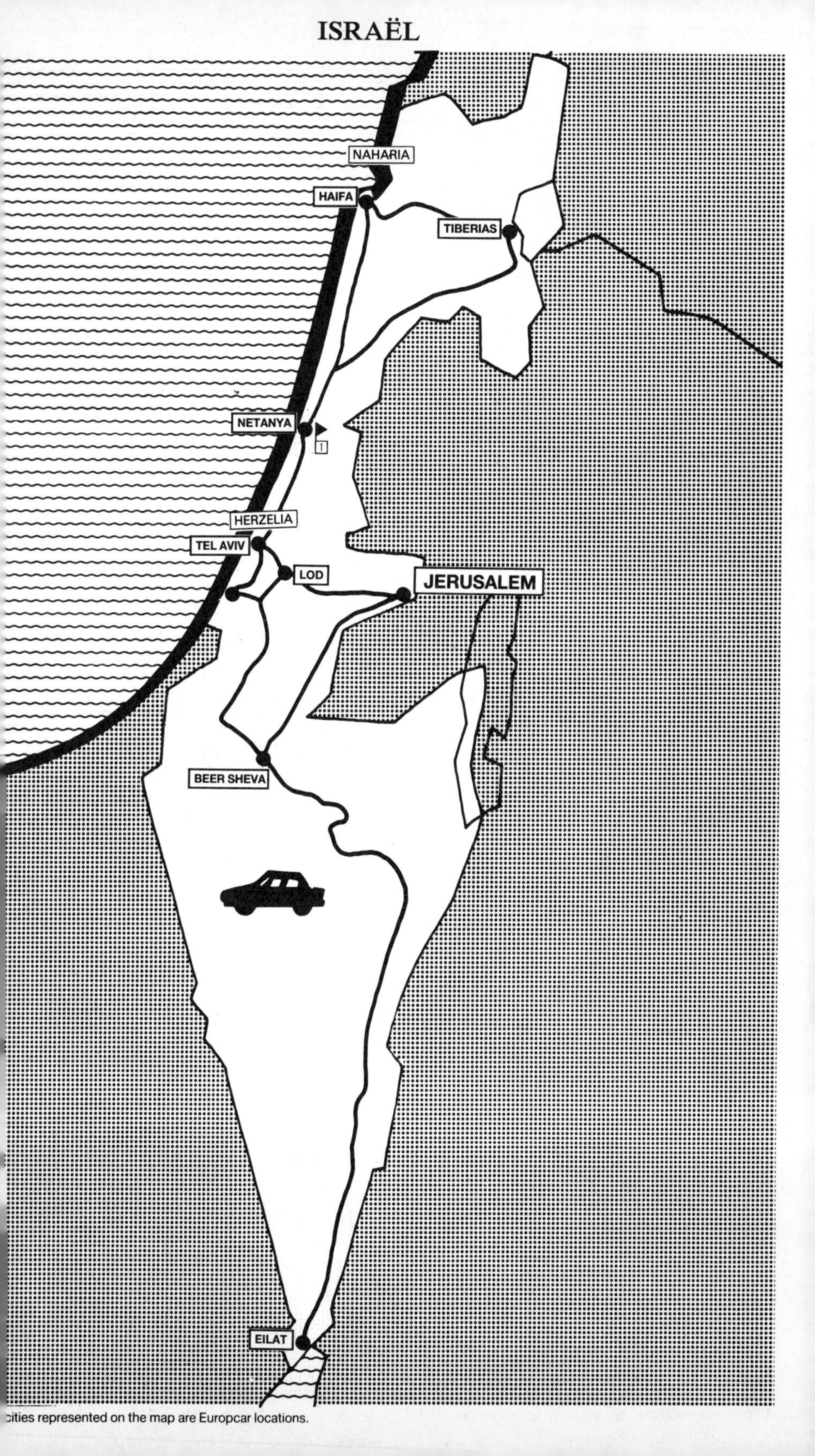

cities represented on the map are Europcar locations.

TUNISIA

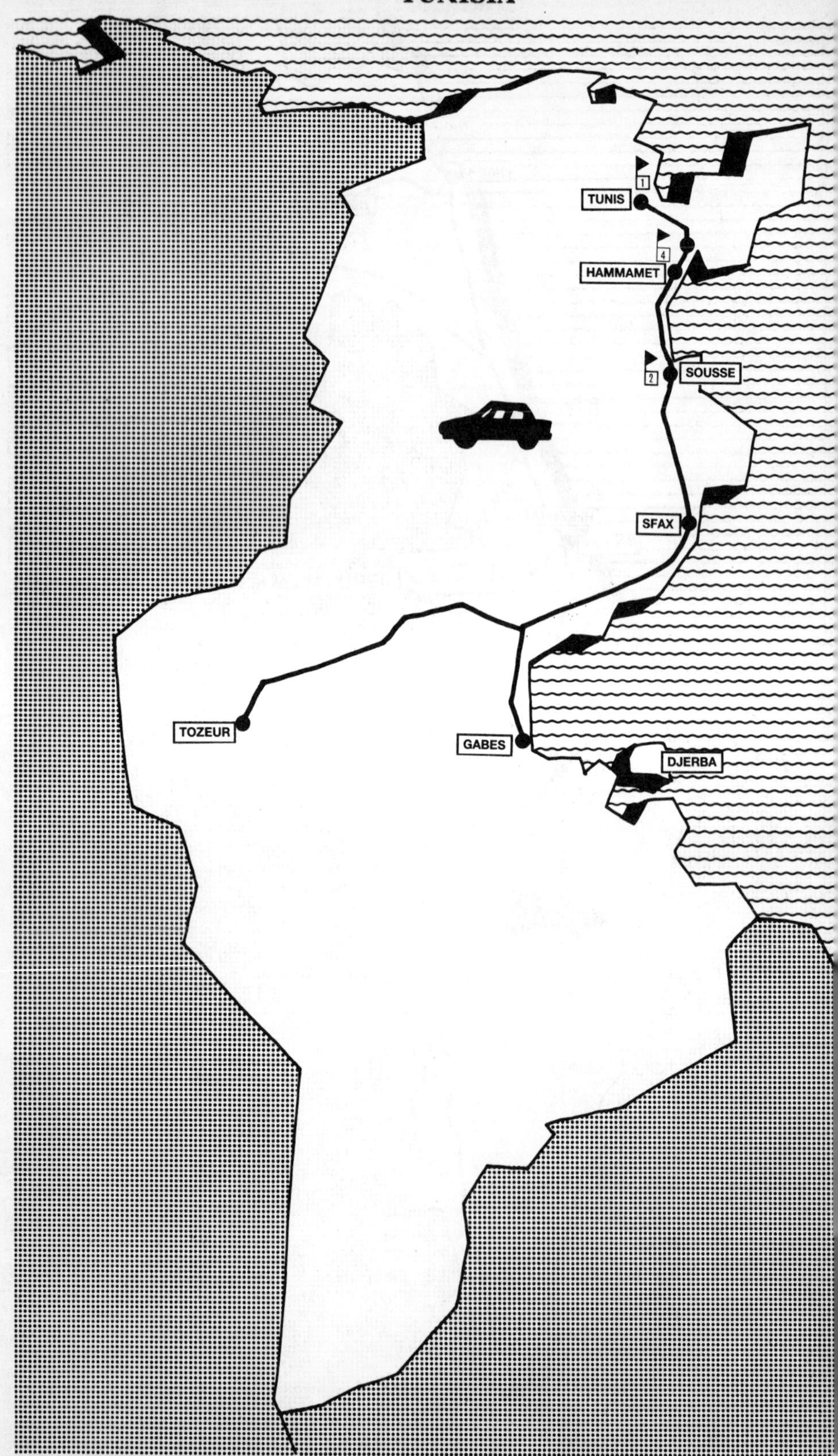

All cities represented on the map are Europcar locations.

MOROCCO

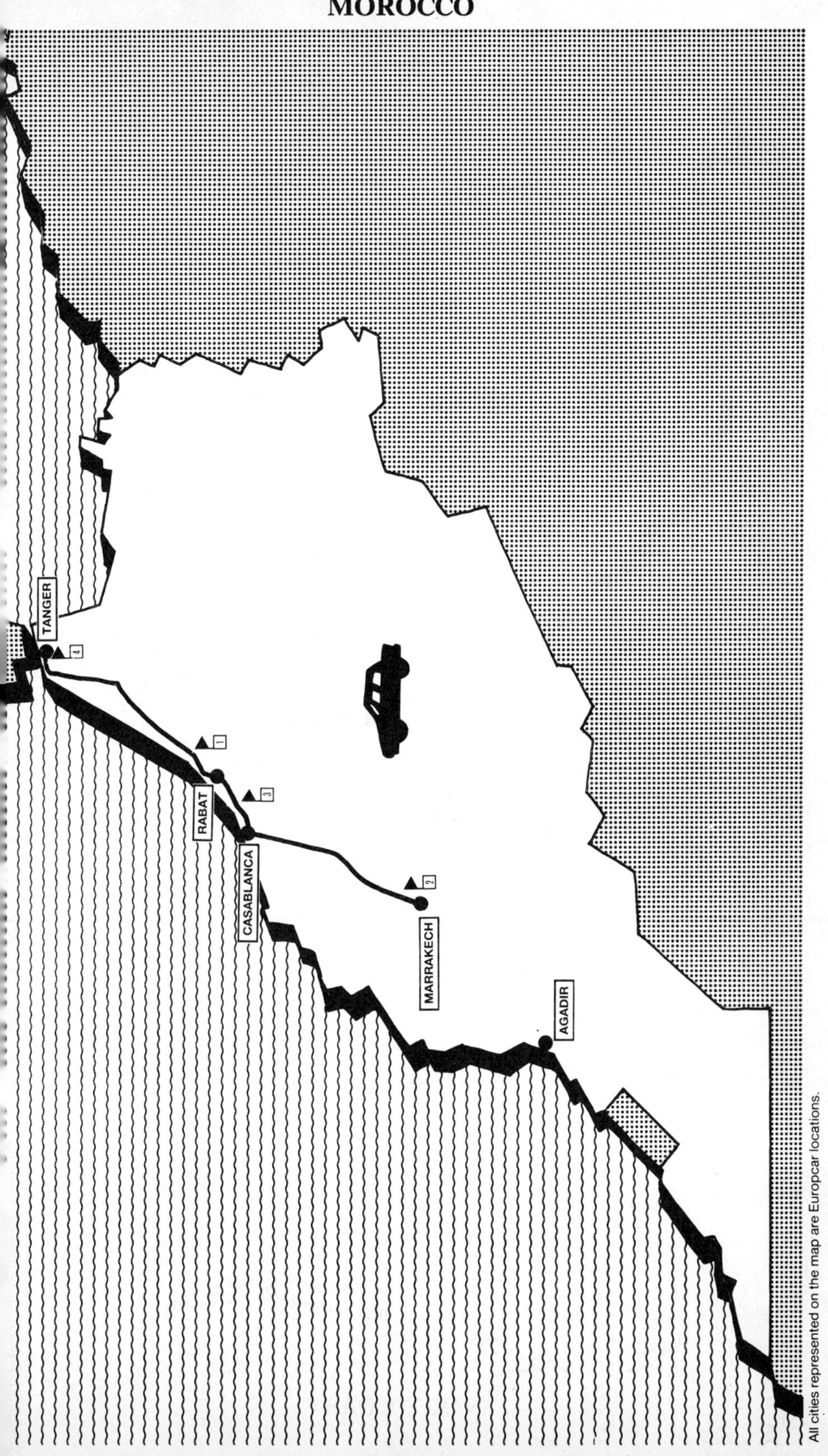

All cities represented on the map are Europcar locations.

MALTA

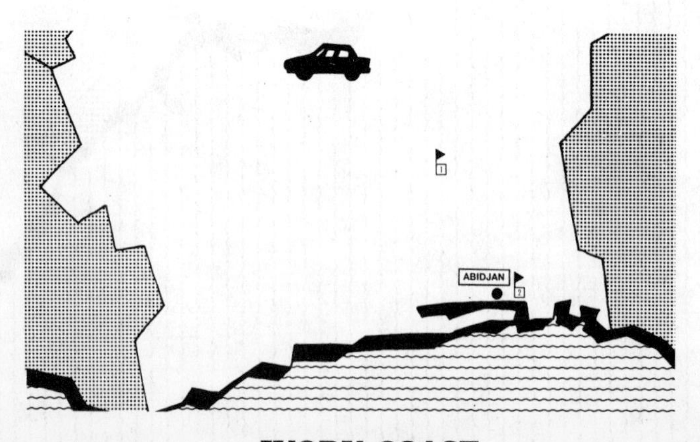

IVORY COAST

IMPERATRICE JOSEPHINE

TEL : (596)683281
LOCATION : 6 km Fort de France by boat
ADDRESS : 97229 Trois-Ilets – Martinique
HOTEL :
Meridien – Trois-Ilets
Tel : (596)660000
RESTAURANT : La Plantation de Leyritz – Basse Pointe
Tel : (596)755392

Designed by Robert Trent Jones, this fine Caribbean holiday course is set on the sea shore backed by low, thickly wooded hills. Its main difficulties are the strategically placed water hazards and bunkers. Among its feature holes is the 16th with an island fairway and an island green. The excellent holiday hotel Meridien is 2km from the course offering many sports and leisure facilities.

GF $

1976

18

—

R. Trent Jones

L 6170 P 71

R

Required : None
Best days : Any day

HOLE	LENGTH MEDAL-TEE	PAR	STROKE INDEX
1	485	5	1
2	350	4	11
3	175	3	15
4	400	4	5
5	325	4	13
6	370	4	7
7	160	3	18
8	340	4	9
9	425	4	3
TOTAL	3030	35	TOTAL

HOLE	LENGTH MEDAL-TEE	PAR	STROKE INDEX
10	375	4	12
11	185	3	10
12	515	5	2
13	345	4	17
14	490	5	6
15	165	3	16
16	470	5	4
17	175	3	14
18	420	4	8
TOTAL	3140	36	TOTAL

SAINT-FRANÇOIS

TEL : (590)844187
LOCATION : 10 km Saint-François
ADDRESS : 97118 Saint-François
HOTEL : HP
Hamak, Tel. : (590)844180, Meridien
Tel : (590)855100
RESTAURANT : La Louisiane-Saint-François
Tel : (590)844434

This international golf course has a varied layout, set on rather hilly terrain, bordering the Atlantic Ocean. Very cunningly bunkered, there are several contrived dog-leg holes demanding accuracy from tee to green. Robert Trent Jones included two strategically placed lakes, guarding several of the fairways. Both hotels, the Hamak and the Meridien, are adjacent to the course. They are set within a tropical garden and offer outstanding facilities.

GF $$ — S

1975 R. Trent Jones

18 L 5970 P 71

Required : Handicap Certificate
Best days : Any day

HOLE	LENGTH MEDAL-TEE	PAR	STROKE INDEX
1	510	5	
2	155	3	
3	355	4	
4	330	4	
5	175	3	
6	470	5	
7	335	4	
8	175	3	
9	365	4	
TOTAL	2870	35	TOTAL

HOLE	LENGTH MEDAL-TEE	PAR	STROKE INDEX
10	325	4	
11	155	3	
12	490	5	
13	375	4	
14	370	4	
15	385	4	
16	185	3	
17	460	5	
18	355	4	
TOTAL	3100	36	TOTAL

CAESAREA

TEL : (06)361172/4
LOCATION : 45 km Haïfa/Tel Aviv
ADDRESS : P.O Box – 1010 Caesarea 30600
HOTEL : HR
Dan Caesarea – Caesarea
Tel : (06)362266

Built on sandy soil near the popular seaside resort of Caesarea, the course is set near the Mediterranean sea front. There are many carob trees scattered over the easy walking course. The modern clubhouse overlooks the 1st hole and the 10th and 18th greens. The five star Dan Caesarea Hotel is adjacent to the golf course with tennis courts, swimming pool, beaches, horse-riding, sailing and windsurfing.

GF $ — 1961 — F. Smith — 18 — L 5956 P 73 — S

RP

Required : Handicap Certificate for competition only
Best days : Any day

HOLE	LENGTH MEDAL-TEE	PAR	STROKE INDEX
1	293	4	13
2	488	5	3
3	340	4	5
4	167	3	15
5	485	5	1
6	322	4	11
7	300	4	9
8	123	3	17
9	435	5	7
TOTAL	2953	37	TOTAL

HOLE	LENGTH MEDAL-TEE	PAR	STROKE INDEX
10	166	3	16
11	370	4	10
12	450	5	4
13	330	4	14
14	440	5	8
15	160	3	18
16	388	4	2
17	389	4	6
18	310	4	12
TOTAL	3003	36	TOTAL

ABIDJAN

TEL : (225)430845
LOCATION : Direction Cocody/Riviera
ADDRESS : 08 – BP 01 – Abidjan 08
HOTEL : 
Golf Hotel
Tel : (225)431044

Designed by the Italian architect Piero Mancinelli, this international golf course, very popular among golfers worldwide, is set on the shores of the Ebrié lagoon, close to the ocean. Superb from any point, the course is beautiful with enormous bunkers, fast greens and twelve Florida-style water hazards. Palm trees are scattered over the fairways. Another feature of the club is the astonishing clubhouse with swimming pools, squash and tennis courts, gymnasium, sauna, and three restaurants. The excellent Golf Hotel is near the course.

GF $$ — Mondays

1979 — P. Mancinelli

27 — L 6289 P 73. 2845 P 36

Required : Handicap Certificate for competitions only
Best days : Any day

HOLE	LENGTH MEDAL-TEE	PAR	STROKE INDEX
1	367	4	7
2	374	4	5
3	462	5	13
4	358	4	15
5	385	4	3
6	164	3	9
7	404	4	1
8	175	3	12
9	500	5	11
TOTAL	3189	36	TOTAL

HOLE	LENGTH MEDAL-TEE	PAR	STROKE INDEX
10	370	4	6
11	160	3	17
12	445	5	10
13	300	4	8
14	490	5	4
15	340	4	16
16	150	3	14
17	395	4	2
18	450	5	18
TOTAL	3100	37	TOTAL

PRESIDENT

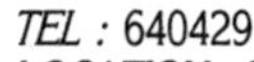

TEL : 640429
LOCATION : 235 km Abidjan
ADDRESS : BP-1024 – Yamoussoukro
HOTEL : HR
Président
Tel : 640181

Hosting the Ivory Coast Open every year, the course is located in the African Savannah in the heart of the country near the city of Yamoussoukro. A testing championship course with difficult roughs and an enormous water hazard in the middle of the course affecting play on several holes. The clubhouse is an amazing building with a large swimming pool.

GF $$ — Mondays — R S 

1980 — D. Thomas  

18 — L 5885 P 72 

Required : Handicap Certificate for competitions only
Best days : Any day

HOLE	LENGTH MEDAL-TEE	PAR	STROKE INDEX
1	520	5	
2	135	3	
3	421	4	
4	346	4	
5	482	5	
6	163	3	
7	386	4	
8	306	4	
9	399	4	
TOTAL	3158	36	

HOLE	LENGTH MEDAL-TEE	PAR	STROKE INDEX
10	493	5	
11	310	4	
12	190	3	
13	338	4	
14	469	5	
15	295	4	
16	121	4	
17	121	3	
18	390	4	
TOTAL	2727	36	

MARSA

✡

TEL : 622914/233851
LOCATION : 10 km Sliema/Valletta
ADDRESS : Marsa Sports Club – Marsa – Isle of Malta
HOTEL :
Preluna – Sliema
Tel : 334001

Set on the picturesque island of Malta, the Marsa golf club is the only course on the island and therefore popular among golfers. It is an attractive inland course with palm trees bordering the fairways and ditches serving as hazards. The Marsa Sports Club is equipped with several tennis and squash courts and a swimming pool, a miniature golf, cricket and polo fields.

GF $

Saturday mornings

—

18

L 5091 y P 68

Required : Handicap Certificate
Best days : Wednesdays, Fridays, Sundays

HOLE	LENGTH MEDAL-TEE	PAR	STROKE INDEX
1	242	4	9
2	248	4	17
3	405	4	1
4	406	4	5
5	164	3	11
6	145	3	13
7	141	3	15
8	481	5	3
9	316	4	7
TOTAL	2548	34	TOTAL

HOLE	LENGTH MEDAL-TEE	PAR	STROKE INDEX
10	328	4	6
11	293	4	8
12	359	4	2
13	164	3	14
14	267	4	16
15	490	5	4
16	216	3	10
17	166	3	12
18	260	4	18
TOTAL	2543	34	TOTAL

MARRAKECH

TEL : (05)447-05/443-41
LOCATION : 5 km Marrakech 31 A
ADDRESS : Route de Ouarzazate – B.P. 634 – Marrakech
HOTEL :
Sémiramis Meridien – Marrakech
Tel : (4)31377
La Mamounia – Marrakech
Tel : (4)48981
Es Saadi – Marrakech
Tel : (4)48811
RESTAURANT : Ksar el Hamra-Marrakech
Tel : (4)23297

Peacefully located near the colourful city of Marrakech, the course is scenically situated overlooking the snow clad mountain tops of the Atlas. It is laid out in a real tropical garden full of orange, eucalyptus and cypress trees. The gently undulating fairways are landscaped among tall palm trees. There is no clubhouse on the Marrakech golf course.

GF $ — S

1923 G. Golias

18 L 5658 P 72

Required : None
Best days : Any day

HOLE	LENGTH MEDAL-TEE	PAR	STROKE INDEX
1	320	4	
2	318	4	
3	346	4	
4	160	3	
5	445	5	
6	295	4	
7	448	5	
8	320	4	
9	178	3	
TOTAL	2830	36	TOTAL

HOLE	LENGTH MEDAL-TEE	PAR	STROKE INDEX
10	317	4	
11	311	4	
12	323	4	
13	307	4	
14	500	5	
15	150	3	
16	450	5	
17	320	4	
18	150	3	
TOTAL	2828	36	TOTAL

MOHAMMEDIA

TEL : (32)2052
LOCATION : 30 km N. Casablanca
ADDRESS : Mohammedia
HOTEL :
Méridien Miramar – Mohammedia
Tel : (32)2021

A fine seaside course, set on the Atlantic coast, ideal for holiday golf. Many of the excellent fairways run through flat terrain and are surrounded by mature palm trees. There is one water hazard which is a pond between the 9th and 18th hole. There is a fine, welcoming clubhouse.

GF $ | Tuesdays

— | —

18 | L 5662 y P 72

S

Required : Handicap Certificate
Best days : Any day with prior booking

HOLE	LENGTH MEDAL-TEE	PAR	STROKE INDEX
1	412	5	7
2	307	4	15
3	328	4	9
4	157	3	17
5	348	4	5
6	326	4	11
7	450	5	3
8	179	3	13
9	378	4	1
TOTAL	2885	36	TOTAL

HOLE	LENGTH MEDAL-TEE	PAR	STROKE INDEX
10	257	4	16
11	135	3	18
12	428	5	8
13	303	4	14
14	345	4	10
15	350	4	4
16	413	5	6
17	163	3	12
18	383	4	2
TOTAL	2777	36	TOTAL

RABAT DAR ES SALAM

TEL : (7)55864
LOCATION : 12 km Rabat
ADDRESS : Rte des Zaiers – Rabat
HOTEL :
Hyatt Regency – Rabat
Tel. : (7)71234
Tour Hassan – Rabat
Tel : (7)21401

Situated in the suburbs of Rabat laid out amongst a forest of cork trees, old oaks and eucalyptus, the Dar es Salam golf course is a masterpiece designed by Robert Trent Jones. There are two 18-hole courses, both varied and interesting. The main championship layout is the Red Course with very fast and undulating greens. It features the scenic 9th hole, set within fields of mimosas and orange trees, and bordered by a lake reserved for flamingos. The Blue Course is less difficult but has an equally scenic layout. There is an Californian style clubhouse. The luxury Hyatt Regency Hotel is situated in a park at 11km from the course. The Tour Hassan Hotel lies right in the center of Rabat.

GF $$

1971

45

Mondays

R. Trent Jones

L 6409 P 73, 5865 P 72, 2060 P 32

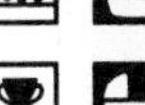

Required : Handicap Certificate
Best days : Tuesdays to Sundays inc.

Red Course

HOLE	LENGTH MEDAL-TEE	PAR	STROKE INDEX
1	355	4	13
2	175	3	9
3	395	4	1
4	358	4	15
5	495	5	17
6	380	4	7
7	368	4	3
8	500	5	5
9	160	3	11
TOTAL	3186	36	TOTAL

HOLE	LENGTH MEDAL-TEE	PAR	STROKE INDEX
10	440	5	18
11	399	4	4
12	495	5	14
13	335	4	8
14	168	3	12
15	342	4	16
16	373	4	2
17	181	3	6
18	490	5	10
TOTAL	3223	37	TOTAL

Blue Course

HOLE	LENGTH MEDAL-TEE	PAR	STROKE INDEX
1	355	4	8
2	445	5	4
3	360	4	6
4	195	3	14
5	270	4	16
6	470	5	2
7	345	4	12
8	150	3	18
9	345	4	10
TOTAL	2935	36	TOTAL

HOLE	LENGTH MEDAL-TEE	PAR	STROKE INDEX
10	335	4	11
11	395	4	1
12	170	3	13
13	290	4	15
14	425	5	5
15	155	3	17
16	350	4	7
17	470	5	3
18	340	4	9
TOTAL	2930	36	TOTAL

HAMMAMET

✡

TEL : (2)82722
ADDRESS : 5 km Hammamet/70 km Tunis
Bir Bou Rekba
HOTEL :
Sheraton - Hammamet
Tel : (2)80555
Abou Nawas - Hammamet
Tel : (2)81344
Sindbad - Hammamet
Tel : (2)80122

Designed by the renowned golf architect Ronald Fream, this course stands amidst hillocks overlooking distant woodlands and the beaches of the seaside resort of Hammamet. It will certainly be recognised as one of Tunisia's finest golfing venues, testing the skill of any golfer, whatever their handicap. Its interesting layout features rather short holes with large fairways, many strategically placed water hazards and difficult three or four level greens. A stylish clubhouse is presently under contruction.

GF $ — — S
1990 — R. Fream
27 — L 6115 P 73 — R

Required : Handicap Certificate
Best days : Any day

HOLE	LENGTH MEDAL-TEE	PAR	STROKE INDEX
1			
2			
3			
4			
5			
6			
7			
8			
9			
TOTAL			TOTAL

HOLE	LENGTH MEDAL-TEE	PAR	STROKE INDEX
10			
11			
12			
13			
14			
15			
16			
17			
18			
TOTAL			TOTAL

MONASTIR

TEL : (3)61095
LOCATION : 12 km Sousse, 2 km Skanés-Monastir
ADDRESS : Route de Ouardanine 5000 Monastir
HOTEL :
Kuriat Palace – Shanes Monastir
Tel : (3)61200
Regency – Monastir
Tel : (3)60033

Opened in december 1988, this new champioship course is the second of seven Tunisian golf courses planned to open in the near future. Designed by Ronald Fream for golfers of all standards due to the use of 5 different departure tees, the course lies inside groves of majestic olive trees not far from the sea front overlooking the Mediterranean, the city of Monastir and several lakes. The course has 4 par 3s, 10 par 4s and 4 par 5s. The new and superb hotel Kuriat Palace is near the course and offers outstanding facilities. It is equipped with a tennis school, swimming pools, beaches, water sport facilities, etc.

  $   —  

 1988  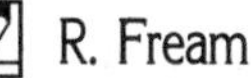 R. Fream 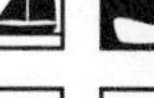

 18 L 6140 P 72  

Required : Handicap Certificate
Best days : Any day

HOLE	LENGTH MEDAL-TEE	PAR	STROKE INDEX
1	365	4	7
2	160	3	13
3	420	4	5
4	470	5	15
5	140	3	9
6	460	5	1
7	375	4	17
8	315	4	3
9	310	4	11
TOTAL	3015	36	TOTAL

HOLE	LENGTH MEDAL-TEE	PAR	STROKE INDEX
10	370	4	2
11	520	5	14
12	200	3	8
13	405	4	18
14	330	4	10
15	150	3	12
16	320	4	16
17	340	4	6
18	490	5	4
TOTAL	3125	36	TOTAL

PORT EL KANTAOUI

TEL : (3)41755/41756
LOCATION : 5 km Sousse
ADDRESS : Port El Kantaoui
HOTEL : HR
Diar El Andalous *Tel. :* (3)40200
Green Park *Tel :* (3)43277
Hasdrubal *Tel. :* (3)41944

Designed by the Californian architect Ronald Fream, this is a great and promising golf course and the venue of the Tunisian Open championship. Set on the borders of the Mediterranean, the first nine holes (blue course) are undulating with several doglegs, set partly in a grove of olive trees with a 75m high cliff in the background. The 8th hole has a fine view over the harbour. The second nine holes (red course) are flat, winding their way through dunes and palm trees. The 12th, 13th and 14th holes are laid out on the beach. The deluxe Green Park and Diar el Andalous hotels are on the course.

GF

1980

27

—

R. Fream

L 3123 P 36, 3060 P 36, 2835 P 36

RP S

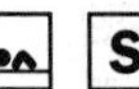

Required : Handicap Certificate
Best days : Any day

HOLE	LENGTH MEDAL-TEE	PAR	STROKE INDEX
1	344	4	8
2	366	4	5
3	142	3	9
4	401	4	2
5	461	5	4
6	296	4	7
7	383	4	3
8	175	3	6
9	555	5	1
TOTAL	3123	36	TOTAL

HOLE	LENGTH MEDAL-TEE	PAR	STROKE INDEX
10	369	4	1
11	489	5	5
12	372	4	6
13	144	3	8
14	343	4	4
15	500	5	3
16	141	3	9
17	330	4	7
18	372	4	2
TOTAL	3060	36	TOTAL

GREAT BRITAIN

ENGLAND
SCOTLAND
WALES

Reservation/Information telephone number :

Country code : 44

Telephone number : 532/422233

Headquarters address :

EUROPCAR U.K. LTD
Bushey House
High street, Bushey
Watford WD2, 1RE – United Kingdom
Tel. : (44) 81 9504080
Telex : 297190
Fax : (44) 81 9504245

1 200 GOLF COURSES, 1 300 000 PLAYERS

★★★ Great golf course
★★ Very good golf course
$ 5-15 Pound
★ Recommended golf course
☼ Holiday golf course
$ $ more than 18 Pound

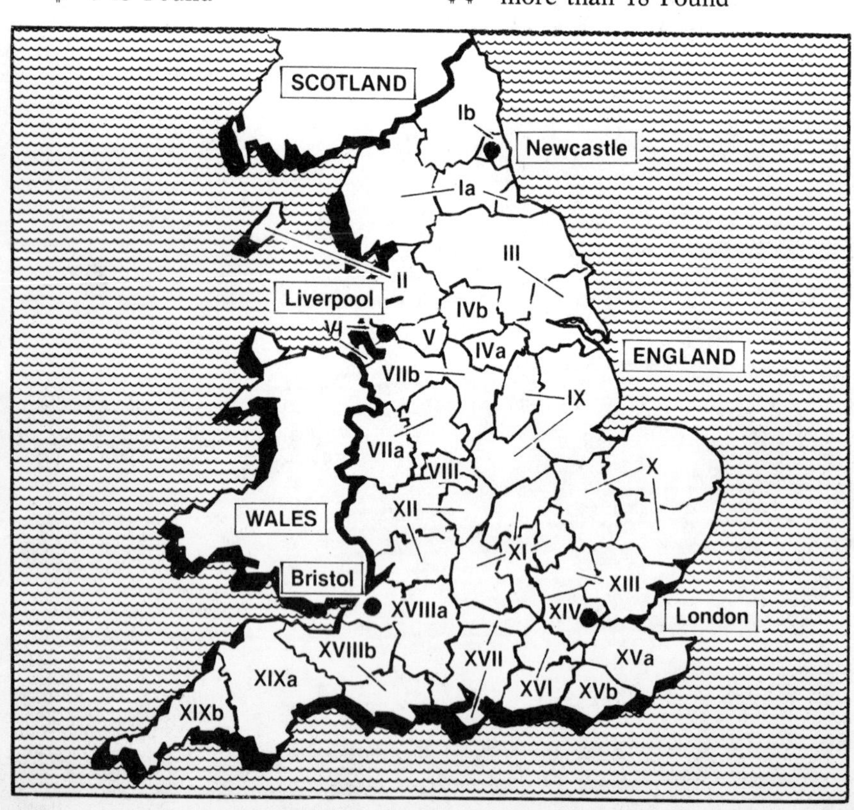

ENGLAND

1 200 GOLF COURSES, 800 000 PLAYERS

Contents : Maps of England

Cleveland • Cumbria • Durham • Northumberland • Tyne & Wear

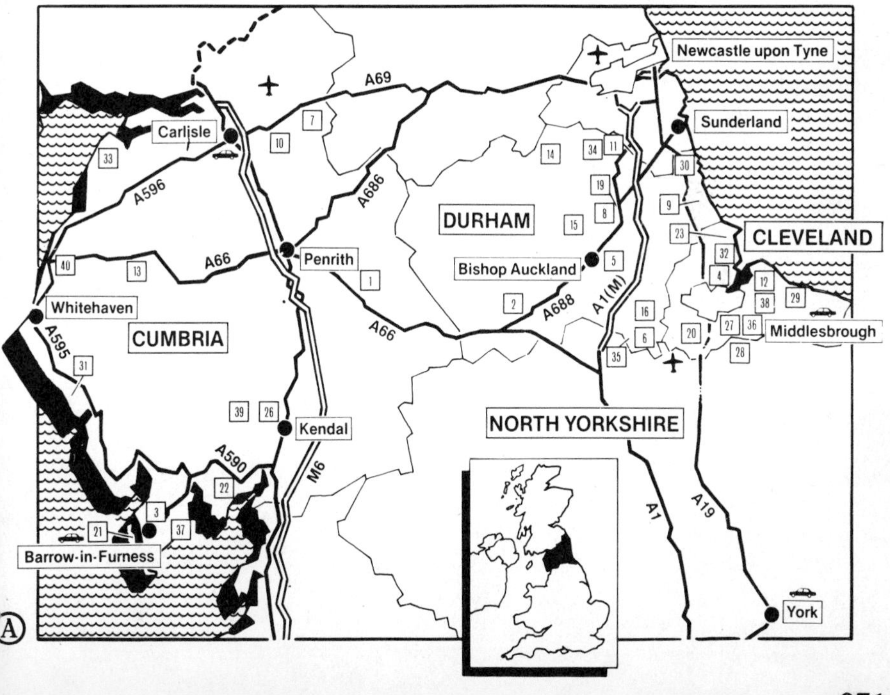

ENGLAND/I

Cleveland • Cumbria • Durham • Northumberland • Tyne & Wear

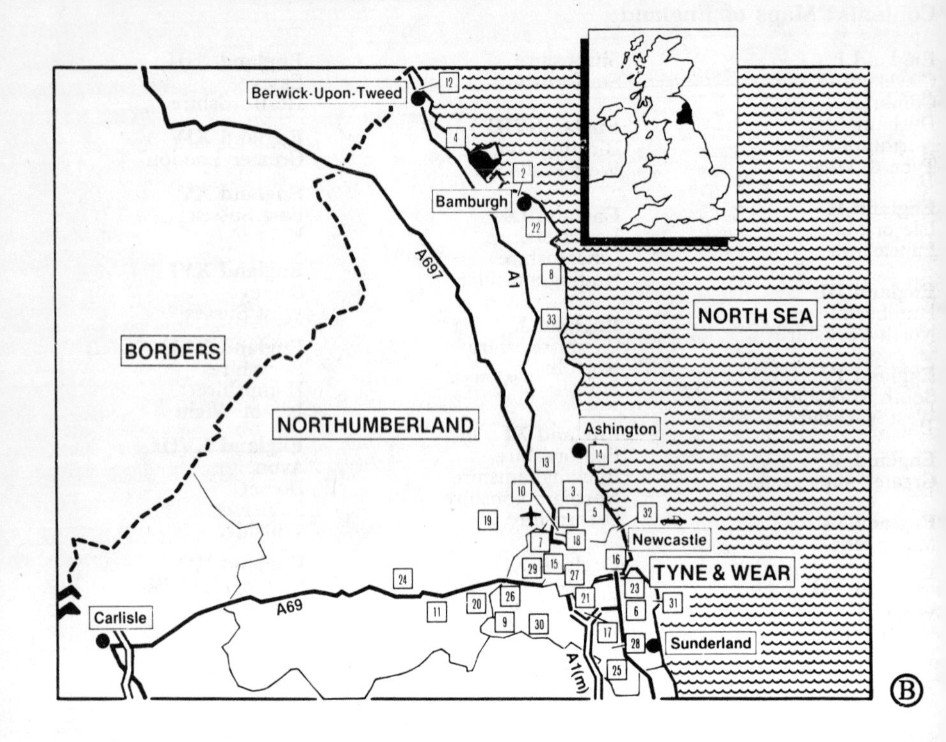

TOWN	GOLF COURSE		TEL	♦	MAP REF.
Alnwick	Alnmouth		(0665) 830368		B 33
	Alnwick	•	(0665) 602632		•
	Dunstanburgh		(066576) 676		B 8
Appleby	Appleby		(0930) 51432		A 1
Ashington	Newbiggin-by-the-Sea		(0670) 817344		B 14
Bamburgh	Bamburgh Castle		(06684) 231		B 2
Barnard Castle	Barnard Castle		(033) 38355		A 2
Barrow-in-Furness	Barrow	✡	(0229) 25444		A 3
	Furness	✡	(0229) 41232		A 21
Bedlington	Bedlingtonshire		(0670) 822087		B 3
Bellingham	Bellingham	•	(0660) 20530		•
Berwick-upon-Tweed	Berwick-upon-Tweed		(0289) 87256		B 4
	Magdalene Fields		(0289) 5109		B 12
Billingham	Billingham		(0642) 554494		A 4
Bishop Auckland	Bishop Auckland		(0388) 602198		A 5
Blyth	Blyth New Course		(06706) 67728		B 5
Carlisle	Brampton		(09677) 2255		A 7
	Carlisle	★	(022872) 303		A 10
	Stoney Holme	•	(0228) 34856		•
Chester-le-Street	Chester-le-Street		(0385) 883218		A 11
Cockermouth	Cockermouth		(059681) 223		A 13
Consett	Consett & District		(0207) 502186		A 14
Darlington	Blackwell Grange		(0325) 464464		A 6
	Darlington		(0325) 463936		A 16
	Dinsdale Spa		(0325) 332222		A 16
Durham	Brancepeth Castle		(0385) 780075		A 8
	Crook		(0388) 762429		A 15
	Durham City		(0385) 780069		A 19
	South Moor		(0207) 232848		A 34
Gateshead	Ravensworth		(091) 4876014		B 21
	Whickham		(091) 4887309		B 30
Gosforth	Gosforth		(091) 2853495		B 10
	Northumberland		(0632) 362498		B 18
Grange-over-Sands	Grange Fells	•	(04484) 2536		•
	Grange-over-Sands	✡	(04484) 3180		A 22
Hartlepool	Castle Eden & Peterlee		(0429) 836510		A 9
	Hartlepool	★	(0429) 74398		A 23
	Seaton Carew	★	(0429) 266249		A 32
Hexham	Hexham		(0434) 603072		B 24
Kendal	Kendal	★	(0539) 24079		A 26
Keswick	Threkeld Hall		(07687) 83324		•
Maryport	Maryport	•	(0900) 812605		•
Middlesbrough	Middlesbrough		(0642) 316430		A 28
	Middlesbrough Municipal		(0642) 315533		A 27
Morpeth	Morpeth		(0670) 512065		B 13
Newcastle-upon-Tyne	Arcot Hall		(0632) 362794		B 1
	City of Newcastle		(091) 2851775		B 7
	Newcastle United		(091) 2864693		B 15
	Ponteland		(0661) 22689		B 19
	Westerhope		(091) 2869125		B 29
Penrith	Penrith		(084) 62217		
Prudhoe	Prudhoe		(0661) 32466		B 20
Redcar	Cleveland		(0642) 483693		A 12
	Wilton		(0642) 465265		A 38
Ryton	Tyneside		(091) 4132742		B 26
Saltburn	Saltburn-by-Sea		(0287) 22812		A 29
Seaham	Seaham		(0783) 812354		A 30
Seahouses	Seahouses		(0665) 720794		B 22
Seascale	Seascale	★★ ✡	(0940) 28202		A 31
Silloth	Silloth-on-Solway	✡	(0965) 31179	♦	A 33
South Shields	South Shields		(091) 568942		B 23
Stocksfield	Stocksfield		(0661) 843041		B 11
Stockton	Eaglescliffe		(0642) 780098		A 20
	Teesside		(0642) 676249		A 36
Sunderland	Boldon		(0783) 364182		B 6
	Wearside		(0783) 342518		B 28
	Whitburn		(0783) 292144		B 31
Tynemouth	Tynemouth		(0632) 574578		B 16
Ulverston	Ulverston	✡	(0229) 52824		A 37
Wallsend	Wallsend		(0632) 621973		B 27
Washington	Washington		(091) 4172626		
Whitley Bay	Whitley Bay		(0632) 520180		B 32
Windermere	Windermere	✡	(09662) 3123		A 39
Workington	Workington		(0900) 3460		A 40

ENGLAND/II

Isle of man • Lancashire (Lancs)

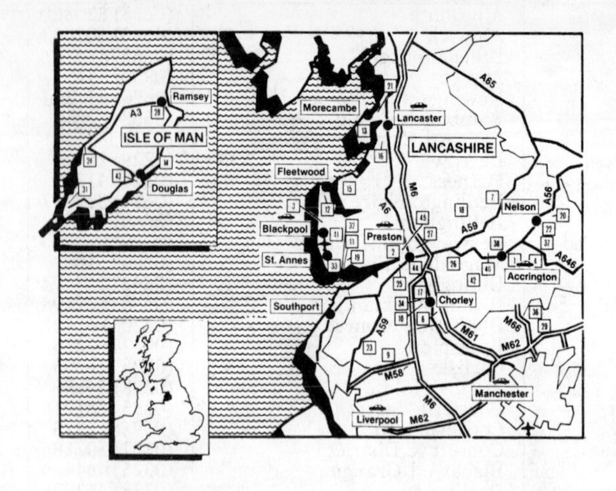

TOWN	GOLF COURSE		TEL	♦	MAP REF.
Accrington	Accrington & District		(0254) 32734		1
Blackburn	Blackburn		(0254) 51122		40
	Pleasington		(0254) 22177		26
	Wilpshire		(0254) 48260		38
Blackpool	Blackpool North Shore		(0253) 52054		3
	Blackpool Park		(0253) 33960		41
	Poulton-le-Fylde	•	(0253) 893150		•
	Knott End		(0253) 810576		15
	Burnley		(0282) 21045		4
	Towneley		(0282) 38473		37
Chorley	Chorley		(0257) 480263		6
	Duxbury Park		(02572) 77049		10
	Shaw Hill		(02572) 69221		34
Clitheroe	Clitheroe	✡	(0200) 22618		7
Darwen	Darwen		(0254) 71287		42
Fleetwood	Fleetwood		(03917) 3661		12
Lancaster	Lancaster		(0524) 751247		16
Lytham St. Annes	Fairhaven	✡	(0253) 736741		11
	Lytham Green Drive		(0253) 737390		19
	Royal Lytham St. Annes	★★★	(0253) 724206	♦	32
	St. Annes Old Links	✡	(0253) 723597		33
Morecambe	Heysham		(0524) 51011		13
	Morecambe		(0524) 412841		21
Nelson	Marsden Park		(0282) 67525		20
Ormskirk	Ormskirk		(0695) 72112		23
Preston	Ashton & Lea		(0772) 726480		2
	Fishwick Hall		(0772) 798300		44
	Ingol		(0772) 734556		45
	Longridge		(077478) 3291		18
	Penwortham		(0772) 744630		25
	Preston		(0772) 700011		27
Rochdale	Rochdale		(0706) 46024		29
	Springfield Park		(070649) 801		36
Silverdale	Silverdale	•	(0524) 701300		•
Wigan	Dean Wood		(0695) 622219		9
Isle of Man					
Castletown	Castletown	✡	(0624) 822201	♦	5
	Rowany	✡	(0624) 834108		31
Douglas	Douglas Municipal	★	(0624) 75952		43
	Howstrake	★★	(0624) 24299		14
Peel	Peel	★	(0624) 4842227		24
Ramsey	Ramsey	★★	(0624) 812244	♦	28

♦ For details, see following pages.

• 9 hole golf course.

Humberside • North Yorkshire (N. Yorks)

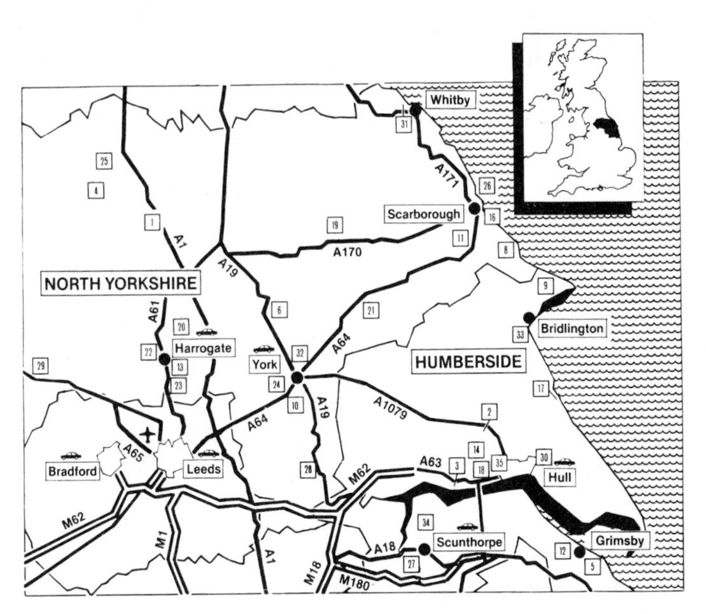

TOWN	GOLF COURSE	TEL	♦	MAP REF.
Barnoldswick	Ghyll •	(0282) 842466		•
Bedale	Bedale	(0677) 22568		1
Beverley	Beverley & East Riding	(0482) 867190		2
Bridlington	Bridlington	(0262) 672092		33
	Flamborough Head	(0262) 850333		9
Cleethorpes	Cleethorpes	(0472) 814060		5
Filey	Filey	(0723) 513293		8
Grimsby	Grimsby	(0472) 42823		12
Harrogate	Harrogate ★	(0423) 863158		13
	Oakdale	(0423) 67162		22
	Pannal ★★	(0423) 871641		23
Hornsea	Hornsea	(04012) 21020		17
Hull	Brough	(0482) 667374		3
	Hessle	(0482) 650171		14
	Hull	(0482) 658919		18
	Springhead Park	(0482) 656309		35
	Sutton Park	(0482) 781954		30
Knaresborough	Knaresborough	(0423) 863219		20
Malton	Malton & Norton	(0653) 2959		21
Pickering	Kirkbymoorside	(0751) 31525		19
Richmond	Catterick Garrison	(0748) 833268		4
	Richmond	(0748) 2457		25
Scarborough	Ganton ★★★	(030679) 555	♦	11
	Scarborough North Cliff ☆	(0723) 360786		26
	Scarborough South Cliff ☆	(0723) 374737		16
Scunthorpe	Normanby Hall	(8724) 862141		34
	Scunthorpe	(0742) 842913		27
Selby	Selby	(075782) 622		28
Settle	Settle	(0792) 2617		•
Skipton	Skipton	(0756) 3922		29
Thirsk	Thirsk & Northallerton •	(0845) 22170		•
Whitby	Whitby	(0947) 602768		31
York	Easingwold	(0347) 21486		6
	Fulford ★	(0904) 413579		10
	Pike Hills	(0904) 706566		24
	York ★	(0904) 490304		32

♦ For details, see following pages.

• 9 hole golf course.

ENGLAND/IV

South Yorkshire (S. Yorks) • West Yorkshire (W. Yorks)

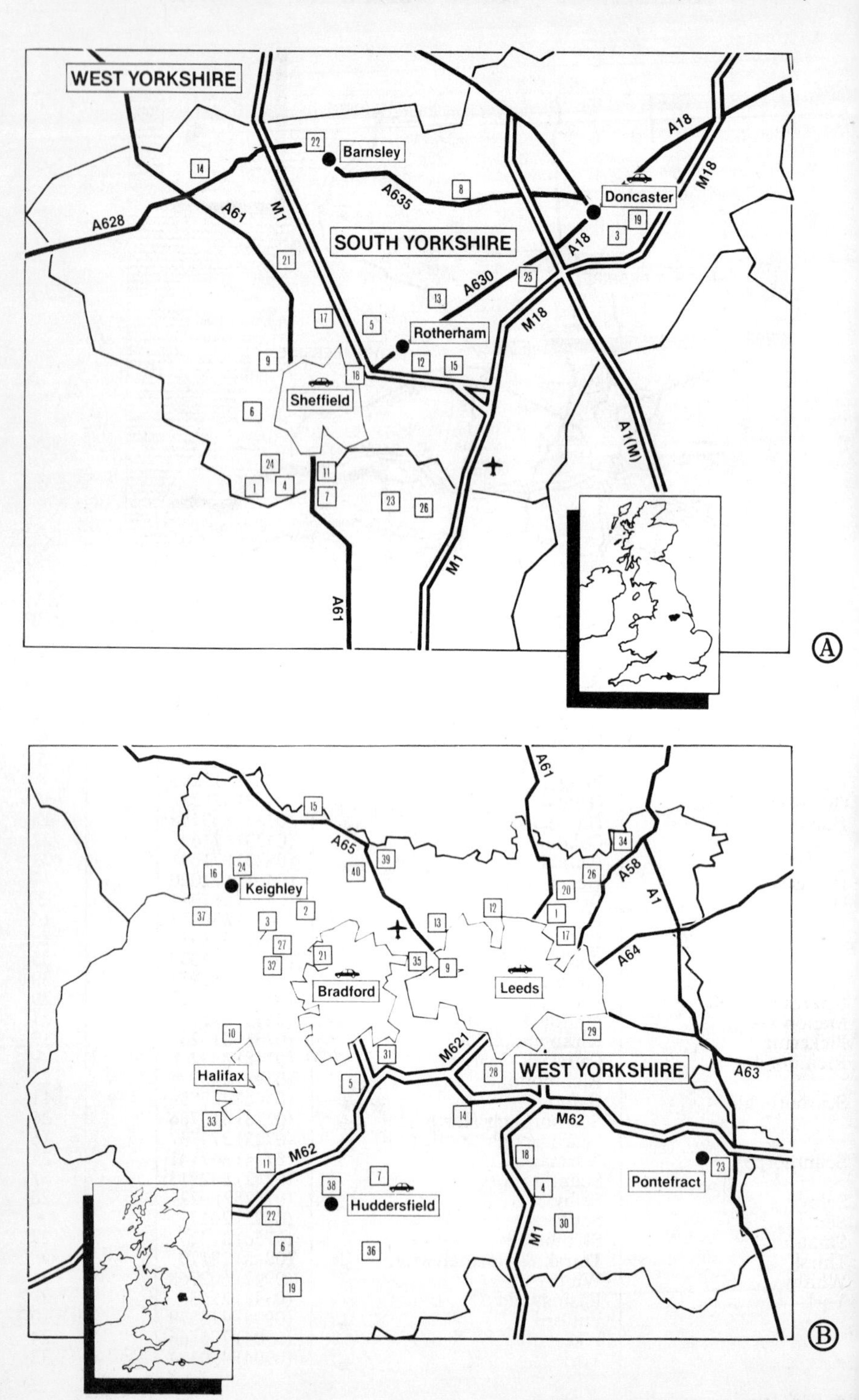

TOWN	GOLF COURSE		TEL	♦	MAP REF.
Barnsley	Barnsley		(0226) 382856		A 22
	Silkstone		(0226) 790328		A 14
Bingley	Bingley		(0274) 562506		B 3
Bradford & Suburbs	Baildon		(0274) 584266		B 2
	Bradford Moor	•	(0274) 638313		•
	Cleckheaton & District		(0274) 877851		B 5
	Headley	•	(0274) 833348		•
	Northcliffe		(0274) 584085		B 21
	Shipley		(0274) 563212		B 27
	South Bradford	•	(0274) 679195		•
	West Bowling		(0274) 724449		B 31
	West Bradford		(0274) 427671		B 32
Dewsbury	Dewsbury District		(0924) 492399		B 7
Doncaster	Crookhill Park		(0709) 862979		A 25
	Doncaster		(0302) 868316		A 3
	Hickleton		(0709) 892496		A 8
	Wheatley		(0302) 831655		A 19
Halifax	Halifax		(0422) 244171		B 10
	Halifax Bradley Hall		(0422) 74108		B 11
	West End		(0422) 53608		B 33
Hebden Bridge	Mount Skip	•	(0422) 842896		•
Huddersfield	Crosland Heath		(0484) 653216		B 6
	Huddersfield		(0484) 26203		B 38
	Woodsome Hall		(0484) 602971		B 36
Ilkley	Ben Rhydding	•	(0943) 608759		•
	Ilkley	✡	(0943) 600214		B 15
Keighley	Branshaw		(0535) 43235		B 37
	Keighley		(0535) 604778		B 16
	Riddlesdon		(0535) 602148		B 24
Leeds & Suburbs	Alwoodley	★★	(0532) 681680		B 1
	Fulneck	•	(0532) 565191		•
	Gotts Park		(0582) 638232		B 9
	Headingley		(0532) 675100		B 12
	Horsforth		(0532) 586819		B 13
	Leeds		(0532) 658775		B 17
	Middleton Park		(0532) 700449		
	Moor Allerton	★★	(0532) 661154	♦	B 20
	Moortown	★★★	(0532) 686521	♦	B 41
	Roundhay	•	(0532) 662695		•
	Sand Moor		(0532) 685180		B 25
	Scarcroft		(0532) 892263		B 26
	South Leeds		(0532) 700479		B 28
	Temple Newsam		(0532) 645624		B 29
Meltham	Meltham		(0484) 850227		B 19
Otley	Otley		(0943) 461015		B 39
Pontefract	Pontefract & District		(0977) 792241		BB 23
Rotherham	Grange Park		(0799) 559497		A 5
	Phoenix		(0709) 363864		A 12
	Rotherham		(0709) 850480		A 13
	Sitwell Park		(0709) 541046		A 15
Sheffield & Suburbs	Abbeydale		(0742) 360763		A 1
	Beauchief Municipal		(0742) 360648		A 24
	Birley Wood		(0742) 390099		A 23
	Dore & Totley		(0742) 360492		A 4
	Hallamshire		(0742) 302153		A 6
	Hallowes		(0246) 413734		A 7
	Hillsborough		(0742) 343608		A 9
	Renishaw Park		(0246) 432044		A 26
	Tankersley Park		(0742) 468247		A 17
	Tinsley Park		(0742) 442237		A 18
	Wortley		(0742) 882139		A 21
Wakefield	City of Wakefield		(0924) 255104		B 4
	Low Laithes		(0924) 273275		B 18
	Painthorpe House	•	(0924) 255083		•
	Wakefield		(0924) 255104		B 30
Wetherby	Wetherby		(0937) 65527		B 34

♦ For details, see following pages.

• 9 hole golf course.

Greater Manchester (Manchester and Suburbs)

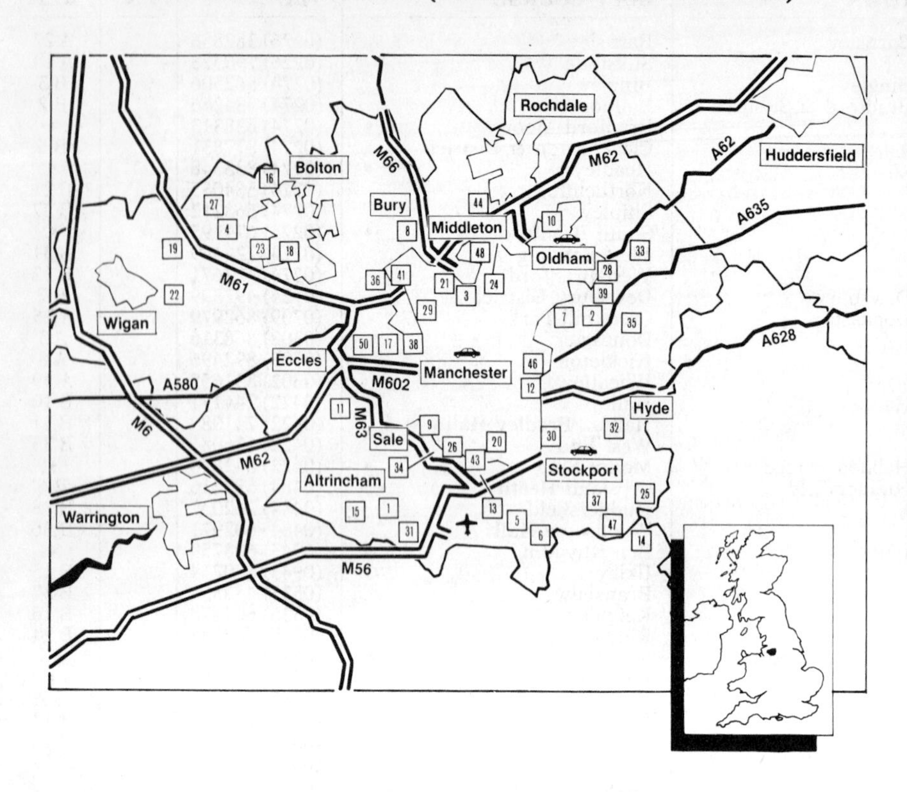

TOWN	GOLF COURSE	TEL	♦	MAP REF.
Altrincham	Altrincham	(061) 9280761		1
	Dunham Forest	(061) 9282605		15
	Ringway	(061) 9802630		31
Ashton-under-Lyne	Ashton-under-Lyne	(061) 3301537		2
Bolton	Bolton	(0204) 42307		4
	Deane	(0204) 61944		23
	Dunscar	(0204) 53321		16
	Great Lever & Farnworth	(0204) 62582		18
	Old Links	(0204) 42307		27
Bury	Bury	(061) 7664897		8
	Lowes Park	(061) 7641231		•
Manchester	Blackley	(061) 6432980		3
	Chorlton-cum-Hardy	(061) 8813139		9
	Denton	(061) 3363218		12
	Ellesmere	(061) 7902122		17
	Fairfield	(061) 3701641		46
	Heaton Park	(061) 7980295		21
	Prestwich	(061) 7732544		29
	Stand	(061) 7662388		36
	Swinton Park	(061) 7941785		38
	Whitefield	(061) 7662409		41
	Worsley	(061) 7894202		50
Middleton	Manchester	(061) 6432718		24
	North Manchester	(061) 6437094		48
Northenden	Didsbury	(061) 9982743		13
	Northenden	(061) 9984738		26
	Withington	(061) 4459544		43
Oldham	Brookdale	(061) 6814534		7

♦ For details, see following pages.

• 9 hole golf course.

TOWN	GOLF COURSE		TEL	♦	MAP REF.
	Crompton & Royton		(061) 6242154		10
	Oldham		(061) 6244986		28
	Saddleworth		(04577) 2059		33
	Werneth		(061) 6241190		39
Rochdale	Castle Hawk		(0706) 40841		44
Sale	Sale		(061) 9733404		34
Stockport	Bramall Park		(061) 4853119		5
	Bramhall		(061) 4394057		6
	Disley		(06632) 2071		14
	Hazel Grove		(061) 4833217		47
	Heaton Moor		(061) 4320846		20
	Marple		(061) 4272311		•
	Mellor & Townscliffe		(061) 4272208		25
	Reddish Vale		(061) 4802959		30
	Romiley		(061) 4302392		32
	Stockport		(061) 4272001		37
Urmston	Davyhulme Park		(061) 7482856		11
Wigan	Arley Hall	•	(0257) 421360		22
	Haigh Hall		(0942) 831107		22
	Hindley Hall		(0942) 55131		22
	Pennington	•	(0942) 672823		22

♦ For details, see following pages.

• 9 hole golf course.

Merseyside

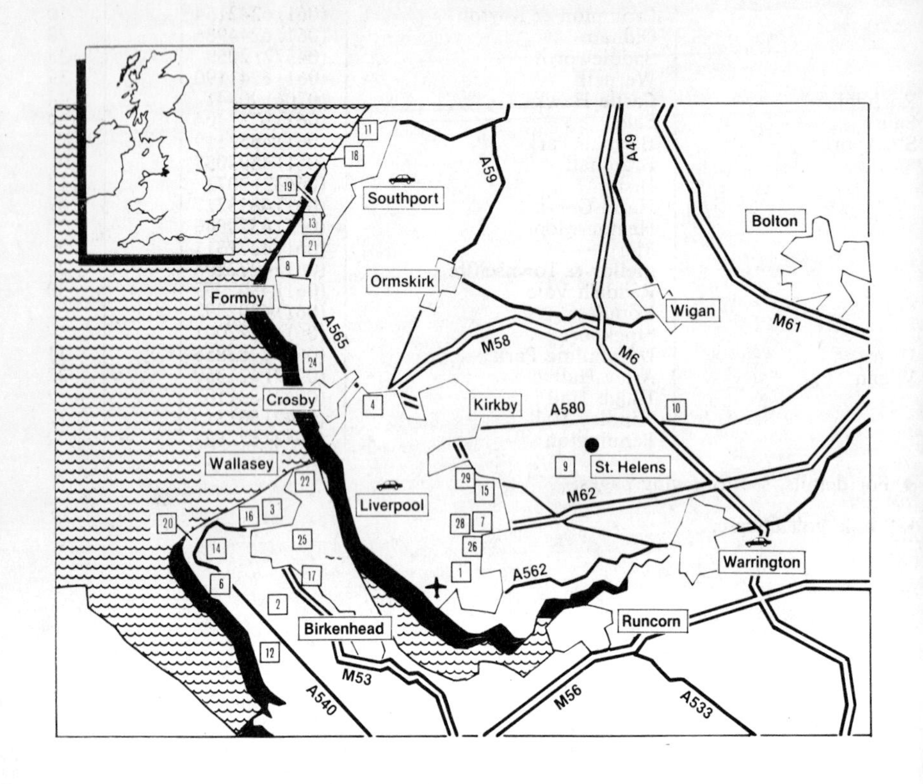

TOWN	GOLF COURSE		TEL	♦	MAP REF.
Birkenhead	Arrowe Park		(051) 6771527		2
	Prenton		(051) 6081053		17
	Wirral Ladies		(051) 6521255		25
Formby	Formby	★★★	(07048) 72164	♦	8
Heswall	Heswall		(051) 3422193		12
Hoylake	Caldy	★★	(051) 6255660		6
	Hoylake		(051) 6322956		14
	Royal Liverpool	★★★	(051) 6323101	♦	20
Liverpool	Allerton Park		(051) 4281046		1
	Bootle		(051) 9281371		4
	Childwall		(051) 4870654		7
	Huyton & Preston		(051) 4893948		15
	Lee Park		(051) 4873882		28
	Liverpool Municipal		(051) 5465435		29
	West Lancashire		(051) 9241036		24
Newton-le-Willows	Haddock Park		(09252) 28525		10
St Helens	Grange Park		(0744) 26318		9
Southport	Hesketh	★	(0704) 36897		11
	Hillside	★	(0704) 67169		13
	Park		(0704) 35286		18
	Royal Birkdale	★★★	(0704) 69903	♦	19
	Southport & Ainsdale	★★★	(0704) 78000	♦	21
Wallasey	Bidston		(051) 6383412		3
	Leasowe		(051) 6775852		16
	Wallasey		(051) 6393630		22

♦ For details, see following pages.

ENGLAND/VII

Cheshire • Derbyshire (Derbys) • Shropshire • Staffordshire (Staffs)

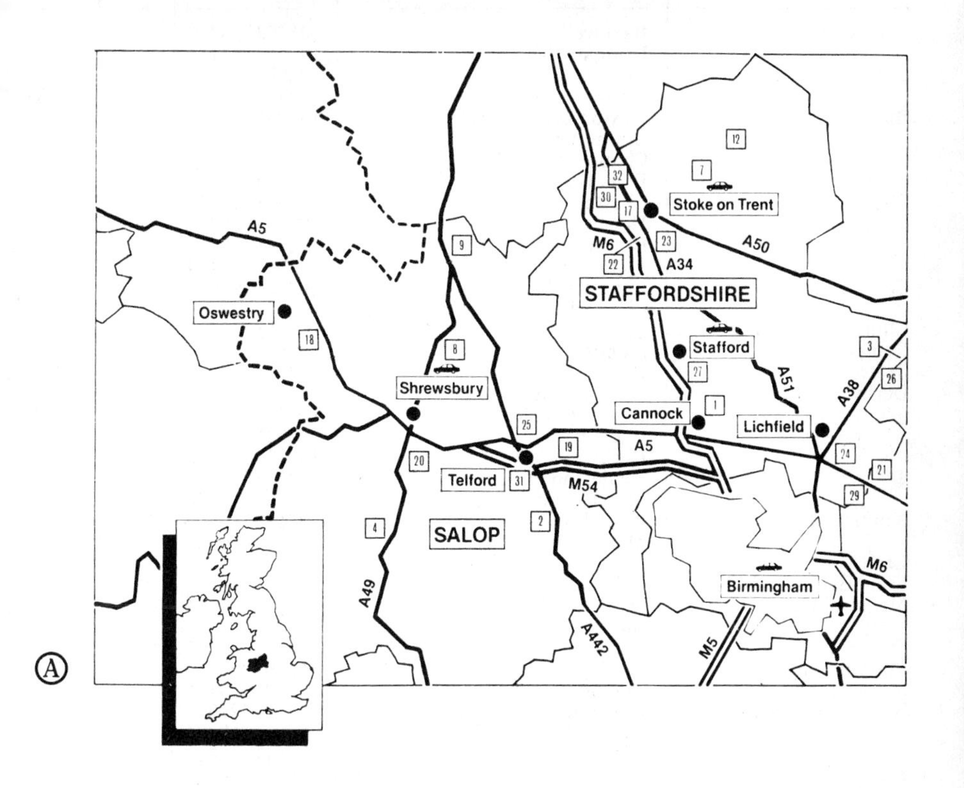

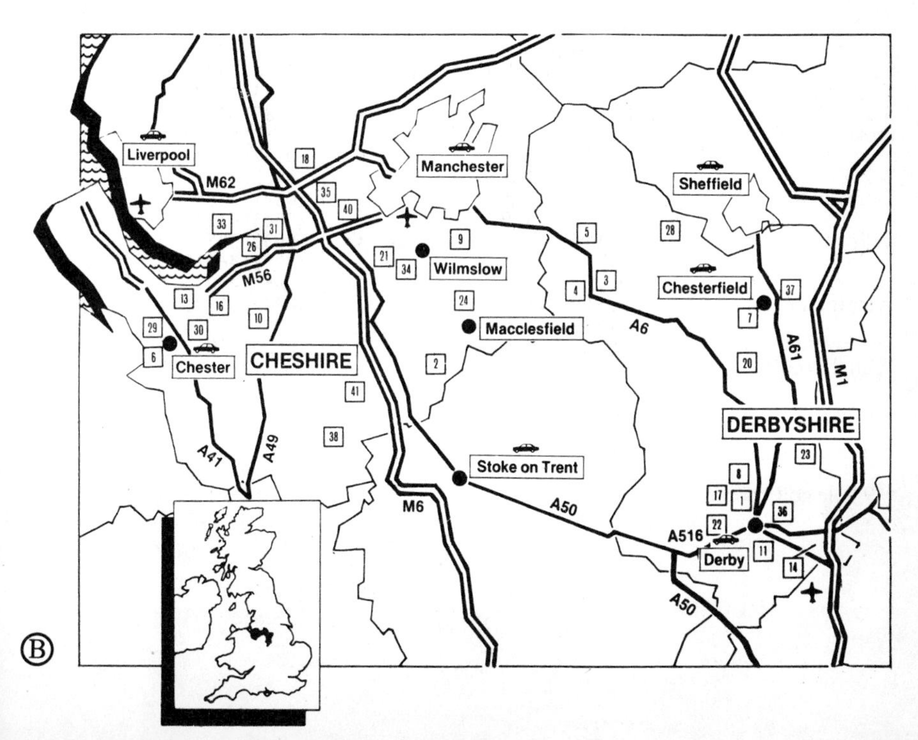

TOWN	GOLF COURSE		TEL	♦	MAP REF.
Bakewell	Bakewell	•	(062981) 3229		•
Bridgnorth	Bridgnorth		(07462) 3315		A 2
Burton-on-Trent	Branston		(0283) 43207		A 26
	Burton-on-Trent		(0283) 44551		A 3
Buxton	Buxton & High Peak		(0298) 3453		B 3
	Cavendish		(0298) 3494		B 4
	Chapel-en-le-Frith		(0298) 812118		B 5
Cannock	Beau Desert		(05438) 2692		A 1
Chester	Chester		(0244) 675130		B 6
	Helsby		(0928) 2202		B 16
	Upton-by-Chester		(0244) 381183		B 29
	Vicars Cross		(0244) 335174		B 30
Chesterfield	Chesterfield		(0246) 79256		B 7
	Chesterfield Municipal		(0246) 73887		B 37
Church Stretton	Church Stretton		(0694) 722281		A 4
Congleton	Astbury		(0260) 272772		•
Crewe	Crewe		(0270) 584227		B 38
Derby	Allestree Park		(0332) 550616		B 1
	Breadsall Priory	✡	(0332) 832235		B 36
	Chevin		(0332) 841864		B 8
	Derby		(0332) 766462		B 11
	Kedleston Park		(0332) 840035		B 17
	Mickleover		(0332) 512092		B 22
Knutsford	Knutsford	•	(0565) 3355		•
	Mere	★	(0565) 830155		B 21
Leek	Leek		(0538) 384779		A 12
Long Eaton	Erewash Valley		(0602) 322984		B 14
Macclesfield	Davenport		(0625) 896951		B 9
	Macclesfield	•	(0625) 23227		•
	Prestbury		(0625) 828241		B 24
Market Drayton	Market Drayton	•	(0630) 2266		•
Matlock	Matlock		(0629) 2191		B 20
Newcastle-under-Lyme	Newcastle Municipal		(0782) 627596		A 30
	Newcastle-under-Lyme		(0782) 617006		A 17
	Wolstanton		(0782) 622413		B 32
New Mills	New Mills	•	(0663) 43485		•
Northwich	Delamere Forest		(0606) 882807		B 10
Oswestry	Aston Park		(069188) 221		A 10
Runcorn	Runcorn		(09285) 72093		B 26
Sandbach	Malkins Bank Municipal		(09367) 5931		B 41
Shrewsbury	Shrewsbury		(074372) 2976		A 20
Stafford	Brocton Hall		(0785) 661901		A 27
Stoke-on-Trent	Greenway Hall		(0782) 502204		A 7
	Trentham		(0782) 658100		A 23
	Trentham Park		(0782) 657317		A 22
Tamworth	Tamworth Municipal		(0827) 53850		A 21
	Whittington Barracks		(0543) 432212		A 24
Telford	Telford	✡	(0952) 585642		A 31
	Shifnal		(0952) 460330		A 19
	Wrekin		(0952) 44032		A 25
Warrington	Birchwood		(0925) 818819		B 35
	Hill Warren		(0925) 61775		B 35
	Walton Hall		(0925) 630619		B 31
Whitchurch	Hawkstone Park	★	(093924) 611	♦	A 8
	Hill Valley	★	(0948) 3584		A 9
Wilmslow	Wilmslow		(056587) 2148		B 34

♦ For details, see following pages.

• 9 hole golf course.

West Midlands (W. Midlands)

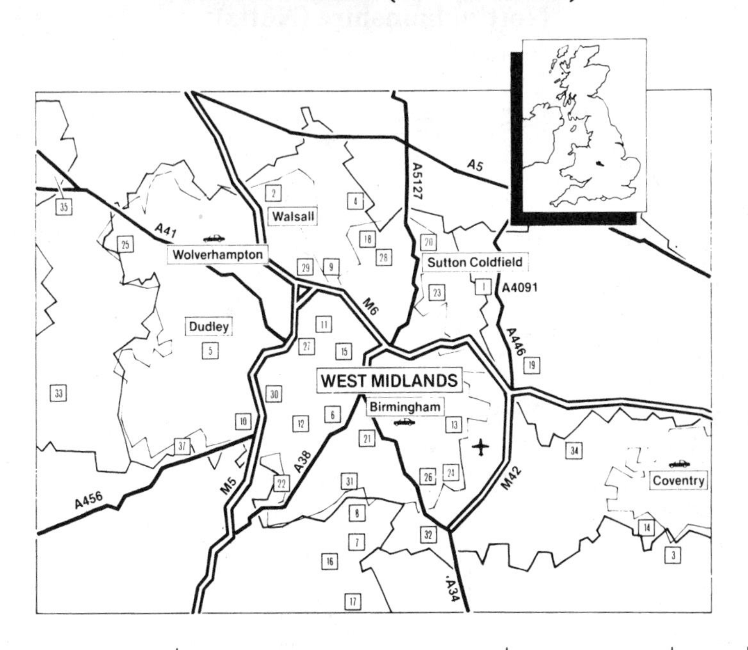

TOWN	GOLF COURSE		TEL	♦	MAP REF.
Birmingham	Brand Hall		(021) 5527475		30
	Cocks Moor Woods		(021) 4443584		31
	Edgbaston		(021) 4541736		6
	Gay Hill		(021) 4306523		8
	Halesowen		(021) 5501041		10
	Handsworth		(021) 5540599		11
	Harborne		(021) 4271728		12
	Hilltop & Manwood Farm		(021) 5544463		15
	King's Norton	★★	(0564) 826706		16
	Moseley		(021) 4442115		21
	North Worcestershire		(021) 4751026		22
	Warley		(021) 4292440		•
Coleshill	Maxstoke Park		(0675) 62158		19
Coventry	City of Coventry		(0203) 543141		19
	Coventry		(0203) 414152		3
	Forest of Arden	★	(06767) 22118		34
	Hearsall		(0293) 713156		14
	Sphinx		(0203) 458890		19
Solihull	Olton		(021) 7051083		24
	Robin Hood		(021) 7060061		26
	Shirley		(021) 7446001		32
Stourbridge	Enville		(0384) 872551		33
	Stourbridge		(0384) 393062		37
Sutton Coldfield	Belfry	★★	(0675) 70301	♦	1
	Little Aston	★★★	(021) 3532066	♦	18
	Moor Hall		(021) 3086130		20
	Sutton Coldfield		(021) 3539633		28
	Walmley		(021) 3730029		23
Walsall/Barr	Bloxwich		(0922) 405724		2
	Great Barr		(021) 3571232		9
	Walsall		(0922) 673512		29
West Bromwich	Dartmouth	•	(021) 5882131		•
	Sandwell Park		(021) 5534637		27
Wolverthampton	Patshull Park	★	(0902) 700100		35
	Penn		(0902) 341142		25

♦ For details, see following pages.

• 9 hole golf course.

Leicestershire (Leics) • Lincolnshire (Lincs) • Nottinghamshire (Notts)

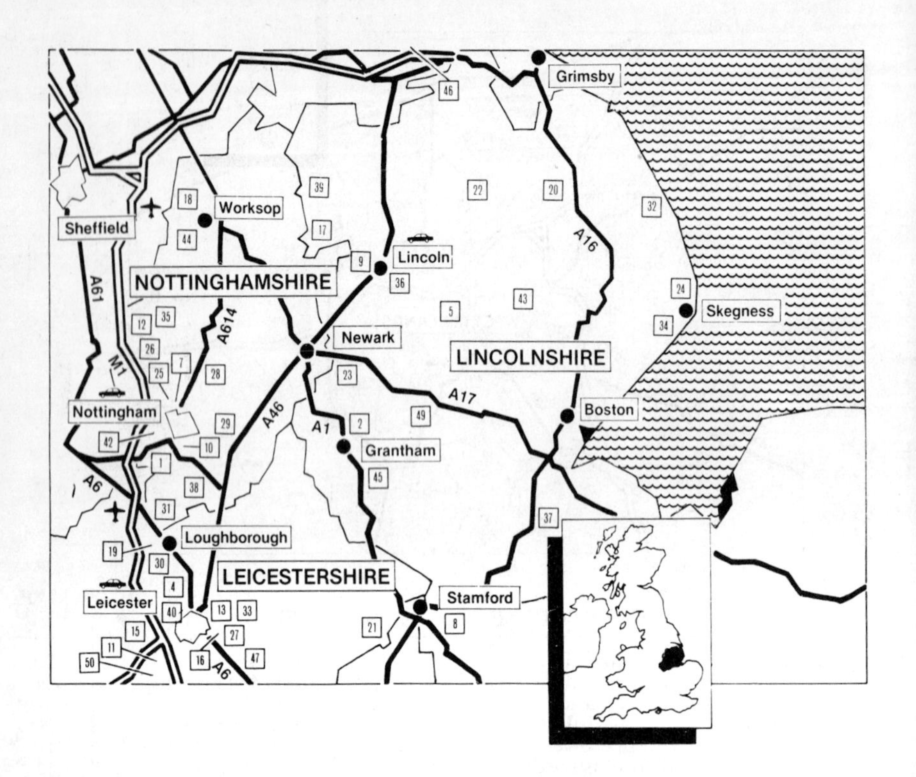

TOWN	GOLF COURSE	TEL	♦	MAP REF.
Brigg	Elsham	(0652) 688382		46
Grantham	Belton Park	(0476) 67399		2
	Stoke Rochford	(047683) 275		45
Hinckley	Hinckley	(0455) 615124		
Leicester	Birstall	(0533) 674322		4
	Cosby	(0533) 864759		11
	Glen Gorse	(0533) 714159		47
	Humberstone Heights	(0533) 764674		13
	Kirby Muxloe	(0533) 393457		15
	Leicestershire	(0533) 738835		16
	Oadby	(0533) 700326		27
	Rothley Park	(0533) 302809		30
	Scraptoft	(0533) 419000		33
	Western Park	(0533) 876158		40
	Whetstone •	(0533) 861424		•
Lincoln	Blankney	(0526) 20263		5
	Carholme	(0522) 23725		9
	Lincoln	(042771) 210		17
	Southcliffe & Canwick	(0522) 22166		36
Loughborough	Lingdale •	(0509) 890035		•
	Longcliffe	(0509) 239129		19
	Rushcliffe	(0509) 822209		31
Louth	Louth	(0507) 603681		20
Lutterworth	Lutterworth •	(04555) 2532		•
	Ullesthorpe	(0455) 209023		50
Mansfield	Coxmoor	(0623) 557359		12
	Sherwood Forest	(0623) 23327		35
Market Rasen	Market Rasen & District	(0673) 842416		22
Newark	Newark	(0636) 84282		23
Nottingham	Beeston Fields	(0602) 257062		1
	Bulwell Forest	(0602) 278008		7
	Chilwell Manor	(0602) 257050		10
	Mapperley	(0602) 265611		•
	Nottingham City	(0602) 278021		25
	Notts ★	(0623) 753225		26
	Oxton	(0602) 653545		28
	Wollaton Park ★	(0602) 787585		42
Skegness	North Shore ✡	(0754) 3298		24
	Seacroft ✡	(0754) 3020		34
Sleaford	Sleaford	(05298) 273		49
Spalding	Spalding	(077585) 386		37
Stamford	Burghley Park	(0780) 53789		8
	Luffenham Heath	(0780) 720205		21
Sutton-on-Sea	Sandilands ✡	(0521) 41432		32
Woodhall Spa	Woodhall Spa ★★★	(0526) 52511	♦	43
Worksop	Lindrick	(0909) 472120		18
	Worksop	(0909) 477731		44

♦ For details, see following pages.

• 9 hole golf course.

Cambridgeshire (Cambs) • Norfolk • Suffolk

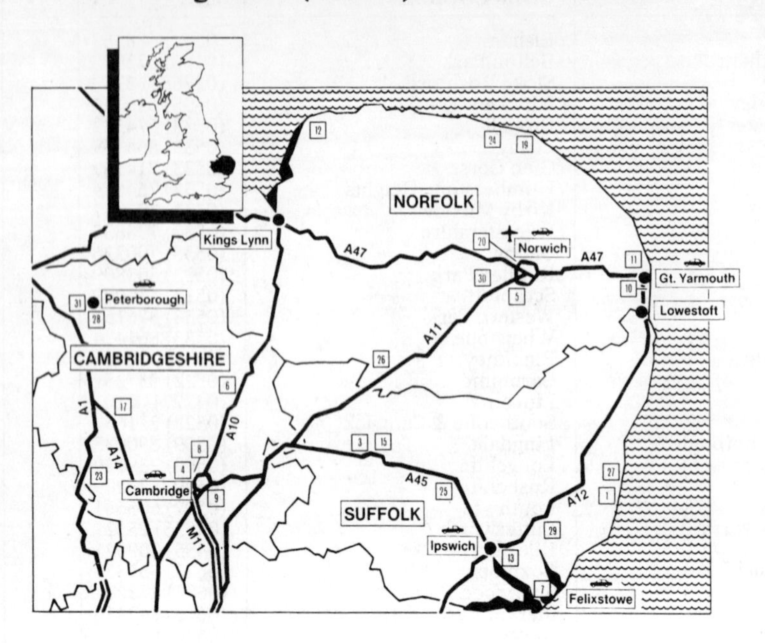

TOWN	GOLF COURSE		TEL	♦	MAP REF.
Aldeburgh	Aldeburgh	★	(072885) 2890		1
	Thorpeness	★	(072885) 2176		27
Bury-St-Edmonds	Bury-St-Edmonds		(0284) 5979		3
	Flempton		(028484) 219		•
	Lark Valley		(0284) 63426		15
Cambridge	Cambridgeshire Hotel	✡	(0954) 80555		4
	Girton		(0223) 276169		8
	Gog Magog	★	(0223) 247626	♦	9
Cromer	Mundesley		(0263) 720095		•
	Links Country Park		(026375) 691		•
	Royal Cromer	★★	(0263) 512884	♦	19
	Sheringham	★	(0263) 822038		24
Diss	Diss		(0379) 2847		•
Ely	Ely City	★	(0353) 2751		6
Felixstowe	Felixstowe Ferry		(0394) 283060		7
Great Yarmouth	Gorleston	✡	(0493) 661911		10
	Great Yarmouth & Caister	✡	(0493) 728699		11
Huntingdon	Ramsey	✡	(0487) 812600	♦	17
	St-Neots		(0480) 72363		23
Hunstanton	Hunstanton	★★	(04853) 2811	♦	12
	Royal West Norfolk	★★	(0485) 210223		21
Ipswich	Ipswich		(0473) 78941		13
	Rushmere		(0473) 77109		22
Lowestoft	Southwold		(0502) 723234		•
Newmarket	Links		(0638) 663000		16
	Royal Worlington & Newmarket		(0638) 72216		•
Norwich	Barnham Broom	✡	(060545) 437		30
	Eaton		(0603) 52881		5
	Royal Norwich	★★	(0603) 49928		20
Peterborough	Peterborough Milton		(073121) 204		31
	Thorpe Wood		(0733) 267701		28
Stowmarket	Stowmarket		(04493) 473		25
Thetford	Thetford	★	(0842) 2258		26
Woodbridge	Woodbridge	★	(03943) 2038		29

♦ For details, see following pages.

• 9 hole golf course.

ENGLAND/XI

Bedfordshire (Beds) • Buckinghamshire (Bucks) • Oxfordshire (Oxon) • Northamptonshire (Northants)

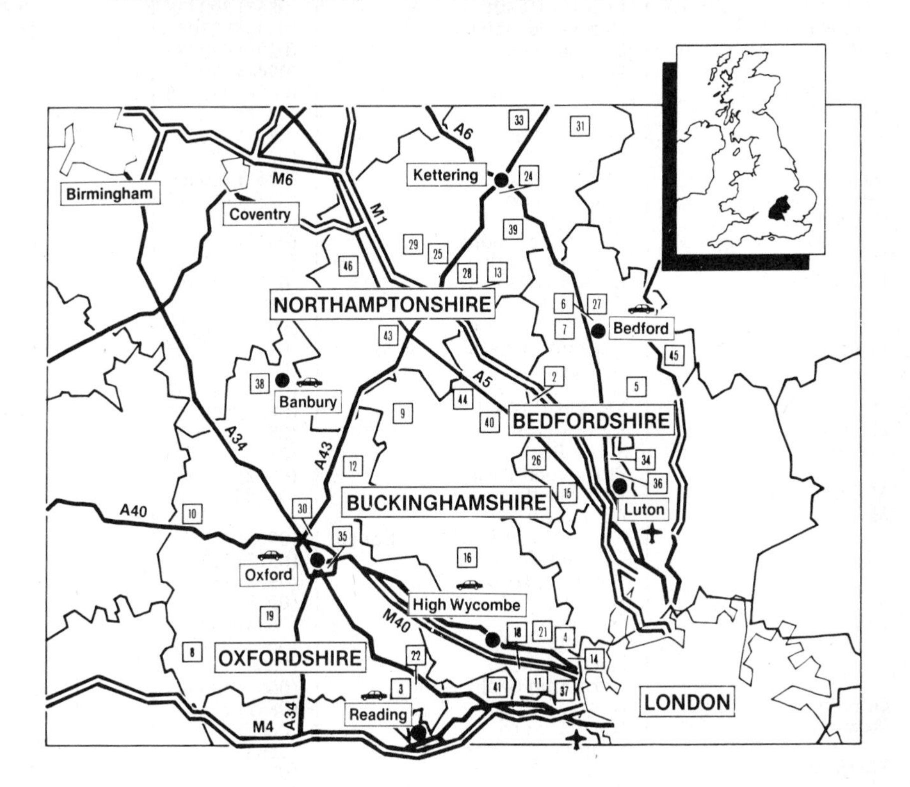

TOWN	GOLF COURSE	TEL	♦	MAP REF.
Abingdon	Frilford Heath	(0865) 390428		19
Amersham	Harewood Downs	(02404) 2308		21
Aylesbury	Ellesborough	(0296) 622375		16
	Whiteleaf	(08444) 3097		•
Banbury	Tadmarton Heath	(0608) 737278		38
Bedford	Bedford & County	(0234) 52617		6
	Bedfordshire	(0234) 61669		7
	Mowsbury	(0234) 771041		27
Biggleswade	John O'Gaunt ★	(0767) 260360		45
Buckingham	Buckingham	(0280) 813282		9
Burford	Burford	(099382) 2583		10
Chesterton	Chesterton Country	(0869) 241204		12
Daventry	Staverton Park	(0327) 705911		46
Dunstable	Dunstable Downs	(0582) 63634		15
	Tilsworth	(0525) 210721		•
Gerrards Cross	Denham	(0895) 832022		14
Henley-on-Thames	Badgemore Park	(0491) 572206		3
	Henley	(0491) 575742		22
	Huntercombe	(0491) 641207		23
High Wycombe	Flackwell Heath	(06285) 20929		18
Kettering	Kettering	(0536) 512074		24
Luton	South Beds	(0582) 591500		34
	Stockwood Park	(0582) 413704		36
Maidenhead	Winter Hill	(06285) 276139		41
Milton Keynes	Abbey Hill	(0908) 563845		44
	Aspley Guise & Woburn Sands	(0908) 583596		2
	Leighton Buzzard	(0525) 373811		27
	Windmill Hill	(0908) 78623		40
	Woburn	(0908) 70756		42
Northampton	Delapre	(0604) 64036		13
	Kingsthorpe	(0604) 71173		25
	Northampton	(0604) 719453		28
	Northamptonshire	(0604) 843025		29
Oundle	Oundle	(0832) 73267		31
Oxford	North Oxford	(0865) 54415		30
	Southfield	(0865) 242158		35
Shefford	Beadlow Manor	(0525) 60800		5
Slough	Beaconsfield	(04946) 6545		4
	Burnham Beeches	(0628) 61448		11
	Stoke Poges	(0753) 26985		37
	Wexham Park	(02816) 3271		
Swindon	Bremhill Park	(0793) 782946		8
Towcester	Woodlands	(032736) 291		43
Wellingborough	Wellingborough	(0933) 673022		39

♦ For details, see following pages.

• 9 hole golf course.

ENGLAND/XII

Gloucestershire (Glos.) • Hereford & Worcester (Here & Worcs) • Warwickshire (Warwicks)

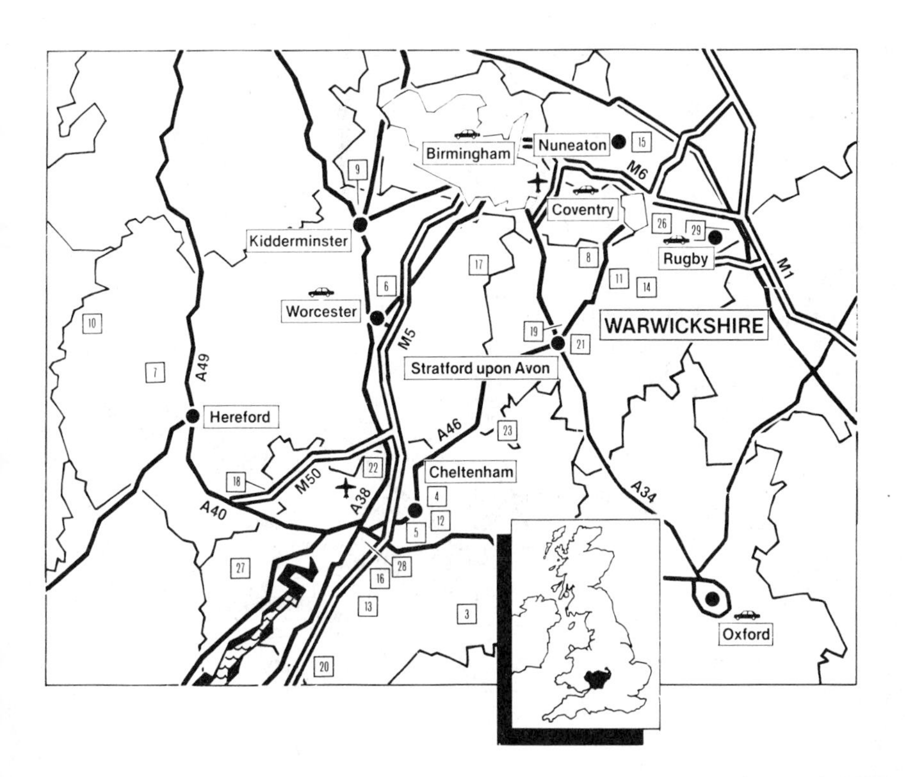

TOWN	GOLF COURSE		TEL	♦	MAP REF.
Broadway	Broadway		(0386) 853683		23
Cheltenham	Cleeve Hill		(024267) 2592		4
	Cotswold Hills		(0242) 515264		5
	Lilley Brook		(0242) 526785		12
Cirencester	Cirencester	★	(0285) 2465		3
Coleford	Coleford	★	(0594) 32583		27
Droitwich	Droitwich		(0905) 770129		6
Gloucester	Gloucester Hotel	✡	(0452) 411331		28
	Stinchcombe Hill		(0453) 2015		20
Great Malvern	Worcestershire		(06845) 64428		25
Hereford	Herefordshire		(0432) 71219		7
Kidderminster	Habberley	•	(0562) 745756		•
Kington	Kington		(0544) 230340		10
Leamington Spa	Leamington Spa		(0926) 25961		11
	Newbold Comyn		(0926) 21157		14
Leominster	Leominster	•	(0568) 2863		•
Nuneaton	Nuneaton		(0203) 347810		15
Redditch	Redditch		(0527) 43309		17
Stratford-upon-Avon	Avon (Welcombe)	✡	(0789) 295252	♦	19
	Stratford-upon-Avon	★	(0789) 205749		21
Stroud	Minchinhampton	★	(045383) 3866		13
	Painswick		(0452) 812180		16
Tewkesbury	Tewkesbury Park	✡	(0684) 295405		22
Warwick	Warwick	•	(0926) 494316		•
Worcester	Worcester		(0905) 422555		24

♦ For details, see following pages.

• 9 hole golf course.

Essex • Hertfordshire (Herts)

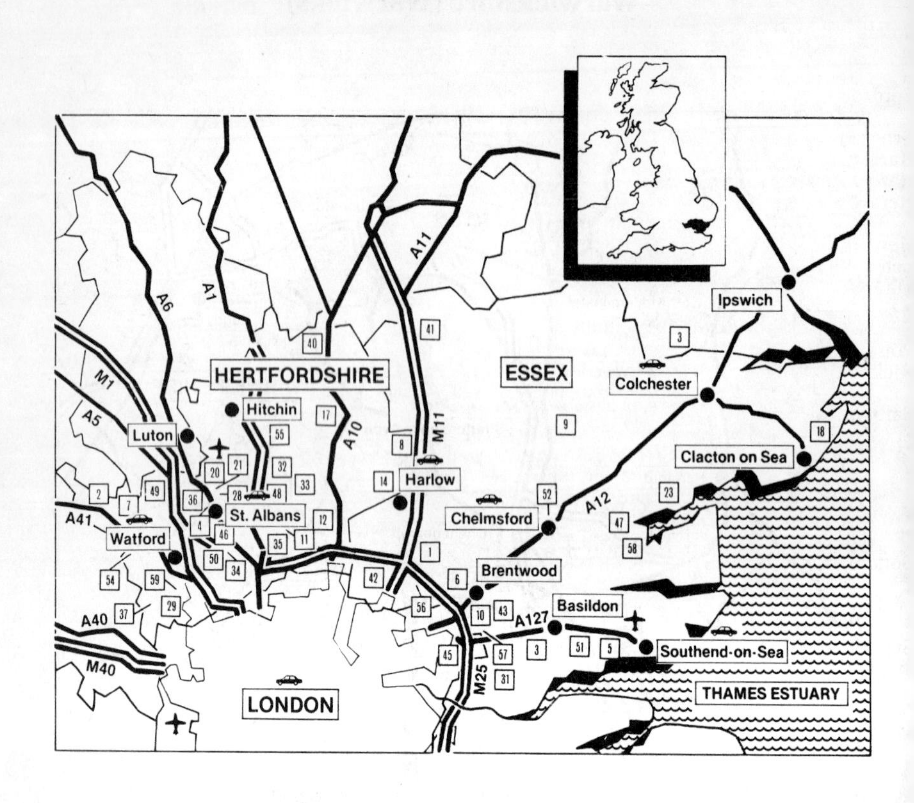

TOWN	GOLF COURSE	TEL	♦	MAP REF.
Basildon	Basildon	(0268) 2297		3
Berkhamsted	Ashridge	(044284) 2244		2
	Berkhamsted	(04427) 5832		7
	Whipsnade	(044284) 2330		49
Bishop's Stortford	Bishop's Stortford	(0279) 54715		8
Braintree	Braintree	(0376) 24117		9
Brentwood	Bentley	(0277) 73179		6
	Brentwood (Hartswood)	(0277) 218714		10
	King George's	(0277) 218850		
	Thorndon Park	(0277) 811666		43
	Warley Park	(0277) 224891	★	57
Burnham-on-Crouch	Burnham-on-Crouch	(0621) 782282	★★	12
Chelmsford	Channels	(0245) 440005		52
	Chelmsford	(0245) 50555		
Clacton-on-Sea	Frinton	(02556) 4618		18

TOWN	GOLF COURSE	TEL	♦	MAP REF.
Colchester	Birch Grove •	(020634) 276		•
	Manifold	(0621) 860410		23
	Stoke-by-Nayland	(0206) 262836		39
Epping	Abridge	(04028) 396		1
	Theydon Bois	(0378) 881		42
Grays	Orsett	(0375) 891352		31
Harlow	Canon's Brook ★	(0279) 21482		14
Hatfield	Brookmans Park	(0707) 52487		11
Hemel Hempstead	Boxmoor •	(0442) 42434		•
	Little Hay	(0442) 833798		54
Hertford	Brickendon Grange	(0992) 86228		12
Letchworth	Letchworth	(04626) 3203		
Maldon	Maldon •	(0621) 891406		•
	Warren	(024541) 3258		47
	Westcliff (Three Rivers)	(0621) 828631		58
Potters Bar	P.L. London	(0707) 42624		33
Rickmansworth	Moor Park ★	(0923) 773146		29
	Rickmansworth	(0923) 773163		37
Saffron Walden	Saffron Walden	(0799) 22786		41
St. Albans	Batchwood Hall	(0727) 52101		4
	Harpenden	(05827) 2580		20
	Harpenden Common	(05827) 2856		21
	Mid Herts	(058283) 2242		28
	Porters Park	(09276) 4127		34
	Redbourn	(058285) 3493		36
Southend-on-Sea	Belfairs	(0702) 525345		5
	Boyce's Hill	(03745) 3625		51
	Rochford Hundred	(0702) 544302		38
	Thorpe Hall ★	(0702) 582205		44
Stevenage	Stevenage	(043888) 424		55
Watford	Aldenham	(09276) 7775		50
	Hartsbourne Country Club ★	(01) 9501133		53
	West Herts ★	(0923) 36484		59
Welwyn Garden City	Panshanger	(07073) 33350		32
	Welwyn Garden City	(07073) 22722		48

♦ For details, see following pages.

• 9 hole golf course.

Greater London (London & Suburbs)

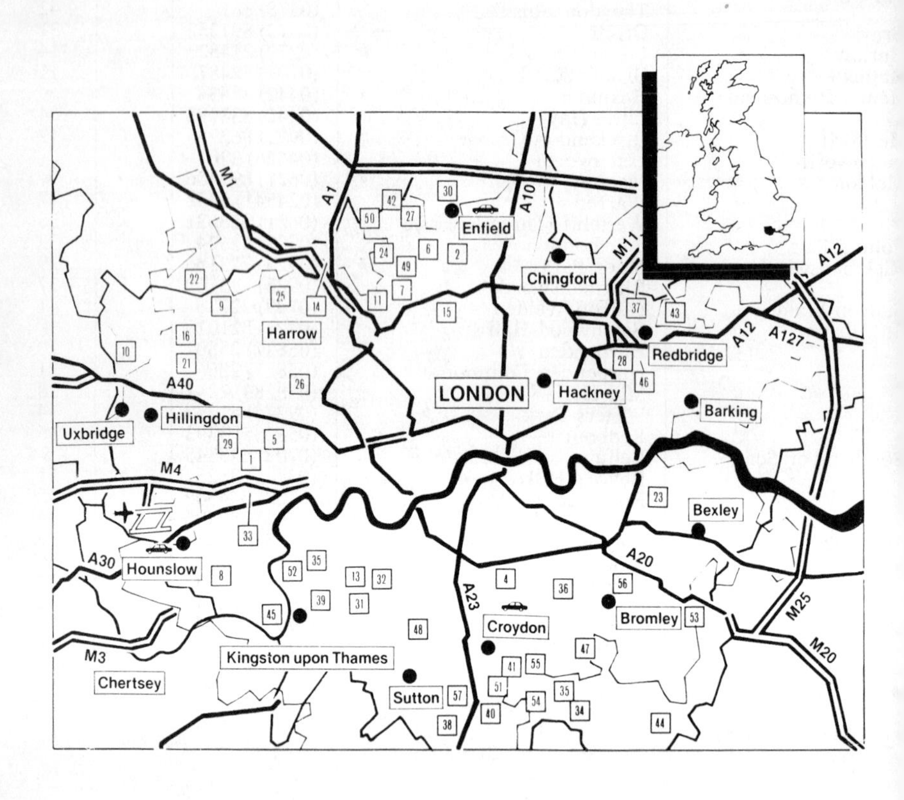

TOWN	GOLF COURSE		TEL	♦	MAP REF.
London	Addington Court		(01) 6570281		34
	Addington Palace		(01) 6543061		35
	Beckenham Place Park		(01) 8579513		36
	Brent Valley		(01) 5674230		1
	Bush Hill Park		(01) 3605738		2
	Chigwell		(01) 5002059		37
	Chipstead		(07375) 55781		38
	Coombe Hill		(01) 9422284		39
	Coombe Wood		(01) 9420388		39
	Coulsdon Court		(01) 6600468		40
	Croham Hurst		(01) 6572075		41
	Dulwich & Sydenham Hill		(01) 6933961		4
	Ealing		(01) 9970937		5
	Enfield		(01) 3666500		6
	Finchley	★	(01) 3462436	♦	7

♦ For details, see following pages.

TOWN	GOLF COURSE		TEL	♦	MAP REF.
	Fulwell		(01) 9772733		8
	Grim's Dyke		(01) 4284539		9
	Hadley Wood		(01) 4494328		42
	Hainault Forest		(01) 5002097		43
	Hampton Wick		(01) 9776645		
	Harefield Place		(0895) 31169		10
	Hendon		(01) 3466023		11
	High Elms		(0689) 58175		44
	Holiday		(0895) 444232		
	Home Park		(01) 9772423		45
	Ilford		(01) 5545174		46
	Langley Park		(01) 6586849		47
	London Scottish		(01) 7880135		13
	Mill Hill		(01) 9592339		14
	Mitcham		(01) 6484197		48
	Muswell Hill		(01) 8881764		15
	North Middlesex		(01) 4451604		49
	Northwood		(09274) 21384		16
	Oak Sports Centre		(01) 6438363		
	Old Fold Manor		(01) 4409185		50
	Picketts Lock	•	(01) 8033611		•
	Purley Downs		(01) 6578347		51
	Richmond		(01) 9401463		
	Richmond Park		(01) 8763205		35
	Royal Blackheath	★★★	(01) 8501795	♦	18
	Royal Epping Forest		(01) 5292195		19
	Royal Mid-Surrey	★★	(01) 9401894		52
	Royal Wimbledon		(01) 9462125		20
	Ruislip	★★	(09285) 72093		21
	Selsdon Park Hotel	✡	(01) 6578811		54
	Shirley Park		(01) 6541143		55
	Shooters Hill		(01) 8541216		23
	South Herts		(01) 4452035		24
	Stanmore		(01) 9544661		25
	Sudbury		(01) 9023713		26
	Sundridge Park		(01) 4600278		56
	Trent Park		(01) 3667432		27
	Twickenham	•	(01) 9410032		•
	West Middlesex		(01) 5743450		29
	White Webbs		(01) 3632951		30
	Wimbledon Common		(01) 9460294		31
	Wimbledon Park		(01) 9461002		32
	Woodcote Park		(01) 6682788		57
	Wyke Green		(01) 5608777		33

♦ For details, see following pages.

• 9 hole golf course.

East Sussex • Kent

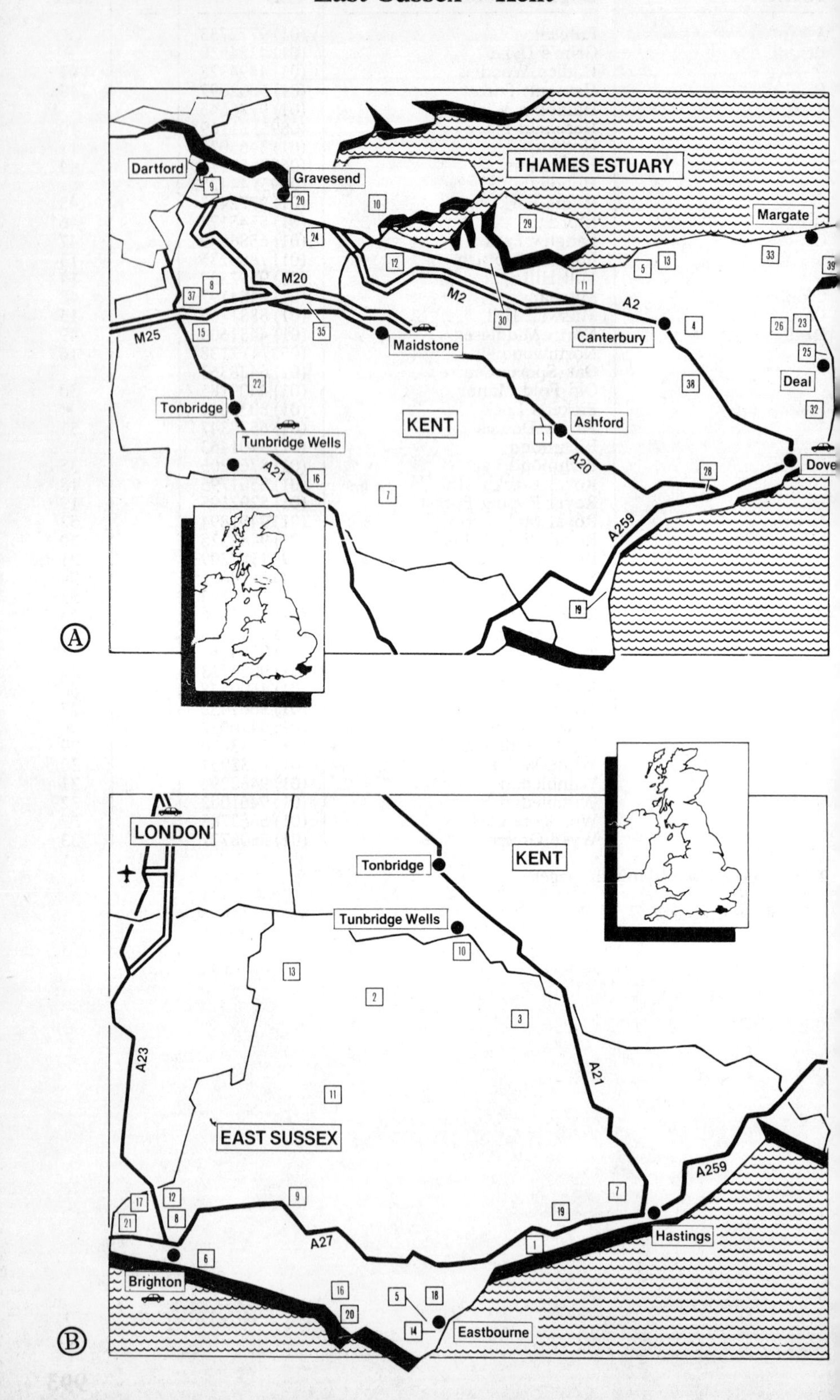

TOWN	GOLF COURSE		TEL	♦	MAP REF.
Ashford	Ashford		(0223) 20180		A 1
Bexhill	Cooden Beach	✩	(04243) 2040		B 1
	Highwoods		(0424) 212625		B 19
Brighton	Brighton & Hove	✩	(0273) 556482		•
	Dyke	✩	(079156) 296		B 4
	East Brighton	✩	(0273) 604838		B 6
	Hollingbury Park	✩	(0273) 552010		B 8
	Pyecombe	✩	(07918) 5372		B 12
	Waterhall	✩	(0273) 508658		B 17
	West Hove	✩	(0273) 419738		B 21
Broadstairs	North Foreland	★	(0843) 62140		A 21
Canterbury	Broome Park		(0304) 831701		A 38
	Canterbury	★	(0227) 63586		A 4
	Faversham		(0795) 89251		A 11
Cranbrook	Cranbrook		(0580) 712833		A 7
Dartford	Dartford		(0322) 23616		A 9
Deal	Prince's	★★★	(0304) 611118	♦	A 23
	Royal Cinque Ports	★★★	(0304) 374007	♦	A 25
	Royal St Georges	★★★	(0304) 613070	♦	A 26
	Walmer & Kingsdown	✩	(0304) 373256		A 32
Eastbourne	Eastbourne Downs	✩	(0323) 20827		B 5
	Royal Eastbourne	✩	(0323) 29738		B 14
	Willingdon	★	(0323) 32383		B 18
Folkestone	Sene Valley	★	(0303) 68513		A 28
Gravesend	Mid Kent		(0474) 68035		A 20
Hastings	Hastings		(0424) 52977		B 7
Lewes	Lewes		(0273) 473245		B 9
Maidstone	Bearsted		(0622) 38198		A 2
	Cobtree Manor Park		(0622) 53276		
Newhaven	Peacehaven	•	(0273) 514049		•
New Romney	Littlestone		(0679) 63355		A 19
Ramsgate	St Augustine's	★	(0843) 821346		A 39
Rochester	Deangate Ridge		(0634) 251180		A 10
	Gillingham		(0634) 51546		A 12
	Rochester & Cobham Park		(047482) 3411		A 24
Rye	Rye	★★	(0797) 225241		B 15
Seaford	Seaford	✩	(0323) 892442		B 16
	Seaford Head	★	(0323) 890137		B 20
Sevenoaks	Knole Park		(0732) 452150		A 15
	Wildernesse		(0732) 61526		A 36
	Woodlands Manor		(09592) 3806		A 37
Sittingbourne	Sheerness	✩	(0795) 662585		A 29
	Sittingbourne & Milton Regis	✩	(0795) 842261		A 30
Tonbridge	Poult Wood		(0732) 364039		A 22
Tunbridge Wells	Ashdown Forest	✩	(034282) 4866		B 13
	Crowborough Beacon	✩	(08926) 61511		B 2
	Lamberhurst		(0892) 890241		A 16
	Nevill		(0892) 25818		B 10
	Royal Ashdown Forest	★★★	(034282) 2010		B 13
	Tunbridge Wells	•	(0892) 23034		•
Uckfield	East Sussex	★★	(082575) 577		B 11
Westgate	Westgate & Birchington		(0843) 31115		A 33
Whitstable	Herne Bay	✩	(0227) 373964		A 13
	Whitstable & Seasalter		(0227) 272020		•

♦ For details, see following pages.

• 9 hole golf course.

West Sussex • Surrey

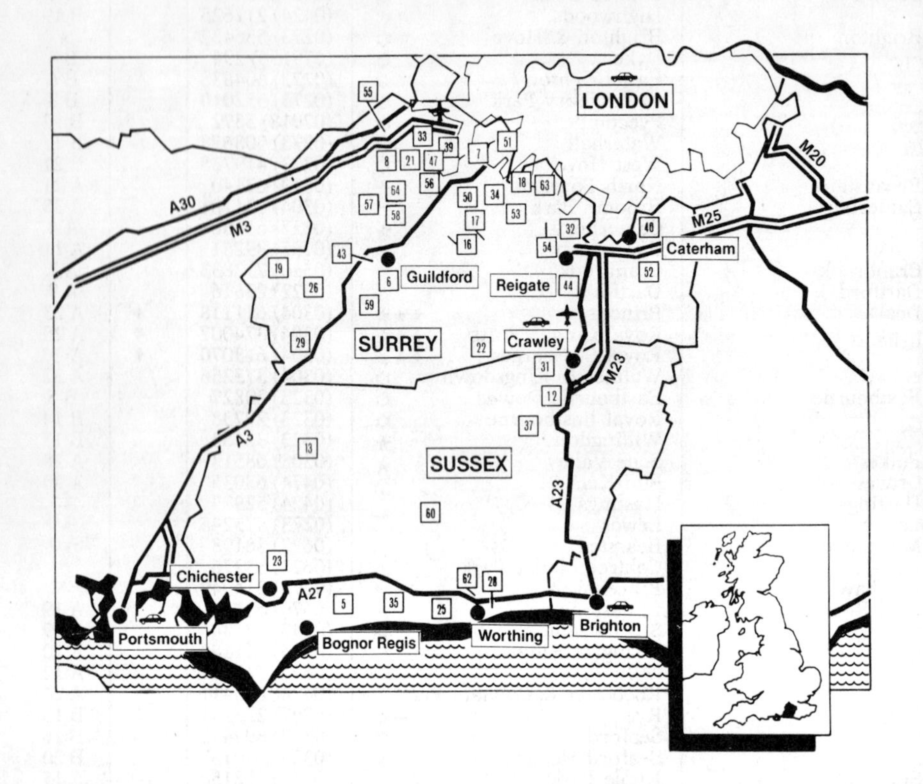

TOWN	GOLF COURSE		TEL	♦	MAP REF.
Banstead	Cuddington		(01) 3930952		15
Bognor Regis	Bognor Regis	★	(0243) 865867		5
	Littlehampton	★★	(09064) 7170		35
Camberley	Camberley Heath	★★	(0276) 23258		8
Chichester	Goodwood	★	(0234) 774964		23
	Selsey	•	(0243) 602203		•
Cobham	St George's Hill		(0932) 42406		47
	Silvermere		(0932) 67275		50
Crawley	Cottesmore	✡	(0293) 28256	♦	12
	Ifield		(0293) 20222		31
	Mannings Heath		(0403) 66217		37
Dorking	Betchworth Park		(0306) 882052		
	Dorking	•	(0306) 889786		•
	Gatton Manor	✡	(030679) 555		22
Epsom	Epsom		(03727) 21666		18
	R.A.C. Country Club		(03722) 76311		63
	Walton Heath	★★★	(073781) 2380	♦	54
Esher	Moore Place	•	(0372) 63533		•
	Surbiton		(01) 3983101		51
Farnham	Farnham		(02518) 2109		19
	Hankley Common		(094825) 2493		26
Gatwick	Gatwick Manor	•	(0293) 24470		•
Godalming	West Surrey		(04868) 21275		59
Guildford	Bramley		(0483) 892696		6
	Drift		(04865) 4641		16
	Effingham		(0372) 52203		17
	Guildford		(0483) 63941		24
Haslemere	Hindhead		(042873) 4614		29
Leatherhead	Tyrrels Wood		(0372) 376025		53
Midhurst	Cowdray Park		(073081) 3599		13
Oxted	Tandridge		(08833) 2273		52
Reigate	Redhill & Reigate		(07372) 40777		44
Storrington	West Sussex	★★★	(07982) 25639		60
Woking	Foxhills		(093287) 2050		21
	Hoebridge		(04862) 22611		
	Wentworth	★★★	(09904) 2201	♦	55
	West Byfleet		(09323) 45230		56
	West Hill		(04867) 2110		57
	Woking		(04862) 60053		64
	Worplesdon		(04867) 2277		58
Worthing	Hill Barn	★	(0903) 37301		28
	Worthing	★	(0903) 60801		62

♦ For details, see following pages.

• 9 hole golf course.

ENGLAND/XVII

Berkshire (Berks) • Hampshire (Hants) • Isle of Wight

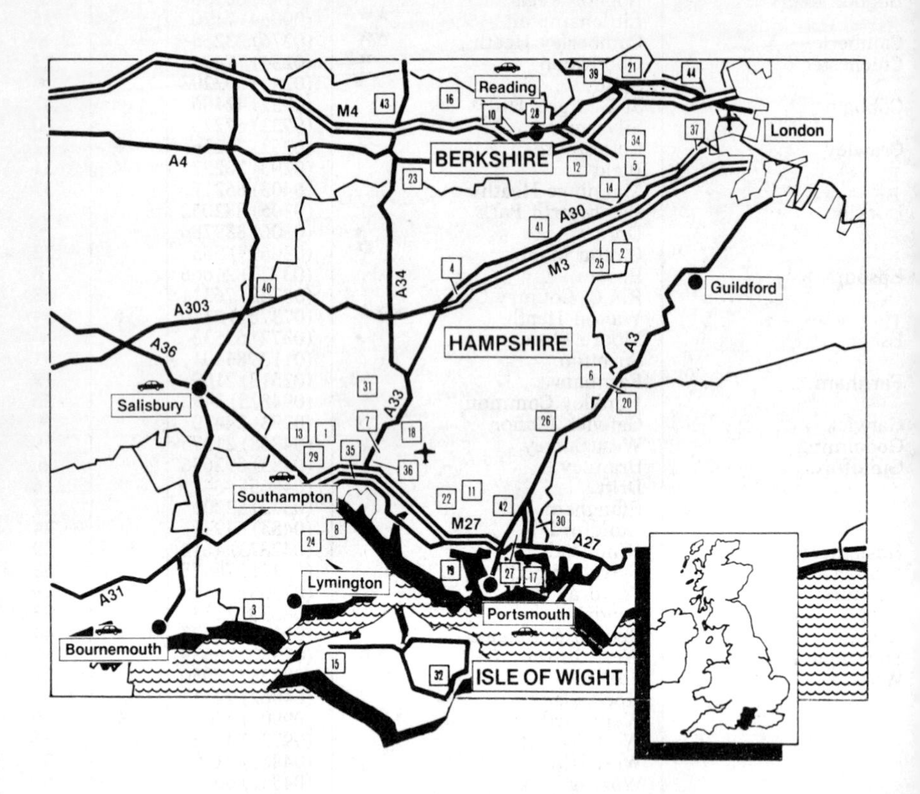

TOWN	GOLF COURSE		TEL	♦	MAP REF.
Alton	Alton		(0420) 82042		•
Amesbury	Tidworth & Garrison		(0980) 42301		40
Andover	Andover		(0264) 3980		•
Ascot/Bracknell	Berkshire	★★★	(0990) 21495	♦	5
	Downshire		(0344) 424066		12
	East Berkshire		(0344) 2041		14
	Royal Ascot		(0990) 25175		34
	Sunningdale	★★★	(0990) 21681	♦	37
	Swinley Forest		(0990) 201975		38
Basingstoke	Basingstoke		(0256) 465990		4
Bishopswood	Tylney Park		(07356) 5213		41
Brokenhurst	Brokenhurst Manor	★	(0590) 23332		9
Droxford	Corhampton		(0489) 877279		11
Fareham	Lee-on-the-Solent		(0705) 551170		19
Farnborough	Army		(0252) 540638		2
	North Hants		(02514) 6443		25
	Southwood	•	(0502) 723234		•
Haslemere	Blackmoor		(04203) 2775		6
	Liphook	★★	(0428) 723271		20
	Old Thorns		(0428) 724555		
Havant	Hayling	★	(07016) 46446		17
	Rowlands Castle		(07054) 2216		30
Lyndhurst	Bramshaw	✡	(0703) 813433		7
	New Forest	✡	(042128) 2450		24
Maidenhead	Maidenhead		(0628) 24693		21
	Temple		(062882) 4248		39
	Winter Hill		(06285) 276139		
New Milton	Barton-on-Sea	✡	(0425) 615308		3
Petersfield	Petersfield		(0730) 63725		26
Portsmouth	Great Salterns		(0705) 664549		
	Portsmouth Municipal		(0705) 372210		27
Reading	Calcot Park		(07357) 27134		10
	Goring & Streatley		(0491) 872688		16
	Reading		(0734) 472909		28
Romsey	Ampfield Par Three		(0794) 68480		1
	Dunwood Manor		(0794) 40549		13
	Romsey		(0703) 734637		29
Slough	Wexham Park		(02816) 3271		44
Sonning	Sonning		(0734) 693332		33
Southampton	Bramshott Hill (Dibden)		(0703) 845596		8
	Fleming Park		(0707) 612797		7
	Meon Valley	✡	(0329) 833455		22
	Southampton		(0703) 760472		35
	Stoneham		(0703) 768151		36
	West Side		(0703) 768407		
Winchester	Hockley		(0692) 713165		18
	Royal Winchester	★	(0962) 52462		31
Isle of Wight					
Cowes	Osborne		(0983) 297758		•
Newport	St-George's Down		(0983) 525076		•
Ryde	Ryde		(0983) 614809		•
Sandown	Shanklin & Sandown	✡	(0983) 403217		32
Yarmouth	Freshwater Bay	✡	(0983) 752955	♦	15

♦ For details, see following pages.

• 9 hole golf course.

Avon • Dorset • Somerset • Wiltshire

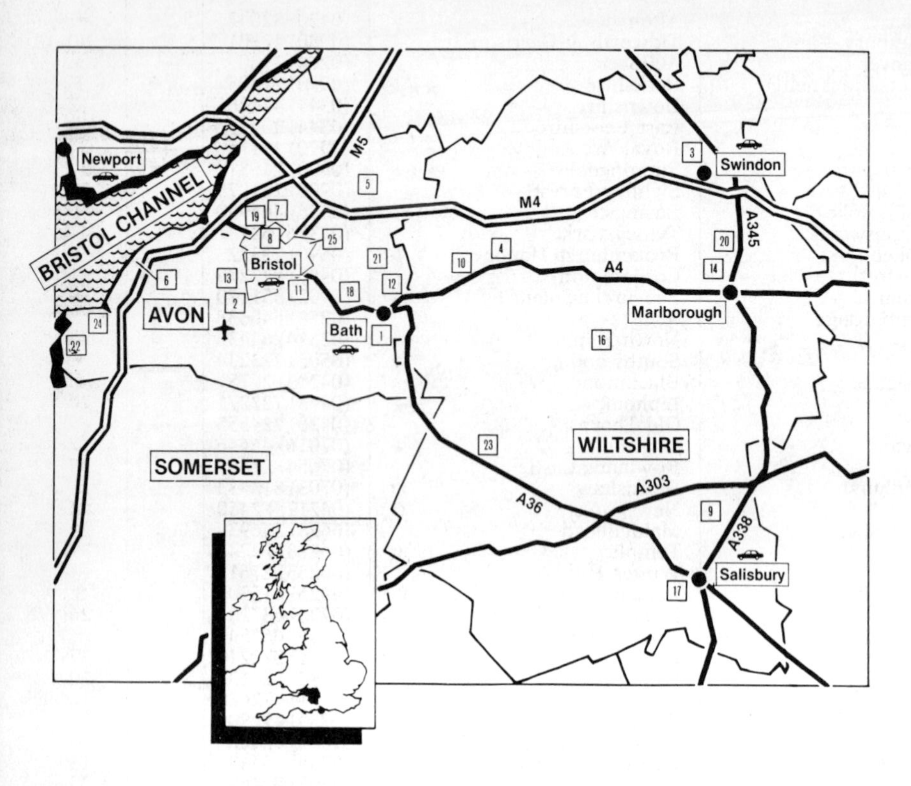

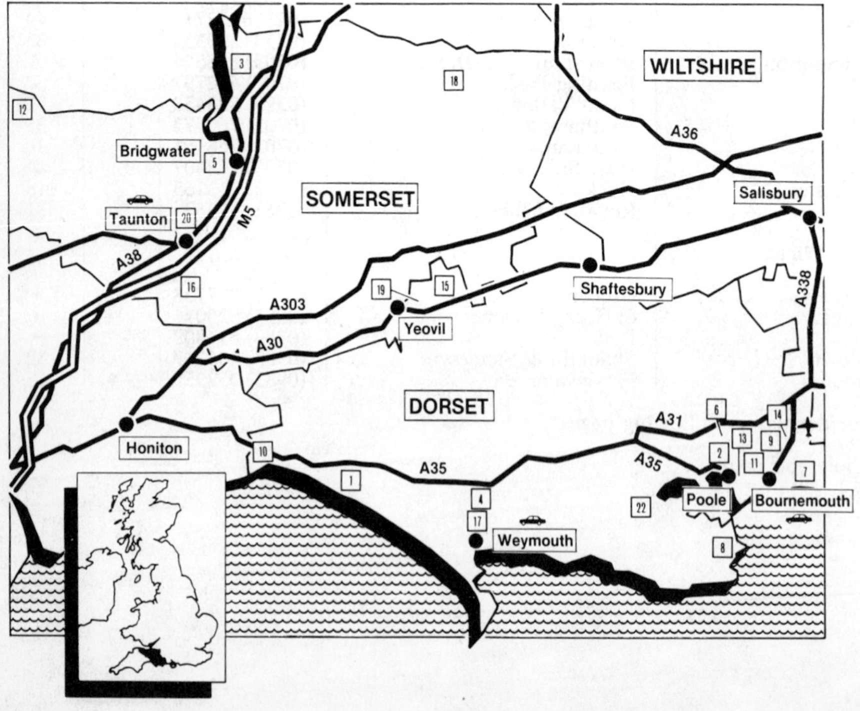

TOWN	GOLF COURSE		TEL	♦	MAP REF.
Bath	Bath		(0225) 63834		A 1
	Fosseway	•	(0761) 412214		•
	Kingsdown		(0225) 742530		A 10
	Lansdown		(0225) 22138		A 12
	Mendip	★	(0749) 840570		B 18
	Saltford		(02217) 3220		A 18
Blandford	Ashley Wood	★★	(0258) 52253	♦	•
Bournemouth	Ferndown		(0202) 874602		B 6
	Isle of Purbeck	✡	(092944) 361		B 8
	Knighton Heath		(0202) 572633		B 9
	Meyrick Park	★	(0202) 290871		B 11
	Parkstone	✡	(0202) 707138		B 13
	Queens Park	★	(0202) 36198		B 14
Bridgwater	Enmore Park		(0278) 67481		B 5
Bridport	Bridport & West Dorset		(0308) 22597		B 1
Burnham-on-Sea	Burnham & Berrow	★★	(0278) 783137	♦	B 3
Bristol	Bristol & Clifton	★	(0272) 393117		A 2
	Chipping Sodbury	★	(0454) 319042		A 5
	Filton		(0272) 694169		A 7
	Henbury		(0272) 500660		A 8
	Knowle		(0272) 776341		A 11
	Long Ashton		(0272) 392229		A 13
	Mangotsfield		(0272) 565501		A 25
	Shirehampton Park		(0272) 822083		A 19
	Tracy Park		(027582) 2251		A 21
Chard	Windwhistle	•	(046030) 231		•
Chippenham	Chippenham		(0249) 652040		A 4
Clevedon	Clevedon		(0272) 874057		A 6
Devizes	North Wilts		(038086) 627		A 16
Dorchester	Came Down		(030581) 2531		B 4
Lyme Regis	Lyme Regis	★★	(02974) 2043		B 10
Marlborough	The Common		(0672) 52147		
Minehead	Minehead & West Somerset	✡	(0643) 2057	♦	B 12
Poole	Broadstone	★	(0202) 693363		B 12
Salisbury	High Post	★	(0722) 73231		A 9
	Salisbury & South Wilts		(0722) 2645		A 17
Sherborne	Sherborne		(0935) 814431		B 15
Swindon	Broome Manor		(0793) 32403		A 3
Taunton	Deane (Vivary Park)		(0823) 73875		B 20
	Taunton & Pickeridge		(082342) 240		B 16
Wareham	Lakey Hill		(0929) 471776		B 22
Warminster	West Wiltshire		(0985) 212110		A 23
Wells	Wells	•	(0749) 72868		•
Weston-super-Mare	Weston-super-Mare	★	(0995) 21360		A 22
	Worlebury		(0934) 23214		A 24
Weymouth	Weymouth	★	(0305) 784994		B 17
Yeovil	Yeovil		(0935) 75949		B 19

♦ For details, see following pages.

• 9 hole golf course.

Channel Islands • Cornwall • Devon

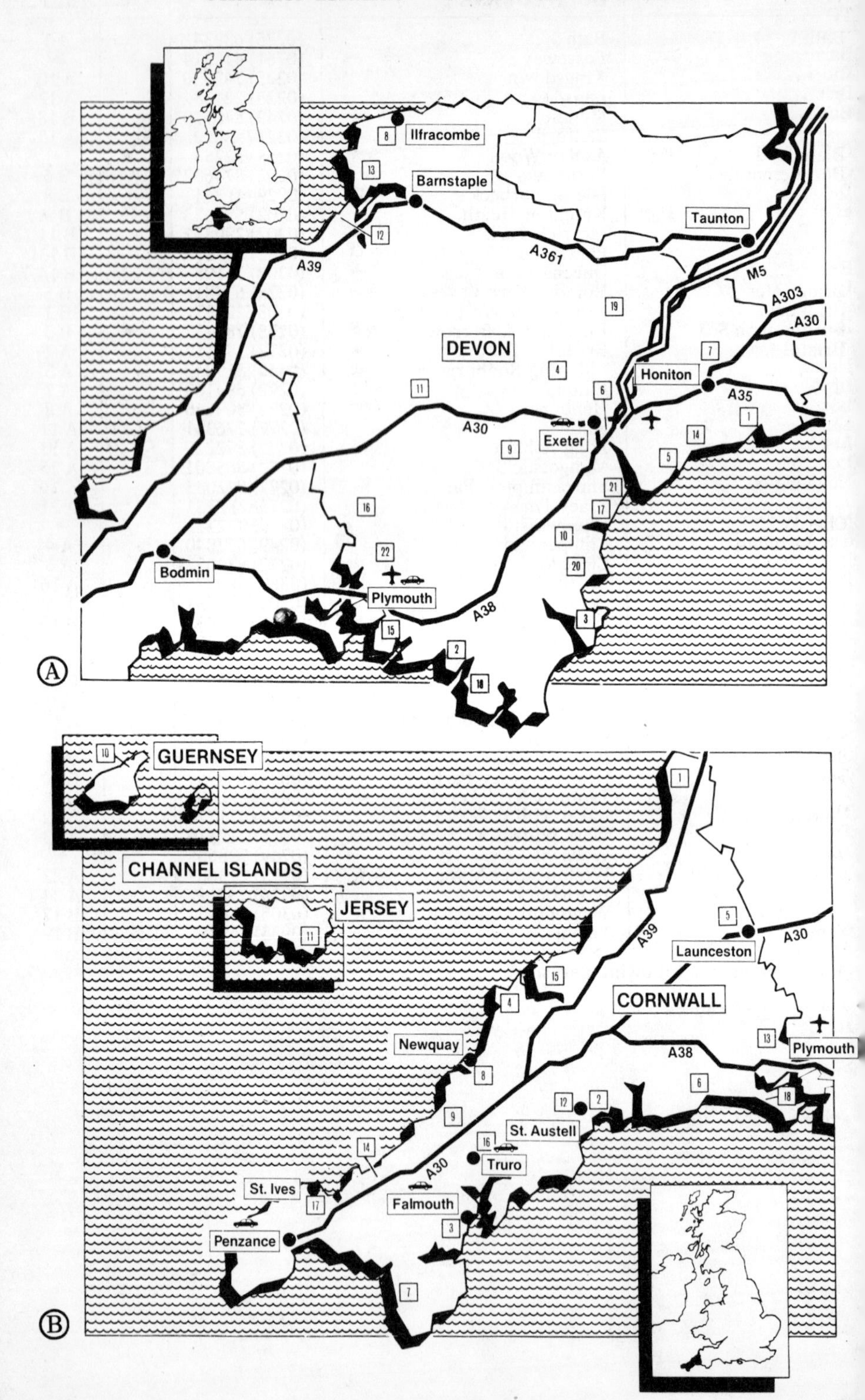

TOWN	GOLF COURSE		TEL	♦	MAP REF.
Barnstaple	Saunton	★★★	(0271) 812436	♦	A 13
Bideford	Royal North Devon	★★	(02372) 73817	♦	A 12
Brixham	Churston	✡	(0803) 842751		A 3
Bude	Bude & North Cornwall	✡	(0288) 2006		B 1
	Holsworthy		(0409) 253177		•
Callington	St. Mellion	✡	(0579) 50101		B 13
Camborne	Tehidy Park		(0209) 842208		B 14
Dawlish	Warren		(0626) 862255		
Exeter	Downes Crediton		(03632) 3991		A 4
	Exeter		(039287) 4139		A 6
	Manor House Hotel	✡	(0647) 40355	♦	A 9
Exmouth	East Devon	✡	(03954) 3370		A 5
Falmouth	Budock Vean	•	(0326) 250288		
	Falmouth	✡	(0326) 311262		AB 3
Helston	Mullion	✡	(0326) 240276		B 7
	Praa Sands	•	(0736) 763445		•
Honiton	Honiton		(0404) 2934		A 7
Ilfracombe	Ilfracombe	✡	(0271) 62176		A 8
Isles of Scilly	Isles of Scilly	•	(0720) 22692		•
Kingsbridge	Bigbury	✡	(054881) 207		A 2
Launceston	Launceston		(0566) 3442		B 5
Looe	Looe Bin Down	★	(05034) 247		B 6
Newquay	Newquay	✡	(06373) 4354		B 8
	Perranporth	✡	(087257) 2454		B 9
Newton Abbot	Newton Abbot		(0626) 2460		A 10
Okehampton	Okehampton		(0837) 2113		A 11
Padstow	Trevose	★★	(0841) 520208	♦	B 4
Plymouth	Elfordleigh	•	(0752) 336428		•
	Staddon Heights		(0752) 42475		A 15
	Whitsand Bay Hotel	✡	(0503) 30276	♦	B 18
	Wrangaton	•	(03647) 3229		•
	Yelverton		(0822) 852824		A 22
St. Austell	Carlyon Bay	✡	(072681) 4250		B 2
	St. Austell	✡	(0726) 72649		B 12
St. Ives	West Cornwall	✡	(0736) 753401		B 17
Seaton	Axe Cliff	✡	(0297) 20499		A 1
Sidmouth	Sidmouth		(0395) 3451		A 14
Tavistock	Tavistock		(0822) 2049		A 16
Teignmouth	Teignmouth		(06267) 4194		A 17
Thurlestone	Thurlestone	✡	(0548) 560405		A 18
Tiverton	Tiverton		(0884) 252187		A 19
Torquay	Torquay	✡	(0803) 37471		A 20
Truro	Truro	✡	(0872) 72640		B 6
Wadebridge	St. Enodoc	★	(020886) 3216		B 15
Channel Islands :					
Alderney					
St. Annes	Alderney	•	(048182) 2835		•
Guernsey					
Vale	Royal Guernsey	★	(0481) 46523		B 10
Jersey					
St. Clements	St. Clements	•	(0534) 21938		•
St. Helier	La Moye	★★ ✡	(0584) 43401	♦	B 4
	Royal Jersey	★★★	(0534) 54416	♦	B 11

♦ For details, see following pages.

• 9 hole golf course.

AVON (WELCOMBE)

★

TEL : (0789)295252
LOCATION : 3 km Stratford-upon-Avon A 46
ADDRESS : Warwick Rd – Stratford-upon-Avon – Warwicks
HOTEL : HR
Welcombe Hotel
Tel : (0789)295252
Ettington Park – Stratford
Tel : (0789)740740
Shakespeare – Stratford
Tel : (0789)294771

Set on mature undulating parkland in the grounds of the magnificent Welcombe Hotel, and overlooking the picturesque river Avon and the Cotswolds, this is a course with an attractive layout. It features five testing short holes and a scenic lake guarding the 10th and 18th holes. The luxury hotel, a Jacobean-style mansion built in 1869 and former home of the historian Trevelyan, stands in the middle of the course. *SSS 70*

GF $ | Wednesdays | S

1980 | — |

18 | L 6202 y P 70 | R

Required : Handicap Certificate
Best days : Mondays and Tuesdays; any day for hotel residents

HOLE	LENGTH MEDAL-TEE	PAR	STROKE INDEX
1	400	4	5
2	490	5	13
3	477	5	8
4	162	3	17
5	447	4	1
6	390	4	6
7	308	4	7
8	181	3	18
9	362	4	4
TOTAL	3217	36	TOTAL

HOLE	LENGTH MEDAL-TEE	PAR	STROKE INDEX
10	392	4	12
11	186	3	9
12	362	4	11
13	201	3	2
14	358	4	15
15	390	4	10
16	173	3	16
17	402	4	14
18	521	5	3
TOTAL	2985	34	TOTAL

BELFRY

★★

TEL : (0675)70301
LOCATION : 9 m Birmingham off A 446
ADDRESS : Lichfield Rd – Wishaw – Sutton Coldfield – W. Midlands
HOTEL : HR
Belfry
Tel : (0675)70301
Moxhull Hall – Sutton Coldfield
Tel : (021)3292056
Sutton Court – Sutton Coldfield
Tel : (021)3556071

The Belfry is one of England's leading and most picturesque country hotels, peacefully situated in the middle of a lush parkland landscape. Since 1977, it has had its own golf courses, the scenic Brabazon course and the excellent Derby course, laid out in the grounds of the hotel, amidst lakes and streams affectig play on several holes. Both courses are of championship standard and very popular with golfers.

GF $$
1977
36
—
D. Thomas, P. Allis
L 6975 y P 73, 5953 y P 70
R S

Required : Handicap Certificate
Best days : Any day

HOLE	LENGTH MEDAL-TEE	PAR	STROKE INDEX
1	408	4	15
2	340	4	17
3	455	4	7
4	569	5	3
5	389	4	11
6	386	4	1
7	173	3	9
8	476	5	13
9	390	4	5
TOTAL	3586	37	TOTAL

HOLE	LENGTH MEDAL-TEE	PAR	STROKE INDEX
10	301	4	8
11	365	4	18
12	225	3	2
13	364	4	12
14	184	3	16
15	540	5	4
16	400	4	10
17	555	5	14
18	455	4	6
TOTAL	3389	36	TOTAL

BERKSHIRE

TEL : (0990)21495
LOCATION : 5 km SW. Ascot A 332
ADDRESS : Swinley Rd – Ascot – Berks
HOTEL :
Berystede – Ascot
Tel : (0990)23311
Royal Berkshire – Ascot
Tel : (0990)23322
Royal Foresters – Ascot
Tel : (0344)884747

The Berkshire with its thirty-six outstanding holes, is one of the world's best inland golf courses. Both courses run through undulating heathland and are landscaped amongst pine, chestnut and silver birch woods. Several ditches serve as hazards. The courses command fine views of the surrounding Ascot countryside. The actual championship course is made out of holes from both courses. There is a spacious well-appointed clubhouse. *SSS 70*

GF $$

Weekends

R S

1928

H. Fowler

36

L 6356 y P 72, 6258 y P 71

Required : Handicap Certificate
Best days : Weekdays by prior arrangement only

Red Course

HOLE	LENGTH MEDAL-TEE	PAR	STROKE INDEX
1	518	5	5
2	146	3	18
3	481	5	13
4	394	4	1
5	182	3	9
6	353	4	14
7	201	3	7
8	427	4	3
9	477	5	11
TOTAL	3179	36	TOTAL

HOLE	LENGTH MEDAL-TEE	PAR	STROKE INDEX
10	187	3	12
11	338	4	4
12	328	4	15
13	484	5	10
14	436	4	2
15	477	5	16
16	221	3	6
17	529	5	8
18	177	3	17
TOTAL	3177	36	TOTAL

Blue Course

HOLE	LENGTH MEDAL-TEE	PAR	STROKE INDEX
1	217	3	8
2	340	4	12
3	477	5	3
4	152	3	17
5	316	4	10
6	481	5	5
7	363	4	13
8	405	4	1
9	310	4	15
TOTAL	3061	36	TOTAL

HOLE	LENGTH MEDAL-TEE	PAR	STROKE INDEX
10	200	3	9
11	478	5	11
12	360	4	4
13	159	3	18
14	365	4	6
15	406	4	14
16	452	4	2
17	375	4	16
18	402	4	7
TOTAL	3197	35	TOTAL

BURNHAM & BERROW

★★

TEL : (0278)785760
LOCATION : 2 km N. Burnham-on-Sea, Jct 22/M 5
ADDRESS : Burnham-on-Sea – Somerset
HOTEL :
Cloisters – Burnham-on-Sea
Tel : (0278)782946
Grange – Burnham-on-Sea
Tel : (0278)784214
RESTAURANT : Batch Farm Country – Lympsham
Tel : (0934)750371

This is a classical links courses and one of the oldest in England. It is laid out on the Somerset coast, overlooking the Bristol Channel with the coastline of Wales in the dim distance. Its holes run through enormous sand hills which are full of natural hazards. The nine hole course was desiged by Fred Hawtree. Adjacent to the clubhouse is a Dormy House with four bedrooms. *SSS 73*

GF $$

1890

27

—

J. Taylor, F. Hawtree

L 6547 y P 71, 6550 y P 72

S

R

Required : Handicap Certificate
Best days : Any day by prior arrangement only

HOLE	LENGTH MEDAL-TEE	PAR	STROKE INDEX
1	381	4	9
2	396	4	3
3	384	4	13
4	480	5	7
5	160	3	15
6	397	4	1
7	450	4	5
8	483	5	16
9	163	3	17
TOTAL	3294	36	TOTAL

HOLE	LENGTH MEDAL-TEE	PAR	STROKE INDEX
10	370	4	12
11	422	4	2
12	388	4	6
13	475	5	14
14	181	3	11
15	438	4	4
16	329	4	18
17	201	3	10
18	449	4	8
TOTAL	3253	35	TOTAL

CASTLETOWN

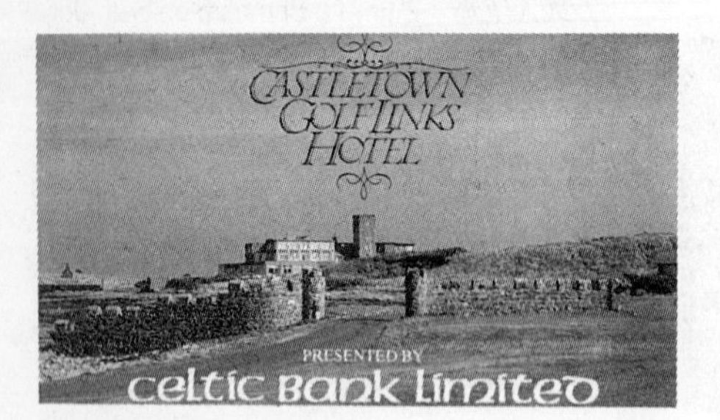

TEL : (0624)822201
LOCATION : 3,5 km E. Castletown
ADDRESS : Fort Island – Castletown – Isle of Man
HOTEL : HR
Castletown Golf Links
Tel : (0624)822201
Grand Island – Ramsey
Tel : (0624)812455
Mannin – Douglas
Tel : (0624)75480

The Castletown golf club lies in the southern part of the Isle of Man. It is a typical links which is bordered by the sea on three sides. It features seveal fine holes such as the 18th laid out on a promontory with panoramic views of the coast. The Castletown Golf Links Hotel adjoins the course.

GF $

—

18

—

M. MacKenzie Ross

L 6567 y P 72

S

R

Required : None
Best days : Any day

HOLE	LENGTH MEDAL-TEE	PAR	STROKE INDEX
1	251	4	18
2	390	4	3
3	516	5	11
4	367	4	5
5	486	5	13
6	135	3	17
7	350	4	7
8	410	4	1
9	368	4	9
TOTAL	3273	37	TOTAL

HOLE	LENGTH MEDAL-TEE	PAR	STROKE INDEX
10	550	5	4
11	173	3	15
12	366	4	10
13	345	4	14
14	468	4	2
15	375	4	6
16	193	3	16
17	414	4	8
18	410	4	12
TOTAL	3294	35	TOTAL

COTTESMORE

★

TEL : (0293)28256
LOCATION : 3 m S. Crawley M 23
ADDRESS : Pease Pottage – Crawley – W. Sussex
HOTEL : HR
Country Club Cottesmore
Tel : (0293)28256
Copthorne – Copthorne
Tel : (0342)714971
George – Crawley
Tel : (0293)24215

The Cottesmore golf courses are picturesquely set on undulating landscape with woodlands and scenic lakes. The fairways are lined with silver birch, pine, oak and colourful rhododendrons. The clubhouse is an attractive French style farmhouse with fifteen bedrooms and three squash courts.

GF $ — S

1974 M.D. Rogerson

36 L 6097 y P 71, 5321 y P 68 R

Required : Handicap Certificate
Best days : Any day

HOLE	LENGTH MEDAL-TEE	PAR	STROKE INDEX
1	493	5	8
2	135	3	18
3	380	4	6
4	172	3	16
5	450	4	2
6	310	4	12
7	417	4	4
8	192	3	14
9	304	4	10
TOTAL	2853	34	TOTAL

HOLE	LENGTH MEDAL-TEE	PAR	STROKE INDEX
10	280	4	17
11	332	4	7
12	227	3	13
13	390	4	3
14	476	5	11
15	576	5	1
16	312	4	5
17	176	3	15
18	476	5	9
TOTAL	3245	37	TOTAL

FERNDOWN

★★

TEL : (0202)874602
LOCATION : 6 m N. Bournemouth
ADDRESS : Golf Links Road - Wimborne - Dorset
HOTEL : HP
Dormy - Ferndown
Tel : (0202)872121
Bridge House - Longham
Tel : (0202)578828
Coach House - Ferndown
Tel : (0202)861222

The Ferndown golf course is built on sandy subsoil with its 18 holes running through pine woods and heather. The 9 hole course was designed by Hamilton Stutt. The Dormy Hotel, adjoining the golf club, is one of England's most celebrated golf hotels. It is set within lush gardens featuring, a scenic lily pond, a water fall, a swimming pool and several tennis and squash courts. *SSS 71*

GF $$

1926

27

—

H. Hilton, H. Stutt

L 6442 y P 71, 2797 y P 35

R S

Required : Handicap Certificate
Best days : Any day by prior arrangement only

HOLE	LENGTH MEDAL-TEE	PAR	STROKE INDEX
1	396	4	13
2	175	3	17
3	398	4	3
4	395	4	11
5	206	3	9
6	409	4	1
7	480	5	7
8	304	4	15
9	427	4	5
TOTAL	3190	35	TOTAL

HOLE	LENGTH MEDAL-TEE	PAR	STROKE INDEX
10	485	5	10
11	438	4	2
12	186	3	12
13	488	5	6
14	152	3	18
15	398	4	4
16	305	4	16
17	397	4	8
18	403	4	14
TOTAL	3252	36	TOTAL

FINCHLEY

★

TEL : (01)3462436
LOCATION : 8 m N.W. Charing Cross
ADDRESS : Nether Court – Frith Lane – London N.W.7
HOTEL :
Travel Lodge – Mill Hill
Tel : (01)9060611
Hendon Hall – Hendon
Tel : (01)2033341
Scratchwood Travelodge
Tel : (01)9060611
RESTAURANT : Good Earth – Mill Hill
Tel : (01)9597011

Designed by the celebrated James Braid, Finchley is one of the golf clubs nearest to London. It is laid out on mature and gently rolling parkland with its fairways landscaped with tall trees. It features several tight holes demanding accuracy from tee to green. The club boasts an imposing clubhouse standing in the middle of the course.

GF $ | Weekends | S
1929 | J. Braid
18 | L 6411 y P 72 | R

Required : None
Best days : Weekdays

HOLE	LENGTH MEDAL-TEE	PAR	STROKE INDEX
1	300	4	15
2	390	4	7
3	167	3	17
4	395	4	3
5	427	4	9
6	415	4	1
7	215	3	11
8	526	5	5
9	481	5	13
TOTAL	3316	36	TOTAL

HOLE	LENGTH MEDAL-TEE	PAR	STROKE INDEX
10	262	4	16
11	300	4	14
12	160	3	10
13	490	5	6
14	399	4	2
15	124	3	18
16	448	4	4
17	484	5	12
18	428	4	8
TOTAL	3095	36	TOTAL

FORMBY

★★★

TEL : (07048)72164
LOCATION : 10 m N. Liverpool/18 m S. Southport
ADDRESS : Golf Rd – Formby – Liverpool – Merseyside
HOTEL :
Grapes – Formby
Tel : (07048)70818
Prince of Wales – Southport
Tel : (0704)36688
Talbot – Southport
Tel : (0704)33975
RESTAURANT : Don Luigi – Formby
Tel : (07048)79424

Laid out on the Merseyside coast between the sea and a railway line, Formby is considered one of the greatest links courses in the world. The course runs through sand hills and tall pine trees with strategically placed bunkers and challenging drives. The club hosted the World Amateur Championships in 1957, 1967 and in 1984. There is an imposing clubhouse with a dormy house accomodation for men only. Formby is one of those golf courses owning a special but separate "Ladies" course with its proper clubhouse. *SSS 73*

GF $$  Weekends  

1884  W. Park, H. Colt 

18 L 6781 y P 72 

Required : Introduction Letter
Best days : Weekdays

HOLE	LENGTH MEDAL-TEE	PAR	STROKE INDEX
1	415	4	11
2	381	4	9
3	518	5	3
4	312	4	15
5	162	3	17
6	402	4	7
7	377	4	13
8	493	5	1
9	450	4	5
TOTAL	3510	37	TOTAL

HOLE	LENGTH MEDAL-TEE	PAR	STROKE INDEX
10	214	3	16
11	384	4	12
12	405	4	4
13	434	4	6
14	420	4	10
15	403	4	2
16	127	3	18
17	494	5	8
18	390	4	14
TOTAL	3271	35	TOTAL

FRESHWATER BAY

TEL : (0983)752955
LOCATION : 2,5 m Yarmouth
ADDRESS : Afton Down – Freshwater Bay – Isle of Wight
HOTEL :
Albion – Freshwater Bay
Tel : (0983)753631
Bugle – Newport
Tel : (0983)522800
Farringford – Freshwater Bay
Tel : (0983)752500
RESTAURANT : Sentry Mead – Totland
Tel : (0983)753212

Freshwater Bay is an attractive seaside golf course scenically situated on the Isle of Wight. Ideal for holiday golf, the course is laid out on high cliffs commanding panoramic views of the bay and the rugged countryside. Its 18 holes run through undulating and open terrain.

 $  —  

 — 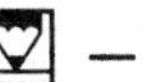 — 

18 L 5662 y P 68

Required : Handicap Certificate
Best days : Weekdays by prior arrangement

HOLE	LENGTH MEDAL-TEE	PAR	STROKE INDEX
1	136	3	17
2	394	4	3
3	157	3	15
4	322	4	9
5	180	3	13
6	397	4	1
7	421	4	7
8	437	4	5
9	341	4	11
TOTAL	2785	33	TOTAL

HOLE	LENGTH MEDAL-TEE	PAR	STROKE INDEX
10	322	4	12
11	492	5	6
12	512	5	2
13	323	4	10
14	184	3	18
15	188	3	14
16	275	4	8
17	151	3	16
18	430	4	4
TOTAL	2877	35	TOTAL

GANTON

★★

TEL : (09444)70329
LOCATION : 16 km W. Scarborough A 64
ADDRESS : Ganton – Scarborough – N Yorks
HOTEL :
St-Nicholas – Scarborough
Tel : (0723)364101
Red Lea – Scarborough
Tel : (0723)362431
Royal – Scarborough
Tel : (0723)364333
RESTAURANT : Lanterna – Scarborough
Tel : (0723)363616

Ganton, an inland course with a seaside character, is one of England's celebrated golf clubs and the home course of Harry Vardon, one of the world's most famous golfers. It is set on mostly flat open heathland with ditches on four holes, and a lake guarding the 5th and 6th holes. The bunkers are of excellent quality and protect many of the fairways. The club has hosted a great number of championships, such as the Dunlop Masters, the Ryder Cup and various National and European championships. *SSS 73*

GF $$ | — | S
1891 | H. Colt |
18 | L 6720 y P 72 | R

Required : Handicap Certificate
Best days : Weekdays by prior arrangement

HOLE	LENGTH MEDAL-TEE	PAR	STROKE INDEX
1	373	4	15
2	418	4	7
3	334	4	13
4	406	4	5
5	157	3	17
6	449	4	1
7	431	4	9
8	392	4	11
9	494	5	3
TOTAL	3454	36	TOTAL

HOLE	LENGTH MEDAL-TEE	PAR	STROKE INDEX
10	168	3	18
11	417	4	6
12	363	4	10
13	499	5	2
14	282	4	14
15	437	4	4
16	448	4	8
17	252	4	16
18	400	4	12
TOTAL	3266	36	TOTAL

GOG MAGOG

★

TEL : (0223)247626
LOCATION : 2 m S. Cambridge A 1307
ADDRESS : Babraham Rd – Cambridge – Cambs CB 24 AB
HOTEL :
Cambridgeshire Moat House – Cambridge
Tel : (0954)80555
Arundel House – Cambridge
Tel : (0223)67701
Post House – Cambridge
Tel : (022023)7000
RESTAURANT : Cunard – Barr Hill
Tel : (0954)80555

Gog Magog is a fine championship course near Cambridge. The course is laid out on undulating and mostly open Cambridgeshire countryside with strategically placed trees serving as hazards on several holes. The short 9 hole course was designed by Fred Hawtree.
SSS 70

GF $$ — R S

1901 J. Braid, F. Hawtree 

27 L 6354 y P 70, 2935 y P 34

Required : Handicap Certificate
Best days : Weekdays

HOLE	LENGTH MEDAL-TEE	PAR	STROKE INDEX	HOLE	LENGTH MEDAL-TEE	PAR	STROKE INDEX	HOLE	LENGTH MEDAL-TEE	PAR	STROKE INDEX
1	391	4	6	10	396	4	3	1	369	4	6
2	367	4	8	11	377	4	11	2	355	4	12
3	382	4	4	12	416	4	7	3	318	4	16
4	181	3	10	13	205	3	15	4	151	3	18
5	343	4	16	14	506	5	2	5	383	4	2
6	194	3	14	15	386	4	13	6	181	3	8
7	529	5	1	16	446	4	5	7	321	4	14
8	491	5	12	17	162	3	17	8	376	4	4
9	140	3	18	18	443	4	9	9	471	5	10
TOTAL	3017	35	TOTAL	TOTAL	3337	35	TOTAL	TOTAL	2925	35	TOTAL

HAWKSTONE PARK HOTEL

★★

TEL : (093924)611
LOCATION : 14 m N. Shrewsbury A 49
ADDRESS : Weston-under-Redcastle – Shrewsbury – Shropshire
HOTEL : HP
Hawkstone Park
Tel : (093924)611
Albrighton Hall – Albrighton
Tel : (0939)291000
Prince Rupert – Shrewsbury
Tel : (0743)236000

Two beautiful inland courses laid out amongst wooded, undulating parkland with each hole having its own distinct character. Several holes are set alongside Hawk lake. The Weston Course is the newer one, laid out on more open Shropshire countryside. It is the home base for Sandy Lyle, one of the world's top golfers, and for Ian Woosnam being its touring pro. The scenic Hawkstone Park Hotel, a castle dating back to the 13th century, has fifty bedrooms, grass tennis courts, a croquet lawn and a swimming pool. *SSS 70/65*

 $

 1930

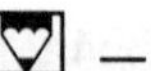 —

—

6465 y P 72, 5368 y P 66

Required : Handicap Certificate
Best days : Any day

Hawkstone Course

HOLE	LENGTH MEDAL-TEE	PAR	STROKE INDEX
1	322	4	11
2	367	4	7
3	362	4	13
4	436	4	1
5	481	5	5
6	188	3	15
7	525	5	9
8	441	4	3
9	147	3	17
TOTAL	3269	36	TOTAL

HOLE	LENGTH MEDAL-TEE	PAR	STROKE INDEX
10	373	4	10
11	476	5/4	4
12	317	4	14
13	255	4	18
14	386	4	8
15	398	4	2
16	217	3	16
17	364	4	12
18	410	4	6
TOTAL	3196	36/35	TOTAL

Weston Course

HOLE	LENGTH MEDAL-TEE	PAR	STROKE INDEX
1	266	4	12
2	141	3	16
3	474	4	2
4	372	4	9
5	150	3	14
6	412	4	6
7	395	4	8
8	123	3	18
9	432	4	1
TOTAL	2765	33	TOTAL

HOLE	LENGTH MEDAL-TEE	PAR	STROKE INDEX
10	254	4	13
11	434	4	4
12	400	4	7
13	407	4	5
14	323	4	10
15	132	3	17
16	219	3	3
17	138	3	15
18	302	4	11
TOTAL	2603	33	TOTAL

HUNSTANTON

★★

TEL : (04853)2811
LOCATION : 1 km Hunstanton A 149
ADDRESS : Hunstanton – Norfolk
HOTEL :
Strange Arms – Hunstanton
Tel : (04853)34411
Holly Lodge – Heacham
Tel : (0485)70790
Lodge – Hunstanton
Tel : (04583)2896
RESTAURANT : Holly Lodge – Hunstanton
Tel : (0485)70790

Hunstanton is one of the fine championship courses in the Norfolk area and the venue of most of the National Mens and Ladies Amateurs championships. The course borders the windy northern Norfolk coast on one side, and the river Hun on the other side. The holes run over an undulating dune landscape with sandy hills serving as hazards. The 16th hole is considered one of the best short holes in England. *SSS 72*

 GF $$

 –

 S

1891

 J. Braid, J. Sherlock

18

L 6670 y P 72

Required : Handicap Certificate
Best days : Weekdays

HOLE	LENGTH MEDAL-TEE	PAR	STROKE INDEX
1	343	4	15
2	532	5	7
3	443	4	1
4	165	3	17
5	424	4	5
6	332	4	9
7	162	3	13
8	483	5	11
9	508	5	3
TOTAL	3392	37	TOTAL

HOLE	LENGTH MEDAL-TEE	PAR	STROKE INDEX
10	372	4	14
11	439	4	4
12	356	4	12
13	387	4	6
14	216	3	18
15	476	5	2
16	188	3	10
17	446	4	8
18	398	4	16
TOTAL	3278	35	TOTAL

LA MOYE

TEL : (0534)43401
LOCATION : 6 m St-Helier
ADDRESS : La Moye – Jersey – Channel Islands
HOTEL :
Beaufort – St-Helier
Tel : (0534)32471
De la Plage – St Helier
Tel : (0534)23474
Little Grove – St Helier
Tel : (0534)25321
RESTAURANT : Victoria's – St-Helier
Tel : (0534)72255

La Moye lies on the picturesque island of Jersey. It is a fine seaside course of championship standard, laid out on flat ground and commanding fine views of the surroundings. There are no water hazards. The course is an enjoyable experience for any holiday golfer and therefore can be very crowded in summer time. *SSS 71*

GF $$

1902

18

—

G. Boomer

L 6512 y P 72

S

Required : Handicap Certificate
Best days : Any day by prior arrangement

HOLE	LENGTH MEDAL-TEE	PAR	STROKE INDEX
1	136	3	17
2	513	5	7
3	177	3	15
4	431	4	1
5	437	4	3
6	477	5	11
7	372	4	9
8	404	4	13
9	399	4	5
TOTAL	3346	36	TOTAL

HOLE	LENGTH MEDAL-TEE	PAR	STROKE INDEX
10	358	4	14
11	494	5	2
12	132	3	18
13	387	4	6
14	183	3	16
15	333	4	12
16	477	5	8
17	412	4	4
18	390	4	10
TOTAL	3166	36	TOTAL

LITTLE ASTON

TEL : (021)3532066
LOCATION : 4 m Sutton Coldfield, off A 452
ADDRESS : Streetly – Sutton Coldfield – W. Midlands
HOTEL :
Sutton Court – Sutton Coldfield
Tel : (021)3556071
Moxhull Hall – Sutton Coldfield
Tel : (021)3292056
New Hall – Sutton Coldfield
Tel : (021)3782442
RESTAURANT : La Gondola – Sutton Coldfield
Tel : (021)3086782

Little Aston was designed by Harry Vardon and altered by Harry Colt and Charles Lawrie. It is now one of England's finest inland courses laid out on a subsoil of sand and gravel in Little Aston Park. The course runs over lush and mature parkland and woodland with lakes guarding the 12th and 17th holes. The club has hosted the Dunlop Masters on several occasions. *SSS 73*

GF $$ — Weekends — R S
1908 — H. Vardon, H. Colt, C. Lawrie
18 — L 6427 y P 72

Required : Handicap Certificate
Best days : Weekdays by prior arrangement

HOLE	LENGTH MEDAL-TEE	PAR	STROKE INDEX
1	390	4	13
2	437	4	5
3	505	5	7
4	316	4	1
5	160	3	1
6	426	4	9
7	374	4	4
8	394	4	11
9	197	3	18
TOTAL	3199	35	TOTAL

HOLE	LENGTH MEDAL-TEE	PAR	STROKE INDEX
10	438	4	3
11	398	4	10
12	491	5	6
13	164	3	17
14	313	4	16
15	566	5	2
16	402	4	8
17	364	4	14
18	389	4	12
TOTAL	3525	37	TOTAL

MOOR ALLERTON

★★

TEL : (0532)661154
LOCATION : 5,5 m N. Leeds off A 61
ADDRESS : Coal Rd – Wike – Leeds – W. Yorks
HOTEL :
Stakis Windmill – Seacroft
Tel : (0532)732323
Ladbroke – Leeds
Tel : (0532)866556
Merrion – Leeds
Tel : (0532)439191
RESTAURANT : Low Hall – Horsforth
Tel : (0532)58822

This is a leading championship course, with three separate loops of nine holes, set in undulating Yorkshire countryside with streams and lakes serving as hazards. Each hole is in its own picturesque setting and many of the greens are elevated in typical Trent Jones style, making them fast. The club has a spacious clubhouse adjacent to the 9th, 18th and 27th greens. Sports facilities include seven tennis courts and a full sized bowling green. *SSS 70/71/70*

GF $$

1923

27

Sundays

R. Trent Jones

L 3122 y P 36, 2908 y P 35, 3280 y P 36

S

R

Required : Handicap Certificate
Best days : Weekdays

HOLE	LENGTH MEDAL-TEE	PAR	STROKE INDEX	HOLE	LENGTH MEDAL-TEE	PAR	STROKE INDEX	HOLE	LENGTH MEDAL-TEE	PAR	STROKE INDEX
1	424	4	4	1	426	4	4	1	422	4	4
2	381	4	2	2	327	4	9	2	148	3	9
3	322	4	7	3	362	4	2	3	489	5	2
4	128	3	9	4	143	3	6	4	397	4	6
5	478	5	1	5	475	5	1	5	381	4	1
6	280	4	8	6	316	3	7	6	174	3	8
7	170	3	6	7	372	4	8	7	354	4	5
8	550	5	5	8	140	4	5	8	357	4	7
9	389	4	3	9	345	4	3	9	558	5	3
TOTAL	3122	36	TOTAL	TOTAL	2908	35	TOTAL	TOTAL	3280	36	TOTAL

MOORTOWN

★★

TEL : (0532)686521
LOCATION : 5 m N. Leeds A 61
ADDRESS : Harrogate Rd – Alwoodley – Leeds – W. Yorks
HOTEL :
Merrion – Leeds
Tel : (0532)439191
Ladbroke Dragonara – Leeds
Tel : (0532)442000
Queens – Leeds
Tel : (0532)431323
RESTAURANT : Emmott Arms – Rawdon
Tel : (0532)502079

A testing moorland course laid out in Yorkshire landscape amidst tall birch woods. The course is of championship standard and hosted the first Ryder Cup match played in England in 1929. A lot of accuracy is needed here as most of the fairways have punishing rough, and are flanked by scrub and heather. Most of the greens are guarded by tricky sand traps. Moortown has hosted almost every major amateur tournament since its creation in 1909. *SSS 74*

GF $$ — Weekends — RP S
1909 — A. MacKenzie
18 — L 7020 y P 71

Required : None
Best days : Weekdays

HOLE	LENGTH MEDAL-TEE	PAR	STROKE INDEX
1	490	5	11
2	456	4	9
3	446	4	3
4	174	3	17
5	388	4	13
6	446	4	1
7	516	5	7
8	220	3	15
9	470	4	5
TOTAL	3606	36	TOTAL

HOLE	LENGTH MEDAL-TEE	PAR	STROKE INDEX
10	176	3	8
11	367	4	10
12	554	5	2
13	439	4	8
14	437	4	4
15	397	4	14
16	417	4	6
17	191	3	16
18	436	4	12
TOTAL	3414	35	TOTAL

PRINCE'S

★★★

TEL : (0304)611118/612000
LOCATION : 5 km Sandwich A 257
ADDRESS : Prince's Drive – Sandwich-Kent
HOTEL : HF
Dormy House
Tel : (0304)611147
Bell – Sandwich
Tel : (0304)613388
Fleur de lis – Sandwich
Tel : (0304)611131

Founded in 1904, the course was redesigned in 1945 by J. Morrison and Sir Guy Campbell. Prince's is a memorable and challenging links laid out on flat landscape alongside Sandwich Bay. There are three loops of nine holes, named Dunes, Shore and Himalaya. Each of them is characterized by long and generous fairways, sometimes covered by huge dunes. The heavily bunkered greens are fast and undulating. There is a comfortable clubhouse with dormy house accomodation for 18 persons. Prince's is building its own hotel due to open soon.

GF $$

1904

27

—

J. Morrison, G. Campbell

L 3347 P y P 36, 3343 y P 36, 3163 y P 35

R S

Required : Handicap Certificate
Best days : Any day

HOLE	LENGTH MEDAL-TEE	PAR	STROKE INDEX	HOLE	LENGTH MEDAL-TEE	PAR	STROKE INDEX	HOLE	LENGTH MEDAL-TEE	PAR	STROKE INDEX
1	420	4		1	440	4		1	377	4	
2	485	5		2	147	3		2	376	4	
3	161	3		3	484	5		3	172	3	
4	385	4		4	400	4		4	319	4	
5	377	4		5	406	4		5	380	4	
6	393	4		6	487	5		6	570	5	
7	538	5		7	363	4		7	183	3	
8	176	3		8	200	3		8	407	4	
9	412	4		9	416	4		9	379	4	
TOTAL	3347	36	TOTAL	TOTAL	3343	36	TOTAL	TOTAL	3163	35	TOTAL

ROYAL BIRKDALE

TEL : (0704)69903
LOCATION : 20 m N. Liverpool
ADDRESS : Waterloo Road – Southport – Merseyside
HOTEL :
Prince of Wales – Southport
Tel : (0704)36688
Scarisbrick – Southport
Tel : (0704)43000
Royal Clifton
Tel : (0704)33771
RESTAURANT : Lockerbie House – Southport
Tel : (0704)65298

The Royal Birkdale is a memorable golf course rated as one of the great links courses in the world. It features many outstanding holes with the fairways running in valleys between towering sand hills and dunes. Situated on the Lancashire coast, an area once described as the most heavenly golfing country in the world, it is never free of wind. Royal Birkdale has hosted more famous championships than any other Club in the British isles, including the Open Championship, the Ryder Cup, the British Amateur, the Walker Cup, the Ladies British Open and the Curtis Cup. *SSS 73*

GF $$ — Weekends —  S

1889 — G. Low, F. Hawtree, J. Taylor — 

18 — L 6703 P 72 — 

Required : Handicap Certificate, Introduction Letter
Best days : Weekdays

HOLE	LENGTH MEDAL-TEE	PAR	STROKE INDEX
1	447	4	11
2	416	4	3
3	407	4	7
4	202	3	15
5	341	4	13
6	488	5	1
7	150	3	17
8	414	4	9
9	413	4	5
TOTAL	3278	35	TOTAL

HOLE	LENGTH MEDAL-TEE	PAR	STROKE INDEX
10	372	4	14
11	374	4	8
12	181	3	18
13	436	4	4
14	198	3	16
15	542	5	2
16	344	4	12
17	502	5	6
18	476	5	10
TOTAL	3425	37	TOTAL

ROYAL BLACKHEATH

★★★

TEL : (01)8501795
LOCATION : 7 m Charing Cross
ADDRESS : Court Rd – Eltham – London S.E.9
HOTEL :
Bromley Court – Bromley
Tel : (01)4645011
Blakes – London South Kensington
Tel : (01)3706701
Halcyon – London Kensington
Tel : (01)7277288
RESTAURANT : La Goulue – Blackheath
Tel : (01)8529226

Royal Blackheath is one of the world's oldest golf clubs as golf goes back here to 1608. It was designed by James Braid and laid out on lush parkland close to the British capital. Many of the fairways are landscaped with majestic silver birch, oak and fir trees. Water obstacles, such as ditches crossing the fairways and ponds, affect play on six holes. Most of the greens are well protected by strategic bunkes. *SSS 70*

GF $$ — Weekends — R S
1608 — J. Braid
18 — L 6214 y P 70

Required : Handicap Certificate, Introduction Letter
Best days : Weekdays

HOLE	LENGTH MEDAL-TEE	PAR	STROKE INDEX
1	473	4	
2	386	4	
3	428	4	
4	197	3	
5	348	4	
6	482	5	
7	374	4	
8	158	3	
9	357	4	
TOTAL	3203	35	TOTAL

HOLE	LENGTH MEDAL-TEE	PAR	STROKE INDEX
10	349	4	
11	376	4	
12	180	3	
13	523	5	
14	377	4	
15	348	4	
16	174	3	
17	400	4	
18	284	4	
TOTAL	3011	35	TOTAL

ROYAL CINQUE PORTS

TEL : (0304)374007
LOCATION : 15 km N. Dover A 258
ADDRESS : Golf Rd – Deal – Kent
HOTEL :
Royal-Deal
Tel : (0304)375555
Black Horse – Deal
Tel : (0304)374074
Sutherland – Deal
Tel : (0304)362853

Royal Cinque Ports is a true links course and one of Britain's most challenging courses. It is adjoining the seaside resort of Old Deal Town and is laid out on rugged landscape amidst hummock. Fairways and greens are heavily bunkered. Another important obstacle is that the course is seldom free of wind. The club has hosted many major golf tournaments.
SSS 72

GF $$ | Weekends | 

1892 | H. Vardon | 

18 | L 6407 y P 70

Required : Handicap Certificate, Introduction Letter
Best days : Weekdays

HOLE	LENGTH MEDAL-TEE	PAR	STROKE INDEX
1	325	4	14
2	364	4	8
3	453	4	4
4	153	3	13
5	494	5	2
6	304	4	12
7	358	4	6
8	164	3	16
9	383	4	10
TOTAL	2998	35	TOTAL

HOLE	LENGTH MEDAL-TEE	PAR	STROKE INDEX
10	362	4	11
11	382	4	1
12	418	4	13
13	400	4	5
14	215	3	15
15	420	4	7
16	456	4	3
17	360	4	14
18	396	4	9
TOTAL	3409	35	TOTAL

ROYAL CROMER

★★

TEL : (0263)512884
LOCATION : 1,5 km E. Cromer
ADDRESS : Overstrand Rd – Cromer-Norfolk
HOTEL :
Cliftonville-Cromer
Tel : (0263)512543
Anglia Court – Cromer
Tel : (0263)512443
RESTAURANT : Cliffhouse-Cromer
Tel : (0263)512445

This is a splendid seaside course laid out in beautiful rolling countryside and ideal for holiday golf. It has a varied layout with several holes winding through links countryside and others through verdant parkland. One of its feature holes is the 6th set on a clifftop. The Cliftonville hotel overlooks the putting green of the Royal Cromer. *SSS 71*

GF $ — Sunday mornings — R S

1888 — T. Morris

18 — L 6508 y P 72

Required : Handicap Certificate
Best days : Weekdays

HOLE	LENGTH MEDAL-TEE	PAR	STROKE INDEX
1	439	4	7
2	383	4	11
3	315	4	13
4	456	4	3
5	492	5	9
6	457	4	1
7	411	4	5
8	310	4	15
9	161	3	17
TOTAL	3424	36	TOTAL

HOLE	LENGTH MEDAL-TEE	PAR	STROKE INDEX
10	509	5	6
11	501	5	8
12	285	4	16
13	182	3	12
14	399	4	2
15	391	4	4
16	317	4	14
17	119	3	18
18	381	4	10
TOTAL	3084	36	TOTAL

ROYAL JERSEY

TEL : (0534)52233/54416
LOCATION : 4 m E. St. Helier
ADDRESS : Grouville – Jersey – Channel Islands
HOTEL :
La Plage – St-Helier
Tel : (0534)23474
Lavender Villa – Grouville
Tel : (0534)54937
Pomme d'Or – St-Helier
Tel : (0534)78644
RESTAURANT : Victoria's – St-Helier
Tel : (0534)72255

Formed in 1878, the Royal Jersey is a picturesque seaside course laid out alongside Grouville Bay. It has a varied and testing layout, and features several challenging holes demanding a great deal of accuracy. The golf club is very popular and therefore crowded during the summer season.

GF $$

 1878

18

—

—

L 6023 y P 70

 S

R 

Required : Handicap Certificate
Best days : Any day by prior arrangement only

HOLE	LENGTH MEDAL-TEE	PAR	STROKE INDEX
1	468	5	3
2	143	3	15
3	554	5	5
4	180	3	18
5	369	4	7
6	378	4	11
7	398	4	1
8	129	3	17
9	506	5	9
TOTAL	3125	36	TOTAL

HOLE	LENGTH MEDAL-TEE	PAR	STROKE INDEX
10	342	4	13
11	378	4	12
12	389	4	2
13	404	4	4
14	328	4	8
15	191	3	16
16	181	3	10
17	364	4	6
18	321	4	14
TOTAL	2898	34	TOTAL

ROYAL LIVERPOOL

TEL : (051)6323101
LOCATION : 10 m Liverpool, off A 553
ADDRESS : Meols Drive – Hoylake – Wirral – Merseyside
HOTEL :
Stanley – Hoylake
Tel : (051)6323311
Atlantic Tower – Liverpool
Tel : (051)2274444
Grange – Liverpool
Tel : (051)4272950
RESTAURANT : Linas – Hoylake
Tel : (051)6321408

Royal Liverpool, sometimes called "Hoylake", is a great and noble golf course, providing one of the finest tests of golf in the world. Laid out alongside the Irish Sea on typical links countryside, its 18 holes run through sand hills overlooking the distant hills of Wales and Hilbre Island. A fearsome wind serves as a constant hazard. There are many tough holes, especially the 17th hole where many championships are decided. Hoylake has hosted the British Open no less than ten times. *SSS 74*

GF $$

1869

18

Weekends

—

L 6804 y P 72

Required : Handicap Certificate, Introduction Letter
Best days : Weekdays

HOLE	LENGTH MEDAL-TEE	PAR	STROKE INDEX
1	428	4	5
2	369	4	15
3	505	5	7
4	184	3	13
5	407	4	1
6	383	4	9
7	200	3	17
8	479	5	3
9	393	4	11
TOTAL	3348	36	TOTAL

HOLE	LENGTH MEDAL-TEE	PAR	STROKE INDEX
10	409	4	12
11	200	3	14
12	395	4	4
13	157	3	18
14	516	5	8
15	460	4	2
16	533	5	10
17	391	4	6
18	395	4	16
TOTAL	3456	36	TOTAL

ROYAL LYTHAM & ST-ANNES

TEL : (0253)724206
LOCATION : 1,7 km NW. Lytham St-Annes, 3 m S. Blackpool
ADDRESS : Links Gate – St-Annes on Sea – Lancs
HOTEL :
Clifton Arms – Lytham St-Annes
Tel : (0253)739898
Bedford – Lytham St-Annes
Tel : (0253)724636
RESTAURANT : Grand Osprey – Lytham St-Annes
Tel : (0253)721288

The Royal Lytham St Annes is not physically attractive. Nevertheless it is one of the world's greatest links courses and one of the most severe tests of golf. The course winds through a wild dune landscape. It has fast fairways which are defended by deep bunkers. The 17th and 18th finishing holes are among the world's best. Royal Lytham St Annes is one of the seven golf courses hosting the British Open regularly. The stately and Victorian style clubhouse lies behind the 18th green. There is a dormy house with accomodation for men only. *SSS 73*

GF $$ — Weekends — S

1886 — — — R

27 — L 6673 y P 71

Required : Handicap Certificate, Introduction Letter
Best days : Mondays, Thursdays and Fridays

HOLE	LENGTH MEDAL-TEE	PAR	STROKE INDEX
1	206	3	13
2	420	4	5
3	458	4	1
4	393	4	9
5	188	3	15
6	486	5	7
7	551	5	3
8	394	4	11
9	162	3	17
TOTAL	3258	35	TOTAL

HOLE	LENGTH MEDAL-TEE	PAR	STROKE INDEX
10	334	4	10
11	485	5	4
12	189	3	14
13	339	4	18
14	445	4	6
15	468	4	2
16	356	4	16
17	413	4	8
18	386	4	12
TOTAL	3415	36	TOTAL

ROYAL NORTH DEVON

TEL : (02372)73817
LOCATION : 1 m Northam
ADDRESS : Westward Ho – Devon
HOTEL :
Durrant House – Bideford
Tel : (02372)72361
Portledge – Fairy Cross
Tel : (02375)262
Riversford – Bideford
Tel : (02372)74239
RESTAURANT : Yeoldon House – Bideford
Tel : (02372)74400

Royal North Devon is the second oldest golf club in England. Originally designed by Old Tom Morris of St Andrews in 1864, the course was redesigned in 1908 by Herbert Fowler. It is a great links course laid out alongside Barnstaple Bay on flat and open land. It has many fine natural hazards such as the Great Sea Rushes which are tall marshland reeds guarding the 9th to 13th holes. Several of the greens are narrow and heavily bunkered.
SSS 72

GF $

1864

18

—

T. Morris, H. Fowler

L 6662 y P 71

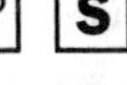

Required : Handicap Certificate
Best days : Any day by prior arrangement

HOLE	LENGTH MEDAL-TEE	PAR	STROKE INDEX
1	485	5	15
2	424	4	5
3	418	4	5
4	354	4	11
5	137	3	16
6	413	4	1
7	400	4	9
8	197	3	13
9	481	5	3
TOTAL	3309	36	TOTAL

HOLE	LENGTH MEDAL-TEE	PAR	STROKE INDEX
10	372	4	10
11	371	4	12
12	425	4	2
13	440	4	8
14	205	3	14
15	431	4	4
16	145	3	17
17	548	5	6
18	416	4	18
TOTAL	3353	35	TOTAL

ROYAL ST-GEORGE'S

TEL : (0304)613090
LOCATION : 1 m Sandwich
ADDRESS : Sandwich – Kent
HOTEL :
Bell – Sandwich
Tel : (0304)613388
De Fleur de Lis – Sandwich
Tel : (0304)611131
St-Crispin – Worth
Tel : (0304)612081

Royal St Georges is one of the seven British golf courses where the Open is held regularly. It is one of the most famous golf clubs in the world and a great test of golf. It is a classic links with its fairways and greens modified by Frank Pennink. The course, which is heavily bunkered, changes level frequently and is enclosed by tricky sand dunes. There is only one water hazard which is a stream crossing the 14th fairway. The golf club has hosted the Open eleven times and has been the venue for the Walker Cup, the Dunlop Masters and the European Team Championships. *SSS 72*

GF $$ — Weekends  

1887 —  F. Pennink — 

18 —  6534 y P 70 — 

Required : Handicap Certificate, Introduction Letter
Best days : Weekdays

HOLE	LENGTH MEDAL-TEE	PAR	STROKE INDEX
1	400	4	5
2	341	4	14
3	200	3	11
4	420	4	2
5	422	4	9
6	156	3	17
7	475	5	8
8	410	4	3
9	376	4	16
TOTAL	3200	35	TOTAL

HOLE	LENGTH MEDAL-TEE	PAR	STROKE INDEX
10	377	4	15
11	216	3	6
12	343	4	13
13	438	4	1
14	497	5	12
15	439	4	7
16	165	3	18
17	422	4	4
18	437	4	10
TOTAL	3334	35	TOTAL

SAUNTON

TEL : (0271)812436
LOCATION : 13,5 km Barnstaple
ADDRESS : Saunton - Braunton - Devon
HOTEL : HP
Saunton Sands - Braunton
Tel : (0271)890212
Brookdale - Braunton
Tel : (0271)812075
Poyers - Wrafton
Tel : (0271)812149
RESTAURANT : Poyers - Braunton
Tel : (0271)812149

Extended to 18 holes in 1924 by Herbert Fowler, the course was redesigned by C.K. Cotton in 1950. Saunton is a noble links laid out on rugged terrain amongst rushes, sand hills and scrub. It is bordered by the beach on one side and the marshes of the Taw estuary on the other side. Its most testing hole is the tough 16th, a lefthand dogleg carrying over a huge sand hill to an elevated green flanked by further sand hills. The New Course was designed by Frank Pennink and is ideal for family golf. The fine holiday hotel Saunton Sands with ninety-three bedrooms is near the course. *SSS 73*

GF $

1897

36

Weekends

H. Fowler, C.K. Cotton, F. Pennink

L 6703 y P 73, 6356 y P 71

Required : Handicap Certificate
Best days : Weekdays by prior arrangement only

HOLE	LENGTH MEDAL-TEE	PAR	STROKE INDEX
1	470	4	
2	476	5	
3	402	4	
4	444	4	
5	112	3	
6	370	4	
7	428	4	
8	380	4	
9	382	4	
TOTAL	3464	36	TOTAL

HOLE	LENGTH MEDAL-TEE	PAR	STROKE INDEX
10	337	4	
11	362	4	
12	418	4	
13	136	3	
14	461	4	
15	485	5	
16	430	4	
17	202	3	
18	408	4	
TOTAL	3239	35	TOTAL

SILLOTH-ON-SOLWAY

TEL : (0965)31179
LOCATION : 24 m W. Carlisle A 395
ADDRESS : The Club House – Silloth – Cumbria
HOTEL : HP
Golf – Silloth
Tel : (0965)31438
RESTAURANT : Skinburness – Silloth
Tel : (0965)31468

Bordering the Solway Firth, this is a classic links of championship status with a challenging layout. The course features hazards such as natural sand bunkers, gorse, hillocks and heather. The greens are of excellent quality. There are panoramic views across the Solway Firth to the Scottish Hills, the mountains of the Lake District and the Isle of Man in the distance. The British Ladies Championship was held here in 1976 and in 1983. The Golf Hotel is a few minutes walk from the club. *SSS 70*

GF $ — — 

1892 — 

18 — L 6343 y P 72 

Required : Introduction Letter
Best days : Weekdays

HOLE	LENGTH MEDAL-TEE	PAR	STROKE INDEX
1	380	4	6
2	325	4	13
3	362	4	10
4	377	4	8
5	486	5	1
6	184	3	17
7	408	4	3
8	370	4	12
9	127	3	18
TOTAL	3019	35	TOTAL

HOLE	LENGTH MEDAL-TEE	PAR	STROKE INDEX
10	308	4	14
11	389	4	4
12	192	3	15
13	482	5	2
14	484	5	9
15	417	4	5
16	179	3	16
17	486	5	7
18	387	4	11
TOTAL	3324	37	TOTAL

SOUTHPORT & AINSDALE

★★★

TEL : (0704)78000
LOCATION : 3 m S. Southport on A 565
ADDRESS : Bradshaws Lane – Liverpool Rd – Ainsdale – Southport
HOTEL :
Royal Clifton – Southport
Tel : (0704)33771
Prince of Wales – Southport
Tel : (0704)36688
Scarisbrick – Southport
Tel : (0704)38321
RESTAURANT : Dolce Vita – Ainsdale
Tel : (0704)75535

This is one of the leading golf courses along the South Lancashire coast. Its holes run through rugged links land and are flanked by sand hills. Its most challenging hole is the 16th, alongside the railway line, featuring an enormous bunker and huge sand hills. The links command panoramic views of the Welsh Hills and the Cumberland mountains. The club has hosted various prestigeous tournaments such as the Ryder Cup, the Dunlop Masters, and the British Ladies Open. *SSS 73*

GF $

Wed. and Weekends

1907

J. Braid

18

L 6612 y P 72

Required : Handicap Certificate, Club Membership Card
Best days : Mondays, Tuesdays, Fridays by prior arrangement

HOLE	LENGTH MEDAL-TEE	PAR	STROKE INDEX
1	200	3	13
2	520	5	3
3	418	4	11
4	316	4	15
5	447	4	1
6	386	4	9
7	480	5	5
8	157	3	17
9	482	5	7
TOTAL	3406	37	TOTAL

HOLE	LENGTH MEDAL-TEE	PAR	STROKE INDEX
10	160	3	18
11	447	4	4
12	401	4	10
13	154	3	16
14	383	4	6
15	353	4	12
16	510	5	2
17	443	4	8
18	355	4	14
TOTAL	3206	35	TOTAL

SUNNINGDALE

TEL : (0990)21681
LOCATION : 0,5 m Sunningdale Station, 25 m W. London
ADDRESS : Ridgmount Rd – Sunningdale – Ascot – Berks
HOTEL :
Berystede – Ascot
Tel : (0990)23311
Royal Berkshire – Ascot
Tel : (0990)23322
RESTAURANT : Royal Foresters – Ascot
Tel : (03447)884747

Sunningdale is a masterpiece and one of the world's greatest golf courses laid out on firm heathland. It is scenically situated, with its thirty-six outstanding holes running through woodland, heather, bracken, pine and silver birch. The main championship layout is the Old Course designed in 1901 by the great English golf champion Willie Park. The sterner New Course, inaugurated in 1922, was the brainchild of Harry Colt. Each hole of the two courses has its own distinctive challenge. Most of them are very long having elevated tees and strategic trees serving as hazards. Sunningdale Old has hosted most of the major golf tournaments except the British Open which is held on a links course. The club boasts an old-fashioned but stately clubhouse.

GF $$

Weekends

R S

1901

W. Park, H. Colt

36

L 6341 P 70/74, 6033 P 72
SSS 70/72

Required : Handicap Certificate 18
Best days : Weekdays by prior arrangement only

HOLE	LENGTH MEDAL-TEE	PAR	STROKE INDEX
1	494	5	9
2	456	4/5	4
3	296	4	14
4	161	3	16
5	400	4	2
6	388	4	11
7	383	4	6
8	172	3	18
9	267	4	8
TOTAL	3017	35/36	TOTAL

HOLE	LENGTH MEDAL-TEE	PAR	STROKE INDEX
10	463	4/5	7
11	299	4	15
12	423	4/5	1
13	178	3	17
14	477	5	3
15	226	3	12
16	423	4/5	10
17	421	4	5
18	414	4	13
TOTAL	3324	35/38	TOTAL

TREVOSE

TEL : (0841)520208
LOCATION : 5 m W. Padstow
ADDRESS : Constantine Bay – Padstow – Cornwall
HOTEL :
Treglos – Padstow Constantine Bay
Tel : (0841)520727
Old Custom House Inn – Padstow
Tel : (0841)532359
The Metropole – Padstow
Tel : (0841)532486

Trevose is situated on fine natural links land on the north coast of Cornwall with sandy beaches surrounding it. It is a true links course having undulating fairways which are flanked by sand hills and large rolling greens. Trevose is full of natural hazards such as several deep grass hollows and a stream crossing four fairways. The links commands panoramic views of Cornwall. Sports facilities include a heated swimming pool and three tennis courts. The club accomodation consists of cottages, flats, chalets and bungalows. The elegant Treglos hotel is nearby. *SSS 71*

GF $

1924

27

—

H. Colt

L 6461 y P 71, 1357 y P 29

RP S

Required : Handicap Certificate
Best days : Any day

HOLE	LENGTH MEDAL-TEE	PAR	STROKE INDEX
1	443	4	5
2	346	4	11
3	166	3	17
4	450	5	9
5	461	4	2
6	323	4	15
7	371	4	3
8	156	3	13
9	451	5	7
TOTAL	3167	36	TOTAL

HOLE	LENGTH MEDAL-TEE	PAR	STROKE INDEX
10	467	4	8
11	199	3	6
12	448	4	1
13	507	5	12
14	317	4	18
15	327	4	16
16	225	3	10
17	388	4	4
18	416	4	14
TOTAL	3294	35	TOTAL

WALTON HEATH

TEL : (073781)2380
LOCATION : 3 m S. Epsom
ADDRESS : Deans Lane – Tadworth – Surrey
HOTEL :
White Horse – Dorking
Tel : (0306)81138
Burford Bridge – Dorking
Tel : (0306)884561
White House – Epsom
Tel : (03727)22472
RESTAURANT : Drift Bridge – Epsom
Tel : (07373)52163

Walton Heath is one of the leading golf courses in England and was the home for forty-five years of the legendary James Braid, famous golf architect and five times winner of the Open. It consists of two championship courses, the Old and the New Course. Both are glorious heathland courses with their fairways flanked by strategic heather and bracken. It is characterized by large, deep bunkers, big greens, difficult rough, and a prevailing wind. There is a fine clubhouse. *SSS Old Course 73, New Course 72*

GF $$

Weekends

S

1904

H. Fowler

36

L 6813 y P 73, 6659 y P 72

R

Required : Handicap Certificate, Introduction Letter
Best days : Weekdays

Old course

HOLE	LENGTH MEDAL-TEE	PAR	STROKE INDEX
1	298	4	14
2	439	4	3
3	289	4	16
4	443	4	5
5	391	4	10
6	422	4	7
7	174	3	17
8	489	5	1
9	390	4	12
TOTAL	3335	36	TOTAL

HOLE	LENGTH MEDAL-TEE	PAR	STROKE INDEX
10	395	4	6
11	189	3	9
12	371	4	15
13	507	5	8
14	517	5	2
15	404	4	11
16	510	5	4
17	181	3	18
18	404	4	13
TOTAL	3478	37	TOTAL

New Course

HOLE	LENGTH MEDAL-TEE	PAR	STROKE INDEX
1	310	4	14
2	140	3	18
3	424	4	5
4	260	4	12
5	469	4	1
6	169	3	16
7	385	4	10
8	499	5	7
9	455	4	3
TOTAL	3111	35	TOTAL

HOLE	LENGTH MEDAL-TEE	PAR	STROKE INDEX
10	189	3	15
11	389	4	8
12	426	4	4
13	489	5	13
14	408	4	2
15	410	4	11
16	511	5	6
17	353	4	17
18	373	4	9
TOTAL	3548	37	TOTAL

WENTWORTH

TEL : (09904)2201
LOCATION : 21 m London A 30
ADDRESS : Virginia Water – Surrey
HOTEL :
Berystede – Ascot
Tel : (0990)23311
Royal Berkshire – Ascot
Tel : (0990)23322
Royal Foresters – Ascot
Tel : (0344)884747
RESTAURANT : Royal Foresters – Ascot
Tel : (0344)884747

Wentworth is a noble golf club owning two golf courses, each considered being a masterpiece. The new South Course, designed by John Jacobs, Bernard Gallacher and Gary Player will be open for play in 1990. This will be one of the longest courses in Europe measuring 6700m long. The shorter East Course was laid out by Harry Colt in 1924, the championship West Course was inaugurated three years later. All three are typical inland courses cut out of Surrey heathland, with pine, heather and silver birch trees surrounding each hole. The bunkers are deep and large demanding a great deal of accuracy. Streams and paths crossing the fairways serve a hazards. Wentworth has hosted the Ryder Cup, the Dunlop Masters, the World Cup, the Piccadilly World Match Play, welcoming the greatest golfers in history. It boasts an imposing Victorian style clubhouse.

GF $$

1924

63

Weekends

H. Colt

L 6365 P 72, 5644 P 68
SSS 70/74

Required : Handicap Certificate, Introduction Letter
Best days : Weekdays only

HOLE	LENGTH MEDAL-TEE	PAR	STROKE INDEX
1	431	4	
2	142	3	
3	413	4	
4	458	5	
5	175	3	
6	314	4	
7	365	4	
8	364	4	
9	412	4	
TOTAL	3074	35	TOTAL

HOLE	LENGTH MEDAL-TEE	PAR	STROKE INDEX
10	170	3	
11	344	4	
12	442	5	
13	403	4	
14	164	3	
15	439	4	
16	348	4	
17	522	5	
18	459	5	
TOTAL	3291	37	TOTAL

WHITSAND BAY HOTEL

TEL : (0503)30276
LOCATION : 6 m Plymouth
ADDRESS : Portwrinkle – Torpoint – Cornwall
HOTEL : HP
Whitsand Bay
Tel : (0503)30276
Holiday Inn – Plymouth
Tel : (0752)662866
Mayflower Post House – Plymouth
Tel : (0752)662828

The golf course was designed in 1906 by Fernie of Troon. It is a fine seaside course set on open countryside and scenically laid out on cliffs. The course commands excellent views of the picturesque Cornish coast and Plymouth. A road comes into play on several holes. The attractive Whitsand Bay Hotel stands high up overlooking the sea and the course. *SSS 67*

GF $ — 1906 — 18

— — W. Fernie — L 5512 y P 68

S  RP

Required : Handicap Certificate
Best days : Any day

HOLE	LENGTH MEDAL-TEE	PAR	STROKE INDEX
1	420	4	3
2	300	4	7
3	177	3	9
4	322	4	12
5	425	4	1
6	490	5	11
7	143	3	15
8	476	5	5
9	125	3	17
TOTAL	2878	35	TOTAL

HOLE	LENGTH MEDAL-TEE	PAR	STROKE INDEX
10	498	5	10
11	144	3	16
12	270	4	18
13	410	4	2
14	165	3	14
15	210	3	8
16	376	4	6
17	353	4	4
18	208	3	13
TOTAL	2634	33	TOTAL

WOODHALL SPA

TEL : (0526)52511
LOCATION : 18 m NW. Lincoln
ADDRESS : Woodhall Spa – Lincs
HOTEL : HF
Golf – Woodhall Spa
Tel : (0526)52434
Dower House – Woodhall Spa
Tel : (0526)52588
RESTAURANT : Dower House – Woodhall Spa
Tel : (0526)52588

Woodhall Spa is one of Britain's leading inland courses built on sandy soil. It runs through moorland with heather, silver birch and pine trees serving as natural hazards. The course was originally designed by Harry Vardon, then altered by H. Colt and totally redesigned by Colonel Hotchkin. Many important tournaments have been held here, such as the Brabazon Trophy, the Home Internationals, and other national championships. The Golf Hotel is a Tudor style country house with fifty bedrooms and several tennis courts.

GF $$ — RF S

1906 H. Vardon, H. Colt, S. Hotchkin

18 L 6867 y P 73

Required : Handicap Certificate, Introduction Letter
Best days : Weekdays

HOLE	LENGTH MEDAL-TEE	PAR	STROKE INDEX
1	363	4	7
2	408	4	17
3	417	4	3
4	415	4	11
5	155	3	16
6	506	5	1
7	435	4	9
8	193	3	13
9	560	5	5
TOTAL	3452	36	TOTAL

HOLE	LENGTH MEDAL-TEE	PAR	STROKE INDEX
10	334	4	12
11	442	4	6
12	152	3	18
13	437	4	2
14	489	5	10
15	325	4	14
16	398	4	4
17	322	4	15
18	516	5	8
TOTAL	3415	37	TOTAL

SCOTLAND

450 GOLF COURSES, 400 000 PLAYERS

★★★ Great golf course
★★ Very good golf course
$ 5-15 Pound
★ Recommended golf course
✡ Holiday golf course
$ $ more than 18 Pound

LOTHIAN

TOWN	GOLF COURSE		TEL	♦	MAP REF.
Bathgate	Bathgate		(0506) 52232		36
Dalkeith	Newbattle		(031) 6632123		23
Dunbar	Dunbar	★	(0368) 62317		6
	Winterfield	✡	(0368) 63562		34
Edinburgh and Suburbs	Baberton		(031) 4533361		35
	Braid Hills		(031) 4476666		37
	Broomieknowe		(031) 6639317		1
	Bruntsfield Links	★	(031) 3361479	♦	2
	Craigmillar Park		(031) 6672837		3
	Dalmahoy	★★	(031) 3331845	♦	4
	Duddingston	★	(031) 6617688		5
	Glencorse		(0968) 77177		7
	Kingsknowe		(031) 4411145		14
	Liberton		(031) 6643009		15
	Lothianburn		(031) 4452206		40
	Merchants of Edinburgh		(031) 4471219		19
	Mortonhall		(031) 4472411		20
	Murrayfield		(031) 3373478		21
	Prestonfield		(031) 6671273		25
	Ratho Park		(031) 3331752		26
	Royal Burgess Golfing Society	★★	(031) 3392075	♦	27
	Royal Musselburgh		(0875) 810276	♦	28

♦ For details, see following pages.

TOWN	GOLF COURSE		TEL	♦	MAP REF.
	Silverknowes		(031) 3363843		41
	Swanston		(031) 4452239		29
	Torphin Hill		(031) 4411100		30
	Turnhouse		(031) 3391014		31
Gullane	Gullane	★★★	(0620) 842255	♦	9
	Honorouble Company of Edinburgh Golfers	★★★	(0620) 842123	♦	12
	Kilspindie	★	(08757) 216		13
	Luffness New	★	(0620) 843114		18
Haddington	Haddington		(062082) 3627		10
Linlithgow	Linlithgow		(0506) 826030		16
Livingston	Deer Park		(0506) 38843		39
Longniddry	Longniddry	★	(0875) 52141		17
Musselburgh	Musselburgh	★	(031) 6652005		22
North Berwick	East Links		(0620) 2726		38
	North Berwick	★★	(0620) 2135	♦	24
Uphall	Uphall		(0506) 856404		32
West Calder	Harburn		(0506) 871256		11
Whitburn	Greenburn		(0501) 43905		8

♦ For details, see following pages.

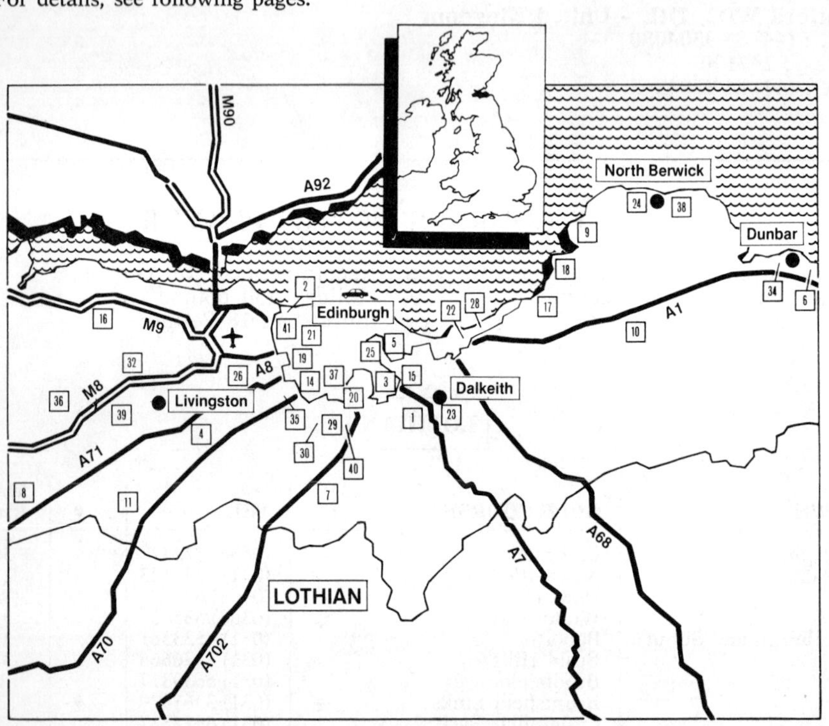

BORDERS

TOWN	GOLF COURSE		TEL	♦	MAP REF.
Coldstream	Hirsel	•	(08890) 2678		•
Galashiels	Galashiels	★	(0896) 3724		8
	Torwoodlee	•	(0896) 2260		•
Hawick	Hawick		(0450) 72293		4
	Minto		(0450) 72267		5
Jedburgh	Jedburgh	•	(08356) 3587		•
Lauder	Lauder	•	(05783) 381		•
Melrose	Melrose	•	(089682) 2855		•
	St Boswells	•	(0835) 22359		•
Peebles	Peebles Municipal		(0721) 20197		7
	West Linton		(0968) 60589		33
Selkirk	Selkirk	•	(0750) 20621		•

• 9 hole golf course.

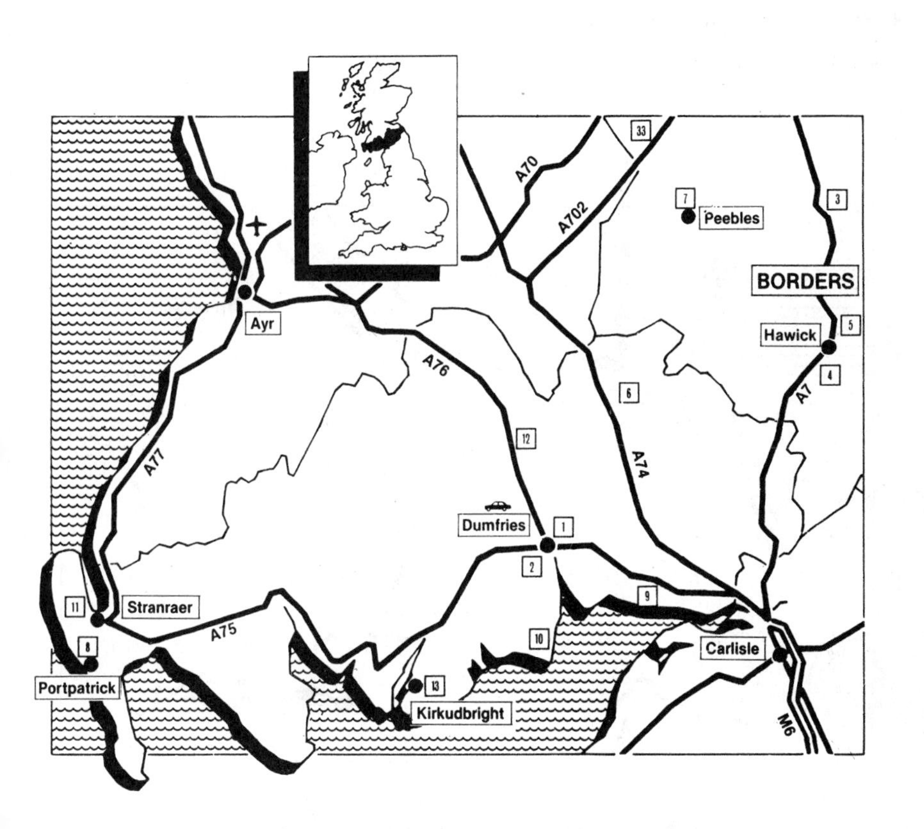

DUMFRIES & GALLOWAY

TOWN	GOLF COURSE		TEL	♦	MAP REF.
Annan	Powfoot	✡	(0461) 227		9
Castle Douglas	Castle Douglas	•	(0556) 2801		•
Dumfries	Dumfries & County		(0387) 53585		1
	Dumfries & Galloway		(0387) 3582		2
	Southerness	✡	(038788) 677		10
Kirkcudbright	Kirkcudbright				13
Langholm	Langholm	•			•
Lockerbie	Lockerbie	•	(038781) 552		•
Moffat	Moffat	★★	(0683) 20020	♦	6
Portpatrick	Portpatrick		(0776) 81725		8
Port William	St Medan	•	(09887) 577		•
Stranraer	Stranraer	✡	(0776) 87245		11
Thornhill	Thornhill		(0848) 30546		12
Wigtown	Wigtown Bladnoch	•	(09884) 3354		•

♦ For details, see following pages.

• 9 hole golf course.

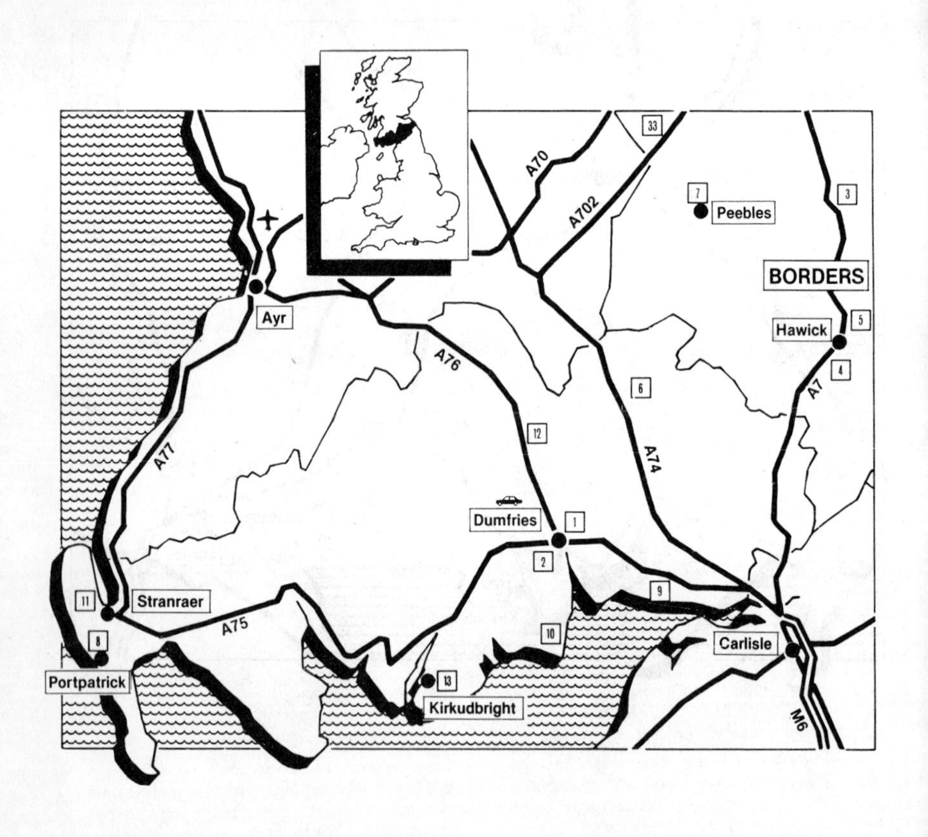

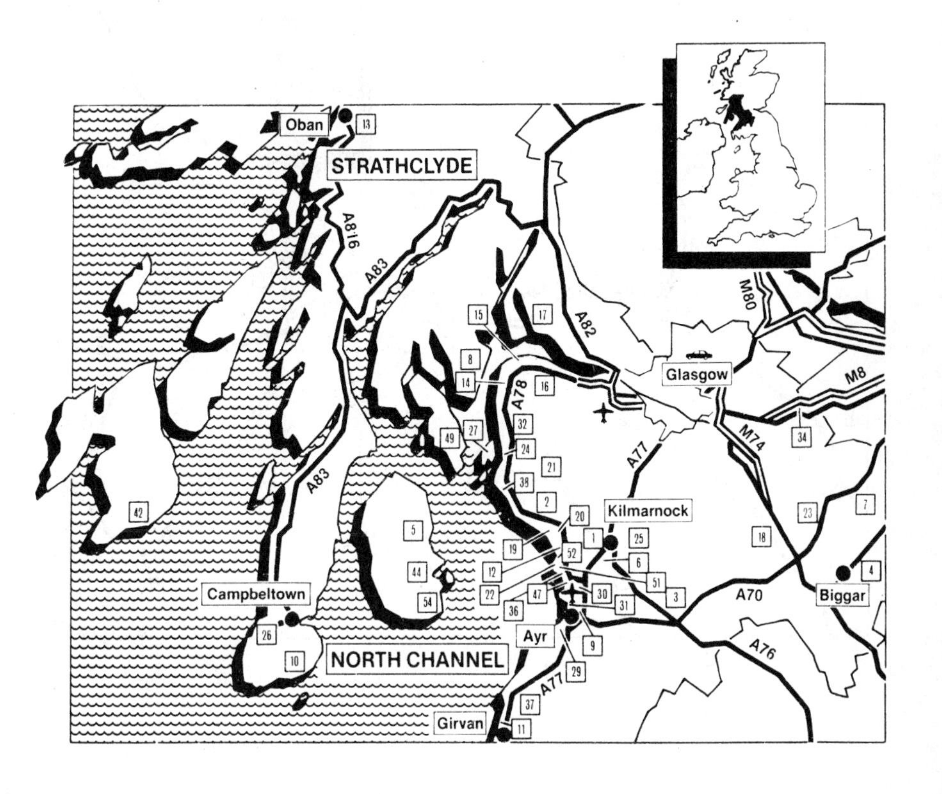

STRATHCLYDE

TOWN	GOLF COURSE		TEL	♦	MAP REF.
Ayr	Ayr Belleisle	★	(0292) 41258	♦	A 29
	Ayr Dalmilling	★	(0292) 41258		A 9
Beith	Beith		(05055) 3166		•
Biggar	Biggar		(0899) 20618		A 4
Brodick	Brodick	☆	(0770) 2349	♦	A 5
	Lamlash	☆	(07706) 296		A 44
Campbeltown	Carradale		(05833) 624		•
	Machrihanish	★	(0586) 81213		A 26
Cumnock	Ballochmyle		(0290) 50469		A 3
Dunoon	Cowal		(0369) 2216		A 8
Girvan	Girvan		(0465) 4272		A 11
	Turnberry	★★★	(0655) 31000	♦	A 37
Greenock	Gourock		(0475) 31001		A 14
	Greenock		(0475) 20793		A 15
	Whinhill		(0475) 24694		A 53
Helensburgh	Helensburgh		(0463) 4173		A 17
Irvine	Ardeer		(0294) 64542		A 2
	Glasgow Gailes	★	(0294) 311347		A 12
	Irvine		(0294) 75979		A 19
	Irvine Ravenspark		(0294) 79550		A 20
	Western Gailes		(0294) 311357		A 52

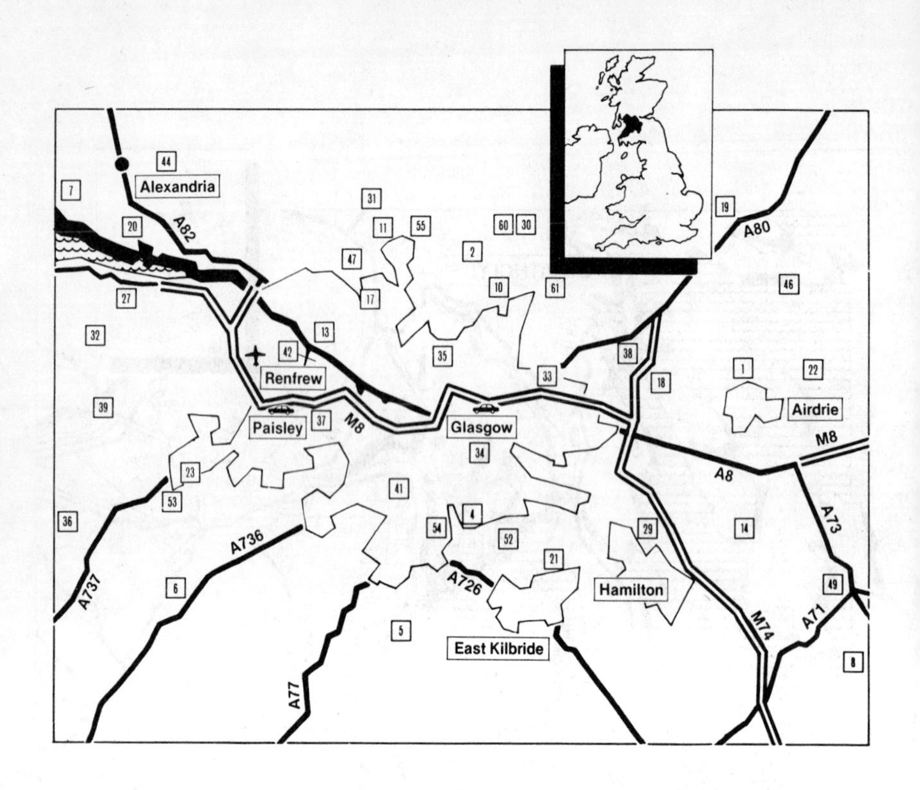

TOWN	GOLF COURSE		TEL	♦	MAP REF.
Islay	Islay	✡	(0496) 2310	♦	A 42
Kilmarnock	Annanhill		(0563) 21644		A 1
	Caprington		(0563) 23702		A 6
	Loudoun		(0563) 820551		A 25
Kilsyth	Kilsyth Lennox	•	(0236) 822190		•
Lanark	Carnwath		(0555) 840251		A 7
	Hollandbush		(0555) 893484		A 18
	Lanark	★	(0555) 3219		A 23
Largs	Kirbirnie Place		(0505) 823398		A 21
	Largs		(0475) 673594		A 24
	Routenburn		(0475) 673230		A 32
	West Kilbride		(0294) 833128		A 38
Oban	Glencruitten	✡	(0631) 62868		A 13
Prestwick	Prestwick	★★★	(0292) 77404	♦	A 47
	Prestwick St-Cuthbert	✡	(0292) 77101		A 30
	Prestwick St-Nicholas	✡	(0292) 70359		A 31
Rothesay	Rothesay		(0700) 2244		A 49
Shotts	Shotts		(0501) 20431		A 34
Troon	Kilmarnock	★	(0292) 311077		A 22
	Royal Troon	★★★	(0292) 311555	♦	A 36
	Troon Municipal		(0292) 312464		A 51
Whiting Bay	Whiting Bay		(07707) 487		A 54

♦ For details, see following pages.

• 9 hole golf course.

GLASGOW CITY

TOWN	GOLF COURSE		TEL	♦	MAP REF.
Glasgow	Knightswood Park	•	(041) 9592131		•
	Lethamhill		(041) 7706220		B 33
	Linn Park		(041) 6375871		B 34
	Pollok		(041) 6321080		B 41

GLASGOW SURROUNDINGS

TOWN	GOLF COURSE		TEL	♦	MAP REF.
Airdrie	Airdrie	✩	(02364) 62195		B 1
	Easter Moffat		(0236) 842289		B 22
Alexandria	Vale of Leven		(0389) 52351		B 44
Bearsden	Douglas Park		(041) 9422220		B 17
	Glasgow	★	(041) 9422011		B 27
	Windyhill		(041) 9422349		B 47
Bishopbriggs	Bishopbriggs		(041) 7221810		B 3
	Cawder		(041) 7727360		B 10
	Littlehill		(041) 7231916		B 35
Bridge of Weir	Old Course Ranfurly		(0505) 613612		B 39
Clydebank	Clydebank Overtoun		(041) 9526372		B 13
Coatbridge	Drumpellier		(0236) 24139		B 18
Cumbernauld	Dullatur		(02367) 23230		B 19
	Palacerigg		(02367) 34969		B 46
Dumbarton	Cardross		(0389) 841213		B 7
	Dumbarton		(0389) 841213		B 20
Eaglesham	Bonnyton		(03553) 2781		B 6
East Kilbride	East Kilbride		(03552) 20913		B 21
Giffnock	Deaconsbank		(041) 5521855		B 54
	East Renfrewshire		(03555) 256		B 22
Hamilton	Bothwell Castle	★	(0698) 853177		B 29
	Carluke		(0555) 71770		B 8
Johnstone	Cochrane Castle		(0505) 20146		B 53
Kilmacolm	Kilmacolm		(050587) 2139		B 32
Kirkintilloch	Hayston		(041) 7761244		B 30
	Kirkintilloch		(041) 7761256		B 60
	Lenzie		(041) 7761535		B 61
Langbank	Gleddoch House		(047554) 304		B 27
Milngavie	Balmore		(03602) 240		B 2
	Clober		(041) 9561685		B 11
	Dougalston		(041) 9565750		B 35
	Hilton Park		(041) 9564657		B 31
	Milngavie		(041) 9561619		B 25
Motherwell	Colville Park		(0698) 63017		B 14
Paisley	Barshaw		(041) 8892908		B 37
	Lochwinnoch		(0505) 842710		B 36
	Paisley	★	(041) 8842292		B 40
Renfrew	Renfrew		(041) 8866692		B 42
Rutherglen	Blairbeth		(041) 6343355		B 4
	Cathkin Braes		(041) 6344007		B 52
Stepps	Mount Ellen		(0236) 872277		B 38
Strathaven	Strathaven		(0357) 20539		B 43
Uplawmoor	Caldwell		(050) 585329		B 6
Wishaw	Wishaw		(0698) 372869		B 49

♦ For details, see following pages.

• 9 hole golf course.

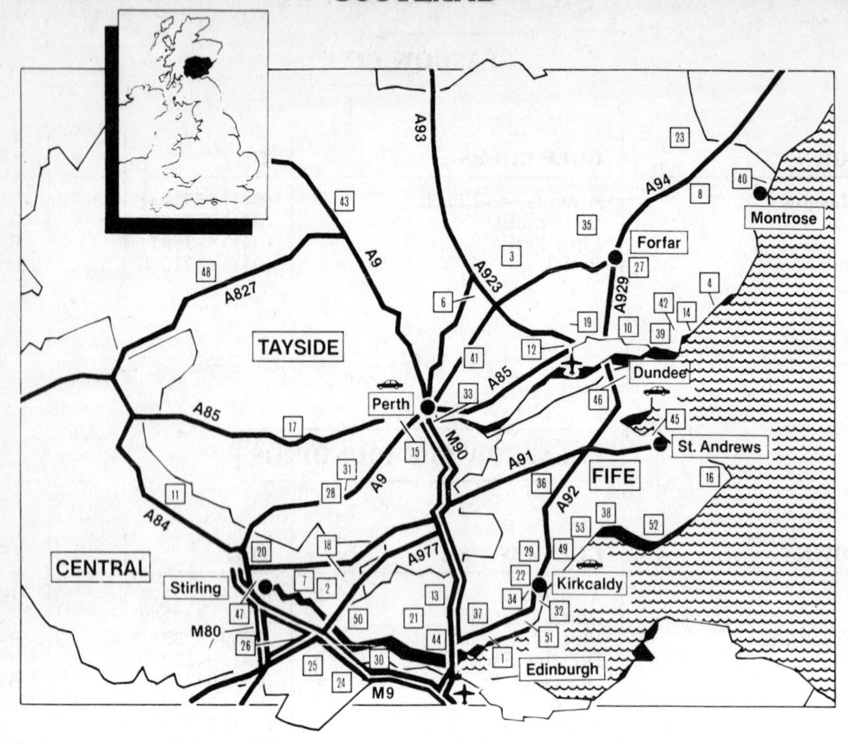

TAYSIDE

TOWN	GOLF COURSE		TEL	◆	MAP REF.
Aberfeldy	Taymouth Castle	✡	(08873) 228		48
Alyth	Alyth		(08283) 2268		3
Arbroath	Arbroath		(0241) 72272		4
Auchterarder	Auchterarder		(07646) 2804		31
	Gleneagles	★★★	(0764) 62231	◆	28
Blairgowrie	Blairgowrie	★★	(0250) 2383	◆	6
	Dalmunzie		(025085) 226		•
Brechin	Brechin		(03562) 2383		8
	Edzell		(03564) 235		23
Crieff	Comrie		(0764) 70544		•
	Crieff	✡	(0764) 2909		17
	Muthill		(0764) 3319		•
	St. Fillans		(076485) 312		•
Dundee	Caird Park		(0382) 453606		10
	Camperdown		(0382) 645450		12
	Carnoustie	★★★	(0241) 53249	◆	14
			(0241) 53789		
	Downfield	★	(0382) 825595	◆	19
	Monifieth	★★	(0382) 532767	◆	39
	Panmure	★	(024) 53120	◆	42
Dunkeld	Dunkeld Birnam	•	(03502) 524		•
Forfar	Forfar		(0307) 62120		27
Kinross	Green Hotel		(0577) 63467		
Kirriemuir	Kirriemuir		(0575) 72144		35
Montrose	Montrose	★	(0674) 72634		40
Perth	Craigie Hill	★	(0738) 24377		16
	King James VI		(0738) 32440		33
	Murrayshall		(0738) 52784		41
Pitlochry	Blair Atholl	•	(079681) 407		•
	Pitlochry	★	(0796) 2792		43

◆ For details, see following pages.

CENTRAL

TOWN	GOLF COURSE		TEL	♦	MAP REF.
Alloa	Alloa		(0259) 722745		2
	Braehead	✡	(0259) 722078		7
	Tulliallan		(0259) 30396		50
Callander	Callander		(0877) 30090		11
Falkirk	Falkirk		(0324) 23457		24
	Falkirk Tryst		(09324) 562415		25
	Glenbervie		(0324) 562605		26
	Grangemouth	★	(0324) 711500		30
Killin	Killin		(05672) 312		•
Stirling	Dunblane		(0786) 823711		20
	Stirling		(0786) 64098		47

♦ For details, see following pages.

• 9 hole golf course.

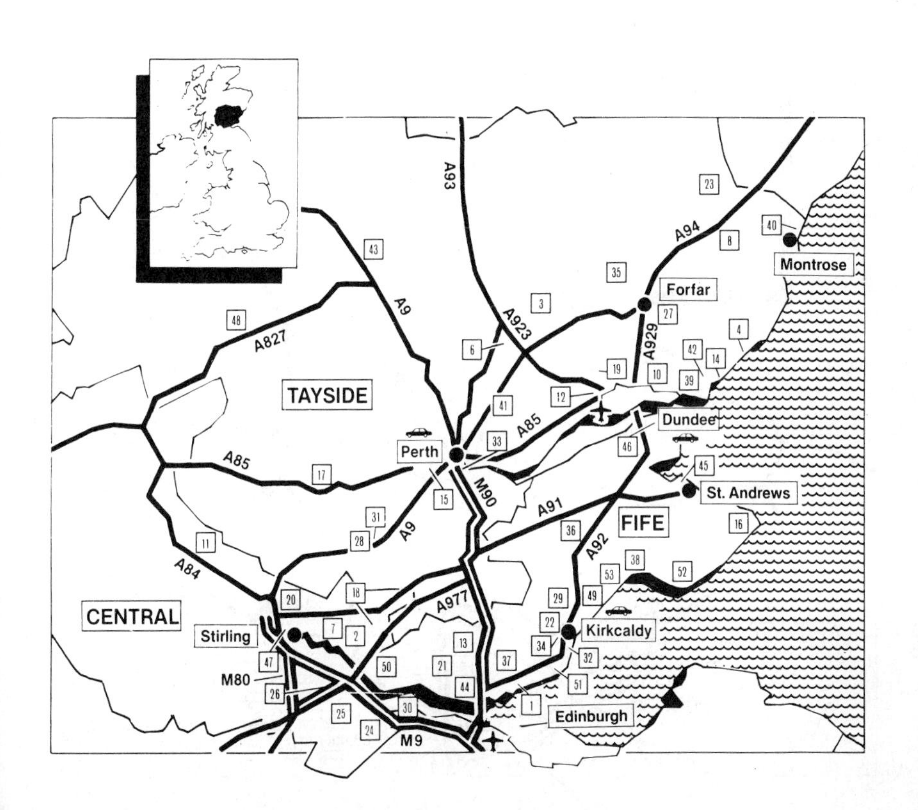

FIFE

TOWN	GOLF COURSE		TEL	♦	MAP REF.
Aberdour	Aberdour	✡	(0383) 860256		1
Crail	Golfing Society	★	(0333) 50686	♦	16
Cupar	Cupar		(0334) 53549		•
	Ladybank	✡	(0337) 30814		36
Dunfermline	Canmore		(0383) 724969		13
	Dunfermline		(0383) 723534		21
	Pitreavie		(0383) 722591		44
Elie	Golf House Club	✡	(0333) 330327		52
Glenrothes	Leslie		(0592) 742511		•
	Thornton		(0592) 771111		49
Kirkcaldy	Burntisland		(0592) 874093		51
	Dunnikier Park		(0592) 261599		22
	Kinghorn		(0592) 890345		32
	Kirkcaldy		(0592) 260370		34
	Lochgelly		(0592) 780174		37
Leven	Leven Links	★	(0333) 26096		53
	Lundin	✡	(0333) 320202		38
St. Andrews	St. Andrews	★★★	(0334) 75757	♦	45
	St. Michaels		(033483) 365		•
Wormit	Scotscraig	✡	(0382) 552515		46

♦ For details, see following pages.

• 9 hole golf course.

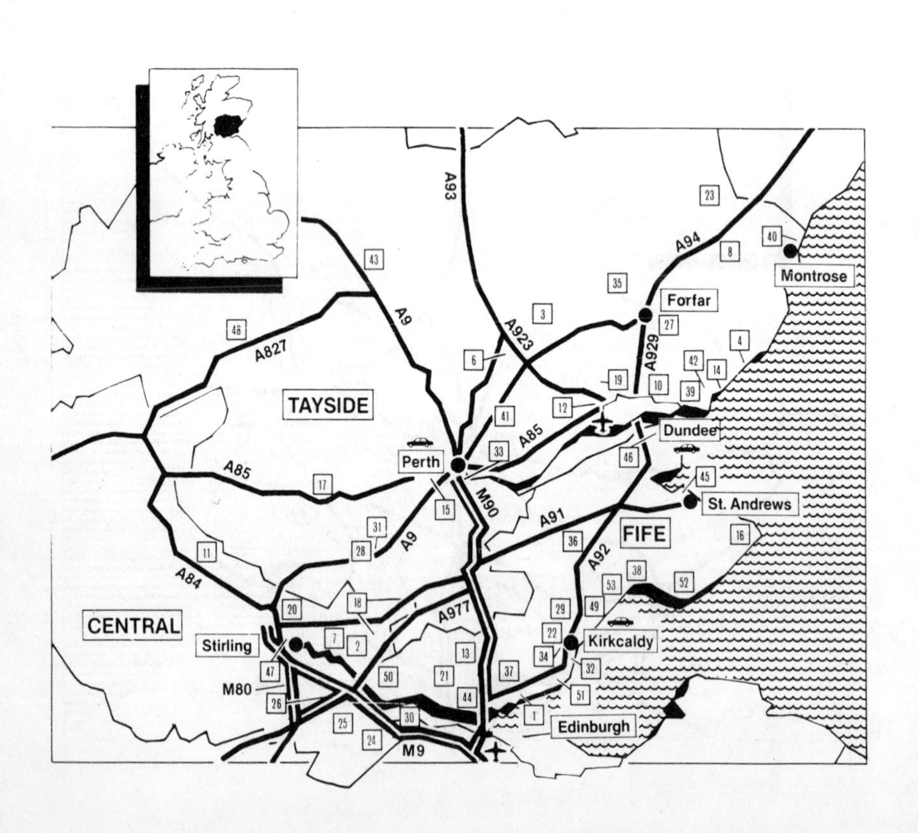

HIGHLAND

TOWN	GOLF COURSE		TEL	◆	MAP REF.
Achnasheen	Gairloch		(0445) 2407		•
Aviemore	Boat of Garten	★	(047983) 282	◆	5
	Kingussie	☆	(05402) 374		24
	Newtonmore		(05403) 128		30
Dingwall	Alness				•
	Invergordon				•
	Strathpeffer Spa		(0997) 21219		42
Dornoch	Brora	☆	(04082) 1417	◆	7
	Golspie			◆	18
	Royal Dornoch	★★★	(0862) 810219	◆	35
Fort August	Fort August		(0320) 6333		•
Fort William	Fort William	☆	(0397) 4464		16
Grantown-on-Spey	Grantown-on-Spey	☆	(0479) 2079		12
Inverness	Fortrose & Rosemarkie	☆	(0381) 20529		15
	Inverness	★	(0463) 239882		21
	Muir of Ord		(0463) 870286		26
Nairn	Nairn	★★★	(0667) 53208	◆	28
	Nairn Dunbar	☆	(0667) 52741		29
Portree	Sconser				•
Tain	Tain		(0862) 2314		44
Thurso	Reay		(084781) 288		33
	Thurso		(0847) 63807		45
Wick	Wick	☆	(0955) 2726		•

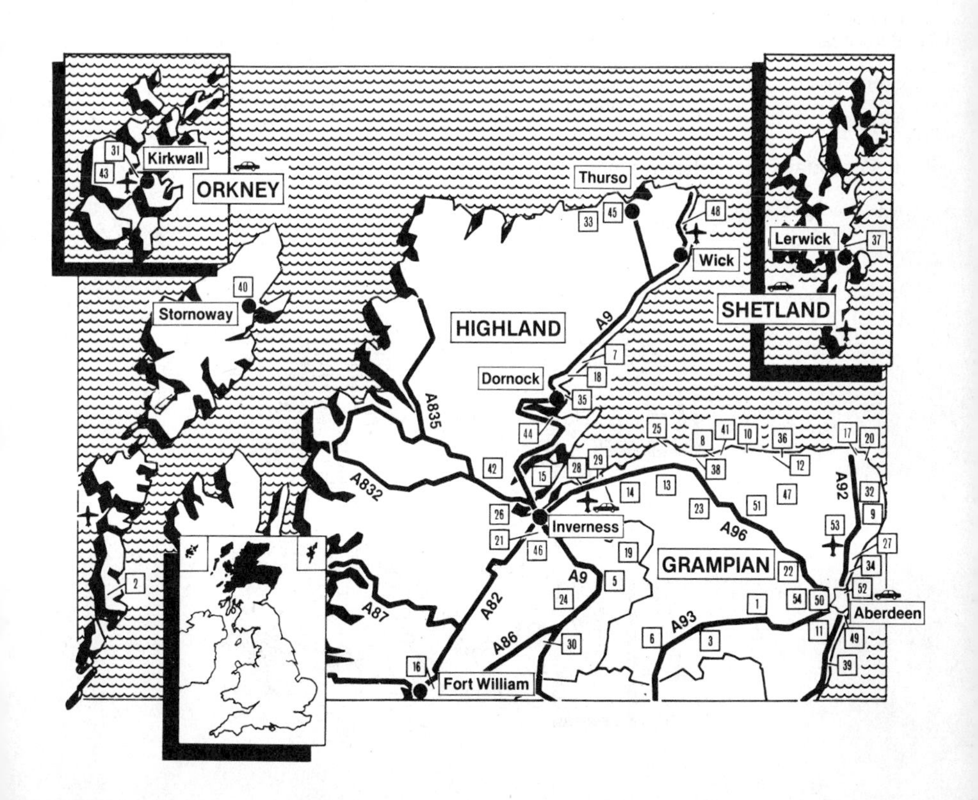

GRAMPIAN

TOWN	GOLF COURSE		TEL	♦	MAP REF.
Aberdeen	Deesside		(0224) 867697		11
	Hazlehead		(0224) 23456		50
	King's Links		(0224) 632269		52
	Murcar	☆	(0224) 704354		27
	Royal Aberdeen	★★	(0224) 702571	♦	34
	Westhill		(0224) 740159		54
Aboyne	Aboyne	☆	(0339) 2328		1
	Tarland		(033981) 413		•
Banchory	Banchory		(03302) 2365		4
	Torphins		(033982) 493		•
Banff	Duff House Royal	★	(02612) 2062		12
	Royal Tarlair	☆	(0261) 32897		36
Braemar	Ballater		(0338) 55567		3
	Braemar	☆	(03383) 618		6
Buckie	Buckpool		(0542) 32236		8
	Cullen	☆	(0542) 40685		10
	Strathlene		(0542) 31798		41
Elgin	Elgin	☆	(0343) 2338		13
	Hopeman		(0343) 830578		•
Ellon	McDonald		(0358) 20576		53
Forres	Forres		(0309) 72949		14
Fraserburgh	Fraserburgh	★	(0346) 28287		17
Huntly	Huntly		(0466) 2643		51
Inverurie	Inverurie		(0467) 24080		22
	Kintore				•
Lossiemouth	Moray	★★	(034381) 2018	♦	25
	Spey Bay	☆	(0343) 820362		38
Old Meldrum	Old Meldrum		(0467) 20314		•
Peterhead	Cruden Bay	☆	(0779) 812285		9
	Peterhead		(0779) 72149		32
Stonehaven	Auchenblae				•
	Stonehaven	★	(0569) 62124		39
Turriff	Turriff		(0888) 62745		47

♦ For details, see following pages.

• 9 hole golf course.

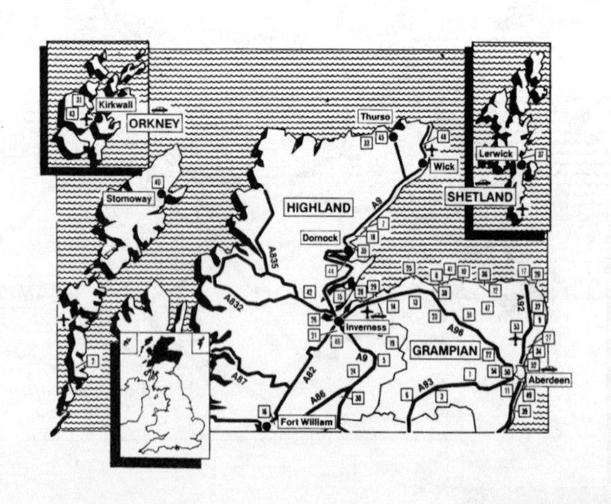

WESTERN ISLES

TOWN	GOLF COURSE	TEL	♦	MAP REF.
Stornoway	Stornoway	(0851) 2240		40

ORKNEY & SHETLAND

TOWN	GOLF COURSE	TEL	♦	MAP REF.
Kirkwall	Orkney	(0856) 2457		31
Lerwick	Shetland	(059584) 369		37
Stromness (Orkney)	Stromness	(0856) 850245		43
Westray (Orkney)	Westray	(0856) 2197		•

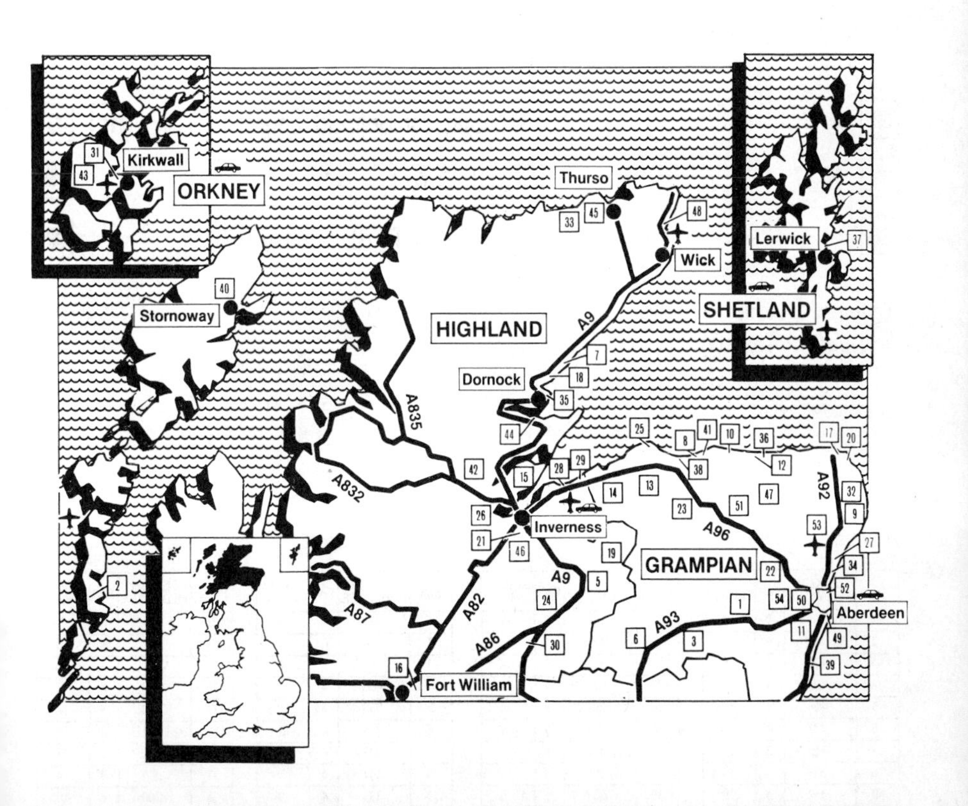

AYR BELLEISLE

★

TEL : (0292)41258
LOCATION : 2 m Ayr A 719
ADDRESS : Doonfoot Rd – Ayr – Ayrshire
HOTEL :
Belleisle House – Ayr
Tel : (0292)42331
Balgarth – Alloway
Tel : (0292)42441
Pickwick – Ayr
Tel : (0292)260111
RESTAURANT : Miller's Table – Ayr
Tel : (0292)63268

These two popular inland courses are run by the municipality of Ayr. The Belleisle course, designed by James Braid, is a parkland course of championship standard with various fine dogleg holes. The fairways are tree-lined with beeches and streams meander their way through several of them. The course commands fine views overlooking the sea and the Island of Arran. The Seafield course has shorter holes with small greens and is ideal for family golf. *SSS 71*

GF $

1927

36

Sun. for Seafield Course

J. Braid

L 6540 y P 70, 5244 y P 66

Required : None
Best days : Any day

Belleisle Course

HOLE	LENGTH MEDAL-TEE	PAR	STROKE INDEX
1	477	5	10
2	471	4	3
3	179	3	15
4	424	4	7
5	408	4	11
6	431	4	1
7	145	3	17
8	338	4	13
9	352	4	5
TOTAL	3225	35	TOTAL

HOLE	LENGTH MEDAL-TEE	PAR	STROKE INDEX
10	192	3	18
11	433	4	4
12	428	4	12
13	435	4	8
14	202	3	14
15	481	5	9
16	407	4	2
17	200	3	16
18	537	5	6
TOTAL	3315	35	TOTAL

Seafield Course

HOLE	LENGTH MEDAL-TEE	PAR	STROKE INDEX
1	221	3	15
2	374	4	3
3	167	3	17
4	400	4	1
5	255	4	11
6	245	3	13
7	337	4	7
8	347	4	5
9	333	4	9
TOTAL	2679	33	TOTAL

HOLE	LENGTH MEDAL-TEE	PAR	STROKE INDEX
217	3	14	
11	307	4	8
12	411	4	6
13	437	4	2
14	260	4	12
15	127	3	18
16	202	3	16
17	304	4	4
18	300	4	10
TOTAL	2565	33	TOTAL

BLAIRGOWRIE

TEL : (0250)2383
LOCATION : 15 m Dundee A 93
ADDRESS : Rosemount – Blairgowrie – Perthshire
HOTEL :
Dalmunzie – Blairgowrie
Tel : (025085)224
Altamount House – Blairgowrie
Tel : (0250)3512
Kinloch House – Blairgowrie
Tel : (025084)237
RESTAURANT : Stormont Lodge – Blairgowrie
Tel : (0250)2853

Of the two 18 hole courses, the Rosemount course, laid out in the dense Rosemount Woods, is considered one of Scotland's best inland courses, picturesquely set amid pine, fir, silver birch and heather. Each isolated hole has its own individual character, with generous lush fairways and large greens. Its feature hole is the 16th crossing a lake 'the Black Loch', to a narrow green in the woods. *SSS 72/73*

 $

 1889

45

 Wednesdays

 A. Mackenzie

L 6581 y P 72, 6865 y P 72

Required : Handicap Certificate, Introduction Letter
Best days : Weekdays

Rosemount Course

HOLE	LENGTH MEDAL-TEE	PAR	STROKE INDEX
1	442	4	5
2	338	4	12
3	221	3	15
4	407	4	1
5	537	5	7
6	189	3	17
7	378	4	10
8	365	4	3
9	328	4	14
TOTAL	3205	35	TOTAL

HOLE	LENGTH MEDAL-TEE	PAR	STROKE INDEX
10	509	5	11
11	505	5	4
12	295	4	13
13	401	4	8
14	511	5	2
15	129	3	18
16	469	4	6
17	169	3	16
18	388	4	9
TOTAL	3376	37	TOTAL

Landsdowne

HOLE	LENGTH MEDAL-TEE	PAR	STROKE INDEX
1	486	5	9
2	375	4	7
3	454	4	1
4	367	4	13
5	167	3	15
6	391	4	5
7	448	4	3
8	533	5	11
9	153	3	17
TOTAL	3374	36	TOTAL

HOLE	LENGTH MEDAL-TEE	PAR	STROKE INDEX
10	379	4	6
11	366	4	18
12	407	4	4
13	371	4	10
14	211	3	14
15	440	4	2
16	363	4	16
17	552	5	12
18	402	4	8
TOTAL	3491	36	TOTAL

BOAT OF GARTEN

★

TEL : (047983)282
LOCATION : 10 km N. Aviemore
ADDRESS : Boat of Garten – Inverness-shire
HOTEL :
Craigard – Boat of Garten
Tel : (047983)206
Moorfield House – Boat of Garten
Tel : (047983)646
The Boat – Boat of Garten
Tel : (047983)258

A very challenging and picturesque inland course, considered one of the best in Scotland. Laid out on undulating terrain, the holes are cut partly on moorland, partly through silver birch woods. Its feature holes include the 6th, one of the most testing Scottish dogleg holes. The course is backed by the snow capped Cairngorm mountains. *SSS 68*

GF $ — 1898 — 18

— J. Braid — L 5720 y P 69

S — R

Required : None
Best days : Any day

HOLE	LENGTH MEDAL-TEE	PAR	STROKE INDEX
1	186	3	
2	347	4	
3	146	3	
4	484	5	
5	333	4	
6	403	4	
7	382	4	
8	353	4	
9	150	3	
TOTAL	2784	34	TOTAL

HOLE	LENGTH MEDAL-TEE	PAR	STROKE INDEX
10	265	4	
11	369	4	
12	339	4	
13	436	4	
14	274	4	
15	305	4	
16	167	3	
17	346	4	
18	435	4	
TOTAL	2936	35	TOTAL

BRODICK

TEL : (0770)2349
LOCATION : 1 km Brodick Pier
ADDRESS : Brodick – Isle of Arran
HOTEL :
Douglas – Brodick
Tel : (0770)2155
Auchrannie – Brodick
Tel : (0770)2234
Kinloch – Blackwaterfoot
Tel : (077086)444
RESTAURANT : Kingsley – Brodick
Tel : (0770)2226

Set on the island of Arran near the Clyde coast of Scotland, the short Brodick course is ideal for holiday golf. It is laid out alongside the beach on rugged countryside with trees landscaping the holes. *SSS 62*

 $ — — 

1897 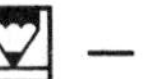 — 

  4404 y P 62 

Required : None
Best days : Any day

HOLE	LENGTH MEDAL-TEE	PAR	STROKE INDEX
1	216	3	
2	148	3	
3	233	3	
4	401	4	
5	293	4	
6	133	3	
7	126	3	
8	170	3	
9	374	4	
TOTAL	2094	30	TOTAL

HOLE	LENGTH MEDAL-TEE	PAR	STROKE INDEX
10	377	4	
11	368	4	
12	287	4	
13	191	3	
14	163	3	
15	127	3	
16	278	4	
17	299	4	
18	220	3	
TOTAL	2310	32	TOTAL

BRORA

TEL : (04082)1417
LOCATION : 25 km N. Dornoch A 9
ADDRESS : Golf Road – Brora – Sutherland
HOTEL :
Golf Links
Tel : (04082)225
RESTAURANT : Golden Fry – Brora
Tel : (04082)327

Designed by James Braid in 1889, Brora is a natural links built on rising ground overlooking the tiny village of Brora. A fine holiday course with a pleasant layout in the Dornoch area. *SSS 69*

GF $

1889

18

—

J. Braid

L 6110 y P 69

Required : None
Best days : Any day

HOLE	LENGTH MEDAL-TEE	PAR	STROKE INDEX
1	297	4	13
2	344	4	9
3	447	4	1
4	325	4	15
5	428	4	3
6	174	3	7
7	350	4	11
8	501	5	5
9	162	3	17
TOTAL	3028	35	TOTAL

HOLE	LENGTH MEDAL-TEE	PAR	STROKE INDEX
10	435	4	6
11	412	4	8
12	362	4	10
13	125	3	18
14	334	4	16
15	430	4	2
16	345	4	12
17	438	4	4
18	201	3	14
TOTAL	3082	34	TOTAL

BRUNTSFIELD LINKS

EDINBURGH

★

TEL : (031)3361479
LOCATION : 5 m W. Edinburgh off A 90
ADDRESS : Barnton Av. – Davidson's Mains – Edinburgh – Midlothian
HOTEL :
Barnton – Edinburgh
Tel : (031)3391144
Carlton Highland – Edinburgh
Tel : (031)5567277
Embassy – Ellersley House – Edinburgh
Tel : (031)3376888
RESTAURANT : Doric Tavern – Edinburgh
Tel : (031)2251084

The Bruntsfield Links Golfing Society is adjacent to the equally famous Royal Burgess Golfing Society, laid out in beautiful verdant parkland on the edge of Edinburgh. One of the most ancient and prestigious clubs in the world as golf goes back here to 1761.
SSS 71

GF $$
1761
18

Weekends
J. Braid
L 6407 y P 71

R S

Required : Handicap Certificate, Introduction Letter
Best days : Weekdays

HOLE	LENGTH MEDAL-TEE	PAR	STROKE INDEX
1	419	4	7
2	381	4	11
3	487	5	9
4	549	5	1
5	205	3	15
6	332	4	5
7	157	3	18
8	382	4	13
9	354	4	4
TOTAL	3266	36	TOTAL

HOLE	LENGTH MEDAL-TEE	PAR	STROKE INDEX
10	339	4	10
11	415	4	3
12	168	3	16
13	455	4	8
14	493	5	2
15	170	3	17
16	373	4	12
17	381	4	6
18	347	4	14
TOTAL	3141	35	TOTAL

CARNOUSTIE COURSES

★★★

TEL : (0241)53789/53249
LOCATION : 12 m E. of Dundee
ADDRESS : Links Parade – Carnoustie – Angus
HOTEL :
Glencoe – Carnoustie
Tel : (0241)53273
Stakis Earl Grey – Dundee
Tel : (0382)29271
Queen's – Dundee
Tel : (0382)22515
RESTAURANT : Brax – Carnoustie
Tel : (0241)53032

The world famous and legendary Carnoustie links, consists of three fine courses, the great Championship layout, the less tough but subtler Burnside course and the recently constructed Buddon Links course. Golf goes back to the 16th century in Carnoustie when Sir Robert Maule, one of the first known golfers, hit a ball here. Most important is the Championship course, a tough course with very long holes, a prevailing wind, and fast greens. Set on flat terrain between the estuary and distant low hills, every hole has its own character with the treacherous Jockie's burn, and the winding Barry burn, crossing several of them. Carnoustie has hosted the Open numerous times welcoming the greatest golfers in history. *SSS 74/69/71*

GF $

1845

54

—

A. Robertson, T. Morris, J. Braid

L 6936 y P 72, 5732 y P 69, 6020 y P 68

S

R

Required : Handicap Certificate
Best days : Weekdays only

HOLE	LENGTH MEDAL-TEE	PAR	STROKE INDEX
1	407	4	7
2	425	4	3
3	342	4	15
4	375	4	11
5	387	4	13
6	524	5	1
7	390	4	9
8	168	3	17
9	420	4	5
TOTAL	3438	36	TOTAL

HOLE	LENGTH MEDAL-TEE	PAR	STROKE INDEX
10	446	4	8
11	353	4	14
12	477	5	4
13	161	3	18
14	483	5	2
15	456	4	12
16	245	3	16
17	433	4	6
18	444	4	10
TOTAL	3498	36	TOTAL

CARNOUSTIE COURSES

Burnside Course

HOLE	LENGTH MEDAL-TEE	PAR	STROKE INDEX
1	324	4	7
2	450	4	3
3	175	3	17
4	460	4	1
5	158	3	9
6	348	4	15
7	360	4	11
8	432	4	5
9	163	3	13
TOTAL	2870	33	TOTAL

HOLE	LENGTH MEDAL-TEE	PAR	STROKE INDEX
10	336	4	14
11	375	4	10
12	386	4	6
13	382	4	8
14	228	3	12
15	500	5	2
16	163	3	18
17	473	4	4
18	307	4	16
TOTAL	3150	35	TOTAL

Buddon Links

HOLE	LENGTH MEDAL-TEE	PAR	STROKE INDEX
1	280	4	13
2	184	3	15
3	395	4	9
4	525	5	1
5	403	4	3
6	176	3	17
7	393	4	7
8	326	4	11
9	480	5	5
TOTAL	3162	36	TOTAL

HOLE	LENGTH MEDAL-TEE	PAR	STROKE INDEX
10	364	4	8
11	386	4	6
12	175	3	12
13	410	4	2
14	165	3	14
15	486	5	4
16	166	3	18
17	148	3	16
18	270	4	10
TOTAL	2570	33	TOTAL

CRAIL GOLFING SOCIETY

★

BALCOMIE GOLF COURSE

TEL : (0333)50686
LOCATION : 15 km SE St-Andrews
ADDRESS : Balcomie Clubhouse – Fifeness – Crail
HOTEL :
Marine – Crail
Tel : (0333)50207
Rufflets Country House – St-Andrews
Tel : (0334)72594
Rusacks – St-Andrews
Tel : (0334)74321
RESTAURANT : Croma – Crail
Tel : (0333)50239

A most renowned golf club (the seventh oldest in the world) dating back to 1786 with a fine classic links course, set on rugged countryside and some parkland near the outstanding golfing resort of St. Andrews in the Fife region. The course follows the coastline and every hole is within sight of the sea. The clubhouse stands on a commanding position offering panoramic views out to the North Sea. *SSS 68*

GF $

1786

18

—

—

L 5720 y P 69

S

R

Required : None
Best days : Weekdays

HOLE	LENGTH MEDAL-TEE	PAR	STROKE INDEX
1	312	4	15
2	480	5	3
3	179	3	17
4	348	4	7
5	346	4	5
6	334	4	11
7	421	4	1
8	306	4	13
9	334	4	9
TOTAL	3060	36	TOTAL

HOLE	LENGTH MEDAL-TEE	PAR	STROKE INDEX
10	209	3	12
11	500	5	2
12	489	5	6
13	215	3	8
14	149	3	16
15	265	4	18
16	163	3	14
17	461	4	4
18	209	3	10
TOTAL	2660	33	TOTAL

DALMAHOY

★★

TEL : (031)3331845/3332055
LOCATION : 12 m SW. Edinburgh A 71
ADDRESS : Kirknewton - Midlothian
HOTEL : HP
Dalmahoy House
Tel : (031)3331845
Ladbroke Dragonara - Edinburgh
Tel : (031)3322545
Post House - Edinburgh
Tel : (031)3348221

Both courses were laid out by James Braid on rolling woodland with a picturesque lake. The East Course is of championship standard and set on varied countryside, the West Course is more suitable for the less experienced golfers. The clubhouse, Dalmahoy House, was built in 1725 for the Earl of Morton and is still owned by the family. It is a magnificent Georgian House set in 1000 acres of countryside at the foot of the Pentland Hills. Other sports facilities include horse riding, trout fishing, clay pigeon shooting and archery. The Dalmahoy Hotel opposite the club is a small country hotel. *SSS 72/66*

GF $$

1927

36

—

J. Braid

L 6664 y P 72, 5212 y P 67

 S

R 

Required : None
Best days : Any day

East Course

HOLE	LENGTH MEDAL-TEE	PAR	STROKE INDEX
1	505	5	13
2	435	4	3
3	416	4	7
4	430	4	11
5	461	4	5
6	149	3	17
7	423	4	1
8	309	4	15
9	321	4	9
TOTAL	3449	36	TOTAL

HOLE	LENGTH MEDAL-TEE	PAR	STROKE INDEX
10	495	5	10
11	406	4	6
12	431	4	2
13	145	3	18
14	306	4	16
15	390	4	4
16	206	3	14
17	356	4	8
18	480	5	12
TOTAL	3215	36	TOTAL

West Course

HOLE	LENGTH MEDAL-TEE	PAR	STROKE INDEX
1	368	4	2
2	278	4	9
3	128	3	18
4	375	4	3
5	311	4	7
6	273	4	12
7	260	4	14
8	336	4	5
9	246	3	17
TOTAL	2575	34	TOTAL

HOLE	LENGTH MEDAL-TEE	PAR	STROKE INDEX
10	169	3	11
11	366	4	6
12	341	4	8
13	543	5	1
14	343	4	13
15	129	3	15
16	248	3	4
17	244	3	10
18	254	4	16
TOTAL	2637	33	TOTAL

DOWNFIELD

★★

TEL : (0382)825595
LOCATION : N. Dundee A 923
ADDRESS : Turnberry Ave – Dundee – Angus
HOTEL :
Queens – Dundee
Tel : (0382)22515
Angus Thistle – Dundee
Tel : (0382)26874
Swallow – Dundee
Tel : (0382)641122
RESTAURANT : Gunga Din – Dundee
Tel : (0382)65672

This fine championship golf course is a typical, gently rolling inland course (one of Scotlands best) with tree-lined fairways, numerous water hazards such as ponds, ditches and the Gelly Burn winding its way through several fairways. The club hosted the Scottish Professional Championships and the British Ladies Stroke Play championships. *SSS 73*

GF $ — Weekends — R S
1932 — —
18 — L 6804 y P 73

Required : None
Best days : Weekdays only

HOLE	LENGTH MEDAL-TEE	PAR	STROKE INDEX
1	425	4	9
2	408	4	5
3	228	3	15
4	538	5	1
5	412	4	7
6	177	3	17
7	491	5	3
8	407	4	13
9	414	4	11
TOTAL	3500	36	TOTAL

HOLE	LENGTH MEDAL-TEE	PAR	STROKE INDEX
10	434	4	8
11	480	5	4
12	182	3	16
13	480	5	6
14	515	5	2
15	326	4	14
16	352	4	12
17	151	3	18
18	384	4	10
TOTAL	3304	37	TOTAL

GLENEAGLES HOTEL

TEL : (0764)62231
Telex 76105
LOCATION : 16 m S.W. Perth A 9,
2 m SW. Auchterarder
ADDRESS : Auchterarder – Perthshire
HOTEL : HR
Gleneagles Hotel
Tel : (0764)62231

Situated amidst the beautiful Perthshire moors at 500 feet above sea level on undulating terrain, Gleneagles Hotel and its four marvellous golf courses have grown into a legend, attracting golfers worldwide. Gleneagles, Scotland's finest hotel awarded a five-star rating, is set amid 830 acres and surrounded by unspoiled countryside. A 'Versailles' style castle with 210 bedrooms, as well as an indoor swimming pool, jaccuzzi, sauna, turkish bath, tennis and squash courts, bowling, crocket, shooting school, equestrian centre and a 9 hole pitch and putt course. The King's and the Queen's courses were designed by the legendary James Braid. The noble King's is the longest and most renowned of the four, scenically laid out overlooking the Ochil Hills. Bunkers are deep and punishing, whilst the greens are very large and undulating. It features one of the world's most famous holes, the relentless 13th, 'Braid's Brawest'. The Queen's course is shorter with fairways tree-lined with firs, two severe dogleg holes, the 13th and 14th, as well as a scenic lake 'Loch-an-Eerie'. The Prince's course, opened in 1930 and the Glendevon course, opened in 1980, are being combined with some new land to make a new championship course which is going to be designed by Jack Nicklaus. *SSS 69/69*

GF $$ — S
1919 J. Braid 
72 L 6471 y P 70, 5965 y P 68 RF 

Required : None
Best days : Any day

GLENEAGLES HOTEL

King's Course

HOLE	LENGTH MEDAL-TEE	PAR	STROKE INDEX
1	362	4	6
2	405	4	14
3	374	4	9
4	466	4	2
5	161	3	16
6	476	5	8
7	439	4	4
8	158	3	17
9	351	4	12
TOTAL	3195	35	TOTAL

HOLE	LENGTH MEDAL-TEE	PAR	STROKE INDEX
10	447	4	1
11	230	3	10
12	395	4	13
13	448	4	7
14	260	4	15
15	459	4	3
16	135	3	18
17	377	4	11
18	525	5	5
TOTAL	3276	35	TOTAL

Queen's Course

HOLE	LENGTH MEDAL-TEE	PAR	STROKE INDEX
1	409	4	5
2	146	3	17
3	421	4	1
4	355	4	10
5	177	3	15
6	437	4	6
7	491	5	8
8	337	4	12
9	419	4	2
TOTAL	3192	35	TOTAL

HOLE	LENGTH MEDAL-TEE	PAR	STROKE INDEX
10	421	4	4
11	318	4	13
12	433	4	3
13	140	3	18
14	215	3	9
15	252	4	16
16	378	4	11
17	204	3	14
18	412	4	7
TOTAL	2773	33	TOTAL

GULLANE

TEL : (0620)842255
LOCATION : 29 km NE. Edinburgh, off A 198
ADDRESS : Gullane – East Lothian
HOTEL :
Greywalls – Gullane
Tel : (0620)842144
Bisset's – Gullane
Tel : (0620)842230
Open Arms – Dirleton
Tel : (062085)241
RESTAURANT : La Potinière – Gullane
Tel : (0620)843214

Located in the great and sporty golfing resort of Gullane, the Gullane golf courses rate among the best in Scotland. There are three first-class seaside and downland courses adjacent to the Muirfield and Luffness golf courses. The excellent No 1 course, partly laid out on a hill, is the most testing one with fine views of the sea, the Lothians and Edinburgh. The course is of championship standard and is used as a qualifying course when the Open is held at Muirfield. The No 2 course is less tough, and the short No 3 course is ideal for holiday golf. *SSS 71/69/64*

GF $$

1882

54

—

—

L 6491 y P 71, 6127 y P 70, 5035 y P 65

S

R

Required : None
Best days : Any day ; booking in advance for N°1 Course

HOLE	LENGTH MEDAL-TEE	PAR	STROKE INDEX
1	304	4	14
2	378	4	4
3	498	5	8
4	142	3	18
5	445	4	1
6	325	4	16
7	400	4	6
8	364	4	10
9	152	3	12
TOTAL	3008	35	TOTAL

HOLE	LENGTH MEDAL-TEE	PAR	STROKE INDEX
10	470	4	7
11	472	4	2
12	478	5	11
13	165	3	15
14	430	4	3
15	538	5	9
16	187	3	13
17	384	4	5
18	359	4	17
TOTAL	3483	36	TOTAL

GULLANE

Nº2 Course

HOLE	LENGTH MEDAL-TEE	PAR	STROKE INDEX
1	366	4	9
2	334	4	3
3	237	3	13
4	425	4	1
5	171	3	17
6	498	5	5
7	358	4	15
8	393	4	7
9	354	4	11
TOTAL	3136	35	TOTAL

HOLE	LENGTH MEDAL-TEE	PAR	STROKE INDEX
10	350	4	6
11	215	3	16
12	408	4	10
13	386	4	2
14	336	4	12
15	164	3	18
16	476	5	4
17	361	4	8
18	295	4	14
TOTAL	2991	35	TOTAL

Nº3 Course

HOLE	LENGTH MEDAL-TEE	PAR	STROKE INDEX
1	345	4	3
2	144	3	17
3	257	4	5
4	250	3	13
5	314	4	7
6	342	4	1
7	311	4	11
8	165	3	15
9	327	4	9
TOTAL	2455	33	TOTAL

HOLE	LENGTH MEDAL-TEE	PAR	STROKE INDEX
10	450	4	4
11	360	4	8
12	186	3	14
13	426	4	2
14	169	3	12
15	281	4	10
16	149	3	18
17	328	4	6
18	231	3	16
TOTAL	2580	32	TOTAL

HONOURABLE COMPANY OF EDINBURGH GOLFERS (Muirfield)

★★★

TEL : (0620)842123
LOCATION : 15 m E. Edinburgh
ADDRESS : Muirfield – Gullane – East Lothian
HOTEL : HP
Greywalls – Gullane
Tel : (0620)842144
Bisset's – Gullane
Tel : (0620)842230
Marine – North Berwick
Tel : (0620)2406
RESTAURANT : La Potinière – Gullane
Tel : (0620)843214

Muirfield is the home of the Honourable Company of Edinburgh Golfers, and one of the noblest and oldest golf clubs in the world, having been founded in 1744. They are the lineal descendants of the 'Gentlemen Golfers' who played at Leith Links from at least the 15th century. In 1744 they drew up the first set of golf rules. The Honourable Company arrived at Muirfield in 1891, previously playing at Luffness and Musselburgh. The course is a classic links with around 150 well-designed bunkers and fast greens. It has hosted more championships than any other club in Britain, welcoming the British Open thirteen times. Preserving all the traditional qualities of the game on the course and in the clubhouse, they do not permit medal-play, four-ball games during weekends. Women are still not permitted in the clubhouse. The adjoining Greywalls Hotel is one of Scotland's most famous and elegant golf hotels. *SSS 73*

GF $$ | Weekends, Mon., Wed. | S
1744 | D. Plenderleith, T. Morris | R
18 | L 6601 y P 70

Required : Handicap Certificate, Introduction Letter
Best days : Tuesdays, Thursday and Friday mornings only

HOLE	LENGTH MEDAL-TEE	PAR	STROKE INDEX
1	444	4	
2	345	4	
3	374	4	
4	174	3	
5	506	5	
6	436	4	
7	151	3	
8	439	4	
9	460	4	
TOTAL	3329	35	TOTAL

HOLE	LENGTH MEDAL-TEE	PAR	STROKE INDEX
10	471	4	
11	350	4	
12	376	4	
13	146	3	
14	442	4	
15	391	4	
16	181	3	
17	501	5	
18	414	4	
TOTAL	3272	35	TOTAL

ISLAY

TEL : (0496)2310
LOCATION : In Port Ellen
ADDRESS : Port Ellen – Isle of Islay – Argyll
HOTEL : Hr
Machrie
Tel : (0496)2310
Lochside – Bowmore
Tel : (049681)244
Port Askaig – Port Askaig
Tel : (049684)245

Originally set out by Willie Campbell in 1891 and redesigned in 1978 by Donald Steele, this scenic links is located on one of the Hebridean Islands, the Isle of Islay. It borders Laggan Bay overlooking beaches, mountains, headlands, sandhills and sea. The only building for miles is the Machrie Hotel with its 22 bedrooms and 15 de-luxe cottages with facilities such as fishing (salmon, trout), clay pigeon shooting, trekking, sailing, riding plus visits to numerous malt whisky distilleries. *SSS 70*

GF $ — R S

1891 W. Campbell, D. Steele 

18 L 6226 y P 71  

Required : None
Best days : Any day

HOLE	LENGTH MEDAL-TEE	PAR	STROKE INDEX
1	308	4	12
2	508	5	2
3	319	4	17
4	390	4	8
5	163	3	18
6	344	4	10
7	395	4	3
8	337	4	14
9	392	4	15
TOTAL	3156	36	TOTAL

HOLE	LENGTH MEDAL-TEE	PAR	STROKE INDEX
10	156	3	16
11	357	4	15
12	174	3	7
13	488	5	9
14	423	4	1
15	335	4	13
16	411	4	4
17	352	4	11
18	374	4	6
TOTAL	3070	35	TOTAL

MOFFAT

★★

TEL : (0683)20020
LOCATION : On A 701, N. of Moffat
ADDRESS : Coateshill – Moffat – Dumfriesshire
HOTEL :
Beechwood Country House – Moffat
Tel : (0683)20210
Ladbroke – Moffat
Tel : (0683)20464
Moffat House – Moffat
Tel : (0683)20039
RESTAURANT : Arden House – Moffat
Tel : (0683)20220

A first class moorland course laid out high above the former spa town of Moffat with panomaric views over Upper Annandale town, the mountains and on a good day the Solway coast and Anna Valley. *SSS 66*

GF $ — Wednesdays — R 

1884 —  B. Sayer — 

18 — L 5218 y P 69 — 

Required : Handicap Certificate
Best days : Weekdays

HOLE	LENGTH MEDAL-TEE	PAR	STROKE INDEX
1	203	3	
2	331	4	
3	346	4	
4	276	4	
5	291	4	
6	267	4	
7	334	4	
8	390	4	
9	125	3	
TOTAL	2563	34	TOTAL

HOLE	LENGTH MEDAL-TEE	PAR	STROKE INDEX
10	342	4	
11	381	4	
12	251	4	
13	141	3	
14	476	5	
15	364	4	
16	144	3	
17	285	4	
18	271	4	
TOTAL	2655	35	TOTAL

MONIFIETH

TEL : (0382)532767
LOCATION : 6 m Dundee A 930
ADDRESS : Princes Str. – Monifieth
HOTEL :
Monifieth – Monifieth
Tel : (0382)532630
Glencoe – Carnoustie
Tel : (0241)53272
Queen's – Dundee
Tel : (0382)22515

Situated between Dundee and Carnoustie, these are two fine traditional links courses but different from most in that a great number of holes are tree-lined with pines. The championship Medal Course is used as a qualifying course when the British Open is at Carnoustie. It is set between a railway line and the town of Monifieth. A burn affects play on the 6th and 7th holes. The shorter Ashludie course features several testing holes demanding great accuracy. Records have shown that golf was being played at Monifieth in the beginning of the 17th century. *SSS 72/66*

GF $

1858

36

Saturdays

—

L 6657 y P 71, 5123 y P 68

Required : None
Best days : Any day

Medal Course

HOLE	LENGTH MEDAL-TEE	PAR	STROKE INDEX
1	324	4	13
2	416	4	9
3	431	4	11
4	454	4	5
5	195	3	15
6	378	4	3
7	419	4	7
8	285	4	17
9	544	5	1
TOTAL	3446	36	TOTAL

HOLE	LENGTH MEDAL-TEE	PAR	STROKE INDEX
10	371	4	14
11	183	3	16
12	378	4	6
13	436	4	2
14	154	3	18
15	380	4	10
16	342	4	12
17	437	4	4
18	530	5	8
TOTAL	3211	35	TOTAL

Ashludie Course

HOLE	LENGTH MEDAL-TEE	PAR	STROKE INDEX
1	275	4	
2	338	4	
3	100	3	
4	274	4	
5	296	4	
6	143	3	
7	445	4	
8	339	4	
9	160	3	
TOTAL	2370	33	TOTAL

HOLE	LENGTH MEDAL-TEE	PAR	STROKE INDEX
10	312	4	
11	294	4	
12	379	4	
13	259	4	
14	252	4	
15	338	4	
16	143	3	
17	448	4	
18	328	4	
TOTAL	2753	35	TOTAL

★★

TEL : (034381)2018
LOCATION : 9 km N. Elgin A 96
ADDRESS : Stofield Rd – Lossiemouth – Morayshire
HOTEL :
Stotfield – Lossiemouth
Tel : (034381)2011
Mansion House – Elgin
Tel : (0343)48811
Park House – Elgin
Tel : (0343)7695
RESTAURANT : Huntly House – Lossiemouth
Tel : (034381)2085

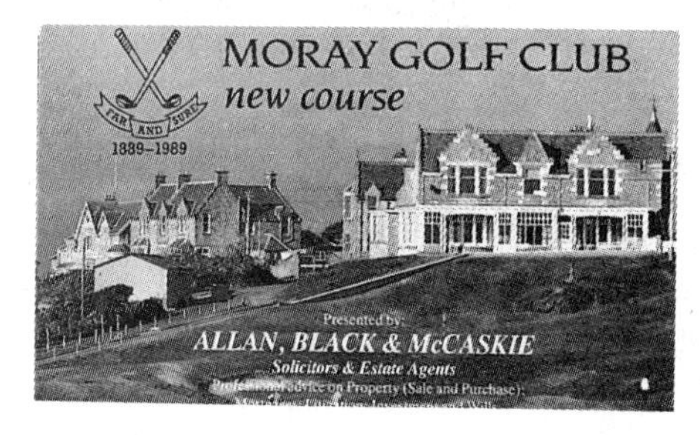

'Old Moray' was laid out in 1889 by Tom Morris and 'New Moray' was designed by Henry Cotton and inaugurated in 1979. Both courses are first class natural links courses set behind the beach and the dunes with each hole having its own personality. The fairways are undulating and flanked by sandhills and gorse, the greens are large and flat. The 18th of the fine Old Course, laid out along a valley, is considered to be the noblest finishing hole in Scotland. 'New Moray' is ideal for family golf. *SSS 72/71*

$$

1889

—

T. Morris, H. Cotton

6643 P 71, 6005 P 70

R

Required : Handicap Certificate
Best days : Any day

Old Moray

HOLE	LENGTH MEDAL-TEE	PAR	STROKE INDEX
1	333	4	11
2	493	5	3
3	400	4	8
4	203	3	13
5	419	4	6
6	141	3	17
7	439	4	9
8	460	4	1
9	316	4	15
TOTAL	3204	35	TOTAL

HOLE	LENGTH MEDAL-TEE	PAR	STROKE INDEX
10	314	4	14
11	415	4	2
12	402	4	10
13	422	4	4
14	417	4	7
15	190	3	18
16	359	4	12
17	497	5	5
18	423	4	16
TOTAL	3439	36	TOTAL

New Moray

HOLE	LENGTH MEDAL-TEE	PAR	STROKE INDEX
1	361	4	10
2	322	4	14
3	420	4	2
4	141	3	16
5	362	4	5
6	103	3	18
7	426	4	7
8	411	4	3
9	364	4	12
TOTAL	2910	34	TOTAL

HOLE	LENGTH MEDAL-TEE	PAR	STROKE INDEX
10	323	4	9
11	158	3	17
12	445	4	4
13	347	4	11
14	503	5	1
15	404	4	6
16	319	4	13
17	177	3	15
18	419	4	8
TOTAL	3095	35	TOTAL

NAIRN

TEL : (0667)53208
LOCATION : 1,5 km W. Nairn A 96
ADDRESS : Seabank Rd – Nairnshire
HOTEL : HR
Golf View
Tel : (0667)52301
Clifton – Nairn
Tel : (0667)53119
Newton – Nairn
Tel : (0667)53144
RESTAURANT : Windsor – Nairn
Tel : (0667)53108

One of the great and challenging Scottish championship links laid out by Andrew Simpson, altered by Tom Morris and improved by James Braid. Situated on the south shore of the Moray Firth, Nairn looks north to the Black Isle and the mountains of Ross. Its sometimes windy fairways run through gorse, heather, and sand dunes. The beach is a hazard for the first seven holes. Many tees are elevated and most of the greens are huge and very fast. Nairn has hosted many championships including both the Scottish Amateurs and Ladies' championship in 1987. The excellent Golf View hotel is adjacent to Nairn. *SSS 71*

GF $$

 1887

27

—

A. Simpson, T. Morris, J. Braid

L 6556 y P 72, 2035 y P 31

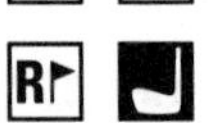

Required : None
Best days : Weekdays

HOLE	LENGTH MEDAL-TEE	PAR	STROKE INDEX
1	400	4	
2	499	5	
3	400	4	
4	145	3	
5	378	4	
6	183	3	
7	507	5	
8	330	4	
9	359	4	
TOTAL	3201	36	TOTAL

HOLE	LENGTH MEDAL-TEE	PAR	STROKE INDEX
10	500	5	
11	161	3	
12	445	4	
13	435	4	
14	206	3	
15	309	4	
16	422	4	
17	361	4	
18	516	5	
TOTAL	3355	36	TOTAL

NORTH BERWICK

★★

TEL : (0620)2135
LOCATION : 24 m E. Edinburgh A 198
ADDRESS : Beach Rd – North Berwick – East Lothian
HOTEL : HP
Marine – North Berwick
Tel : (0620)2406
Nether Abbey – North Berwick
Tel : (0620)2802
Point Garry – North Berwick
Tel : (0620)2380
RESTAURANT : Blenheim House – North Berwick
Tel : (0620)2385

The thirteenth oldest golf club in the world, the course is a classic championship links with many hazards including the beach, streams, bunkers, light rough and some walls across the links. The stately and luxury Marine hotel, with 85 bedrooms, overlooks the course. *SSS 70*

GF $

1832

18

—

—

L 6298 y P 70

S

RP

Required : Handicap Certificate, Introduction Letter
Best days : Weekdays

HOLE	LENGTH MEDAL-TEE	PAR	STROKE INDEX
1	324	4	9
2	453	4	5
3	459	4	1
4	171	3	15
5	378	4	11
6	161	3	17
7	354	4	3
8	467	4	13
9	489	5	7
TOTAL	3256	35	TOTAL

HOLE	LENGTH MEDAL-TEE	PAR	STROKE INDEX
10	161	3	18
11	515	5	2
12	374	4	10
13	348	4	12
14	377	4	6
15	191	3	14
16	383	4	4
17	423	4	8
18	270	4	16
TOTAL	3042	35	TOTAL

PANMURE

★

TEL : (0241)53120
LOCATION : 2 m W. Carnoustie, 7 m E. Dundee A 930
ADDRESS : Barry – Carnoustie – Angus
HOTEL :
Glencoe – Carnoustie
Tel : (0241)53273
Queen's – Dundee
Tel : (0382)22515
RESTAURANT : Brax – Carnoustie
Tel : (0241)53032

The course, touching the Monifieth links at its eastern end, is a fine and rugged championship links with gorse and pines flanking the holes. The 'Buddon Burn' meanders its way through several of the holes. There is a splendid clubhouse built near the railway station. *SSS 70*

GF $

1845

18

Saturdays

—

L 6317 y P 70

R S

Required : None
Best days : Any day

HOLE	LENGTH MEDAL-TEE	PAR	STROKE INDEX
1	289	4	15
2	488	5	3
3	398	4	9
4	348	4	8
5	147	3	17
6	387	4	1
7	418	4	11
8	360	4	6
9	174	3	13
TOTAL	3009	35	TOTAL

HOLE	LENGTH MEDAL-TEE	PAR	STROKE INDEX
10	416	4	4
11	171	3	18
12	363	4	7
13	398	4	12
14	535	5	2
15	234	3	14
16	382	4	5
17	401	4	10
18	408	4	16
TOTAL	3308	35	TOTAL

PRESTWICK (Old Prestwick)

TEL : (0292)77404
LOCATION : 1 m W. Prestwick Airport
ADDRESS : 2 Links Rd – Prestwick – Ayrshire
HOTEL :
Fairways – Prestwick
Tel : (0292)70396
Parkstone – Prestwick
Tel : (0292)77286
St Nicholas – Prestwick
Tel : (0292)79568
RESTAURANT : Pinewood – Prestwick
Tel : (0292)78966

A memorable links and one of the world's best, hosting the very first Open Championship in 1860 and regularly used for it until 1925 when crowd control was no longer possible. All the great historic golf champions like Old and Young Tom Morris, Harry Vardon, James Braid, and James Taylor have won here. Set along the coast of Ayrshire with wild rough, deep bunkers, a winding burn, small greens, it features the Cardinal hole, the 3rd, with enormous bunkers, considered by many to be the best par 5 hole in the world. *SSS 72*

GF $$

1851

18

Saturdays, Sundays

—

L 6544 y P 71

S

RP

Required : Introduction Letter
Best days : Weekdays

HOLE	LENGTH MEDAL-TEE	PAR	STROKE INDEX
1	346	4	8
2	167	3	18
3	482	5	2
4	382	4	14
5	206	3	10
6	362	4	4
7	430	4	16
8	431	4	6
9	444	4	12
TOTAL	3250	35	TOTAL

HOLE	LENGTH MEDAL-TEE	PAR	STROKE INDEX
10	454	4	1
11	195	3	17
12	513	5	7
13	460	4	3
14	362	4	9
15	347	4	13
16	288	4	11
17	391	4	5
18	284	4	15
TOTAL	3294	36	TOTAL

ROYAL ABERDEEN

TEL : (0224)702571.
LOCATION : 2 m N. Aberdeen A 92
ADDRESS : Balgownie – Bridge of Don – Aberdeen
HOTEL :
Atholl – Aberdeen
Tel : (0224)323505
Altens Skean Dhu – Aberdeen
Tel : (0224)877000
Cairn Northern – Aberdeen
Tel : (0224)483342
RESTAURANT : Gerard's – Aberdeen
Tel : (0224)571782

Formally set up in 1780, the club is the sixth oldest in the world. Laid out on uneven ground on Scotland's east coast adjacent to the Murcar course, this is a traditional links with many of its fairways flanked by gorse. The sea is close by, but little is seen of it. There is a ladies' course of 15 holes nearby, including the Aberdeen Ladies clubhouse. *SSS 71*

GF $$

 Weekends

 1780

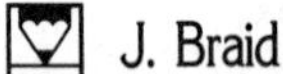 J. Braid

27

L 6372 y P 70, 2512 y P 34

Required : Handicap Certificate
Best days : Weekdays

HOLE	LENGTH MEDAL-TEE	PAR	STROKE INDEX
1	409	4	9
2	530	5	11
3	223	3	13
4	423	4	2
5	326	4	15
6	486	5	7
7	375	4	3
8	147	3	17
9	453	4	5
TOTAL	3372	36	TOTAL

HOLE	LENGTH MEDAL-TEE	PAR	STROKE INDEX
10	342	4	8
11	166	3	16
12	383	4	4
13	375	4	10
14	390	4	1
15	341	4	14
16	389	4	6
17	180	3	18
18	434	4	12
TOTAL	3000	34	TOTAL

ROYAL BURGESS GOLFING SOCIETY OF EDINBURGH

★★

TEL : (031)3392075
LOCATION : 5 m W. Edinburgh
ADDRESS : Whitehouse Road – Barnton – Edinburgh 4 – Midlothian
HOTEL :
Carlton – Edinburgh
Tel : (031)5567277
Norton House – Edinburgh
Tel : (031)3331275
Post House – Edinburgh
Tel : (031)3348221
RESTAURANT : Prestonfield House – Edinburgh
Tel : (031)6683346

Dating back to 1735, the much respected Royal Burgess Golfing Society is the oldest established golf club in the world. Located in beautiful parkland in Edinburgh, the course is a testing one with a varied layout, hosting many international championships. There is a stately looking clubhouse. *SSS 72*

GF $$

1735

18

Weekends

T. Morris, J. Braid

L 6167 y P 68

R S

Required : Introduction Letter (recommended especially to Ladies' golfers)
Best days : Weekdays

HOLE	LENGTH MEDAL-TEE	PAR	STROKE INDEX
1	387	4	9
2	282	4	17
3	427	4	5
4	443	4	1
5	139	3	13
6	470	4	15
7	416	4	3
8	135	3	11
9	377	4	7
TOTAL	3071	34	TOTAL

HOLE	LENGTH MEDAL-TEE	PAR	STROKE INDEX
10	366	4	4
11	366	4	14
12	306	4	16
13	187	3	10
14	381	4	8
15	384	4	2
16	456	4	12
17	414	4	6
18	236	3	18
TOTAL	3096	34	TOTAL

ROYAL DORNOCH

TEL : (0862)810219
LOCATION : 80 km N. Inverness A 9,
3 km Dornoch A 949
ADDRESS : Dornoch – Sutherland
HOTEL : HR
Royal Golf
Tel : (0862)810283
Dornoch Castle – Dornoch
Tel : (0862)810216

A splendid seaside links rated by the American magazine 'Golf Monthly' as one of the six best in the world. Each hole has a different character and presents a real test to any golfer. Many of the holes (9th to 16th) are along the sea shore. There are water hazards such as a burn in front of the 8th tee and ditches on the 9th fairway. There is also a short 9 hole links course. The stately Royal Hotel with 34 bedrooms and various garden chalets has a private entrance to the courses and overlooks the Dornoch Firth and its golf courses. *SSS 72*

GF $

1877

27

—

T. Morris

L 6577 y P 70, 2485 y P 32

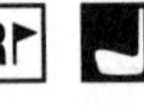

Required : Handicap Certificate
Best days : Weekdays

HOLE	LENGTH MEDAL-TEE	PAR	STROKE INDEX
1	336	4	7
2	179	3	15
3	414	4	11
4	418	4	3
5	361	4	9
6	165	3	17
7	465	4	1
8	437	4	5
9	499	5	13
TOTAL	3274	35	TOTAL

HOLE	LENGTH MEDAL-TEE	PAR	STROKE INDEX
10	148	3	16
11	445	4	4
12	504	5	12
13	168	3	18
14	448	4	2
15	322	4	10
16	405	4	6
17	406	4	8
18	457	4	14
TOTAL	3303	35	TOTAL

ROYAL MUSSELBURGH

★

TEL : (0875)810276
LOCATION : 8 m SE. Edinburgh A 198
ADDRESS : Prestonpans - East Lothian
HOTEL :
Caledonian - Edinburgh
Tel : (031)2252433
Carlton Highland - Edinburgh
Tel : (031)5567277
Embassy Ellersley House - Edinburgh
Tel : (031)3376888
RESTAURANT : Howtowdie - Edinburgh
Tel : (031)2256291

One of Scotlands oldest golf clubs having been founded in 1774, this is a fine parkland course of championship standard, laid out by James Braid on undulating countryside. The clubhouse is a magnificent castle, standing in the middle of the course. *SSS 70*

GF $ — S

1774 J. Braid

18 L 5675 P 70 R

Required : Handicap Certificate
Best days : Weekdays

HOLE	LENGTH MEDAL-TEE	PAR	STROKE INDEX
1	319	4	8
2	270	4	18
3	337	4	6
4	334	4	14
5	284	4	16
6	161	3	2
7	358	4	4
8	384	4	10
9	436	5	12
TOTAL	2883	36	TOTAL

HOLE	LENGTH MEDAL-TEE	PAR	STROKE INDEX
10	326	4	7
11	340	4	15
12	331	4	11
13	413	4	1
14	133	3	17
15	390	4	3
16	161	3	9
17	324	4	13
18	374	4	5
TOTAL	2792	34	TOTAL

ROYAL TROON

TEL : (0292)311555
LOCATION : 28 m Glasgow A 77
ADDRESS : Craigend Rd – Troon – Ayrshire
HOTEL : HR
Marine
Tel : (0292)314444
Piersland House – Troon
Tel : (0292)314747
Sun Court – Troon
Tel : (0292)312727

The Old Course, hosting the Open numerous times, is another of Britain's famous and testing links composed of wild rough, sand dunes, hillocks, rough pasture land, brambles and heather. Troon has the longest (the 6th) and the shortest (the 8th) holes in the British championship courses featuring the famous and treacherous 8th hole the 'Postage Stamp', claiming many victims among the world's greatest golfers. Henry Cotton considered the dogleg 11th one of the world's most difficult holes and Bobby Locke selected the bunkerless 13th as one of the world's best holes. The Portland course, is shorter but nevertheless testing. The Marine Hotel is a first class deluxe hotel overlooking the course, the clubhouse and the sea. *SSS 73/71*

GF $$ — Weekends, Fridays — S

1878 — — — RP

36 — L 6641 y P 71, 6274 y P 70

Required : Handicap Certificate, Introduction Letter at least 4 weeks in advance
Best days : Mondays to Thursdays inc.
Note : No Ladies are accepted

Old Course

HOLE	LENGTH MEDAL-TEE	PAR	STROKE INDEX
1	357	4	16
2	381	4	7
3	371	4	11
4	522	5	4
5	194	3	14
6	544	5	2
7	381	4	9
8	123	3	18
9	387	4	5
TOTAL	3260	36	TOTAL

HOLE	LENGTH MEDAL-TEE	PAR	STROKE INDEX
10	385	4	10
11	421	4	1
12	427	4	6
13	411	4	12
14	175	3	15
15	445	4	3
16	533	5	8
17	210	3	13
18	374	4	17
TOTAL	3381	35	TOTAL

Portland Course

HOLE	LENGTH MEDAL-TEE	PAR	STROKE INDEX
1	462	4	9
2	427	4	5
3	352	4	13
4	194	3	7
5	349	4	15
6	409	4	1
7	368	4	11
8	147	3	17
9	420	4	3
TOTAL	3128	34	TOTAL

HOLE	LENGTH MEDAL-TEE	PAR	STROKE INDEX
10	154	3	16
11	494	5	6
12	470	4	2
13	353	4	12
14	214	3	10
15	498	5	4
16	155	3	18
17	311	4	8
18	497	5	14
TOTAL	3146	36	TOTAL

ST-ANDREWS

TEL : (0334)75757/
Starter 73393
LOCATION : 14 m Dundee
ADDRESS : St-Andrews
HOTEL : HP
St-Andrews
Tel : (0334)72611
Old Course
Tel : (0334)74371
Rusack's Marine
Tel : (0334)74321

It is claimed that golf originated at St Andrews, as records show that golf has been played here since 1547. It is the home of the famous Royal and Ancient Golf Club playing golf here for centuries. They drew up the rules which continue to regulate the game all over the world. Run by the Municipality, there are four 18 hole courses at St Andrews, including the Old Course, considered by many to be the greatest links course in the world and masterminded by James Braid. Mostly flat, it has very long holes with enormous greens and frightening bunkers. The 17th hole, the "Road Hole", is known as the greatest hole in the world. The Old Course has been the frequent venue for the Open, the Walker Cup and British Amateur Championship. The other three 18 hole courses include the long and testing New Course also designed by James Braid. The shorter Jubilee is laid out nearest the sea bordered by sand dunes. The Eden is ideal for the average player. There are several clubhouses located near the 18th hole of the Old Course welcoming golfers, such as the St Andrews Golfing Society, St Regulus, and others. There are three equally famous hotels adjacent to this golfing Mecca: the luxury Old Course Hotel overlooking the 2nd and 17th holes of the Old Course, the modern St Andrews Hotel near the Royal and Ancient Clubhouse, and the charming Rusack's Marine opposite the 18th hole of the Old Course. *SSS 72/72/70/69*

GF $$ — Old C. : Sun., March 

1400 — J. Braid 

81 — L 6004 P 72, 6604 y P 71, 6284 y P 69, 5971 y P 69 

Required : Handicap Certificate for the Old Course
Best days : Any day

ST-ANDREWS

Old Course

HOLE	LENGTH MEDAL-TEE	PAR	STROKE INDEX
1	338	4	15
2	377	4	3
3	322	4	13
4	383	4	9
5	470	5	1
6	342	4	11
7	328	4	7
8	152	3	18
9	281	4	5
TOTAL	2993	36	TOTAL

HOLE	LENGTH MEDAL-TEE	PAR	STROKE INDEX
10	291	4	10
11	157	3	17
12	289	4	6
13	364	4	12
14	478	5	2
15	366	4	8
16	321	4	14
17	421	4	4
18	324	4	16
TOTAL	3011	36	TOTAL

New Course

HOLE	LENGTH MEDAL-TEE	PAR	STROKE INDEX
1	336	4	7
2	367	4	13
3	511	5	3
4	369	4	9
5	180	3	17
6	445	4	5
7	356	4	11
8	481	5	1
9	225	3	15
TOTAL	3270	36	TOTAL

HOLE	LENGTH MEDAL-TEE	PAR	STROKE INDEX
10	464	4	6
11	347	4	14
12	518	5	4
13	157	3	18
14	386	4	8
15	394	4	12
16	431	4	2
17	229	3	16
18	408	4	10
TOTAL	3334	35	TOTAL

ST-ANDREWS

Jubilee Course

HOLE	LENGTH MEDAL-TEE	PAR	STROKE INDEX
1	457	4	7
2	250	3	16
3	393	4	3
4	342	4	10
5	346	4	8
6	356	4	5
7	147	3	18
8	380	4	1
9	373	4	13
TOTAL	3044	34	TOTAL

HOLE	LENGTH MEDAL-TEE	PAR	STROKE INDEX
10	395	4	9
11	331	4	14
12	180	3	17
13	398	4	11
14	441	4	4
15	319	4	15
16	454	4	2
17	333	4	12
18	389	4	6
TOTAL	3240	35	TOTAL

Eden Course

HOLE	LENGTH MEDAL-TEE	PAR	STROKE INDEX
1	303	4	14
2	428	4	6
3	205	3	16
4	454	4	1
5	435	4	10
6	270	4	8
7	145	3	18
8	367	4	4
9	344	4	12
TOTAL	2951	34	TOTAL

HOLE	LENGTH MEDAL-TEE	PAR	STROKE INDEX
10	407	4	9
11	422	4	3
12	415	4	13
13	313	4	7
14	179	3	15
15	504	5	2
16	154	3	17
17	365	4	5
18	261	4	11
TOTAL	3020	35	TOTAL

TURNBERRY

TEL : (0655)31000
Telex : 777779
LOCATION : 6 m N. Girvan A 77
ADDRESS : Turnberry – Ayrshire
HOTEL : HR
Turnberry and Dormy House
Tel : (0655)31000

The Ailsa and Arran courses are both memorable links courses. They are set on the coast of South West Ayrshire with the Arran mountains in the background and commanding fine views of the surroundings including the Ailsa rock. The Ailsa links, designed by MacKenzie Ross, set along the dunes and the sea, is the most famous and demanding of the two. It has rather flat fairways featuring treacherous bunkers and thick rough. The Arran is shorter and set more inland. Both courses have hosted numerous championships such as the Open in 1977 and 1986, the 1979 European Open, the 1983 British Amateur Championship, the Walker Cup, the Volvo British Open in 1987, 88 and 89 and major PGA events. The scenic and renowned Turnberry Hotel with 124 bedrooms including a dormy house with 115 rooms, owns both courses. Facilities include a swimming pool, sauna, gymnasium, solarium, billiards room plus a private airstrip and helipad. *SSS 70/71*

GF $$
1883
36

—
A. MacKenzie Ross
L 6249 y P 69, 6408 y P 69

S
R

Required : Handicap Certificate
Best days : Any day after 12h with priority for hotel residents

TURNBERRY

Arran Course

HOLE	LENGTH MEDAL-TEE	PAR	STROKE INDEX
1	352	4	10
2	506	5	2
3	160	3	18
4	330	4	14
5	426	4	6
6	394	4	12
7	228	3	16
8	388	4	8
9	454	4	4
TOTAL	3238	35	TOTAL

HOLE	LENGTH MEDAL-TEE	PAR	STROKE INDEX
10	163	3	17
11	312	4	13
12	456	4	1
13	422	4	3
14	390	4	9
15	334	4	5
16	367	4	11
17	216	3	15
18	351	4	7
TOTAL	3011	34	TOTAL

Ailsa Course

HOLE	LENGTH MEDAL-TEE	PAR	STROKE INDEX
1	362	4	9
2	378	4	13
3	393	4	5
4	167	3	17
5	411	4	3
6	222	3	15
7	465	4	1
8	427	4	11
9	413	4	7
TOTAL	3238	34	TOTAL

HOLE	LENGTH MEDAL-TEE	PAR	STROKE INDEX
10	430	4	6
11	157	3	18
12	391	4	8
13	379	4	14
14	400	4	2
15	168	3	16
16	381	4	10
17	487	5	4
18	377	4	12
TOTAL	3170	35	TOTAL

WALES

Car Rental

Reservation/Information telephone number :

Country code : 44

Telephone number : 532/422233

Headquarters address :

EUROPCAR U.K. LTD
Bushey House
High street, Bushey
Watford WD2, 1RE – United Kingdom
Tel. : (44) 81 9504080
Telex : 297190
Fax : (44) 81 9504245

---

100 GOLF COURSES, 80 000 PLAYERS

★★★ Great golf course
★★ Very good golf course
$ 5-15 Pound
★ Recommended golf course
✡ Holiday golf course
$ $ more than 18 Pound

TOWN	GOLF COURSE		TEL	♦	MAP REF.
Aberdare	Aberdare		(0685) 871188		48
Aberdovey	Aberdovey	✡	(065472) 493		22
Abergavenny	Monmouthshire	★	(0873) 2606		57
	Old Rectory	•	(0873) 810373		•
	West Monmouthshire		(0495) 310233		32
Abersoch	Abersoch	•	(075881) 2622		•
Aberystwyth	Aberystwyth		(0970) 615104		26
	Borth & Ynyslas	✡	(097081) 202		23
Ammanford	Glynhir		(0269) 850472		31
Bala	Bala	•	(0678) 520539		•
Barry	Brynhill		(0446) 745061		68
Bangor	St Deiniol		(0248) 353098		12
Beaumaris	Baron Hill	•	(0248) 810231		•
Blackwood	Bargoed		(0443) 830143		53
	Blackwood	•	(0495) 223152		•
	Bryn Meadows		(0495) 225590		56
Brecon	Brecon	•	(0874) 2004		•
	Cradoc		(0874) 3658		29
Builth Wells	Builth Wells	•	(0982) 553296		•
Caernarfon	Caernarfon		(0286) 3783		15
Caerphilly	Caerphilly	•	(0222) 883481		•
Cardiff	Cardiff	★	(0222) 753320		63
	Creigiau		(0222) 890263		•
	Dinas Powis		(0222) 512727		61
	Glamorganshire		(0222) 701185		65
	Llanishen		(0222) 755078		55
	Radyr		(0222) 842408		60
	St Mellons		(0633) 680408		66
	Wenvoe Castle		(0222) 594371		62

TOWN	GOLF COURSE		TEL	♦	MAP REF.
	Whitchurch		(0222) 60125		50
Cardigan	Cardigan		(0239) 612035		27
Carmarthen	Carmarthen	✡	(026787) 493		30
Chepstow	St Pierre	★★★	(0291) 625261	♦	51
Colwyn Bay	Abergele	✡	(0745) 824034		6
	Old Colwyn	•	(0492) 515581		•
	Rhos-on-Sea	✡	(0492) 49641		5
Conwy	Caernarvonshire	★★	(049263) 3400		2
	Penmaenmawr	•	(0492) 623330		•
Cwmbran	Pontnewydd	•	(06333) 2170		•
Denbigh	Denbigh		(074571) 4159		•
Dolgellau	Dolgellau	•	(0341) 422603		•
Ffestiniog	Ffestiniog	•	(076676) 2687		•
Harlech	Royal St Davids	★★★	(0766) 780361	♦	21
Haverfordwest	Haverfordwest	•	(0437) 3565		•
Hawarden	Hawarden	•	(0244) 531447		•
Holyhead	Anglesey		(0407) 810219		11
	Bull Bay	✡	(0407) 830960		1
	Holyhead	★	(0407) 3279		10
Holywell	Holywell	•	(0352) 71040		•
Knighton	Knighton	•	(0457) 528646		•
Lladrindod Wells	Llandrindod Wells		(0597) 2010		28
Llandudno	Llandudno	★	(0492) 76450		4
	North Wales	✡	(0492) 75325		3
Llanelli	Ashburnham	★	(05546) 2269		35
Llangollen	Vale of Llangollen		(0978) 860040		16
Machynlleth	Machynlleth	•	(0654) 2000		•
Merthyr Tydfil	Merthyr Tydfil	•	(0685) 3308		•
	Morlais Castle	•	(0685) 2822		•
Milford Haven	Milford Haven	✡	(06462) 2368		33
Mold	Mold		(0352) 740318		9
	Padeswood & Buckle		(0244) 542537		13
Monmouth	The Rolls of Monmouth	•	(0600) 5353		•
Neath	Glenneath	•	(0639) 720452		•
	Neath		(0639) 3615		38
	Swansea Bay	✡	(0639) 814153		45
Nefyn	Nefyn & District	✡	(0758) 720218		17
Nelson	Whitehall	•	(0222) 740245		•
Newport	Llanwern		(0633) 2029		67
	Newport		(0633) 894496		54
	Tredegar Park		(0633) 894433		64
Oswestry	Llanymynech		(069188) 221		24
Pembroke	South Pembrokeshire	•	(06463) 683817		•
Pontardawe	Pontardawe		(0792) 863118		36
Pontypool	Pontypool		(04955) 3655		40
Pontypridd	Mountain Ash		(0443) 472265		39
	Pontypridd		(0443) 402359		47
Porthcawl	Pyle & Kenfig	★	(065671) 3093		52
	Royal Porthcawl	★★★	(065671) 2251	♦	58
	Southerndown	★	(0656) 880476		59
Portmadoc	Criccieth		(076671) 2154		19
	Portmadoc	✡	(0766) 2037		20
Port Talbot	Maesteg		(0656) 732037		46
Prestatyn	Prestatyn	✡	(07456) 4320		8
	St Melyd	•	(07456) 4405		•
Pwllheli	Pwllheli		(0758) 612520		18
Rhondda	Rhondda		(0443) 433204		49
Rhyl	Rhuddlan		(0745) 590217		7
	Rhyl	•	(0745) 63171		•
Ruthin	Ruthin Pwllglas	•	(08242) 2296		•
Swansea	Clyne		(0792) 401989		44
	Fairwood Park		(0792) 203648		42
	Langland Bay	✡	(0792) 66023		43
	Morriston		(0792) 71079		37
	Pennard	✡	(044128) 3131		41
Tenby	Tenby	✡	(0834) 2787	♦	34
Welshpool	Welshpool		(093883) 249		25
Wrexham	Wrexham		(0978) 364268		14

♦ For details, see following pages.
• 9 hole golf course.

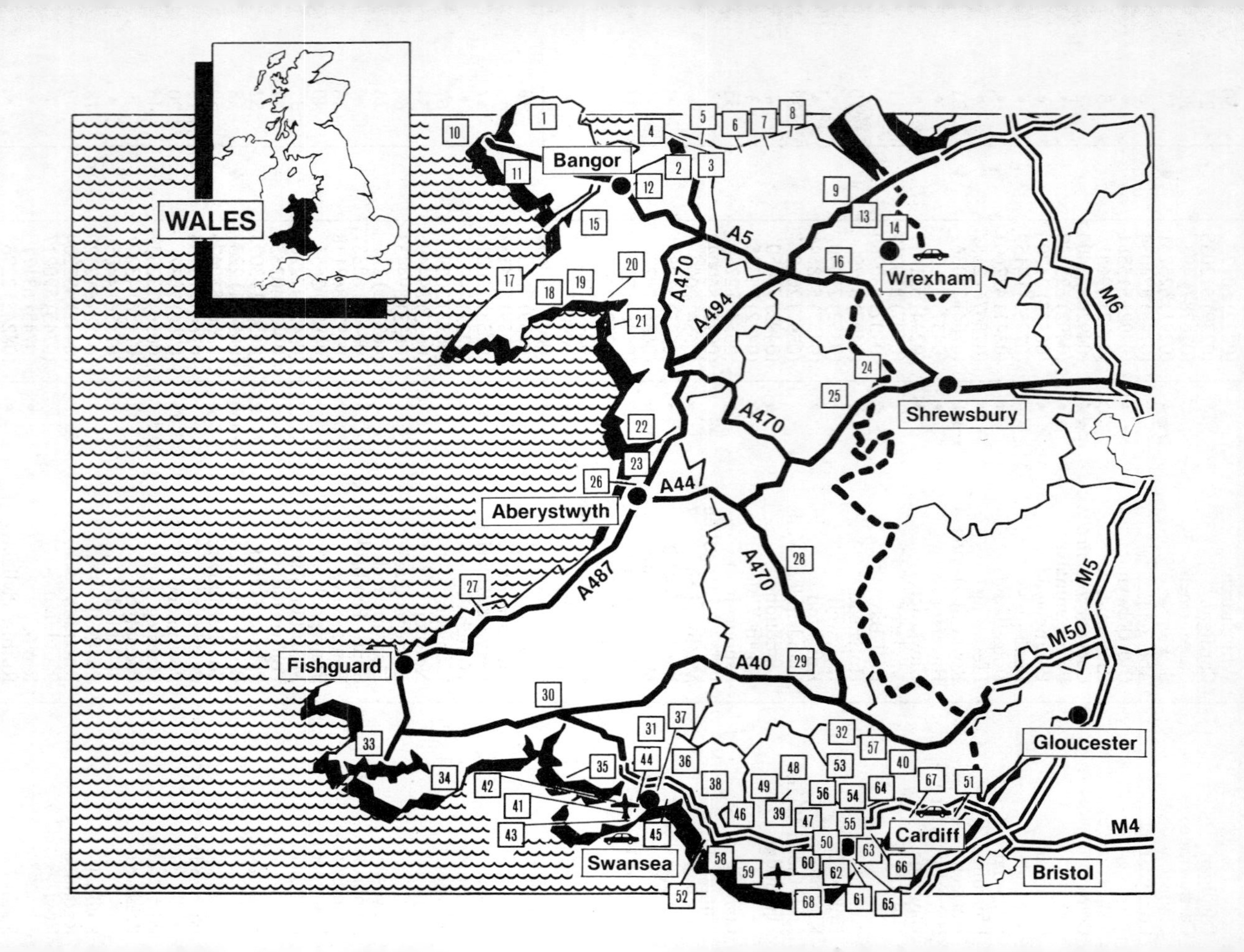
WALES
Bangor
Wrexham
Shrewsbury
Aberystwyth
Fishguard
Swansea
Cardiff
Gloucester
Bristol
A5
A470
A494
A44
A487
A40
M6
M5
M50
M4
1
2
3
4
5
6
7
8
9
10
11
12
13
14
15
16
17
18
19
20
21
22
23
24
25
26
27
28
29
30
31
32
33
34
35
36
37
38
39
40
41
42
43
44
45
46
47
48
49
50
51
52
53
54
55
56
57
58
59
60
61
62
63
64
65
66
67
68

CARDIFF

TEL : (0222)753320
LOCATION : 3 m Cardiff
ADDRESS : Sherborne Ave – Cyncoed – Cardiff – South Glamorgan
HOTEL :
Post House – Cyncoed
Tel : (0222)731212
Angel – Cardiff
Tel : (0222)32633
Holiday Inn – Cardiff
Tel : (0222)399944
RESTAURANT : Inn on the Avenue – Cardiff
Tel : (0222)732520

Located on the outskirts of the Welsh capital, this is a pleasant parkland course laid out in a residential area of Cardiff. There are magnificent oak trees flanking various fairways with brooks and streams meandering their way through them. There is a comfortable mansion style clubhouse. *SSS 70*

GF $ | Weekends | R S
1922 | — |
18 | L 6016 y P 70 |

Required : Handicap Certificate
Best days : Mondays and Fridays

HOLE	LENGTH MEDAL-TEE	PAR	STROKE INDEX
1	419	4	9
2	154	3	15
3	440	4	3
4	497	5	5
5	150	3	17
6	417	4	1
7	271	4	13
8	491	5	7
9	193	3	11
TOTAL	3032	35	TOTAL

HOLE	LENGTH MEDAL-TEE	PAR	STROKE INDEX
10	476	5	6
11	501	5	10
12	169	3	16
13	432	4	2
14	302	4	12
15	394	4	4
16	179	3	14
17	399	4	8
18	132	3	18
TOTAL	2984	35	TOTAL

ROYAL PORTHCAWL

TEL : (065671)2251
LOCATION : 15 m E. Swansea/0,5 m NW. Porthcawl
ADDRESS : Porthcawl – Mid Glamorgan
HOTEL :
Seabank – Porthcawl
Tel : (065671)2261
Rose & Crown – Porthcawl
Tel : (065671)4850
The Lorelei – Porthcawl
Tel : (065671)2683
RESTAURANT : Atlantic – Porthcawl
Tel : (065671)5011

Royal Porthcawl is a memorable seaside course and one of the best links in the world, set on the rocky southern shores of Wales alongside the British Channel. The opening holes follow the coast line, the finishing holes are laid out in heathland featuring gorse and hummocks. There are deep bunkers and a strong wind frequently causes trouble to the golfers. *SSS 73*

GF $$ — 1891 — J. Braid — 18 — L 6409 y P 72 — S — R

Required : Handicap Certificate
Best days : Weekdays only

HOLE	LENGTH MEDAL-TEE	PAR	STROKE INDEX
1	326	4	16
2	411	4	5
3	377	4	11
4	193	3	8
5	476	5	14
6	391	4	3
7	116	3	18
8	476	5	9
9	368	4	1
TOTAL	3139	36	TOTAL

HOLE	LENGTH MEDAL-TEE	PAR	STROKE INDEX
10	327	4	15
11	187	3	7
12	476	5	10
13	413	4	2
14	152	3	17
15	421	4	4
16	420	4	12
17	489	5	6
18	385	4	13
TOTAL	3270	36	TOTAL

ROYAL ST-DAVID

TEL : (0766)780361
LOCATION : W. Harlech
ADDRESS : Harlech – Gwynedd
HOTEL : HR
St-Davids – Harlech
Tel : (0766)780366
Maes-y-Neuadd – Harlech
Tel : (0766)780200
The Cemlyn – Harlech
Tel : (0766)780425
RESTAURANT : Castle – Harlech
Tel : (0766)780416

Royal St David is a magnificent links course ranking among the world's best. The course is separated from the sea by sand hills and overlooks historic Harlech castle and Cardigan Bay. There are many great holes with excellent large greens. Among its feature holes is the 15th, doglegged from the tee and winding between sandhills, with no bunkers and with Mount Snowdon in the background. The St Davids Hotel commands fine views of the course, the bay and the mountains. *SSS 71*

GF $$ — S
1898 — R
18 L 6427 y P 69

Required : Handicap Certificate
Best days : Weekdays only

HOLE	LENGTH MEDAL-TEE	PAR	STROKE INDEX
1	436	4	9
2	346	4	15
3	463	4	2
4	188	3	13
5	393	4	8
6	371	4	11
7	476	5	4
8	491	5	6
9	173	3	16
TOTAL	3337	36	TOTAL

HOLE	LENGTH MEDAL-TEE	PAR	STROKE INDEX
10	430	4	1
11	144	3	17
12	437	4	10
13	451	4	7
14	218	3	12
15	427	4	3
16	354	4	14
17	427	4	5
18	202	3	18
TOTAL	3090	33	TOTAL

SOUTHERNDOWN

★

TEL : (0656)880476
LOCATION : 7 m SE. Porthcawl
ADDRESS : Ewenny – Bridgend-Mid Glamorgan
HOTEL :
Heronston – Bridgend
Tel : (0656)68811
Coed-y-Mwstwr – Coychurch
Tel : (0656)860621
RESTAURANT : Coed-y-Mwstwr – Bridgend
Tel : (0656)860621

A typical downland course with rolling fairways and fast greens. It is scenically laid out overlooking the town of Porthcawl, and the mouth of the Ogmore river. Among its feature holes is the scenic 5th played across a valley. The course is very pleasant and boasts an equally pleasant clubhouse. *SSS 73*

GF $

 Sundays

 S

1905

 W. Fowler, H. Colt

18

L 6613 y P 70

Required : Handicap Certificate
Best days : Mondays, Wednesdays and Fridays

HOLE	LENGTH MEDAL-TEE	PAR	STROKE INDEX
1	373	4	9
2	448	4	3
3	412	4	13
4	401	4	1
5	172	3	16
6	484	5	2
7	231	3	11
8	428	4	5
9	367	4	15
TOTAL	3316	35	TOTAL

HOLE	LENGTH MEDAL-TEE	PAR	STROKE INDEX
10	181	3	17
11	427	4	1
12	411	4	12
13	478	5	6
14	146	3	18
15	377	4	10
16	412	4	4
17	428	4	14
18	437	4	8
TOTAL	3297	35	TOTAL

ST. PIERRE

TEL : (0291)625261
LOCATION : 2 m Chepstow off A 48, jct 22/M4
ADDRESS : St Pierre Park – Chepstow – Gwent
HOTEL :
St. Pierre
Tel : (0291)625261
George – Chepstow
Tel : (02912)2497
Two Rivers – Chepstow
Tel : (02912)5151

The St Pierre Country Club features two 18 hole championship courses: The Old Course designed by Ken Cotton, and the New Course designed by Bill Cox. The Old Course is a parkland course with age-old trees and an 11 acre lake. It has been selected numerous times as the venue for the Dunlop Masters (renamed the Silk Cut Masters). The New Course is a not too testing meadowland course. The elegant St. Pierre Hotel, a restored castle dating back to the 14th century, has 150 rooms, a restaurant overlooking the 18th green, and sports facilities for tennis, squash, swimming, snooker, badminton and a gymnasium. *SSS 71/69*

GF $$
1964
36
—
K. Cotton, B. Cox
L 6285 y P 71, 5593 y P 68

Required : Handicap Certificate
Best days : Weekdays

Old Course

HOLE	LENGTH MEDAL-TEE	PAR	STROKE INDEX
1	557	5	3
2	345	4	13
3	135	3	15
4	364	4	9
5	377	4	1
6	150	3	11
7	420	4	5
8	299	4	17
9	423	4	7
TOTAL	3070	35	TOTAL

HOLE	LENGTH MEDAL-TEE	PAR	STROKE INDEX
10	339	4	6
11	345	4	18
12	516	5	4
13	198	3	14
14	483	5	10
15	326	4	16
16	407	4	2
17	373	4	12
18	228	3	8
TOTAL	3215	36	TOTAL

New Course

HOLE	LENGTH MEDAL-TEE	PAR	STROKE INDEX
1	335	4	11
2	114	3	17
3	384	4	5
4	495	5	3
5	184	3	7
6	423	4	1
7	345	4	13
8	209	3	9
9	290	4	15
TOTAL	2779	34	TOTAL

HOLE	LENGTH MEDAL-TEE	PAR	STROKE INDEX
10	252	4	18
11	195	3	10
12	300	4	16
13	344	4	6
14	416	4	4
15	391	4	2
16	357	4	12
17	373	4	8
18	186	3	14
TOTAL	2814	34	TOTAL

TENBY

TEL : (0834)2787
LOCATION : 1 m S. Tenby
ADDRESS : Tenby – The Burrows – Dyfed
HOTEL :
Imperial – Tenby
Tel : (0834)3737
Kinloch Court – Tenby
Tel : (0834)2777
Waterwynch House – Tenby
Tel : (0834)2464
RESTAURANT : Royal Lion – Tenby
Tel : (0834)2127

One of the oldest links courses in Wales, having been founded in 1888 and ideal for holiday golf with several fine and sporting holes. The course is always in excellent condition. The Imperial Hotel, nearby the golf club, is set on the South Cliff with direct access to the beach. *SSS 71*

GF $ — — R S

1888 —

18 L 6239 y P 69

Required : Handicap Certificate
Best days : Any day

HOLE	LENGTH MEDAL-TEE	PAR	STROKE INDEX
1	470	4	5
2	429	4	11
3	382	4	1
4	415	4	7
5	354	4	13
6	117	3	17
7	419	4	3
8	367	4	9
9	186	3	15
TOTAL	3139	34	TOTAL

HOLE	LENGTH MEDAL-TEE	PAR	STROKE INDEX
10	426	4	2
11	409	4	6
12	175	3	16
13	284	4	14
14	481	5	10
15	350	4	12
16	382	4	4
17	174	3	18
18	419	4	8
TOTAL	3100	35	TOTAL

GOLF PARTNER PRESS
2040 Avenue of the Stars
Suite 400
CENTURY CITY, CALIFORNIA 90067

Maury-Eurolivres S.A., 45300 Manchecourt
N° d'éditeur : 905 277 – N° d'imprimeur : 91/09/M0113
Dépôt légal : juillet 1984
Printed in France

 CNUF : 35285
ISBN 2.90527701.7